ANNUAL REVIEW OF PHYSIOLOGY

ANNUAL REVIEW OF PHYSIOLOGY

I. S. EDELMAN, *Editor*
Columbia University College of Physicians and Surgeons

STANLEY G. SCHULTZ, *Associate Editor*
University of Pittsburgh School of Medicine

VOLUME 41

1979

ANNUAL REVIEWS INC.   4139 EL CAMINO WAY   PALO ALTO, CALIFORNIA 94306

ANNUAL REVIEWS INC.
Palo Alto, California, USA

REPRINTS The conspicuous number aligned in the margin with the title of each article in this volume is a key for use in ordering reprints. Available reprints are priced at the uniform rate of $1.00 each postpaid. The minimum acceptable reprint order is 5 reprints and/or $5.00 prepaid. A quantity discount is available.

International Standard Serial Number: 0066-4278
International Standard Book Number: 0-8243-0341-5
Library of Congress Catalog Card Number: 39-15404

PREFACE

For the past four decades the *Annual Review of Physiology* has been dedicated to the ideal of the intellectual unity of this branch of biology. Previous volumes, at least for three decades, could reasonably be expected to provide critical reviews of many of the frontiers in physiology. The range and diversity of contemporary physiology, however, demand intense specialization by most of its practitioners. Physiology has been transformed into a complex of interrelated sciences with evolving boundaries. The establishment of the *Annual Review of Neuroscience* in 1978 attested to the need for expanded coverage of what was once a subdividion of the present series.

Recently our Editorial Committee concluded that the time had come to inaugurate a new format recognizing the major subsectors that now exist in physiology. Beginning with this volume (Volume 41, 1979), the *Annual Review of Physiology* will comprise seven sections, each with its own Section Editor—Respiratory and Cardiovascular Physiology (in future volumes to be divided into two sections: Circulatory and Respiratory Physiology); Endocrinology and Metabolism; Renal and Electrolyte Physiology; Cell and Membrane Physiology; Comparative and Integrative Physiology; Gastrointestinal and Nutritional Physiology; and Special Topics (this year, Neurophysiology). Each Section Editor will formulate themes to be covered by a series of complementary articles emphasizing his sector's most timely and important developments. Thus the single volume maintains unity while facilitating, by the juxtaposition of subdomains, access to a wide range of current research in physiology. The new format is intended to benefit both the active researcher and the specialized scholar; for the generalist—the bravest of scholars—it will be possible to delve into the many fields represented in each issue.

The transition to the new thematic format was made possible by the scholarly contributions of recent Editors, Editorial Committees, and authors. A special debt of gratitude is owed to J. H. Comroe, Jr., who, during his tenure as Editor, began to explore new ways for the *Annual Review of Physiology* to fulfill its responsibilities. Ernst Knobil, my immediate predecessor as Editor, fulfilled his obligations with a remarkable combination of energy and depth of understanding of physiology; he provided a sterling example for us to follow. In addition, the *Annual Review of Physiology* has profited immeasurably from the extraordinary service rendered by Ralph Sonnenschein as Associate Editor for 15 years. It is also a pleasure to salute Walter J. Freeman and Samuel M. McCann for their devoted and outstanding service on the Editorial Committee.

Just as the quality of past issues of the *Annual Review of Physiology* was determined by the quality of these formidable academics (Comroe, Knobil, Sonnenschein, Freeman, McCann), the future volumes regardless of format depend on the dedication and talents of the new Associate Editor, Stanley G. Schultz, and his fellow Section Editors: T. E. Andreoli, R. M. Berne, W. R. Dawson, A. P. Fishman, J. Gergely and D. T. Krieger. This cast of editorial characters is superb; it is a privilege for me to serve with them.

I. S. EDELMAN
EDITOR

Annual Review of Physiology
Volume 41, 1979

CONTENTS

K S Cole

Ann. Rev. Physiol. 1979. 41:1–24

MOSTLY MEMBRANES[1] ♦1202

Kenneth S. Cole

Laboratory of Biophysics, IRP, NINCDS, National Institutes of Health,
Bethesda, Maryland 20014 and Marine Biological Laboratory, Woods Hole,
Massachusetts 02543

My first formal connection with physiology, and my first job, began in 1929 when I became Assistant Professor of Physiology at Columbia's College of Physicians and Surgeons in New York City. The association with physiology has been very happy and rewarding. Physiology and physiologists have been kind, generous, and forgiving. Now I am invited to write the Prefatory Chapter of the *Annual Review* which, in the words of the editor "is traditionally authored by a physiologist of great distinction." I am highly honored to join this group and more than a little flattered.

I switched to biology after I obtained a degree in physics in 1926; but I had been committed after the first summer at Woods Hole in 1924. I had gone to Woods Hole because I liked my first taste of biophysics at the Cleveland Clinic the summer before.

I had decided on physics research during the more than a year at the General Electric Research Laboratory, 1920–1922. There I saw electrical engineers at work and it was not for me, in spite of the fact that earlier, during a five week inspection as a merchant seaman, I had been inspired by the magnificence of the Panama Canal, and during a trip with Dad I'd felt the grandeur of the generators and the thrill of molten aluminum being cast at Niagara Falls.

As a youngster I had been lonesome but too busy to worry about it. Even then, although I spent summers as a machinist and as a deck hand on the Great Lakes, I was an electrician. I produced sparks and shocks with worn out parts from the telephone company and put together a licensed wireless station with a Ford spark coil and galena (for a detector) begged from the head of the Geology Department.

It all goes back to my amazing parents—a Mother who, when I asked her why the big lumps came to the top when I jiggled the sugar bowl, said "Maybe they don't," and a Father who devoted his career to shaping the academic excellence of Oberlin College. As a parent and a Dean he must have been sorely tried by my pranks—especially by those he suspected but I didn't get caught at. When I asked about a couple of faculty members, he told me they could keep warm on a very cold day just by talking about him. But I don't remember ever acting against paternal advice!

COLLEGE

My scientific career really began with the year at Schenectady. S. R. Williams at Oberlin persuaded me to write for a summer job to the Bureau of Standards, which promptly turned me down, and to General Electric, where W. R. Whitney asked me to visit and promised me a job if I *had* to work there. It was a marvelous experience. I worked on my own on high frequency heating of silicon steel and evolved gas analysis in high vacuum. The techniques were all new to me. Come fall, I didn't have my first analysis.

Dad suggested I take a year off from college, and GE raised my salary so that I could quit my job as a boarding-house waiter. At the research laboratory I got to know everyone and what they were doing. I prowled the works from a battleship turbo-generator to tests of a rolling mill motor. I was properly chewed out for indiscretions and mistakes but I was really hurt when Irving Langmuir ignored me after a glance at my puzzling data. The next time he said "You *do* have a problem," and we worked on it. When I said I was interested in his octet atom, he spent the afternoon explaining and defending it, and we became friends! During this period, solo canoeing on the Mohawk out of the Edison Club and a vacation up Schoharie Creek were my principal diversions.

By far my luckiest move was to take a course at Union College on "Modern Physical Theories" by F. K. Richtmyer of Cornell. He was consultant to GE and gave several lectures on each visit. His book became the first year grad student's bible for several decades and a model for mine almost fifty years later.

My senior year was spent catching up on sophomore and junior year courses I'd missed while in the Army and on the high seas. Dad was Oberlin representative to Farrand's inauguration at Cornell. As he departed for the occasion in academic regalia and soup and fish, I told him that I didn't care about the ceremonies but that he must meet the rough-hewn Richtmyer. He was as much impressed by the man as I, and advised me to take the half-time instructorship Richtmyer had offered me. So, having considered MIT, Chicago, and Harvard, I settled on Cornell. That summer my favorite girlfriend was married, and I went on the Lakes, a rough, tough high-seas bos'n—aged 22.

PHYSICS

The first semester at Cornell was so grim that I was ready to quit, but Dad told me I couldn't quit as a loser. Then a notice appeared on the bulletin board: "Wanted—Two biophysicists at the Cleveland Clinic." I knew of the Clinic and of G. W. Crile. Richtmyer said "Darned if I know what a biophysicist is, but I'll tell you something I think is biophysics." He told me of a day at Woods Hole when W. J. V. Osterhout explained the electrical conductivity of the kelp, *Laminaria*. "I think he's right," Richtmyer concluded, "and it looks like darned good fun." But Hugo Fricke wanted two physics PhDs, not a summering first year grad student. He went on vacation to Denmark with no word of what I was to do, so I had to talk myself into the job twice.

Fricke (10) measured the resistance and capacity of blood and calculated the cell membrane at nearly 1 μF cm^{-2}, to give a lipid thickness of 33 Å. He published this finding in the spring of 1923—barely ahead of the extraction and spreading experiments of Gorter & Grendel. I recalibrated his bridge and struggled futilely with his analysis, but it was a good summer. I liked Fricke and admired his history-making combination of theory and experiment. I also learned something of his principal love, the chemical effects of X rays. I knew most of the staff, including several who died in the Clinic fire a few years later. The medical atmosphere was interesting and exciting.

I spent the next summer at the Marine Biology Laboratory at Woods Hole. C. G. Rogers took me in to work on heat production of the eggs of the sea urchin, *Arbacia*. R. A. Budington told me that he was glad to see me interested in a live subject. Rogers had superb measuring equipment, but I had to design and make my first thermopile and stirring gadget while the new Lillie building was being built. The results of the *Arbacia* work were solid and spectacular, but they were first repeated and confirmed 50 years later—at my urging—by Ed Prosen of the National Bureau of Standards.

I went to most of the Physiology and Friday evening lectures as well as the MBL Club dances. I bought a decrepit sailing dory and taught myself to sail while I eased into the sailing crowd led by Ghosty Bridges, of genetics fame. I saw so many interesting and useful things that I thought I could do and had such a wonderful time that I became a Woods Hole addict and set out to try to mix biology with my physics.

Back at Cornell I turned to doing a thesis that involved chasing electrons in circles onto photographic emulsions in a brass box. Most of my fellow graduate students were in the graduate fraternity but, as I found out later, my name was always blackballed. I wasn't even curious about this; I joined a group of fellow barbarians that included a couple of my first-year students. We had some hilarious times to more than compensate for living at home during college.

In the mad scramble to finish up I applied for an NRC post-doc fellowship that would let me follow Fricke and measure the membrane capacity of sea urchin eggs. It seemed easy because they were large and beautifully spherical. But the physics division said that eggs weren't in their jurisdiction; they told me to try biology. Biology said that I didn't have the appropriate training; they told me to try physics. Richtmyer somehow persuaded the sporting biology board to play the long shot and support me at Harvard and Woods Hole under W. J. Crozier and E. L. Chaffee. When my diploma came, Dad said "It's very pretty but it doesn't mean a thing —except that now you won't have to explain why you don't have one."

BIOLOGY

So I became a biologist. Tramping the hot sidewalks of Cambridge looking for a room was discouraging until I came to the last place on my list— opposite Radcliffe—on the second day. Jack Fife clattered down, invited me in, made me a cup of tea, and sold me on the other third floor room. Then he sold his landlady on me as a roomer, and I moved in to the center of my social activities for two happy years. Lucky? Jack was an English grad student. Mrs. Williams, the landlady, had been a student of Osterhout's, was the widow of a Harvard anatomist, and was putting their two children through Radcliffe and Harvard. Her husband had done his thesis on "The Anatomy of the Common Squid, *Loligo*," in which he discovered and described the giant nerve system. But I didn't see the monograph for ten years; I don't know why I didn't cite it in my book.

While I was trying to duplicate Fricke's bridge, my roommate at Cruft, H. B. Vincent, suggested that I use two vacuum thermocouples such as he was using for his shot-noise work. I tried the idea out on Fricke's data and it gave me his result with half of his data. So I designed and built an oscillator and an egg cell—where stirring and aerating the egg suspension were problems, as were electrodes—and got to Woods Hole before the *Arbacia*. I visited New York to meet Osterhout and Selig Hecht, who were to become lifelong friends.

The work went well with minor modifications, but the cell required the eggs from as many as five females. Preliminary calculations following M.

Philippson showed a large dependence of capacity on frequency—contrary to postulate. But I was stuck with the experiment and took as much data as possible on both unfertilized and fertilized eggs. I hoped to sort it out later. I made many friends. E. N. Harvey was a lab neighbor and listened to my woes. When Keffer Hartline complained about his experiment, my vacuum tube and circuit cured the troubles; he upbraided me some years later when his amplifier misbehaved: "It's your fault, you started me on this miserable business." I got another old sailing dory, promptly christened "Hunky"; we sailed as much and as often as possible in it and in Ghosty's beautiful Herreschoff "Virge."

The next year was mixed. In trying to make sense out of my data, I spent long periods in Widner Library. I went back into the fundamentals and tried to derive the relations that (as I didn't know) Kramer & Kronig were just then publishing. But I was very lucky. Browsing through Maxwell's text I discovered his neat derivation for the resistance of a suspension of spheres and then, a few pages earlier, his expression for a two-phase sphere. Extrapolating the outer phase to a thin capacitor and putting it into the suspension, I arrived at considerable improvements on Fricke.

From K. S. Johnson of Bell Labs, who was a visiting professor, I learned about equivalent circuits and complex plane plots. Gildemeister had plotted human skin impedance on the complex plane to give a small, short, straight line; I was able to show that for a constant phase angle impedance this became the circular arc with a depressed center that has since been widely used. I wrote up the two papers alone in Randall Cottage—where, in one of his puckish moods, G. W. Pierce designated me Director. L. R. Blinks came up from Rockefeller with a thermos full of *Laminaria* to check out their high-frequency behavior. I got some understanding of Crozier's thermal coefficients and became acquainted with Hudson Hoagland and Gregory Pincus, who later did "the pill." Crozier really went to work on my two manuscripts. He whipped them and me into shape, both grammatically and logically, for which I've been very grateful. The theory paper (2) is still useful. The experimental one only reminds me to be generous with brash youngsters.

I was intrigued by what little I knew of nerve. I got a fellowship to work with A. V. Hill, but he wouldn't have me unless I'd go back to heat. Then Osterhout called from Washington to ask if I'd like a year with Peter Debye in Leipzig. Would I ever! "Get an application in the mail today and maybe you'll get a fellowship." I missed the last mail, but a long telegram did the trick—except that Debye wouldn't have me. Then Richtmyer interceded, and I had a fabulous year. I worked over my head on Nernst-Planck theory. When I asked what one problem had to do with membranes, Debye stomped to the window muttering "You and your damned membranes."

We both laughed and that was our password. But Debye was frustrated; in a letter to Richtmyer he said, "I've enjoyed having Cole—but please don't send me any more like him." Working with Debye was a rare privilege; I was convinced that he, like Langmuir, was a different kind of mortal.

PHYSIOLOGY

Soon I was to take my first real job as a physiologist. During the winter in Leipzig I'd had a very satisfactory offer from H. B. Williams at Columbia P & S. I accepted twice—once in a letter from Athens that didn't arrive. Williams had battled for the position for a physicist and had asked Richtmyer for a recommendation once he'd gotten it. More luck! The other two PhDs on the P & S faculty, Hans Clarke and Michael Heidelberger, were chemists; I was an oddball. (But Williams himself had been a math major, had been in charge of sound ranging in World War I, and had written a couple of papers on string galvanometer theory and design.) Williams' help and understanding were nearly unbelievable. He took me to the Mens Faculty Club occasionally; usually we ate at the Attendings Dining Room of Presbyterian Hospital. My next best friend was Ross Golden of radiology. He gave me the job of calibrating his therapy machines, and soon I was consulting physicist to the hospital.

We'd had an ethylene explosion in an Operating Room soon after I arrived. Williams and I made recommendations, which fell by the wayside. A fatal cyclopropane explosion some years later was devastating. The Executive Vice President decreed there would be no more cyclo operations until I could assure him that they would be absolutely safe. When we had things under reasonable control I told him I could make the rooms safe for cyclo only by means that would make surgery impossible. I told him I would give the surgeons a probability of an explosion, which they could then consider along with all the other hazards—including those of other anesthetics. He was disgusted but convinced.

I did all sorts of odd jobs. I measured potential differences between teeth, calibrated a skin-temperature gadget, overhauled (with Williams and Hoyt) the first-year medical physiology laboratory, and gave a few of the lectures. The Department was then concentrated on circulatory physiology. B. G. King and E. Oppenheimer injected some 100 dogs with Evans Blue dye and took blood samples between a few minutes and 24 hours afterward. I found the concentrations were beautiful linear functions of the square root of time and wrote up a picture for diffusion of the serum albumin that bound the dye. But this was against the local establishment and also the journal wouldn't publish anything so absurd.

I've been very proud of my aortic aneurysm operation. After being bombarded by reports about everything that had been tried, I finally realized that a wire laid down on the wall and heated to a controlled temperature might work. We used enamelled wire, pushed the bight through a needle and heated it electrically in a bridge. After animal experiments and our first patient we had a long series of successful immobilizations. Our chief of surgery, Alan Whipple, came in once, watched the wire being inserted, looked at me and my rheostats, galvanometer, slide rule, and log-log graph paper, and, twinkling, said "I've seen strange things in operating rooms, but this is the damnedest yet." I was let down when my collaborators wrote up the operation; they gave me credit only for the circuit.

It was Ashley Weech who finally sold me to the Center staff. According to him, I could diagnose, prescribe and cure a patient by phone. He told me of his new and expensive glass electrode pH meter. I kept my reservations to myself. During the summer he reported that his meter was completely unreliable. I told him how to keep the quartz insulation dry, and that did it.

RESEARCH

My own work was slow starting. I got minimum equipment and set up a crude bridge that I used to measure everything from potato, to nerve, to a cat's diaphragm. Then I managed to approximate them on the impedance plane by depressed-center circular arcs. At Woods Hole Harvey was working on *Arbacia* eggs in the centrifuge microscope he'd built (following the design I'd sent him from Leipzig). He came up with an incredibly low value for the surface tension. This I confirmed by dropping a bit of cover slip onto eggs in a dish. I spent much of the winter building an "egg crusher" designed around specially rolled gold wire from a friend at Leeds & Northrup. The results gave me the internal pressure and elasticity I'd long wanted. Harvey hurried me into publication in the *Journal of Cellular & Comparative Physiology*, Vol. 1, No. 1, p. 1, 1932. With no little sentiment I remember that the symposium, which W. J. Adelman, R. A. Sjodin, and R. E. Taylor arranged around my 65th birthday at Woods Hole, appeared as a supplement to the last issue of the *Journal* before it changed its name. This was also about the time that M. Yoneda et al showed I'd probably been too lazy in not integrating the moment of the profile of the egg—which I had built a balance to do. They found the membrane tension independent of the area. (Recently, this question became controversial again!)

The next winter I improved the crusher. Eva Michaelis came with me to work on fertilized eggs during the summer. My brother, R. H. Cole, came to work on a fancy but stupid idea of mine to measure *Arbacia* heat. I'd shopped most of the Cape to find a knockabout I could afford; I called it "Nike." About the first thing I did was to sail it down from Monument Beach single-handed in enough of a breeze to cause Ed Norman to allow as how I must be a good sailor. He had a Herreschoff "S" and was about to rejuvenate the long-dormant Woods Hole Yacht Club. Once, when ballast shifted, my brother Bob and I were dumped in the Hole! That summer Elizabeth Roberts, a Chicago attorney whom I'd known since she was two years old, came to New York and we were married. I took her to Woods Hole. She complained that all I cared about was sailing; she got sea sick. We were to share our lives happily, through thick and thin, for a third of a century. She died with her boots on.

R. G. Harris asked me to help with a symposium he was organizing at Cold Spring Harbor in late '32. I came up with the name, Cold Spring Harbor Symposium on Quantitative Biology, and gave three papers to replace dropouts. It seems a shame to me that lately there have been so many pressures as to preclude the leisurely eight-week programs that were the rule until Reg died.

Bruce Hogg, a medical student, had volunteered to help in New York. Using a micropipette, he and C. M. Goss had explored potentials around a heart-muscle culture. The 2 μm tip killed the cells when he tried to cross a membrane, but there were one or two hot spots in some cultures where the action potentials exceeded the rest potential. He came with me to work on *Laminaria* the first Cold Spring Harbor summer in Fricke's lab. We collected the kelp by diving off Eaton's Neck at chilly dawn and repeated some of Osterhout's experiments. The kinetics were provocative but I couldn't understand them. So the graphs sat in our lab collecting Medical Center grime until we found the answers with *Nitella*. The next summer Bob Cole helped Emil Bozler and me on frog sartorius with a rather good bridge I'd put together. I calculated the resistance and capacity for parallel cylinders following Maxwell, only to find later that Rayleigh had given my resistance as his first approximation. Again we had a constant phase angle impedance, but I finally realized that this gave no information on the absolute value of the frequency-dependent capacity. Remembering my '28 trick for calculating this, I went to work before breakfast to see if the exponents checked. To my vast relief, they did. By sugar substitution, we got an early value of membrane resistance as 40 Ω cm^2.

I'd been remembering E. N. Harvey's telling me of a big white Bermuda sea urchin, then called *Hipponoë*, which he'd found with a few eggs at Christmas. When Dr. Horace Davenport told us of the delights of the Bermuda Station, Elizabeth and I decided to go on a working vacation in the fall. Will Beebe and his group were recovering from their bathysphere deep dive and included us in all their fun, from helmet diving at Almost Island to motor boating to St. Georges for dinner and moonlight dancing. Elizabeth had a rough time with her bicycle and was black and blue from running into ditches and hibiscus bushes. With the captain of the Bermuda water polo team we collected eggs from every possible source. Our last collection gave two ripe female *Hipponoë* and 100% fertilization, as Harvey had suspected. So we planned another expedition the next fall and the H. J. Curtises came along for a couple of weeks. One memory is of the four of us racing our bikes back from Swizzle Inn.

Our second experiment gave a 90° phase angle—*Hipponoë's* membrane was a perfect capacitor, altogether different from my *Arbacia*. Also the capacity increased on fertilization and decreased on swelling. (Bob Taylor recently asked about the capacity per egg—not per square cm—and it was near enough constant to suggest microscopic dimples and pimples or wrinkles and crinkles.) So we had to do *Arbacia* again. The next summer Bob and I imposed on Fricke's hospitality again; for eggs from starfish we found the same result as for *Hipponoë*. When we used urchins from Woods Hole it was the same story. Why did three echinoderm eggs have a perfect capacity while all tissues showed what I've come to call dielectric loss? And how did the capacity increase on fertilization? And what was the high-frequency dispersion at several MHz?

My ideas on a wheatstone bridge had jelled enough to justify my taking 1935 off to design and build it. Dottie Curtis and Elizabeth decided that Curtis should work with me. The Rockefeller Foundation supported the idea; he arrived at New Years, just in time to solder a few of the last joints. Joe Spencer had been dropped from Princeton, and he was volunteered to help us; we'd been invited to give a paper at the '36 CSH Symposium on nerve and muscle; Ted Jahn wanted to work on grasshopper egg cuticle during this summer: We had a feverish rush.

We knew that muscle fibers varied considerably in size and, since cell radius is a factor, whole muscles could give an apparent membrane loss. Years later, Paul Fatt showed, gently but firmly by calculation, that the contribution of the size spread was negligible. In our paper we also derived the longitudinal impedance of a single nerve fiber with narrow and also with wide electrodes. The wide-electrode result looked too difficult to be useful.

At Woods Hole, Joe Spencer did a precision job on *Arbacia* eggs. He confirmed the findings of *Hipponoë* and *Asterias* while showing that Bob and I had tried to do too much on too few eggs at Cold Spring Harbor. As Curtis worked with single eggs at Woods Hole, Rita Guttman studied frog eggs in New York. One of these was held in a cylindrical hole in the disc between the electrodes. I couldn't solve the potential theory so she got an analog solution using progressively larger glass beads as a model system. But I thought the resistance effect would be too small to measure with red cells when Coulter proposed his counter. How wrong can you be? Recently it was found that W. R. Smythe had solved the problem in an entirely different connection. Smythe was certainly pleased when I told him our data agreed with his solution. How widespread has been the use of the Coulter counter! (Then Smythe was bewildered and deeply grateful when I pointed out an old mistake in the last edition of his book!)

SQUID

The spectacular events of the summer of 1936 involved J. Z. Young and his squid giant axon. Squid were brought from the south shore of Long Island in milk cans; they arrived thoroughly inked and more dead than alive. The two axons we tried looked just like sea water but Young convinced us of their importance. "If you want to find out about nerve, you've got to work on this axon." When I asked how everyone had missed this half-mm tube as an axon, Young said he'd not done the literature until he'd mostly finished at Naples and then had found a 1912 monograph—by an American —on the giant axon system of squid. "Would that American be L. W. Williams?" I asked. I told him the story of my landlady's husband—to his utter amazement.

Elizabeth became pregnant and our lives were going to be different for a while. We went to England on an elegant small Cunarder because U.S. lines were struck, taking with us *Time* magazine with its center spread on Wallis Simpson and King Edward. This was all news to Britain and we kept current with the Paris Herald. We had a delightful lunch with J. Z. Young at Oxford, and I probably first met Alan Hodgkin in Cambridge during this visit. We took one of the first ferry trains to Paris where we visited A. M. Monnier and his wife. Elizabeth had her first, and I my second, encounter with bitter winter weather in the Atlantic in a small American freighter coming back. We were four or five days late, but home by Christmas.

The squid axon was a bigger break by far than we knew then. Our first interest was to see if 1 μF cm^{-2} and dielectric loss were characteristic of a single cell membrane. Curtis suggested that we use *Nitella* during the winter. We got the 1 μF cm^{-2} and a considerable loss—as had Blinks—but the *Nitella* had far too low a resistance. Finally when we pulled the cellulose sheath over a glass rod we found we had what came to be called an ion exchanger—the conductivity was nearly independent of that of the medium, as has been confirmed.

We arrived at Woods Hole with the squid and soon had another 1 μF cm^{-2} with considerable loss—70° to 80°. Out of plate glass Curtis ground a new cell with much larger electrodes; it made no difference to our findings. We also had a second, high-frequency dispersion, which we ignored. More disturbing was the fact that there was no change of impedance during excitation nor during deterioration until an hour or so after the axon became inexcitable (9). A constant critic kept his record clean: "I always thought you were carefully measuring something quite unimportant!"

We went back to *Nitella* in the fall of '37; using narrow electrodes we saw the transverse impedance decrease as an impulse went past. For the first time, I calculated the effect of a pure membrane resistance decrease. Our points taken from movies of the unbalance Lissajous figures during impulses could be interpreted as an average 15% decrease of membrane capacity from its resting value of 0.9 μF cm^{-2} and an average maximum resistance decrease of 500 Ωcm^2 which was independent of frequency. So the capacity change seemed negligible compared to the 200-fold decrease of membrane resistance. But the lowest resistance (500 Ωcm^2) was considerable. It was also interesting to do some analysis on the characteristics of a partial short circuit travelling with constant speed. The paper we wrote is a pride and joy to me (5). If (as we've been accused of doing) we started a new era of axonology, it was in this paper that we had to be original.

We built a new cell and a new amplifier; we modified our first commercial oscilloscope to give single, but highly nonlinear, sweeps. Then we waited, miserably, at Woods Hole for the first squid. Our first two axons showed nothing. We put in the whole nerve. With everything wide open we observed a very slight change. Curtis swore it was a decrease; I wasn't sure. But it got larger and larger as we used better and better axons, until finally we got the picture shown in Figure 1 (6). The photo was taken in the dark with my '29 Leica. I set and tripped the Lucas spring rheotome some twenty times for the impedance change, ΔZ, and half a dozen times for the action potential, V. I had a bloody thumb sometimes. Hodgkin visited when we had ΔZ on the scope. He was as excited as I've ever seen him, jumping up and down as we explained it. He also appreciated the importance of the resting membrane resistance and thought longitudinal measurements between long electrodes could give it. He assembled the equipment in New York and took the data back to Cambridge to find about 1000 Ωcm^2 (7).

On my way to the 1938 Zurich congress I stopped in London; Otto Schmitt was there; Bernard Katz had just come from Leipzig; A. V. Hill instructed me on talking to the multilingual audience I would face. Brian Matthews and I travelled together and talked sailboats most of the way. After a bad case of jitters I was truly surprised by the enthusiastic reception of my talk.

Near the end of the Congress a cable sent me to Vienna. Elizabeth's sister had married a Viennese doctor, and they wanted me to bring his mother back with me. It was very distressing that Frau Frey, her relatives, and her friends could only go to each other's homes in the evenings and talk about the Nazi restrictions and what had happened to whom. I could only get transit visas for Switzerland and France when we had to leave—two weeks before our boat sailed. The inspector on the boat train nearly had apoplexy when I showed him Frau Frey's passport. Frau Frey was the belle of the boat; she could go anywhere, do anything, and talk to everybody—which she did. Then we were met in Hoboken by the Jewish Relief, who insisted I was not an adequate escort! Frau Frey had a wonderful time in Chicago with her children, going to tea rooms and movies for the few years she had left.

Curtis had talked with Hodgkin about recording the internal potential of an axon but I wasn't enthusiastic. Why bother about an upside down action potential? We used a metal core needle. Hodgkin and Huxley got a certain overshoot, with a micropipette and reported this in a note in *Nature*. We did better the next summer (except for an overcompensation of the 100 μm glass tube).

It most certainly was a serious mistake in general for us to have directed so much attention to our single exception to the mean behavior of all our other axons. Hodgkin (11) blames it and the dextrose effect for a year's delay in proposing the "sodium hypothesis." The dextrose effect I neither understand nor remember.

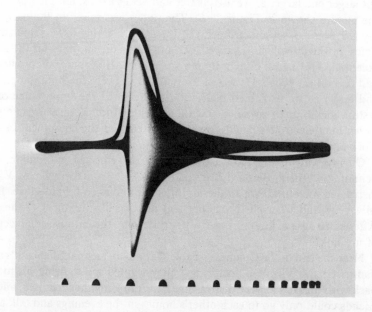

Figure 1 Oscillograms from passing squid-axon impulse. Action potential is the single line, *V;* impedance decrease, ΔZ, is the band; time mark are 1 msec apart. [After (6), 1938.]

But the Battle of Britain had begun. Curtis and I measured the potential under an external electrode and I found a neat trick to get the membrane V-I rectification curve. Hodgkin dubbed it Cole's Theorem. Years later I was disgusted to find I'd assumed linearity in one step; I'm still puzzled about why several better derivations give the same answer.

Curtis wanted to become a real physiologist and went to Johns Hopkins with Phil Bard. R. F. Baker came to us having written a mass-spectrometer thesis; we found that impedance changes by current flow duplicated those during a passing impulse at intermediate frequencies. We also measured the inductive reactance that Hodgkin and I had found in the membrane. It could be explained by the time needed to establish a nonlinear steady state and could also be a capacitive reactance.

As Baker became interested in microscopic spectroscopy and electron microscopy, George Marmont came from Cal Tech. We investigated the effects of K^+ and Ca^{2+} on longitudinal impedance. The results were striking (4) but were only published in abstract at the time. I thought the capacitive and inductive reactances might be permanent structures, seen only as allowed by shunt or series resistances, but the complexity was hideous. The time constant of nonlinearity and Mott's semiconductor theory adapted for K^+ made much more sense.

I'd studied the calculus of variations under Marston Morse at Cornell (along with I. I. Rabi) and had listened to his lectures on mechanics at Harvard. Still, I was surprised to have him suggest that I come to the Institute for Advanced Study on leave after he'd been there a while. I was tired of the medical atmosphere at the College of Physicians and Surgeons, and I got a Guggenheim for one of our very happy years. We had just moved to the Bronx, but we moved again with our very new little girl. I was set up in Fine Hall in mathematics with physics next door and the joint library upstairs. L. A. MacColl of Bell Labs had told me of V. Bush's lecture, "The Engineer Grapples with Nonlinearity." With that and Mott's semiconductor theory for starts, I chased nonlinearity and negative resistances through the mostly Japanese and Russian literature. John Tukey set up an IBM card-sort solution for a membrane, but I couldn't tell him the membrane characteristics. Riding into New York one day, I sat with Solomon Lefschetz. I told him I was planning to bring him a question.

"What is it?"

"How to tell one side of a line from the other."

"That's a good question for a topologist. Why do you want to know?"

"I want to know what makes a nerve impulse go."

"You come see me day after tomorrow and we'll talk."

Talk we did for practically a solid week. After a few days he said that because he wanted to know more, he would give a course. After the second week he had decided to translate the pertinent Russian literature. Decades later, shortly before he died, he introduced me to a friend as the man who had started him on the work he'd been doing for the past 25–30 years.

WAR

There were all kinds of visits and phone calls to enlist me in war work, but I was determined to finish the sabbatical that was starting so well. Luring me to Chicago for consultation, A. H. Compton and N. Hillberry told me the story of nuclear fission and demanded that I take charge of the biomedical problems. I knew at least how to start; and after I had persuaded them I could take no medical responsibility, it was an exciting four years. Our group grew exponentially to nearly 400 before staffing Site X (Oak Ridge). It was six months before our first laboratory was ready. It occupied the disinfected stable of an extinct ice plant on the south side of the Midway, and it was extended twice. Soon we had the first practical hunk of uranium from Spedding. We fought battles for survival with Groves; we struggled to get support from DuPont. Meanwhile the pile went critical.

Soon after R. E. Zinkle came with me, we interviewed Pat Lear for the job of animal farm manager. She told Ray she could cook. She was a tower of strength—even though she could not cook.

George Svihla and I decided to try an autoradiograph for fission product dose. An exposed guinea pig was frozen, sawed into thick sections, and reassembled with X-ray film between the sections. Svihla noticed that the machinist who had watched the procedure put on gloves to replace the band saw blade. Joe Hamilton, who supplied much of our distribution data from Berkeley, could never understand why we used thick sections.

I stole Curtis from an aviation project to head up Site X biology. In a sea of mud in the early days I had to be carried by men in hip boots. Ladd Prosser was my unhappy, able, number two at Chicago. Jo Graff was our beautiful administrator, who kept things going while her husband was interning. Only by the few times she wept on my shoulder could I guess what it cost her to be so tough.

It was all tightly programmed—except for the free 10% man days I insisted upon—but after Hiroshima and Nagasaki the place blew up. Everybody had kept his pet hates to himself until the war was won.

War is so disgusting, so futile.

PEACE

The University of Chicago set up the new Institutes. Zinkle became head of Radiobiology and Biophysics, and I resigned from Columbia to head up

Biophysics. It was a real wrench. At Columbia I'd found myself, I'd been happy. The years there were the best I've had.

George Marmont came to Chicago; we took equipment to Woods Hole for squid studies in 1946. It was not a good summer; we tried futilely to extend our prewar results on longitudinal impedance to low-frequency effects of current flow. Jimmie Savage had worked with Warren Weaver, who had thrust upon Jimmie a fellowship to work with me. Savage visited us late in the summer; after listening to our woes, he suggested putting a long current-carrying electrode inside the axon. I explained how the electrode polarization would probably defeat us; but Marmont took him seriously and soon proposed a reduced silver axial electrode, a central outside electrode with a guard at each end, and electronic control of the membrane current. I promptly added the inverse of membrane potential control.

In 1947 Carlos Chagas had invited me to Rio de Janeiro to lecture and consult at the new Instituto de Biofisica. It was a long, hard trip, but I was met by an enthusiastic delegation. During a courtesy visit to the Rector it was decided that my lectures would be published as the first of a series. There have been several reprints of the *Four Lectures on Biophysics*. I was able to help E. Leão with his spreading-depression impedance decrease; it could be interpreted as a membrane-resistance decrease. I couldn't do anything with the Instituto's favorite electric eel and I got back in time to go to Woods Hole.

After the usual start-up troubles but with Will Rall's help, we had the Mach I cell in operation in 1947. We confirmed the 1 μF cm^{-2} and 1000 Ωcm^2 findings and ran strength-duration curves with direct data. We found the initial resistance to be much too high unless there was a series resistance associated with the membrane; we had trouble with anode block of an impulse. My dream of making excitation stand still in space and time was half-fulfilled; it was not until J. W. Moore showed that excitation for the squid axon in iso-osmotic KCl and CaCl$_2$ was stable in time that I had the other half. However, Marmont was firmly opposed to my insistence on membrane potential control, and I got only a few runs—including that shown in Figure 2 (3). These I found spectacular. There was no trace of a threshold; the early inward current was a mystery, but it was a transient negative resistance that could account—at least qualitatively—for the rise and height of a spike and its propagation. The outward currents corresponded to our ideas about K$^+$.

In the fall Hodgkin told me of his Na$^+$ results with Katz; but I was more impressed by my own data, which I told him about. He wanted to visit us; still, he wasn't altogether happy to find I'd booked him for the annual biology division lecture, which he gave on the Na$^+$ work—to a full house. We went over the equipment and my results in great detail. He vigorously

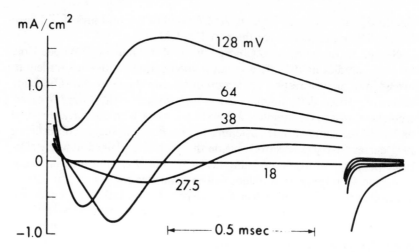

Figure 2   Squid-axon membrane currents after step depolarizations as indicated from resting potential (voltage clamps). [After (3), 1947.]

defended his and A. L. Huxley's carrier theory and blamed the slow rise of inward current on apparatus; but I believed my results, and he later confirmed them. I also pointed out troubles with electrode polarization (which they corrected) and with the membrane resistance (which they compensated for).

Through the winter, while Marmont designed and built the elegant Mach II cell, I tried all sorts of outrageous schemes to explain the potential-control data and did various Institute chores. We got a new Director, who didn't care what biophysics was, so long as it was physical chemistry. He told Savage to go back to mathematics where he belonged; Jimmie became Mr. Statistics, first at Chicago and then at Yale. The Director didn't mind having me, but he didn't want any more like me. I felt less than wanted at Chicago and our friends agreed.

DEFENSE

It was a most auspicious time for Admiral Clarence Brown to offer me the new position of Technical Director at the Naval Medical Research Institute in Bethesda and announce that he was going to stay in Chicago until I accepted. From the latter intention he was dissuaded; he sat out my indecision in Washington. Leaving the Institute was not easy—the breadth of the University was so great, and we had many good friends—but I felt I had to try the unknown again. I had not realized how discouraged Elizabeth had been in Chicago; she was delighted to be going to Washington.

I had to interrupt making friends and enemies at NMRI to go to Paris by way of London for the electrophysiology conference in honor of Louis Lapicque and his gallant war stand. I spoke for the visitors and included an April-in-Paris note. It was my first chance to present my '47 results, which I could only do briefly as an introduction, really, for Hodgkin, Huxley and Katz (14). In a little over a year they had corrected most of my difficulties, caught up and run past me. I was pleased that we had been their starting point and that they had confirmed my results, although I was not entirely happy to have the concept and the technique dubbed the "voltage clamp."

My simple plan for NMRI was to have a group of small, strong centers of research distributed as well over the medical field as possible so that any emergency would be within reach of one or perhaps two staffed working laboratories. This would avoid some of what caused our slow start up at Chicago. Manuel Morales was a fountain of good ideas (e.g. that we should invite Terrell Hill to join us). Moore, one of several students of Jesse Beams who turned to biology, came with us to work on muscle impedance; we had Dave Goldman, who started to construct an analog computer. The energetic submariner Al Behnke kept things moving as Executive Officer. Early on, Admiral Brown transferred to us his long-time right-hand man, Vic King, with instructions to get done the things we wanted done. W. E. (Bill) Kellum became CO and soon had the admiration and respect of civilians and military alike. Although he confessed it took him a year to understand what I was trying to do, he could straighten out my mistakes almost before I made them. But it was slow business, with much diversion, backtracking, and backbiting. Then we lost momentum. Ed Condon was hounded out of the Bureau of Standards; McCarthy forced out two of the most unlikely subversives of our staff—one now a full professor at Yale; A. V. Astin was only saved in the battery additive fiasco at the NBS after a slow protest from outside government and the Bureau was weakened by fragmentation; the Office of Naval Research was being forced to curtail its broad effectiveness to "man in the fleet" problems; and good rumor had it that NMRI was next. We were losing key personnel in the antiintellectual movement and couldn't get adequate replacements. I tried to get a more prestigious replacement for me but I couldn't get even medical support in my office. We seemed to be in an apparently endless decline.

Five of us flew Navy via Gander, Azores, Port Leyouty, and London to the 1951 Copenhagen physiological congress. At the Congress dinner, Lord Adrian said that if we were to rank our national preferences he was sure Denmark would be the unanimous choice for second place. One spectacular achievement reported was Ussing's electrochemical identification of an ion pump. But I was much more interested in the preliminary curves Huxley showed me of their Na^+ and K^+ conductances-vs-potential from voltage-clamp data.

The next summer (1952) there was a Cold Spring Harbor repeat run on nerve and nerve systems. Hodgkin sent me near-to-final drafts of their five *Journal of Physiology* manuscripts, and at last I realized fully what they were doing and how enormously successful they had been. Hodgkin gave the paper with his usual calm, convincing enthusiasm. After ten minutes the Chairman, Frank Schmitt, co-opted me to handle the discussion. I infuriated Hodgkin by counting the number of ad hoc analytical forms and numerical values in their equations (12). But he also said they had fully confirmed my 1947 results and had used essentially our experimental approach. Lorente de No said that it was a powerful picture and might be right but that it couldn't work for a frog axon. John Eccles dominated the rest of the all-too-short symposium and won at least grudging admiration from everyone by producing three new theories in three days.

On our way back to Woods Hole I was feeling very sorry for myself because Hodgkin and Huxley (HH) had done all that I had ever hoped to do. Consolingly, Hodgkin said they had just followed my lead. Later Huxley was to say he was only Hodgkin's student, while Eccles only claimed to apply their results. At Woods Hole, Moore and I were trying to clamp with external electrodes. Hodgkin wasn't sympathetic, but he dissected axons for us and tried to teach our other guest, I. Tasaki, to do it—even using Tasaki's favorite needles.

In 1952 the Standards Eastern Automatic Computer was in somewhat erratic operation at NBS. H. A. Antosiewicz and I explored all four quadrants of the HH equations (13) and found a saddle point that was an undoubted threshold. I passed the word to Bonhoeffer, and to his translator, Max Delbrück, that his thermochemical analogy would have to have a threshold. Huxley agreed with Richard FitzHugh's phantom saddle point, and they both thought I was wrong. Several years later I ran onto some unaccountable bumps in the curves. FitzHugh & Antosiewicz finally traced these to an absurd programming mistake that had produced the saddle point. Although important theoretically, the threshold was only 1 part in 10^8 wide and only made a percent or so change in any physiological parameter, but I had to explain and apologize as widely as possible. It was only a decade and a half later when Rita Guttman was getting much more gradual thresholds at temperatures in the 30s C, which F. Bezanilla confirmed with HH calculations.

Moore saw an advantage in using a microcapillary for the internal axon potential, and we practiced on "open chest" squid with intact circulation. Harvey had mixed feelings: "Here is a perfectly good biological experiment being done by two physicists." The undershoot recovery was delayed so much that we could expect it to disappear along with the HH leakage in an undisturbed animal. This Hodgkin and Keynes did find by boring through the mantle directly to the axon!

NATIONAL INSTITUTES OF HEALTH

Seymour Kety was intramural director for the NINDB and NIMH joint operation at National Institutes of Health and planned a biophysics laboratory. I was a very discouraged administrator after four years of war and six of defense, and the squid work I wanted to do was more than I could support at NMRI. So Moore and I moved across the street. With me I took considerable regrets that the Navy might not get what it needed and deserved for some time; I also took a pay cut!

Once again we were starting a new lab from scratch. It is not easy to sort out the apparently intertwining threads of the past twenty-three years at NIH. The most compelling strand has been the voltage clamp, with the squid axon a close second. If (as I've been accused of doing) I revolutionized electrobiology in 1947, Hodgkin and Huxley certainly took the giant step in 1952. Hodgkin (11) recounted it for the centenary of the Physiological Society in 1976. As the concept of the clamp has been accepted, many new techniques (some good, some not so good) have been developed. I guess there are well over 100 voltage clamps around the world; the published papers relying on them must be in the thousands. And now solid-state programming and data reduction are rapidly taking over manipulations far beyond my wildest dreams.

The "abominable notch" was still with us. Moore, Taylor, and I spent a couple of years on it—spurred on by Frankenhauser and Hodgkin, who ignored it, and by Tasaki and collaborators, who insisted that all good axons showed it. (Who wants to work on less than the best?) Although it almost certainly comes from poor electrodes, it is still the constant threat that I, and Hodgkin and Huxley, only narrowly avoided before 1950. Moore and I had been keeping our axons hyperpolarized between pulses to maximize the sodium currents, but all too soon the polarizing currents would begin to run away or the axial electrode would bubble. Only a few msec of prepolarization were adequate to prevent these troubles and prepotential had little effect on the initial sodium current. But after -212 mV the potassium currents were delayed by up to 0.2 msec. Didn't this prove HH were wrong? No, only limited! Our article (8) seems to have been a good start for the *Biophysical Journal,* first volume, first number, first page, 1960. The Cole-Moore delay has been confirmed for squid (Figure 3) and has been a

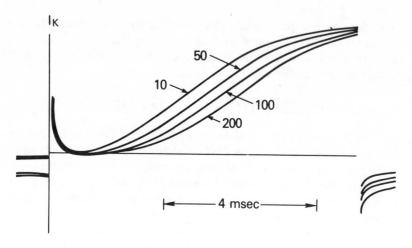

Figure 3 Depolarizations of squid axon with TTX after 3 msec hyperpolarizations to indicated potentials from holding potential. [After Keynes, Kimura & Lecar, unpublished.]

major challenge for theory. For several years there have been rumors that a frog node is different. So it may be that our simple delay is the exception rather than the rule; theorists can then let out their belts.

The work of our group on squid was hampered and finally broken up by dissension that I was unable to ease or prevent without more space. So I made everyone a section chief and went on alone.

We had only the simple analog computer—a descendant of V. Bush's mechanical differential analyzer, which I'd admired—and with it I learned the lessons I got from v. Neumann and E. Teller. The computer succeeds calculus as a way of intellectual life. Richard FitzHugh took it over—he'd always wanted one—and worked up to solutions of the HH equations before turning to keep pace with the digital developments. He worked on topology, developed the BVP (Bonhoeffer–van der Pol) analogy, and moved on to the relatively recent economics of nerve and muscle action. I've loved his teaching gadgets and his cartoons—the "Drink MyxiCola" gag, and the coy squid (which I've stolen).

We had been going along happily with *Loligo* at Woods Hole when I heard (around 1960) that the Humbolt *Dosidicus* off Chile weren't as impossible to work with as I'd been led to believe. Our first expedition didn't come off; but the second, in the fall of '63 with Dan Gilbert in charge, was a good start. Our groups had excellent seasons at Vina del Mar with E. Rojas in spite of crude collecting and laboratory facilities, fantastic logistics, and a tidal wave. But in 1971, with a capacity crowd waiting, not one single *Dosidicus* was to be found—nor have they reappeared. The unlikely troika of Keynes, Rojas, and Taylor has, however, continued to function. In Chile, efforts have been diverted to the giant barnacle muscle fiber; at Bethesda, Leonard Binstock discovered and promoted the cord of the worm, *Myxicola,* which has become a mainstay of the laboratory.

Ross Bean, whom I'd met at a bilayer meeting, came to see us at Bethesda. We persuaded him to try a very low concentration of additives; this gave impressive unit conductances. These studies, along with studies of fluctuations, have continued to expand in the lab under Gerry Ehrenstein and Harold Lecar.

For some time I'd decided that I should step aside at 65—as insurance against mistakes and to let young blood take over. I almost made it. Taylor became Acting Lab Chief in '63 and continued until '71. Adelman came back as Lab Chief and, after considerable shuffling around, moved with two sections to Woods Hole year round, leaving a section in Bethesda.

BIOPHYSICS

My first attempt at formal biophysics was a discussion group I chaired at the first summer meeting of the American Physical Society in 1927 at Cornell. During the war I tangled with Leo Szilard, who had been about to switch from physics to biology when artificial radioactivity was discovered. He dismissed my simple approach to biophysics, and it was only after many hours that I caught on: Biophysics was whatever Szilard did in biology, and that settled the argument. He started to work on phage after the war. When peace came, departments, laboratories, institutes, divisions, and branches of biophysics burst into the open. Many plans arose for national organization and publication. I managed to keep in touch with the more active people and groups, but so much time and effort were wasted in attempting definitions that I finally was able to get them ruled out of order. I was in favor of affiliating with the Institute of Physics; this notion was bitterly attacked. Alan Burton, then President of the American Physiological Society, told me what APS could offer, but I knew that a number of noisy physicists and engineers would have none of it. I had to do the best I could, even though I was a loyal member of the Society.

It was finally obvious that biophysics had to proceed without assistance or entangling alliances. An informal but considerable group at the '56 Federation meeting voted for a trial meeting to be run by the Committee of Four, E. Pollard, O. Schmitt, S. Talbot, and me. We held the first meeting at Columbus with Air Force funds from Colonel A. P. Gagge; Pollard produced the required *Proceedings.* When Hartline said that we had more people he knew and more he wanted to know than any meeting he'd been to, I was sure we had succeeded. Elizabeth and I wrote up both the

Constitution and Bylaws. I worked for their adoption, item by item. After an evening without adverse discussion at Cambridge, the Biophysical Society came into being. It has been very interesting to watch the completely independent development of a division of biological physics in the American Physical Society and the current trial of joint sponsorship of the *Biophysical Journal.* I do hope that the casual cooperation can go on.

H. B. Steinbach was commissioned to organize an ad hoc National Research Council committee to keep track of international biophysics. After considerable manipulation, the first congress was held in Stockholm. United States financing was an important factor in assuring its success, and I was relieved of one of my longest ad hoc services. The organization joined UNESCO to become the International Union of Pure and Applied Biophysics and now meets regularly.

A major effort was made in 1969 to bring MBL up to date. Steinbach and I had talked for some time about having a voltage-clamp researcher working with students at Woods Hole through the winter. Finally Adelman put together a summer program in 1969—the Excitable Membrane Training Program. He edited the book of lectures, *Biophysics and Physiology of Excitable Membranes* (1). Ernie Wright was the angel who kept it going for six years before it was ruled out. It was well worthwhile.

I was named Regents' Professor at the University of California at Berkeley for the first semester of 1963–64, and Elizabeth was determined to go with me. We had a lovely apartment near campus. It overlooked San Francisco Bay and the Golden Gate, which I'd steered a West Coast War Emergency boat in and out of long before there was a bridge. I usually got home early so we could put up our feet at cocktail time and watch the glorious sunsets. I'd decided to write up my lectures as a book, but I was not prepared for what became a five year stint.

I've been back to Berkeley almost every year for the winter quarter. I have gradually entrusted my seminar to C. A. Tobias and have added La Jolla and Galveston to my visiting list. P. E. Lilienthal of Cal Press saw me through the book *Membranes, Ions and Impulses* and its reprinting in 1972 (4). I'm almost convinced it was worth the time and effort. By the time I had recovered it was mandatory retirement time.

RETIRED AND REHIRED

My 70th birthday was ushered in with flair at the Gilberts' by the Piet Oostings' singing Happy Birthday in Dutch at midnight, and I became a rehired annuitant. As an experimentalist I've increasingly depended on Woods Hole, where for some years I've had relative peace and quiet in 150 square feet of space. I've not only gotten my hands dirty, I've cut, burned, and otherwise maltreated them on my own.

I had been somewhat querulous about various aspects of the electrical and electron-micrographic estimates of the Schwann sheath at 1.5 Ωcm^2 until I ran onto a paper Curtis and I published in '38 on the axon-impedance locus with its incomplete high-frequency tail. Could it be the Schwann sheath? Probably so; I calculated the resistance to be 1.6 Ωcm^2. Before 1970, Choh lu Li, Tony Bak, and I had run analogs to show that the low-concentration Rayleigh and Maxwell resistance equations applied to up to 100% volume concentrations of several close-packing cylinders and three dimensional forms. If cylinders made up the sheath, then the extra-cellular space constitutes about one half of one percent of cell volume. But what about the 4 MHz dispersion capacity? Might the low-frequency Rayleigh capacity equation work up to 100%? An analog said it did. Thus, if the membrane capacities are 1 $\mu F\ cm^{-2}$, the sheath should be six cells thick—except that the cells aren't cylinders! Membrane-covered cubes followed the Maxwell capacity up to 100%. This completes at least a sketch of Fricke's beginning in 1923. The 1935 bridge reappeared, after 18 years in hiding and minus crucial transformers, to make it possible, at least, to test guard arrangements and perhaps to find out more about dielectric loss!

IN CONCLUSION

I've had busy and exciting times with membranes since I first heard of them in 1923. In spite of my mistakes, I'm very happy to have had the good luck to participate in the development of the present widespread enthusiasm for them. I'm only slightly modest about the many and good friends who've helped so much and who share in my distinctions. These days I find it difficult to keep track of new concepts, powerful techniques, and obvious conclusions—but I keep on trying.

Literature Cited

1. Adelman, W. J. Jr., ed. 1971. *Biophysics and Physiology of Excitable Membranes.* New York: Van Nostrand Reinhold. 527 pp.
2. Cole, K. S. 1928. Electric impedance of suspensions of spheres. *J. Gen. Physiol.* 12:29–36
3. Cole, K. S. 1949. Dynamic electrical characteristics of the squid giant axon membrane. *Arch. Sci. Physiol.* 3:253–58
4. Cole, K. S. 1972. *Membranes, Ions and Impulses.* Berkeley: Univ. Calif. Press. 569 pp. 2nd printing

5. Cole, K. S., Curtis, H. J. 1938. Electric impedance of *Nitella* during activity. *J. Gen. Physiol.* 22:37–64
6. Cole, K. S., Curtis, H. J. 1939. Electric impedance of the squid giant axon during activity. *J. Gen. Physiol.* 22:649–70
7. Cole, K. S., Hodgkin, A. L. 1939. Membrane and protoplasm resistance in the squid giant axon. *J. Gen. Physiol.* 22:671–87
8. Cole, K. S., Moore, J. W. 1960. Potassium ion current in the squid giant

axon: dynamic characteristics. *Biophys. J.* 1:1–14

9. Curtis, H. J., Cole, K. S. 1938. Transverse electric impedance of the squid giant axon. *J. Gen. Physiol.* 21:757–65

10. Fricke, H. 1923. The electric capacity of cell suspensions. *Phys. Rev.* 21:708–9

11. Hodgkin, A. L. 1976. Chance and design in electrophysiology: an informal account of certain experiments on nerve carried out between 1934 and 1952. *J. Physiol. London* 263:1–21

12. Hodgkin, A. L., Huxley, A. F. 1952. Movements of sodium and potassium ions during nervous activity. *Cold Spring Harbor Symp. Quant. Biol.* 17:43–52

13. Hodgkin, A. L., Huxley, A. F. 1952. A quantitative description of membrane current and its application to conduction and excitation in nerve. *J. Physiol. London* 117:500–44

14. Hodgkin, A. L., Huxley, A. F., Katz, B. 1949. Ionic currents underlying activity in the giant axon of the squid. *Arch. Sci. Physiol.* 3:129–50

GASTROINTESTINAL PHYSIOLOGY

Introduction

The gastrointestinal system is, among other things, a collection of neuro-muscular tissues, a collection of specialized epithelia that exhibit a wide variety of absorptive and secretory functions, a collection of endocrine cells, and a collection of target cells for the gastrointestinal hormones. In addition, it contains vast and complex biochemical factories capable of breaking down the ingesta into absorbable forms, synthesizing triglycerides and proteins, catabolizing endocrine secretions, detoxifying and secreting alien agents, etc. It is difficult to identify any other physiological system that features as many diverse functions and capabilities. During the past few decades all of these areas have developed into highly advanced subspecialties with their own languages and technologies, and the "gastrointestinal physiologist" has become a rare and endangered species much like the "Renaissance man."

The natural evolution of clearly defined subdivisions within the conglomerate referred to as "gastrointestinal physiology" makes this subject ideally suited to the new format adopted by the *Annual Review of Physiology.* Our plan is that each volume will contain 5–7 papers dealing with a central theme or subspecialty and that these themes will recycle at approximately 4–5 year intervals.

The theme for this volume is "The humoral and neural regulation of gastrointestinal secretions." Drs. Morton I. Grossman, John Walsh, and Andrew Sol not only agreed to contribute to this effort, but also helped design the entire section. I, and the Editorial Committee of the *Annual Review of Physiology,* are grateful for their gracious and expert assistance.

The theme for Volume 42, already underway, is "Mechanisms of absorption and secretion by gastrointestinal epithelia;" the subject for Volume 43 will be "Gastrointestinal motility."

Stanley G. Schultz
Section Editor

25

Ann. Rev. Physiol. 1979. 41:27–33
Copyright © 1979 by Annual Reviews Inc. All rights reserved

NEURAL AND HORMONAL REGULATION OF GASTROINTESTINAL FUNCTION: AN OVERVIEW

♦1203

Morton I. Grossman

VA Wadsworth Hospital Center and UCLA School of Medicine,
Los Angeles, California

During the past decade physiologists have been so preoccupied with the newly isolated peptide hormones of the gut that nerves have been neglected. This imbalance is now being redressed because we are learning that nerves are more important than we have supposed. The interactions between nerves and hormones are pervasive. For an understanding of gastrointestinal regulation it is usually necessary to study both.

Since all gastrointestinal hormones had been found to be peptides, it was assumed that the converse was also true—i.e. that all biologically active gastrointestinal peptides are hormones. It is now apparent that this is not so. Some gastrointestinal peptides are in nerves and some are in endocrine-like cells which, however, do not discharge their product into the blood and therefore are presumed to perform a paracrine function. The recent discovery that many peptides are found in both neurons of the brain and endocrine cells of the gut (20) has revolutionized our ideas about how the activities of the digestive tract are regulated.

THE BRAIN-GUT AXIS

In 1931, von Euler & Gaddum (28) were using a bioassay system, contraction of rabbit jejunum, to study the distribution of acetylcholine in various tissues. They serendipitously found that extracts of brain and of intestine contained a substance that reacted in the system but was not

27

acetylcholine since its action was not inhibited by atropine. The active principle came to be known as substance P and many years later was isolated both from brain (6) and from intestine (25) and identified as a peptide with 11 amino acid residues. In recent years we have come to recognize that substance P is the prototype of a long and still-growing list of peptides found in both brain and gut. Neurotensin is the only peptide other than substance P that has been isolated from both brain (5) and gut (16) and shown to have the same composition in both sites. The other peptides found in both brain and gut have been isolated and sequenced from only one of these sites and then shown by radioimmunoassay or immunohistochemistry to have immunological cross-reacting counterparts in the other site. Thus we cannot be sure that we are dealing with identical peptides in both sites. Peptides first isolated from the gastrointestinal tract and then shown to have immunoreactive counterparts in brain include cholecystokinin (9), vasoactive intestinal peptide (4), and motilin (30). Peptides first isolated from brain and later shown to have immunological counterparts in the digestive tract include somatostatin (1), enkephalin (21), and thyrotropin releasing hormone (19). Bombesin, a peptide isolated from frog skin, has been found to have immunoreactive counterparts in both brain (3) and digestive tract (11). In the digestive tract, these peptides are found in endocrine-type cells; several, including vasoactive intestinal peptide (17), somatostatin (7), gastrin (27), and enkephalin (18), are also present in the nerves of the gut. Not every peptide found in brain or gut is also present at the other site. At present we do not know what determines which ones will be present at both sites. Each peptide has a distinctive pattern of distribution at each of the sites where it is found. For peptides found in endocrine-paracrine cells there is a distinctive cell type for each peptide.

The finding that the same peptide may be present both in neurons of the brain and gut and in endocrine cells suggests that the same peptide may serve both as a neurotransmitter and as an endocrine transmitter. Do the many peptides found in neurons in the brain and in the periphery actually serve a transmitter function? That is, are there peptidergic nerves? This is a plausible hypothesis but has not yet been established by adequate supporting evidence. For example, vasoactive intestinal peptide is widely distributed in the nerves of the gut, is released by vagal stimulation (12), and has a number of the actions that would make it a good candidate for the long-sought transmitter of the noncholinergic, nonadrenergic inhibitory nerves of the gut [often referred to as purinergic nerves (14)].

When Bayliss & Starling discovered secretin, they recognized that it exemplified a concept with broad biological implications, namely chemical coordination of bodily functions. Like the nervous system, this system of blood-borne chemical coordinators provided a means whereby stimuli acting in one part of the body could produce effects on organs at a distance.

Bayliss & Starling sought a name for this group of substances that would convey the meaning of "chemical messengers" but failed to find one and adopted the word suggested by Hardy, namely hormone. Now that we recognize that the "chemical messengers" or "chemical transmitters" of the neural, endocrine, and paracrine systems belong to a single family, it would seem appropriate to coin a name to designate this entire group of substances. Perhaps the word "chemitter" (from *chem*ical trans*mitter*) might serve.

This concept of shared transmitters has caused a reexamination of the interrelation of the nervous and endocrine-paracrine systems.

CHEMICAL MESSENGERS

Bodily processes are regulated in response to perturbations arising within or outside the body. The perturbation may act directly on the responding cell or on a receptor cell that in turn sends a chemical message to the responding cell. These chemical messages are transmitted by one of three modes: neurocrine, endocrine, or paracrine. Neurocrine transmission spans the very short distance of the synaptic cleft, endocrine transmission occurs by way of the blood, and paracrine transmission occurs by diffusion of the chemical messenger through the intercellular space between the receptor and target cells. The unifying link among these three systems is that all three utilize amino acids or derivatives of amino acids, amines and peptides, as chemical messengers. Just as some of the same peptides are found in nerves and endocrine cells, so too the same amines may be found at both sites. For example, histamine, dopamine, and serotonin have been found in both nerves and endocrine-type cells (1). The endocrine glands derived from entoderm and ectoderm use peptides as chemical messengers, whereas those derived from mesoderm use steroids.

KINDS OF REGULATION

Some bodily processes are continuous, either because the target cells are intrinsically spontaneously active or because they receive continuous stimulation. Examples of continuous intrinsic activity in the digestive tract are the basal contraction of the lower esophageal sphincter (14) and the basal secretion of certain salivary glands such as the parotid of sheep (10). These processes continue even after the target has been isolated in vitro and all neural and hormonal influences have been removed. Examples of continuous activity depending on continuous stimulation include the basal contraction of the upper esophageal sphincter and of the external anal sphincter (2). These depend on continuous nervous stimulation and are abolished by cutting the extrinsic nerves.

Regardless of whether a process does or does not show continuous activity, it is subject to regulation in response to perturbations arising within or outside the body. The perturbation may act directly on the target cell. Some examples of such direct action in the digestive tract are: contraction of gut muscle in response to stretch, secretion of acid in response to amino acids and peptides topically applied to oxyntic mucosa (8), and active transport of hexoses, amino acids, and peptides by absorptive cells of the intestinal mucosa in response to being bathed by these substances.

Such direct action is uncommon; more often the perturbation acts on a receptor cell that in turn sends a chemical message over a long or short distance to the target cell and thus alters its activity. As indicated above, the chemical message may be delivered by neurocrine, endocrine, or paracrine paths. Neurocrine delivery crosses the narrow synaptic cleft, allowing highly selective delivery to only those cells receiving the neural impulses. Even though many kinds of target cells may be capable of responding to the transmitter, only those to which transmitter is actually delivered as a result of neural activity will respond.

Endocrine delivery by way of the blood exposes all cells to the hormone but produces reactions only in those with appropriate receptors coupled to intracellular activating mechanisms. Endocrine delivery may be more selective when a portal system of blood flow exists. For example, the hypothalamo-pituitary portal blood system allows selective delivery from the hypothalamus to the pituitary without necessarily producing sufficiently high levels in the systemic circulation to have systemic effects. Although the gastrointestinal hormones are all delivered into the hepatic portal system, in most instances these selective high concentrations in the liver have no physiological importance: For most gastrointestinal hormones the liver is neither an important target nor an important site of degradation (24). By contrast, the liver is an important target and an important site of degradation of the pancreatic hormones insulin and glucagon.

The concept of paracrine delivery (simple diffusion of the chemical messenger across the intercellular space from its cell of origin to the target cell) is a new one, and no fully substantiated examples are yet available. However, it promises to be an important mechanism of gastrointestinal regulation. Now that it is possible to isolate paracrine-type cells in vitro (24), we can expect progress in identifying the factors that regulate the release of these agents. The dispersion of the endocrine-like cells of the gastrointestinal mucosa among the nonendocrine mucosal cells provides the anatomical arrangement for efficient paracrine delivery.

The path between receptor and target may consist of a chain of cells rather than a single cell. The chain may comprise cells from only one of the three delivery systems (e.g. all neurons) or it may be a mixture. For example, the stimulus may act on a neuron that in turn activates an endocrine cell, and so on.

Outside the digestive tract endocrine-paracrine cells respond only to neural or blood-borne stimuli. The endocrine-paracrine cells of the digestive tract have microvillous borders exposed to the lumen, and thus they can respond to chemicals in the gut content as well.

GASTRIC ACID SECRETION AS AN EXAMPLE OF THE INTERPLAY OF NEURO-, ENDO-, AND PARACRINE FACTORS

Soll's recent studies on isolated parietal cells, reviewed in a later chapter in this section, show that the paracrine transmitter histamine, the neurocrine transmitter acetylcholine, and the endocrine transmitter gastrin have strong potentiating interactions in regulating gastric acid secretion. Several principles are illustrated by his work. First, in intact mucosa it may not be possible to analyze meaningfully the relative contributions of various stimulants and modulators. Second, a single substance, e.g. histamine, may act both as a sensitizer and as a direct stimulant. And third, potentiating stimulants may utilize different second-messenger pathways in the cell before converging at the final cellular event—e.g. hydrogen ion secretion.

INTERACTIONS OF NERVES AND HORMONES

Release of Hormones by Nerves

The most obvious form of interaction between nerves and hormones is the release of hormone in response to nervous stimulation. In the digestive tract, only two clear examples of this have been established. One is the release of gastrin by vagal nerve stimulation. Atropine enhances rather than inhibits vagal release of gastrin (24), suggesting that there are both stimulatory and inhibitory components to the action of the vagus on gastrin release. This raises two as yet unanswered questions: (*a*) What is the neuroeffector transmitter for vagal release of gastrin, and (*b*) what is the locus of the atropine-sensitive mechanism for inhibition of gastrin release? The second example of neural release of hormone is vagal release of pancreatic polypeptide (13), an orphan hormone whose physiological role is as yet unknown.

Nervous Modulation of Hormone Release

For some years it has been assumed that secretion of pancreatic enzymes in response to intestinal stimulants was mediated solely by release of cholecystokinin. As a corollary, it was further assumed that the decrease in pancreatic response to intestinal stimulants caused by vagotomy and by atropine was attributable to removal of vagal cholinergic facilitation of release of cholecystokinin. It has recently been shown (23) that atropine and vagotomy do not decrease release of cholecystokinin by intestinal stimulants; thus the most plausible explanation for their action is interruption of vagovagal enteropancreatic reflexes, a mechanism postulated by Pavlov but not taken seriously after the discovery of pancreozymin (cholecystokinin).

Vagotomy enhances rather than suppresses release of gastrin by meals (29). Whether this is due to removal of the inhibitory component of vagal action on gastrin release, mentioned above, or to some other mechanism is not yet known.

Nervous Modulation of Response to Hormones

Vagotomy and atropine markedly depress gastric acid secretion in response to gastrin (29). The effect of vagotomy cannot be reversed by giving a background of a cholinomimetic agent (22); unidentified factors in addition to removal of cholinergic tone must be involved. By contrast, vagotomy and atropine have no effect on the action of cholecystokinin on the pancreas (15) and only moderately inhibit the action of secretin (26).

A LOOK AHEAD

Within the next few years we can expect to see the repertoire of transmitters of nervous effects greatly enlarged from the current pair (acetylcholine and norepinephrine) to include additional amines (histamine, serotonin, dopamine) and many peptides. The role of paracrine substances, chemical regulators that are delivered by diffusion across intercellular spaces from their site of origin to their targets, will almost certainly be clarified. The endocrine, neurocrine, and paracrine roles of the many peptides now being discovered will be sorted out. Most important, we will learn much more about the harmonious interplay that allows these modalities to achieve their regulatory actions.

Literature cited

1. Arimura, A., Sato, H., Dupont, A., Nishi, N., Schally, A. V. 1975. Somatostatin: abundance of immunoreactive hormone in rat stomach and pancreas. *Science* 189:1007–9
2. Asoh, R., Goyal, R. J. 1978. Manometry and electromyography of the upper esophageal sphincter in the opossum. *Gastroenterology* 74:514–20
3. Brown, M., Rivier, J., Kobayashi, R., Vale, W. 1978. Neurotensin-like and bombesin-like peptides: CNS distribution and actions. In *Gut Hormones*, ed.

S. R. Bloom, pp. 550–58. Edinburgh: Churchill Livingstone
4. Bryant, M. G., Polak, J. M., Modlin, I., Bloom, S. R., Albuquerque, R. H., Pearse, A. G. E. 1976. Possible dual role for vasoactive intestinal peptide as gastrointestinal hormone and neurotransmitter substance. *Lancet* I:991–93
5. Carraway, R., Leeman, S. E. 1975. The amino acid sequence of a hypothalamic peptide, neurotensin. *J. Biol. Chem.* 250:1907–11
6. Chang, M. M., Leeman, S. E., Niall, H. D. 1971. Amino-acid sequence of sub-

stance P. *Nature* [*New Biol*] 232:86–87
7. Costa, M., Patel, J. B., Furness, J. B., Arimura, A. 1977. Evidence that some intrinsic neurons of the intestine contain somatostatin. *Neurosci. Lett.* 6:215
8. Debas, H. T., Grossman, M. I. 1975. Chemicals bathing the oxyntic gland area stimulate acid secretion in dog. *Gastroenterology* 69:651–59
9. Dockray, G. J. 1976. Immunochemical evidence of cholecystokinin-like peptides in brain. *Nature* 264:568–70
10. Emmelin, N. 1967. Secretion from denervated salivary glands. In *Secretory Mechanisms of Salivary Glands,* ed. L. H. Schneyer, C. A. Schneyer, pp. 127–140. New York: Academic
11. Erspamer, V., Melchiorri, P., Falconieri Erspamer, C., Negri, L. 1978. Polypeptides of the amphibian skin active on the gut and their mammalian counterparts. In *Gastrointestinal Hormones and Pathology of the Digestive System,* ed. V. Speranza, N. Basso, E. Lezoche, M. I. Grossman, pp. 51–64. New York: Plenum
12. Fahrenkrug, J., Schaffalitzky de Muckadell, O. B., Holst, J. J. 1978. Nervous release of VIP. See Ref. 3, pp. 488–91
13. Feldman, M., Richardson, C. T., Taylor, I. A., Walsh, J. H. 1978. Neural regulation of gastrin and pancreatic polypeptide release in man. *Clin. Res.* 26:497A
14. Goyal, R. J., Rattan, S. 1978. Neurohumoral, hormonal, and drug receptors for the lower esophageal sphincter. *Gastroenterology* 74:598–619
15. Henriksen, F. W. 1969. Effect of vagotomy or atropine on the canine pancreatic response to secretin and pancreozymin. *Scand. J. Gastroenterol.* 4:137–44
16. Kitabgi, P., Carraway, R., Leeman, S. E. 1976. Isolation of a tridecapeptide from bovine intestinal tissue and its partial characterization as neurotensin. *J. Biol. Chem.* 251:7053–58
17. Larsson, L.-I., Fahrenkrug, J., Schaffalitzky de Muckadell, O. B., Sundler, F., Hakanson, R. 1976. Localization of vasoactive intestinal peptide (VIP) to central and peripheral neurons. *Proc. Natl. Acad. Sci. USA* 73:3197–3200
18. Linnoila, I., DiAugustine, R. P., Miller, R., Chang, I., Cuatrecasas, P. 1978. Distribution of [Met^5]- and [Leu^5]-enke-phalin in the gastrointestinal tract. *Fed. Proc.* 37:666
19. Morley, J. E., Garvin, T. J., Pekary, A. E., Hershman, J. M. 1977. Thyrotropin-releasing hormone in the gastrointestinal tract. *Biochem. Biophys. Res. Commun.* 79:314–18
20. Pearse, A. G. E. 1977. The diffuse neuroendocrine system and the APUD concept: related 'endocrine' peptides in brain, intestine, pituitary, placenta, and anuran cutaneous glands. *Med. Biol.* 55:115–25
21. Polak, J. M., Bloom, S. R., Sullivan, S. N., Facer, P., Pearse, A. G. E. 1977. Enkephalin-like immunoreactivity in the human gastrointestinal tract. *Lancet* I:972–74
22. Roland, M., Berstad, A., Liavag, I. 1975. Effect of urecholine and carbacholine on pentagastrin-stimulated gastric secretion after proximal gastric vagotomy in duodenal ulcer patients. *Scand. J. Gastroenterol.* 10:315–19
23. Solomon, T. E., Grossman, M. I. 1977. Cholecystokinin and secretin release are not affected by vagotomy or atropine. *Gastroenterology* 72:1134
24. Strunz, U. T., Walsh, J. H., Grossman, M. I. 1978. Removal of gastrin by various organs in dogs. *Gastroenterology* 74:32–33
25. Studer, R. O., Trzeciak, A., Lergier, W. 1973. Isolierung und Aminosäuresequenz von Substans P aus Pferdedarm. *Helv. Chim. Acta* 56:860–66
26. Thomas, J. E. 1964. Mechanism of action of pancreatic stimuli studied by means of atropine-like drugs. *Am. J. Physiol.* 206:124–28
27. Uvnas-Wallensten, K., Rehfeld, J. F., Larsson, L.-I., Uvnas, B. 1977. Heptadecapeptide gastrin in the vagal nerve. *Proc. Natl. Acad. Sci. USA* 74:5707–10
28. van Euler, U. S., Gaddum, J. H. 1931. An unidentified depressor substance in certain tissue extracts. *J. Physiol. London* 72:74–87
29. Walsh, J. H., Grossman, M. I. 1975. Gastrin. *N. Engl. J. Med.* 292:1324–34, 1377–84
30. Yanaihara, C., Sato, H., Yanaihara, N., Naruse, S., Forssmann, W. G., Helmstaedter, V., Fujita, T., Yamaguchi, K., Abe, K. 1978. Motilin-, substance P- and somatostatin-like immunoreactivities in extracts from dog, tupaia and monkey brain and GI tract. See Ref 11, pp. 269–83

Ann. Rev. Physiol. 1979. 41:35–53

REGULATION OF GASTRIC ACID SECRETION

♦1204

Andrew H. Soll and John H. Walsh

Center for Ulcer Research and Education, Veterans Administration Center, Wadsworth Hospital, Los Angeles, California 90073

REGULATION OF GASTRIC SECRETION

Hydrochloric acid is secreted by the oxyntic, or parietal, cells located in the oxyntic gland area of the stomach. Acid secretion is regulated by several chemical messengers that appear to act separately on the parietal cell but that have important interactions in the overall regulation of acid secretion (36, 82). The best-defined chemical messengers are acetylcholine, histamine, and gastrin. Additional evidence obtained by physiological studies in vivo suggests that at least one additional stimulant and one or more inhibitors of parietal cell secretion are released into the blood or tissues when acid or various food components are present in the lumen of the gut. We examine the evidence obtained in intact mammals and with isolated parietal cells that supports the current concept of multiple and overlapping regulatory mechanisms acting on the parietal cell to control the rate of secretion of hydrochloric acid.

Chemical Messengers

ACETYLCHOLINE   The neurotransmitter released by muscarinic nerve endings of the parasympathetic nervous system in the gastric mucosa is acetylcholine. The nerves that innervate the gastric glands are postganglionic fibers that originate in ganglia located in submucosal and muscular layers of the stomach. Most of the preganglionic fibers that synapse in these ganglia have their cell bodies in the plexuses of the stomach and form local reflex arcs within the wall of the stomach. The remainder of the postganglionic cells synapse with preganglionic fibers from the vagus nerve and are part of the vagal reflex system. Atropine and other anticholinergic agents

35

can be used to define the action of acetylcholine at muscarinic neuro-effector junctions in the stomach by specific inhibition of cholinergic transmission.

HISTAMINE   Histamine is present in large quantities, about 40 micrograms per gram wet weight, in the oxyntic mucosa of humans and other mammals (65, 89). Until recently the role of histamine in regulation of acid secretion was a mystery, primarily because specific antagonists of the acid-stimulating action of histamine were not available. The development of a series of histamine antagonists that act on a set of receptors (H_2) distinct from those antagonized by ordinary antihistaminic drugs has made it clear that histamine plays an important role in physiologic stimulation of parietal cells (10).

The cellular source of histamine in the gastric mucosa is not known. In rats it appears to be localized in specialized cells in the epithelium called enterochromaffin-like (ECL) cells (88). Other species lack histamine in ECL cells. In the dog, most of the gastric mucosal histamine appears to be located in cells that morphologically resemble tissue mast cells, found in the lamina propria near the parietal cells (3, 19). If these cells are the source of histamine for the oxyntic glands, it is likely that histamine must diffuse through the lamina propria in order to reach the parietal cells. It is not likely that histamine originating from the stomach is carried through the portal circulation and back to the stomach through the systemic circulation because the liver removes histamine from the circulation almost quantitatively. The chemical and physiological mechanisms for the synthesis and release of histamine in the gastric mucosa are unknown (3).

GASTRIN   Gastrin is the peptide hormone most clearly identified as an important stimulant of gastric acid secretion. The subject of gastrin release was reviewed recently (92, 94). The two principal biologically active forms of gastrin in pyloric gland mucosa and in the circulation are little gastrin (G-17) and big gastrin (G-34) (93). The potency of G-17 is 6–8 times that of G-34 and it appears that G-17 is the principal biologically active circulating form. Both G-17 and G-34 exist in sulfated and nonsulfated forms, but sulfation does not affect acid-stimulating activity. G-17 is the most abundant form in pyloric gland extracts while the reverse is true for circulating gastrin, probably because of the slower disappearance rate of circulating G-34.

Gastrin is released by amino acids and peptides bathing the pyloric gland mucosa. The specific amino acids that are the most potent gastrin releasers in humans are tryptophan and phenylalanine; these same two amino acids are the most potent stimulants of acid secretion (14). However, there is evidence that certain amino acids have acid-stimulating effects independent of circulating gastrin concentrations. For example, aspartic acid is a moderately potent stimulant of acid secretion in humans but does not cause an increase in serum gastrin. Also, administration of mixtures of amino acids into the small intestine or intravenously causes stimulation of acid secretion without change in serum gastrin concentrations (48).

The effects of vagal and cholinergic stimulation on the release of gastrin are confusing (94). Direct electric vagal stimulation in animals causes gastrin release, but this release is resistant to inhibition by atropine. Topical acetylcholine applied to the pyloric mucosa in dogs causes gastrin release that is at least partially antagonized by atropine (22). Sham feeding causes a small increase in serum gastrin in both dogs and humans (58, 60). Insulin hypoglycemia also causes gastrin release. High doses of atropine antagonize the gastrin responses to sham feeding and to insulin hypoglycemia in the dog (20, 60). All of these observations suggest that there is a vagal, cholinergic mechanism for release of gastrin.

In contrast, small doses of atropine enhance the serum gastrin response to food in humans (96) and dogs (45) and enhance the gastrin responses to insulin hypoglycemia (27) and sham feeding in man (29), even when intragastric pH is kept at a constant level. Vagotomy also increases the gastrin response to feeding in both species (94). The serum gastrin response to insulin hypoglycemia in humans is maintained after vagotomy (16), and there is evidence that this form of gastrin release is mediated by circulating epinephrine (17).

Gastrin is released by distention of isolated antral pouches in dogs (22). This release is diminished after parasympathetic denervation of the pouch or by administration of atropine (20, 87). On the other hand, distention of the intact stomach of dog or human with balloons or saline does not cause significant release of gastrin (76).

The only known physiological inhibition of gastrin release is caused by acidification of the gastric contents below pH 3 (95). Several peptides present in the gut have the ability to inhibit gastrin release when administered in large doses exogenously, but none appears to inhibit at concentrations likely to exist in the circulation under normal circumstances (2). Somatostatin, which is present in large quantities in the pyloric mucosa, is a potent inhibitor of gastrin release (63, 91). Somatostatin may modulate gastrin release by local action on gastrin cells. The same possibility exists for vasoactive intestinal peptide, which is found in nerve fibers in the stomach (61).

Two major questions emerge from the studies on vagal and cholinergic mechanisms for release and inhibition of release of gastrin. First, which neurotransmitters are released by vagal stimulation? Second, does the vagus act directly on the gastrin cell or are there mechanisms of endocrine or paracrine intermediation of vagal effects? Whatever the mechanisms, it is apparent that vagal inhibition of gastrin release is more sensitive to low doses of atropine than vagal stimulation of gastrin release.

Phases of Acid Secretion in Vivo

Acid secretion is commonly divided into basal or fasting and stimulated or postprandial phases. Basal secretion varies considerably over time and usually represents 5–10% of maximal rates, although periods of achlorhydria are not uncommon. There is a diurnal variation in fasting humans with highest rates found in the evening and lowest rates in the morning. This diurnal variation in acid secretion is not correlated with serum gastrin concentration (59).

Stimulated secretion is commonly subdivided somewhat arbitrarily into cephalic, gastric, and intestinal phases. The cephalic phase begins with the sight, smell, taste, and chewing of appetizing food; the gastric phase begins when food enters the stomach; and the intestinal phase begins when food components begin to enter the intestine. Obviously these phases overlap. The mechanisms that mediate these phases are multiple, and several mechanisms may be operative during the same period.

CEPHALIC PHASE   The cephalic phase appears to be mediated by efferent impulses transmitted through fibers of the vagus nerve to the stomach. The sensory receptors for cephalic stimulation have not been identified, nor have the pathways been mapped in the central nervous system (11, 64). Cephalic stimulation is abolished by vagotomy (87). Maximal stimulation by sham feeding can cause near-maximal rates of acid secretion in dogs and more than half-maximal rates in humans (58, 60, 67, 85). At least two mechanisms are operative during sham feeding. The most significant mechanism is direct cholinergic stimulation of the parietal cell. However, small amounts of gastrin are also released from the gastrin cells. This background of gastrin is necessary for full stimulation of acid secretion in the dog. There is also evidence that sham feeding in dogs releases one or more substances that inhibit acid secretion in denervated gastric pouches: Sham feeding in dogs inhibits pentagastrin-stimulated acid secretion in Heidenhain pouches (75). Such an inhibitor probably accounts for the difficulty that plagued earlier investigators who attempted to demonstrate gastrin release in response to vagal stimulation and antral distention in dogs with denervated fundic pouches before the development of radioimmunoassays for gastrin. The cephalic phase probably makes a significant contribution to the overall response to a meal. In humans, the acid response to an eaten meal is significantly greater than the response to the same meal infused directly into the stomach (67). Sham feeding in humans also increases the acid responses to gastric distention with glucose or saline solutions (67). The increased acid responses to sham feeding in humans are accompanied by greater increases in serum gastrin than those achieved by introduction of food directly into the stomach.

GASTRIC PHASE   The two factors known to be operative when food is present in the stomach are distention of the stomach and chemical stimulation of gastrin release.

Distention   Distention of the intact stomach results in a small but significant stimulation of acid secretion. Presumably this results from activation of reflexes, since serum gastrin concentrations are not increased. The maximal response to distention with saline in humans is about 25% of maximal acid secretion; increasing the intragastric pressure does not increase acid secretion (76). Distention of the human fundus with a balloon was reported to cause progressive pressure-dependent increases in acid output up to about 50% of maximal, while distention of the normal human antrum produced only minimal responses (6, 37).

In dogs with separated antral pouches and gastric fistulas, distention of the antral pouch with neutral or acid solutions caused increased acid secretion from the gastric fistula (23). At acid pH no gastrin was released and the response was apparently due to a pyloro-oxyntic reflex. Evidence for the existence of an oxynto-pyloric reflex was also obtained in dogs with a similar preparation by demonstration of gastrin release during distention of the acid-secreting mucosa (25). Distention may also activate a mechanism for inhibition of acid secretion. In some human subjects, balloon distention of the fundus decreased the acid response to maximal doses of pentagastrin (39).

The response to fundic distention in humans is markedly inhibited by atropine or by proximal gastric vagotomy; this agrees with the concept that the acid response is mediated by an atropine-sensitive cholinergic reflex conveyed by both short intramural and long vago-vagal pathways (38).

Chemical stimulation   The gastric secretory response to food can be studied directly by intragastric titration (33). Alkali is added to maintain intragastric pH at a predetermined value; the amount of base added is equal to the acid secreted. Similar measurements also can be obtained by multiple sampling techniques performed with gastric and intestinal dilution markers without alteration of the natural intragastric pH (57).

When various food components were studied for acid-stimulating activity in humans, amino acids and partially digested protein were found to be effective while glucose and fat caused no stimulation (68). The increase in gastrin caused by gastric instillation of mixed amino acids in humans was sufficient to account for most of the observed acid secretory response, since intravenous infusion of gastrin at doses sufficient to reproduce the increase in serum gastrin also caused similar stimulation of acid secretion (30). Progressive lowering of intragastric pH from 5.5 to 2.5 abolished the gastrin response to amino acids in humans but only decreased the acid response by half, which again implies that amino acids stimulate acid secretion by more than one mechanism (95). Of the specific amino acids tested individually, phenylalanine and tryptophan are the most potent releasers of gastrin in dogs and humans and are the most potent stimulants of acid secretion in man (14, 86). Gastric administration of calcium salts also causes stimulation of acid secretion not associated with an increase in serum calcium (54). Caffeine stimulates acid secretion in humans without an increase in gastrin (94). Alcohol appears to cause gastrin release and stimulation of acid secretion in the dog but not in the human (94).

INTESTINAL PHASE   Food substances entering the intestine may cause stimulation or inhibition of gastric secretion. Several groups have reported that intraduodenal administration of peptone or liver extract caused an increase in gastric acid secretion that could not be explained by changes in gastrin (34, 47). Gastrin is present in the proximal duodenum in relatively high concentrations, but it is not known whether or not duodenal gastrin is released by a normal meal. Reinfusion of intestinal contents in human subjects caused acid secretory rates higher than those found when intestinal contents were aspirated at the ligament of Treitz (18). There is some evidence that the acid response to peptides in the small intestine may be due at least in part to effects of absorbed amino acids, since intravenous administration of amino acids in humans caused significant stimulation of acid secretion (48). In dogs, there is evidence that peptone releases from the intestine a substance that potentiates the action of pentagastrin on vagally denervated oxyntic pouches and that this substance is distinct from gastrin (24).

Introduction of fat into the intestine produces marked inhibition of gastric acid secretion (15, 72). The agent responsible for this inhibition has been called "enterogastrone." Many peptides isolated from the mucosa of the gut and pancreas can produce inhibition of acid secretion when administered in large doses (2). However, none of these has been shown to meet the criteria required for identification as the major enterogastrone. The two inhibitory peptides released by fat are cholecystokinin (CCK) (12) and gastric inhibitory peptide (GIP) (62). The doses of both required to produce inhibition are probably larger than the amount released by fat in the intestine. Both of these hormones are released by amino acids in the intestine as well as by fat. However, intestinal amino acids do not inhibit acid secretion. Hypertonic glucose is a moderately potent inhibitor of acid secretion but is effective when given intravenously as well as orally or intraduodenally (55, 97). Acidification of the duodenum, especially the duodenal bulb, inhibits gastric secretion (9, 90). It is unlikely that the amount of secretin released is sufficient to account for this effect, since relatively high doses of secretin are needed to inhibit acid secretion (21). It is possible that a major part of the effect of intraduodenal administration of acid and other inhibitory substances is due to stimulation of an inhibitory reflex (51).

Inhibitors of Acid Secretion

ANTICHOLINERGIC AGENTS   Atropine and other anticholinergic agents produce moderate inhibition of acid secretion stimulated by food in humans and somewhat greater inhibition of secretion stimulated by sham feeding and by gastric distention. Although it has long been felt that large doses of anticholinergics were necessary to produce significant inhibition, recent studies in humans have shown that doses much lower than those needed to produce undesirable side effects caused similar inhibition (28). The maximal inhibition of food-stimulated acid secretion achieved with anticholinergics in humans has been about 30–40%

HISTAMINE ANTAGONISTS   Ordinary antihistaminic agents that inhibit histamine action on smooth muscle (H_1 receptors) do not block stimulation of acid secretion. A second class of histamine antagonists (H_2 receptor antagonists) markedly inhibit gastric acid secretion but do not inhibit histamine action at the H_1 sites (66). Two of the H_2 receptor antagonists, metiamide and cimetidine, have been tested extensively in humans and other animals and have been found to inhibit strongly both basal acid secretion and secretion stimulated by histamine, insulin, sham feeding, food, gastrin, and caffeine. The inhibitory effects of H_2 antagonists are augmented by simultaneous administration of anticholinergic agents (28).

PROSTAGLANDINS   Prostaglandins E_1 and E_2 inhibit basal, histamine- , and pentagastrin-stimulated acid secretion in humans and other species (69). Synthetic analogs have been developed that are resistant to intestinal inactivation and are effective orally. One of these analogs, 16,16-dimethyl prostaglandin E_2, was found to produce almost complete inhibition of meal-stimulated acid secretion in humans when administered into the stomach and lesser inhibition when given intraduodenally (46). A parallel inhibition of gastrin release also was observed with this drug. Parenteral prostaglandin E_1 was found not to inhibit gastrin release in the dog (4); presumably this inhibition is caused by a local effect on the gastric mucosa.

Interdependence in the Actions of Secretagogues

The preceding discussion leaves little question that the regulation of acid secretion is a complex matter. Probably the most confusing aspect of this regulation is the fact that the stimulants of acid secretion do not act independently. Instead, there is an interdependence of secretagogue action that is most clearly evident in the *apparent* lack of specificity of cimetidine (66) and atropine (43, 52) in vivo; these agents, which are pharmacologically specific for the histamine and acetylcholine receptors, also inhibit the action of pharmacologically unrelated stimulants such as gastrin. Secretagogue interdependence is also evident in that the simultaneous administration of two stimulants can lead to a potentiated response (42, 50), although the failure to demonstrate interactions in this manner has also been reported (44). Effects of secretagogue interactions may also, in part, underlie the observations that antrectomy inhibits the response to exogenous histamine, gastrin, and vagally mediated stimulation as well as stimulation by food (5). Furthermore, vagotomy inhibits the acid-secretory response to histamine and gastrin as well as to vagally mediated stimuli (35).

The interdependence between secretagogues in their action on acid secretion is therefore a major element determining the level of parietal cell function. The mechanisms involved are of interest not only to the physiologist, but also to the physician treating ulcer disease, since the available therapies for treating ulcer disease work at least in part by interfering with the interactions between secretagogues. Three theories have been proposed to explain these interactions. The first supposes that the parietal cell has receptors only for histamine, with gastrin and acetylcholine promoting the release of mucosal histamine stores. Although this theory explains the inhibition of gastrin and acetylcholine action by cimetidine, it fails to explain how atropine inhibits gastrin action. Furthermore, in the isolated rat stomach, concentrations of cimetidine that totally block the response to exogenous histamine fail to block stimulation by cholinergic analogs and only partially inhibit stimulation by gastrin (56). A second theory proposes that the parietal cell has specific receptors for histamine, gastrin and carbachol and that potentiating interactions at the parietal cell itself explain the interdependency of secretagogue action. Data obtained in studies with isolated parietal cells support this theory, as discussed further below. Finally, it is possible that drugs such as cimetidine have actions independent of H_2 receptor blockade, thus accounting for the inhibition of pharmacologically unrelated stimulants (74).

STUDIES WITH ISOLATED PARIETAL CELLS

It is likely that the parietal cell in vivo is continuously exposed to endogenous histamine and acetylcholine, which are present in the intact fundic mucosa. Since there are no means for determining the actual concentrations of histamine and acetylcholine released at the parietal cell in vivo and since these agents may interact with each other and with circulating stimuli such as gastrin, it is desirable to have model systems in which agents can be studied both singly and in defined combinations. By isolating the parietal cell, it is possible to remove and add back individual stimulants and inhibitors, markedly facilitating the study of actions and interactions of hormones and drugs that regulate the function of this cell.

Cell Isolation

It was essential to develop a technique that allowed the isolation of parietal cells without disruption of functional integrity. One such technique, adapted from the studies on pancreatic acinar cells by Amsterdam & Jamieson (1), involves sequential exposure of gastric mucosa that has been bluntly separated from submucosa to low concentrations of collagenase and EDTA (78). The functional responses of parietal cells isolated by these techniques indicated that at least some of the damaging effects of proteolytic enzymes on cell surfaces were circumvented.

Cell Separation

Cell separation has been accomplished using the Beckman elutriator rotor. This rotor operates on a counterflow principle, separating cells by sedimentation velocity, which for practical purposes reflects cell size. When fractions of varying parietal cell content were prepared, secretagogue stimulation of both oxygen consumption and AP uptake correlated closely with the parietal cell content (77, 78).

Three Indexes of Parietal Cell Response to Stimulation

In intact mucosa, for each hydrogen ion secreted by the parietal cell into the lumen, a bicarbonate ion is secreted at the basal surface. Since this polarity is lost with dispersion it is not possible to measure acid secretion by isolated parietal cells directly. Therefore the following indirect measures of the stimulation of the parietal cell have been used:

OXYGEN CONSUMPTION The cytoplasm of the parietal cell is packed with mitochondria, reflecting high energy requirements for the secretion of acid. In systems such as the ex vivo preparation of canine stomach, where it is possible to monitor both the consumption of oxygen and the secretion of acid, these two indexes of parietal cell function are closely related (53). Oxygen consumption by isolated parietal cells can be measured readily using polarographic techniques (78).

MORPHOLOGICAL TRANSFORMATION   With stimulation in vivo, the parietal cell undergoes a morphological transformation characterized by coalescence of the tubulovesicles that fill the cytoplasm in the basal state into secretory canaliculi lined with microvilli that drain into the glandular lumen (32). A similar transformation occurs when parietal cells prepared by these techniques are stimulated by treatment with histamine, carbachol, and gastrin (83).

[14]C-AMINOPYRINE (^{14}C-AP) ACCUMULATION   Berglindh and co-workers (7) in their studies on isolated gastric glands were the first to use ^{14}C-AP uptake as an index of parietal cell function in vitro. AP uptake has also been used as an index of function of isolated parietal cells (77). AP is a weak base and its accumulation by stimulated parietal cells appears to reflect a pH partition phenomenon as originally described for the secretion of weak bases into gastric juice (73). AP readily diffuses across plasma membranes but only in the un-ionized form. When AP enters an acidic environment (pH $\ll$ pKa = 5.0) it acquires a hydrogen ion to become ionized and no longer diffusable. AP is presumably trapped in the tubulovesicles and secretory canaliculi of the parietal cell.

Both AP accumulation and oxygen consumption show similar patterns for the actions and interactions of secretagogues: Stimulation is produced by carbachol, histamine, gastrin, the phosphodiesterase inhibitor IMX, and the cyclic AMP analog dibutyryl cyclic AMP (dbcAMP).

Receptor Specificity

Histamine, gastrin, and cholinergic agents each appear to act on specific receptors on the parietal cell. Evidence for this conclusion comes from study of the effects of cimetidine and atropine on stimulation of both oxygen consumption and AP accumulation by carbachol, gastrin, and histamine (77, 78). Atropine caused parallel displacement of the dose response curve to carbachol, but in the same concentrations failed to inhibit stimulation by gastrin, histamine, dbcAMP or IMX. Cimetidine, on the other hand, caused parallel displacement of the dose response curve to histamine, while at the same concentrations failed to inhibit the responses to gastrin, carbachol or dbcAMP. In order to further characterize these receptors, dissociation constants (K_b) for cimetidine inhibition of histamine and atropine inhibition of carbachol were determined and found to be 1.0 μM and 0.89 nM respectively. Since these constants are similar to those found in other tissues, these findings indicate that parietal cells isolated by these techniques possess typical H_2-histamine and muscarinic cholinergic receptors. Apparently the rigors of tissue dispersion did not alter the properties of these two receptors. It is also clear that gastrin acts on yet a third receptor on the parietal cell.

NONSPECIFIC ACTIONS OF INHIBITORS   Atropine at very high concentrations (1 mM) inhibited AP uptake in response to dbcAMP and histamine (77). Since these effects were limited to a concentration 10^6-fold greater than the K_b, these effects should not be interpreted as reflecting blockade at the muscarinic receptor. The H_1 blocking drug mepyramine at concentrations below 10 μM did not alter stimulation by carbachol, histamine, or dbcAMP. Mepyramine at 0.1 mM did, however, inhibit the response to all three of these stimulants. Since these effects were limited to concentrations 10^6-fold higher than the dissociation constant for the H_1 receptor (1 nM for histamine action on guinea pig ileum) it is unlikely that this action on isolated parietal cells reflects specific H_1 receptor blockade.

Interactions Between Secretagogues

The findings reviewed above indicate that cimetidine and atropine are pharmacologically specific in their inhibition of the actions of single agents on the isolated parietal cell and appear to conflict with the apparent nonspecificity in their actions in vivo. The existence of potentiating interactions between secretagogues may explain this inconsistency. For the purposes of the present discussion, potentiating interactions exist when the response to a combination of agents is significantly greater than the sum of the individual responses. By this definition, the study of either AP uptake (80) or oxygen consumption (79) reveals potentiating interactions between histamine and gastrin and histamine and carbachol but not between carbachol and gastrin. However, in studies using AP uptake as an index of response, the addition of histamine, carbachol, and gastrin together in concentrations that each produced threshold stimulation caused a three-way potentiation. This three-way potentiated response was not only greater than the sum of the three individual responses but was also greater than the sum of the two-way interaction responses plus the response to the third agent.

THE EFFECTS OF CIMETIDINE AND ATROPINE ON SECRETAGOGUE INTERACTIONS   When atropine and cimetidine were tested against combinations of agents that produced potentiated responses, they displayed an apparent cross-specificity reminiscent of that found in vivo and clearly resulted from specific blockade of the histaminic and cholinergic components of these potentiated responses. For example, when the response to gastrin was potentiated by histamine, this combination was not inhibited by atropine, presumably because there was no cholinergic component to block, whereas cimetidine caused marked inhibition as a result of blocking histamine enhancement of gastrin action. When the effects of cimetidine and atropine were tested against the three-way potentiated response to histamine, gastrin, and carbachol, treatment with atropine reduced the response to that seen with histamine plus gastrin, treatment with cimetidine inhibited the response to that produced by carbachol plus gastrin, and treatment with both cimetidine and atropine inhibited the response to that produced by gastrin alone. Thus when the response of the isolated parietal cell to gastrin is potentiated by interaction with histamine and carbachol, this potentiated gastrin stimulation is inhibited by both atropine and cimetidine to the extent of the potentiation by carbachol and histamine respectively.

In vivo, the parietal cell is continuously exposed to histamine released from mucosal stores and to acetylcholine released from local nerve endings. If this endogenous histamine and acetylcholine were to be released in amounts sufficient to support potentiating interactions with a superimposed stimulus such as gastrin, then the apparent lack of specificity of atropine and cimetidine in vivo might be explained by the above findings. Under these circumstances, administration of gastrin would produce a response potentiated by interaction with endogenous histamine and acetylcholine, and this potentiated response would be inhibited by cimetidine and atropine.

The existence of potentiating interactions between secretagogues may provide the parietal cell with a mechanism for finely controlling the response to stimulation. This mechanism appears to be of particular importance for the parietal cell since there are at least three final effectors at the parietal itself that mediate physiological stimulation of acid secretion. The potentiating interactions may serve to integrate the responses to these various stimuli. For example, increasing the degree of vagal stimulation will not only directly stimulate the parietal cell but will also modulate the response to gastrin and histamine. Since all of the potentiating interactions involve histamine (histamine plus gastrin, histamine plus carbachol, and histamine plus carbachol plus gastrin), the potency of cimetidine in inhibiting all forms of acid secretion is understandable. In the studies with isolated parietal cells, gastrin alone was a weak stimulant, producing marked stimulation only in the presence of histamine. Although this response to gastrin may have been impaired by damage resulting from the isolation of the cells, it is of interest to note that gastrin may also be an intrinsically weak stimulant in vivo, in that stimulation by gastrin is markedly impaired by treatment with cimetidine (66).

Secondary Effectors of Secretagogue Action

CYCLIC AMP   The role of cyclic nucleotides in the response of the parietal cell to stimulation has been controversial (49), largely because it has been difficult to study the role of cyclic nucleotides in the complex mixture of cell types in intact mucosa. However, when cells are dispersed and cell separation techniques applied, the study of these problems is greatly facilitated. In the isolated parietal cell preparation, histamine but neither carbachol nor gastrin stimulates cyclic AMP production (84). In cell separation experiments, this effect of histamine was localized to the parietal cell itself. The dose-response relations for histamine stimulation of cyclic AMP production correlated quite closely with histamine stimulation of the parietal cell acid secretory mechanisms as indicated by stimulation of both oxygen uptake and aminopyrine accumulation. Phosphodiesterase inhibitors, such as IMX, produced similar potentiation of histamine stimulation of AP uptake and histamine stimulation of cyclic AMP production. Finally, both the actions and the interactions of histamine are mimicked by the cyclic AMP analogs dbcAMP and 8-bromo cyclic AMP. These four points represent the major criteria set out by Sutherland and co-workers (70) for deciding whether cyclic AMP is involved as a mediator of hormone action.

With the parietal cell, one further obstacle limited the acceptance of cyclic AMP as a secondary effector for hormone action: the dilemma posed by studies with prostaglandins. Prostaglandins inhibit acid secretion (4, 46, 69) but also stimulate cyclic AMP production by intact gastric mucosa (49, 98). Initial attempts to resolve this paradox in isolated cells indicated that prostaglandins stimulated cyclic AMP production by nonparietal cells, with little or no stimulation of cyclic AMP production by the parietal cell itself (84). However, in low concentrations PGE_2 directly inhibits parietal cell function in vitro, specifically blocking histamine-stimulated AP accumulation (81). PGE_2 in concentrations up to 0.1 mM did not inhibit the response to dbcAMP, to gastrin, or to carbachol. However, when the response to carbachol was enhanced by potentiating interactions with histamine, then PGE_2 did inhibit to the extent of histamine's enhancement of carbachol action. When gastrin stimulation of AP uptake was enhanced by potentiating interactions with histamine, then PGE_2 also inhibited the combined response, whereas when gastrin action was potentiated by interaction with dbcAMP, no inhibition of this gastrin-dbcAMP response was found. Since histamine but neither carbachol nor gastrin stimulated cyclic AMP generation by parietal cells, the above findings suggested that prostaglandin was acting by means of blocking histamine activation of adenylate cyclase.

This mechanism for prostaglandin action has been described previously in other tissues. Butcher & Baird (13), studying epinephrine-stimulated lipolysis, noted that prostaglandin inhibited this response by blocking epi-nephrine-stimulated cyclic AMP generation. In isolated canine parietal cells, PGE_2 inhibited histamine-stimulated cyclic AMP production and AP accumulation over the same concentration range (81). Furthermore, in experiments in which the dose-response relation to histamine was studied in the presence of three concentrations of prostaglandin, PGE_2 inhibition of histamine-stimulated AP accumulation correlated with the inhibition of cyclic AMP levels, with a correlation coefficient of 0.94 (81). Thus these data taken together provide strong support for the view that cyclic AMP mediates histamine action on the parietal cell.

SECONDARY EFFECTORS FOR CHOLINERGIC STIMULATION AND FOR GASTRIN   It is clear that the actions of carbachol and gastrin are mediated by intracellular effectors different from those mediating the action of histamine. Not only do the direct studies described above indicate that only histamine stimulates cyclic AMP production, but the existence of potentiating interactions on AP accumulation and oxygen uptake between histamine and carbachol and histamine and gastrin also suggests that the biochemical effectors for carbachol and gastrin are distinct from that for histamine. Two agents that show potentiating interactions would be ex-pected to have effector mechanisms that to a certain point are biochemically distinct but that eventually converge upon a common effector mechanism or final response. The finding of the three-way potentiation between hista-mine, gastrin, and carbachol furthermore indicates that the biochemical effectors mediating the responses to these later two agents will also be biochemically distinct.

Only negative information is available regarding specific effectors for carbachol and gastrin. The actions of these two agents do not appear to be mediated by cyclic GMP: The response to carbachol and gastrin was not enhanced by IMX in the same fashion as histamine action (80). Further-more, neither exogenous dibutyryl cyclic GMP nor 8-bromo cyclic GMP stimulated AP accumulation by parietal cells (77). Finally, direct measure-ment of cyclic GMP content of cells indicated that treatment with carba-chol and gastrin failed to elevate cellular cyclic GMP content above the levels produced by treatment with IMX alone (A. W. Wollin, A. H. Soll, unpublished observations). Since the cells in these studies did respond to carbachol and gastrin (as indicated by studies of AP accumulation) these negative findings appear to be valid.

Alteration of calcium fluxes across the plasma membrane or alteration in the membrane cellular calcium may play a role in the responses to carbachol and gastrin, but there are no direct data to support these possibili-ties.

SUMMARY

The three stimulants of gastric acid secretion likely to have physiological roles in regulation of secretion are acetylcholine, gastrin, and histamine. Acetylcholine is released by vagal and intramucosal reflex stimulation, acting directly on the parietal cell. Gastrin is released by peptides and free amino acids in the stomach and is the only known hormonal stimulant of acid secretion. Release of gastrin by acetylcholine may occur. However, cholinergic control of gastrin release is complex since under certain conditions anticholinergic drugs may actually enhance gastrin release. Factors regulating histamine release have not been defined, but studies with H_2-receptor antagonists leave little doubt that histamine has an important role in acid secretion.

Studies with isolated parietal cells indicate that histamine, gastrin, and acetylcholine each appear to act at separate receptors on the parietal cell. Anticholinergic agents specifically prevent the cellular actions of acetylcholine, cimetidine specifically inhibits stimulation by histamine, and neither inhibitor blocks the small direct response to gastrin. Furthermore potentiating interactions occur between histamine, gastrin, and cholinergic agents which may account for the interdependence of secretagogue action observed in vivo. Direct potentiating interactions occur between histamine and gastrin and histamine and carbachol but not between carbachol and gastrin. However, in the presence of histamine, carbachol, and gastrin, a three-way potentiation does occur. By interfering with the potentiating interactions between stimulants, anticholinergic agents and cimetidine display an apparent cross-specificity in vitro that resembles the effects of these agents in intact mucosa. The mechanisms underlying these interactions are unknown, but the actions of histamine appear to be mediated through increased production of cyclic AMP and cyclic AMP analogs, which mimic the interactions involving histamine itself. The secondary effectors for acetylcholine and gastrin and the mechanisms for amplification of the response to combinations of stimulants remain to be elucidated.

ACKNOWLEDGMENTS

This work was supported by NIAMDD grants 17294, 17328 and 19984. The authors are indebted to Dr. Morton I. Grossman for his very helpful suggestions and comments.

Literature Cited

1. Amsterdam, A., Jamieson, J. D. 1974. Studies on dispersed pancreatic exocrine cells. I. Dissociation technique and morphologic characteristics of separated cells. *J. Cell. Biol.* 63:1037–56
2. Baron, J. H., 1976. Inhibition of gastric separation by intestinal hormones. *Scand. J. Gastroenterol.* 11 (Suppl 42): 17–24
3. Beaven, M. A. 1978. Histamine: its role in physiological and pathological processes. *Monogr. Allergy* 13:1–114
4. Becker, H. D., Reeder, D. D., Thompson, J. C. 1973. The effect of prostaglandin E_1 on the release of gastrin and gastric acid secretion in dogs. *Endocrinology* 93:1148–51
5. Bergegardh, S., Broman, G., Knutson, U., Palmer, L., Olbe, L. 1976. Gastric acid responses to graded i.v. infusions of pentagastrin and histalog in peptic ulcer patients before and after antrum-bulb resection. *Scand. J. Gastroenterol.* 11: 337, 346
6. Bergegardh, S., Olbe, L. 1975. Gastric acid response to antrum distension in man. *Scand. J. Gastroenterol.* 10: 171–76
7. Berglindh, T., Helander, H. F., Obrink, K. J. 1976. Effects of secretagogues on oxygen consumption, aminopyrine accumulation, and morphology in isolated gastric glands. *Acta Physiol. Scand.* 97:401–14
8. Berglindh, T. 1977. Absolute dependence on chloride for acid secretion in isolated gastric glands. *Gastroenterology* 73:874–80
9. Berstad, A., Petersen, H. 1972. Effect of duodenal acidification on the gastric secretory response to pentagastrin in man. *Digestion* 6:193–204
10. Black, J. W., Duncan, W. A. M., Durant, C. J., Ganellin, C. R., Parsons, E. M. 1972. Definition and antagonism of histamine H_2-receptors. *Nature* 236: 385–90
11. Brooks, F. P. 1967. In *Handbook of Physiology*, ed. C. F. Code, Vol. II, Sect. 6, p. 805. Washington DC: Am. Physiol. Soc.
12. Brooks, A. M., Grossman, M. I. 1970. Effect of secretin and cholecystokinin on pentagastrin stimulated gastric secretion in man. *Gastroenterology* 59:114–19
13. Butcher, R. W., Baird, C. E. 1968. Effects of prostaglandins on adenosine 3',5'-monophosphate levels in fat and other tissues. *J. Biol. Chem.* 243: 1713–17
14. Byrne, W. J., Christie, D. L., Ament, M. E., Walsh, J. H. 1977. *Clin. Res.* 25:108A (Abstr.)
15. Christiansen, J., Rehfeld, J. F., Stadil, F. 1976. Effect of intrajejunal fat on meal-stimulated acid and gastrin secretion in man. *Scand. J. Gastroenterol.* 11:673–76
16. Christensen, K. C., Stadil, F. 1976. On the beta-adrenergic contribution to the gastric acid and gastrin responses to hypoglycaemia in man. *Scand. J. Gastroenterol.* 11 (Suppl. 37):81–86
17. Christensen, K. C., Stadil, F. 1976. Effect of epinephrine and norepinephrine on gastrin release and gastric secretion of acid in man. *Scand. J. Gastroenterol.* 11 (Suppl. 37):81–86
18. Clain, J. E., Malagelada, J. R., Go, V. L., Summerskill, W. H. 1977. Participation of the jejunum and ileum in postprandial gastric secretion in man. *Gastroenterology* 73:211–14
19. Cross, S. A. M., Ewen, S. W. B., Rost, F. W. D. 1971. A study of methods available for the cytochemical localization of histamine by fluorescence induced with O-pthalaldehyde or acetaldehyde. *Histochem. J.* 3:471–76
20. Csendes, A., Walsh, J. H., Grossman, M. I. 1972. Effects of atropine and of antral acidification on gastrin release and acid secretion in response to insulin and feeding in dogs. *Gastroenterology* 63:257–63
21. Dalton, M. D., Eisenstein, A. M., Walsh, J. H., Fordtran, J. S. 1976. Effect of secretin on gastric function in normal subjects and in patients with duodenal ulcer. *Gastroenterology* 71: 24–29
22. Debas, H. T., Csendes, A., Walsh, J. H., Grossman, M. I. 1974. In *Endocrinology of the Gut*, ed. W. Y. Chey, S. P. Brooks, pp. 222–32. Thorofare, NJ: Charles B. Slack, Inc.
23. Debas, H. T., Konturek, S. J., Walsh, J. H., Grossman, M. I. 1974. Proof of a pyloro-oxyntic reflex for stimulation of acid secretion. *Gastroenterology* 66: 526–32
24. Debas, H. T., Slaff, G. F., Grossman, M. I. 1974. Intestinal phase of gastric acid secretion: augmentation of maximal response of Heidenhain pouch to gastrin and histamine. *Gastroenterology* 68:691–98
25. Debas, H. T., Walsh, J. H., Grossman, M. I. 1975. Evidence for oxynto-pyloric reflex for release of gastrin. *Gastroenterology* 68:687–90

26. Durbin, R. P. 1977. Chloride transport and acid secretion in stomach. *Gastroenterology* 73:927–30

27. Farooq, O., Walsh, J. H. 1975. Atropine enhances serum gastrin response to insulin in man. *Gastroenterology* 68: 662–66

28. Feldman, M., Richardson, C. T., Peterson, W. L., Walsh, J. H., Fordtran, J. S. 1977. Effect of low-dose propantheline on food-stimulated gastric acid secretion: comparison with an "optimal effective dose" and interaction with cimetidine. *N. Engl. J. Med.* 297: 1427–30

29. Feldman, M., Richardson, C. T., Taylor, I. A., Walsh, J. H. 1978. Neural regulation of gastrin and pancreatic polypeptide release in man. *Clin. Res.* 26:497A (Abstr.)

30. Feldman, M., Walsh, J. H., Wong, H., Richardson, C. T. 1978. Role of gastrin heptadecapeptide in the acid secretory response to amino acids in man. *J. Clin. Invest.* 61:308–13

31. Forte, J. G., Lee, H. C. 1977. Gastric adenosine triphosphatases: a review of their possible role in HCl secretion. *Gastroenterology* 73:921–26

32. Forte, T. M., Machen, T. E., Forte, J. G. 1977. Ultrastructural changes in oxyntic cells associated with secretory function: a membrane-recycling hypothesis. *Gastroenterology* 73:941–55

33. Fordtran, J. S., Walsh, J. H. 1973. Gastric acid secretion rate and buffer content of the stomach after eating: results in normal subjects and in patients with duodenal ulcer. *J. Clin. Invest.* 52: 645–57

34. Grabner, P., Semb, L. S., Schrumpf, E., Myren, J. 1977. Plasma gastrin and gastric secretory response to duodenal perfusion with liver extract in healthy human subjects. *Scand. J. Gastroenterol.* 12:865–68

35. Grossman, M. I. 1974. Some minor heresies about vagotomy. *Gastroenterology* 67:1016–19

36. Grossman, M. I. 1978. Control of gastric secretion. In *Gastrointestinal Disease*, ed. M. H. Sleisenger, J. S. Fordtran, pp. 640–59. Philadelphia: Saunders

37. Grötzinger, U., Bergegardh, S., Olbe, L. 1977. Effect of fundic distension on gastric acid secretion in man. *Gut* 18:105–10

38. Grötzinger, U., Bergegardh, S., Olbe, L. 1977. Effect of atropine and proximal gastric vagotomy on the acid response

39. Grötzinger, U., Bergegardh, S., Olbe, L. 1977. Effects of fundic distension on pentagastrin-stimulated gastric acid secretion in man. *Gastroenterology* 73: 447–52

40. Hersey, S. J. 1974. Interactions between oxidative metabolism and acid secretion in gastric mucosa. *Biochim. Biophys. Acta* 344:157–203

41. Hersey, S. J. 1977. Metabolic changes associated with gastric stimulation. *Gastroenterology* 73:914–19

42. Hirschowitz, B. I., Hutchison, G. A. 1973. A working hypothesis for urecholine effects of histamine stimulation on gastric secretion. *Scand. J. Gastroent.* 8:569–76

43. Hirschowitz, B. I., Hutchison, G. A. 1977. Kinetics of atropine inhibition of pentagastrin-stimulated H^+, electrolyte, and pepsin secretion in the dog. *Am. J. Dig. Dis.* 22:99–107

44. Hirschowitz, B. I., Sachs, S., Hutchison, G. 1973. Lack of potentiation or synergism between histamine and pentagastrin in the fistula dog. *Am. J. Physiol.* 224:509–13

45. Impicciatore, M., Walsh, J. H., Grossman, M. I. 1977. Low doses of atropine enhance serum gastrin response to food in dogs. *Gastroenterology* 72:995–96

46. Ippoliti, A. F., Isenberg, J. I., Maxwell, V., Walsh, J. H. 1976. The effect of 16,16-dimethyl prostaglandin E2 on meal-stimulated gastric acid secretion and serum gastrin in duodenal ulcer patients. *Gastroenterology* 70:488–91

47. Isenberg, J. I., Ippoliti, A. F., Maxwell, V. L. 1977. Perfusion of the proximal small intestine with peptone stimulates gastric acid secretion in man. *Gastroenterology* 73:746–752

48. Isenberg, J. I., Maxwell, V. 1978. Intravenous infusion of amino acids stimulates gastric acid secretion in man. *N. Engl. J. Med.* 298:27–29

49. Jacobson, E. D., Thompson, W. J. 1976. Cyclic AMP and gastric secretion: the illusive second messenger. *Adv. Cyclic Nucleotide Res.* 7:199–224

50. Johnson, L. R., Grossman, M. I. 1969. Potentiation of gastric acid response in the dog. *Gastroenterology* 56:687–92

51. Konturek, S. J., Johnson, L. R. 1971. Evidence for an enterogastric reflex for the inhibition of acid secretion. *Gastroenterology* 61:667–74

52. Konturek, S. J., Wysocki, A., Oleksy, J. 1968. Effect of medical and surgical vagotomy on gastric response to graded

doses of pentagastrin and histamine. *Gastroenterology* 54:392–400

53. Kowalewski, K., Kolodej, A. 1972. Relation between hydrogen ion secretion and oxygen consumption by *ex vivo* isolated canine stomach, perfused with homologous blood. *Can. J. Physiol. Pharmacol.* 50:955–61

54. Levant, J. A., Walsh, J. H., Isenberg, J. I. 1973. Stimulation of gastric secretion and gastrin release by single oral doses of calcium carbonate in man. *New Engl. J. Med.* 289:555–59

55. MacGregor, I. L., Deveney, C., Way, L. W., Meyer, J. H. 1976. The effect of acute hyperglycemia on meal-stimulated gastric, biliary, and pancreatic secretion, and serum gastrin. *Gastroenterology* 70:197–202

56. Main, I. H. M., Pearce, J. B. 1977. Histamine output from the rat isolated gastric mucosa during acid secretion stimulated by pentagastrin, methacholine, and dibutyryl cyclic adenosine 3′,5′-monophosphate. *Br. J. Pharmacol.* 61:461P

57. Malagelada, J. R., Longstreth, G. F., Deering, T. B., Summerskill, W. H., Go, V. L. 1977. Gastric secretion and emptying after ordinary meals in duodenal ulcer. *Gastroenterology* 73:989–94

58. Mayer, G., Arnold, R., Feurle, G., Fuchs, K., Ketterer, H., Track, N. S., Creutzfeldt, W. 1974. Influence of feeding and sham feeding upon serum gastrin and gastric acid secretion in control subjects and duodenal ulcer patients. *Scand. J. Gastroenterol.* 9:703–10

59. Moore, J. G., Wolfe, M. 1973. The relation of plasma gastrin to the circadian rhythm of gastric acid secretion in man. *Digestion* 9:97–105

60. Nilsson, G., Simon, H., Yalow, R. S., Berson, S. A. 1972. Plasma gastrin and gastric acid responses to sham feeding and feeding in dogs. *Gastroenterology* 63:51–59

61. Pearse, A. G. E., Polak, J. M., Bloom, S. R. 1977. The new gut hormones: cellular sources, physiology, pathology, and clinical aspects. *Gastroenterology* 72:746–61

62. Pederson, R. A., Brown, J. C. 1972. Inhibition of histamine-, pentagastrin-, and insulin-stimulated canine gastric secretion by pure "gastric inhibitory polypeptide." *Gastroenterology* 62:393–400

63. Phillip, J., Domschke, S., Domschke, W., Urbach, H. J., Reiss, M., Demling, L. 1977. Inhibition by somatostatin of

gastrin release and gastric acid responses to meals and to pentagastrin in man. *Scand. J. Gastroenterol.* 12:261–65

64. Ramamurthi, B., Mascreen, M., Valmikinathan, K. 1977. Role of the amygdala and hypothalamus in control of gastric secretion in human beings. *Acta Neurochir. (Wien)* (Suppl. 24:) 187–90

65. Reite, O. B. 1972. Comparative physiology of histamine. *Physiol. Rev.* 52:778–819

66. Richardson, C. T. 1978. Effect of H2-receptor antagonists on gastric acid secretion and serum gastrin concentration: a review. *Gastroenterology* 74:366–70

67. Richardson, C. T., Walsh, J. H., Cooper, K. A., Feldman, M., Fordtran, J. S. 1977. Studies on the role of cephalic-vagal stimulation in the acid secretory response to eating in normal human subjects. *J. Clin. Invest.* 60:435–41

68. Richardson, C. T., Walsh, J. H., Hicks, M. I., Fordtran, J. S. 1976. Studies on the mechanisms of food-stimulated gastric acid secretion in normal human subjects. *J. Clin. Invest.* 58:623–31

69. Robert, A. 1976. Antisecretory, antiulcer, cytoprotective and diarrheogenic properties of prostaglandins. In *Advances in Prostaglandin and and Thromboxane Research,* ed. B. Samuelson, R. Paoletti, Vol. 1, pp. 507–20. New York: Raven

70. Robison, G. A., Butcher, R. W., Sutherland, E. W. 1968. Cyclic AMP. *Ann. Rev. Biochem.* 37:149–74

71. Sachs, G., Chang, H., Rabon, E., Shackman, R., Sarau, H. M., Saccomani, G. 1977. Metabolic and membrane aspects of gastrin H^+ transport. *Gastroenterology* 73:931–40

72. Schmidt-Wilcke, H. A., Stienhagen, P., Steinhagen, E., Martini, G. A. 1975. Effect of fatty acids on the stimulated gastric secretion in man. *Digestion* 13:8–14

73. Shore, P. A., Brodie, B. B., Hogben, C. A. M. 1957. The gastric secretion of drugs: a pH partition hypothesis. *J. Pharmacol. Exp. Ther.* 119:361–69

74. Simay, D. A., Peskin, G. W., Saik, R. P. 1978. Metiamide: more than an H2-receptor antagonist. *Am. J. Dig. Dis.* 23:169–72

75. Sjodin, L. 1975. Inhibition of gastrin-stimulated canine acid secretion by sham-feeding. *Scand. J. Gastroenterol.* 10:73–80

76. Soares, E. C., Zaterka, S., Walsh, J. H. 1977. Acid secretion and serum gastrin

at graded intragastric pressures in man. *Gastroenterology* 72:676–79

77. Soll, A. H. 1977. Secretagogue stimulation of O_2 consumption and ^{14}C-aminopyrine uptake by enriched canine parietal cells. *Gastroenterology* 72:1166 (Abstr.)

78. Soll, A. H. 1978. The actions of secretagogues on oxygen uptake by isolated mammalian parietal cells. *J. Clin. Invest.* 61:370–80

79. Soll, A. H. 1978. The interaction of histamine with gastrin and carbamylcholine on oxygen uptake by isolated mammalian parietal cells. *J. Clin. Invest.* 61:381–89

80. Soll, A. H. 1978. Three-way interactions between histamine, carbachol, and gastrin on aminopyrine uptake by isolated canine parietal cells. *Gastroenterology* 74:1146 (Abstr.)

81. Soll, A. H. 1978. Prostaglandin inhibition of histamine-stimulated aminopyrine uptake and cyclic AMP generation by isolated canine parietal cells. *Gastroenterology* 74:1146 (Abstr.)

82. Soll, A. H., Grossman, M. I. 1978. Cellular mechanisms in acid secretion. *Ann. Rev. Med.* 29:495–507

83. Soll, A. H., Lechago, J., Walsh, J. H. 1976. The isolated mammalian parietal cell: Morphological transformation induced by secretagogues. *Gastroenterology* 70:975 (Abstr.)

84. Soll, A. H., Wollin, A. 1977. The effects of histamine, prostaglandin E_2, and secretin on cyclic AMP in separated canine fundic mucosal cells. *Gastroenterology* 72:1166 (Abstr.)

85. Stenquist, B., Knutson, U., Olbe, L. 1978. Gastric acid responses to adequate and modified sham feeding and to insulin hypoglycemia in duodenal ulcer patients. *Scand. J. Gastroenterol.* 13:357–63

86. Strunz, U. T., Walsh, J. H., Grossman, M. I. 1978. Stimulation of gastrin release in dogs by individual amino acids. *Proc. Soc. Biol. Med.* 157:440–41

87. Tepperman, B. L., Walsh, J. H., Preshaw, R. M. 1973. Effect of antral denervation on gastrin release by sham feeding and insulin hypoglycemia in dogs. *Gastroenterology* 63:973–80

88. Thunberg, R. 1967. Localization of cells containing and forming histamine in the gastric mucosa of the rat. *Exp. Cell. Res.* 47:108

89. Troidl, H., Lorenz, W., Rohde, H., Häfner, G., Ronzheimer, M., Schmal, A. 1975. Histamine content in human gastric mucosa: its relation to the pentagastrin-stimulated acid secretion and to selective-gastric vagotomy with drainage. *Agents Actions* 5:427–28

90. Uvnas, B. 1971. Role of duodenum in inhibition of gastric acid secretion. *Scand. J. Gastroenterol.* 6:113–25

91. Vatn, M. H., Schrumpf, E., Hanssen, K. F., Myren, J. 1977. The effect of somatostatin on pentagastrin-stimulated gastric secretion and on plasma gastrin in man. *Scand. J. Gastroenterol.* 12:833–39

92. Walsh, J. H. 1975. Circulating gastrin. *Ann. Rev. Physiol.* 37:81–104

93. Walsh, J. H. 1977. Gastrin heterogeneity: Biological significance. *Fed. Proc.* 36:1948–51

94. Walsh, J. H., Grossman, M. I. 1975. Gastrin (Parts I and II). *New Engl. J. Med.* 292:1324–34; 1377–84

95. Walsh, J. H., Richardson, C. T., Fordtran, J. S. 1975. pH dependence of acid secretion and gastrin release in normal and ulcer patients. *J. Clin. Invest.* 55:462–69

96. Walsh, J. H., Yalow, R. S., Berson, S. A. 1971. The effect of atropine on plasma gastrin response to feeding. *Gastroenterology* 60:16–21

97. Ward, A. S., Wilkins, R. A., Cockel, R., Windsor, C. W. O. 1969. Duodenal inhibition of gastric secretion by osmotic agents in normal subjects and patients with duodenal ulcer. *Gut* 10:1020–28

98. Wollin, A., Code, C. F., Dousa, T. P. 1976. Interaction of prostaglandins and histamine with enzymes of cyclic AMP metabolism from guinea pig gastric mucosa. *J. Clin. Invest.* 57:1548–53

Ann. Rev. Physiol. 1979. 41:55–66
Copyright © 1979 by Annual Reviews Inc. All rights reserved

REGULATION OF PANCREATIC ❖1205
EXOCRINE FUNCTION IN VITRO:
INITIAL STEPS IN THE ACTIONS
OF SECRETAGOGUES

Jerry D. Gardner

Section on Gastroenterology, Digestive Diseases Branch, National Institute
Arthritis, Metabolism, and Digestive Disease, National Institutes of Health,
Bethesda, Md. 20014

INTRODUCTION[1]

The sequence of morphological and biochemical events in the pancreas during the synthesis and secretion of pancreatic enzymes is reasonably well-established (23); however, only during the past 5 years have we begun to elucidate the mechanisms through which pancreatic secretagogues regulate the secretory process. This recent progress has resulted primarily from the development of in vitro preparations such as slices of pancreas, microdissected acini, and dispersed acinar cells. Studies using these preparations coupled with the application of electrophysiologic techniques have provided insight into the biochemical and electrical changes that constitute the initial steps in the action of secretagogues on pancreatic enzyme secretion. The present paper reviews the major findings that have helped to elucidate the initial sequence of changes effected by secretagogues in various in vitro preparations of pancreas.

CALCIUM

The actions of secretagogues on pancreatic enzyme secretion were initially thought to result from their ability to increase the inward movement of

[1]Because of the limited space available for this paper I have not cited every report which documents a particular observation but, instead, have selected representative studies. Whenever possible I have cited review articles which do contain comprehensive bibliographies.

55

0066-4278/79/0301-0055$01.00

calcium into acinar cells (10). This conclusion was based primarily on the observation that stimulation of pancreatic enzyme secretion is reduced or abolished in calcium-free incubation solutions (3, 40, 48). With one exception, however, measurements of transport of ^{45}Ca in vitro showed that pancreatic secretagogues such as acetylcholine or cholecystokinin (CCK) do not increase calcium influx but cause a significant increase in calcium outflux and that the increase in calcium outflux does not depend on extracellular calcium (3, 7, 9, 14, 16, 30, 45, 48). In pancreatic acinar cells most of the calcium is nonexchangeable (3, 26, 45, 48) and although secretagogues can increase outflux of exchangeable calcium, this effect does not alter total tissue calcium (3, 26, 45, 48). In the studies in which CCK and cholinergic agents were reported to increase the uptake of ^{45}Ca (26, 27), the cells were washed with iced, isosmotic choline chloride. A subsequent study (16) showed that under these conditions the increased uptake of ^{45}Ca caused by the secretagogues reflected cellular uptake of radioactivity from the wash solution, not from the incubation medium.

The precise cellular localization of the calcium released by pancreatic secretagogues has not been determined, but measurements of changes in fluorescence of chlorotetracycline (4) as well as the amount of exchangeable cellular calcium retained on a Millipore filter after hypotonic lysis of acinar cells (45) suggest that most, if not all, of the calcium is released from intracellular, bound stores. Although release of cellular calcium is a step in the mechanism through which secretagogues increase amylase secretion, it is not known whether the critical event is the release of calcium per se or a resulting increase in cytoplasmic calcium.

Recent studies have shown that peptides isolated from amphibian skin (caerulein, bombesin, litorin, and physalaemin) as well as eledoisin, a peptide isolated from the posterior salivary gland of a Mediterranean octopod, can increase amylase release and outflux of calcium from pancreatic fragments and dispersed acinar cells (9, 30). This action of caerulein is not surprising since this decapeptide has seven of its eight C-terminal amino acids in positions identical to those in the C-terminal octapeptide of CCK (12, 30). The other four peptides have amino acid sequences which differ significantly from those of CCK (12), and their actions are probably mediated by receptors different from those with which CCK, gastrin, and caerulein interact.

In addition to its role in initiating the action of various secretagogues, cellular calcium also functions to control the enzyme secretory process. The available evidence suggests that these actions reflect two functionally distinct components of cellular calcium. Without extracellular calcium the ability of secretagogues to increase enzyme secretion is reduced or abolished (3, 40, 48), but the ability of secretagogues to cause release of cellular calcium is unaltered (3, 7, 9, 14, 16, 30, 45, 48).

The antibiotic A23187 promotes transfer of divalent cations across biological as well as artificial membranes (39) and increases release of amylase from pancreas in vitro (5, 7, 11). Removing extracellular calcium abolishes the increase in amylase secretion caused by A23187 (5, 11). This finding was initially cited as evidence that secretagogues cause pancreatic enzyme secretion by increasing calcium influx (11). However, in dispersed acinar cells, A23187 increases both influx and outflux of ^{45}Ca (7). In the presence of extracellular calcium, the A23187-induced increase in influx is greater than the increase in outflux and the net effect is that the ionophore increases the uptake of calcium. In the absence of extracellular calcium, the ionophore-induced increase in calcium outflux causes a rapid depletion of exchangeable cellular calcium. The lack of effect of A23187 in calcium-free solutions may reflect the accelerated depletion of cellular calcium rather than simply the absence of the ionophore-mediated increase in calcium influx.

CYCLIC GMP

Pancreatic secretagogues that cause release of cellular calcium also increase cyclic GMP (1, 7, 18, 30); this increase can occur in a calcium-free solution. There has been a close correlation between the dose-response curve for the action of a secretagogue on cellular cyclic GMP and that for its action on calcium release. Three findings suggest that secretagogues increase cellular cyclic GMP by causing mobilization of cellular calcium: (a) Calcium can influence guanylate cyclase activity in broken cell preparations from various tissues (e.g. 25). (b) A23187 increases cellular cyclic GMP in dispersed acinar cells, and this action can occur in a calcium-free medium (7). (c) Exogenous derivatives of cyclic GMP do not increase calcium outflux from in vitro preparations of pancreas (7), but these nucleotides can increase amylase secretion (17, 18).

Although secretagogues can increase cellular cyclic GMP in vitro (1, 7, 18, 30), and some (17, 18) but not all (19) investigators have found exogenous derivatives of cyclic GMP to increase amylase release, the role of cyclic GMP as a potential mediator of the action of secretagogues on pancreatic enzyme secretion is still unclear. No secretagogue that increases cellular cyclic GMP has been reported to activate guanylate cyclase in a broken-cell preparation. Analogs of cyclic nucleotides can inhibit cyclic nucleotide phosphodiesterase (2) and by so doing could increase cellular cyclic AMP. This might account for their ability to increase secretion of amylase from pancreas in vitro. The action of cyclic nucleotides on cell function is thought to occur from their ability to activate cyclic nucleotide–dependent protein kinase (28). To date there has been only one study of cyclic GMP–dependent protein kinase in pancreas (47); the characteristics of this enzyme differ from those reported for other tissues. In tissues incubated with agents whose action on cell function is mediated by a cyclic nucleotide there is endogenous activation of the cyclic nucleotide–dependent protein kinase and occupation of binding sites on the enzyme by the cyclic nucleotide. No such studies have been reported using pancreas.

The finding that CCK could increase cyclic AMP in pancreas (8) plus the finding that CCK as well as C-terminal fragments and analogs could activate adenylate cyclase in broken cell preparations from pancreas (29, 44, 46) suggested that cyclic AMP mediated the action of CCK. However, several subsequent findings indicated that cyclic AMP does not mediate the action of CCK on pancreatic enzyme secretion. Concentrations of CCK that increase calcium outflux, cyclic GMP, and amylase release do not increase cellular cyclic AMP (8, 29). Synthetic C-terminal fragments of CCK do not increase cyclic AMP in the pancreas in vitro (29) and this finding suggests that the increase in cyclic AMP observed with natural CCK (8) may have reflected contamination with small amounts of secretin- or VIP-like material. The concentrations of CCK required to activate adenylate cyclase (29, 44, 46) are substantially higher than those required to increase enzyme secretion (17, 42), and the structural requirements for CCK to activate adenylate cyclase differ significantly from the requirements for stimulation of amylase release (29). Finally, some analogs of the C-terminal octapeptide of CCK are partial agonists for adenylate cyclase but full agonists for amylase secretion (42).

CYCLIC AMP

Secretin and VIP can increase pancreatic enzyme secretion in some (8, 17) but not all (43) species. The increase in amylase secretion caused by secretin or VIP is accompanied by an increase in cellular cyclic AMP (15, 41, 43) with no change in calcium fluxes or cellular cyclic GMP (7, 14). Inhibitors of cyclic nucleotide phosphodiesterase augment the action of secretin or VIP on cellular cyclic AMP as well as on enzyme secretion (8, 17), and both peptides can activate adenylate cyclase in membrane preparations from pancreatic acinar cells (29, 44, 46). Furthermore, derivatives of cyclic AMP can increase enzyme secretion from the pancreas in vitro (17, 18), and the increase in enzyme secretion caused by secretin or VIP plus exogenous derivatives of cyclic AMP is the same as that obtained with secretin or VIP alone (17).

The basis for the species variation in the ability of secretin and VIP to increase amylase release is not known. Robberecht et al (43) found that although secretin and VIP increase cyclic AMP in fragments of pancreas from mouse, dog, cat, rat, and guinea pig, these peptides increase enzyme secretion only in pancreas from rat or guinea pig. Furthermore, in acinar cells from guinea pig, the dose-response curve for the action of VIP on cyclic AMP is biphasic, but only the first component correlates with the action of VIP on enzyme secretion (17, 41). Finally, the major increase in cyclic AMP in guinea pig pancreas incubated with secretin is not accompanied by an increase in enzyme secretion (17, 41). Although some of these discrepancies are only apparent and can be resolved by critical examination of studies of receptors for VIP and secretin (discussed below in section on Receptors), additional studies are required to establish clearly the degree of correlation between the actions of secretin and VIP on cellular cyclic AMP and the increase in enzyme secretion.

VIP and secretin do not alter calcium fluxes or cyclic GMP and do not alter the action of other secretagogues on these functions (7, 14, 30). Similarly, secretagogues that increase calcium outflux and cellular cyclic GMP do not alter cellular cyclic AMP or the increase in cellular cyclic AMP caused by VIP or secretin (8, 29, 41, 43).

PHOSPHOLIPIDS

A number of agents such as cholinergic and α-adrenergic compounds increase degradation of phosphatidylinositol in a variety of tissues and frequently change cellular calcium transport or cyclic GMP, but do not alter cyclic AMP (31). Agents whose effects on their target tissues are mediated by cyclic AMP, however, do not affect phosphatidylinositol turnover. In the pancreas, cholinergic compounds and CCK increase the turnover of phosphatidylinositol by accelerating its degradation to diacylglycerol and inositolphosphate (20, 24, 31, 32). Secretin does not affect degradation of phosphatidylinositol (31).

The actions of various agents on phosphatidylinositol turnover persist in tissues incubated in calcium-free solutions (24, 31). Furthermore, A23187 does not accelerate degradation of phosphatidylinositol under conditions where the ionophore causes changes in other cell functions (24, 31). Thus, in tissues in which calcium may mediate the actions of various agonists, the change in phosphatidylinositol turnover is thought to precede the change in calcium movement. Some (24, 31, 32) have suggested that phosphatidylinositol or a related compound may be closely associated with the membrane receptors for agents that accelerate degradation of phosphatidylinositol.

RECEPTORS

Studies of the interaction of ^{125}I-VIP with intact acinar cells from guinea pig pancreas have shown that acinar cells possess two distinct classes of receptors, each of which interacts with VIP and secretin but not glucagon (6). One class is "VIP-preferring" in that it has a high affinity for VIP and a low affinity for secretin; the other is "secretin-preferring" in that it has a high affinity for secretin and a low affinity for VIP (6). These two classes of receptors can also be distinguished by whether or not they are sensitive to structural changes in fragments and analogs of secretin (6, 15, 41). There is a close correlation between the ability of native VIP to inhibit binding of ^{125}I-VIP and its ability to increase cellular cyclic AMP (6, 41). The increase in cyclic AMP caused by secretin correlates with its ability to inhibit binding of ^{125}I-VIP to the secretin-preferring receptors (6, 41). There is no detectable increase in cyclic AMP caused by secretin acting through the VIP-preferring receptors—probably because the increase is too small to be detected in the presence of the increase in cyclic AMP resulting from secretin acting through the secretin-preferring receptors (6, 15, 41). Although occupation of secretin-preferring receptors by VIP or secretin causes a greater increase in cellular cyclic AMP than does occupation of the VIP-preferring receptors by these peptides, stimulation of enzyme secretion from guinea pig acinar cells appears to be mediated exclusively by the VIP-preferring receptors. What cellular function, if any, is altered as a consequence of the increase in cyclic AMP caused by the secretin-preferring receptors is not known. These findings offer a possible explanation for the inability of secretin and VIP to increase enzyme secretion from dog, cat, or mouse pancreas, even though secretin and VIP increase cyclic AMP in these tissues. Acinar cells from dog, cat, and mouse pancreas may possess secretin-preferring receptors that mediate the increase in cyclic AMP but may lack the VIP-preferring receptors that mediate the stimulation of enzyme secretion. One finding in support of this possibility is that studies of ^{125}I-secretin binding to partially purified membranes from cat pancreas showed a single class of binding sites that had a high affinity for secretin and a low affinity for VIP (33).

Studies of the interaction of [^{3}H]caerulein with plasma membranes from rat pancreas (42) have shown that the *relative* potencies with which caerulein, CCK, and chemically related peptides inhibit binding of [^{3}H]caerulein were similar to their *relative* potencies for increasing enzyme secretion from fragments of pancreas. However, the potency of a given peptide for inhibiting binding was 10–100 times less than its potency for increasing amylase release (42). This discrepancy may reflect the fact that the studies were performed under different incubation conditions and with different tissue preparations, the presence of "spare receptors" (i.e. only a small percentage of the receptors need to be occupied to cause a maximal response), or the existence of a class of binding sites unrelated to the receptors that mediate the action of these peptides on enzyme secretion. A derivative of the C-terminal pentapeptide shared by CCK and gastrin (2-nitro-5-azidobenzoyl-Gly-Trp-Met-Asp-Phe-NH$_2$) has been used to attempt to photoaffinity label acinar cell receptors for CCK (13). Photolysis of the derivative in the presence of pancreatic lobules caused persistent stimulation of protein secretion. In contrast to what one would expect with a photoaffinity label of the receptor, native secretagogues such as CCK or caerulein failed to inhibit the photolysis-catalyzed stimulation of protein discharge caused by the derivative; its mechanism of action is unknown.

INTERACTION BETWEEN REGULATORY PATHWAYS

With appropriate pairs of secretagogues the increase in enzyme secretion caused by two agents in combination is significantly greater than the sum of the increase caused by each agent alone (8, 17). This potentiation of enzyme secretion occurs when a secretagogue that increases cyclic AMP (e.g. VIP or secretin) is added to a secretagogue that increases calcium outflux and cyclic GMP (e.g. CCK or carbachol) but not with two agents that act through the same mechanism (e.g. not with CCK plus carbachol or secretin plus VIP). Although the biochemical basis for potentiation is not known, it appears to occur from an interaction at a step distal to the secretagogue-induced changes in cellular cyclic nucleotides.

ELECTROPHYSIOLOGY

In recent years there has been a substantial increase in our knowledge of the electrical properties of glandular tissue in general and of pancreatic acinar cells in particular (for review see 36). Secretagogues that increase both calcium outflux and cellular cyclic GMP cause depolarization of pancreatic acinar cells. Secretagogue-induced depolarization of acinar cells is accompanied by a reduction in the cell surface membrane resistance (22, 34–36) and by changes in the membrane conductance of sodium, potassium, and chloride ions (34). The dose-response curve for secretagogue-induced depolarization correlates closely with those for change in surface membrane resistance since high extracellular potassium can cause depolarization of acinar cells but does not cause enzyme secretion or a change in resistance (36, 38). Secretin does not cause depolarization of pancreatic acinar cells (35). One laboratory has reported that in rat acinar cells acetylcholine and CCK cause hyperpolarization and increase surface membrane resistance (36). The basis for this discrepancy is not clear; it is not due to a species difference because others (36) using rat acinar cells have observed depolarization with acetylcholine and CCK.

The secretagogue-induced electrical changes in pancreatic acinar cells appear to result from the effects of these agents on cellular calcium described previously. Electrical changes caused by various secretagogues do not require extracellular calcium (34, 36). Either incubation of acinar cells with A23187 (38) or intracellular injection of calcium (21) causes depolarization and a reduction in surface membrane resistance. Thus, effects of secretagogues on depolarization and membrane resistance are thought to result from an increased concentration in cytoplasmic calcium caused by secretagogue-induced mobilization of cellular calcium stores. Although these electrical changes appear to be caused by secretagogue-induced mobilization of cellular calcium, it is the change in calcium, not the change in electrical properties, that appears to play the causal role in increasing enzyme secretion.

Pancreatic acinar cells are electrically coupled because the junctional cell membranes have a specific resistance substantially lower than that of the surface cell membranes (36, 37). Furthermore, an acinar cell is coupled to other cells within the same acinus but does not interact electrically with cells in adjacent acini (36, 37). At relatively high concentrations, those pancreatic secretagogues that cause depolarization can also cause electrical uncoupling (21, 22). Repeated injection of intracellular calcium, like high concentrations of secretagogues, causes electrical uncoupling of pancreatic acinar cells (21). This finding suggests that at high concentrations, secretagogues increase the concentration of cytoplasmic calcium to an extent sufficient to cause electrical uncoupling. The functional significance of electrical coupling of pancreatic acinar cells is not known; however, this coupling could provide a potential amplification mechanism whereby signals initiated by interaction of a secretagogue with a few cells could be transmitted to all of the cells within the same acinus. Just as electrical coupling may amplify the response of the system to low secretagogue concentrations, electrical uncoupling may serve as an attenuation mechanism to buffer the response of the system to high secretagogue concentrations.

WORKING HYPOTHESIS

As illustrated in Figure 1, acinar cells can be viewed as having five classes of membrane receptors for various secretagogues. Four of these classes mediate secretagogue-induced changes in calcium fluxes and cyclic GMP while the fifth mediates changes in adenylate cyclase and cellular cyclic AMP. The receptors that interact with cholinergic agents can be distinguished by their susceptibility to inhibition by muscarinic cholinergic antagonists, and those that interact with VIP and secretin have been demonstrated directly. The hypothesis that there are three other classes of receptors is based on the chemical structures of the secretagogues, not on direct experimental evidence. That is, in terms of amino acid sequences one can postulate that acinar cells possess a class of receptors that interacts with CCK, caerulein, and gastrin, a class that interacts with bombesin and litorin, and a class that interacts with physalaemin and eledoisin.

Pancreatic secretagogues that mobilize cellular calcium and increase cyclic GMP also increase degradation of phosphatidylinositol. In Figure 1, the arrow from "breakdown of phosphatidylinositol" to "release cellular calcium" is not intended to indicate that the former causes the latter, although this may be the case, but rather that the secretagogue-induced turnover of phospholipid precedes the release of cellular calcium. This conclusion is based solely on the finding in parotid gland that A23187 does not accelerate degradation of phosphatidylinositol (24, 31); it should be viewed as hypothetical until confirmed in pancreas. Furthermore, effects of bombesin, litorin, physalaemin, and eledoisin on phosphatidylinositol turnover in pancreas have not been reported. In Figure 1 they are postulated to have this

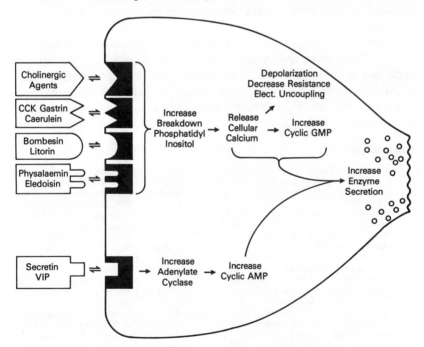

Figure 1 Working hypothesis that outlines the initial steps in the actions of secretagogues on pancreatic acinar cells.

action because their effects on calcium outflux, cellular cyclic GMP, and electrical changes in pancreatic acinar cells are similar to those of CCK, caerulein, and cholinergic agents. Secretagogue-induced release of cellular calcium causes increased cellular cyclic GMP and changes in the electrical properties of pancreatic acinar cell surface and junctional membranes. The electrical changes appear to result from an increase in the concentration of cytosolic calcium, but it is not known whether the increase in cellular cyclic GMP is caused by the release of stored calcium per se or by an increase in cytosolic calcium.

In acinar cells from guinea pig and rat (but not those from dog, cat, or mouse) the increase in cyclic AMP caused by VIP and secretin evokes an increase in amylase secretion. Other secretagogues cause release of cellular calcium and increase cyclic GMP; however, it is not known which of these two phenomena is causally linked to secretagogue-induced increase enzyme secretion. In terms of playing a causal role in increasing enzyme secretion, the relation between cyclic GMP and calcium release may be analogous to that between the electrical changes and calcium release. That is, although release of cellular calcium increases cyclic GMP, it may be the change in calcium, not the cyclic nucleotide, that causes the increase in enzyme secretion.

Although the two pathways for stimulating pancreatic enzyme secretion are initially separate, they converge at some step distal to the generation of cyclic nucleotides. The nature of this convergence is such that potentiation of enzyme secretion occurs when a secretagogue that causes calcium release and a secretagogue that increases cyclic AMP are combined. The mechanism by which these potentiating interactions occurs is not known.

Literature Cited

1. Albano, J., Bhoola, K. D., Harvey, R. F. 1976. Intracellular messenger role of cyclic GMP in exocrine pancreas. *Nature,* 404–6
2. Appleman, M. M., Thompson, W. J., Russell, T. R. 1973. Cyclic nucleotide phosphodiesterases. *Adv. Cyclic Nucleotide Res.* 3:65–98
3. Case, R. M., Clausen, T. 1973. The relationship between calcium exchange and enzyme secretion in the isolated rat pancreas. *J. Physiol. London* 235:75–102
3. Chandler, D. E., Williams, J. A. 1977. Fluorescent probe detects redistribution of cell calcium during stimulus-secretion coupling. *Nature* 268:659–60
5. Chandler, D. E., Williams, J. A. 1977. Intracellular uptake and α-amylase and lactate dehydrogenase releasing actions of the divalent cation ionophore A23187 in dissociated pancreatic acinar cells. *J. Membr. Biol.* 32:201–30
6. Christophe, J. P., Conlon, T. P., Gardner, J. D. 1976. Interaction of porcine vasoactive intestinal peptide with dispersed pancreatic acinar cells from the guinea pig. Binding of radioiodinated peptide. *J. Biol. Chem.* 251:4629–34
7. Christophe, J. P., Frandsen, E. K., Conlon, T. P., Krishna, G., Gardner, J. D. 1976. Action of cholecystockinin, cholinergic agents and A23187 on accumulation of guanosine 3',5'-monophosphate in dispersed guinea pig pancreatic acinar cells. *J. Biol. Chem.* 251:4640–45
8. Deschodt-Lanckman, M., Robberecht, P., DeNeef, P., Labrie, F., Christophe, J. 1975. *In vitro* interactions of gastrointestinal hormones on cyclic adenosine 3',5'-monophosphate levels and amy-

lase output in the rat pancreas. *Gastroenterology* 68:318–25

9. Deschodt-Lanckman, M., Robberecht, P., DeNeef, P., Lammens, M., Christophe, J. 1976. In vitro action of bombesin and bombesin-like peptides on amylase secretion, calcium efflux and adenylate cyclase activity in the rat pancreas. *J. Clin. Invest.* 58:891–98

10. Douglas, W. W. 1968. Stimulus-secretion coupling: the concept and clues from chromaffin and other cells. *Br. J. Pharmacol.* 34:451–74

11. Eimerl, S., Savion, N., Heichal, O., Selinger, Z. 1974. Induction of enzyme secretion in rat pancreatic slices using the ionophore A-23187 and calcium. An experimental bypass of the hormone receptor pathway. *J. Biol. Chem.* 249:3991–93

12. Erspamer, V., Melchiorri, P. 1973. Active polypeptides of the amphibian skin and their synthetic analogs. *Pure Appl. Chem.* 35:463–94

13. Galardy, R. E., Jamieson, J. D. 1977. Photoaffinity labeling of a peptide secretagogue receptor in the exocrine pancreas. *Mol. Pharmacol.* 13:852–63

14. Gardner, J. D., Conlon, T. P., Klaeveman, H. L., Adams, T. D., Ondetti, M. A. 1975. Action of cholecystokinin and cholinergic agents on calcium transport in isolated pancreatic acinar cells. *J. Clin. Invest.* 56:366–75

15. Gardner, J. D., Conlon, T. P., Fink, M. L., Bodanszky, M. 1976. Interactions of peptides related to secretin with hormone receptors on pancreatic acinar cells. *Gastroenterology* 71:965–70

16. Gardner, J. D., Hahne, W. F. 1977. Calcium transport in dispersed acinar cells from rat pancreas. *Biochem. Biophys. Acta* 471:466–76

17. Gardner, J. D., Jackson, M. J. 1977. Regulation of amylase release from dispersed pancreatic acinar cells. *J. Physiol. London* 270:439–54

18. Haymovits, A., Scheele, G. A. 1976. Cellular cyclic nucleotides and enzyme secretion in the pancreatic acinar cell. *Proc. Natl. Acad. Sci. USA* 73:156–60

19. Heisler, S., Grondin, G. 1975. Absence of effects of dibutyryl cyclic guanosine 3',5'-monophosphate on release of α-amylase, ^{45}Ca efflux, and protein synthesis in rat pancreas in vitro. *Experientia* 31:936–38

20. Hokin, M. R. 1974. Breakdown of phosphatidylinositol in the pancreas in response to pancreozymin and acetylcholine. In *Secretory Mechanisms of Exocrine Glands*, ed. N. A. Thorn, O. H. Petersen, pp. 101–12. New York: Academic

21. Iwatsuki, N., Petersen, O. H. 1977. Acetylcholine-like effects of intracellular calcium: application in pancreatic acinar cells. *Nature* 268:147–49

22. Iwatsuki, N., Petersen, O. H. 1978. *In vitro* action of bombesin on amylase secretion, membrane potential, and membrane resistance in rat and mouse pancreatic acinar cells. *J. Clin. Invest.* 61:41–46

23. Jamieson, J. D. 1973. The secretory process in the pancreatic exocrine cell: morphologic and biochemical aspects. In *Secretin, Cholecystokinin, Pancreozymin and Gastrin*, ed. J. E. Jorpes, V. Mutt, pp. 195–217. New York: Springer

24. Jones, L. M., Michell, R. H. 1975. The relationship of calcium to receptor-controlled stimulation of phosphatidylinositol turnover. *Biochem. J.* 148:479–85

25. Kimura, H., Murad, F. 1974. Evidence for two different forms of guanylate cyclase in rat heart. *J. Biol. Chem.* 249:6910–16

26. Kondo, S., Schulz, I. 1976. Calcium ion uptake in isolated pancreas cells induced by secretagogues. *Biochem. Biophys. Acta* 419:76–92

27. Kondo, S., Schulz, I. 1976. Ca^{++} fluxes in isolated cells of rat pancreas: effect of secretagogues and different Ca^{++} concentrations. *J. Memb. Biol.* 29:185–203

28. Langan, T. A. 1973. Protein kinase and protein kinase substrates. *Adv. Cyclic Nucleotide Res.* 3:99–154

29. Long, B. W., Gardner, J. D. 1977. Effects of cholecystokinin on adenylate cyclase activity in dispersed pancreatic acinar cells. *Gastroenterology* 73:1008–14

30. May, R. J., Conlon, T. P., Erspamer, V., Gardner, J. D. 1978. Actions of peptides isolated from amphibian skin on pancreatic acinar cells. *Am. J. Physiol. London* In press

31. Michell, R. 1975. Inositol phospholipids and cell surface receptor function. *Biochem. Biophys. Acta* 415:81–147

32. Michell, R. H., Jones, L. M., Jafferji, S. S. 1976. The relationship between agonist-stimulated phosphatidylinositol metabolism and the mechanisms of receptor systems. In *Stimulus-secretion Coupling in the Gastrointestinal Tract*, ed. R. M. Case, H. Goebel, pp. 89–106. Baltimore: University Park Press

33. Milutinovic, S., Schulz, I., Rosselin, G. 1976. The interactions of secretin with

pancreatic membranes. *Biochem. Biophys. Acta* 436:113–27

34. Nishiyama, A., Petersen, O. H. 1975. Pancreatic acinar cells: ionic dependence of acetylcholine-induced membrane potential and resistance change. *J. Physiol. London* 244:431–65

35. Petersen, O. H., Ueda, N. 1975. Pancreatic acinar cells: effect of acetylcholine, pancreozymin, gastrin and secretin on membrane potential and resistance *in vivo* and *in vitro. J. Physiol. London* 247:461–71

36. Petersen, O. H. 1976. Electrophysiology of mammalian gland cells. *Physiol. Rev.* 56:535–77

37. Petersen, O. H., Ueda, N. 1976. Pancreatic acinar cell: the role of calcium in stimulus secretion coupling. *J. Physiol. London* 254:583–606

38. Poulsen, J. H., Willims, J. A. 1977. Effects of ionophore A23187 on pancreatic acinar cell membrane potentials and amylase release. *J. Physiol. London* 264:323–39

39. Reed, P. W., Lardy, H. A. 1972. A23187: A divalent cation ionophore. *J. Biol. Chem.* 247:6970–77

40. Robberecht, P., Christophe, J. 1971. Secretion of hydrolases by perfused fragments of rat pancreas: effects of calcium. *Am. J. Physiol.* 220:911–17

41. Robberecht, P., Conlon, T. P., Gardner, J. D. 1976. Interaction of porcine vasoactive intestinal peptide with dispersed pancreatic acinar cells from guinea pig: structural requirements for effects of VIP and secretin on cellular cyclic AMP. *J. Biol. Chem.* 251:4635–39

42. Robberecht, P., Deschodt-Lanckman, M., Camus, J., Christophe, J. 1977. Specific binding and mode of action of caerulein on plasma membranes of rat pancreas. In *Hormonal Receptors in Digestive Tract Physiology*, e., S. Bonfils, P. Fromageot, G. Rosselin, pp. 261–74. Amsterdam: North-Holland

43. Robberecht, P., Deschodt-Lanckman, M., Lammens, M., DeNeef, P., Christophe, J. 1977. *In vitro* effects of secretin and vasoactive intestinal polypeptide on hydrolase secretion and cyclic AMP levels in the pancreas of five animal species. A comparison with caerulein. *Gastroenterol. Clin. Biol.* 1:519–25

44. Rutten, W. J., DePont, J. J. H. H. M., Bonting, S. L. 1972. Adenylate cyclase in the rat pancreas. Properties and stimulation by hormones. *Biochem. Biophys. Acta* 274:201–13

45. Shelby, H. T., Gross, L. P., Lichty, P., Gardner, J. D. 1976. Action of cholecystokinin and cholinergic agents on membrane-bound calcium in dispersed pancreatic acinar cells. *J. Clin. Invest.* 58:1482–93

46. Svoboda, M., Robberecht, P., Camus, J., Deschodt-Lanckman, M., Christophe, J. 1976. Subcellular distribution and response to gastrointestinal hormones of adenylate cyclase in rat pancreas. *Eur. J. Biochem.* 69:185–93

47. Van Leemput-Coutrez, M., Camus, J., Christophe, J. 1973. Cyclic nucleotide-dependent protein kinases of rat pancreas. *Biochem. Biophys. Res. Commun.* 54:182–90

48. Williams, J. A., Chandler, D. 1975. Ca^{++} and pancreatic amylase release. *Am. J. Physiol.* 228:1729–32

Ann. Rev. Physiol. 1979. 41:67–82
Copyright © 1979 by Annual Reviews Inc. All rights reserved

REGULATION OF HEPATIC   ♦1206
BILIARY SECRETION

R. Scott Jones and William C. Meyers

Departments of Surgery and Physiology, Duke University Medical Center, Durham, North Carolina 27710

INTRODUCTION

Bile formation is a complex process comprised of four separate physiologic mechanisms operating at two anatomical sites (29, 129, 131). The initial event occurs in the hepatocyte or at the bile canaliculus, and at least two processes are responsible for total canalicular secretion: the active transport of bile acids into the canalicular lumen, and the production of the bile salt–independent canalicular fraction (BSICF), which is unrelated to bile salt secretion at the canaliculus and which may involve the active transport of sodium (25, 26). As canalicular bile moves into the biliary ducts the secretion may be further modified by the addition of water and electrolytes from the biliary ductular epithelium or, in some cases, by absorption of water and electrolytes.

During digestion, bile secretion increases considerably. Many of the factors involved in this regulation are not known. This review deals primarily with the neurohumoral factors thought likely to be important regulators of bile water and electrolyte secretion. Although a brief description of current understanding of the mechanisms of bile formation is necessary, the subject has been reviewed extensively recently (23, 24, 33, 55, 130).

MECHANISM OF BILE FORMATION

Bile Salt–Dependent Secretion

Since the observation by Schiff (110) that feeding bile caused an increase in bile flow, investigators have recognized the importance of bile salts in stimulating the formation of hepatic bile (35). It remained for Sperber (118,

67

0066-4278/79/0301-0067$01.00

119) to formulate an hypothesis that the active transport of bile salts from plasma to bile provided a primary stimulus for bile formation. Sperber suggested that the osmotic effect of actively transported bile acids was responsible for the movement of water and ions into bile. Although conventional techniques for demonstrating active transport cannot be applied to the process of canalicular bile formation, there is abundant evidence to indicate that active transport processes contribute to bile formation. For example, the concentration of bile salts in bile is 100 times that in plasma (118). Also, studies by Brauer et al (15, 16) in isolated perfused rat liver indicated that bile secretory pressure exceeded the perfusion pressure, which suggested that energy other than hemodynamic forces were important in bile formation.

There is a linear relationship between bile salt secretory rate and bile flow over a wide range of bile salt outputs in many species including man (11, 13, 20, 25, 75, 100, 109, 120, 121, 132). The formation of micelles alters the colligative properties of bile salts in solution so that the osmotic effect of most bile salts in bile is less than that predicted from molar concentrations (129). Bile salts that are avid micelle formers, such as taurocholic acid, are less potent choleretics than bile salts that do not form micelles readily, such as the synthetic substance dehydrocholic acid (94).

Bile Salt–Independent Secretion

CANALICULAR   Schanker & Hogben (108) observed that intravenously administered, uncharged, inert, lipid-insoluble solutes, such as mannitol, passed rapidly into bile. Subsequently, Forker (29–34) and Wheeler, Ross & Bradley (133) provided persuasive arguments that the biliary clearance of such molecules estimates canalicular bile production. Using such techniques, Wheeler, Ross & Bradley (133) demonstrated in dogs that the biliary clearance of mannitol was linearly related to bile acid output over a wide range of secretory rates. They observed further that if one extrapolated the regression line of biliary clearance of mannitol upon bile acid secretory rate, there was a significantly positive intercept, which indicated that substantial cannilicular secretion occurred in the absence of bile acid secretion. This portion of bile secretion was labelled the bile salt–independent canalicular fraction (BSICF). The BSICF has been observed repeatedly in various species including dog, rat, rabbit, and man (9, 12, 25, 99, 109, 120, 121, 133). This fraction comprised 40% of spontaneous basal bile secretion in man (81) and is larger in rodents. Although it is true that the osmotic characteristics of bile salts change (17) near their critical micellar concentrations, studies in the isolated perfused liver have demonstrated definite secretory pressures when negligible bile salts were being secreted by the liver (13).

The mechanism of this bile salt–independent canalicular fraction has not been established, but several observations implicate a sodium pump driven by a sodium potassium ATPase. Sodium potassium ATPase was originally suggested by Erlinger et al (25, 26), who observed that the bile salt–independent canalicular fraction was inhibited by ouabain, ethacrynic acid, and amiloride. However, subsequent reports on the choleretic action of inhibitors of sodium transport have been contradictory (18, 45, 112). More recent studies employing the isolation of canalicular enriched plasma membranes from rat liver disclosed large amounts of sodium potassium ATPase activity stimulated by thyroxine (78), correlating with increased bile flows. That this was not a nonspecific increase in enzymes in the cell was evidenced by thyroxine's failing to stimulate other plasma membrane marker enzymes such as 5'nucleotidase.

The responsibility of sodium potassium ATPase (40) for the bile salt–independent canalicular fraction has not been conclusively demonstrated. Recent studies, in fact, have shown increased $NA^+K^+ATPase$ actively stimulated by bile acids (128). In these studies in rats, increased bile acid also caused adaptive increases in the bile salt–independent canalicular fraction.

Theophylline (6, 27), a phosphodiesterase inhibitor, glucagon (73), a stimulator of cyclic AMP, and dibutyrl cAMP (86) all stimulate the BSICF. These observations suggest, but do not prove, that cAMP may be of fundamental importance in regulating the BSICF.

DUCTAL   When comparing the composition of bile secreted during taurocholate choleresis with secretin-stimulated bile, Preisig, Cooper & Wheeler (100) noted differences in inorganic electrolyte composition. Secretin-stimulated bile characteristically contained bicarbonate in higher concentration. This suggested that although taurocholate stimulated canalicular secretion, secretin acted differently, perhaps stimulating another site in the liver. Several observations indicated that secretin stimulated water and bicarbonate secretion from the biliary ductules. BSP "washout" studies demonstrated that secretin acted at a site distal to taurocholate (131). Furthermore, when secretin was injected into the hepatic artery the choleresis was greater than with intravenous injection. Because the hepatic arterioles are closely related to the ducts, a ductal action of secretin was suggested. Perhaps the strongest evidence for secretin's ductal action is that it stimulated secretion from the isolated bile duct in dogs (88). Also, in most studies secretin failed to stimulate the biliary clearance of erythritol (7, 29).

CONTROL OF BILE SECRETION

Bile Salt–Dependent Secretion

The volume of bile secreted by the bile salt–dependent fraction is determined primarily by the rate at which bile salts are delivered into the canaliculi (133). The availability of bile salts to the hepatocyte is determined by the enterohepatic circulation and by the synthesis of new bile salts (129). The bile salt pool size (49, 53, 85, 114) in humans is about 2–3 g and the pool circulates 2–3 times during each meal so that a person would secrete about 15–30 g of bile salt daily. About 0.3–0.6 g day^{-1} are lost in the feces, but the bile salt pool size remains constant because the liver synthesizes 0.3–0.6 g bile salts daily.

The extraction of bile salts from the plasma by hepatocytes is about 90% efficient (93, 102, 103) in one circulation, probably because of a specific bile salt uptake mechanism in the sinusoidal membrane. This carrier-mediated transport system follows Michalis-Mention kinetics (41–43, 111) and is not the rate-limiting step in secretion of taurocholate. Although bile salts are not bound by Y or Z proteins (79), there is evidence for protein binding of bile salts in the hepatocytes (1); but the specific binding protein has not been characterized. Prior to secretion, free bile salts are conjugated with either taurine or glycine (92, 95), and this process probably plays a minor role in regulation of secretion (74).

The secretion of bile salts from hepatocytes into the canaliculus also seems to occur via a carrier-mediated active transport process. The T_M for taurocholate secretion in dogs was 8–8.5 μmole min^{-1}kg^{-1} (132). A recent interesting study (2) indicated that when the ducts of 3 lobes of the rat liver were obstructed, the T_M for bile salt secretion by the unobstructed lobe rose substantially; this indicated that the T_M for bile salts is not a fixed value but may vary. The investigators suggested that the increased bile salt presented to the unobstructed lobes increased the T_M.

The choleresis produced by bile salts can be characterized by plotting bile flow against bile salt output and calculating the slope of the line. During taurocholate choleresis the dog secretes 8 μl of water per μmole of bile salt (100, 132).

Neurohumoral Control

FEEDING When cholecystectomized dogs were fed during bile collection and stabilization of bile salt output by intravenous or intraduodenal replacement of bile salts, bile flow markedly increased (62, 90). The magnitude of the feeding choleresis is related to meal size (62). This increase in bile secretion was belived to be due to ductal secretion stimulated by the gastrointestinal hormones. One recent study, however, detected an increase in erythritol clearance and stable bile salt secretion during feeding choleresis (4), which suggested that feeding stimulated the bile salt–independent canalicular fraction. The variability of bile salt–independent secretion is generally not well understood.

SECRETIN   Much of the earlier work in hormonal control of bile secretion was done with secretin, a 27-residue helical peptide hormone having a molecular weight of about 3000 (101). Bayliss & Starling (8) described the choleretic action of the hormone in 1902 and explained why duodenal acidification stimulated increased bile secretion. Synthesis of the hormone (10) provided a chemically pure peptide that was used to prove that the choleresis was an effect of the hormone molecule rather than a contaminant of the mucosal extract (126).

Choleretic properties of secretin   Early studies reveled that secretin-stimulated bile was watery; the term hydrocholeresis was suggested to describe secretin's choleretic action (48). Subsequent investigation demonstrated that secretin stimulated secretion of water, bicarbonate, and chloride (61, 116). The output and concentration of both bicarbonate and chloride rise as flow increases during secretin choleresis in dogs (58, 61, 100). As expected, the bile salt concentration in bile decreases during secretin choleresis (129). A study of secretin choleresis in isolated pig liver demonstrated decreased chloride concentration initially with increased bicarbonate concentration (50, 51). The changes in chloride and bicarbonate concentration in pig bile were similar to those in Wheeler's "electrolyte fraction" (100). Bile salt output is unaffected by secretin administration. During secretin stimulation bile pH and osmolality rise (100). Changes in osmolality may be due to increased osmotic effect of bile salts because of the effect of dilution on the behavior of micelles (52).

Site of action   Because bile composition during secretin choleresis differed from that observed during bile salt choleresis, Wheeler, Ross & Bradley (133) suggested that secretin acted upon the bile ducts or ductules to promote secretion. Substantial evidence has accumulated to support that hypothesis. After observing the "washout volume" (131) with BSP during taurocholate choleresis and comparing the values with "washout volumes" during secretin choleresis, Wheeler concluded that secretin stimulated secretion at a site distal to taurocholate. In the same study Wheeler injected secretin into the hepatic artery and observed greater choleresis than when secretin was given into the splenic or a systemic vein, which suggested a ductal site of action because of the anatomical proximity of the hepatic arterioles to the ducts or ductules.

Studies employing the biliary clearance of erythritol or mannitol provided additional evidence that secretin and bile salts act at different sites (106, 133). Bile salts produced clearance of erythritol or mannitol linearly related to bile salt output (133). However, secretin failed to increase the biliary clearance of mannitol in dogs or of erythritol in guinea pigs, which suggested that secretin did not act at the canalicular membrane. In a subsequent study Russell et al (106) observed secretin to produce small but statistically significant increases in the biliary clearance of erythritol in dogs and concluded that either small amounts of erythritol entered the bile through the bile ducts or secretin stimulated canalicular secretion. A more recent study (7) investigated in detail the biliary clearance of erythritol and mannitol during secretin or taurocholate choleresis in dogs and observed a substantial increase in the biliary clearance of both during secretin choleresis. These observations raise questions about the validity of erythritol or mannitol clearance studies and the evaluation of secretin choleresis; in any case, there can be little doubt from clearance studies that secretin promotes choleresis in a manner distinctly different from bile salts. As mentioned before, secretin-stimulated secretion from the isolated dog bile duct (88) provided the most convincing evidence for a ductal site of secretin action.

How secretin promotes choleresis is not understood. Levine & Hall (80) observed that secretin caused secretion of cAMP into the bile of humans and baboons but not dogs.

Although investigation of bile secretion using secretin injection have provided important information, such studies permit no conclusion regarding the physiologic role of the hormone. Acidification of the duodenal mucosa increases bile secretion (107), and secretin may be important in that response. Whether secretin is important in bile secretion during meals is not clear because studies using secretion radioimmunoassay fail to detect increased serum secretin concentrations after feeding (101).

CCK   Cholecystokinin (pancreozymin, CCK) is a 33-residue peptide hormone (101) with a C-terminal tetrapeptide (tryptophane-methianine–aspartic acid–phenylalanylamide) identical to the C-terminal tetrapeptide of gastrin. CCK has a sulfated tyrosyl residue seven positions from the C-terminal. CCK is synthesized in the duodenal mucosa and secreted into blood upon contact of the mucosa with fat or protein. Jorpes et al (65) described the choleretic action of natural CCK and suggested it acted as secretin did. More recent studies show that CCK stimulated bicarbonate and chloride secretion as well as increasing bile flow (37, 60, 125). When given alone, CCK did not influence bile salt output (60). The relative choleretic potency of natural CCK is greater than that of gastrin II but considerably smaller than secretin (60). The synthetic octapeptide of CCK

(CCK-OP) also causes choleresis, which confirms the hypothesis that the increased bile flow is due to CCK rather than to a contaminant from the mucosal extract (113, 125). Because CCK stimulated water and bicarbonate secretion without altering bile salt output it seemed likely that CCK stimulated ductal secretion in the manner of secretin. Recent experiments with dogs revealed that erythritol clearance did not rise during natural CCK choleresis (113), making it probable that CCK stimulated the ducts. High doses of CCK-OP, however, caused small but statistically significant elevations of erythritol clearance.

The role of endogenously secreted CCK in stimulating bile secretion has not been studied in detail. Sum et al (122) perfused Thiry-Vella loops with Bacto Peptone, a known releaser of CCK, and failed to observe increased bile secretion in bile-fistula dogs. An explanation for the failure to observe choleresis in those studies is that the quantity of mucosa in the loop was insufficient to release enough CCK to cause bile stimulation. We have perfused the duodena of bile-fistula dogs with L-phenylalanine, a releaser of CCK, and observed significant increases in bile secretion (R. S. Jones, unpublished observation).

GASTRIN   There are several molecular forms of gastrin. The first described was a 17-residue peptide (127) with a C-terminal tetrapeptide of tryptophane-methianine–aspartic acid–phenylalanlylamide. The sixth amino acid from the C-terminal is tyrosine, which may (gastrin II) or may not (gastrin I) be sulfated. In addition, there are larger forms of the molecule containing 34 residues (big gastrin).

Gregory & Tracy (46) first suggested gastrin may stimulate bile secretion. Then Zaterka & Grossman (135) observed choleresis in totally gastrectomized conscious dogs following intravenous gastrin administration. Subsequent studies suggested that endogenously secreted gastrin stimulated bile secretion (89) and that antrectomy reduced the choleretic effect of insulin (57). Studies by Ross, Saubermann & Silen (105) in dogs with antral pouches, Heindenhain pouches, bile fistulas, and gastric fistulas failed to reveal any increase in bile flow when the antral pouch was stimulated. These investigations suggested that all changes in bile flow during gastrin stimulation were the result of secretin release caused by acid entry into the intestine. Additional studies with gastrin II administered to dogs with bile fistulas revealed gastrin to be the weakest choleretic of the gastrointestinal peptides (60). The gastrin analog pentagastrin failed to stimulate bile secretion when administered to dog (67), rat (77), human (76), or isolated perfused calf liver (96). Pentagastrin did stimulate secretion from the isolated dog common bile duct (91). Because (a) antrectomy failed to reduce feeding choleresis, (b) the potency of intravenously administered gastrin is very low, (c) pentagastrin failed to stimulate bile secretion, and (d) endogenously secreted gastrin failed to cause choleresis, we must conclude that the choleretic action of gastrin is of little physiologic significance unless gastrin potentiates the action of other hormones during meals.

INSULIN   While investigating the role of the vagus nerves in regulating bile secretion, Fritz & Brooks (36) observed that insulin caused marked increases in bile production in dogs. Numerous subsequent experiments have confirmed the choleretic effect of insulin (5, 38, 39, 44, 56, 57, 59, 68). Choleretic dose-response studies in dogs revealed a significant increase in bile flow with an intravenous dose of 0.03 units kg^{-1} and maximal choleresis with a dose of 1.0 unit kg^{-1} (59). Insulin choleresis is characterized by increased chloride concentration and output, increased bicarbonate output, decreased bile salt concentration, and in general unchanged bile salt output (39). Recent studies revealed increased biliary clearance of erythritol during insulin choleresis, which suggested canalicular stimulation (56). Taurocholate dose-response tests with or without insulin permitted calculation of the BSICF by plotting erythritol clearance against bile salt output and extrapolating the line to the ordinate. The intercept was significantly greater with insulin, which indicated that insulin stimulated the BSICF (115).

The mechanism of insulin choleresis is not well understood. Insulin hypoglycemia causes potent vagal stimulation (47). Studies using anticholinergic drugs indicate that cholinergic mechanisms are important in insulin choleresis (70, 82, 84). Such drugs reduce the choleretic effect of insulin in dog (70, 84), human (5), and guinea pig (82).

The question of the influence of vagotomy on insulin choleresis is unsettled. Fritz & Brooks (36) reported that vagotomy abolished insulin choleresis. In subsequent studies selective hepatic, selective extrahepatic, or truncal vagotomy, failed to abolish insulin choleresis in dogs (39, 44, 68). Although vagal stimulation may play a role in insulin choleresis, the data presently available suggest an important nonvagal mechanism. Therefore, insulin must either act directly on the liver or cause the secretion of another choleretic hormone. An early study in dogs (57) with totally interrupted enterohepatic circulation revealed that antrectomy reduced the choleretic effect of insulin. More recent studies in dogs with bile flow stabilized by intravenous infusion of bile salts indicated that evisceration failed to prevent insulin choleresis (3). Although insulin may stimulate bile secretion when given intravenously in pharmacological doses, there is no good evidence to suggest a role for insulin in physiologically regulating bile secretion. To investigate whether endogenously secreted insulin was important in regulating meal-stimulated bile secretion, we observed feeding choleresis in streptozotocin-induced diabetic dogs (T. Shires, III, et al, unpublished observation). There was no significant difference between the pre- and poststreptozotocin choleresis, which indicated that reduction of insulin secretion did not affect feeding choleresis.

GLUCAGON   Because of similarities in structure between glucagon and secretin the choleretic effect of glucagon has been investigated. An early study on the choleretic action of glucagon in dogs indicated that glucagon increased bile flow and taurocholate secretion; it also stimulated increased liver blood flow (87). Subsequent studies indicated that glucagon can increase bile flow, increase chloride concentration, increase chloride output, increase bicarbonate output, and decrease bile salt concentration, without changing bile salt output (22, 58). The choleretic action of secretin is about five times that of glucagon in dogs (58). The structural similarity between glucagon and secretin suggests that the hormones may act on the same receptor, but erythritol clearance studies indicate that this is not the case (105). Because glucagon stimulates adenylcyclase activity in hepatic membrane (19, 97) it is interesting to speculate that cAMP may be involved in producing the increased bile secretion stimulated by glucagon.

HYDROCORTISONE AND THYROXINE   Macarol et al (83) characterized the choleretic effect of hydrocortisone in dogs and found that it stimulated the BSICF. A similar result was reported from studies in the rat (21). Thyroxine administration caused increased BSICF, bile flow, and Na^+K^+ ATPase in hepatic plasma membrane enriched in canaliculi (78), which suggests that Na^+K^+ATPase is related to the BSICF because other plasma membrane marker enzymes were not affected.

HORMONE INTERACTION   Grossman suggested that because the GI hormones stimulated the same target organs, the various hormones stimulate the same receptor (47). Because of basic structural similarities CCK and gastrin may act at the same receptor site while secretin and glucagon may act at another site on the same receptor. Therefore the receptor would contain two receptor sites: one for gastrin-CCK compounds, the other for secretin-glucagon peptides. This hypothesis is supported by interaction of GI hormones on several organs. Perhaps the stimulation of the bile salt–independent fraction during feeding is the result of interaction of the various GI hormones. Of course during a meal, delivery of bile salts into the duodenum, intestinal transit, and ileal absorption are also important in providing bile salts to be secreted. The total biliary response may depend upon neural and hormonal integration of secretion and motility.

Pentagastrin interaction with secretin or CCK   Kaminski, Rose & Nahrwold studied the interaction of pentagastrin with secretin or CCK, using dogs prepared with duodenal cannulas for bile collections (71). Pentagastrin caused no change in the choleresis stimulated by secretin or CCK. They concluded that pentagastrin was ineffective in stimulating the dog biliary system. Jablonski, Sali & Watts (54), on the other hand, observed potentiation between pentagastrin and secretin in the isolated perfused pig liver. Furthermore, in the pig liver pentagastrin and secretin caused increased bile salt output.

Interaction between secretin and CCK   Tavoloni & Angelucci (124) studied anesthetized dogs with bile fistulas. When secretin or CCK were given alone, characteristic secretin and CCK choleresis was observed. However, when the hormones were given together there was augmentation of flow and a marked increase in bile salt secretion, which suggested that the combination stimulated canalicular secretion.

Interaction between glucagon and secretin   The interaction of glucagon and secretin on bile secretion in dogs revealed noncompetitive augmentation (69). This finding suggested that secretin and glucagon caused increased bile secretion by acting at separate sites; this accords with studies showing increased erythritol clearance with glucagon (73) but not with secretin (133), and increased bicarbonate concentration with secretin but not with glucagon (58).

HISTAMINE   Zaterka & Grossman (135) demonstrated in totally gastrectomized dogs that histamine stimulated bile flow. Because the stomach was removed, duodenal acidification and resultant endogenous secretin release could not explain the effect. The choleretic effect of histamine in dogs was confirmed in a subsequent dose-response study (63). It is interesting that the H_2 receptor blocker metiamide reduced histamine choleresis by noncompetitive inhibition (72). Whether histamine is physiologically important in regulating bile secretion is not known.

ROLE OF THE VAGUS IN CONTROLLING BILE SECRETION   Tanturi & Ivy demonstrated that stimulation of the distal cut end of the vagus nerve increased bile secretion in dogs (123). Furthermore, stimulation of the central cut end of a vagus nerve increased bile flow when the contralateral nerve was intact. These studies suggested that vagal stimulation may be important in regulating bile formation. A more recent study of electrical vagal stimulation and bile secretion was performed in conscious dogs with and without intravenous bile salt replacement (66). No increase in bile flow occurred during studies when bile salts were replaced; however, a small increase occurred when the stimulus was applied during interruption of the enterohepatic circulation. The investigation concluded that vagal stimulation played little if any role in regulating bile flow. Sham feeding, a potent vagal stimulant, caused a very small increase in bile flow in dogs (98), which also suggested a small effect of vagal stimulation on bile flow.

Numerous experiments have been done to observe the effect of vagotomy on bile flow and composition (28, 39, 44, 64, 68, 134). Most were performed in such as way as to prevent evaluation of the direct effect of the vagotomy on the bile secretion. In dogs with intact gallbladders vagotomy caused decreased bile flow and cholate concentration (28). A study evaluating the effect of vagotomy on bile salt kinetics in dogs revealed an increased pool size after vagotomy (134). Vagotomy may influence gallbladder function or the movement of bile salts through the intestine and thereby influence bile secretion. However, vagotomy has had no effect on either secretin or taurocholate dose-response tests (64). Most of the available recent evidence suggests that the vagus nerves play a minor or indirect role in regulating the bile secretory processes.

CONCLUSIONS

Our understanding of bile secretion has lagged behind other areas of endeavor (e.g. renal physiology) because of technological problems in studying the secretory unit directly. In the last few years progress in the understanding of biliary secretion has accompanied improved and refined techniques, such as study of canalicular enriched plasma membranes (14, 117). Interesting topics for investigation will be the role of cyclic nucleotides in regulating secretion and the role of $Na^+K^+ATPase$. The possibility that hormones may influence canalicular secretion will provide abundant questions for research.

Literature Cited

1. Accatino, L., Simon, F. R. 1976. Identification and characterization of a bile acid receptor in isolated liver surface membranes. *J. Clin. Invest.* 57:496–508
2. Adler, R. D., Wannagat, F. J., Ockner, R. K. 1977. Bile secretion in selective biliary obstruction. Adaptation of taurocholate transport maximum to increased secretory load in rat. *Gastroenterology* 73(1):129–36
3. Austin, G. L. et al. 1977. Effect of evisceration on insulin-stimulated bile secretion. *Surg. Forum* 28:381–82
4. Austin, G. L. et al. 1978. The effect of feeding on bile salt independent

canalicular bile secretion in dogs. *Am. J. Surg.* 135:36–39
5. Baldwin, J. et al. 1969. Effect of vagus nerve stimulation on hepatic secretion of bile in human subjects. *Am. J. Surg.* 111:66–69
6. Barnhart, J. L., Combes, B. 1974. Effect of theophylline on hepatic excretory function. *Am. J. Physiol.* 227:194–99
7. Barnhart, J. L., Combes, B. 1978. Erythritol and mannitol clearances with taurocholate and secretin-induced choleresis. *Am. J. Physiol.* 234(2):146–56
8. Bayliss, W. M., Starling, E. H. 1902.

The mechanism of pancreatic secretion. *J. Physiol. London* 28:325–53

9. Berthelot, P. et al. 1970. Mechanism of phenobarbital-induced hypercholeresis in the rat. *Am. J. Physiol.* 219:809–13

10. Bodanszky, M., Ondetti, M. A. et al. 1966. Synthesis of a heptacosapeptide-amide with the hormonal activity of secretin. *Chem. Ind.* 42:1757

11. Boyer, J. L. 1971. Canalicular bile formation in the isolated perfused rat liver. *Am. J. Physiol.* 221:1156–63

12. Boyer, J. L., Bloomer, J. R. 1974. Canalicular bile secretion in man. Studies utilizing the biliary clearance of (^{14}C) mannitol. *J. Clin. Invest.* 54:773–81

13. Boyer, J. L., Klatskin, G. 1970. Canalicular bile flow and bile secretory pressure: evidence for a non bile salt dependent fraction in the isolated perfused rat liver. *Gastroenterology* 59:853–59

14. Boyer, J. L., Reno, D. 1975. Properties of (NA^+K^+) activated ATPase in rat liver plasma membranes enriched with bile canaliculi. *Biochem. Biophys. Acta* 401:59–72

15. Brauer, R. W., Leong, G. F., Holloway, R. J. 1954. Mechanics of bile secretion. Effect of perfusion pressure and temperature on bile flow and bile secretion pressure. *Am. J. Physiol.* 177:103–19

16. Brauer, R. W., Pessotti, R. L., Pizzilato, P. 1951. Isolated rat liver preparation. Bile production and other basic properties. *Proc. Soc. Exp. Biol. Med.* 78:174–81

17. Carey, M. C., Small, D. M. 1972. Micelle formation by bile salts. Physical-chemical and thermodynamic considerations. *Arch. Intern. Med.* 130:506–27

18. Chenderovitch, J., Raizman, A., Infante, R. 1975. Mechanism of ethacrynic acid-induced choleresis in the rat. *Am. J. Physiol.* 229:1180–87

19. Christoffersen, T., Berg, R. 1974. Glucagon control of cyclic AMP accumulation in isolated intact rat liver parenchymal cells in vitro. *Biochim. Biophys. Acta* 338:408–17

20. Dowling, R. H., Mack, E., Small, D. M. 1971. Biliary lipid secretion and bile composition after acute and chronic interruption of the enterohepatic circulation in the Rhesus monkey. IV. Primate biliary physiology. *J. Clin. Invest.* 50:1917–26

21. Dumont, M., Erlinger, S. 1973. Influence of hydrocortisone on bile formation in the rat. *Biol. Gastroenterol.* 6:197–203

22. Dyck, W. P., Janowitz, H. D. 1971. Effect of glucagon on hepatic bile secretion in man. *Gastroenterology* 60:400–4

23. Erlinger, S. 1972. Physiology of bile flow. In *Progress in Liver Diseases*, ed. H. Popper, F. Schaffner, pp. 563–82. New York: Grune & Stratton

24. Erlinger, S., Dhumeaux, D. P. 1974. Mechanisms and control of secretion of bile, water, and electrolytes. *Gastroenterology* 66:281–304

25. Erlinger, S. et al. 1970. Effect of inhibitors of sodium transport on bile formation in the rabbit. *Am. J. Physiol.* 219:416–22

26. Erlinger, S., Dhumeaux, D., Benhamon, J. P. 1969. Effect on bile formation of inhibitors of sodium transport. *Nature* 223:1276–77

27. Erlinger, S., Dumont, M. 1973. Influence of theophylline on bile formation in the dog. *Biomedicine* 19:27–32

28. Fletcher, D. M., Clark, C. G. 1969. Changes in canine bile flow and composition after vagotomy. *Br. J. Surg.* 56:103–6

29. Forker, E. L. 1967. Two sites of bile formation as determined by mannitol and erythritol clearance in the guinea pig. *J. Clin. Invest.* 46:1189–95

30. Forker, E. L. 1968. Bile formation in guinea pigs: Analysis with inert solutes of graded molecular radius. *Am. J. Physiol.* 215:56–62

31. Forker, E. L. 1970. Hepatocellular uptake of inulin, sucrose, and mannitol in rats. *Am. J. Physiol.* 219:1568–71

32. Forker, E. L. 1972. Assessing changes in canalicular permeability. *Gastroenterology* 63:205–8

33. Forker, E. L. 1977. Mechanisms of hepatic bile formation. *Ann. Rev. Physiol.* 39:323–47

34. Forker, E. L., Hicklin, T., Sornson, H. 1967. The clearance of mannitol and erythritol in rat bile. *Proc. Soc. Exp. Biol. Med.* 126:115–19

35. Foster, M. G., Hooper, C. W., Whipple, G. H. 1919. Metabolism of bile acids: III. Administration by stomach of bile, bile acids, taurine, and cholic acid to show the influence upon bile acid elimination. *J. Biol. Chem.* 38:379–92

36. Fritz, M. E., Brooks, F. P. 1963. Control of bile flow in the cholecystectomized dog. *Am. J. Physiol.* 204:825–28

37. Gardner, B. N., Small, D. M. 1976. Simultaneous measurement of the pancreatic and biliary response to CCK and secretin. Primate biliary physiology XIII. *Gastroenterology* 70:403–7

38. Geist, R. E., Jones, R. S. 1971. The effect of atropine on bile secretion in dogs. *Surgery* 69:563–68

39. Geist, R. E., Jones, R. S. 1971. Effect of selective and truncal vagotomy on insulin-stimulated bile secretion in dogs. *Gastroenterology* 60:566–71

40. Gelrud, L. G. et al. 1977. The interrelationship of microtubules, bile acids, bile flow, and canalicular (Na^+K^+) ATPase, a unifying concept. *Gastroenterology* 72:1185 (Abstr.)

41. Glasinovic, J. C. et al. 1975. Heptocellular uptake of taurocholate in the dog. *J. Clin. Invest.* 55:419–26

42. Glasinovic, J. C., Dumont, M., Erlinger, S. 1974. Hepatocellular uptake of bile acids: Further evidence for a carrier-mediated transport system. *Digestion* 10:323–24 (Abstr.)

43. Glasinovic, J. C. et al. 1975. Hepatocellular uptake of bile acids in the dog: Evidence for a common carrier-mediated transport system. *Gastroenterology* 69(4):973–81

44. Gourlay, S. J., Jones, R. S. 1972. Effect of truncal vagotomy on 2-deoxy-D-glucose and insulin choleresis. *Ann. Surg.* 176:645–48

45. Graf, J., Peterlik, M. 1976. Ouabain-mediated sodium uptake and bile formation by isolated perfused rat liver. *Am. J. Physiol.* 230(4):876–85

46. Gregory, R. A., Tracey, H. J. 1964. The constitution and properties of two gastrins. *Gut* 5:103–17

47. Grossman, M. I. 1974. Gastrointestinal hormones: spectrum of actions and structure—activity relations. In *Endocrinology of the Gut*, ed. W. Chey, F. B. Brooks, pp. 163–77. Thorofare, NJ: Slack, Inc.

48. Grossman, M. I. et al. 1949. The effect of secretin on bile formation in man. *Gastroenterology* 12:133–38

49. Hanson, R. F., Pries, J. M. 1977. Synthesis and enterohepatic circulation of bile salts. *Gastroenterology* 73(3): 611–18

50. Hardison, W. G., Norman, J. C. 1967. Effect of bile salt and secretin upon bile flow from the isolated perfused pig liver. *Gastroenterology* 53:412–17

51. Hardison, W. G., Norman, J. C. 1968. Electrolyte composition of the secretin fraction of bile from the perfused pig liver. *Am. J. Physiol.* 214:758–63

52. Hardison, W. G., Norman, J. C. 1969. Effect of secretin on bile osmolality *J. Lab. Clin. Med.* 73:34–41

53. Hofmann, A. F. 1976. The entero-hepatic circulation of bile acids in man. *Adv. Intern. Med.* 21:501–34

54. Jablonski, P., Sali, A., Watts, J. 1974. Gastrointestinal hormones and bile secretion in the perfused pig liver: the effects of secretin, cholecystokinin and pentagastrin. *Aust. N.Z.J. Surg.* 44: 173–78

55. Javitt, N. B. 1976. Hepatic bile formation, Parts I&II. *N. Eng. J. Med.* 295: 1464–69; 1511–16

56. Jones, R. S. 1976. Effect of insulin on canalicular bile formation. *Am. J. Physiol.* 231:40–43

57. Jones, R. S., Brooks, F. P. 1967. The role of pyloric antrum in choleresis after insulin and feeding. *Am. J. Physiol.* 213:1406–11

58. Jones, R. S., Geist, R. E., Hall, A. D. 1971. The choleretic effects of glucagon and secretin in the dog. *Gastroenterology* 60:64

59. Jones, R. S., Geist, R. E., Hall, A. D. 1970. Comparison of dose-response relations of insulin and 2-deoxy-D-glucose for biliary and gastric acid secretion. *Gastroenterology* 59:665–70

60. Jones, R. S., Grossman, M. I. 1970. The choleretic effects of cholecystokinin (CCK), gastrin II, and caerulein in the dog. *Am. J. Physiol.* 219:1014–18

61. Jones, R. S., Grossman, M. I. 1969. Choleretic effects of secretin and histamine in the dog. *Am. J. Physiol.* 217: 532–35

62. Jones, R. S., Grossman, M. I. 1969. The choleretic response to feeding in dogs. *Proc. Soc. Exp. Biol. Med.* 132:708–11

63. Jones, R. S., Grossman, M. I. 1969. Dose-response relationship of the choleretic effect of histamine. *Am. J. Physiol.* 216:335–39

64. Jones, R. S., Smith, B. M. 1977. The effect of truncal vagotomy on taurocholate choleresis, and secretin choleresis. *J. Surg. Res.* 23:149–54

65. Jorpes, E. et al. 1965. The influence of secretin and cholecystokinin on bile flow. In *The Biliary System*, ed. W. Taylor. Oxford: Blackwell. pp. 293–301

66. Kaminski, D. L., Dorighi, J., Jellinek, M. 1974. Effect of electrical vagal stimulation on canine hepatic bile flow. *Am. J. Physiol.* 227:487–93

67. Kaminski, D. L., Rose, R. C., Nahrwold, D. L. 1973. Effect of pentagastrin on canine bile flow. *Gastroenterology* 64:630–33

68. Kaminski, D. L., Rose, R. C., Nahrwold, D. L. 1973. Effect of truncal vagotomy on insulin choleresis. *Surgery* 74:758–63

69. Kaminski, D. L., Ruwart, M. J., Jellinek, M. 1975. Effect of glucagon on secretin-stimulated bile flow. *Am. J. Physiol.* 229:1450–55
70. Kaminski, D. L., Rose, R., Nahrwold, D. L. 1974. Effect of cholinergic blockade on insulin choleresis in dogs. *Ann. Surg.* 179:505–9
71. Kaminski, D. L., Rose, R., Nahrwold, D. L. 1974. Effect of pentagastrin on cholecystokinin and secretin choleresis in the dog. *J. Surg. Res.* 17:26–29
72. Kaminski, D. L., Ruwart, M. J., Jellinek, M. 1976. Effect of the histamine (H₂) inhibitor metiamide or histamine-stimulated bile flow in dogs. *Am. J. Physiol.* 231(2):516–21
73. Khedis, A. et al. 1974. Influence of glucagon on canalicular bile production in the dog. *Biomedicine* 21:176–81
74. Klaassen, C. D. 1973. Comparison of the choleretic properties of bile acids. *Eur. J. Pharmacol.* 23:270–75
75. Klaassen, C. D. 1974. Bile flow and composition during bile acid depletion and administration. *Can. J. Physiol. Pharmacol.* 52:334–48
76. Konturek, S. J. 1969. The effect of secretin, gastrin-pentapeptides, and histamine on gastric acid and hepatic bile secretion in man. *Am. J. Dig. Dis.* 14:900–7
77. Kowalewski, K. 1972. The effect of histamine and pentagastrin on secretion of bile in rats. *Arch. Int. Pharmacol. Dyn.* 200:370–77
78. Layden, T. J., Boyer, J. L. 1976. The effect of thyroid hormone on bile salt independent bile flow and Na⁺K⁺AT-Pase activity in liver plasma membranes enriched in bile canaliculi. *J. Clin. Invest.* 57(4):1009–18
79. Levi, A. J., Gatmaitan, Z., Arias, I. M. 1969. Two hepatic proteins Y and Z. *J. Clin. Invest.* 48:2156–67
80. Levine, R. A., Hall, R. S. 1976. Cyclic AMP in secretin choleresis. Evidence for a regulatory role in man and baboons but not in dogs. *Gastroenterology* 70:537–44
81. Lindblad, L., Schersten, T. 1976. Influence of cholic and chenodeoxycholic acid on canalicular bile flow in man. *Gastroenterology* 70(6);1121–24
82. Lundy, E. G., Migliori, J., Jones, R. S. 1973. An analysis of the choleretic effect of insulin. *J. Surg. Res.* 14:181–85
83. Macarol, V. et al. 1970. Hydrocortisone choleresis in the dog. *J. Clin. Invest.* 49:1714–23
84. MacDonald, A. C., Mackay, C., McAllister, R. 1977. The effect of insulin and

atropine on bile volume and composition. *J. Surg. Res.* 23(3):155–60
85. Mok, H. Y., Von Bergmann, K., Grundy, S. M. 1977. Regulation of pool size of bile acids in man. *Gastroenterology* 73:684–90
86. Morris, T. Q. 1972. Choleretic responses to cyclic AMP and theophylline in the dog. *Gastroenterology* 62:187 (Abstr.)
87. Morris, T. Q., Sardi, G. F., Bradley, S. E. 1967. Character of glucagon induced choleresis. *Fed. Proc.* 26:774 (Abstr.)
88. Nahrwold, D. L. 1971. Secretion by the common duct in response to secretin. *Surg. Forum* 22:386–87
89. Nahrwold, D. L., Cooke, A. R., Grossman, M. I. 1967. Choleresis induced by stimulation of the gastric antrum. *Gastroenterology* 52:18–22
90. Nahrwold, D. L., Grossman, M. I. 1967. Secretion of bile in response to food with and without bile in the intestine. *Gastroenterology* 53:11–17
91. Nahrwold, D. L., Shariatzedeh, A. N. 1971. Role of the common bile duct in formation of bile and in gastrin-induced choleresis. *Surgery* 70:147–53
92. O'Maille, E. R., Richards, T. G., Short, A. H. 1965. Acute taurine depletion and maximal rates of hepatic conjugation and secretion of cholic acid in the dog. *J. Physiol. London* 180:67–79
93. O'Maille, E. R., Richards, T. G., Short, A. H. 1967. The influence of conjugation of cholic acid on its uptake and secretion: hepatic extraction of taurocholate and cholate in the dog. *J. Physiol. London* 189:337–50
94. O'Maille, E. R., Richards, T. G. 1976. The secretory characteristics of dehydrocholate in the dog: comparison with the natural bile salts. *J. Physiol. London* 261(2):337–57
95. O'Maille, E. R., Richards, T. G. 1977. Possible explanations for the differences in secretory characteristics between conjugated and free bile acids. *J. Physiol. London* 265(3):855–66
96. Pissidis, A. G. et al. 1969. Hormonal regulation of bile secretion: a study in the isolated perfused liver. *Surgery* 66:1075–84
97. Pohl, S. L., Birnbaumer, L., Rodbell, M. 1971. The glucagon-sensitive adenyl cyclase system in plasma membranes of rat liver. I. Properties. *J. Biol. Chem.* 246:1849–56
98. Powell, K. C., Miller, L. C., Brooks, F. P. 1965. Effect of sham feeding on cholecystectomized dogs. *Proc. Soc. Exp. Biol. Med.* 118:481–83

99. Prandi, D. et al. 1975. Canalicular bile production in man. *Eur. J. Clin. Invest.* 5:1-6

100. Preisig, R., Cooper, H. L., Wheeler, H. O. 1962. The relationship between taurocholate secretion rate and bile production in the unanesthetized dog during cholinergic blockade during secretin administration. *J. Clin. Invest.* 41:1152-62

101. Rayford, P. L., Miller, T. A., Thompson, J. C. 1976. Secretin, cholecystokinin and newer gastrointestinal hormones. Parts I and II. *N. Engl. J. Med.* 294:1093-1102; 1157-74

102. Reichen, J., Paumgartner, G. 1975. Kinetics of taurocholate uptake by the perfused rat liver. *Gastroenterology* 68: 132-36

103. Reichen, J., Paumgartner, G. 1976. Uptake of bile acids by perfused rat liver. *Am. J. Physiol.* 231(3):734-42

104. Reichen, J., Paumgartner, G. 1977. Relationship between bile flow and $Na^+K^+ATPase$ in liver plasma membrane enriched in bile canaliculi. *J. Clin. Invest.* 60(2):429-34

105. Ross, H., Saubermann, A., Silen, W. 1969. The effect of gastric antral stimulation upon the secretion of hepatic bile. *Proc. Soc. Exp. Biol. Med.* 130:278-83

106. Russell, T. R., Searle, G. L., Jones, R. S. 1975. The choleretic mechanisms of sodium taurocholate, secretin, and glucagon. *Surgery* 77:498-504

107. Rutherford, W. et al. 1879. A report on the biliary secretion of the dog; with reference to the action of cholagogue. *Br. Med. J.* 1:177-79

108. Schanker, L. S., Hogben, C. A., 1961. Biliary excretion of inulin, sucrose, and mannitol: analysis of bile formation. *Am. J. Physiol.* 200:1087-90

109. Schersten, T. et al. 1971. Relationship between the biliary excretion of bile acids and the excretion of water, lecithin, and cholesterol in man. *Eur. J. Clin. Invest.* 1:242-47

110. Schiff, M. 1870. Gallenbildung, abhängig von der Aufsaugung der Gallenstoffe. *Pfluegers Arch.* 3:598-613

111. Schwarz, L. R. et al. 1975. Uptake of taurocholic acid into isolated rat liver cells. *Eur. J. Biochem.* 55:617-23

112. Shaw, H. M., Caple, I., Heath, T. J. 1972. Effect of ethacrynic acid on bile formation in sheep, dogs, rats, guinea pigs, and rabbits. *J. Pharmacol. Exp. Ther.* 182:27-33

113. Shaw, H. A., Jones, R. S. 1978. The choleretic effect of CCK and CCK-OP in dogs. In press

114. Small, D. M., Dowling, R. H., Redinger, R. N. 1965. The enterohepatic circulation of bile salts. *Arch. Intern. Med.* 130:552-73

115. Snow, J. R., Jones, R. S. 1978. The effect of insulin on bile salt independent canalicular secretion. *Surgery* 83: 458-63

116. Soloway, R. D. et al. 1972. Effects of secretin and bile salt infusions on canine bile composition and flow. *Am. J. Physiol.* 222:681-86

117. Song, C. S. et al. 1969. Plasma membranes in rat liver. *J. Cell. Biol.* 41: 124-32

118. Sperber, I. 1959. Secretion of organic anions in the formation of urine and bile. *Pharmacol. Rev.* 11:109-34

119. Sperber, I. 1965. Biliary secretion of organic anions and its influence on bile flow. See Ref. 65, p. 457

120. Strasberg, S. M. et al. 1975. Analysis of the components of bile flow in rhesus monkey. *Am. J. Physiol.* 228:115-21

121. Strasberg, S. M., Siminovitch, K. A., Ilson, R. G. 1974. Bile production in fasted and fed primates. *Ann. Surg.* 180:356-63

122. Sum, P. T. et al. 1970. Studies on the regulation of hepatic bile flow. The intestinal phase of biliary secretion. *Am. J. Surg.* 120:160-65

123. Tanturi, C. A., Ivy, A. C. 1938. On the existence of secretory nerves in the vagi for the reflex excitation and inhibition of bile secretion *Am. J. Physiol.* 121: 270-83

124. Tavoloni, N., Angelucci, L. 1975. Polypeptide stimulation of choleresis in the dog. *Rend. Gastroenterol.* 7:165-72

125. Thulin, L. 1973. The choleretic effect of pure natural cholecystokinin in dogs. *Acta Chir. Scand.* 139:635-40

126. Vagne, M. et al. 1968. Synthetic secretin: comparison with natural secretin for potency and spectrum of physiological action. *Gastroenterology* 55:260-67

127. Walsh, J., Grossman, M. I. 1975. Gastrin. *N. Engl. J. Med.* Parts I&II. 292:1324-34; 1377-84

128. Wannagat, F. J., Adler, R. D., Ockner, R. K. 1978. Bile acid induced increase in bile acid independent flow and plasma membrane $Na^+K^+ATPase$ activity in rat liver. *J. Clin. Invest.* 61(2): 297-307

129. Wheeler, H. O. 1968. Water and electrolytes in bile. In *Handbook of Physiology*, Sect. 6, ed. C. Code, 5:2409. Baltimore: Am. Physiol. Soc.

130. Wheeler, H. O. 1972. Secretion of bile acids by the liver and their role in the

formation of hepatic bile. *Arch. Intern. Med.* 130:533–41
131. Wheeler, H. O., Mancusi-Ungaro, P. L. 1966. Role of bile ducts during secretin choleresis in dogs. *Am. J. Physiol.* 210:1153–59
132. Wheeler, H. O., Ramos, O. L. 1960. Determinants of the flow and composition of bile in the unanesthetized dog during constant infusions of sodium taurocholate. *J. Clin. Invest.* 39:161–70

133. Wheeler, H. O., Ross, E. D., Bradley, S. E. 1968. Canalicular bile production in dogs. *Am. J. Physiol.* 214:866–74
134. White, T. T. et al. 1974. The effect of vagotomy on biliary secretions and bile salt pools in dogs. *Ann. Surg.* 179: 406–11
135. Zaterka, S., Grossman, M. I. 1966. The effect of gastrin and histamine on secretion of bile. *Gastroenterology* 50:500–5

Ann. Rev. Physiol. 1979. 41:83-95

COMPARATIVE BIOCHEMISTRY AND PHYSIOLOGY OF GUT HORMONES

♦1207

G. J. Dockray

Physiological Laboratory, University of Liverpool, Liverpool, U.K.

Until recently comparative studies on the gut hormones were sparse and fragmentary. Earlier studies, starting with that of Bayliss & Starling in 1903 (7), dealt with the identification of hormone-like biological activity in gut extracts of different species and were thought to suggest that mechanisms of control in the gut were both simple and uniform throughout the vertebrates. Recent developments leave no doubt that this position is now untenable (6, 13). A considerable number of hormonal and related peptides have now been identified in the gastrointestinal tract, and at least some of these are known to exist in different molecular forms and to vary in their species and tissue distributions. The physiological role of many of these molecules is still poorly understood, but the available evidence suggests that most possess a wide spectrum of biological activity and that there are likely to be complex patterns of interaction between different hormones, and between nerves and hormones. A number of these peptides occur not only in gut endocrine cells but also in central or peripheral neurons and so may well have dual functions as both hormones and neurotransmitters. These advances pose fundamental questions about the factors governing the distribution, nature, and mode of action of peptide hormones and neurotransmitters, the answers to which depend at least in part on an understanding of the phylogenetic aspects of these systems. There is good reason to think that certain of the gut hormones have a common evolutionary history; comparative studies at the cellular and molecular levels are therefore likely to prove rewarding in elucidating basic patterns of organization and development in the gastrointestinal endocrine system.

0066-4278/79/0301-0083$01.00

CELLULAR AND MOLECULAR RELATIONSHIPS

Several authors have suggested that gut hormones and related peptides originated as modified digestive enzymes, or their fragments, which were secreted into the blood rather than the gut lumen. Supposed similarities in the sequences of selected enzymes and hormones have been cited in favor of this view, and attention has also been drawn to the possible embryological origin of gut endocrine cells in the endoderm (1, 44). However, rapidly accumulating evidence gathered largely from the application of immuno-chemical methods of analysis (radioimmunoassay and immunocytochem-istry) makes it clear that peptides such as somatostatin, substance P, neurotensin, vasoactive intestinal polypeptide (VIP), cholecystokinin (CCK), bombesin, and enkephalin occur in both gut endocrine cells and central or peripheral neurons. Obviously this dual distribution must receive full attention in any analysis of phylogenetic origins. The widespread capac-ity of neurons to produce active peptides has been appreciated for many years. Indeed, as Scharrer has pointed out, neurons specialized for neurosecretion (presumably producing polypeptides) can be identified in lower metazoans (such as coelenterates) that do not possess endocrine cells as such (34). Thus the ability of neurons to produce and secrete peptides would seem to precede the development of peptide-secreting endocrine cells.

Other evidence also points to similarities at the cellular level in peptide secreting neurons and endocrine cells. For example, Pearse has repeatedly drawn attention to the similar histochemical properties of gut endocrine cells and certain other cells that are either neurons or of neuronal origin (32). These properties are conveniently summarized in the acronym, APUD: *a*mine *p*recursor *u*ptake (or storage) and *d*ecarboxylation, to which may be added other properties discussed by Pearse (32). All APUD cells are said to have a common embryological origin in the neuroectoderm (neuroendocrine programmed epiblast). Experimental evidence supports a neural crest origin for certain APUD cells—e.g. thyroid C cells and adrenal chromaffin cells. But evidence for a neuroectodermal origin of the gut endocrine cells is less convincing. In particular, Le Douarin has concluded from the results of heterospecific transplantation of quail tissues—which are readily distinguished by cells containing a prominant neucleolus—into chicken embryos that the gut and pancreatic endocrine cells are likely to derive from the endoderm at least as it stands at the end of gastrulation (18). It seems more realistic therefore to view the dual distribution of peptides in nerves and endocrine cells not as a consequence of a common embryolog-ical origin of these cell types but rather as an expression of the capacity of all cells to produce a particular peptide. This capacity could well be drawn upon independently by different cell types so that the same peptide functions in otherwise unrelated systems.

At the molecular level there are striking similarities in the sequences of certain gut hormones , notably in gastrin and CCK on the one hand and in secretin, glucagon, VIP, and gastric inhibitory peptide (GIP) on the other. Together these similarities emphasize that the gut hormones are not a collection of isolated molecules but are likely to be united by a common ancestry (6, 13). The genes that coded for ancestral members of these two groups are therefore believed to have undergone duplication to produce daughter genes. Through independent mutation these then diverged to yield distinct but related peptide hormones. Elucidation of the sequences of submammalian peptides should help clarify the early evolutionary history of these molecules.

There are also limited similarities in sequence between certain other brain and gut peptides—e.g. substance P and neurotensin (26)—but in general the structural affinities of these and other molecules such as somatostatin and motilin are less clear. However, most or perhaps all secretory peptides are synthesized as part of large precursor molecules, and further examples of structural homologies may well come to light in the precursor forms. The possibility also deserves consideration that apparently distinct peptides are derived from a single biosynthetic precursor. There is evidence, for example, that the pituitary peptide β lipotrophin (β LPH) is a precursor for both β melanotrophin and the endogenous opiate peptides (enkephalin and endorphins), even though these molecules have seemingly unrelated patterns of biological activity. Recent evidence suggests that in a mouse pituitary tumor cell line, β LPH is itself a product of a larger precursor (31 k) which also contains the sequence of corticotrophin (27). These interrelationships are of direct interest in gut endocrinology since both enkephalin and corticotrophin immunoreactivities have been reported in gastrin (G-) cells of the pyloric antral mucosa (23, 33). However, in a wider sense they indicate that different cell types may process a single precursor by alternative pathways to produce different peptides.

GASTRIN AND CHOLECYSTOKININ

Structure and Distribution

Porcine gastrin and cholecystokinin share a common COOH-terminal pentapeptide (-Gly-Trp-Met-Asp-Phe-NH$_2$). In addition, CCK has a sulfated tyrosine residue at position seven from the COOH-terminus, and gastrin has a tyrosine at position six from the COOH-terminus, which may or may not be sulfated (20, 22). Natural selection would be expected to conserve functionally important residues, and so it is not surprising that the COOH-terminal regions of gastrin and CCK also contain the minimum sequences required for their characteristic actions (tetrapeptide for gastrin, heptapeptide for CCK). Recently we isolated from sheep brain two peptides with the sequences of the COOH-terminal octapeptide of CCK (CCK8). The peptides were indistinguishable from synthetic CCK8 in biological and immunochemical properties; and although they differ slightly in charge, the basis for this difference is not yet clear (15). These findings raise the possibility that a single structural gene for CCK is expressed in brain and gut. If so, the structure of the active COOH-terminal portion of CCK is likely to be strongly conserved, since mutations leading to amino acid substitution will be subject to selective pressures in two systems and must be acceptable in both to survive. Further evidence of strong pressures working on CCK is provided by the amphibian decapeptide caerulein. This peptide shares with porcine CCK an identical COOH-terminal octapeptide sequence but for a single substitution of threonine for methionine, and also has a similar spectrum of biological actions and potency (2). Although originally isolated from the skin of certain amphibian species such as *Hyla caerulea* and *Xenopus laevis*, recent evidence suggests caerulein-like peptides are also present in gut endocrine cells in amphibia and might therefore function as hormones (24).

There are almost no similarities in structure in the NH_2-terminal regions of CCK and gastrin, which suggests that these regions are poorly conserved, perhaps because they are relatively unimportant in determining biological activity. In the mammalian heptadecapeptide gastrins (G17) so far sequenced (human, pig, dog, cat, cow, and sheep) amino acid substitutions are known in three positions, all in the mid- or NH_2-terminal parts of the molecule and all having little or no influence on biological activity.

About 5% of human and hog antral gastrin is accounted for by a component (big gastrin, G34) consisting of G17 extended at its NH_2-terminus by a further seventeen residues (20). Although the biological activity of gastrin is determined by the COOH-terminal region it may be modified by the NH_2-terminal part. Thus in both human and dog, circulating G34 is about 20% as potent as G17 in stimulating acid secretion (42); G34 is also cleared more slowly than G17, and so contributes a higher proportion of total gastrin concentration in blood than in antrum. Trypsin cleaves G34 at lysine residues in positions 16 and 17 to yield G17 and an NH_2-terminal peptide (NT G34) (20). Recent evidence suggests that equimolar amounts of G17 and NT G34 occur in antral G-cells; this is consistent with the idea that G34 is a biosynthetic precursor of G17 (16). In mammals like dog and pig, gastrin occurs in highest concentrations in pyloric antral mucosa and in relatively low concentration in duodenum; minute amounts may also occur in pancreas, vagus, and pituitary. In humans, however, duodenal gastrin concentration is 10–50% that in antrum, and about half of this is G34. Moreover in neonatal rats, gastrin concentrations in duodenum and pancreas are considerably higher than in antrum, and in duodenum there is also a relatively high proportion of G34 (25). Early in life duodenal and pancreatic gastrin concentrations decrease while antral concentrations increase (25). The relative rates of synthesis and conversion of G34 to G17 therefore seem to depend on the species, tissue, and stage of development. Because G17 and G34 differ in biological properties, the factors governing their relative concentrations are of physiological significance. Cholecystokinin also exists in several forms that differ in species and tissue distribution probably as a consequence of differences in the rate of conversion of larger to smaller forms (14). Cholecystokinin was isolated from hog duodenum in the form of peptides of 33 and 39 residues (22), but immunochemical evidence suggests CCK8 and an intermediate-size peptide also occur in significant amounts (14). In contrast, in hog brain we are able to find significant quantities of CCK8 but only negligible amounts of CCK33 (14).

The recent development of region specific antisera for gastrin and CCK has considerably extended the scope of comparative studies of these molecules. The structural relationships of otherwise uncharacterized peptides can now be examined on the basis of their patterns of cross-reactivity with antisera known to be specific for particular regions of the mammalian forms of gastrin or CCK. The results of this approach indicate that relatively small CCK-like peptides resembling CCK8 occur widely in extracts of brain and intestine of many species including cyclostomes (*Lampetra*), teleost fish (cod), amphibia (*Rana*), reptiles (*Testudo*), birds (chicken and turkey), and a variety of mammals [(13, 24); G. J. Dockray, unpublished observations]. These results therefore emphasize the conserved nature of the COOH-terminal regions of gastrin and CCK. They also supplement and extend earlier studies in which it was shown that extracts of many species, including representatives of the cyclostomes, teleosts, elasmobranchs, amphibia, and birds, had gastrin- or CCK-like activity in mammalian bioassays (5, 13). The results obtained in the cyclostomes are of particular significance, for these animals belong to the oldest of the vertebrate groups, the Agnatha. It would seem therefore that the distribution of CCK-like peptides in brain and gut is of considerable antiquity and was very likely established in the earliest vertebrates. A similar distribution may even exist in certain invertebrates, for there is evidence of gastrin-like immunoreactivity in the neurosecretory system of an insect (*Manduca sexta*) and in the gut of certain molluscs (*Aplysia, Otala*) (21, 37).

The application of region-specific antisera in immunocytochemical studies has also provided important information on the comparative aspects of cellular origins. For example, in the stomach and intestine of teleost and amphibian species Larsson & Rehfeld were able to identify only a single cell type cross-reacting with gastrin/CCK antisera, and this appeared to contain caerulein-like peptides (24). In contrast, in birds, reptiles, and mammals there were two distinct cell types, one in antral mucosa associated with gastrin-like immunoreactivity, the other in intestine and associated with CCK. On this evidence it is postulated that the divergence of gastrin and CCK from a common ancestor occurred after the amphibian line separated from that giving reptiles. However, the possibility cannot yet be excluded that in lower vertebrates there are peptides of the gastrin/CCK series that fail to cross-react with antisera to the mammalian hormones. The immunocytochemical studies of Van Noorden and her colleagues indicate that in the intestine of cyclostomes (*Lampetra fluviatilis, Myxine glutinosa*) and in a cephalochordate (amphioxus), gastrin/CCK-like factors are found in the same cells as a factor with glucagon-like immunoreactivity (31, 39, 40). These results imply a common cellular origin for the two main families of gut hormones and suggest that amphioxus and the cyclostomes represent a stage in the emergence of the gut endocrine system before the localization of these peptides to discrete cell types.

Comparative Physiology

Both gastrin and CCK act at numerous sites throughout the mammalian gastrointestinal tract (43). Few of these actions are likely to be evoked by concentrations of hormone circulating after a normal meal; in this sense they may be considered pharmacological. The identification of physiological actions of a hormone is now seen to depend on the capacity to match quantitatively a response with the concentrations of endogenous peptide in blood after a normal stimulus (feeding), and to duplicate this response with exogenous hormone giving comparable blood concentrations (43). This approach obviously depends on the availability of pure native peptide for each species; the opportunities for truly physiological studies are therefore still restricted to a few species. In dog and human there is strong evidence that gastrin exerts a physiological action on acid secretion; it is also widely believed that the actions on gastric motility and the growth of gastric mucosa are physiological (43). The main physiological actions of CCK are generally accepted as stimulation of gall bladder contraction and pancreatic enzyme secretion.

Considerable attention has been devoted to elucidating the relationships between the structure of gastrin and CCK and their biological activity. In mammals the COOH-terminal tetrapeptide is recognized as the minimal fragment with appreciable activity on acid secretion (gastrin activity). The tetrapeptide also has weak activity on gall bladder and pancreas, but for full potency on these targets (i.e. for CCK-like activity) a sulfated tyrosine residue must occupy position 7 from the COOH-terminus (43). In mammals CCK has relatively low potency for gastric acid secretion. However, there are marked differences in the pattern of structure-activity relationships in lower vertebrates, which illustrates that at the molecular level the evolution of endocrine systems involves changes not only in the structure of hormones but also in the specificity of their receptors. For example, in the frog, *Rana esculenta,* Negri & Erspamer (29) have shown that acid secretion and short circuit current of gastric mucosa in vitro were stimulated by low doses of caerulein and CCK8. Peptides with considerably reduced activity were obtained when the tyrosine was desulfated or was displaced from position 7 from the COOH-terminus—e.g. to position 6 as in the mammalian gastrins. The structure-activity relationships of amphibian oxyntic cells therefore bear a closer resemblance to those of mammalian gall bladder than mammalian parietal cells. Taken together with the evidence of caerulein-like activity in antral endocrine cells in *R. esculenta* (24) the results are also consistent with a role for caerulein in the regulation of acid secretion in amphibia.

In the chicken, caerulein is reported to be a stronger stimulant of acid secretion than human G17 (4). However, little is known of the structure and activity of avian gastrin and so the physiological significance of these observations is uncertain. Relatively low doses of caerulein and CCK8 strongly stimulate chicken and turkey gall bladder contraction and pancreatic enzyme secretion; since there is immunochemical evidence of CCK8-like peptides in intestine, there may well be endocrine mechanisms controlling the avian gall bladder and pancreas similar to those in mammals [(3); G. J. Dockray, unpublished observations].

Similar mechanisms are probably also involved in the control of the gall bladder in teleost fish. Intestinal extracts of certain teleost species (pike and eel) have been shown to have CCK-like activity on mammalian gall bladder and pancreas (5). Moreover Vigna & Gorbman recently reported that sulfated forms of both porcine CCK8 and G17 were strong stimulants of salmon gall bladder contractions in vitro, whereas unsulfated peptides were about 1000 times less potent (41). It would seem that the structural requirements for activity on teleost gall bladder were similar but less stringent than for mammals, since the teleost gall bladder discriminates between sulfated and unsulfated peptides but not between sulfated tyrosine residues at position 6 or position 7 from the COOH-terminus.

THE SECRETIN FAMILY

Structure and Distribution

When porcine secretin, glucagon, VIP, and GIP are aligned from the NH_2-terminus identical residues occur in at least three of the four peptides at 13 of 27 positions, including 8 in the NH_2-terminal decapeptide, and there are identical residues in pairs of peptides in no fewer than 25 of 27 positions. These similarities in structure justify a belief in the evolution of these peptides from a common ancestor. Peptides resembling porcine secretin, glucagon, and VIP have been isolated from chicken intestine or pancreas, so these molecules were probably well established in the reptilian ancestors common to birds and mammals (13, 30). Little is known of the distribution of GIP in submammalian species, and so the early history of this hormone is largely obscure.

The structure of glucagon is strongly conserved, there being identical sequences in all the mammalian species so far examined (human, cow, rat, rabbit, pig) and only a single residue difference between chicken and mammalian glucagons. The structure of VIP is also conserved: Chicken and porcine peptides differ in only 4 of 28 residues, and these differences appear to have little influence on biological activity (30). These observations suggest that glucagon and VIP have precisely defined structure-activity relationships such that relatively limited opportunity exists for amino acid substitution without loss of biological activity. This view implies an important biological role for glucagon and VIP; the physiological importance of glucagon is not in question, but the physiological significance of VIP in mammals is still uncertain. The sequence of chicken secretin has not yet been reported, but preliminary evidence suggests that its structure may be significantly different from that of porcine secretin (30).

Crude extracts of the intestine of many species including representatives of all the major vertebrate groups have been reported to evoke secretin-like increases in the flow of juice and bicarbonate output of the pancreas in mammals like rat and dog (6, 13). However, these bioassays cannot be regarded as specific for secretin since VIP and CCK also show weak secretin-like activity in many mammals. Partially purified extracts of the intestine of a teleost fish (*Esox lucius*), which had little or no CCK-like activity, resembled VIP more closely than secretin in their pattern of activity on pancreatic secretion in birds and mammals (12). Since there is also evidence of glucagon-like activity in teleosts it appears that the molecular diversity characteristic of this family was established relatively early.

Immunocytochemical evidence indicates that secretin and GIP occur only in endocrine cells in the duodenum and jejunum of mammals (35). In contrast, there are differing opinions about the presence of VIP in endocrine cells, although there is general agreement that VIP occurs in nerves of the myenteric plexuses (35). The failure of some antisera to reveal VIP in endocrine cells could well be due to the presence in these cells of different immunoreactive forms of the peptide. In support of this we have recently shown that in extracts of human colon mucosa—which contains both endocrine cells and nerve fibers—there were in addition to VIP three components cross-reacting with NH_2-terminal specific antisera that were less basic than the porcine octacosapeptide. However, in extracts of human colon muscle—where VIP is localized in nerve plexuses only—there was a single immunoreactive form indistinguishabe in chromatographic properties from porcine VIP (10).

Glucagon is united with the other members of the secretin group not only by structural simularities but also phylogenetic and morphological grounds. Abundant chemical, immunochemical, and histological evidence indicates that glucagon originates in A cells of the endocrine pancreas of the gnathostome vertebrates (17). However, there is also glucagon-like material in gut endocrine cells, and this may be a primitive feature reflecting the early origins of the hormone. This idea is supported by the observation that in primitive vertebrates such as the cyclostomes glucagon-like immunoreactivity appears to be restricted to endocrine cells dispersed throughout the intestinal mucosa, although there are insulin- and perhaps somatostatin-containing cells in the pancreatic islets (17, 31, 38, 39). In a protochordate (amphioxus), both glucagon- and insulin-like factors are localized in cells scattered throughout the intestinal mucosa (40). On this evidence the hormones of the endocrine pancreas would seem to have appeared first in gut endocrine cells that later associated into islets. It is striking that in chordates ranging from amphioxus to the mammals almost all endocrine cells of the gut are dispersed throughout the mucosal layers and reach from basement membrane to lumen. These cells are clearly well-fitted for a direct response to luminal stimuli by the secretion of hormone into the blood. At an early stage insulin and glucagon would seem to have become involved in the control of metabolism, and the subsequent localization of these hormones in the pancreatic islets could well reflect the advantages obtained by linking their secretion to blood-borne factors (glucose, amino acids, and endocrine stimuli) rather than directly to the presence of food in the gut.

The glucagon-like factors extracted from mammalian gut are distinguishable in both immunochemical and chromatographic properties from pancreatic glucagon (28). An exception is the glucagon-like activity in dog fundic mucosa that appears to be identical to that of the pancreatic peptide. Recently Moody et al isolated from hog intestine a peptide of 100 residues (glicentin) that contains within its structure the sequence of pancreatic glucagon (28). Experimental evidence obtained from studies in teleost fish, birds, and mammals, indicates that glucagon, like other peptide hormones, is synthesized initially in a large precursor form. Glicentin may well be a biosynthetic precursor that in pancreas is more or less completely converted to glucagon but in gut endocrine cells remains essentially unconverted.

Comparative Physiology

Like gastrin and CCK, the peptides of the secretin family exert numerous actions on motility, secretion, and absorption in many parts of the gut; in addition, they have important effects on metabolism. Many of these actions are seen only in response to high doses of exogenous peptide and are therefore often regarded as pharmacological. In some instances such actions can be accounted for by low affinity of a peptide for the receptors of a structurally related molecule, and these effects may justifiably be called pharmacological. In other cases, however, we must consider the possibility that responses evoked by high doses of exogenous peptide reflect physiological events normally produced by locally high concentrations of peptide, as for example at the terminals of peptidergic neurons or in the immediate vicinity of mucosal endocrine cells. The physiological actions of the secretin-like peptides are likely to range from neuromodulator roles in the central nervous system (VIP) to hormonal regulation of the exocrine (secretin) and endocrine (GIP) pancreas and the control of blood sugar (glucagon).

In mammals, only minute increases in plasma secretin concentrations occur during normal digestion (36), but these are probably effective in stimulating the pancreas because of strong potentiation of secretin by CCK. VIP has low potency and is a partial agonist for the flow and bicarbonate output from the pancreas in mammals such as dog, human, and rat, and is not likely to be of physiological significance (11, 13). In contrast, in birds like the chicken and turkey, VIP is a strong stimulant of the flow of pancreatic juice (11). Chicken VIP is about twice as potent as porcine VIP and 50–100 times more potent than either chicken or porcine secretin on the avian pancreas (R. Dimaline & G. J. Dockray, unpublished observations). These results cast doubt on the role of secretin in the regulation of the avian pancreas; they suggest instead that in birds VIP might have a physiological role analogous to that of secretin in mammals. The differences in activity of secretin and VIP in birds and mammals could be explained by differences in the properties of target organ receptors. In this context it is interesting that recent evidence suggests guinea pig pancreatic acinar cell membranes have a relatively small population of receptors with high affinity for VIP but low affinity for secretin, and a larger population of receptors with high affinity for secretin and low affinity for VIP (8). Differences in the action of secretin and VIP in birds and mammals might therefore be explained by changes either in the relative numbers of different receptors or in their specificity. It is of further interest that there are also receptors with high affinity for VIP and low affinity for secretin on the plasma membranes of rat liver and fat cells; these probably mediate the hyperglycemic and lipolytic actions of VIP (9). Similar actions are evoked by glucagon, but the available evidence suggests these actions are mediated via a receptor distinct from that for VIP (9). In the chicken, glucagon stimulates lipolysis, but VIP and secretin are ineffective; it seems possible that the VIP/secretin receptor is absent from these cells (19). The obvious diversity in the numbers and specificity of receptors revealed by these studies could be of considerable phylogenetic significance, for the existence of a pool of variability in both receptors and their peptide ligands would be a clear requirement for the development and evolution of new and diverse relationships between peptides and their target organs.

CONCLUSIONS

Representatives of the two main groups of gut hormones, the secretin and gastrin families, are widely distributed in gut endocrine cells throughout the vertebrates. It seems probable that these families arose by duplication of ancestral genes and their subsequent divergence by independent mutation. Since several peptides occur in both gut endocrine cells and neurons, the evolution of this system must also involve important changes in the patterns of gene expression in different tissues. The physiological roles of these molecules have been established in only a few instances but probably include not only hormonal control of many aspects of digestion and metabolism but also neuromodulator functions in the central nervous system. Recent studies on the mode of action of these peptides at the molecular level suggest the existence of distinct but related target organ receptors and provide a basis for interpreting species differences in actions in terms of the number of receptors as well as their affinity for different ligands.

Literature Cited

1. Adelson, J. W. 1971. Enterosecretory proteins. *Nature* 229:321–25
2. Anastasi, A., Erspamer, V., Endean, R. 1968. Isolation and amino acid sequence of caerulein, the active decapeptide of the skin of *Hyla caerulea. Arch. Biochem. Biophys.* 125:57–68
3. Angelucci, L., Baldieri, M., Linari, G. 1970. The action of caerulein on pancreatic and biliary secretions of the chicken. *Eur. J. Pharmacol.* 11:217–32
4. Angelucci, L., Linari, G. 1970. The action of caerulein on gastric secretion of the chicken. *Eur. J. Pharmacol.* 11:204–16
5. Barrington, E. J. W., Dockray, G. J. 1972. Cholecystokinin-pancreozymin-like activity in the eel (*Anguilla anguilla L.*). *Gen. Comp. Endocrinol.* 19:80–87
6. Barrington, E. J. W., Dockray, G. J. 1976. Gastrointestinal hormones. *J. Endocrinol.* 69:299–325
7. Bayliss, W. M., Starling, E. H. 1903. On the uniformity of the pancreatic mechanism in Vertebrata. *J. Physiol. London* 29:174–80
8. Christophe, J. P., Conlon, T. P., Gardner, J. D. 1976. Interactions of porcine vasoactive intestinal peptide with dispersed pancreatic acinar cells from the

guinea pig. *J. Biol. Chem.* 251:4629–34
9. Desbuquois, B., Laudat, M. H., Laudat, Ph. 1973. Vasoactive intestinal polypeptide and glucagon: Stimulation of adenylate cyclase via distinct receptors in liver and fat cell membranes. *Biochem. Biophys. Res. Commun.* 53:1187–194
10. Dimaline, R., Dockray, G. J. 1978. Multiple immunoreactive forms of vasoactive intestinal peptide in human colonic mucosa. *Gastroenterology.* 75: 387–92
11. Dockray, G. J. 1973. Vasoactive intestinal peptide: secretin-like action on the avian pancreas. *Experientia* 29:1510–11
12. Dockray, G. J. 1974. Extraction of a secretin-like factor from the intestine of pike (*Esox lucius*). *Gen. Comp. Endocrinol.* 23:340–47
13. Dockray, G. J. 1977. Molecular evolution of gut hormones: application of comparative studies on the regulation of disgestion. *Gastroenterology* 72:344–58
14. Dockray, G. J. 1977. Immunoreactive component resembling cholecystokinin octapeptide in intestine. *Nature* 270: 359–61
15. Dockray, G. J., Gregory, R. A., Harris, J. I., Hutchison, J., Runswick, M. J. 1978. *J. Physiol. London* 280:16–17P (Abstr.)
16. Dockray, G. J., Vaillant, C., Hopkins, C. R. 1978. Biosynthetic relationships of big and little gastrins. *Nature* 273:770–72
17. Falkmer, S., Cutfield, J. F., Cutfield, S. M. et al. 1975. Comparative endocrinology of insulin and glucagon production. *Am. Zool.* 15 (Suppl. 1): 255–70
18. Fontaine, J., Le Douarin, N. M. 1977. Analysis of endoderm formation in the avian blastoderm by the use of quail-chicken chimeras. *J. Embryol. Exp. Morphol.* 14:209–22
19. Frandsen, E. K., Moody, A. J. 1973. Lipolytic action of a newly isolated vasoactive intestinal peptide. *Horm. Metab. Res.* 5:196–99
20. Gregory, R. A., Tracy, H. J. 1975. In *Gastrointestinal Hormones,* ed. J. C. Thompson, pp. 13–24. Austin, Texas: Univ. Texas Press
21. Kramer, K. J., Speirs, R. D., Childs, C. N. 1977: Immunochemical evidence for a gastrin-like peptide in insect neuroendocrine system. *Gen. Comp. Endocrinol.* 32:423–26
22. Jorpes, J. E., Mutt, V. 1973. Secretin and cholecystokinin (CCK). *Handb. Exp. Pharmacol.* 34:1–179

23. Larsson, L.-I. 1977. Corticotrophin-like peptides in central nerves and in endocrine cells of gut and pancreas. *Lancet* 2:1321–23
24. Larsson, L.-I., Rehfeld, J. F. 1977. Evidence for a common evolutionary origin of gastrin and cholecystokinin. *Nature* 269:335–38
25. Larsson, L.-I., Rehfeld, J. F., Sundler, F., Hakanson, R. 1976. Pancreatic gastrin in foetal and neonatal rats. *Nature* 262:609–10
26. Leeman, S. E., Mroz, E. A., Carraway, R. E. 1977. In *Peptides in Neurobiology,* ed. H. Gainer, pp. 99–144. New York: Plenum
27. Mains, R. E., Eipper, B. A., Ling, N. 1977. Common precursor to corticotrophin and endorphins. *Proc. Natl. Acad. Sci. USA* 74:3014–18
28. Moody, A. J., Jacobsen, H., Sundby, F. 1978. In *Gut Hormones,* ed. S. R. Bloom, pp. 369–78. Edinburgh: Churchill, Livingston
29. Negri, L., Erspamer, V. 1973. Action of caerulein and caerulein-like peptides on "short circuit current" and acid secretion in the isolated gastric mucosa of amphibians. *Naunyn Schmiedebergs Arch. Pharmacol.* 277:401–12
30. Nilsson, A. 1974. Isolation, amino acid composition and terminal amino acid residues of the vasoactive octacosapeptide from chicken intestine. Partial purification of chicken secretin. *FEBS Lett.* 47:284–89
31. Ostberg, Y., Van Noorden, S., Pearse, A. G. E., Thomas, N. W. 1976. Cytochemical, immunofluorescence and ultrastructural investigations on polypeptide hormone containing cells in the intestinal mucosa of a cyclostome, *Myxine glutinosa. Gen. Comp. Endocrinol.* 28:213–27
32. Pearse, A. G. E., 1975. Neurocristopathy, neuroendocrine pathology and the APUD concept. *Z. Krebsforsch.* 84: 1–18
33. Polak, J. M., Sullivan, S. N., Bloom, S. R., Facer, P., Pearse, A. G. E. 1977. Enkephalin-immunoreactivity in the human gastrointestinal tract. *Lancet* 1:972–74
34. Scharrer, B. 1976. Neurosecretion—comparative and evolutionary aspects. *Prog. Brain Res.* 45:125–37
35. Solcia, E., Polak, J. M., Pearse, A. G. E. et al. 1978. See Ref. 28, pp. 40–48
36. Straus, E. 1978. Radioimmunoassay of gastrointestinal hormones. *Gastroenterology* 74:141–52

37. Straus, E., Yalow, R. S., Gainer, H. 1975. Molluscan gastrin: concentration and molecular forms. *Science* 190: 687–89
38. Van Noorden, S., Ostberg, Y., Pearse, A. G. E. 1977. Localisation of somatostatin-like immunoreactivity in the pancreatic islets of the hagfish, *Myxine glutinosa*, and the lamprey, *Lampetra fluviatilis. Cell Tiss. Res.* 177:281–85
39. Van Noorden, S., Pearse, A. G. E. 1974. Immunoreactive polypeptide hormones in the pancreas and gut of the lamprey. *Gen. Comp. Endocrinol.* 23:311–24
40. Van Noorden, S., Pearse, A. G. E. 1976. In *The Evolution of the Pancreatic Islets,* ed. T. A. I. Grillo, L. Liebson, A. Epple, pp. 163–78. Oxford: Pergamon
41. Vigna, S. R., Gorbman, A. 1977. Effects of cholecystokinin, gastrin and related peptides on coho salmon gallbladder contraction in vitro. *Am. J. Physiol.* 232:E485–91
42. Walsh, J. H. 1975. See Ref. 20, pp. 75–83
43. Walsh, J. H., Grossman, M. I. 1975. Gastrin. *New Engl. J. Med.* 292: 1324–32
44. Weinstein, B. 1972. A generalized homology correlation for various hormones and proteins. *Experientia* 28: 1517–22

SPECIAL TOPIC: NEUROPHYSIOLOGY

Introduction

The main concern of these essays is with the substrates of motor control systems. Houk raises the question: What is the property that is controlled by the gamma efferent feedback loop—muscle length, tension, or some combination of these? He reviews evidence showing that the controlled parameter is muscle stiffness, which is defined as the ratio of force change to length change, and suggests that the advantage is simplification of the properties of the muscle as observed and used by the central nervous system.

Kostyuk & Vasilenko review evidence on the organization of identified groups of spinal interneurons (dorsal sensory nuclear IN, Renshaw IN, group Ia-IN, and various propriospinal IN), including their functional interconnections and interactions and the specialized sites of entry for spinal afferent and descending (cortico-, tecto-, rubro-, vestibulo-, and reticulo-spinal) activities. They show the pattern of analysis that may be required for understanding somato- and viscero-motor integration.

The review by Peterson describes properties of the rapidly conducting reticulospinal tracts extending to spinal motor nuclei, including their topographic organization in the brain stem in relation to axial and limb musculature, direct and indirect excitatory and inhibitory connections to motoneurons, and their function in reticulo-motor control.

Darian-Smith, Johnson & Goodwin review the topography of the posterior parietal cortex in primates, the effects of lesions on behavior, the behavioral correlates of unit activity, and corticocortical connections of neurons in this area. Emphasis is on conceptual rather than technical problems.

Somjen reviews evidence showing that the blood-brain barrier very effectively insulates the brain from fluctuations in potassium concentration, but that significant extracellular changes occur in the CNS that may modulate or regulate normal as well as abnormal function of local regions.

Walter J. Freeman
Section Editor

Ann. Rev. Physiol. 1979. 41:99–114

REGULATION OF STIFFNESS ♦1208
BY SKELETOMOTOR REFLEXES

James C. Houk

Department of Physiology, Northwestern University Medical
and Dental Schools, Chicago, Illinois 60611

Since the early 1950s when Merton (44) first introduced his "follow-up servo hypothesis" of movement control, the dominant opinion has held that stretch and unloading reflexes function to control the length of a muscle in opposition to changes in mechanical load, thus providing *load compensation*. In this article I review recent evidence indicating that this notion is wrong, or at least incomplete, and proceed to develop an alternative idea (47) that neither muscle length nor force are regulated as individual variables, but that a property called stiffness (the ratio of force change to length change) is maintained relatively constant by skeletomotor reflexes. This leads to a discussion of the actions of descending motor commands on the segmental system, from which I conclude that these may be much less versatile than was formerly believed.

The reader is referred to another review (55) and to Matthews' monograph (42) for additional information.

AUTOGENETIC REFLEXES AND THE MOTOR SERVO

Stretch and unloading reflexes are mediated by combined actions of several autogenetic neural pathways. "Autogenetic" means that the stimulus excites receptors located in the same muscle that is the target of the reflex response. The most important of these muscle receptors are the primary and secondary endings in muscle spindles, sensitive to length change, and the Golgi tendon organs, sensitive to contractile force. The autogenetic circuits appear to function as servoregulatory loops that convey continuously graded amounts of excitation and inhibition to the large (alpha) skeletomo-

0066-4278/79/0301-0099$01.00

tor neurons. Small (gamma) fusimotor neurons innervate the contractile poles of muscle spindles and function to modulate spindle-receptor discharge. The term *motor servo* (29) will be used to refer to this entire control system, summarized by the block diagram in Figure 1.

Prior to a study by Matthews (41, 42) in 1969 it was widely assumed that secondary endings belong to the mixed population of "flexor reflex afferents," so called because their activation provokes the flexor reflex pattern —excitation of flexor motoneurons and inhibition of extensor motoneurons. This should interfere with extensor stretch reflexes while reinforcing flexor ones, which is difficult to reconcile with the fact that stretch reflexes in the decerebrate preparation are strong in extensor muscles and weak in flexors. Matthews' results (obtained with a vibratory technique that occludes stretch responses of primary endings) indicated that some category of muscle stretch receptor other than the primary ending provides important excitation to extensor muscles, and he argued forcefully that it must be the secondary ending. The classical finding that inhibition results when secondary spindle afferents are activated electrically was attributed to other afferents inadvertently excited by the same stimuli, perhaps group II nociceptors. Subsequent studies by other investigators provided both support

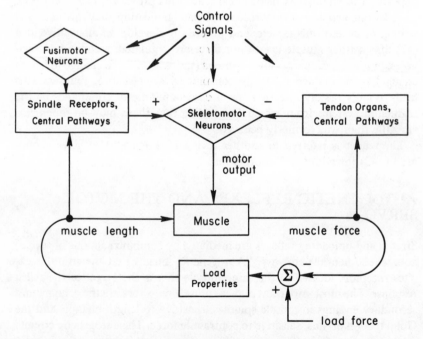

Figure 1   Basic organizational plan of the motor servo.

for and opposition to Matthew's conclusion. The reader may consult two recent studies (34, 54) that support excitation by secondaries and also summarize other studies. The conclusion that the discharge of both primary and secondary endings contributes excitation now seems firmly established, in the opinion of this author. However, the classical inhibitory actions evoked by electrical stimulation, and in some cases by stretch, require further explanation (cf 52).

The pathways from primary and secondary endings are treated commonly in Figure 1, since both receptors are sensitive to muscle length and both provoke reflex excitation. However, primary endings show an additional sensitivity to the dynamic phase of length change, called dynamic responsiveness, and they also show a much-enhanced sensitivity to small changes in muscle length (42). Recent studies indicate that both of these special response features of primary endings derive from a common nonlinear property, which is a decreasing sensitivity to length change that occurs whenever the muscle is stretched beyond a certain point (25). Prior to this study it usually had been assumed that the dynamic response is a velocity response that provides velocity feedback. In fact, the dependence on velocity is both weak and highly nonlinear (53), and the role of the dynamic component of feedback must be reevaluated (cf 30, 51).

Two features omitted from the block diagram of the motor servo may have to be added to it in the future. One concerns the motor fibers that send branches to both the main muscle and to spindles, referred to as skeletofusimotor (or beta) fibers. There is now increasing evidence of the importance of skeletofusimotor innervation in mammals as well as lower vertebrates (24). The other omission concerns feedback to fusimotor neurons, the existence of which has been demonstrated in several laboratories (4, 10, 17, 32). What remains unclear at present is the specific modality and actual importance of these projections. The incorporation of both of these features into theories of muscle control has been considered elsewhere (28). Neither modification alters the theoretical conclusion drawn in the next section.

STRUCTURAL ANALYSIS OF THE MOTOR SERVO

The motor servo comprises three closed circuits (Figure 1), two neural feedback pathways, and one circuit representing the mechanical interaction between a muscle and its load. One of the feedback pathways, that from spindle receptors, conveys information concerning muscle length, and it follows that this loop will act to keep muscle length constant. The other feedback pathway, that from tendon organs, conveys information concerning muscle force, and it acts to keep force constant.

In general, it is physically impossible to maintain both muscle length and force constant when external loads vary; in this situation the action of the two feedback loops will oppose each other. For example, an increased load force will lengthen the muscle and cause muscular force to increase as the muscle is stretched out on its length-tension curve. The increased length will lead to excitation of motoneurons, whereas the increased force will lead to inhibition. It follows that the net regulatory action conveyed by skeletomotor output will depend on some relationship between force change and length change and on the strength of the feedback from muscle spindles and tendon organs. A simple mathematical derivation (47) demonstrates that the change in skeletomotor output, the error signal of the motor servo, should be proportional to the difference between a *regulated stiffness* and the actual stiffness provided by the mechanical properties of the muscle, where stiffness has the units of force change divided by length change. The regulated stiffness is determined by the ratio of the gain of length to force feedback.

It follows that the combination of spindle receptor and tendon organ feedback will tend to maintain the stiffness of the neuromuscular apparatus at some regulated level. If this level is high, due to a high gain of length feedback and a low gain of force feedback, one could simply forget about force feedback and treat muscle length as the regulated variable of the system. However, if the regulated level of stiffness is intermediate in value, i.e. not appreciably different from the average stiffness arising from muscle mechanical properties in the absence of reflex actions, one would conclude that stiffness, or its inverse, compliance, is the regulated property of the motor servo.

EVIDENCE FAVORING STIFFNESS, RATHER THAN MUSCLE LENGTH, AS THE REGULATED PROPERTY OF THE MOTOR SERVO

For the past several decades most investigators have assumed, either explicitly or implicitly, that the regulated property of the stretch reflex is muscle length, or one of its derivatives such as velocity. The contemporary notion that the stretch reflex is a mechanism for load compensation derives directly from this assumption, since effective length (or velocity) regulation would prevent load changes from appreciably affecting movements or postures.

Recently several authors have reported that the load compensating capabilities of the stretch reflex system are rather modest. In particular, Vallbo (58) has shown, with a calculation based on spindle responses in human subjects during voluntarily graded contractions, that the stiffness of the motor servo is rather low. Bizzi, Dev, Morasso & Polit (7) compared load compensation before and after dorsal rhizotomy and found only relatively small differences. Rack (50) has emphasized that muscle mechanical properties can contribute an appreciable amount of stiffness without the assistance of a reflex, and it has been shown that this muscular stiffness may not differ substantially from the stiffness of an intact decerebrate stretch reflex, at least in some situations (22, 49).

If the assumption that muscle length is the regulated property of the motor servo were correct, this evidence would indicate that the system is rather ineffective and indeed of minor importance in normal motor control. Another interpretation is that the motor servo is actually designed to regulate stiffness. All of the findings just discussed are compatible with the idea of stiffness regulation, but they provide no direct test of it. Two recent studies, one in the decerebrate cat (47) and the other in normal humans (8), were designed specifically to test the hypothesis of stiffness regulation and to assess its efficacy.

The rationale for these experiments is that the inherent mechanical stiffness of a muscle varies, depending on the amplitude and the direction of length change (33, 47). Thus, if the function of the motor servo is to regulate stiffness, reflex action should vary to maintain stiffness approximately constant. In the animal experiments reflex action was assessed mechanically, as the difference between a net change in reflex force and the force change attributable to the purely mechanical response of the muscle. In the human experiments reflex action was assessed more indirectly, by the changes in electromyographic (EMG) activity. In both cases, it was found that reflex action is greater during muscle stretch than it is during release, and this difference effectively compensates for an opposite asymmetry in the mechanical response of the unregulated muscle. In the cat experiments the dependence of stiffness on the amplitude of length change was also studied. Muscular stiffness was shown to vary widely and in some instances actually to assume negative values. Although the stiffness of the motor servo was not absolutely constant, the variations were small in comparison with those of the unregulated muscle, which indicated that the regulation of stiffness was quite effective.

Although the results obtained with human subjects were qualitatively similar to those obtained in the decerebrate cat, there were two potentially important differences. Changes in the state of a decerebrate preparation were sometimes accompanied by alterations in reflex stiffness, even when it was assessed at the same initial length and force (46). These changes must be attributed to extrinsic neural signals that alter gain in the motoservo pathways, and it is notable that such changes could not be demonstrated in the experiments with normal human subjects. The second difference was that the human reflex actions in response to unloading were often in a direction that assisted rather than opposed length change. This observation provides strong evidence against the hypothesis for length regulation, suggests a higher gain of tendon organ feedback in intact man than in decerebrate cat (8), and indicates that the regulated stiffness may be more compliant than the inherent stiffness of the muscle under some circumstances.

The results just described test the efficacy of stiffness regulation when the amplitude and direction of length change are varied. Another test of the theory would be to explore differences in initial force, since muscular stiffness is known to increase in approximate proportion with initial force (47) and effective servo action would be expected to diminish this dependence.

Matthews (39, 40) studied the relation between muscle force and length under a wide range of conditions by applying stretch at a low and constant velocity to the soleus muscle of the decerebrate cat. He showed that the stiffness (the slope of the stretch reflex curves) was low near the threshold of the reflex, increased as the stretch progressed, and then tended to reach a constant value as indicated by a linear relationship between muscle force and length. The dependence of stiffness on initial force has also been assessed from incremental responses to length change, with similar results (31). The evidence from both of these studies suggests that the stiffness of the motor servo remains relatively constant whenever the initial force exceeds approximately 15% of its maximal value, and decreases progressively with lower forces. The latter authors suggested that the more appreciable variation at low initial forces might be accentuated by the presence of a "recruitment nonlinearity," which was postulated to arise from the recruitment of motor units in the order small to large [the size principle (26)]. This factor would compound with the dependence of muscular stiffness on initial force mentioned earlier. The fact that the stiffness of the motor servo depends so little on initial force (in the range 15–100% of maximum) is good evidence in support of stiffness regulation.

The relation of stiffness to initial force appears to be similar in humans to that demonstrated in the decerebrate cat, although most of the available measurements were made in the range of low initial forces where stiffness varies most (5, 15, 37).

SIMPLIFIED MODELS OF THE MOTOR SERVO

I now consider how these results relate to more general problems of motor control. Here it is useful to have a summary model of the motor servo that accounts for its net responses to mechanical disturbances and to control signals that may be sent to it from other regions of the central nervous system.

Figure 2 shows two alternative models. The simple mechanical analog on the left represents the regulatory actions of the motor servo by a spring of constant stiffness. The solid curve on the right shows an alternative model, expressed as a graph of muscle force versus muscle length.

There are only two basic modes by which higher motor processes might control the motor servo. One involves changing the reference, or set point of the servo, which is analogous to cranking the rack and pinion in Figure 2, or to the change in *threshold length* (dashed curve on the right). The other involves changing the gain (or responsiveness) of the servoregulatory loops, and this has an effect analogous to modifying the properties of the spring, either changing the spring constant or altering the damping of the system. The dotted curve in Figure 2 illustrates a decrease in stiffness that would occur if the gain of force feedback were increased.

CONTROL OF THE MOTOR SERVO BY HIGHER MOTOR PROCESSES

Pathways descending from the brain to the spinal cord have direct actions on alpha and gamma motoneurons, as well as actions upon interneurons in reflex pathways and upon presynaptic terminals (35). It is sometimes presumed that the interneuronal and presynaptic actions are particularly important in controlling reflex responsiveness and that movements are controlled instead by direct actions on motoneurons. Certainly, there is now good evidence that movement commands are sent to both skeletomotor and fusimotor neurons (21); it is also clear that reflex transmission, as tested by

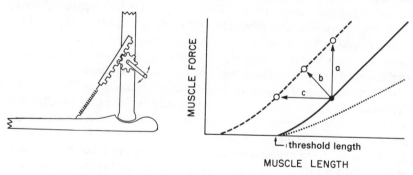

Figure 2 Two summary models of the motor servo. (*left*) Simple mechanical analog showing the regulatory actions of the motor servo as a spring of constant stiffness. A more accurate model would include a parallel element for damping and would replace the linear spring by a slightly nonlinear one. (*right*) The alternative, expressed as a graph of muscle force versus muscle length (solid curve), again neglects damping but shows the observed nonlinearity of the stretch reflex by the curvature of the relationship. Stiffness, shown by the slope of the curve, increases as the initial force increases.

electrophysiological techniques, can be altered by descending activity. However, changes in reflex transmission only demonstrate the anatomical convergence of descending and reflex pathways; the normal actions of a convergent circuit might be ones that change the reference of the motor servo by adding to an ongoing input from the periphery (a change in threshold length), rather than ones that alter the gain of the reflex pathway (a change in stiffness). This question can only be answered by studies that employ natural stimuli and as much as possible preserve normal activity states of the spinal cord. The decerebrate cat preparation, during ongoing reflex activity, approximates these requirements, but the best tests are made in intact animal and human subjects.

Studies in decerebrate animals in which electrical stimulation mimics motor commands show that these sources of excitatory and inhibitory input simply bias the threshold of the stretch reflex (the alteration in threshold length shown by the dashed curve in Figure 2) without appreciably altering its slope (16, 40). In terms of the analog of the motor servo (Figure 2), these actions crank the rack and pinion without altering stiffness. Of course, there is no guarantee that the electrical stimuli used in these studies are actually analogous to normal motor commands.

In experiments with human subjects it is easy to provoke authentic motor commands by asking the subject to move to a new position, but it is more difficult to ascertain that responses to mechanical disturbances applied at that new position are, in fact, purely reflexive. Asatryan and Fel'dman (5) introduced the procedure of instructing their subjects not to intervene voluntarily as a means for obtaining responses to mechanical disturbances that were presumed to be reflexive. Fairly conclusive evidence that this can be accomplished has been given recently by Crago, Houk & Hasan (8).

Asatryan and Fel'dman (5) showed that when the subject is asked to move to a new initial position the relations between elbow moment and angle, described in an earlier section, are shifted along the abscissa of the torque versus angle graph with little additional change in the relation. Fel'dman (15) also demonstrated by mechanical analysis that this shift was accounted for by assuming that the thresholds of the stretch reflexes of the muscles acting about the elbow were biased in the manner discussed above. The effects of altered loads on head movements described recently by Bizzi, Polit & Morasso (6) are also well accounted for on this basis. Thus, the available evidence indicates that motor commands alter threshold length, an effect analogous to cranking the rack and pinion of the motoservo analog.

One concludes that descending motor commands control neither muscle forces nor movements but rather the threshold length of the spring that characterizes the properties of the motor servo (the threshold of the stretch reflex). A controlled change in threshold length leads to movement if (or when) the mechanical load yields; if the load is isometric, the same motor command controls the force of contraction. This effect of load on the peripheral outcome of a given central motor command is illustrated in Figure 2 by the three trajectories. The one labeled *a* corresponds to pulling on an immovable object, *b* to pulling on a spring, and *c* to pulling against a constant force load. The absence of load compensation is illustrated by the fact that the length change resulting from the same motor command differs so markedly in the three cases.

ABSENCE OF EVIDENCE FOR THE CONTROL OF MOTOSERVO GAIN

Other types of neural control signals sent by central motor processes might operate by controlling the gain of the reflex loops, which would alter the stiffness that is then regulated by motoservo action. This mode of control could form the efferent mechanism of an adaptive control process in the brain that adjusts the mechanical impedance of the neuromuscular apparatus to match the requirements of the task at hand. A rigid control of muscle length might be desirable in many tasks, while a more compliant system would improve the suspension of the body during locomotion over rough terrain (cf 28, 36). Thus, there is reason enough to expect gain control, and, indeed, numerous authors have suggested that it occurs.

Most of the available studies that are thought to demonstrate gain control suffer from technical limitations. Unnatural stimuli and abnormal spinal states have already been mentioned. A second problem is that nonlinearities in the properties of motoservo components can be confused with changes in gain thought to be controlled by a central adaptive mechanism. Although gain variations having this origin may subserve some useful function [e.g. compensation for fatigue, as suggested in (37)], they are of no direct concern to central motor processes, since they cannot be controlled in any independent fashion but occur in an obligatory manner along with motor commands that control movements. The possibility that observed changes in responsiveness result from motoservo nonlinearities is minimized if initial length, force, and motoneuronal output are held constant while testing for a gain change of central origin.

A third problem (a special case of the second) arises if the relevant motoneuronal pools are biased below the threshold for motor output, which happens whenever a limb is initially unloaded. The experimenter then loses control over the initial excitability of the motoneurons. Subthreshold changes in excitability produce apparent changes in reflex responsiveness, but these changes can be due either to motor commands that do not reach threshold or to control signals that actually change gain. While changes in responsiveness under passive conditions (e.g. 12, 14) cannot be taken as evidence for gain control, they may contribute to the preparedness of a subject for a transition from an inactive to an active state.

A fourth and major problem concerns the admixture of reaction-time movements with motoservo responses. The former are not servoregulatory actions, yet their presence in one response and absence in another might be interpreted (falsely) as the result of a change in motoservo gain. Since the movements are delayed by a reaction time, many authors have simply restricted their analysis to events occurring at times prior to the supposed onset of a reaction. The two disadvantages of this approach are that it neglects later phases of reflex response and it relies heavily on a valid measure of the minimal reaction time. This measure is difficult to obtain since reaction times depend upon several parameters, such as the intensity and modality of the stimulus, the number of choices in the task, and the degree of attention and practice (59). The usual procedure in stretch-reflex studies has been to measure a reaction time to stimuli other than muscle stretch, or to small tendon taps that provoke no appreciable reflex, and to assume that the latency of a reaction in response to a large stretch would be no shorter (e.g. 23, 37, 43). Unfortunately this is not true.

An alternative procedure has been proposed by Evarts & Granit (12), who suggested that the time at which EMG activity recommences after initially being silenced by an unloading reflex is indicative of the onset of a reaction-time movement ("intended movement" in their terminology). They reported a latency as brief as 70 msec. A potential problem with this method is that an enhancement of EMG activity during unloading might also be explained on the basis of a segmental reflex action (3, 8). Furthermore, the method does not provide a means for studying later (beyond 70 msec) phases of reflex response.

In addition to a delayed onset, reaction-time movements have several special properties useful in distinguishing them from motoservo actions (8). For example, the latency of a reaction becomes longer and more variable when the subject is required to choose between alternative responses, as contrasted with performance in a simple reaction-time task. Also, subjects in a choice-reaction task will occasionally make errors; if the task is appropriately designed, the errors will appear as responses of opposite direction, which are easily detected in movement traces.

Very few studies of adaptive responsiveness meet all of the objections raised in this section; if only those that do are considered (5, 8), one finds no evidence at present that demonstrates an ability of the central nervous system to control the gain of the motor servo in an adaptive manner. This result is surprising since neural mechanisms for gain change are available, as evidenced by authentic alterations that have been observed in reduced animal preparations (46, 52) and that may occur also in human pathology.

While it is premature to conclude that there are no situations in which normal humans adaptively alter the gain of their motoservo loops, the available evidence does suggest that gain change is not a usual mode of control. Ordinarily the motor servo operates in a rather stereotypic manner when it is brought to action by a central motor command.

EVIDENCE CONCERNING SUPRASPINAL SERVOREGULATORY LOOPS

The recent hypothesis that a supraspinal servo loop is largely responsible for the stretch reflex can be traced to Hammond's (23) observations that the first major temporal component of EMG response to an abrupt stretch has a latency of 50–60 msec and that its amplitude can be influenced by prior instructions. Hammond suggested that this latency is too long to represent segmental reflex action and too short to represent a reaction-time movement. He explained both the latency and the modifiability by proposing a long servo loop that ascends to the brain where a modification of the gain of reflex transmission was supposed to occur. This interpretation of the so-called "long-loop reflex" has been accepted by several subsequent investigators. For example, the same arguments led Phillips (48) to propose that a pathway from primary spindle receptors to cortical area 3a constitutes the afferent limb of a *transcortical servo loop* that was supposed to provide negative feedback compensation for changes in load. Evarts (11) supported Phillips' proposal in reporting that single pyramidal tract neurons in behaving primates responded at short latency to load perturbations, and, later, that the responses of these neurons are subject to the influence of 'set' (13).

We now know that reaction times can be as short as 50–60 msec in man (cf 29) and even shorter in trained cats (19). The modifiable aspect of stretch response seems to be accounted for by the versatility of the reaction-time movements superimposed upon motoservo actions (8, 29). It is also well known that the segmental reflex pathways that participate in the operations of the motor servo are both monosynaptic and polysynaptic, and that transmission through these pathways, particularly when natural stimuli are employed, will not necessarily be as rapid as conduction through the monosynaptic pathway (42).

A second influential observation by Hammond (23) indicated that the monosynaptic component of EMG response is not followed by a large force response. Because of this, and because it was assumed that the later component at 50 msec was unrelated to spinal mechanisms, Hammond suggested that the segmental stretch reflex might be unimportant in man, perhaps being replaced by the supraspinal servo loop with adjustable gain mentioned earlier. This proposal, reinforced by Phillips (48) and by Melvill, Jones & Watt (43), has been difficult to reconcile with the large body of literature illustrating the importance of the segmental mechanisms (42). One should consider first that the size of the stretch reflex response is not an adequate measure of motoservo action, since the response to a load change reflects inhibitory as well as excitatory components. Also, the segmental reflex response in man undoubtedly continues beyond the time of the monosynaptic peak, which only signals its onset.

Some arguments in support of a supraspinal servo loop are independent of the previous criticisms. Evarts (11) pointed out that the initial perturbation response of some pyramidal tract neurons occurs sufficiently early to postulate that it is conducted to spinal motoneurons in advance of the signals that initiate reaction-time movements. This short-duration phase of discharge is sensitive to the direction of the perturbation, whereas a later, longer-lasting phase is sensitive to the direction of the intended movement (14). There is also evidence in support of the assumption that the perturbation-sensitive neurons project to the relevant spinal motoneurons (45). While this and other evidence is consistent with the hypothesis that a transcortical servo loop contributes to motoservo action, the efficacy of the proposed loop has not been demonstrated, nor has it been compared with the efficacy of segmental pathways.

Marsden, Merton & Morton (38) reported that an early peak in the EMG response to stretch has longer latencies in muscles of the lower limb than in those of the upper limb. They pointed out that this observation is consistent with a supraspinal pathway; however, there are numerous problems associated with the interpretation of EMG peaks. Ghez & Shinoda (18) showed recently that the peaks of longer latency formerly attributed to supraspinal pathways are, in fact, present also in spinalized cats.

Another argument is based on the effects of lesions and cooling of supraspinal structures on stretch reflex function (e.g. 1, 56, 57). The difficulty is that changes in motoservo actions can be interpreted in two different ways. They may indicate interference with supraspinal loops or they may reflect a depression or enhancement of purely segmental mechanisms caused by a removal of the normal tonic activity in descending pathways. The latter interpretation is reinforced by the observations that normal stretch reflexes, which disappear after cord transection, are observed in chronic spinal animals and in acute preparations after the administration of 5-HTP or L-DOPA (2, 20). These drugs are known to reverse the generalized depression of spinal reflex transmission caused by interruption of descending pathways.

In an earlier section I compared motoservo actions in decerebrate animals (which appear not to differ from those in spinal animals as mentioned above) with those in normal subjects, and concluded that there is a great deal of similarity between the two. The only major difference is that human motoservo action sometimes assists length change, whereas this has not been observed in the decerebrate cat preparation. A likely explanation of this difference is that inhibitory feedback from Golgi tendon organs has a higher gain in intact man than in the decerebrate cat (8). While the high gain might be attributed to an *inhibitory* supraspinal loop, a more parsimonious explanation is that the Ib segmental pathway is relatively depressed in the decerebrate, as contrasted with intact animals; moreover, there is independent evidence favoring this interpretation (9, 27, 31).

In summary, it appears likely that the motor servo is in large part a segmental reflex mechanism. If this reflex system does employ supraspinal loops, it is not clear what they add to the servoregulatory actions known to be mediated by segmental pathways. Formerly it was believed that improved load compensation and adaptive responsiveness might be added, but it now seems clear that these features result from reaction-time responses rather than from the servoregulatory actions of the stretch reflex.

CONCLUSIONS

Stretch and unloading reflexes are controlled by the combined actions of several autogenetic reflex pathways, which are part of a negative feedback system referred to as the *motor servo.* This fundamental skeletomotor reflex system is organized segmentally within the spinal cord; recent claims that the segmental system is dominated by supraspinal servo loops are found to be weak when evaluated critically.

The older view that this system functions to regulate muscle length and to provide load compensation is not supported by recent experimental studies, nor does it have a sound theoretical basis. Length feedback from muscle spindles when combined with force feedback from tendon organs should give rise to *stiffness regulation,* and experimental studies have demonstrated that motoservo actions are, in fact, effective in compensating for known variations in the inherent mechanical stiffness of skeletal muscle.

Descending motor commands could act to shift the *threshold length* of the motor servo (i.e. the threshold of the stretch reflex), and they could act also to modify the stiffness regulated by length and force feedback (an adaptive type of control that requires a change in gain of the feedback pathways). Current experimental evidence clearly supports the former action, while there is no good evidence that the latter mode of control is actually used by normal intact subjects. However, gain changes probably do occur in pathology.

These results provide an answer to the often-posed question concerning which mechanical variable, muscle length or force, or some derivative of these variables, is actually controlled by descending motor commands. The answer appears to be none of these individually, since a controlled change in threshold length acts to shift the entire relationship between length and force that is then regulated locally by length and force feedback. The actual values of length and force resulting from a central motor command depend on the mechanical load to which the muscle is attached.

One advantage of stiffness regulation is that it provides a spring-like interface between the body and its mechanical environment. The compliance of this interface probably serves to absorb the impacts of abrupt changes in load, thus attenuating their transmission to the body and head. For example, in the standing posture with bent knees, stiffness regulation probably insures a good suspension system for the body.

The apparent absence of an adaptive control of stiffness might be viewed as a disadvantage, since flexibility is clearly sacrificed. On the other hand, the relative constancy of motoservo properties should simplify the task of higher motor control processes that must generate appropriate motor commands. Such commands must be adjusted to account for the properties of the system they control, and, if these properties are constant, the adjustments can be made routine.

Literature Cited

1. Adam, J., Marsden, C. D., Merton, P. A., Morton, H. B. 1975. The effect of lesions in the internal capsule and the sensorimotor cortex on servo action in the human thumb. *J. Physiol. London* 254:27P
2. Ahlman, H., Grillner, S., Udo, M. 1971. The effect of 5-HTP on the static fusimotor activity and the tonic stretch reflex of an extensor muscle. *Brain Res.* 27:393–96
3. Alston, W., Angel, R. W., Fink, F. S., Hoffman, W. W. 1967. Motor activity following the silent period in human muscle. *J. Physiol. London* 190:189–202
4. Appelberg, B., Johansson, H., Kalistratov, G. 1977. The influence of Group II muscle afferents and low threshold skin afferents on dynamic fusimotor neurons to the triceps surae of the cat. *Brain Res.* 132:153–58
5. Asatryan, D. G., Fel'dman, A. G. 1965. Functional tuning of the nervous system with control of movement or maintenance of posture-I. Mechanographic analysis of the work of the joint on execution of a postural task. *Biophysics* 10:925–35
6. Bizzi, E., Polit, A., Morasso, P. 1976. Mechanisms underlying achievement of final head position. *J. Neurophysiol.* 39:435–44

7. Bizzi, E., Dev, P., Morasso, P., Polit, A. 1978. Effect of load disturbances during centrally initiated movements. *J. Neurophysiol.* 41:542–57
8. Crago, P. E., Houk, J. C., Hasan, Z. 1976. Regulatory actions of the human stretch reflex. *J. Neurophysiol.* 39:925–35
9. Eccles, R. M., Lundberg, A. 1959. Supraspinal control of interneurons mediating spinal reflexes. *J. Physiol. London* 147:565–84
10. Ellaway, P. H., Trott, J. R. 1976. Reflex connections from muscle stretch receptors to their own fusimotor neurons. *Progr. Brain Res.* 44:113–21
11. Evarts, E. V. 1973. Motor cortex reflexes associated with learned movements. *Science* 179:501–3
12. Evarts, E. V., Granit, R. 1976. Relations of reflexes and intended movements. *Progr. Brain Res.* 44:1–14
13. Evarts, E. V., Tanji, J. 1974. Gating of motor cortex reflexes by prior instruction. *Brain Res.* 71:479–94
14. Evarts, E. V., Tanji, J. 1976. Reflex and intended responses in motor pyramidal tract neurons of monkey. *J. Neurophysiol.* 39:1069–80
15. Fel'dman, A. G. 1966. Functional tuning of the nervous system with control of movement or maintenance of a

steady posture. II. Controllable parameters of the muscle. *Biophysics* 11:565–78

16. Fel'dman, A. G., Orlovsky, G. N. 1972. The influence of different descending systems on the tonic stretch reflex in the cat. *Exp. Neurol.* 37:481–94

17. Fromm, C., Haase, J., Noth, J. 1974. Length dependent autogenetic inhibition of extensor gamma motoneurons in the decerebrate cat. *Pfluegers Arch.* 346:251–62

18. Ghez, C., Shinoda, Y. 1978. Spinal mechanisms of the functional stretch reflex. *Brain Res.* 32:55–68

19. Ghez, C., Vicario, D. 1978. The control of rapid limb movement in the cat. I. Response latency. *Brain Res.* 33: 173–89

20. Goodwin, G. M., McGrath, G. J., Matthews, P. B. C. 1973. The tonic vibration reflex seen in the acute spinal cat after treatment with DOPA. *Brain Res.* 49:463–66

21. Granit, R. 1975. The functional role of the muscle spindles—facts and hypotheses. *Brain* 98:531–56

22. Grillner, S. 1972. A role for muscular stiffness in meeting the changing postural and locomotor requirements for force development by the ankle extensors. *Acta Physiol. Scand.* 86:92–108

23. Hammond, P. H. 1960. An experimental study of servo action in human muscular control. In *Proc III Int. Congr. Med. Electron.*, pp. 190–99. London: Inst. Electr. Eng.

24. Harker, D. W., Jami, L., Laporte, Y., Petit, J. 1977. Fast-conduction skeletofusimotor axons supplying intrafusal chain fibers in the cat peroneus tertius muscle. *J. Neurophysiol.* 40:791–99

25. Hasan, Z., Houk, J. C. 1975. The transition in the sensitivity of spindle receptors that occurs when the muscle is stretched more than a fraction of a millimeter. *J. Neurophysiol.* 38:673–89

26. Henneman, E., Somjen, G., Carpenter, D. O. 1965. Functional significance of cell size in spinal motoneurons. *J. Neurophysiol.* 28:599–620

27. Hongo, T., Jankowska, E., Lundberg, A. 1969. The rubrospinal tract. II. Facilitation of interneuronal-transmission in reflex paths to motoneurons. *Exp. Brain Res.* 7:365–91

28. Houk, J. C. 1972. The phylogeny of muscular control configurations. In *Biocybernetics*, ed. H. Drischel, P. Dettmar, 4:125–44. Jena: Fisher

29. Houk, J. C. 1978. Participation of reflex mechanisms and reaction-time processes in the compensatory adjustments to mechanical disturbances. *Progr. Clin. Neurophysiol.* 4:193–215

30. Houk, J. C., Rymer, W. Z., Crago, P. E. 1977. Complex velocity dependence of the electromyographic component of the stretch reflex. *Proc. XXVIII Int. Congr. Physiol. Sci., Paris.* (Abstr. #981)

31. Houk, J. C., Singer, J. J., Goldman, M. R. 1970. An evaluation of length and force feedback to soleus muscles of decerebrate cats. *J. Neurophysiol.* 33: 784–811

32. Hunt, C. C. 1951. The reflex activity of mammalian small-nerve fibres. *J. Physiol. London* 115:456–69

33. Joyce, C. G., Rack, P. M. H., Westbury, D. F. 1969. The mechanical properties of cat soleus muscle during controlled lengthening and shortening movements. *J. Physiol. London* 204:461–74

34. Kanda, K., Rymer, W. Z. 1977. An estimate of the secondary spindle receptor afferent contribution to the stretch reflex in extensor muscle of the decerebrate cat. *J. Physiol. London* 264:63–87

35. Lundberg, A. 1967. The supraspinal control of transmission in spinal reflex pathways. *Electroencephalogr. Clin. Neurophysiol. Suppl.* 25:35–46

36. Lundberg, A. 1969. Reflex control of stepping. *Nasen Mem. Lect., V.*, pp. 1–42. Oslo: Universitetsforlaget

37. Marsden, C. D., Merton, P. A., Morton, H. B. 1976. Servo action in the human thumb. *J. Physiol. London* 257:1–44

38. Marsden, C. D., Merton, P. A., Morton, H. B. 1976. Stretch reflexes and servo actions in a variety of human muscles. *J. Physiol. London* 259:531–60

39. Matthews, P. B. C. 1959. The dependence of tension upon extension in the stretch reflex of the soleus muscle of the decerebrate cat. *J. Physiol. London* 147:521–46

40. Matthews, P. B. C. 1959. A study of certain factors influencing the stretch reflex of the decerebrate cat. *J. Physiol. London* 147:547–64

41. Matthews, P. B. C. 1969. Evidence that the secondary as well as the primary endings of the muscle spindles may be responsible for the tonic stretch reflex of the decerebrate cat. *J. Physiol. London* 204:365–93

42. Matthews, P. B. C. 1972. *Mammalian Muscle Receptors and Their Central Actions.* Baltimore: Williams and Wilkins.

43. Melvill Jones, G., Watt, D. G. D. 1971.

Observations on the control of stepping and hopping movements in man. *J. Physiol. London* 291:709–27

44. Merton, P. A. 1953. Speculations on the servo control of movement. *The Spinal Cord,* pp. 183–98. Boston: Little, Brown

45. Murphy, J. T., Wong, Y. C., Kwan, H. C. 1975. Afferent-efferent linkages in motor cortex for single forelimb muscles. *J. Neurophysiol.* 38:990–1014

46. Nichols, T. R. 1974. *Soleus muscle stiffness and its reflex control.* Ph.D. thesis, Harvard University, Cambridge, Mass.

47. Nichols, T. R., Houk, J. C. 1976. The improvement in linearity and the regulation of stiffness that results from the actions of the stretch reflex. *J. Neurophysiol.* 39:119–42

48. Phillips, C. G. 1969. Motor apparatus of the baboon's hand. *Proc. R. Soc. London Ser. B* 173:141–74

49. Pompeiano, O. 1960. Alpha types of "release" studied in tension-extension diagrams from cat's forelimb triceps muscle. *Arch. Ital. Biol.* 98:92–117

50. Rack, P. M. H. 1970. The significance of mechanical properties of muscle in the reflex control of posture. In *Excitatory Synaptic Mechanisms,* ed. P. Andersen, J. K. S. Jansen, pp. 317–21. Oslo: Universitetsforlaget

51. Rymer, W. Z., Houk, J. C., Crago, P. E. 1976. Vibratory occlusion of compensation for muscle yielding. *Neurosci. Abstr.* #758

52. Rymer, W. Z., Houk, J. C., Crago, P. E.

1977. Mechanisms of the clasp-knife reflex. *Neurosci. Abstr.* #887

53. Rymer, W. Z., Houk, J. C., Crago, P. E. 1977. The relation between dynamic response and velocity sensitivity for muscle spindle receptors. *Proc. XXVIII Int. Congr. Physiol. Sci., Paris.* (Abstr. #1922)

54. Stauffer, E. K., Watt, D. G. D., Taylor, A., Reinking, R. M., Stuart, D. B. 1976. Analysis of muscle receptor connections by spike-triggered averaging. 2. Spindle group II afferents. *J. Neurophysiol.* 39:1393–1402

55. Stein, R. B. 1974. Peripheral control of movement. *Physiol. Rev.* 54:215–43

56. Tatton, W. G., Forner, S. D., Gerstein, G. L., Chambers, W. W., Liu, C. N. 1975. The effect of postcentral cortical lesions on motor responses to sudden upper limb displacement in monkeys. *Brain Res.* 96:108–13

57. Terzuolo, C. A., Viviani, P. 1974. Movements' parameters and EMG activities during some simple motor tasks in normal subjects and cerebellar patients. In *Cerebellum, Epilepsy and Behavior,* ed. I. Cooper, M. Riklan, R. S. Snider, pp. 173–215. London: Pergamon

58. Vallbo, A. B. 1974. Human muscle spindle discharge during isometric voluntary contractions. Amplitude relations between spindle frequency and torque. *Acta Physiol. Scand.* 90:319–36

59. Welford, A. T. 1968. *Fundamentals of Skill.* London: Methuen. pp. 27–104

Ann. Rev. Physiol. 1979. 41:115–26

SPINAL INTERNEURONS   ♦1209

P. G. Kostyuk and D. A. Vasilenko

A. A. Bogomoletz Institute of Physiology, Academy of Sciences of the
Ukrainian SSR, Kiev, USSR

The present survey does not claim to be a complete description of the
organization of all spinal interneuronal populations and their functions. Of
primary interest here are those interneuronal groups whose structural and
functional organization can at present be rather completely identified, as
well as the participation of these populations in control and coordination
of some types of motor activity.

GENERAL PROBLEMS

Investigation of the activities of spinal interneurons (IN) began almost
immediately after microelectrode recordings were obtained from motoneurones (MN) (18, 21). In contrast to MN, the IN could not be identified by
antidromic excitation from their axons, and therefore the patterns of responses to volleys arriving through different primary afferents were chosen
for their functional differentiation. Eccles, Eccles & Lundberg (11) found
that group I and II muscle and low-threshold cutaneous afferents monosynaptically excite separate groups of IN. This feature formed the basis for
the whole subsequent analysis of the systemic organization of the spinal
interneuronal apparatus.

Besides the IN monosynaptically connected to low-threshold muscle and
cutaneous afferents, a large group of cells was found that received synaptic
inputs only from high-threshold muscle, skin and joint afferents (so-called
flexor reflex afferents, FRA) (22). These afferents can also produce EPSP
and/or IPSP in the IN of the former groups, but only polysynaptically.
Therefore the classification of IN according to their afferent inputs was
found to be justified only in respect to *monosynaptic* responses.

Wall (80) was the first to show that IN that are connected to cutaneous
touch receptors form a layer in the central part of the dorsal horn; the cells

115

0066-4278/79/0301-0115$01.00

in this region do not respond to muscle stretch. IN responding to stretch are also located in a layer-like but more ventral pool. This topographic separation [which corresponds to the data about spatial distribution of focal potentials evoked by the stimulation of different primary afferents (12)] was found to correspond quite well in the lumbar region to the laminar organization of the spinal gray matter according to Rexed (62). Later the same correspondence was demonstrated for the thoracic region (20). The topographic organization of the interneuronal system may be briefly summarized as follows:

Low-threshold cutaneous afferents from touch receptors activate (monosynaptically) the IN in the lamina IV and (polysynaptically) the neurons in the lamina V. High-threshold afferents excite IN located in the lamina V monosynaptically, and units of the lamina IV polysynaptically. Among the neurons in the lamina IV one can differentiate several subgroups according to the pattern of polysynaptic effects from high-threshold afferents. Low-threshold muscle afferents activate the IN in the lamina VI monosynaptically.

This relatively regular laminar organization becomes less pronounced in more ventral parts of the gray matter. Laminae VII and VIII contain IN with different input characteristics. In more dorsal parts (laminae II and III, which correspond to the gelatinous substance) it was not possible to determine such characteristics precisely because of the extreme difficulty of microelectrode recording; very small cells are packed here in a dense longitudinal bundle. Only recently have data been obtained (9) about the features of synaptic activation of identified neurons in these layers. (9). The same can be said about neurons of the marginal zone (lamina I).

Somewhat later the connections of·the spinal IN to the main descending pathways were analyzed in a similar way. It was possible to demonstrate a certain spatial separation of interneuronal populations activated monosynaptically from different cerebrospinal systems. The IN connected to cortico- and rubrospinal pathways are concentrated in the most lateral parts of laminae V–VII; zones of "cortical" and "rubral" activation overlap, but the former is more dorsal and the latter more ventral [for patterns of field potentials see (45, 46); for a survey of the whole problem see (43)]. Spatial separation of the interneuronal groups activated primarily from segmental afferents and descending tracts allowed one to suppose that some spinal IN are relatively specialized in respect to their synaptic connections to descending tracts (see below); but in many IN, a wide convergence of segmental and descending effects was found [for the cortico- and rubrofugal actions see (23, 24, 58)]. The IN connected monosynaptically to the reticulo- and vestibulospinal pathways are located predominantly in the medial parts of laminae VII and VIII (8, 69).

From the above data the following generalization can be made: The whole mass of spinal IN is divided into several functional groups, each taking part in the realization of a certain type of spinal activity determined by the signals arriving from corresponding peripheral receptors or supraspinal centers. At the same time, the vast convergence of excitatory and inhibitory synaptic actions of IN of one type upon other types of IN forms the mechanisms of mutual interaction of these groups in cases of concomitant activity.

To make this general statement more precise we require more information about the function of identified spinal IN, in particular about their output projections and the way they are involved in definite forms of natural activity of the spinal cord. Some progress along these lines has already been achieved.

RENSHAW INTERNEURONS

Morphological data obtained mainly by the Golgi technique indicate that the axons of many IN project to MN as well as to other IN of the same segment; in this respect they can be defined as segmental IN. Functional tracing of the connections of such IN was achieved by antidromic excitation after stimulation of various points of the gray and white matter.

The first studies of this type were made on Renshaw cells, which are monosynaptically excited by the axon collaterals of MN. Recent studies (42, 64) have shown that the trajectories and connections of Renshaw-cell axons are much more complex than would be expected from classical morphological data. Antidromic responses could be obtained in such cells after stimulation of the ventral funicles at a distance of 12 mm, with the conduction velocity exceeding 30 m sec^{-1}. The terminals of their axons could be traced in the motor nuclei as well as in more dorsomedial parts of the gray matter. Obviously, each Renshaw IN is able to exert its action upon a considerable population of both MN and IN.

Ia INTERNEURONS

The IN monosynaptically activated by group Ia muscle afferents (Ia-IN) exert a direct inhibitory effect upon the MN, and those located immediately dorsomedially to the motor nuclei receive inhibitory inputs from the Renshaw IN (27). The activity of the Ia-IN spreads over even larger populations of other cells than does that of the Renshaw cells. Such IN can be fired antidromically from both the ventral and the lateral funicles at a distance of many millimeters, and the conduction velocity reaches 70 m sec^{-1} (40, 41). By using direct stimulation of a single Ia-IN through an intracellular microelectrode (40, 41) it was possible to produce unitary monosynaptic IPSP in MN with an amplitude of 80–220 μV. The latter value is 0.1–0.005 the amplitude of maximal Ia-IPSP in the same MN, which indicates that Ia-IN widely converge upon individual MN. Intracellular injections of both procion-yellow and horseradish peroxidase verified the results of local microstimulations and have shown that the axons of Ia-In are myelinated and may be divided in the funicles into an ascending and a descending branch or even pass to the contralateral side; their terminals contact MN as well as some other IN (10, 38).

The following general features of Ia-IN can be listed: Low-threshold group Ia afferents from several muscles converge upon single Ia-IN, and their excitatory synaptic actions can summate (29). The excitatory influences from the vestibular (Deiters') nucleus and medial longitudinal fasciculus also converge upon Ia-IN (26, 28). Other types of primary afferents (low-threshold cutaneous, high-threshold cutaneous, and muscle) exert a facilitatory effect upon Ia-IN only through polysynaptic pathways (15). Curiously, such facilitatory effect from the contralateral side was observed only in spinal animals under chloralose anesthesia; in the decerebrate state the effect was depressive (16). Finally, the Ia-IN are subject to Ia inhibition from muscles strictly antagonistic to the muscles that send the excitatory Ia fibers. This inhibition can also be facilitated by the activity of different ipsi- and contralateral primary afferents and several descending pathways (25).

On the basis of these data one can now consider the Ia-IN as a system that is usually activated in parallel to the activation of MN of a certain muscle, exerting its inhibitory effect on several antagonistic muscles. At the same time, this system is under inhibitory feedback control from the Renshaw cells and similar Ia interneuronal systems of antagonistic muscles.

OTHER TYPES OF SEGMENTAL INTERNEURONS

By comparison to data on Renshaw IN and Ia-IN, the data about the projections of other types of segmental IN are very scant. Regarding the EPSP allegedly produced in MN by the group Ib, group II, low-threshold cutaneous and flexor reflex–afferents can have a latency compatible with disynaptic central transmission; it is possible to postulate that at least some of the IN connected directly to these primary afferents may in turn project directly to MN and evoke excitatory synaptic responses. The inhibitory effects seem always to be trisynaptic at least (55–57).

The IN linked to high-threshold cutaneous and muscle afferents (FRA) form an extensive system whose projections and synaptic connections have not been well studied. These neurons receive both ipsi- and contralateral afferent volleys and project also bilaterally. A huge increase and prolongation of their activity are observed after stimulation of the descending monoaminergic systems (see below).

NEURONS OF GELATINOUS SUBSTANCE

According to morphological data, the IN of the gelatinous substance project into a dense bundle of longitudinal fibers; they receive synaptic inputs also from this bundle. Recent electrophysiological data have shown that stimulation of the Lissauer's tract at a point 2–3 segments rostral to the recording site can produce both antidromic and synaptic excitation of these IN (9). The axon conduction velocity varies between 4 and 10 m sec^{-1}. Obviously, after passing a certain distance they terminate upon other neurons of the same type. High-threshold cutaneous and muscle afferents (group $A\delta$ or $A\delta + C$) produce EPSP in gelatinous neurons; low-threshold cutaneous and group II muscle fibers exert upon them a long-lasting inhibitory action. The described organization can be considered as a basis for the long-lasting reverberation of activity and the corresponding tonic influence upon other spinal structures. A role of the gelatinous neurons in the presynaptic inhibition has been suggested (72). However, a precise answer to the question of the functional significance of this interneuronal system is still lacking.

PROPRIOSPINAL INTERNEURONS

The IN may be classified as propriospinal units in the full sense if their axons pass in the white matter for a distance of more than one spinal segment.

A considerable portion of the IN localized in the lateral and central regions of laminae V-VII and in the lamina VIII and ventromedial parts of lamina VII can be identified as typical propriospinal cells (51, 60, 65, 67, 70, 71); axons pass into the lateral or ventral funicle for a distance of over 5 segments or less to form short propriospinal pathways. Long descending and ascending propriospinal fibers interconnecting cervical and lumbar regions originate from the neurons mainly localized in the ventral cord quadrants. Their axons also pass into the lateral (except its dorsal parts) and the ventral funicles (3), but direct data concerning the synaptic inputs to the long descending and ascending propriospinal IN are still absent.

Mean values of conduction velocity via the short propriospinal pathways in the dorsolateral funicle of the cat lumbar cord were 35–40 m sec⁻¹ (48, 49); in the cervical region they were somewhat higher (7). The maximum values in some fibers of these pathways in the lumbar region are about 70 m sec⁻¹ (77, 78). The conduction velocities for short propriospinal pathways in the ventrolateral and ventral funicles were established to be 45–65 m sec⁻¹ for the mass discharge and around 95–100 m sec⁻¹ in the fastest single axons (50, 67, 73, 74). Similar results were obtained in monkeys (51, 67). The fastest-conducting propriospinal axons (up to 110–120 m sec⁻¹) were found in the long pathways descending in the central parts of the lateral funicle (39) and in short lateral pathways in the upper cervical cord (30).

Short propriospinal IN are the recipients of a considerable portion of the main cerebrospinal projections (1, 4, 5, 30, 34, 35, 51, 67, 74, 76–78), the lateral ones being activated from the cortico-, rubro-, and partially tecto- and reticulo-spinal fibers, while the ventromedial ones are activated mainly from the vestibulo- and reticulo-spinal fibers. Monosynaptic excitation from the descending tracts is usually accompanied by a di- and/or polysynaptic action (74, 76, 77). Primary afferent stimulation evokes only polysynaptic and often very weak effects in most of the short lateral propriospinal IN of the lumbar cord (45, 77, 78). Despite reservations (54, 67) this neuronal group appears to be relatively specialized in the transmission of descending signals with limited participation in segmental reflex actions (43, 47; see also 35, 74). Excitatory and inhibitory interconnections among propriospinal IN themselves have been reported (44, 63, 70). The inhibitory system could be organized in a fashion similar to the recurrent inhibitory network in the motoneuronal pools (75, 76).

Short axons from the lateral funicle terminate ipsilaterally in laminae V-VII; their termination zone is oriented to the motoneuronal pools supplying the distal muscles of extremities. Propriospinal axons from the ventral funicles (both long and short ones) terminate bilaterally in the medial parts of the laminae VII and VIII and are directed to the MN of proximal and axial muscles (63).

Monosynaptic excitation is the main initial effect in most flexor MN and in some extensor ones produced by short lateral pathways in the cat lumbar cord, while monosynaptic inhibition is observed in some units (predominantly extensor ones) (48, 49). Thus, it can be concluded that certain portions of short lateral propriospinal neurons are inhibitory IN. In the cervical region the short lateral propriospinal pathways evoke monosynaptic excitatory action in all but a few MN (6, 35).

Propriospinal pathways can also activate the IN of segmental reflex arcs: The pronounced excitatory and inhibitory polysynaptic actions usually follow the initial monosynaptic PSP in the IN (6, 48, 49). In the cervical region the intensity of the "propriospinal" action on the segmental IN is noticeably higher than in the lumbar region (6).

Stimulation of short propriospinal pathways in the ventral funicles also evokes mono- and polysynaptic PSP in the MN; polysynaptic action is transmitted via segmental IN, Ia interneurons in particular (50, 67, 73). Contradictory data were obtained about the existence of direct inhibitory connections of these pathways to MN (50; but see 73). An attempt was undertaken to evaluate the intensity of synaptic action from a single propriospinal axon in a MN; it seems to be usually less than 100 μV (52).

A definite difference is observed in the relative intensity of the action of short lateral and ventral propriospinal pathways upon the MN: The former exert more pronounced synaptic drive on the MN of distal muscles, the latter on the MN of proximal muscle groups (49, 73). Long descending propriospinal axons coming into the central parts of the lateral funicle have a direct effect upon MN. Direct projections of these axons to the Ia and FRA-IN were also demonstrated (39). Similar patterns of connections were demonstrated for the long propriospinal pathways in the ventral funicles, but in this case direct action upon MN was either absent or very scanty (73).

According to indirect data, long ascending propriospinal pathways project mainly to the MN of the axial muscle groups (59).

The data presented above allow one to consider the short propriospinal IN as an interneuronal system participating in the transmission of signals from the lateral and medial descending systems (53), which ensure disynaptic linkage of corresponding tracts with the motoneuronal pools (31, 33, 47, 50–52, 73, 77, 78). Integration of signals from different descending fiber systems and to some extent from primary afferents is probably performed in these propriospinal populations (30, 32, 34, 35, 47, 51, 67, 74, 76, 77), but it is necessary to recognize that functional significance of transmission via both the short and long (39) propriospinal neurons can be explained mainly on the hypothetical and speculative level.

INTERNEURONAL ACTIVITIES DURING NATURAL MOTOR ACTS

Direct recording from identified IN during natural activities has met with considerable technical difficulties. Therefore, experiments with models of spinal activity are of interest. Studies of DOPA action on reflex transmission in the spinal cord (2) are closely related to those involving "controlled" (68) and "fictive" (66) locomotion and scratching in the high decerebrate cat. In spinal cats, administration of DOPA creates basic conditions for rhythmic alternation of flexor and extensor limb movements, i.e. the most essential component of stepping. Since DOPA stimulates a release of nor-adrenaline from sectioned descending monoaminergic pathways, it is suggested that tonic action of such pathways releases the appropriate spinal interneuronal mechanisms from stable inhibition.

Investigations of interneuronal activity in spinal animals after administration of DOPA have been performed by Jankowska et al (36, 37). IN that can transmit late responses to MN were found in dorsolateral parts of the ventral horn. Most of them (group A) are excited from ipsilateral high-threshold afferents and inhibited from contralateral ones. Some IN (group B) responded to co-FRA stimulation and were inhibited from ipsi-FRA; few IN (group C) revealed late excitation at stimulation of both ipsi-FRA and co-FRA. These results suggested that FRA-IN responsible for late discharges are organized as two "half-centers" coupled via special cross-inhibitory IN.

Orlovsky & Feldman (61) recorded the interneuronal activity during controlled locomotion in the high decerebrate cat. The volleys in IN (non-identified) were shown to arise both in supporting and moving phases; there was no difference in distribution of the two types of neurons in spinal cross sections. These volleys were recorded after deafferentation of the limb and, consequently, were not related to the supply of afferent signals. Neurons were located mainly in the lateral part of intermedial zone and vertral horn. Similar results have been obtained with "fictive" locomotion induced in spinal animals by DOPA + nyalamide injection (13, 14); maxima of the rhythmic activity in IN of various kinds corresponded to different phases of stepping.

Since Ia-IN could be exactly identified, their behavior was considered in more detail. These neurons are intensively involved in late discharges induced by DOPA injection. If such neurons were monosynaptically activated by Ia flexor afferents (and, consequently, inhibited extensor MN), late discharges in them appeared from ipsilateral high-threshold afferents. Neurons inhibiting flexor MN, on the contrary, were excited with large delay from co-FRA. Thus, the hypothesis proved correct that these neurons form a system supporting reciprocal changes of excitability of MN (19). The study of activity of the same neurons during locomotion gave compatible results. Ia-IN were activated simultaneously with the muscle that is a source of Ia fibers monosynaptically connected to these units. Since the activation took place under deafferentation, it could be due to a spinal generator responsible for locomotor programming (17).

To determine the neuronal organization of such a generator, detailed information concerning the involvement of other types of identified IN in locomotor activity is needed. Now such information is beginning to be available, as for example in the work of Viala & Viala (79) in decorticated, curarized rabbits.

CONCLUSION

A detailed description of functional connections of spinal IN and the ways of their involvement in complex forms of neural activity is now possible. Practically, such description has been done so far only for some IN, first of all connected to Ia afferents. Progress in research on short propriospinal neurons may be expected. But a thorough examination of the largest interneuronal systems (e.g. cutaneous IN or FRA-neurones, etc) is still required. It should be noted that in most studies the function of spinal IN has been regarded in view of their participation in coordination of motor activity. However, the regulation of visceral functions is undoubtedly also connected to the complex integrative activity of IN, whose detailed systemic investigation is still needed.

Literature Cited

1. Anastasievič, R., Vasilenko, D. A., Kostyukov, A. I., Preobrazhensky, N. N. 1973. Reticulofugal activation of interneurones in the lateral region of spinal grey matter in the cat. *Neirofiziologiya (Kiev)* 5:525–36

2. Anden, N.-E., Jukes, M. G. M., Lundberg, A., Vyklicky, L. 1966. The effect of DOPA on the spinal cord. I. Influences on transmission from primary afferents. *Acta Physiol. Scand.* 67:373–86

3. Barilari, M. G., Kuypers, H. G. J. M. 1969. Propriospinal fibres interconnecting the spinal enlargements in the cat. *Brain Res.* 14:321–30

4. Bayev, K. V., Kostyuk, P. G. 1972. A study of connections of cortico- and rubrospinal tracts with neuronal elements in the cervical region of cat spinal cord. *Neirofiziologiya (Kiev)* 4:158–67

5. Bayev, K. V., Kostyuk, P. G. 1973. Convergence of cortico- and rubrospinal influences on interneurones of cat cervical spinal cord. *Brain Res.* 52:159–72

6. Bayev, K. V., Vasilenko, D. A., Kostyuk, P. G. 1973. Synaptic processes in the neurones of cervical spinal cord of the cat evoked by stimulation of propriospinal pathways in the dorsolateral funiculus. *Neirofiziologiya (Kiev)* 5:61–69

7. Bayev, K. V., Vasilenko, D. A., Manzhelo, L. I. 1973. Functional properties of propriospinal pathways in the dorsolateral funiculus of the cat spinal cord. *Neirofiziologiya (Kiev)* 5:54–60

8. Bezhenaru, I. S., Gokin, A. P., Zadorozhny, A. G., Preobrazhensky, N. N. 1972. Synaptic activation of the interneurones in the thoracic region of spinal cord from the reticulospinal pathways. *Neirofiziologiya (Kiev)* 4:566–78

9. Cervero, F., Molony, V., Iggo, A. 1977. Extracellular and intracellular recordings from neurones in the substantia gelatinosa Rolandi. *Brain Res.* 136:565–69

10. Czarkowska, J., Jankowska, E., Sybirska, E. 1976. Axonal projections of spinal interneurones excited by group I afferents in the cat, revealed by intracellular staining with horseradish peroxidase. *Brain Res.* 118:115–18

11. Eccles, J. C., Eccles, R. M., Lundberg, A. 1960. Types of neurons in and around the intermediate nucleus of the lumbosacral cord. *J. Physiol. (London)* 154:89–114

12. Eccles, J. C., Fatt, P., Landgren, S., Winsbury, G. J. 1954. Spinal cord potentials generated by volley in the large muscle afferents. *J. Physiol. (London)* 125:590–606

13. Edgerton, V. R., Grillner, S., Sjöström, A., Zangger, P. 1975. The spinal generator for locomotion in the cat. *Exp. Brain Res.* 23:64

14. Edgerton, V. R., Grillner, S., Sjöström, A., Zangger, P. 1976. Central generation of locomotion in vertebrates. In *Neural control of locomotion,* ed. R. M. Herman, S. Grillner, P. S. G. Sten, D. G. Stuart, pp. 439–64. New York and London: Plenum

15. Fedina, L., Hultborn, H. 1972. Facilitation from ipsilateral primary afferents of interneuronal transmission in the Ia inhibitory pathway to motoneurones. *Acta Physiol. Scand.* 86:59–81

16. Fedina, L., Hultborn, H., Illert, M. 1975. Facilitation from contralateral primary afferents of interneuronal transmission in the Ia inhibitory pathway to motoneurones. *Acta Physiol. Scand.* 94:198–221

17. Feldman, A. G., Orlovsky, G. N. 1975. Activity of interneurones mediating reciprocal Ia inhibition during locomotion. *Brain Res.* 84:181–94

18. Frank, K., Fuortes, M. G. F. 1956. Unitary activity of spinal interneurones of cats. *J. Physiol. (London)* 131:424–35

19. Fu, T.-C., Jankowska, E., Lundberg, A. 1975. Reciprocal Ia inhibition during the late reflexes evoked from the flexor reflex afferents after DOPA. *Brain Res.* 85:99–102

20. Gokin, A. P. 1970. Synaptic activation of interneurones in the thoracic spinal cord segments from the cutaneous, muscle and visceral afferents. *Neirofiziologiya (Kiev)* 2:563–72

21. Haapanen, L., Kolmodin, G. M., Skoglund, C. R. 1958. Membrane and action potentials of spinal interneurons in the cat. *Acta Physiol. Scand.* 43:315–48

22. Hongo, T., Jankowska, E., Lundberg, A. 1966. Convergence of excitatory and inhibitory action on interneurones in the lumbosacral cord. *Exp. Brain Res.* 1:338–58

23. Hongo, T., Jankowska, E., Lundberg, A. 1969. The rubrospinal tract. I. Facilitation of interneuronal transmission in reflex paths to motoneurones. *Exp. Brain Res.* 7:365–91

24. Hongo, T., Jankowska, E., Lundberg, A. 1972. The rubrospinal tract. IV. Effects on interneurones. *Exp. Brain Res.* 15:54–78

25. Hultborn, H., Illert, M., Santini, M. 1976. Convergence on interneurones mediating the reciprocal Ia inhibition of motoneurones. I. Disynaptic Ia inhibition of Ia inhibitory interneurones. *Acta Physiol. Scand.* 96:193–201

26. Hultborn, H., Illert, M., Santini, M. 1976. Convergence on interneurones mediating the reciprocal Ia inhibition of motoneurones. III. Effects from supraspinal pathways. *Acta Physiol. Scand.* 96:368–91

27. Hultborn, H., Jankowska, E., Lindström, S. 1971. Recurrent inhibition of interneurones monosynaptically activated from group Ia afferents. *J. Physiol. (London)* 215:613–36

28. Hultborn, H., Udo, M. 1972. Convergence in the reciprocal Ia inhibitory pathway of excitation from descending pathways and inhibition from motor axon collaterals. *Acta Physiol. Scand.* 84:95–108

29. Hultborn, H., Udo, M. 1972. Convergence of large muscle spindle (Ia) afferents at interneuronal level in the reciprocal Ia inhibitory pathway to motoneurones. *Acta Physiol. Scand.* 84:493–99

30. Illert, M., Lundberg, A., Padel, Y., Tanaka, R. 1975. Convergence on propriospinal neurones which may mediate disynaptic corticospinal excitation to forelimb motoneurones in the cat. *Brain Res.* 93:530–34

31. Illert, M., Lundberg, A., Tanaka, R. 1974. Disynaptic corticospinal effects in forelimb motoneurones in the cat. *Brain Res.* 75:312–15

32. Illert, M., Lundberg, A., Tanaka, R. 1975. Integration in a disynaptic cortico-motoneuronal pathway to the forelimb of the cat. *Brain Res.* 93:525–29

33. Illert, M., Lundberg, A., Tanaka, R. 1976. Integration in descending motor pathways controlling the forelimb in the cat. I. Pyramidal effects on motoneurones. *Exp. Brain Res.* 26:509–19

34. Illert, M., Lundberg, A., Tanaka, R. 1976. Integration in descending motor pathways controlling the forelimb in the cat. 2. Convergence on neurones mediating disynaptic cortico-motoneuronal excitation. *Exp. Brain Res.* 26:521–40

35. Illert, M., Lundberg, A., Tanaka, R. 1977. Integration in descending motor pathways controlling the forelimb in the cat. 3. Convergence on propriospinal neurones transmitting disynaptic excitation from the corticospinal tract and other descending tracts. *Exp. Brain Res.* 29:323–46

36. Jankowska, E., Jukes, M. G. M., Lund, S., Lundberg, A. 1965. Reciprocal innervation through interneuronal inhibition. *Nature* 206:198–99

37. Jankowska, E., Jukes, M. G., Lund, S., Lundberg, A. 1967. The effect of DOPA on the spinal cord. 6. Half-centre organization of interneurones transmitting effects from the flexor reflex afferents. *Acta Physiol. Scand.* 70:389–402

38. Jankowska, E., Lindström, S. 1972. Morphology of interneurones mediating Ia reciprocal inhibition of motoneurones in the spinal cord of the cat. *J. Physiol. (London)* 226:805–23

39. Jankowska, E., Lundberg, A., Roberts, W. J., Stuart, D. 1974. A long propriospinal system with direct effect on motoneurones and on interneurones in

the cat lumbosacral cord. *Exp. Brain Res.* 21:169–94

40. Jankowska, E., Roberts, W. J. 1972. An electrophysiological demonstration of the axonal projections of single spinal interneurones in the cat. *J. Physiol. (London)* 222:597–622

41. Jankowska, E., Roberts, W. J. 1972. Synaptic actions of single interneurones mediating reciprocal Ia inhibition of motoneurones. *J. Physiol. (London)* 222:623–42

42. Jankowska, E., Smith, D. O. 1973. Antidromic activation of Renshaw cells and their axonal projections. *Acta Physiol. Scand.* 88:198–214

43. Kostyuk, P. G. 1973. *Structure and Function of Descending Systems of the Spinal Cord,* pp. 120–53; 154–68. Leningrad: Nauka. 280 pp.

44. Kostyuk, P. G., Maisky, V. A. 1972. Propriospinal projections in the lumbar spinal cord of the cat. *Brain Res.* 39:530–35

45. Kostyuk, P. G., Pilyavsky, A. I. 1969. Synaptic processes in the spinal cord interneurones evoked by the rubrospinal influences. *Neirofiziologiya (Kiev)* 1:158–66

46. Kostyuk, P. G., Vasilenko, D. A. 1965. Peculiarities of activation of different spinal neuronal populations after sensorimotor cortex stimulation in cat. *J. Higher Nerv. Activity (Moscow)* 15:695–703

47. Kostyuk, P. G., Vasilenko, D. A. 1968. Transformation of cortical motor signals in spinal cord. *Proc. IEEE* 56:1049–58

48. Kostyuk, P. G., Vasilenko, D. A., Lang, E. 1971. Propriospinal pathways in the dorsolateral funiculus and their effects on lumbosacral motoneuronal pools. *Brain Res.* 28:233–49

49. Kostyuk, P. G., Vasilenko, D. A., Zadorozhny, A. G. 1969. Reactions of lumbar motoneurones produced by actions of propriospinal pathways. *Neirofiziologiya (Kiev)* 1:5–14

50. Kozhanov, V. M. 1974. The propriospinal monosynaptic effects of the ventral descending pathways on the cat lumbar motoneurones. *Sechenov Fiziol. Zh. SSSR (Leningrad)* 60:171–78

51. Kozhanov, V. M., Shapovalov, A. I. 1977. Synaptic organization of the supraspinal control of propriospinal ventral horn interneurons in cat and monkey spinal cord. *Neirofiziologiya (Kiev)* 9:177–86

52. Kozhanov, V. M., Shapovalov, A. I. 1977. Synaptic actions evoked in

motoneurons by stimulation of individual propriospinal neurons. *Neirofiziologiya (Kiev)* 9:300–6

53. Kuypers, H. G. J. M. 1964. The descending pathways to the spinal cord, their anatomy and function. *Prog. Brain Res.* 11:178–200

54. Lundberg, A. 1972. The significance of segmental spinal mechanisms in motor control. *Symp. Pap. 4th Int. Biophys. Congr. (Moscow)* pp. 1–13

55. Lundberg, A., Malmgren, K., Schomburg, E. 1975. Convergence from Ib, cutaneous and joint afferents in reflex pathways to motoneurones. *Brain Res.* 87:81–84

56. Lundberg, A., Malmgren, K., Schomburg, E. D. 1975. Characteristics of the excitatory pathway from group II muscle afferents to alpha motoneurones. *Brain Res.* 88:538–42

57. Lundberg, A., Malmgren, K., Schomburg, E. D. 1977. Cutaneous facilitation of transmission in reflex pathways from Ib afferents to motoneurones. *J. Physiol. (London)* 265:763–80

58. Lundberg, A., Norrsell, U., Voorhoeve, P. 1962. Pyramidal effects on lumbosacral interneurones activated by somatic afferents. *Acta Physiol. Scand.* 56:220–29

59. Miller, S., Reitsma, D. J., Van der Meche, F. G. A. 1973. Functional organization of long ascending propriospinal pathways linking lumbosacral and cervical segments in the cat. *Brain Res.* 62:169–88

60. Molenaar, I., Rustioni, A., Kuypers, H. G. J. M. 1974. The location of cells of origin of the fibres in the ventral and lateral funiculus of the cat's lumbosacral cord. *Brain Res.* 78:239–54

61. Orlovsky, G. N., Feldman, A. G. 1972. Classification of the interneurones in the lumbosacral spinal cord in respect to their discharges during evoked locomotion. *Neirofiziologiya (Kiev)* 4:410–17

62. Pomeranz, B., Wall, P. D., Weber, W. V. 1968. Cord cells responding to fine myelinated afferents from viscera, muscle and skin. *J. Physiol. (London)* 199:511–32

63. Rustioni, A., Kuypers, H. G. J. M., Holstege, G. 1971. Propriospinal projections from the ventral and lateral funiculi to the motoneurons in the lumbosacral cord of the cat. *Brain Res.* 34:255–75

64. Ryall, R. W., Piercey, M. F., Polosa, C. 1971. Intersegmental and intrasegmental distribution of mutual inhibition

126   KOSTYUK & VASILENKO

of Renshaw cells. *J. Neurophysiol.* 34:700–7
65. Scheibel, M. E., Scheibel, A. B. 1966. Spinal motoneurons, interneurons and Renshaw cells. A Golgi study. *Arch. Ital. Biol.* 104:328–53
66. Severin, F. V., Shik, M. L. Orlovsky, G. N. 1967. Muscle and unitary motoneuronal activity during controlled locomotion. *Biofizika (Moscow)* 12:660–68
67. Shapovalov, A. I. 1975. *Neurones and Synapses of Supraspinal Motor Systems.* Leningrad: Nauka. pp. 58–64
68. Shik, M. L., Severin, F. V., Orlovsky, G. N. 1966. Walking and running control by midbrain electrical stimulation. *Biofizika (Moscow)* 11:659–66
69. Skinner, R. D., Willis, W. D. 1970. Spinal cord potentials produced by ventral cord volleys in the cat. *Exp. Neurol.* 27:318–33
70. Sterling, P., Kuypers, H. G. J. M. 1968. Anatomical organization of the brachial spinal cord of the cat. III. The propriospinal connections. *Brain Res.* 7:419–43
71. Szentágothai, J. 1964. Propriospinal pathways and their synapses. *Prog. Brain Res.* 11:155–77
72. Szentágothai, J. 1966/1968. Synaptic structure and the concept of presynaptic inhibition. In *Structure and Function of Inhibitory Neuronal Mechanisms,* ed. C. von Euler, S. Skoglund, U. Söderberg, pp. 15–31. Oxford: Pergamon
73. Vasilenko, D. A. 1975. Propriospinal pathways in the ventral funicles of the cat spinal cord: their effects on lumbosa-

cral motoneurones. *Brain Res.* 93: 502–6
74. Vasilenko, D. A., Kostyukov, A. I. 1976. Brain stem and primary afferent projections to the ventromedial group of propriospinal neurones in the cat. *Brain Res.* 117:141–46
75. Vasilenko, D. A., Kostyukov, A. I. 1976. Postactivation inhibitory process in the interneurones transmitting activity from lateral descending systems. *Neirofiziologiya (Kiev)* 8:538–41
76. Vasilenko, D. A., Kostyukov, A. I. 1977. Transmission of reticulofugal activities via ventromedial group of propriospinal neurones in the cat. *Neirofiziologiya (Kiev)* 9:205–9
77. Vasilenko, D. A., Kostyukov, A. I., Pilyavsky, A. I. 1972. Cortico- and rubrofugal activation of propriospinal interneurones sending axons into the dorsolateral funiculus of the cat spinal cord. *Neirofiziologiya (Kiev)* 4:489–500
78. Vasilenko, D. A., Zadorozhny, A. G., Kostyuk, P. G. 1967. Synaptic processes in spinal neurons monosynaptically activated from the pyramidal tract. *Bull. Exp. Biol. Med. (Moscow)* 64(11):20–25
79. Viala, G., Viala, D. 1977. Elements of locomotor programming in the rabbit. *Proc. XXVII Int. Congr. Physiol. Sci. Satell. Symp., Paris.*
80. Wall, P. D. 1960. Cord cells responding to touch, damage, and temperature of skin. *J. Neurophysiol.* 23:197–210

Ann. Rev. Physiol. 1979. 41:127–40

RETICULOSPINAL PROJECTIONS TO SPINAL MOTOR NUCLEI

♦1210

Barry W. Peterson

The Rockefeller University, New York, N.Y. 10021

INTRODUCTION

As described by Brodal (5), the medial pontomedullary reticular formation is a complex brainstem region with a bewildering array of intrinsic interconnections, long ascending projections to diencephalic levels and beyond, and long reticulospinal projections reaching all levels of the spinal cord. According to our present understanding, this region is involved in such functions as descending control of motor activity or of sensory relays, ascending control of cortical arousal, or control of autonomic activity. Each of these functions may be mediated either by fast, myelinated reticular efferent fibers or by the slowly conducting, unmyelinated aminergic systems that originate from nuclei classified (in the past, at least) as belonging to the reticular formation.

Because of the complexity of reticular efferent systems, most investigations dealing with the reticular formation have focused upon a single reticular function and a restricted subset of reticular efferent pathways. This review, too, focuses on a single reticular efferent system—the fast, myelinated reticulospinal projection to spinal motor nuclei—in an attempt to evaluate our current understanding of this system and to point out questions that need to be answered as we move toward a more integrative understanding of reticular function.

MOTOR ACTIVITY EVOKED BY STIMULATION OF THE MEDIAL RETICULAR FORMATION

Interest in the possible motor role of the medial pontomedullary reticular formation was stimulated by the work of Lloyd (22), who showed that

127

0066-4278/79/0301-0127$01.00

activation of long bulbospinal fibers leads to discharge of spinal interneurons and facilitation of hindlimb motoneurons. Lloyd emphasized that most of this facilitation is mediated by indirect pathways that include propriospinal or segmental relay neurons, but his results suggested that there might also be weak direct excitatory connections between reticulospinal fibers and motoneurons.

The locus of brainstem sites from which facilitation of hindlimb reflexes could be evoked was explored by Rhines & Magoun (38) in the cat. They found that facilitation could be evoked by repetitive stimulation of a region beginning with the dorsal and anterior part of the pontomedullary reticular formation and extending anterior into the mesencephalic reticular formation and midline thalamic nuclei. The same investigators (26) also observed that stimulation of the remainder of the pontomedullary reticular formation (i.e. its ventral and posterior region) produced a profound inhibition of reflexes in all four limbs. Recordings made in animals with spinal cord lesions indicated that both facilitatory and inhibitory influences were transmitted by fibers travelling in the ventral half of the spinal cord.

The work of Magoun & Rhines gave rise to the concept that the reticulospinal system has a global excitatory or inhibitory action on motoneurons supplying muscles throughout the body, a concept still found in textbooks today. In fact, however, Sprague & Chambers (42) found that relatively weak stimuli applied to the medial reticular formation in decerebrate cats could evoke a much wider variety of postural responses than those described by Magoun & Rhines (26) and Rhines & Magoun (38). With the weakest stimuli it was sometimes possible to obtain changes in the position of one limb or body part in isolation. As the stimulus was increased, they commonly obtained a postural pattern characterized by flexion of the ipsilateral limbs, extension of the contralateral limbs, and turning of the head toward the side with the flexed limbs. Only when the stimulus was increased still further did global facilitation or inhibition of muscles in all four limbs appear.

Thus, while stimulation studies indicate that the medial reticular formation has excitatory and inhibitory access to motoneurons supplying muscles throughout the body, reticulospinal projections appear to be organized with sufficient specificity that local activation of a relatively small number of reticular elements can produce fractionated body movements that might form the components of a wide variety of motor behaviors. Therefore the reticulospinal pathways must be considered as an extrapyramidal motor system that is likely to participate in many different kinds of motor behaviors.

ANATOMY OF THE RETICULOSPINAL SYSTEM

Medial and Lateral Reticulospinal Tracts

Both anatomical (27, 35) and physiological (16, 33) studies have shown that the medial pontomedullary reticular formation gives rise to three groups of descending fibers: one in the ventromedial funiculus (RST_m), one in the ipsilateral ventrolateral funiculus (RST_i) and one in the contralateral ventrolateral funiculus (RST_c). As shown in Figure 1B, RST_m originates primarily from neurons in the pons and in dorsorostral *nucleus reticularis* (*n.r.*) *gigantocellularis*, although a few RST_m neurons are found more caudally (16, 33). The descending RST_m fibers run in or close to the medial longitudinal fasciculus (MLF), continue in the spinal ventromedial funiculus, and then terminate in Rexed's (37) laminae VI–IX at all levels of the spinal cord (27, 35). As indicated by the symbols in Figure 1B, the great majority of RST_m neurons project at least as far as the upper lumbar spinal cord, and there is no clear segregation of neurons that terminate at different spinal levels.

The anatomical organization of the lateral reticulospinal tracts, RST_i and RST_c, is somewhat more complex. As shown in Figure 1, both pathways originate from neurons in the medullary reticular formation. Thus medullary lesions cause degeneration of both RST_i and RST_c fibers together with degeneration of RST_m fibers that are transected by the lesion. Collectively these degenerating fibers extend to all levels of the spinal cord giving off terminals to Rexed's laminae V–IX. Because of the combined damage to all three reticulospinal fiber systems, it is difficult to be certain which terminals are those of RST_i or RST_c fibers as opposed to RST_m fibers. Nevertheless, the former terminate heavily in regions at the base of the dorsal horn (which receives relatively few RST_m terminals) and probably also contribute to the degeneration observed throughout the ventral horn. This wide distribution of their terminals suggests that lateral reticulospinal fibers act upon a wider population of spinal neurons than RST_m fibers, which have a more restricted area of termination.

As shown in Figure 1C, most RST_i fibers extend as far as the lumbar cord. There is, however, a significant group of RST_i neurons that project only to the neck (N cells), and these neurons have a distribution within the medullary reticular formation different from RST_i neurons projecting further. The latter neurons tend to cluster in the ventrocaudal portion of *n.r. gigantocellularis*, while N cells are found both in that region and in the dorsorostral region just behind the abducens nucleus. The data shown in Figure 1C thus suggest that the RST_i pathway has a somatotopic organization, a property not previously ascribed to reticulospinal systems. The presence of such an

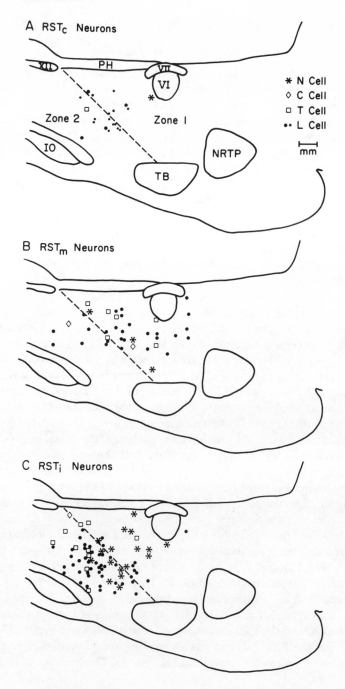

organization has recently been confirmed (B. W. Peterson and J. D. Coulter, unpublished observations) using the technique of retrograde labeling with horseradish peroxidase (HRP). The distribution of labeled reticular neurons following injection of HRP into the grey matter at various levels of the spinal cord indicated that reticulospinal neurons projecting to the neck tend to cluster in the dorsal medullary reticular formation, while neurons projecting to thoracic or to lumbar levels are clustered progressively more ventrally. Neurons projecting to the neck also extended more posteriorly into *n.r. ventralis* than did neurons projecting to lower spinal levels.

Neuroanatomical data thus show that the reticulospinal projection area in the medial pontomedullary reticular formation is subdivided into distinct subregions. Two major subregions are the dorsorostral region, which gives rise to RST_m fibers, and the ventrocaudal region, which gives rise to lateral reticulospinal fibers. The latter region is further subdivided into a somatotopically arranged set of subregions projecting to different spinal levels. The functional correlates of these anatomical subdivisions are considered in later sections.

Reticulospinal Tracts as a Medial Descending System

An important outgrowth of anatomical investigations of descending motor pathways is Kuypers' (19) concept of medial and lateral descending systems. This concept is based both upon the patterns of termination of descending systems in the spinal grey matter and upon the deficits in motor behavior that result from interruption of various descending pathways.

Kuypers' medial systems include the reticulospinal, vestibulospinal, tectospinal, and interstiospinal tracts. Collectively these pathways tend to terminate most heavily in the ventromedial parts of the ventral horn (20, 27, 35), which Sterling & Kuypers (43) have shown to be closely associated with motoneuron nuclei that innervate the axial and proximal limb muscles. In experimental animals, medial bulbar lesions, interrupting medial fiber systems, produce deficits in righting and in the control of postural and antigravity muscles without impairment of the control of distal muscles.

Figure 1 Locations of reticulospinal neurons. Histologically determined locations of reticulospinal neurons projecting in RST_c, RST_m and RST_i are shown on three drawings of a schematic parasagittal section through the pons (right) and medulla (left). As shown by key, different symbols indicate neurons identified as projecting to different spinal levels (N cells to neck above C_4, C cells to cervical enlargement above T_1, T cells to thoracic cord above L_1, L cells beyond L_1). Diagonal dashed lines indicate border between two reticular regions labeled zone 1 and 2 in A. Other structures indicated in A are: IO, inferior olivary nucleus; NRTP, nucleus reticularis tegmenti pontis; PH, prepositus hypoglossi nucleus; TB, trapezoid body; VI, abducens nucleus; VII, genu of facial nerve; XII, hypoglossal nucleus. From (33)

In sharp contrast to medial systems, the corticospinal and rubrospinal tracts that Kuypers (19) classifies as lateral descending systems terminate in the dorsolateral parts of the spinal grey matter—a region associated with motoneuron pools supplying the distal musculature (43). Lesions of lateral systems result in a severe impairment in control of the distal musculature but relatively little deficit in postural reactions that are executed by the axial and proximal limb muscles.

The value of the medial/lateral system dichotomy is that it provides a framework for forming hypotheses about the motor functions mediated by a descending pathway. Thus functions performed by reticulospinal pathways should fall within that group of motor behaviors that preferentially utilize the proximal musculature. Behaviors that satisfy this criterion include righting responses and vestibular reflexes, which produce strong activation of the proximal musculature coupled with movements of many parts of the body. The role of reticulospinal pathways is probably not restricted to such whole-body movements, however. These pathways are likely to be involved in producing the synergistic activation of postural muscles that accompanies many movements, and lesion studies reported by Brinkman & Kuypers (4) suggest that reticulospinal pathways may also play a key role in mediating visually guided arm movements. They found that split-brain, chiasm-sectioned monkeys were able to make visually controlled reaching movements with the arm ipsilateral to their seeing eye but were unable to initiate distal grasping movements. Thus the predominately crossed lateral systems are required for fine distal movements, whereas reaching movements can be mediated by uncrossed descending pathways. Electrophysiological data (discussed below) indicate that one of the most direct routes by which cortical activity can reach the ipsilateral spinal cord is via a corticoreticulo-spinal pathway. Thus the reticulospinal system, under the control of higher motor centers, likely participates in mediating relatively discrete movements such as reaching with a single limb.

Branching of Reticulospinal Axons

As discussed in the previous section, many of the motor actions mediated by medial descending systems involve activation of muscles at more than one level of the body. A possible anatomical basis for these complex patterns of motor activity has recently been found in studies of the projection and branching of vestibulospinal (1) and reticulospinal axons (33). In the reticulospinal system, my colleagues and I found that 86% of the reticulospinal neurons that send terminal branches to the cervical enlargement also have axon branches extending to lower spinal levels. Some of these axons extend to lumbar levels and thus could be involved in coordinated activation of fore- and hindlimb muscles. In other cases the long descending axons of reticulospinal neurons innervating the cervical enlargement continue only into the thoracic segments, which suggests that these neurons have an influence on both forelimb and back muscles.

My colleagues and I also traced the arborization of individual reticulospinal axon branches within the grey matter of the cervical enlargement. By so doing we were able to show that an individual neuron may not only project to several different spinal levels but can also act upon neurons on both sides of the spinal cord. While we cannot at present prove that such widely branching neurons act upon motoneurons in each of the spinal regions they innervate, such a "hard-wired" coordination of motor action would be consistent with Sprague & Chambers' (42) observations that even the weakest effective reticular stimulation often causes contraction or relaxation of muscles in several parts of the body and with the idea that reticulospinal neurons may function as motor-command neurons for the execution of complex postural reflexes.

ELECTROPHYSIOLOGICAL STUDIES OF RETICULO-MOTOR PATHWAYS

Reticulospinal Excitation of Motoneurons

Reticulospinal actions on spinal motoneurons were first studied at the single cell level in the 1960s. Grillner & Lund (12) mapped out a brainstem region including *n.r. pontis caudalis,* the dorsorostral part of *n.r. gigantocellularis,* and the MLF that had direct, excitatory connections with both flexor and extensor motoneurons of the hindlimb. Their work was extended by Wilson & Yoshida (45), and by Wilson et al (46), who showed that stimuli applied at the midline within this region also gave rise to monosynaptic excitation of motoneurons supplying muscles of the neck, back, and forelimbs. In fact, extensive mapping of brainstem regions that produce monosynaptic excitation of motoneurons in all parts of the body (34, 36) has indicated that stimuli applied throughout the region originally described by Grillner & Lund (12) may evoke monosynaptic excitation of motoneurons supplying muscles throughout the ipsilateral half of the body.

The reticular region that has a direct excitatory action on both axial and limb muscles is indicated by the light area labeled zone 1 in Figure 2 and its actions on different groups of motoneurons are listed in Table 1. Comparison of Figures 1 and 2 shows that zone 1 lies within the region of origin of RST_m fibers. The RST_m system is therefore likely to play a major role in producing the widespread excitation of motoneurons evoked by stimulation of zone 1, although lesion studies (17) have shown that some fibers in the ventrolateral funiculus also participate in reticulospinal excitation of hindlimb motoneurons. Not all RST_m neurons are involved in producing

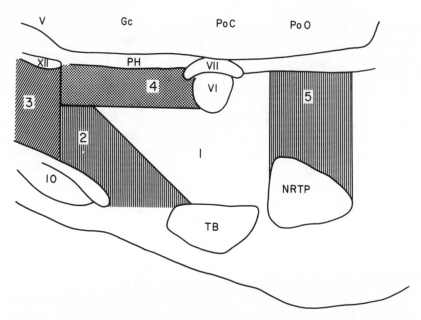

Figure 2   Schematic parasagittal section showing division of medial pontomedullary reticular formation into five zones. V, Gc, PoC, and PoO indicate *nuclei reticularis ventralis, gigantocellularis, pontis caudalis,* and *pontis oralis.* Zone 1 includes *n.r. pontis caudalis* and the dorsorostral part of *n.r. gigantocellularis* beginning 2 mm from the surface of the 4th ventricle. Zone 2 includes the ventrocaudal part of *n.r. gigantocellularis;* zone 3, *n.r. ventralis;* zone 4, the dorsal 2 mm of *n.r. gigantocellularis,* and zone, 5 *n.r. pontis oralis.* Other abbreviations as in Figure 1. From (28)

such excitation of motoneurons, however. Zone 1 does not include the most anterior portion of the RST_m projection area, which lies within *n.r. pontis oralis.* Stimulation of this region, which corresponds to zone 5 of Figure 2, produces virtually no direct excitation of motoneurons. Thus, while they project to all levels of the spinal cord (see Figure 1), the more anteriorly located RST_m neurons apparently have only indirect connections with spinal motoneurons.

The data in Table 1 also indicate that the monosynaptic excitation from zone 1 in the ipsilateral reticular formation was most prevalent in neck motoneurons and least prevalent in limb motoneurons; back motoneurons were intermediate between the two. Examination of amplitudes of the monosynaptic EPSPs in those motoneurons where they were present revealed a similar hierarchy of zone-1 action: Monosynaptic EPSP amplitude was largest in neck motoneurons and smallest in limb motoneurons. Our data do not reveal any difference between reticulospinal excitation of forelimb versus hindlimb motoneurons or between reticulospinal excitation of

Table 1   Responses of somatic motoneurons to stimulation of different reticular zones[a]

Motoneuron	PSP	Zone				
		1	2	3	4	5
Neck	EPSP	35/52	69/78	71/78	26/28	1/17
Back	EPSP	13/26	10/27	9/21	0/7	0/7
Forelimb	EPSP	18/64	1/39	2/21	0/10	1/43
Hindlimb	EPSP	8/33	1/23	1/24	2/22	0/8
Neck	IPSP	4/17	2/32	39/45	14/21	0/12

[a]Entries indicate fraction of motoneurons at each level that exhibited monosynaptic EPSPs or IPSPs when a 100–150μA stimulus was applied to the zone indicated in the ipsilateral reticular formation. No clearly monosynaptic inhibition was seen in back or limb motoneurons.

flexor versus extensor motoneurons. Thus, like Wilson & Yoshida (45), we were unable to confirm the reports of Grillner & Lund (12) and Grillner et al (13) that reticulospinal excitation is found predominantly in flexor motoneurons.

Grillner & Lund (12) found that stimuli applied to reticular regions outside zone 1 did not evoke direct excitation of hindlimb motoneurons. Our data in Table 1 confirm this finding and indicate that it applies to forelimb motoneurons as well. On the other hand, motoneurons supplying muscles of the neck and back receive direct excitation from a much more extensive region. Both of these groups of axial motoneurons exhibit monosynaptic EPSPs when zones 2 or 3 are stimulated. Since the primary reticulospinal projection from these two zones is via RST_i, it is likely that the EPSPs evoked by stimulating them are produced by activation of RST_i neurons or their axons.

As described in the preceeding discussion of reticulospinal anatomy, RST_i neurons projecting to the neck extend more dorsally and rostrally than those projecting to lower spinal levels. The data in Table 1 reveal one of the physiological correlates of this anatomical distribution: Stimulation of the most dorsal part of *n.r. gigantocellularis,* which is shown as zone 4 in Figure 2, evokes direct excitation only in motoneurons supplying the neck muscles. Thus reticulospinal neurons projecting to motoneurons via RST_i are not only selective in that they act preferentially upon axial motoneurons but are also topographically organized in that neurons that excite neck motoneurons have a much wider spatial distribution than those that excite back motoneurons.

Reticulospinal Inhibition of Motoneurons

Llinás & Terzuolo (21) and Jankowska et al (17) reported that stimulation of Magoun & Rhines' (26) reticular inhibitory area, which corresponds to zones 2 and 3 of Figure 2, produces long-latency, slowly rising inhibitory postsynaptic potentials (IPSPs) in hindlimb motoneurons. The properties of these IPSPs suggested that they were produced by multi-synaptic pathways, although a few motoneurons received somewhat earlier IPSPs that might have been produced by a disynaptic pathway. In our recent studies my colleagues and I (34, 36) have confirmed these earlier observations and have found that they apply to forelimb and back motoneurons as well. The only difference between back and limb motoneurons is that the former are more often seen to receive shorter-latency, presumably disynaptic, IPSPs than are the latter.

A completely different type of reticulospinal inhibitory action is present in motoneurons supplying neck muscles. Stimulation of zones 3 and 4 evokes direct monosynaptic IPSPs in motoneurons supplying the ipsilateral biventer cervicis, complexus, splenius, and trapezius muscles. Mapping and lesion studies have shown that these IPSPs are produced by activation of RST_i neurons (34). In addition to this direct inhibition, neck motoneurons also receive di- or polysynaptic inhibition from zones 1–4 on both sides of the brain stem.

Summary of Reticulo-motor Connections

In addition to monosynaptic inputs from the ipsilateral reticular formation, which have been described above, spinal motoneurons also receive weak, monosynaptic excitation and inhibition from the contralateral reticular formation and indirect, polysynaptic excitation and inhibition from zones 1–5 bilaterally. As originally emphasized by Lloyd (22), the indirect excitation or inhibition is often larger than responses mediated by direct pathways, especially when trains of several stimuli are applied to the reticular formation. Responses mediated by polysynaptic reticulo-motor pathways are difficult to study, however, because they vary with changes in excitability of the interneurons interposed between reticular neurons and motor neurons. Because of this difficulty, most investigations of reticulo-motor connections have concentrated upon the direct pathways.

FUNCTION OF RETICULOSPINAL PATHWAYS

The presence of direct, topographically organized connections between medial pontomedullary reticular neurons and spinal motoneurons strongly suggests that the reticulospinal system plays an important role in controlling the activity of skeletal muscles. The results of studies involving lesions or electrical stimulation of the reticular formation (reviewed above) support this idea and suggest that the reticulospinal system should be considered to be part of the motor apparatus that regulates posture and controls the activity of the axial and girdle muscles. This final section examines information obtained by recording the activity of individual medial reticular neurons to see what conclusions can be reached about participation of these neurons in various motor behaviors.

Studies correlating the activity of pontine reticular neurons with eye movements (6, 15, 18, 23) have provided strong evidence that many of these neurons participate in oculomotor activity. While parallel studies of the relation of reticular activity to body movements are only beginning to appear, there have already been reports (41, 44) that the discharge of some medial pontomedullary reticular neurons in waking animals is specifically correlated with movements of the head or other parts of the body. The same neurons are generally silent during slow wave sleep but become very active during REM sleep (14, 41). This latter activity may be related to the motor activation that accompanies REM sleep or could reflect an involvement of certain reticular neurons in the control of behavioral state. Unfortunately, in this case as in many other studies of neuronal correlates of behavior, there is no proof that the particular neurons studied contributed directly to the corresponding behavior. Hopefully, future experiments will include more complete identification of the locations, projections, and synaptic connections of the neurons studied so that neuronal behavior can be more closely related to the available information on the structure and action of reticular efferent pathways.

Inferences about the functional role of reticulospinal neurons can also be drawn from information about the afferent inputs such neurons receive. These inputs include direct excitatory input from three structures known to be involved in motor control: the sensorimotor cortex (25, 30), the deep cerebellar nuclei (2, 8), and the superior colliculi (11, 30). The presence of such powerful direct pathways indicates that reticulospinal pathways constitute one of the several efferent relay systems that convert the output of higher motor centers into patterns of motor activity. In light of the wide variety of reticular actions mentioned above in the Introduction, it is likely that reticulospinal pathways also act as relays for central control of sensory and autonomic systems.

In addition to inputs from central motor structures, reticulospinal neurons also receive direct excitatory and inhibitory inputs from the spinal cord and vestibular nuclei (8, 25, 29). These spinoreticular and vestibulo-reticular connections constitute pathways by which sensory signals from somatic or labyrinthine receptors may excite or inhibit medial reticular neurons (7, 31, 40). Because they respond to such sensory stimuli, reticular neurons have been considered by some to form part of a central sensory pathway.

For instance, investigators who have observed that reticular neurons respond to somatic stimuli, especially those in the nociceptive range, have concluded that the medial reticular formation may comprise part of an afferent sensory pathway for painful sensations (3, 9, 10).

The hypothesis that the medial reticular formation is part of a sensory pathway encounters some difficulty when reticular responses are observed during repetitive sensory stimulation. As described by Scheibel & Scheibel (39), by Segundo et al (40), and by Peterson et al (32), reticular responses to somatic and vestibular stimuli exhibit strong habituation when these stimuli are presented at moderate rates between 0.25 and 2 Hz. It therefore appears that reticular neurons do not function as simple sensory relay neurons that transmit sensory signals to higher centers. Instead the activity of these neurons is related in some way to behavioral responses to sensory stimuli which typically habituate when those stimuli are repeated. It therefore seems reasonable to conclude that the medial reticular formation is part of the effector apparatus that generates behavioral responses to sudden somatic or vestibular stimuli. The components of those responses mediated by reticular efferent pathways might include ascending activation of the cerebral cortex, modulation of sensory pathways, or autonomic, oculomotor, or skeletomotor activation.

CONCLUSION

Evidence obtained by stimulating the medial reticular formation and by recording the properties of medial reticular neurons in both anesthetized and behaving animals points to the conclusion that the medial pontomedullary reticular formation plays an important role in the control of the skeletal musculature. This reticulo-motor control, which is particularly strong in the case of axial and proximal muscles, in all likelihood forms part of an integrated reticular action on sensory, motor, and autonomic systems that may be elicited either by peripheral sensory stimuli or by command signals from higher nervous centers. The small amount of information now available suggests that the reticulospinal system can elicit both generalized changes in motor activity and relatively specific movements. An important goal of future experiments will be to determine the precise types of motor behavior that are mediated by reticulo-motor pathways.

Acknowledgments

The author's research is supported in part by grant NSF BMS 7500487 from the National Science Foundation and grants NS 02619 and EY 02249 from the N.I.H.

Literature Cited

1. Abzug, C., Maeda, M., Peterson, B. W., Wilson, V. J. 1974. Cervical branching of lumbar vestibulospinal axons. *J. Physiol. London* 243:499–522
2. Bantli, H., Bloedel, J. R. 1975. Monosynaptic activation of a direct reticulospinal pathway by the dentate nucleus. *Pfluegers Arch.* 357:237–42
3. Bowsher, D., Mallart, A., Albe-Fessard, D. 1968. A bulbar relay to centre median. *J. Neurophysiol.* 31:288–300
4. Brinkman, J., Kuypers, H. G. J. M. 1973. Cerebral control of contralateral and ipsilateral arm, hand and finger movements in the split-brain Rhesus monkey. *Brain* 96:653–74
5. Brodal, A. 1957. *The Reticular Formation of the Brain Stem.* Edinburgh: Oliver & Boyd. pp. 8–12
6. Cohen, B., Henn, V. 1972. Unit activity in the pontine reticular formation associated with eye movements. *Brain Res.* 46:403–10
7. Duensing, F., Schaefer, K. P. 1960. Die Aktivität einzelner Neurone der Formatio reticularis des nicht-gefesselten Kaninchens bei Kopfwendungen und vestibulären Reizen. *Arch. Psychiatr. Nervenkr.* 201:97–122
8. Eccles, J. C., Nicoll, R. A., Schwarz, W. F., Taborikova, H., Willey, T. J. 1975. Reticulospinal neurons with and without monosynaptic inputs from cerebellar nuclei. *J. Neurophysiol.* 38:513–30
9. Fields, H. L., Wagner, G. M., Anderson, S. D. 1975. Some properties of spinal neurons projecting to the medial brain-stem reticular formation. *Exp. Neurol.* 47:118–34
10. Fields, H. L., Clanton, C. H., Anderson, S. D. 1977. Somatosensory properties of spinoreticular neurons in the cat. *Brain Res.* 120:49–66
11. Grantyn, A. A., Grantyn, R. 1976. Synaptic actions of tectofugal pathways on abducens motoneurons in the cat. *Brain Res.* 105:269–85
12. Grillner, S., Lund, S. 1968. The origin of a descending pathway with monosynaptic action on flexor motoneurones. *Acta Physiol. Scand.* 74:274–84
13. Grillner, S., Hongo, T., Lund, S. 1971. Convergent effects on alpha motoneurones from the vestibulospinal tract and a pathway descending in the medial longitudinal fasciculus. *Exp. Brain Res.* 12:457–79
14. Hobson, J. A., McCarley, R. W., Pivik, R. T., Freedman, R. 1975. Selective firing of cat pontine brain stem neurons in desynchronized sleep. *J. Neurophysiol.* 37:497–511
15. Hikosaka, O., Kawakami, T. 1977. Inhibitory reticular neurons related to the quick phase of vestibular nystagmus. Their location and projection. *Exp. Brain Res.* 27:377–96
16. Ito, M., Udo, M., Mano, N. 1970. Long inhibitory and excitatory pathways converging onto cat's reticular and Deiters' neurons, and their relevance to the reticulofugal axons. *J. Neurophysiol.* 33:210–26
17. Jankowska, E., Lundberg, A., Roberts, W. J., Stuart, D. 1974. A long propriospinal system with direct effect on motoneurones and interneurones in the cat lumbosacral cord. *Exp. Brain Res.* 21:169–94
18. Keller, E. L. 1974. Participation of medial pontine reticular formation in eye movement generation in monkey. *J. Neurophysiol.* 37:316–32
19. Kuypers, H. G. J. M. 1964. The descending pathways to the spinal cord, their anatomy and function. In *Organization of the Spinal Cord,* ed. J. C. Eccles, J. Schadé, pp. 178–200. New York: Elsevier
20. Kuypers, H. G. J. M., Fleming, W. R., Farinholt, J. W. 1962. Subcorticospinal projections in the rhesus monkey. *J. Comp. Neurol.* 118:107–37
21. Llinás, R., Terzuolo, C. A. 1964. Mechanisms of supraspinal actions upon spinal cord activities. Reticular inhibitory mechanisms on alpha-extensor motoneurons. *J. Neurophysiol.* 27:579–91
22. Lloyd, D. P. C. 1941. Activity in neurons of the bulbospinal correlation system. *J. Neurophysiol.* 4:115–34
23. Luschei, E. S., Fuchs, A. F. 1972. Activity of brain stem neurons during eye movements of alert monkeys. *J. Neurophysiol.* 35:445–61
24. Magni, F., Willis, W. D. 1964. Cortical control of brain stem reticular neurons. *Arch. Ital. Biol.* 102:418–33
25. Magni, F., Willis, W. D. 1964. Subcortical and peripheral control of brain stem reticular neurons. *Arch. Ital. Biol.* 102:434–48
26. Magoun, H. W., Rhines, R. 1946. An inhibitory mechanism in the bulbar reticular formation. *J. Neurophysiol.* 9:165–71
27. Nyberg-Hansen, R. 1966. Functional organization of descending supraspinal fibre systems to the spinal cord. Anatomical observations and physio-

logical correlations. *Ergeb. Anat. Ent-wicklungsgesch.* 39(2):1–48
28. Peterson, B. W. 1977. Identification of reticulospinal projections that may participate in gaze control. In *Control of Gaze by Brain Stem Neurons, Developments in Neuroscience,* ed. R. Baker, A. Berthoz, 1:143–52. Amsterdam: Elsevier
29. Peterson, B. W., Abzug, C. 1975. Properties of projections from vestibular nuclei to medial reticular formation in the cat. *J. Neurophysiol.* 38:1421–35
30. Peterson, B. W., Anderson, M. E., Filion, M. 1974. Responses of pontomedullary reticular neurons to cortical, tectal and cutaneous stimuli. *Exp. Brain Res.* 21:19–44
31. Peterson, B. W., Filion, M., Felpel, L. P., Abzug, C. 1975. Responses of medial reticular neurons to stimulation of the vestibular nerve. *Exp. Brain Res.* 22:335–50
32. Peterson, B. W., Franck, J. I., Pitts, N. G., Daunton, N. G. 1976. Changes in responses of medial pontomedullary reticular neurons during repetitive cutaneous, vestibular, cortical and tectal stimulation. *J. Neurophysiol.* 39:564–81
33. Peterson, B. W., Maunz, R. A., Pitts, N. G., Mackel, R. G. 1975. Patterns of projection and branching of reticulospinal neurons. *Exp. Brain Res.* 23:333–51
34. Peterson, B. W., Pitts, N. G., Fukushima, K., Mackel, R. 1978. Reticulospinal excitation and inhibition of neck motoneurons. *Exp. Brain Res.* 32: 471–89
35. Petras, J. M. 1967. Cortical, tectal and tegmental fiber connections in the spinal cord of the cat. *Brain Res.* 6:275–324
36. Pitts, N. G., Fukushima, K., Peterson, B. W. 1977. Reticulospinal action on cervical, thoracic and lumbar motoneu-rons. *Ann. Meet. Soc. Neurosci., 7th.* No. 276 (Abstr.)
37. Rexed, B. 1952. The cytoarchitectonic organization of the spinal cord in the cat. *J. Comp. Neurol.* 96:415–95
38. Rhines, R., Magoun, H. W. 1946. Brain stem facilitation of cortical motor response. *J. Neurophysiol.* 9:219–29
39. Scheibel, M. E., Scheibel, A. B. 1965. The response of reticular units to repetitive stimuli. *Arch Ital. Biol.* 103:279–99
40. Segundo, J. P., Takenaka, T., Encabo, H. 1967. Somatic sensory properties of bulbar reticular neurons. *J. Neurophysiol.* 30:1221–38
41. Siegel, J. M., McGinty, D. J. 1977. Pontine reticular formation neurons: relationship of discharge to motor activity. *Science* 176:678–80
42. Sprague, J. M., Chambers, W. W. 1954. Control of posture by reticular formation and cerebellum in the intact, anesthetized and unanesthetized and in the decerebrated cat. *Am. J. Physiol.* 176:52–64
43. Sterling, P., Kuypers, H. G. J. M. 1968. Anatomical organization of the brachial spinal cord of the cat III. The propriospinal connections. *Brain Res.* 7:419–43
44. Vertes, R. P. 1977. Selective firing of rat pontine gigantocellular neurons during movement and REM sleep. *Brain Res.* 128:146–52
45. Wilson, V. J., Yoshida, M. 1969. Comparison of effects of stimulation of Deiters' nucleus and medial longitudinal fasciculus on neck, forelimb and hindlimb motoneurons. *J. Neurophysiol.* 32:743–58
46. Wilson, V. J., Yoshida, M., Schor, R. H. 1970. Supraspinal monosynaptic excitation and inhibition of thoracic back motoneurons. *Exp. Brain Res.* 11:282–95

Ann. Rev. Physiol. 1979. 41:141–57

POSTERIOR PARIETAL CORTEX: RELATIONS OF UNIT ACTIVITY TO SENSORIMOTOR FUNCTION

♦1211

Ian Darian-Smith, Kenneth O. Johnson, and Antony W. Goodwin

Sensory Processes Laboratory, Department of Physiology, University of Melbourne, Parkville, Victoria, Australia.

INTRODUCTION

We focus this review of single neuron activity in the cortex on recent work concerning the organization and function of the posterior parietal cortex of the primate. Such restriction of the field involves compromise but seems justified, in part by reviews of recent studies (60, 61) of sensorimotor cortex in the immediate region of the central sulcus, and also by the series of interesting recent investigations of the monkey's posterior parietal cortex (33, 34, 45, 52, 53, 55, 63, 66, 67, 78). We take the view that such single neuron studies must be considered, not alone, but along with other investigations that aim to analyze the functions of parietal cortex in the primate.

The particular interest of the posterior parietal cortex is that although its integrity is essential for normal perceptual and motor function, the nature of this behavioral dependency differs from that relating, say, visual perception with striate cortex, or movement with the neuron populations within the precentral gyrus. Early clinical studies of posterior parietal cortex (11, 14, 15) showed that patients with a lesion of this region, although able to detect and locate a small solid object placed in the hand, may be unable to recognize its form ("astereognosis"). Also the patient, although in no way paralyzed, may have difficulty in using common objects such as a knife or a pencil [various types of "apraxia"; (14)]. A detailed description of the behavioral changes brought about by destruction of the parietal cortex was built up from these clinical studies, and from parallel ablation studies in the monkey (3, 14, 21, 23, 32, 47, 49, 59).

141

0066-4278/79/0301-0141$01.00

It was not until methods for recording the activity of single neurons within the cerebral cortex of the alert, behaviorally responsive animal were devised in the late 1960s (24, 25) that worthwhile neurophysiological studies of the posterior parietal cortex became a reality. When combined with appropriate "shaping" of the animal's behavior, with carefully specified stimulus procedures, and with the appropriate analysis of experimental data, this technique provides a new approach to the study of functions of the neocortex. Further, by using monkeys in these studies, the behavioral and neurophysiological investigations can be more closely compared than is possible when nonprimate mammals are used for the single neuron recording.

New histological methods for tracing neuronal connections within the nervous system—selective silver staining of degenerating axon terminals (26), and tagging procedures dependent on axonal transport (10, 13, 48, 74)—have substantially expanded our knowledge of the connections of the posterior neocortex to both subcortical structures and to other zones of cortex.

The problem of recording the responses of single cortical neurons in the alert animal having been solved, the major stumbling block in studies of posterior parietal cortex is now conceptual rather than technical. What questions should be asked about single neurons located in a region of cortex that may be concerned neither with the simple representation of the spatial and temporal characteristics of some peripheral stimulus, nor with the direct control of movements of skeletal muscle? Should we try to identify and characterize correlations between the neuron's activity and particular sensory stimuli or particular movements of the animal? Should we attempt to relate this neuronal activity to particular behavioral states, such as the monkey's selective attention either to particular sensory or motor events or to previous experience of these events? These questions have been central issues in recent exploratory studies.

We first review the effects of destructive lesions of the posterior parietal cortex in the primate. Next, recent studies of the responses of single neurons in the cortex are examined. Finally, the connections of this cortex, evident from recent investigations, are reviewed. The goal common to these different studies has been the identification of causal relations between sensorimotor behavior and neural events within the posterior parietal cortex—an identification quite difficult to establish, even for the simplest behavior.

Topography of Posterior Parietal Cortex

The homotypical parietal cortex in man and several genera of Old World monkeys (*Macaca, Cercopithecus*) are similar but not identical in their fissural and cytoarchitectural patterns. Two main zones are recognized.

Area 5 of Brodmann in man corresponds approximately with the superior temporal lobule in the macaque, being bound superiorly by area 2 of the postcentral gyrus, posterio-inferiorly by the superior lip of the intraparietal sulcus, and extending onto the medial surface of the hemisphere. The same area is termed PE by Economo (19) and by Bonin & Bailey (6). Area 7 of Brodmann in man corresponds approximately with the inferior parietal lobule of the macaque brain (areas PG and PF of Bonin & Bailey) (6). Antero-superiorly this area constitutes the inferior lip of the intraparietal sulcus, and it is juxtaposed with area 19 along its posterior margin. The lateral boundary of area 7 is poorly defined in the macaque brain (6); it is uncertain whether areas homologous with the supramarginal and angular gyri of man (areas 40 and 39) occur in the macaque (6, 57).

BEHAVIORAL DEFICITS FOLLOWING LESIONS OF POSTERIOR PARIETAL CORTEX

For all their limitations (9, 75), studies of the effects of focal lesions in the central nervous system on behavior provide information not attainable with other methods. Stein's recent report (73) illustrates this. Neuronal activity in small areas of cortex in an alert, active monkey was blocked for a short period by cooling the cortex with a device attached to the skull. On cooling area 5 the monkey developed a severe "clumsiness" of its contralateral arm and hand, and was unable to reach for and grasp a raisin; all movements of the limb were similarly affected. During the same period of cooling all movements in the ipsilateral limb appeared to be normal. When area 7 was cooled, however, the movements of the contralateral arm were much less clumsy until the hand was moved into the contralateral visual field. The monkey then moved his arm and hand "as if visual guidance was lost in this field." Even movements of the ipsilateral hand within the contralateral visual field were clumsy, although normal within the ipsilateral visual field. This spatial disorientation may well have resulted directly from a loss of visual information. Stein did not ascertain whether this apparent visual deficit was the direct result of cooling area 7, or of cooling adjacent structures with a known visual function, such as area 19 or the optic radiation just beneath area 7. By contrast, the clumsiness following blockage of area 5 could have resulted from loss of kinesthetic information, or from some impairment of the control of movements of the limb. Further experimental dissection must decide between these possibilities.

Stein's study follows a long series of investigations of the effects of permanent unilateral and bilateral lesions of the posterior parietal cortex of the monkey (3, 14, 21, 23, 32, 47, 49, 59, 65). Usually, however, the lesion has included both areas 5 and 7 of the cortex. The major effects of a unilateral posterior parietal lesion including areas 5 and 7 are:

1. Imprecision of movement of the contralateral arm and hand when reaching out and attempting to grasp an object in space. This inaccuracy is most apparent when these movements relate to "extrapersonal" or "allocentric" space—i.e. the space external to the body. Limb movements of tactual and visual placing reactions are of this type, and are commonly absent in these animals. By contrast, limb movements relating to "personal" space are not impaired—e.g. movements of the hand to the mouth are normal. In the studies preceding that of Stein the observed spatial disorientation was not explicable in terms of a lack of visual cues, presumably because the parietal lesions examined were rarely limited to area 7.
2. Loss of spontaneous movements of the contralateral limbs, and a reluctance to use them.
3. Impairment in the contralateral limbs of tactile discrimination of two-dimensioned patterns, or three-dimensioned objects, of the discrimination of textured surfaces, and of the discrimination of weights.
4. Impaired visual discrimination of spatial patterns, particularly when the dimensions of the pattern require a shift in the monkey's fixation point in order to scan those features of importance in the differentiation.

In most of these experimental studies no gross sensory loss, such as a visual field defect, loss of visual acuity, or of tactile sensibility, has been demonstrated. Nonetheless, Stein's observations and the fact that lesions involving area 7 commonly also damage the underlying optic radiation [evident from the retrograde degeneration in the medial part of the lateral geniculate body (47, 59)] emphasize that the possibility of sensory loss cannot be lightly dismissed as a factor contributing to the monkey's disorientation in space and to his other disabilities.

Posterior parietal lesions in man cause much more complex disability than that observed in the monkey, largely because of the evolution of cerebral functional asymmetry. However, patients with a posterior parietal lesion in the nondominant hemisphere may develop sensorimotor dysfunction that in many ways resembles the monkey's (14, 15). The striking symptoms in these patients are visual and somesthetic indifference to extrapersonal space contralateral to the lesion and loss of motor responses appropriate to stimuli presented within this space. Denny-Brown (14) termed this behavioral disability amorphosynthesis, and considered the behavioral deficit to stem from a breakdown in the early stages of the perceptual process. Semmes (69, 70) considered that some loss of tactual or visual sensory information, along with a deficit in the processing of all information concerning extrapersonal space contralateral to the lesion, together contribute to the behavioral impairment resulting from a posterior parietal lesion. Semmes, too, considered the deficit to be perceptual. Passingham & Ettlinger (57), on the other hand, advocate caution in accepting a perceptual basis for all the effects of a posterior parietal lesion on behavior. Bates & Ettlinger (3) have also proposed that impaired tactual discrimination observed in the lesioned monkey may be secondary to "selective motor retardation" that limits the manual exploration of patterns and objects, rather than the result of a sensory or perceptual deficit. A motor deficit of this type could account for impaired somesthetic discrimination when the animal cannot see the object to be identified.

Lesions of the posterior parietal cortex in either the nondominant or dominant hemisphere in man may result in a more generalized behavioral disturbance that is not simply related to extrapersonal space contralateral to the lesion (14, 15). The exact specification of these varied behavioral changes has evoked much controversy (4, 11, 12, 20, 22, 46), particularly the so-called visual agnosias, but virtually all investigators at least agree that the patient's primary deficit is perceptual.

SINGLE NEURON ACTIVITY IN POSTERIOR PARIETAL CORTEX

As long as we are concerned with responses within neuron populations virtually dedicated to the representation of particular sensory or motor events, the objectives of single neuron analysis are clear enough. With sensory neuron populations we wish to know what characteristics of a particular stimulus are represented in the responses of individual cells, how well they are represented, how the information signalled by individual neurons is combined with that signalled by other cells in the responding population, and what events in other parts of the nervous system may modify this representation. Similarly, with investigations of neuron populations with a primary motor function the analysis is based on correlation of the responses of the individual neuron and relevant defined movements of the limbs, fingers, etc.

When, however, we examine the responses of a neuron population whose function is uncertain or complex, the questions to be asked may not be at all obvious. Should we now look for correlations between the responses of these neurons and particular sensory stimuli, or particular movements? Or should we seek correlations between the neuron's activity and other behavioral events or behavioral states; and, if so, which of these events or states? These questions can be attacked logically only if we have some realistic concept of the overall function of this neuron population, derived perhaps from lesion studies, or from analysis of the connections of the population. The success of the study will ultimately depend on how well this model reflects the actual function of the neuron population.

In recent studies (33, 34, 45, 52, 53, 55, 63, 66, 67, 78) of single neuron activity in areas 5 and 7 of the monkey's parietal cortex a serious attempt has been made to answer some of these questions. The model of the functions of the posterior parietal cortex proposed by each of the laboratories whose work is reviewed in the following pages differs somewhat, and this is clearly reflected in their experiments. Mountcastle (52) describes the starting point of his analysis of single neuron analysis as follows: "We took our clues from the defects in volition displayed by monkeys with parietal lobe lesions and designed our first task to require that the animal attend visually to signals or targets in his immediate environment and that he explore that space manually in order to earn a reward." In contrast, Robinson and his colleagues (63) considered that studies of the effects of parietal lesions point to a primarily perceptual function for areas 5 and 7.

Single Neuron Responses in Area 5

The most extensive study of area 5 is that of Mountcastle and his colleagues (52, 53, 55), who identified the response properties of 977 neurons in alert, behaviorally responsive monkeys. Most of the neurons responded to passive manipulation of the joints (64%), the skin (12%), muscle (3%), or other deep tissue (9%). One class of neurons identified by them differed markedly from the rest in that they could not be driven by any form of passive manipulation of the somatic tissues. Within this class they identified two subsets: projection neurons (5%) and hand manipulation neurons (4%). Projection neurons discharged only when the animal reached for a behaviorally relevant object such as food or the behavioral testing apparatus associated with the reward. The hand manipulation neurons discharged only when the animal grasped and manipulated these objects. Most of these neurons were silent during other projection and hand manipulation movements, such as those of an aggressive nature. They were identical to a class studied by Mountcastle's group (45) in area 7, except that a smaller percentage were related to movement in the ipsilateral limbs (8% in area 5 versus 29% in area 7).

Earlier studies on waking paralyzed primates by Sakata et al (66, 67) and Duffy & Burchfiel (18) yielded results similar to those of Mountcastle except that they did not, of course, observe any responses related to active movement.

Single Neuron Activity in Area 7

The major study of area 7 is again that of Mountcastle and associates (45, 52, 53, 55, 78). Since they observed no neurons that responded to auditory stimuli, all of their behavioral training was aimed at controlling eye movements, hand and arm movements, and the stimulus to which the animal was attending. By recording all of the behavioral, stimulus, and neural events they were able to test the correlation of the neural events with either stimulus or behavioral events. They developed a classification scheme containing 5 major classes of neurons. Typical responses of these classes of neurons are represented diagrammatically in Figure 1.

Projection and manipulation neurons were observed in area 7 and differed from those in area 5 only in that they more often involved the ipsilateral limb or more than one limb.

Light sensitive neurons were called visual space neurons in the first report (55) but were studied more extensively later (78). These neurons have large, peripheral receptive fields that were never found to include the fovea. This was the only major class reported by Mountcastle and associates that could be driven by a stimulus in the absence of eye or limb movements. The remaining three classes were categorized according to the relationship between their responses and associated eye movements.

Visual fixation neurons formed the largest of the classes in which the response was related to eye movements. Their discharge rate increased significantly when the animal fixated objects that were behaviorally relevant and close to the animal. These neurons were not activated by visual stimuli that were not fixated, nor by any nonvisual stimuli or movement. Many of these neurons had restricted gaze fields, defined by Lynch et al (45) as ". . . that zone in space in which fixation of the light is associated with an increased activity of the cell." Some neurons were active over the entire space (7%). Others were restricted to a quadrant or a hemifield. They observed a moderate bias (approximately 60%) towards contralateral gaze fields. The discharge of these neurons persisted throughout smooth pursuit eye movements tracking the stimulus within the gaze field, but was suppressed following a sudden displacement of the stimulus and during the saccadic eye movement to the new fixation point.

Saccade neurons discharged following a sudden displacement of the fixation stimulus to a new point and usually before the onset of saccadic eye movement to the new location. The onset of discharge in these neurons had a mean latency of 126 ± 39 ms (SD) (78) relative to the stimulus displacement, and in those neurons where the discharge preceded the saccade the average period between the onset of discharge and the onset of the saccade was 73 ± 39 ms (SD) (45). The responses of these neurons were tested for displacement of the target in the four directions left, right, up, and down. Approximately half the saccade neurons responded only in tasks with target displacement in one of the four directions tested; the remainder responded in 2, 3, or all of the directions tested. None responded before spontaneous saccades in the dark, nor did they respond to peripheral visual stimuli

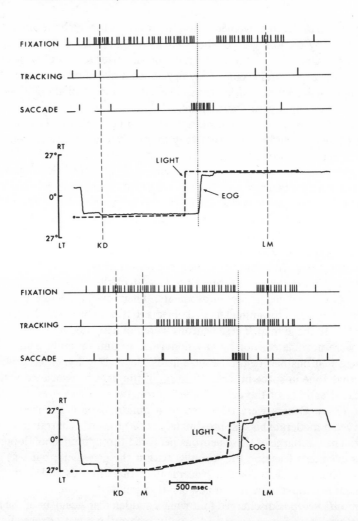

Figure 1 Schematic diagram of the activity of the three classes of visual neurons in area 7 during a visually evoked saccade and during a smooth pursuit movement. Patterns of discharges typical of fixation, tracking, and saccade cells are shown during a period of steady fixation (above) and a smooth pursuit movement (below); each is interrupted by a 27° saccade from left to right. The fixation cell is assumed to subtend a gaze field covering the entire tangent screen so that it is active during periods of steady gaze and during smooth pursuit movements but is abruptly suppressed before and during the saccades. The saccade cell is active before and during rightward saccades. The visual tracking cell is active during smooth pursuit movements to the right; it is not accurate during the steady fixations and is suppressed if a saccadic movement is superimposed on the smooth pursuit. [From (45)]

comparable to those used in the saccade tasks when the animal was required to maintain fixation on the primary spot rather than saccade to the peripheral stimulus.

Visual tracking neurons discharged during smooth pursuit tracking of a moving stimulus but not while fixating a stationary stimulus. Within limits, Mountcastle et al found little relationship between the speed of tracking and the discharge rate. Most of these neurons (90%) responded to movements in one direction only.

The remainder of the neurons observed in area 7 either could not be activated by any of the procedures used, or had complex response properties that required further study. They found no relationship between the response properties of the cells and their locations within area 7 nor did they observe any dramatic relationship between the functional properties of the neurons and their depth relative to the layers of the cortex.

In the second important study of area 7, Robinson and associates (63) examined 289 neurons and reported that almost all cells had response properties similar to those of neurons in area 5, neurons in the frontal eye fields (area 8) (28, 50), or neurons in the superficial layers of the superior colliculus (29, 62, 68). A small fraction (33 units, 12%) could not be activated by their procedures, which consisted of general somatic manipulation, stimuli of the type commonly used in studying visual responses, and behavioral procedures as outlined below. Sixty-two neurons (22%) responded to somesthetic stimuli and not visual stimuli. They reported that these neurons were similar to neurons studied by themselves and others in area 5 (18, 55, 67).

All of the remaining 194 neurons (66%) were responsive to visual stimuli in the absence of eye or hand movements, although some of their responses were modified by the behavioral context. The receptive fields were all large, and no topographic organization was observed except for a bias towards receptive fields in the lower contralateral quadrant of the visual field. Ipsilateral, contralateral, and bilateral fields were observed that occupied a confined circular region, a quadrant, a hemifield, or the entire visual field. No quantitative breakdown of field sizes or locations was reported; however, in one figure illustrating 27 receptive fields in two monkeys, the receptive fields ranged in size from 2° diameter to fields that occupied three quadrants. Six receptive fields in that sample included the monkey's visual fixation point and therefore the fovea. Many cells showed graded, increasing responses to stimuli with increasing area or increasing intensity. No cells had properties typical of neurons in the geniculostriate system such as orientation specificity or surround inhibition. The most remarkable feature of the responses was the lack of specificity for any of the stimulus configurations used.

All of the above properties were determined while the animal fixated on a single stationary spot. Some cells displayed additional properties when tasks requiring eye or hand movements were used; 27 neurons (9%) showed enhanced responses to stimuli in their receptive fields when these stimuli were targets of saccadic eye movements. These enhanced responses were similar to those observed previously in the superior colliculus and the frontal eye fields (30, 51, 76, 77). Fifteen neurons (5%) discharged during smooth pursuit tracking of a target moving in a specific direction but discharged equally well when the eyes fixated a stationary spot and a second moving stimulus was employed. Seven neurons exhibited an enhanced response to a visual stimulus when the animal reached to touch the stimulus.

A third study in area 7 is that of Hyvarinen and associates (33, 34), who studied the response properties of 193 single units. Their analysis is based mainly on observations, in untrained monkeys, of the stimuli and behavioral responses that were effective in activating each of the neurons. Their study was primarily a qualitative survey of the responses observed in area 7, and thus they were unable to assess whether the responses were related to the stimulus or to movement. Nonetheless, they report many phenomena similar to those reported by Mountcastle and associates (45, 55, 78) and by Robinson et al (63).

CONNECTIONS OF POSTERIOR PARIETAL CORTEX

Analysis of the connections of the posterior parietal cortex in the primate has provided additional evidence concerning its functional organization. In the classic model of "association cortex" (27), sensory information was considered to reach the posterior parietal cortex solely through cortico-cortical projections from the postcentral gyrus (areas 3, 1, and 2) and striate cortex. After transformation within the posterior parietal cortex this information was considered to be relayed to the frontal cortex, and ultimately to the motor cortex.

This model was modified somewhat following the identification of thalamic input to the posterior parietal cortex from the pulvinar-posterior nuclear complex (64). In this scheme, thalamic nuclei projecting to the cerebral cortex were considered to be of two types: *extrinsic* nuclei (such as the ventrobasal complex and lateral geniculate body, which received input from structures outside the thalamus—in particular from sense organs—and in turn projected only to the primary sensory cortical areas), and *intrinsic* nuclei, which received input from other thalamic nuclei, and projected only to "association cortex."

In recent years substantial additional connections of the posterior parietal cortex have been demonstrated, so that the possible pathways for the transfer and transformation of sensory information within the neocortex, and for input to the motor systems, have been greatly multiplied. Important new observations include: (a) The pulvinar-posterior-nuclear complex of the thalamus does receive extrathalamic input from the major sense organs (5, 31, 36, 37); (b) the cortico-cortical connections of posterior parietal cortex are more extensive and complex than previous analysis suggested (1, 8, 31, 35, 39, 40, 42, 48, 56, 58, 71, 72); (c) the posterior parietal cortex has extensive potential indirect input to motor systems, at both cortical and subcortical levels (17, 31); (d) the posterior parietal cortex has connections with the cingulate gyrus, which in turn projects to the limbic system (48, 58, 71, 72); and (e) certain of the intralaminar nuclei of the thalamus have connections with the posterior parietal cortex (38).

Input from the Thalamus

The major thalamic relay of somatosensory information to the cortex is the ventrobasal complex, which projects only to somatosensory areas I and II in the postcentral gyrus and not beyond (39, 41). However, other thalamic nuclei do receive input from the skin and other somatic tissues, and also have projections to the neocortex. In the monkey, spinothalamic fibers terminate in rather poorly defined zones along the dorsal and caudal boundaries of the ventrobasal complex (37), and neurons within this region project to the lateral part of the superior parietal lobule (area 5) (2, 43, 47). Spinothalamic fibers also terminate in the central lateral nucleus of the intralaminar complex, from which cells project to a rather extensive area of the parietal cortex (37).

Projections of the retina to the posterior neocortex are complex and still not well defined (36). In the primate, cortical terminations of neurons in the lateral geniculate body have been demonstrated only within area 17. In the extrageniculostriate system the main retinal projection is to the superior colliculus. Neurons in the superficial laminae of the superior colliculus project to various parts of the inferior pulvinar (5), which in turn project to the cerebral cortex to visual areas 17, 18, and 19 of Brodmann (7, 16). The limited data available suggest that these projections retain some retinotopic organization.

These data suggest that the sensory thalamocortical input to posterior neocortex consists of two parallel systems. The first of these consists of visual and somatosensory projections from the lateral geniculate body and the ventrobasal complex to striate cortex (area 17) and somatosensory areas I and II. The second pathway relays in thalamic zones adjacent to the major sensory nuclei, which in turn project to "perisensory cortex" (areas 5, 18, and 19) adjacent to the primary sensory cortical areas (31). Area 7 appears not to have such a direct association with *extrinsic* thalamic nuclei.

Cortico-Cortical Connections of Posterior Parietal Cortex

A structural framework for further cortical processing of sensory information subsequent to its transfer to the primary sensory cortex is provided by the cortico-cortical connections. Recent work of Jones and others (17, 31, 35, 36, 42, 44, 56, 58, 71, 72) has resulted in an elegant synthesis of these connections. In general, each primary sensory area of cortex (areas 3, 1, 2, and 17) projects to both an adjacent zone within the parieto-temporal cortex and also to a particular region of the frontal cortex. Each cortical zone receiving input from primary sensory cortex then projects to another adjacent cortical area within the parieto-temporal cortex, as well as to a new zone in the frontal cortex. In addition, each cortico-cortical projection is matched by a reciprocal connection.

One result of this pattern of connections is that some regions of parietal cortex (areas 5, 18, and 19) have a direct, large, and reciprocal link with one of the areas of primary sensory cortex. The connections of the areas termed "proximal association cortex" by Graybiel (31) (areas 5, 18, and 19) ensure that (*a*) sensory processing within this cortex is largely restricted to a single sensory modality, and (*b*) the topographic representation of the peripheral receptor sheet is retained. Neurophysiological studies of each of these areas of cortex confirm this expectation.

Area 7 differs from the "proximal association cortex" in that it has no direct cortico-cortical link with either visual or somatosensory primary cortex. Sensory information must reach area 7 through indirect cortico-cortical connections, or possibly from projections from the pulvinar-posterior nuclear complex of the thalamus. Both visual and somatosensory information could be relayed by these pathways. Graybiel (31) has used the term "remote association cortex" for cortex, such as area 7, that has no direct input from primary sensory cortical areas.

Connections of Posterior Parietal Cortex with Motor Systems

The various zones of association cortex do have extensive, reciprocal connections with frontal cortex. The different zones of "proximal association cortex," including area 5, each have projections to the periarcuate area, whereas "remote association cortex," including area 7, has connections with the prearcuate area around the principal sulcus (areas 8 and 46). This whole frontal projection area sends fibers to motor cortex (area 4), providing a possible cortical link between association cortex and the motor system (35, 36, 40)—an anatomical link whose functional significance has yet to be demonstrated.

An anatomical link with the limbic system may be similarly traced out for area 7. Connections between area 7 and the cingulate gyrus have been demonstrated using the horseradish peroxidase technique (17, 71).

Pathways linking association cortex with area 4 are not all cortico-cortical. Those cortical zones linked with visual function (areas 18, 19, and 20) have projections to the pulvinar-posterior nuclear complex, which in turn provides a reentrant projection to the periarcuate zone of the frontal cortex (36). Area 7 also has subcortical connections with nucleus ventralis lateralis, n. ventralis anterior, nuclei of the basal forebrain, and with pontine nuclei, each of which has connections with motor pathways (17, 71).

COMMENT

It is not easy to integrate the information about a particular neuron population within the central nervous system obtained from studies of its connections, the functional characteristics of the constituent cells, and the modifications of behavior following destruction of this population. However, with neuron populations in the posterior parietal cortex the combined evidence supports not only the idea that areas 5 and 7 differ in their organization from the adjacent primary sensory cortex, but also that these two areas differ substantially from each other. Area 5 (Graybiel's "proximal association cortex") retains a close functional association with primary somatosensory cortex, evident from the somatic input to most neurons and the maintenance of some degree of topographic representation of the contralateral somatic tissues. On the other hand, area 7 (Graybiel's "remote association cortex") is less directly linked with primary sensory cortex; it receives input from both somatic receptors and from the eye, it lacks a topographic representation of these peripheral receptor sheets, and its destruction modifies limb movements dependent on both somesthetic and visual sensory information.

Recently Mountcastle (54) has presented a provocative account of the intrinsic and extrinsic organization of the whole neocortex. He has sought to separate the common and the dissimilar features of those areas of cortex that are different in their cytoarchitecture and in their overall function—such as primary sensory cortex and the various types of "association" cortex we have examined. Mountcastle argues that the feature common to all types of neocortex is their vertically oriented "columnar" organization, and that the functional differences between different cortical areas results from their extrinsic connections.

One final comment relates to a fundamental difference between single-neuron studies in a cortical region such as area 7 and similar studies in the primary sensory or motor areas. The basic functions and the topographic representation of information in the primary sensory and motor areas had been established by lesions, anatomy, and gross electrophysiology before the first single-neuron studies were undertaken. Thus, in single-neuron studies in these primary areas the investigator was not confronted with the most fundamental questions of function and representation. This is not the case in the analysis of area 7. Neither anatomical nor lesion studies have clearly specified the function of this cortex. Thus single-neuron studies are now faced with solving the most fundamental problems of function and representation. However, the range of possibilities in any such area is enormous. A complex region such as area 7 might serve some basic function such as the transformation, integration, storage, or retrieval of information related to the sensory, motor, or cognitive functions of the brain. Alternatively, it might serve some broad administrative role, such as focussing or sequencing activity in other areas. Moreover, it might serve more than one of these functions concurrently.

How can this question of function and representation be effectively answered by single-neuron studies? Mountcastle, Robinson, and their associates have endeavored to control precisely the stimulus, the motor behavior, the behavioral context, and the data collection in order to test correlations between neural responses and the experimental variables at their disposal. It is hard to see any alternative to the approaches they have taken.

Literature Cited

1. Allman, J. M., Kaas, J. H. 1976. Representation of the visual field on the medial wall of occipital-parietal cortex in the owl monkey. *Science* 191:572–75
2. Baleydier, C., Mauguiere, F. 1977. Pulvinar-latero posterior afferents to cortical area 7 in monkeys demonstrated by horseradish peroxidase tracing technique. *Exp. Brain Res.* 27:501–7
3. Bates, J. A. V., Ettlinger, G. 1960. Posterior biparietal ablations in the monkey. *Arch. Neurol.* 3:177–92
4. Bay, E. 1953. Disturbances of visual perception and their examination. *Brain* 76:515–50
5. Benevento, L. A., Fallon, J. H. 1975. The ascending projections of the superior colliculus in the rhesus monkey (*Macaca mulatta*) *J. Comp. Neurol.* 160:339–62
6. Bonin, G. von, Bailey, P. 1947. *The Neocortex of Macaca mulatta.* Urbana, Ill.: Univ. Illinois Press. pp. 1–100
7. Burton, H., Jones, E. G. 1976. The posterior thalamic region and its cortical projection in new world and old world monkeys. *J. Comp. Neurol.* 168:249–302
8. Chavis, D. A., Pandya, D. N. 1976. Further observations on corticofrontal connections in the rhesus monkey. *Brain Res.* 117:369–86
9. Chow, K. L. 1967. Effects of ablation. In *The Neurosciences: A Study Program,* ed. G. C. Quarton, T. Melnechuck, F. O. Schmitt, pp. 705–13. New York: Rockefeller Univ. Press
10. Cowan, W. M., Gottlieb, F. I., Hendrickson, A. E., Price, J. L., Woolsey, T. A. 1972. The autoradiographic demonstration of axonal connections in the central nervous system. *Brain Res.* 37:21–51
11. Critchley, M. 1953. *The Parietal Lobes.* London: Arnold. 480 pp.
12. Critchley, M. 1964. The problem of visual agnosia. *J. Neurol. Sci.* 1:274–90
13. Dekker, J. J., Kievet, J., Jacobson, S., Kuypers, H. G. J. M. 1975. Retrograde axonal transport of horseradish peroxidase in the forebrain of the rat, cat and monkey. In *Golgi Symp. Proc.,* ed. M. Santini, pp. 201–8. New York: Raven
14. Denny-Brown, D., Chambers, R. A. 1958. The parietal lobe and behavior. *Res. Publ. Assoc. Res. Nerv. Ment. Dis.* 36:35–117
15. Denny-Brown, D., Meyer, J. S., Horenstein, S. 1952. The significance of perceptual rivalry resulting from parietal lesion. *Brain* 75:433–71

16. DeVito, J. L., Simmons, D. M. 1976. Some connections of the posterior thalamus in monkey. *Exp. Neurol.* 51:347–62

17. Divac, I., LaVail, J. H., Rakic, P., Winston, K. R. 1977. Heterogeneous afferents to the inferior parietal lobule of the rhesus monkey revealed by the retrograde transport method. *Brain Res.* 123:197–207

18. Duffy, F. H., Burchfiel, J. L. 1971. Somatosensory system: organizational hierarchy from units in monkey area 5. *Science* 172:273–75

19. Economo, V. von. 1929. *The Cytoarchitectonics of the Human Cerebral Cortex.* London: Oxford Univ. Press. 186 pp.

20. Ettlinger, G. 1956. Sensory deficits in visual agnosia. *J. Neurol. Neurosurg. Psychiatr.* 19:297–307

21. Ettlinger, G., Kalsbeck, J. E. 1962. Changes in tactile discrimination and in visual reaching after successive and simultaneous bilateral posterior parietal ablations in the monkey. *J. Neurol. Neurosurg. Psychiatr.* 25:256–68

22. Ettlinger, G., Warrington, E., Zangwill, O. L. 1957. A further study of visual-spatial agnosia. *Brain* 80:335–61

23. Ettlinger, G., Wegener, J. 1958. Somaesthetic alternation, discrimination and orientation after frontal and parietal lesions in monkeys. *Q. J. Exp. Psychol.* 10:177–86

24. Evarts, E. 1966. Methods for recording activity of individual neurons in moving animals. *Meth. Med. Res.* 11:241–50

25. Evarts, E. 1968. A technique for recording activity of subcortical neurons in moving animals. *Electroencephalogr. Clin. Neurophysiol.* 24:83–86

26. Fink, R., Heimer, L. 1967. Two methods of selective silver impregnation of degenerating axons and their synaptic endings in the central nervous system. *Brain Res.* 4:369–74

27. Flechsig, P. 1896. *Die Localization der geistigen Vorgänge, insbesondere der Sinnesempfindungen des Menschen.* Leipzig: von Veit.

28. Goldberg, M. E., Robinson, D. L. 1977. Visual mechanisms underlying gaze: function of the cerebral cortex. In *Developments in Neuroscience,* ed. R. Baker, A. Berthoz, 1:469–76. Elsevier: Biomedical Press

29. Goldberg, M. E., Wurtz, R. H. 1972. Activity of superior colliculus in behaving monkey. I. Visual receptive fields of single neurons. *J. Neurophysiol.* 35: 542–59

30. Goldberg, M. E., Wurtz, R. H. 1972. Activity of superior colliculus in behaving monkey. II. Effect of attention on neuronal responses. *J. Neurophysiol.* 35:560–74

31. Graybiel, A. M. 1974. Studies on the anatomical organization of posterior association cortex. In *The Neurosciences, Third Study Program,* ed. F. O. Schmidt, F. G. Worden, pp. 205–14. Cambridge, Mass.: MIT Press

32. Hartje, W., Ettlinger, G. 1973. Reaching in light and dark after unilateral posterior parietal ablations in the monkey. *Cortex* 9:346–54

33. Hyvärinen, J., Poranen, A. 1974. Function of the parietal associative area 7 as revealed from cellular discharges in alert monkeys. *Brain* 97:673–92

34. Hyvärinen, J., Poranen, A., Jokinen, Y., Naatanen, R., Linnankoski, I. 1975. Observations on unit activity in the primary somesthetic cortex of behaving monkeys. In *The Somatosensory System,* ed. H. H. Kornhuber, pp. 241–49. Stuttgart: Thieme

35. Jones, E. G. 1969. Interrelationships of parietotemporal and frontal cortex in the rhesus monkey. *Brain Res.* 13: 412–15

36. Jones, E. G. 1974. The anatomy of extrageniculostriate visual mechanisms. See Ref. 31, pp. 215–27

37. Jones, E. G. 1979. Organization of the thalamocortical complex and its relation to sensory processes. In *Handbook of Physiology, Section I: The Nervous System. Vol. 2, Sensory Processes,* ed. J. M. Brookhart, V. B. Mountcastle, I. Darian-Smith. Maryland: Am. Physiol. Soc. In press

38. Jones, E. G., Levitt, R. Y. 1974. Retrograde axonal transport and the demonstration of non-specific projections to the cerebral cortex and striatum for thalamic intralaminar nuclei in the rat, cat and monkey. *J. Comp. Neurol.* 154: 349–78

39. Jones, E. G., Powell, T. P. S. 1969. Connexions of the somatic sensory cortex of the rhesus monkey. I. Ipsilateral cortical connexions. *Brain* 92:477–502

40. Jones, E. G., Powell, T. P. S. 1970. An anatomic study of converging sensory pathways within the cerebral cortex of the monkey. *Brain* 93:793–820

41. Jones, E. G., Powell, T. P. S. 1973. Anatomical organization of the somatosensory cortex. In *Handbook of Sensory Physiology, Vol. II: Somatosensory System,* ed. A. Iggo, pp. 579–620. Berlin: Springer

42. Kaas, J. H., Lin, C. S., Wacor, E. 1977. Cortical projections of posterior parietal cortex in owl monkeys. *J. Comp. Neurol.* 171:387–408
43. Kasdon, D. L., Stein, B. M. 1977. Thalamic afferents to the inferior parietal lobule. *Anat. Rec.* 187:769
44. Lund, J. S., Lund, R., Hendrickson, A. E., Bunt, A. H., Fuchs, A. F. 1975. The origin of efferent pathways from the primary visual cortex, area 17, of the macaque monkey as shown by retrograde transport of horseradish peroxidase. *J. Comp. Neurol.* 164:287–304
45. Lynch, J. C., Mountcastle, V. B., Talbot, W. H., Yin, T. C. T. 1977. Parietal lobe mechanisms for directed visual attention. *J. Neurophysiol.* 40(2):362–89
46. Macrae, D., Trolle, E. 1956. The defect of function in visual agnosia. *Brain* 79:94–110
47. Mendoza, J. E., Thomas, R. K. Jr. 1975. Effects of posterior parietal and frontal neocortical lesions in the squirrel monkey. *J. Comp. Physiol. Psychol.* 89:170–82
48. Mesulam, M. M., Hoesen, G. W. V., Pandya, D. N., Geschwind, N. 1977. Limbic and sensory connections of the inferior parietal lobule (area PG) in the rhesus monkey: a study with a new method for horseradish peroxidase histochemistry. *Brain Res.* 136:393–414
49. Moffett, A., Ettlinger, G., Morton, H. B., Piercey, M. F. 1967. Tactile discrimination performance in the monkey: the effect of ablation of various subdivisions of posterior parietal cortex. *Cortex* 3:59–96
50. Mohler, C. W., Goldberg, M. E., Wurtz, R. H. 1973. Visual receptive fields of frontal eye field neurons. *Brain Res.* 61:385–89
51. Mohler, C. W., Wurtz, R. H. 1976. Organization of monkey superior colliculus: intermediate layer cells discharging before eye movements. *J. Neurophysiol.* 39(4):722–44
52. Mountcastle, V. B. 1975. The world around us: neural command functions for selective attention. In *Neurosciences Research Program Bulletin Vol. 14.* 47 pp.
53. Mountcastle, V. B. 1975. The view from within: pathways to the study of perception. *Johns Hopkins Med. J.* 136:109–31
54. Mountcastle, V. B. 1978. In *The Mindful Brain,* ed. G. M. Edelman, V. B. Mountcastle, pp. 7–50. Cambridge, Mass.: MIT Press
55. Mountcastle, V. B., Lynch, J. C., Georgopoulos, A., Sakata, H., Acuna, C.

1975. Posterior parietal association cortex of the monkey: command functions for operations within extrapersonal space. *J. Neurophysiol.* 38:871–908
56. Pandya, D. N., Kuypers, H. G. J. M. 1969. Cortico-cortical connections in the rhesus monkey. *Brain Res.* 13: 13–36
57. Passingham, R. E., Ettlinger, G. 1974. A comparison of cortical functions in man and the other primates. *Int. Rev. Neurobiol.* 16:233–99
58. Petras, J. M. 1971. Connections of the parietal lobe. *J. Psychiatr. Res.* 8:189–201
59. Pohl, W. 1973. Dissociation of spatial discrimination deficits following frontal and parietal lesions in monkeys. *J. Comp. Physiol. Psychol.* 82:227–39
60. Porter, R. 1973. Functions of the mammalian cerebral cortex in movement. *Prog. Neurobiol. Oxford* 1:1–51
61. Porter, R. 1976. Influences of movement detectors on pyramidal tract neurons in primates. *Ann. Rev. Physiol.* 38:121–38
62. Robinson, D. L., Goldberg, M. E. 1977. Visual mechanisms underlying gaze: function of the superior colliculus. See Ref. 28, pp. 445–51
63. Robinson, D. L., Goldberg, M. E., Stanton, G. B. 1978. Parietal association cortex in the primate: sensory mechanisms and behavioral modulations. *J. Neurophysiol.* In press
64. Rose, J. E., Woolsey, C. N. 1949. Organization of the mammalian thalamus and its relationships to the cerebral cortex. *Electroencephalogr. Clin. Neurophysiol.* 1:391–404
65. Ruch, T. C. 1935. Cortical localization of somatic sensibility. The effect of precentral, postcentral and posterior parietal lesions upon the performance of monkeys trained to discriminate weights. *Res. Publ. Assoc. Res. Nerv. Ment. Dis.* 15:289–330
66. Sakata, H. 1975. Somatic sensory responses of neurons in the parietal association area (area 5) of monkeys. See Ref. 41, pp. 250–61
67. Sakata, H., Takaoka, Y., Kawarasaki, A., Shibutani, H. 1973. Somatosensory properties of neurons in the superior parietal cortex (area 5) of the rhesus monkey. *Brain Res.* 64:85–102
68. Schiller, P. H. 1979. The midbrain and visual function. See Ref. 37
69. Semmes, J. 1973. Somesthetic effects of damage to the central nervous system. See Ref. 41, pp. 719–42

70. Semmes, J., Weinstein, S., Ghent, L., Teuber, H. L. 1963. Correlates of impaired orientation in personal and extrapersonal space. *Brain* 86:747-72
71. Stanton, G. B., Cruce, W. L. R., Goldberg, M. E., Robinson, D. L. 1977. Corticocortical and corticothalamic projections to area 7 of monkey cerebral cortex. *Anat. Rec.* 187:722
72. Stanton, G. B., Cruce, W. L. R., Goldberg, M. E., Robinson, D. L. 1977. Some ipsilateral projections to areas PF and PG of the inferior parietal lobule in monkeys. *Neurosci. Lett.* 6:243-50
73. Stein, J. F. 1976. The effect of cooling parietal lobe areas 5 and 7 upon voluntary movement in awake rhesus monkeys. *J. Physiol. London* 298:62P-63P
74. Trojanowski, J. Q., Jacobson, S. 1975. A combined horseradish peroxidase-autoradiographic investigation of reciprocal connections between superior temporal gyrus and pulvinar in squirrel monkey. *Brain Res.* 85:347-53
75. Weiskrantz, L. 1974. The interaction between occipital and temporal cortex in vision: an overview. See Ref. 31, pp. 189-204
76. Wurtz, R. H., Mohler, C. W. 1976. Organization of monkey superior colliculus: enhanced visual response of superficial layer cells. *J. Neurophysiol.* 39(4):745-65
77. Wurtz, R. H., Mohler, C. W. 1976. Enhancement of visual responses in monkey striate cortex and frontal eye fields. *J. Neurophysiol.* 39(4):766-72
78. Yin, T. C. T., Mountcastle, V. B. 1977. Visual input to the visuomotor mechanisms of the monkey's parietal lobe. *Science* 197:1381-83

Ann. Rev. Physiol. 1979. 41:159–77

EXTRACELLULAR POTASSIUM IN THE MAMMALIAN CENTRAL NERVOUS SYSTEM

♦1212

George G. Somjen

Department of Physiology, Duke University Medical Center, Durham, North Carolina 27710

INTRODUCTORY REMARKS

Potassium, calcium, and magnesium are three inorganic ions that occur in significant quantity in extracellular fluid of the mammalian brain and have powerful effects on the functioning of nervous tissue. In different ways all three influence the excitability of neurons and the release of transmitters from presynaptic terminals. Two different points of view have evolved concerning the regulation of these ions in the central nervous system (CNS). Some authors have emphasized the narrow range of the activity of these ions in the healthy brain and have concluded that stability of brain function requires stability of the extracellular activity of these ions. Others have argued that in the course of evolution the mammalian brain must have found an advantageous use for these powerful agents in the normal regulation of neuronal excitability. According to this view, programmed variations in $[K^+]_o$, $[Ca^{2+}]_o$, and perhaps also $[Mg^{2+}]_o$ may be an integral component in the normal function of the central nervous system.

Due to the recent development of potassium-selective microelectrodes (184) there has been a new surge of interest in the functional significance of potassium distribution in the nervous system. This selective review may be supplemented by consulting more general reviews on brain electrolytes (69, 72, 74, 83, 90, 158, 175).

159

0066-4278/79/0301-0159$01.00

THE EXCHANGES OF K^+ BETWEEN BLOOD, CEREBROSPINAL FLUID (CSF), AND EXTRACELLULAR FLUID (ECF) OF GRAY MATTER.

The Stability of $[K^+]$ in CSF

The concentration of K^+ in the CSF of healthy mammals is between 2.8 and 3.2 mM, which is significantly less than in plasma water (90). The difference is too great to be accounted for by the 2–5 mV potential difference (CSF positive) between the two fluid compartments (66). The CSF-blood potential does vary, however with both $[K^+]$ in plasma and $[K^+]$ in CSF (15, 29, 66), perhaps reflecting changes in the activity of an electrogenic ion pump.

Acute and chronic variations of plasma $[K^+]$ are not reflected in $[K^+]$ of CSF (2, 10, 20, 21, 78, 92), except for small changes induced under severe chronic conditions (138, 139). The independence of $[K^+]$ in CSF from $[K^+]$ in blood is due in part to the low K^+ content of the fluid secreted by the choroid plexus (2, 3, 40, 78). The K^+ contained in the secreting epithelial cells of the choroid plexus is apparently influenced by variations of blood K^+ (84), and therefore the "barrier" and "pump" functions must, in part at least, be located at the interface between cytoplasm of the choroidal epithelial cells and the ventricular fluid. A continued outward transport of K^+ across the CSF-blood interface has been inferred from the drop in K^+ concentration as CSF flows from the lateral ventricle toward the cisterna magna (3, 4, 23).

"Resting" $[K^+]_o$ in ECF of Central Gray Matter

The ependymal lining of the ventricles and the pia-glial membrane present only slight hindrance to the diffusion of K^+ between CSF and brain ECF (20, 35, 49, 89, 146). Measurements made in unstimulated brain and spinal cord with K^+-selective electrodes amply confirmed that "baseline" $[K^+]_o$ is between 2.6 and 3.8 mM, near $[K^+]$ in CSF (52, 101, 102, 122, 152, 182, 183).

In the choroid plexus the capillary endothelium is permeable to K^+ and the blood-CSF barrier is formed by the ependymal lining. In the substance of the brain the endothelial wall of capillaries seems impregnable to K^+, but the pericapillary glial sheath is incomplete and not a true barrier to the diffusion of solutes (31, 90, 128).

Recordings made with ion-selective microelectrodes inserted into gray matter and a neighboring cerebral vein have confirmed the lack of permeability of the blood-brain barrier, either to an induced excess of K^+ in the blood or to a raised level of $[K^+]_o$ in brain ECF during neural excitation and especially during epileptiform seizures (62, 137).

It is not definitely known whether the blood-brain barrier involves active transport of K^+ from brain ECF into capillaries. Subarachnoid fluid contains less K^+ than adjacent CSF (11, 12), and this was taken to prove outward transport of K^+ at least in the tissues of the soft covering of the brain. Simultaneous measurements of $[K^+]$ in CSF, subarachnoid fluid, and ECF of subjacent gray matter would now be possible with K^+-selective microelectrodes, but have not yet been reported. Other arguments have also been marshalled in favor of active transport of K^+ across the blood-brain barrier (22, 23, 35).

Capillary endothelium and pericapillary glial processes are the possible structures involved, but the mechanism has so far not been determined [discussed in detail in (178)].

The Diffusion of K^+ in Cerebral Tissue

In considering the passive movements of K^+ ions in the CNS, account must be taken of their mobility in the solvents and through the membranes separating "compartments," and also of the size of the spaces within which they can move. It has been argued that intercellular clefts are not so narrow that they should interfere with the mobility of K^+ ions contained within them (31, 185). Nevertheless, in early studies McLennan (124, 125) calculated from outflux of $^{42}K^+$ from muscle and brain slices, a diffusion constant only 1/20 of that in aqueous solution and concluded that K^+ diffusion was hindered by the properties of ECF, or by adsorption to cell surfaces. However, the incubation of tissue in isotonic KCl in these experiments may have severely distorted the organization of tissue "compartments."

In intact brain K^+ appeared to diffuse much more freely than in tissue slices. Roughly concordant values were obtained from observing the spread of $^{42}K^+$ in tissue (146); from recording the change of membrane potential of glial cells when the surface was exposed to a solution containing high K^+ (147); from measuring changes of $[K^+]_o$ with the aid of K^+-selective microelectrodes when K^+ was either injected iontophoretically (122) or brought in contact with the cerebral surface (49). In all cases the movement of K^+ could be accounted for by assuming that it diffused freely in an aqueous medium that occupies 15–20% of the tissue volume, and by allowing for a small amount of cellular uptake (147) and for a hindrance to diffusion at the cerebral surface (49, 147).

It is not known how much of the K^+ diffusing through central nervous tissue crosses cell membranes, especially those of glial cells. For glial cells of leech ganglia, a relatively high membrane resistance was calculated (106, 107), and evidence was presented that in this species glial sheaths are an obstacle to the diffusion of K^+ (9). It has been suggested that, in mammals, glial membranes are more freely permeable to K^+ ions (174). A low membrane resistance of mammalian glia was inferred from measurements of input impedance and of membrane time constant (174) and from a comparison of the spatial profile of glial depolarization with the profile of $[K^+]_o$ responses (33, 167).

Gardner-Medwin (55) has recently reported the movements of K^+ ions driven by a voltage imposed upon the cerebral cortex. He concluded that a sizeable fraction of the ion current must have passed through intracellular fluid. If K^+ indeed moves through glial membranes relatively freely, i.e. its movements are not restricted to ECF, then its apparent diffusion constant in cortical tissue (49, 122) must be reinterpreted [see also discussions in (167, 178)].

VARIATIONS OF $[K^+]_o$ IN HEALTHY NERVOUS TISSUE

Transient Responses of $[K^+]_o$ to Stimulation

While the defenses of the brain against fluctuations of plasma $[K^+]$ are nearly impregnable, $[K^+]_o$ in the ECF of central gray matter does vary with changes of neural activity. This has long been suspected on theoretical grounds (58, 111) and has been inferred from indirect evidence such as changes of afterpotentials (9, 86) and depolarization of glial cells (59, 87, 107, 144). In recent years it has been directly demonstrated with the aid of ion-selective microelectrodes (99, 101, 122, 152, 182). Repetitive electrical stimulation of the tissue, or of an afferent pathway, can easily drive $[K^+]_o$ from its "resting" level (around 3.0 mM) to 5 or 6 mM, and sometimes as high as 8 or even 10 mM. This has been observed in the neocortex (52, 115, 118, 152), the hippocampus (51, 113), the cerebellar cortex (28), the cuneate nucleus (101, 102), the gray matter of the spinal cord (99–102, 119, 164, 170, 182), and in the retina (88).

Under more "physiological" conditions, Syková et al (169) found "spontaneous" bursts of impulses of neurons in the reticular formation accompanied by increases of $[K^+]_o$ by not more than 0.2 mM. Changes of similar magnitude were observed during "spindle" activity of the cerebral cortex in barbiturate anesthesia (166), while during cortical EEG "arousal" $[K^+]_o$ was reported to rise from 3.0 to 3.3 mM (95). Moreover, $[K^+]_o$ in the striate cortex increases by about 0.1–0.4 mM in response to optical (i.e. "adequate") stimulation of the visual system (159, 163), or possibly up to 1.0 mM, calculated from glial depolarization (91). Finally, pinching a cat's tail can drive $[K^+]_o$ in the dorsal gray matter of the spinal cord up by 0.2–0.4 mM (162). These observations suggest that under normal conditions in the central nervous system of healthy mammals, $[K^+]_o$ rarely rises above 4.0 mM and probably never above 5.0 mM.

Depression of neural activity by several depressant drugs is not accompanied by a corresponding lowering of the "baseline" level of $[K^+]_o$ (108, 109, 133).

The Source of Excess $[K^+]_o$

The exact distribution of K^+ between "compartments" in gray matter is not known; but, from measurements of $[K^+]_o$ in ECF, and of total K^+ content of central nervous tissue, from the estimates of relative ECF volume and from recordings of the membrane potential of neurons and glial cells, it may be estimated that 1 ml of gray matter contains about 92 μm of K^+ within cells, and less than 0.5 μm in ECF (90, 178). It is clear that releasing a very small fraction of intracellular K^+ can make a very large impact on $[K^+]_o$.

The main source of excess $[K^+]_o$ in stimulated nervous tissue is assumed to be neurons. Glial membranes are passive (107, 160), and glia is not known to give up its content of intracellular potassium, $[K^+]_i$, except probably in hypoxia and perhaps other pathological conditions. Neurons, on the other hand, release a small quantity of K^+ with each impulse. Frankenhaeuser & Hodgkin (50) have inferred from indirect electrophysiological evidence that in the periaxonal space of the squid giant axon a significant quantity of K^+ may accumulate in the wake of impulse activity. From theoretical calculations, Adelman & Fitzhugh (1) estimated the change to amount to nearly 1 mM per impulse.

In the mammalian CNS, unmyelinated fibers may be expected to release larger amounts of K^+ than myelinated ones. In the dorsal white matter where dorsal roots enter the spinal cord, $[K^+]_o$ does not noticeably rise until the intensity of stimulation of a peripheral afferent nerve is raised above the threshold for C fibers (119). With cell bodies and dendritic trees the situation may vary according to the type of neurons and the mode of activation. Antidromic stimulation of spinal ventral roots does not cause a response of $[K^+]_o$ in the ventral horn (164, 171); but impulse activity of cerebellar Purkinje cells is associated with increases up to 0.3–0.5 mM per impulse (28). This may reflect invasion of the dendritic tree by the action potential, although since activation was orthodromic a contribution by synaptic currents cannot be excluded. In the reticular formation, $[K^+]_o$ was measured to increase by only 0.01–0.02 mM per nerve impulse per cell (169).

In addition to impulses, synaptic currents may be a major source of $[K^+]_o$. Gamma-aminobutyric acid (GABA) was found to cause an increase of K^+ efflux from cerebral cortex (25) and GABA as well as other suspected transmitters raised $[K^+]_o$ in spinal cord (105). In the tetrodotoxin-treated necturus retina, C. J. Karwoski & L. M. Proenza (unpublished) have demonstrated $[K^+]_o$ transients in response to illumination, in the absence of spike activity. Finally, extrasynaptic release of K^+ from neurons must also be considered, since local application of GABA causes an increase of $[K^+]_o$ in synapse-free dorsal root ganglia (41). Whether this observation has physiological significance or is a laboratory curiosity remains to be seen.

Recovery Processes of $[K^+]_o$ Following Neuronal Activity

Neurons eventually recover the K^+ they lose, otherwise the brain would cease to function. Before they do, some of the excess $[K^+]_o$ may escape. Is diffusion a mechanism of quantitative importance in the decay of $[K^+]_o$ transients (162, 167, 174, 178)? In two studies of this problem K^+ was considered to be released from point sources or thin sheets (104, 122) into a well-stirred infinite medium. Then diffusion could remove much of the accumulated K^+. In two other studies, release was considered to occur from sizable volumes into an unstirred medium (33, 179). Then diffusion was far too slow to account for more than an insignificant fraction of the dissipation of $[K^+]_o$ transients. Since physiologically significant amounts of $[K^+]_o$ accumulate only when large, dense populations of neural elements are active over a considerable period, the volume-source model (33, 179) probably provides the most valid analysis. A calculation of the current-carrying capacity of extracellular K^+ (167) also suggests that diffusion is of limited significance in removing excess K^+. In cold-blooded animals the significance of diffusion may be greater (19, 71, 145) than in mammals.

Several observations support the conclusion that in the mammalian central nervous system a significant excess of $[K^+]_o$ is cleared by active transport: Increased oxidative metabolism is precisely correlated with the elevation of $[K^+]_o$ (113, 115, 118, 156, 162, 186). "Undershoots" may follow $[K^+]_o$ transients (63, 100, 103). These undershoots disappear, $[K^+]_o$ rises, and the decay of $[K^+]_o$ responses slows down under the influence of inhibitors of membrane ATPase (33, 134), of hypothermia (13, 114), hypoxia (13, 16, 93, 132, 156), ischemia (7, 24, 60, 75, 134), and of hypoglycemia (6, 60).

Which cells actively remove excess $[K^+]_o$? There have been numerous suggestions that this is one of the chief functions of glial cells (17, 18, 36, 67, 71, 72, 110, 143). K^+ could be removed by glial cells near excited neurons, conveyed through gap junctions to neighboring glial cells, and released at some distance where $[K^+]_o$ was at "resting" level (69, 71, 143). Alternatively, glia might take up neutral KCl (17, 18). Such processes would involve little cell swelling (167). Data quoted in support of the idea of glial regulation of $[K^+]_o$ include the demonstration that cellular respiration of glial cells is stimulated by an excess of $[K^+]_o$ (69, 70, 143) and that glial cells accumulate K^+ avidly (18, 69).

During excitation neurons gain $[Na^+]_i$ while they lose $[K^+]_i$. High $[Na^+]_i$ constitutes a powerful additional stimulus for the coupled Na^+-K^+ pump of neurons, which is not experienced by glial cells. For this reason it seems likely that the bulk of the K^+ released by stimulated neurons is rapidly pumped back into the nerve cells that lost them. Glia may have a role in the final "fine tuning" of $[K^+]_o$ toward the homeostatic level of 3 mM (178).

THE POSSIBLE PHYSIOLOGICAL ROLE OF VARIATIONS OF $[K^+]_o$ IN CENTRAL GRAY MATTER

$[K^+]_o$ and Membrane Potential

Excess $[K^+]_o$ first stimulates and then paralyzes excitable tissues (130). The quantitative relationship of $[K^+]_o$ to membrane potential was first accurately defined for the giant axons of squid (37), later for the isolated node of Ranvier of vertebrate nerve (79), and for neuron cell bodies in the nervous system of the leech (106, 107). For neurons in the mammalian central nervous system published data are lacking, but B. Connors (unpublished) has measured the membrane potential of dorsal root ganglion cells at different levels of $[K^+]_o$. In all cases the neuronal membrane potential approaches a linear function of the log $[K^+]_o$ at high, but not at low levels of $[K^+]_o$. Below about 5 or 6 mM the membrane potential is less sensitive than calculated by the Nernst equation for K^+. The accepted explanation for this departure from linearity is the 50:1 ratio of $P_{K_+}:P_{Na_+}$ permeabilities in the "resting" nerve membrane, and the presence of a high concentration of $[Na^+]_o$. Unlike that of neurons, the membrane potential of glial cells bears a straight-line relationship to log $[K^+]_o$ over the entire range of $[K^+]_o$ where measurements are practical. In cold-blooded animals the slope of this function was found to equal that of the Nernst function for K^+ (106, 107, 144). In mammalian glial cells it first appeared that the slope was less than that of the Nernst function (39, 147, 154). Newer measurements indicate that in the steady state [but not when $[K^+]_o$ is rapidly changing (53)] the mammalian glial membrane potential is also determined by the Nernst function (53, 119).

$[K^+]_o$ and Synaptic Transmission

In an investigation of the influence of $[K^+]_o$ on the frequency of spontaneous miniature endplate potentials (mepps), Liley (116) concluded that mepp frequency was a function of the membrane potential of the motor nerve terminals (see also 135). From similar experiments, others (32, 54) have suggested in addition to influencing prejunctional membrane potential, $[K^+]_o$ had a second "specific" stimulant effect on the release of acetylcholine.

Takeuchi & Takeuchi (172) found that an outward (hyperpolarizing) current imposed on the (post-synaptic) skeletal muscle fiber membrane was capable of reducing mepp frequency in the presence of elevated $[K^+]_o$, but not in normal Ringer solution. They took this to mean that the outward current through the (post-synaptic) muscle membrane reduced the concentration of $[K^+]_o$ near the (presynaptic) motor nerve terminal. Whether this observation has a bearing on the function of central inhibitory synapses remains to be determined.

Increased $[K^+]_o$ may affect synaptic transmission in several ways besides stimulating spontaneous transmitter release (mentioned above). By curtailing the presynaptic spike amplitude it may reduce impulse-evoked transmitter release. Finally, depolarization of post-synaptic neurons may render them more than normally excitable. In the case of the giant synapse of the squid, excitatory post-synaptic potentials (EPSPs) were found to be decreased in amplitude, concordant with the diminished amplitude of the presynaptic action potential (45). The input-output function of transmission through the cuneate nucleus was also depressed, though not by very much (134), perhaps because depolarization of post-synaptic elements partially compensated for decreased transmitter output. In the hippocampus, the duration if not the amplitude of evoked potentials was increased when $[K^+]_o$ was elevated up to 11 mM (81). In evaluating any observation relating to the effect of K^+ on synaptic function it should be remembered that the really striking changes of synaptic function usually were found when $[K^+]_o$ was raised well above the "physiological" limit for the CNS of 5 mM. Below that level, the sensitivity of synaptic transmission to $[K^+]_o$, like that of the membrane potential, is functionally negligible.

The Use of K^+ in Biochemical Studies In Vitro

It was noticed several decades ago that elevating $[K^+]_o$ in the bathing solution stimulated both the oxygen consumption and the anaerobic metabolism of slices of excitable tissues, but not nonexcitable organs (5, 43). Since then, raising $[K^+]_o$ sometimes as high as 40–140 mM has become a favorite method of activating excitable tissues in biochemical experiments (e.g. 46, 85, 123, 153, 155). It is usually assumed that the depolarizing action of high $[K^+]_o$ simulates neural excitation. This may be so, but the possibility must not be overlooked that K^+ may have specific effects of its own, as has been suggested in relation to the release of acetylcholine (32, 54). Moreover, incubation in a constant level of high $[K^+]_o$ does not reproduce pulsatile action potentials, nor the waxing and waning of synaptic potentials. Finally, during an active neural response the membrane permeability changes; neurons gain $[Na^+]_i$ and sometimes also $[Ca^{2+}]_i$. This does not necessarily occur when they are exposed to high $[K^+]_o$. However, evidence has been offered that the K^+-induced release of transmitters from synaptosomes in vitro may be similar to the physiological release of transmitter from intact nerve terminals in situ during synaptic transmission (14, 30, 157). In some other cases it seems that the effects observed in vitro are found in situ only during spreading depression, when $[K^+]_o$ can reach very high levels indeed (97, 98).

Theories of the Role of $[K^+]_o$ in Normal Nervous Function

Forty years ago Barron & Matthews (8) suggested that a change of $[K^+]_o$ may be responsible for the slow root potentials that they were first to study in detail. Their suggestion was recently revived as a likely mechanism for the depolarizing potentials of afferent fiber terminals and the related phenomenon of presynaptic inhibition (27, 44, 100, 101, 181, 182). Objections raised against the K^+ theory include the facts that neither time-course, nor magnitude, nor indeed the pharmacology of the negative dorsal root potential corresponds to those of the $[K^+]_o$ responses in dorsal gray matter (27, 119, 161, 164). In defense of the theory it was suggested that ion-specific microelectrodes may not register the full magnitude and true time-course of $[K^+]_o$ experienced by the presynaptic terminals (180, 181). Raising $[K^+]_o$ in cuneate nucleus did not, however, have the differential effect on conditioned and unconditioned presynaptic impulses that is required by the K^+-theory of primary afferent depolarization (38). A compromise, suggesting more than one depolarizing agent acting simultaneously on primary afferent terminals, has also been offered (27, 119, 171).

According to Izquierdo and associates (81, 82), changes of $[K^+]_o$ in hippocampus are the agent of heterosynaptic facilitation and heterosynaptic post-tetanic potentiation. They related this effect with the suggested function of the hippocampus in registering short-term memory (82). Their theory grew out of a discussion by Green (58), whose view it was that in hippocampus, more than elsewhere in the central nervous system, K^+ could accumulate in intercellular clefts during neural activity. However, actual measurements of $[K^+]_o$ in hippocampus have not revealed any remarkable difference in the behavior of K^+ between this and other parts of the central nervous system (49, 113, 115, 149).

Lipton & Heimbach (117) found that in tissue slices isolated from hippocampus, the rate of protein synthesis increased with elevation of $[K^+]_o$ in the bathing medium. Unlike many other investigators, they (117) emphasized the changes that occur within the range of 1.3–8.1 mM $[K^+]_o$, where effects on neuronal membrane potential are minimal and therefore the effect of K^+ may be specific. The authors consider their results to support some of the conclusions by Izquierdo and associates (81, 82) concerning the significance of $[K^+]_o$ in controlling hippocampal function.

Hertz's theory (68, 69) that glia transport significant amounts of K^+ has already been discussed. Hertz suggested that, by distributing K^+ according to some blueprint, glia might regulate the spatial pattern of neuronal excitation. He found that glia isolated from cerebral cortex, but not glia from spinal cord (70), pump K^+ ions more vigorously than neurons. However, oxidative metabolism in spinal cord in situ correlates with $[K^+]_o$ as well as in cortex (156, 162). Whether the in situ response is given by glial cells, neurons, or both cannot be determined as yet.

In the peripheral nervous system, the high $[K^+]_o$ level of endolymph is said to be of significance in setting the excitability of the cochlear responses to acoustic stimulation (94). A similar significance was attributed to the elevated $[K^+]_o$ in the capsular fluid of Pacini's corpuscles (80), though in this case the departure from plasma $[K^+]$ is less impressive.

THE PATHOPHYSIOLOGY OF $[K^+]_o$ IN CENTRAL GRAY MATTER

Spreading Cortical Depression

Brinley et al (26) found that during spreading depression the outflux of K^+ from cerebral cortex increased enormously, approaching that found in the agonal phase of anoxia. With the aid of K^+-selective microelectrodes first Vyskočil et al (183), then several others (34, 77, 112, 118, 127, 140), described the spectacular rise of $[K^+]_o$ during spreading depression. The process usually begins with a gradual increase of $[K^+]_o$, which remains relatively slow and at steady velocity until about 10–15 mM is reached. When that level is exceeded, the process becomes explosive, and $[K^+]_o$ suddenly rises to a maximal level between 30 and 80 mM, accompanied by a negative shift of extracellular potential, massive depolarization of glial cells and neurons, and cessation of all neural activity. $[K^+]_o$ returns to baseline before resumption of EEG activity. An explosive change, resembling spreading depression, also occurs when the cortex is deprived of oxygen (13, 16, 24, 60, 61, 75) or glucose (6). In immature cortex the "critical" or "trigger" level of $[K^+]_o$ is higher than in adults (61, 126, 136); in spinal cord the explosive rise of $[K^+]_o$ does not occur (156, 162).

These observations are in good agreement with a causal role of K^+ in spreading depression (57). However, there are indications that high $[K^+]_o$ may not be the only factor causing spreading depression (176, 177). In hypoxia, EEG activity ceases well before the explosive rise of $[K^+]_o$ (16, 75). The condition can apparently occur independently of spike activity (112) and, in the presence of tetrodotoxin, when impulse discharge is abolished (96, 168). K^+ could, of course, be released with synaptic currents instead of nerve impulses, and it could in turn stimulate the release of synaptic transmitter (14, 30, 116, 157). However, it has also been reported that depolarization of neurons may be delayed sometimes by as much as 10–30 sec after the depolarization of glial cells and the negative shift of extracellular potential (168). Moreover the membrane potential of neurons may turn inside-positive (73); this could not be a "passive" consequence of high $[K^+]_o$, but signifies a change of membrane permeability.

Any nonspecific, intense stimulus causes $[K^+]_o$ in cortex to rise. If the active cellular uptake processes of K^+ are overwhelmed, and the usual "ceiling" level of $[K^+]_o$ (10–12 mM) exceeded, the release of glutamate (176, 177) or of another agent (30, 157) may begin. The latter could cause an increase of Na^+ permeability of neuronal membranes and also the release of more K^+ (105). This in turn would stimulate the further release of glutamate (or other substance), resulting in a positive feedback and the rapid inactivation of excitable membranes.

$[K^+]_o$ and Seizures

This topic has been reviewed in detail recently (163, 165) and a brief summary will suffice here. An excess of $[K^+]_o$ was known to be able to induce seizures (187); K^+ is released from cerebral cortex during epileptiform convulsions (47, 129). Elevated $[K^+]_o$ has therefore been suspected for years of being a common cause of paroxysmal activity (42, 47, 58, 83, 151, 173).

K^+-selective microelectrodes have been applied to the study of seizures (16, 48, 76, 118, 120, 121, 131, 141, 142, 148). Most of these studies concluded that K^+ plays no part in initiating seizures, in the transition from interictal to ictal activity, or in the termination of seizures (48, 65, 118, 120, 131, 148, 149). In all cases $[K^+]_o$ was seen to rise during seizures to a "ceiling" level around 9–12 mM (8–10 mM in spinal cord). If this "ceiling" was breached, spreading depression replaced seizures. The rise of $[K^+]_o$ followed rather than preceded the eruption of seizure activity, and no "threshold" of $[K^+]_o$ could be determined for seizure onset. During postictal depression $[K^+]_o$ returned to its "resting" baseline instead of rising as in spreading depression. In healthy gray matter it was sometimes possible to drive $[K^+]_o$ to levels equal to those seen during seizures without triggering paroxysmal activity. In epileptogenic glial scars the clearing of $[K^+]_o$ was not detectably different from that in normal cortex (56, 150).

Although unlikely to be the cause of seizures, the 8–12 mM $[K^+]_o$ reached during paroxysms must to some degree influence the function of neurons, and therefore the course of the seizure. From available evidence this influence seems minor compared to other factors. Instead of K^+, the movements of Ca^{2+} are now receiving increased attention in relation to the generation of seizures (65, 165).

CONCLUSIONS

Against fluctuations of potassium concentration in blood plasma, the mammalian CNS is well protected. In part the barrier function is performed by active transport of K^+, which keeps the extracellular activity, $[K^+]_o$, in "resting" CNS below that in plasma. Variations of neural activity are associated with measurable changes of $[K^+]_o$ in gray matter, but in a healthy CNS under "natural" conditions $[K^+]_o$ probably never rises above 5.0 mM and rarely above 4.0. Within these limits, variations of $[K^+]_o$ have little if any influence on neural function. Thus, being kept below plasma $[K^+]_o$ level, fluctuations of $[K^+]_o$ in CNS are prevented from interfering with neuronal activity. Above 6 mM, $[K^+]_o$ may cause significant depolarization of membranes, alterations in synaptic function, and changes in a variety of biochemical processes. The level of $[K^+]_o$ reached during seizures may therefore influence neuronal function, but there is no evidence to indicate that the accumulation of $[K^+]_o$ plays an important part in either initiating or terminating seizures. In the initiation of cortical spreading depression the accumulation of $[K^+]_o$ does seem to be a causal factor, but perhaps it is not the only one.

ACKNOWLEDGMENTS

I would like to thank Mrs. Manika (Ibadan) and Mrs. Reynolds (Durham, NC) for typing the manuscript. Work related to $[K^+]_o$ in my laboratory was supported by grant number NS 11933 of the National Institute of Neurological Diseases and Stroke of the USPHS.

Literature Cited

1. Adelman, W. J., Fitzhugh, R. 1975. Solutions of the Hodgkin-Huxley equations modified for potassium accumulation in periaxonal spaces. *Fed. Proc.* 34:1322–29
2. Ames, A. III, Higashi, K., Nesbett, F. B. 1965. Relation of potassium concentration in choroid plexus fluid to that in plasma. *J. Physiol. London* 181:506–15
3. Ames, A. III, Sakanoue, M., Endo, S. 1964. Na, K, Mg and Cl concentrations in choroid plexus fluid and cisternal fluid compared with plasma ultrafiltrate. *J. Neurophysiol.* 27:672–81
4. Anderson, D. K., Heisey, S. R. 1975. Creatinine, potassium and calcium flux from chicken cerebrospinal fluid. *Am. J. Physiol.* 228:415–19
5. Ashford, C. A., Dixon, K. C. 1935. The effect of potassium on the glucolysis of brain tissue with reference to the Pasteur effect. *Biochem. J.* 29:157–68
6. Astrup, J., Norberg. K. 1976. Potassium activity in cerebral cortex in rats during progressive severe hypoglycemia. *Brain Res.* 103:418–23

7. Astrup, J., Symon, L., Branston, N. M., Lassen, N. A. 1977. Cortical evoked potential and extracellular K^+ and H^+ at critical levels of brain ischemia. *Stroke* 8:51–57
8. Barron, D. H., Matthews, B. H. C. 1938. Interpretation of potential changes in the spinal cord. *J. Physiol. London* 92:276–321
9. Baylor, D. A., Nicholls, J. G. 1969. Changes in extracellular potassium concentration produced by neuronal activity in the central nervous system of the leech. *J. Physiol. London* 203:555–69
10. Bekaert, J., Demeester, G. 1954. Influence of the blood on the potassium level of the cerebrospinal fluid. *Exp. Med. Surg* 12:480–501
11. Bito, L. Z. 1969. Blood-brain barrier. Evidence for active cation transport between blood and the extracellular fluid of brain. *Science* 165:81–83
12. Bito, L. Z., Davson, H. 1966. Local variations in cerebrospinal fluid composition and its relationship to the composition of extracellular fluid of cortex. *Exp. Neurol.* 14:264–80

13. Blank, W. F., Kirshner, H. S. 1977. The kinetics of extracellular potassium changes during hypoxia and anoxia in the cat cerebral cortex. *Brain Res.* 123:113–24

14. Blaustein, M. P. 1975. Effects of potassium, veratridine and scorpion venom on calcium accumulation and transmitter release by nerve terminals in vitro. *J. Physiol. London* 247:617–55

15. Bledsoe, S. W., Mines, A. H. 1975. Effects of plasma K^+ on the DC potential and on ion distributions between CSF and blood. *J. Appl. Physiol.* 39:1012–16

16. Bolwig, T. G., Astrup, J., Chistofferson, G. R. 1977. EEG and extracellular K^+ in rat brain during pentylenetetrazol seizures and during respiratory arrest. *Biomed. Express Paris* 27:99–102

17. Bourke, R. S., Nelson, K. M., Nauman, R. A., Young, O. M. 1970. Studies of the production and subsequent reduction of swelling in primate cerebral cortex under isosmotic conditions in vivo. *Exp. Brain Res.* 10:427–46

18. Bourke, R. S., Kimelberg, H. K. 1975. The effect of HCO_3 on the swelling and ion uptake of monkey cerebral cortex under conditions of raised extracellular potassium. *J. Neurochem.* 25:323–28

19. Bracho, H., Orkand, R. K. 1972. Neuron-glia interaction: Dependence on temperature. *Brain Res.* 36:416–19

20. Bradbury, M. W. B., Davson, H. 1965. The transport of potassium between blood, cerebrospinal fluid and brain. *J. Physiol. London* 181:151–74

21. Bradbury, M. W. B., Kleeman, C. R. 1967. Stability of the potassium content of cerebrospinal fluid and brain. *Am. J. Physiol.* 213:519–28

22. Bradbury, M. W. B., Segal, M. B., Wilson, J. 1972. Transport of potassium at the blood-brain barrier. *J. Physiol. London* 22:617–32

23. Bradbury, M. W. B., Stulcová, B. 1970. Efflux mechanism contributing to the stability of the potassium concentration in cerebrospinal fluid. *J. Physiol. London* 208:415–30

24. Branston, N. M., Strong, A. J., Symon, L. 1977. Extracellular potassium activity, evoked potential and tissue blood flow. Relationship during progressive ischaemia in baboon cerebral cortex. *J. Neurol. Sci.* 32:305–21

25. Brinley, F. J., Kandel, E. R., Marshall, W. H. 1960. Effect of gamma-aminobutyric acid (GABA) on K^{42} outflow from rabbit cortex. *J. Neurophysiol.* 23:237–45

26. Brinley, F. J., Kandel, E. R., Marshall, W. H. 1960. Potassium outflux from rabbit cortex during spreading depression. *J. Neurophysiol.* 23:246–56

27. Bruggencate, G. T., Lux, H. D., Liebl, L. 1974. Possible relationship between extracellular potassium activity and presynaptic inhibition in the spinal cord of the cat. *Pfleugers Arch.* 349:301–17

28. Bruggencate, G. T., Nicholson, C., Stöckle, H. 1976. Climbing fiber evoked potassium release in cat cerebellum. *Pfleugers Arch.* 367:107–9

29. Cameron, I. R., Kleeman, C. R. 1970. The effect of acute hyperkalaemia on the blood-CSF potential difference. *J. Physiol. Lond.* 207:68P–69P

30. Clark, R. M., Collins, G. G. 1975. The spontaneous and potassium evoked release of endogeneous amino acids from the mammalian visual cortex. *J. Physiol. London* 246:16P–17P

31. Cohen, M. W. B., Gerschenfeld, H. M., Kuffler, S. W. 1968. Ionic environment of neurones and glial cells in the brain of an amphibian. *J. Physiol. London* 197:363–80

32. Cooke, J. D., Quastel, D. M. J. 1973. The specific effect of potassium on transmitter release by motor nerve terminals. *J. Physiol. London* 228:435–58

33. Cordingley, G. E., Somjen, G. G. 1978. The clearing of excess potassium from extracellular space in spinal cord and cerebral cortex. *Brain Res.* 151:291–306

34. Crowe, W., Mayevsky, A., Mela, L., Silver, H. 1976. Measurements of extracellular potassium, D. C. potential and ECoG in the cortex of the conscious rat during cortical spreading depression. In *Ion and Enzyme Electrodes in Biology and Medicine,* ed. M. Kessler et al, pp. 299–301. Baltimore: Univ. Park Press

35. Cserr, H. 1965. Potassium exchange between cerebrospinal fluid, plasma and brain. *Am. J. Physiol.* 209:1219–26

36. Cummins, J., Hydén, H. 1962. Adenosine triphosphate levels and adenosine triphosphatases in neurons, glia and neuronal membranes of the vestibular nucleus. *Biochim. Biophys. Acta.* 60:271–83

37. Curtis, H. J., Cole, K. S. 1942. Membrane resting and action potentials from the squid giant axon. *J. Cell. Comp. Physiol.* 19:135–44

38. Davidson, N., Simpson, H. K. L. 1976. Concerning the ionic basis of presynaptic inhibition. *Experientia* 32:348–49

39. Dennis, M., Gerschenfeld, H. M. 1965. Some physiological properties of identi-

fied mammalian glial cells. *J. Physiol. London* 203:211–22

40. De Rougemont, J., Ames, A. III, Nesbett, F. B., Hofmann, H. F. 1960. Fluid formed by choroid plexus. *J. Neurophysiol.* 23:485–95

41. Deschenes, M., Feltz, P. 1976. GABA-induced rise of extracellular potassium in rat dorsal root ganglia: an electrophysiological study in vivo. *Brain Res.* 118:494–99

42. Dichter, M. A., Herman, C. J., Selzer, M. 1972. Silent cells during interictal discharges and seizures in hippocampal penicillin foci. Evidence for the role of extracellular K^+ in the transition from the interictal state to seizures. *Brain Res.* 48:173–83

43. Dickens, F., Greville, G. D. 1935. The metabolism of normal and tumor tissue: XIII. Neutral salt effect. *Biochem. J.* 29:1468–83

44. Eccles, J. C., Korn, H., Taborikova, H., Tsukahara, N. 1969. Slow field potentials generated in cerebellar cortex by mossy fiber volleys. *Brain Res.* 15:276–80

45. Erulkar, S. D., Weight, F. F. 1977. Extracellular potassium and transmitter release at the giant synapse of squid. *J. Physiol. London* 266:209–18

46. Ferrendelli, J. A., Rubin, E. H., Knischerf, D. A. 1976. Influence of divalent cations on regulation of cyclic GMP and cyclic AMP levels in brain tissue. *J. Neurochem.* 26:741–48

47. Fertziger, A. P., Ranck, J. B. 1970. Potassium accumulation in interstitial space during epileptiform seizures. *Exp. Neurol.* 26:571–85

48. Fisher, R. S., Pedley, T. A., Moody, W. J. Jr., Prince, D. A. 1976. The role of extracellular potassium in hippocampal epilepsy. *Arch. Neurol.* 33:76–83

49. Fisher, R. S., Pedley, T. A., Prince, D. A. 1976. Kinetics of potassium movement in normal cortex. *Brain Res.* 101:223–37

50. Frankenhaeuser, B., Hodgkin, A. L. 1956. The after-effects of impulses in the giant nerve fibers of *Loligo. J. Physiol. London* 131:341–76

51. Fritz, L. C., Gardner-Medwin, A. R. 1976. The effect of synaptic activation on the extracellular potassium concentration in the hippocampal dentate area, in vitro. *Brain Res.* 112:183–87

52. Futamachi, K. J., Mutani, R., Prince, D. A. 1974. Potassium activity in rabbit cortex. *Brain Res.* 75:5–25

53. Futamachi, K., Pedley, T. A. 1976. Glial cells and potassium: their relationship in mammalian cortex. *Brain Res.* 109:311–22

54. Gage, P. W., Quastel, D. M. J. 1965. Dual effect of potassium on transmitter release. *Nature* 206:625–26

55. Gardner-Medwin, A. R. 1977. The migration of potassium produced by electric current through brain tissue. *J. Physiol. London* 269:32P–33P

56. Glötzner, F. L. 1973. Membrane properties of neuroglia in epileptogenic gliosis. *Brain Res.* 55:159–71

57. Grafstein, B. 1956. Mechanism of spreading cortical depression. *J. Neurophysiol.* 19:154–71

58. Green, J. D. 1964. The hippocampus. *Physiol. Rev.* 44:561–608

59. Grossman, R. G., Hampton, T. 1968. Depolarization of cortical glial cells during electrocortical activity. *Brain Res.* 11:316–24

60. Hansen, A. J. 1978. The extracellular potassium concentration in brain cortex following ischemia in hypo- and hyperglycemic rats. *Acta Physiol. Scand.* 102:324–29

61. Hansen, A. J. 1977. Extracellular potassium concentration in juvenile and adult rat brain cortex during anoxia. *Acta. Physiol. Scand.* 99:412–20

62. Hansen, A. J., Lund-Andersen, H., Crone, C. 1977. K^+ permeability of the brain-blood barrier investigated by aid of a K^+-sensitive microelectrode. *Acta Physiol. Scand.* 101:438–45

63. Heinemann, U., Lux, H. D. 1975. Undershoots following stimulus-induced rises of extracellular potassium concentration in cerebral cortex of cat. *Brain Res.* 93:63–76

64. Heinemann, U., Lux, H. D. 1977. Ceiling of stimulus-induced rises in extracellular potassium concentration in the cerebral cortex of cat. *Brain Res.* 120:231–49

65. Heinemann, U., Lux, H. D., Gutnick, M. J. 1977. Extracellular free calcium and potassium during paroxysmal activity in the cerebral cortex of the cat. *Exp. Brain Res.* 27:237–43

66. Held, D., Fencl, V., Pappenheimer, J. R. 1964. Electrical potential of cerebrospinal fluid. *J. Neurophysiol.* 27:942–59

67. Henn, F. A., Haljamäe, H., Hamberger, A. 1972. Glial cell function: active control of extracellular K^+ concentration. *Brain Res.* 43:437–43

68. Hertz, L. 1965. Possible role of neuroglia: A potassium-mediated neuronal-neuroglial-neuronal impulse transmission system. *Nature* 206:1091–94

69. Hertz, L. 1977. Drug-induced alterations of ion distribution at the cellular level of the central nervous system. *Pharmacol. Rev.* 29:35–65

70. Hertz, L., Clausen, T. 1963. Effects of sodium and potassium on respiration: their specificity to slices from certain brain regions. *Biochem. J.* 89:526–33

71. Hertz, L., Nissen, C. 1976. Differences between leech and mammalian nervous system in metabolic reaction to K as an indicator of differences in potassium homeostatic mechanisms. *Brain Res.* 110:182–88

72. Hertz, L., Schousboe, A. 1975. Ion and energy metabolism of the brain at the cellular level. *Int. Rev. Neurobiol.* 18:141–211

73. Higashida, H., Mitarai, G., Watanabe, S. 1974. A comparative study of membrane potential changes in neurons and neuroglial cells during spreading depression in the rabbit. *Brain Res.* 65:411–25

74. Hillman, H. 1966. The role of potassium and sodium ions as studied in mammalian brain. *Int. Rev. Cytol.* 20:125–37

75. Hossmann, K. A., Sakaki, S., Zimmerman, V. 1977. Cation activities in reversible ischemia of the cat brain. *Stroke* 8:77–81

76. Hotson, J. R., Sypert, G. W., Ward, A. A. 1973. Extracellular potassium concentration changes during propagated seizures. *Exp. Neurol.* 38:20–26

77. Hubschmann, O., Grossman, R., Mehta, P., Abramson, M. 1973. Spreading depression of electrocortical activity studied with K⁺ ion specific microelectrodes. *27th Ann. Meet. Am. EEG Soc. Abstr.*, p. 25

78. Husted, R. F., Reed, D. J. 1976. Regulation of cerebrospinal fluid potassium by the cat choroid plexus. *J. Physiol. London* 259:213–21

79. Huxley, A. F., Stämpfli, R. 1951. Effect of potassium and sodium on resting and action potentials of single myelinated nerve fibers. *J. Physiol. London* 112:496–508

80. Ilyinsky, O. B., Akoev, G. N., Krasnikove, T. L., Elman, S. I. 1976. K⁺ and Na⁺ ion content in the Pacinian corpuscle fluid and its role in the activity of receptors. *Pfluegers Arch.* 361:279–85

81. Izquierdo, I., Nasello, A. G., Marichich, E. S. 1971. The dependence of hippocampal function on extracellular potassium levels. *Curr. Mod. Biol.* 4:35–46

82. Izquierdo, I. 1972. Hippocampal physiology: experiments on regulation of its electrical activity, on the mechanism of seizures, and on a hypothesis of learning. *Behav. Biol.* 7:669–98

83. Izquierdo, J. A., Izquierdo, I. 1967. Electrolytes and excitable tissues. *Ann. Rev. Pharmacol.* 7:125–44

84. Johanson, C. E., Reed, D. J., Woodbury, D. M. 1974. Active transport of sodium and potassium by the choroid plexus of the rat. *J. Physiol. London* 241:359–72

85. Jones, D. A., McIlwain, H. 1971. Amino acid distribution and incorporation into proteins in isolated, electrically stimulated cerebral tissues. *J. Neurochem.* 18:41–58

86. Kandel, E. R., Spencer, W. A. 1961. Electrophysiology of hippocampal neurons II. After-potentials and repetitive firing. *J. Neurophysiol.* 24:243–59

87. Karahashi, Y., Goldring, S. 1966. Intracellular potentials from "idle" cells in cerebral cortex of cat. *Electroencephalogr. Clin. Neurophysiol.* 20:600–7

88. Karwoski, C. J., Proenza, L. M. 1977. Relationship between Müller cell responses, a local transretinal potential, and potassium flux. *J. Neurophysiol.* 40:244–59

89. Katzman, R., Garziani, L., Kaplan, R., Escriva, A. 1965. Exchange of cerebrospinal fluid potassium with blood and brain. *Arch. Neurol. Chicago,* 13:513–24

90. Katzman, R., Pappius, H. M. 1973. *Brain Electrolytes and Fluid Metabolism.* Baltimore: Williams and Wilkins. 419 pp.

91. Kelly, J. P., Van Essen, D. C. 1974. Cell structure and function in the visual cortex of the cat. *J. Physiol. London* 238:515–47

92. Kemény, A., Boldizsár, H., Pethes, G. 1961. The distribution of cations in plasma and cerebrospinal fluid following infusion of solutions of salts of sodium, potassium, magnesium, and calcium. *J. Neurochem.* 7:218–27

93. Kirshner, H. S., Blank, W. F., Myers, R. E. 1975. Brain extracellular potassium activity during hypoxia in the cat. *Neurology* 25:1001–5

94. Konishi, T., Kelsey, E., Singleton, G. T. 1966. Effects of chemical alteration in the endolymph on cochlea potentials. *Acta Oto-Laryngol.* 62:393–404

95. Korytová, H. 1977. Arousal induced increase of cortical [K⁺] in unrestrained rats. *Experientia* 33:242–44

96. Kow, L. M., Van Harreveld, A. 1972. Ion and water movements in isolated chicken retina during spreading depression. *Neurobiology* 2:61–69

97. Krivanek, J. 1974. Changes in the neuronal protein labelling induced by potassium ions in vivo (spreading depression). *J. Neurochem.* 23:1255–62

98. Krivanek, J. 1976. Adenosine 3, 5-monophosphate in rat cerebral cortex: effect of potassium ions in vivo (cortical spreading depression). *J. Neurochem.* 26:413–15

99. Kříž, N., Syková, E., Ujec, E., Vyklický, L. 1974. Changes of extracellular potassium concentration induced by neuronal activity in the spinal cord of the cat. *J. Physiol. London* 238:1–15

100. Kříž, N., Syková, E., Vyklický, L. 1975. Extracellular potassium changes in the spinal cord of the cat and their relation to slow potentials, active transport and impulse transmission. *J. Physiol. London* 248:167–82

101. Krnjević, K., Morris, M. E. 1972. Extracellular K⁺ activity and slow potential changes in spinal cord and medulla. *Can. J. Physiol. Pharmacol.* 50:1214–17

102. Krnjević, K., Morris, M. E. 1974. Extracellular accumulation of K⁺ evoked by activity of primary afferent fibres in the cuneate nucleus and dorsal horn of cats. *Can. J. Physiol. Pharmacol.* 52:852–71

103. Krnjević, K., Morris, M. E. 1975. Correlation between extracellular focal potentials and K⁺ potentials evoked by primary afferent activity. *Can. J. Physiol. Pharmacol.* 53:912–22

104. Krnjević, K., Morris, M. E. 1975. Factors determining the decay of K⁺ potentials and focal potentials in the central nervous system. *Can. J. Physiol. Pharmacol.* 53:923–34

105. Kudo, Y., Fukuda, H. 1976. Alteration of extracellular K⁺ activity induced by amino acids in the frog spinal cord. *Jpn. J. Pharmacol.* 26:385–87

106. Kuffler, S. W. 1967. Neuroglial cells: physiological properties and a potassium mediated effect of neuronal activity on the glial membrane potential. *Proc. R. Soc. London Ser. B.* 168:1–21

107. Kuffler, S. W., Nicholls, J. G. 1966. The physiology of neuroglial cells. *Ergeb. Physiol.* 57:1–90

108. LaManna, J. C., Cordingley, G., Rosenthal, M. 1977. Phenobarbital actions in vivo: effects of extracellular potassium activity and oxidative metabolism in cat cerebral cortex. *J. Pharmacol. Exp. Ther.* 200:560–69

109. LaManna, J., Lothman, E., Rosenthal, M., Somjen, G. G., Younts, W. 1977. Phenytoin, electric, ionic and metabolic responses in cortex and spinal cord. *Epilepsia* 18:317–29

110. Latzkovits, L., Sensenbrenner, M., Mandel, P. 1974. Tracer kinetic model analysis of potassium uptake by dissociated nerve cell culture: glial-neuronal interrelationship. *J. Neurochem.* 23:193–200

111. Lebovitz, R. M. 1970. A theoretical examination of ionic interaction between neural and non-neural elements. *Biophys. J.* 10:423–44

112. Lehmenkühler, A., Speckmann, E. J., Caspers, H. 1976. Cortical spreading depression in relation to potassium activity, oxygen tension, local flow and carbon dioxide tension. See Ref. 34, pp. 311–15

113. Lewis, D. V., Schuette, W. H. 1975. NADH fluorescence and [K⁺]₀ changes during hippocampal electrical stimulation. *J. Neurophysiol.* 38:405–17

114. Lewis, D. V., Schuette, W. H. 1975. Temperature dependence of potassium clearance in the central nervous system. *Brain Res.* 99:175–78

115. Lewis, D., Schuette, W. H. 1976. NADH fluorescence, [K⁺]₀ and oxygen consumption in cat cerebral cortex during direct cortical stimulation. *Brain Res.* 110:523–35

116. Liley, A. W. 1956. The effect of presynaptic polarization on the spontaneous activity at the mammalian neuromuscular junction. *J. Physiol. London* 134:427–43

117. Lipton, P., Heimbach, C. J. 1977. The effect of extracellular potassium concentration on protein synthesis in guinea pig hippocampal slices. *J. Neurochem.* 28:1347–54

118. Lothman, E., LaManna, J., Cordingley, G., Rosenthal, M., Somjen, G. 1975. Responses of electrical potentials, potassium levels and oxidative metabolic activity of cerebral neocortex of cats. *Brain Res.* 88:15–36

119. Lothman, E. W., Somjen, G. G. 1975. Extracellular potassium activity, intracellular and extracellular potential responses in the spinal cord. *J. Physiol. London* 252:115–36

120. Lothman, E. W., Somjen, G. G. 1976. Functions of primary afferents, and responses of extracellular K⁺ during spinal epileptiform seizures. *Electroencephalogr. Clin. Neurophysiol.* 41:253–67

121. Lux, H. D. 1974. The kinetics of extracellular potassium: relation to epileptogenesis. *Epilepsia* 15:375–93

122. Lux, H. D., Neher, E. 1973. The equilibration time course of $[K^+]_o$ in cat cortex. *Exp. Brain Res.* 17:190–205

123. McIlwain, H. 1952. Phosphates of brain during in vitro metabolism: Effects of oxygen, glucose, glutamate, glutamine, calcium and potassium. *Biochem. J.* 52:289–95

124. McLennan, H. 1956. The diffusion of potassium, inulin and thiocyanate in the extracellular spaces of mammalian muscle. *Biochim. Biophys. Acta.* 21:472–81

125. McLennan, H. 1957. The diffusion of potassium, sodium, sucrose and inulin in the extracellular space of mammalian tissues. *Biochim. Biophys. Acta.* 24:1–8

126. Mareš, P., Kříž, N., Brožek, G., Bureš, J. 1976. Anoxic changes of extracellular potassium concentration in the cerebral cortex of young rats. *Exp. Neurol.* 53:12–20

127. Mayevsky, A., Zeuthen, T., Chance, B. 1974. Measurements of extracellular potassium, ECoG and pyridine nucleotide levels during cortical spreading depression in rats. *Brain Res.* 76:347–49

128. Maynard, E. A., Schultz, R. L., Pease, D. C., 1957. Electron microscopy of the vascular bed of rat cerebral cortex. *Am. J. Anat.* 100:409–34

129. Meyer, J. S., Gotoh, F., Tazaki, Y. 1961. Inhibitory action of carbon dioxide and acetazolamide in seizure activity. *Electroencephalogr. Clin. Neurophysiol.* 13:762–75

130. Mines, G. R. 1908. On the spontaneous movements of amphibian skeletal muscle in saline solution, with observations on the influence of potassium and calcium chlorides on muscular excitability. *J. Physiol. London* 37:408–58

131. Moody, W. J., Futamachi, K. J., Prince, D. A. 1974. Extracellular potassium activity during epileptogenesis. *Exp. Neurol.* 42:248–62

132. Morris, M. E. 1974. Hypoxia and extracellular potassium activity in the guinea pig cortex. *Can. J. Physiol. Pharmacol.* 52:872–82

133. Morris, M. E. 1978. Brain extracellular potassium and general anaesthetics. *Can. J. Physiol. Pharmacol.* 56:863–72

134. Morris, M. E., Krnjević, K. 1976. Extracellular K^+ accumulation and modulation of sensory transmission. In *Advances in Pain Research,* ed. J. J. Bonica, D. Albe-Fessard, 1:117–22. New York: Raven Press

135. Muchnik, S., Kotsias, B. A., Arrizurieta de Muchnik, E. E. 1975. In vivo and in vitro miniature endplate potentials at various external K^+ concentrations. *Am. J. Physiol.* 228:1733–37

136. Mutani, R., Futamachi, K. J., Prince, D. A. 1974. Potassium activity in immature cortex. *Brain Res.* 75:27–39

137. Mutsuga, N., Schuette, W. H., Lewis, D. V. 1976. The contribution of local blood flow to the rapid clearance of potassium from the cortical extracellular space. *Brain Res.* 116:431–36

138. Nattie, E. E., Tenney, S. M. 1976. Effect of potassium depletion on cerebrospinal fluid bicarbonate homeostasis. *Am. J. Physiol.* 231:579–87

139. Nattie, E. E., Tenney, S. M. 1976. Effects of potassium depletion on control of breathing in awake rats. *Am. J. Physiol.* 231:588–92

140. Nicholson, C., Kraig, R. P. 1975. Chloride and potassium changes measured during spreading depression in catfish cerebellum. *Brain Res.* 96:384–89

141. Ogata, N., Hori, N., Katsuda, N. 1976. The correlation between extracellular potassium concentration and hippocampal epileptic activity in vitro. *Brain Res.* 110:371–75

142. Ookawa, T., Bureš, J. 1975. Extracellular potassium shifts accompanying epileptic discharge induced in chicken hyperstriatum by systemic injection of metrazol. *Brain Res.* 97:171–76

143. Orkand, P. M., Bracho, H., Orkand, R. K. 1973. Glial metabolism: alteration by potassium levels comparable to those during neuronal activity. *Brain Res.* 55:467–71

144. Orkand, R. K., Nicholls, J. G., Kuffler, S. W. 1966. Effect of nerve impulses on the membrane potential of glial cells in the central nervous system of amphibia. *J. Neurophysiol.* 29:788–806

145. Oswald, R. E., Freeman, J. A. 1976. Extracellular potassium changes associated with the control of retinotectal synaptic transmission in *Bufo Marinus. Soc. Neurosci. VIth Ann. Meet. Abstr.,* p. 995

146. Pape, L. G.. Katzman, R. 1972. K^{42} distribution in brain during simultaneous ventriculo-cisternal and subarachnoid perfusion. *Brain Res.* 38:49–69

147. Pape, L. G., Katzman, R. 1972. Response of glia in cat sensory motor cortex to increase of extracellular potassium. *Brain Res.* 38:71–92

148. Pedley, T. A., Fisher, R. S., Futamachi, K. J., Prince, D. A. 1976. Regulation of extracellular potassium concentration

in epileptogenesis. *Fed. Proc.* 32: 1254–59

149. Pedley, T. A., Fisher, R. S., Moody, W. J., Futamachi, K. J., Prince, D. A. 1974. Extracellular potassium activity during epileptogenesis: a comparison between neocortex and hippocampus. *Trans. Am. Neurol. Assoc.* 99:41–45

150. Pedley, T. A., Fisher, R. S., Prince, D. A. 1976. Focal gliosis and potassium movement in mammalian cortex. *Exp. Neurol.* 50:346–61

151. Pollen, D. A., Trachtenberg, M. C. 1970. Neuroglia: Gliosis and focal epilepsy. *Science* 167:1252–53

152. Prince, D. A., Lux, H. D., Neher, E. 1973. Measurement of extracellular potassium activity in cat cortex. *Brain Res.* 50:489–95

153. Prives, C., Quastel, J. H. 1969. Effect of cerebral stimulation on biosysthesis of nucleotides and RNA in brain slices in vitro. *Biochim. Biophys. Acta.* 182:285–91

154. Ransom, B. R., Goldring, S. 1973. Ionic determinants of membrane potential of cells presumed to be glia in cerebral cortex of cat. *J. Neurophysiol.* 36:855–68

155. Rolleston, F. S., Newsholme, E. A. 1967. Control of glycolysis in cerebral cortex slices. *Biochem. J.* 104:524–33

156. Rosenthal, M., LaManna, J., Yamada, Y., Younts, W., Somjen, G. 1978. Oxidative metabolism, extracellular potassium, and sustained potential shifts in cat spinal cord in situ. *Brain Res.* In press

157. Sellström, A., Hamberger, A. 1977. Potassium-stimulated gamma-aminobutyric acid release from neurons and glia. *Brain Res.* 119:189–98

158. Siesjö, B. K., Sörensen, S. C., eds. 1970. *Ion Homeostasis of the Brain, Alfred Benzon Symposium III.* New York: Academic Press. 479 pp.

159. Singer, W., Lux, H. D. 1975. Extracellular potassium gradients and visual receptive fields in the cat striate cortex. *Brain Res.* 96:378–83

160. Somjen, G. G. 1975. Electrophysiology of neuroglia. *Ann. Rev. Physiol.* 37:163–90

161. Somjen, G. G. 1978. A comment on the effect of potassium on dorsal root potentials. In *Iontophoresis and Transmitter Mechanisms in the Mammalian Central Nervous System,* ed. R. W. Ryall, J. S. Kelly, pp. 282–83. Amsterdam: Elsevier

162. Somjen, G. G. 1978. Metabolic and electrical correlates of the clearing of excess potassium in cortex and spinal

cord. In *Studies of Neurophysiology,* ed R. Porter. Cambridge: Cambridge Univ. Press. In press

163. Somjen, G. G. 1979. The role of potassium and of neuroglia in the generation of seizures and in their treatment. In *Anticonvulsant Mechanisms,* ed. K. Penry et al. New York: Raven Press. In press

164. Somjen, G. G., Lothman, E. W. 1974. Potassium, sustained focal potential shifts, and dorsal root potentials of the mammalian spinal cord. *Brain Res.* 69:153–57

165. Somjen, G. G., Lothman, E., Dunn, P., Dunaway, T., Cordingley, G. 1978. Microphysiology of spinal seizures. In *Abnormal Neuronal Discharges,* ed N. Chalazonitis, M. Boisson, pp. 13–28. New York: Raven Press

166. Somjen, G. G., Rosenthal, M., Cordingley, G., LaManna, J., Lothman, E. 1976. Potassium, neuroglia, and oxidative metabolism in central gray matter. *Fed. Proc.* 35:1266–71

167. Somjen, G. G., Trachtenberg, M. 1978. Neuroglia as generator of extracellular current. In *Cerebral Field Potentials,* ed E. Speckmann, H. Caspers. In press

168. Sugaya, E., Takato, M., Noda, Y. 1975. Neuronal and glial activity during spreading depression in cerebral cortex of rat. *J. Neurophysiol.* 38:822–41

169. Syková, E., Rothenberg, S., Krekule, I. 1974. Changes of extracellular potassium concentration during spontaneous activity in the mesencephalic reticular formation of the rat. *Brain Res.* 79:333–37

170. Syková, E., Shirayev, B., Kříž, N., Vyklický, L. 1976. Accumulation of extracellular potassium in the spinal cord of frog. *Brain Res.* 106:413–17

171. Syková, E., Vyklický, L. 1977. Changes of extracellular potassium activity in isolated spinal cord of frog under high Mg^{2+} concentration. *Neurosci. Lett.* 4:161–65

172. Takeuchi, A., Takeuchi, N. 1961. Changes in potassium concentration around motor nerve terminals produced by current flow and their effects on neuromuscular transmission. *J. Physiol. London* 155:46–58

173. Tower, D. B. 1969. Neurochemical mechanisms. In *Basic Mechanisms of the Epilepsies,* ed. H. Jasper, A. Ward Jr., A. Pope, pp. 611–38. Boston: Little, Brown & Co

174. Trachtenberg, M. C., Pollen, D. A. 1970. Neuroglia: biophysical properties

and physiologcial function. *Science* 167:1248-52

175. Van Harreveld, A. 1966. *Brain Tissue Electrolytes.* Oxford: Butterworth. p. 171

176. Van Harreveld, A., Fifková, E. 1973. Mechanisms involved in spreading depression. *J. Neurobiol.* 4:375-87

177. Van Harreveld, A., Trubatch, J. 1975. Synaptic changes in frog brain after stimulation with potassium chloride. *J. Neurocytol.* 4:33-46

178. Varon, S., Somjen, G. 1978. Neuronglia interactions. *Neurosci. Res. Prog. Bull.* In press

179. Vern, B. A., Schuette, W. H., Thibault, L. E. 1977. [K$^+$]$_o$ clearance in cortex: A new analytical model. *J. Neurophysiol.* 40:1015-23

180. Vyklický, L. 1978. Transient changes in extracellular potassium and presynaptic inhibition. See Ref. 161, pp. 284-86

181. Vyklický, L., Syková, E., & Kříž, N. 1975. Slow potentials induced by changes of extracellular potassium in the spinal cord of the cat. *Brain Res.* 87:77-80

182. Vyklický, L., Syková, E., Kříž, N., Ujec, E. 1972. Post-stimulation changes of extracellular potassium concentration in the spinal cord of the rat. *Brain Res.* 45:608-11

183. Vyskočil, F., Kříž, N., Bureš, J. 1972. Potassium-selective microelectrodes used for measuring the extracellular brain potassium during spreading depression and anoxic depolarization in rats. *Brain Res.* 39:255-59

184. Walker, J. L. 1971. Ion specific liquid ion exchanger microelectrodes. *Anal. Chem.* 43:89A-93A

185. Wendell-Smith, C. P., Blunt, M. J. 1965. Possible role of neuroglia. *Nature* 208:600-1

186. Whittam, R. 1962. The dependence of the respiration of brain cortex on active cation transport. *Biochem. J.* 82:205-12

187. Zuckermann, E. C., Glaser, G. H. 1968. Hippocampal epileptic activity induced by localized ventricular perfusion with high-potassium cerebrospinal fluid. *Exp. Neurol.* 20:87-110

RENAL AND ELECTROLYTE PHYSIOLOGY

Introduction

In keeping with the revised editorial policy of the *Annual Review of Physiology*, the present section on Renal and Electrolyte Physiology is intended to provide a relatively detailed examination, from different points of view, of one cardinal aspect of renal physiology: ion transport by the nephron. The topics discussed this year include: Na^+ and H^+ transport by the nephron; the effect of renal nerves on Na^+ excretion; K^+ transport by the nephron; and polyvalent ion, specifically Ca^{2+} and $HPO_4^{2-}/H_2PO_4^-$, absorption.

In the first paper, "Sugar, amino acid, and Na^+ cotransport in the proximal tubule," K. J. Ullrich examines the molecular specificity of sugar and amino acid transport by the proximal tubule, the interaction of organic nonelectrolyte transport with proximal tubular Na^+ transport, and certain of the theoretical (thermodynamic) and experimental (reconstitution) approaches used to assess proximal tubular sugar and amino acid cotransport with Na^+. In the second paper, "Proton secretion by the kidney," D. G. Warnock and F. C. Rector examine the relations between urinary acidification, presumably H^+ secretion, and net Na^+ absorption in both the proximal and the distal nephron. These authors discuss the differences between the apparent coupling ratios between Na^+ absorption and H^+ secretion in proximal and distal tubules; new observations indicating that the P_{CO_2} of the renal cortex may be higher than in systemic plasma (and that a CO_2 gradient may exist across the proximal tubule); and the implications of such a disparity between luminal and arterial P_{CO_2} for the "disequilibrium pH" argument in support of an Na^+/H^+ exchange mechanism. In the third paper, "Rheogenic and passive Na^+ absorption by the proximal nephron," J. A. Schafer and I review evidence consistent with the view that a portion of proximal tubular Na^+ absorption depends on two different kinds of processes: "simple," active Na^+ absorption, which is rheogenic; and passive

179

NaCl absorption driven by the favorable electrochemical salt gradient produced by preferential $NaHCO_3$ absorption.

The fourth article in this series examines the effects of renal nerve stimulation on Na^+ excretion. Until recently, the notion that renal nerves play a trivial role in regulating Na^+ excretion—except under stressful conditions—has been a prevailing canon of renal physiology. In "Renal nerves and Na^+ excretion," C. W. Gottschalk summarizes recent persuasive evidence that contests this view and is consistent with the possibility that adrenergic nerves exert a direct anti-natriuretic effect on the nephron.

The fifth article, "Potassium transport in the nephron," by G. Giebisch and B. Stanton, summarizes the various mechanisms for K^+ processing by the amphibian and the mammalian kidney. There is an emphasis on the possibility that distal tubular potassium transport may involve: (a) an active peritubular Na^+/K^+ exchange process that is not necessarily electrically silent but, under appropriate conditions, may also be rheogenic; and (b) a passive K^+ transport process across luminal membranes driven by a favorable electrochemical gradient between the cytosol and distal tubular lumen.

Finally, in "Renal handling of phosphate and calcium," V. W. Dennis, W. W. Stead, and J. L. Myers review the renal transport mechanisms for these ionic species, with particular regard to the lessons learned from isolated tubule microperfusion about Ca^{2+} and $HPO_4^{2-}/H_2PO_4^-$ absorption by various segments of the mammalian nephron.

T. E. Andreoli
Section Editor

Ann. Rev. Physiol. 1979. 41:181–95
Copyright © 1979 by Annual Reviews Inc. All rights reserved

SUGAR, AMINO ACID, AND NA⁺ COTRANSPORT IN THE PROXIMAL TUBULE

♦1213

K. J. Ullrich

Max-Planck-Institut für Biophysik, Kennedyallee 70, 6000 Frankfurt (Main) 70, West Germany

INTRODUCTION

For obvious reasons the Na^+-dependence of sugar and amino acid transport was described much earlier for the intestine (5, 15, 19, 61, 62) than for the kidney. Thus, the Na^+-sugar cotransport hypothesis was already well formulated (15) before the sodium dependence of renal glucose transport had been reported in perfused rat (64) and frog kidney (91, 92) and in rabbit kidney cortex slices (52). Similarly, the sodium dependence of renal amino acid transport was studied by uptake into tubular cells (24, 40, 41, 69, 70, 71, 79) before the introduction of new techniques, such as the doubly perfused proximal tubule in situ (86), with transtubular or cellular electrical potential measurements (30) and the preparation of osmotically reactive plasma membrane vesicles from either cell side (51), made it possible to study the single transport steps and to test the sodium gradient hypothesis rigorously. The vesicular transport studies have already been reviewed extensively (48, 65).

ANALYSIS OF SUGAR REABSORPTION IN THE PROXIMAL TUBULE

In the doubly perfused proximal tubule, the zero net flux transtubular concentration difference of all actively transported sugars, which is a measure of the active transport rate, dropped considerably when the perfusion solutions were Na^+-free (86). The same was shown for α-methyl-D-glycoside when the perfusates contained ouabain (84). In the same preparation, Frömter and collaborators have shown that the transepithelial, lumen-

181

positive electrical potential difference as well as the cellular electrical potential difference is reduced when the tubular lumen is perfused with solutions containing actively transported sugars plus sodium ions (27, 28, 30, 85). The explanation for this phenomenon is that the sugars cross the brush-border membrane together with Na^+ ions, resulting in a charge transfer.

In a simple electrical analogy circuit it could easily be shown that a positive ion current entering the cell from the lumen affects the electrical potential difference measured either between lumen and interstitium or between cell and interstitium (27, 28). The driving force for the sodium-coupled glucose influx is not only the concentration difference for glucose across the brush border, but also the concentration difference for Na^+ ions as well as the electrical potential difference for Na^+.

The perfusion data provide strong evidence for the Na^+ gradient hypothesis (16), which postulates (a) a coupled entrance of Na^+ and glucose through the brush-border membrane, the Na^+ gradient across that membrane being the main driving force; and (b) a Na^+-K^+ ATPase, which pumps Na^+ ions out of the cell, thereby creating and maintaining the Na^+ gradient across the brush-border membrane. A sodium- and glucose-dependent depolarization of the luminal cell membrane was also observed in the proximal tubule of amphibia (56). From the D-glucose induced changes of the electrical potential difference and the corresponding electrical resistance values, Frömter & Lüer (31) calculated the maximum electrical current carried by the Na^+-D-glucose cotransport system and compared it with the maximal D-glucose transport rates. They arrived at equal flux rates, which suggests a 1:1 coupling between D-glucose and Na^+ for the luminal cotransport system.

The mutual interaction between glucose and sodium ions has been very elegantly documented by flux studies on closed vesicles of brush-border membranes (4, 51, 58, 82). When the vesicles are incubated in a sodium-free solution or in the presence of phlorrhizin, the same D-glucose influx rate is observed until equilibrium is reached. This influx could be attributed to a passive, probably not carrier-mediated, influx into the vesicles. If, however, a Na^+ gradient is present across the membrane, the initial influx of D-glucose is accelerated ten-fold at 0.1 mM D-glucose in the medium and, transiently, a D-glucose concentration higher than the equilibrium concentration is reached within the vesicles. This "overshoot" of the intravesicular glucose concentration could easily be explained by movement of Na^+ ions from the incubation medium into the vesicles carrying D-glucose via a common carrier in addition to the passive influx of glucose. If this were the case, then no overshoot would be expected if the vesicles were in equilibrium with the surrounding Na^+ ions from the beginning of the D-glucose flux study. Such an absence of overshoot was actually observed.

The electrogenic mode of the Na^+-glucose transfer already seen in electrical measurements leads one to suppose that the rapid movement of sodium ions into the vesicles together with D-glucose would cause the intravesicular space to become electrically positive compared to the medium. If the anions present could not follow as fast, the electrical potential difference would retard further Na^+-glucose influx. That this is indeed so is documented by the fact that with faster moving anions (SCN^-, NO_3^-) the initial influx and overshoot of D-glucose became larger, while with slow-moving ions (SO_4^{2-}) the overshoot is abolished (6, 51). An acceleration of the glucose influx with a larger overshoot could also be observed if an intravesicular negative electrical potential difference was established. This was achieved by preloading the vesicles with K^+ in the presence of the K^+ ionophore, valinomycin, which makes the vesicular wall extremely permeable to K^+. Alternatively, the vesicles were preloaded with H^+ ions in the presence of an uncoupler such as CFCCP, which makes the vesicular wall permeable to H^+ ions. The D-glucose overshoot increased in both cases. All these data support the Na^+-gradient hypothesis (16).

The specificity of the luminal Na^+-glucose transport system was also tested by electrical as well as chemical measurements (85). Both sets of data agreed very well and give the following picture: A free OH in the D-gluco configuration on C atom 2 is most important, the OH in equatorial position of the chair C-1 conformation. A free OH on C-3 in the equatorial configuration is also essential. If the OH on C-4 turns from the equatorial to the axial configuration the transport is reduced by 50%. The OH on C-6 may be missing if the D-glucose configuration is unchanged otherwise. But if in addition the position of OH in C-4 is changed, transport ceases. Furthermore, the presence of a pyranose ring structure is necessary. This configuration is essentially the same as was already proposed by Crane in 1962 (15) for the intestinal hexose transport. Studies of the uptake of different sugars into brush-border vesicles from rabbit and human kidney agree in general with this specificity requirement (4, 82).

The Na^+-gradient hypothesis postulates that glucose accumulated within the cell by the luminal Na^+-glucose cotransport mechanism leaves the cell at the contraluminal cell side passively. So far data from vesicle (51, 77) and electrical studies (66) indicate that the sugar transfer at this cell side is electrically silent, probably Na^+-insensitive, and inhibitable rather by phloretin than by phlorrhizin. Thus the basolateral carrier—not only in the proximal tubule but also in the small intestine (43, 59)—exhibits properties similar to those known in "equilibrating" systems such as the glucose carriers in erythrocytes and other body cells (21, 93).

The driving force for Na^+-glucose cotransport is mainly the electrochemical potential difference for sodium across the brush-border membrane; but, as will be pointed out later, the contribution of the electric field and the concentration gradient to uptake cannot be unequivocally separated. Therefore, it is of great importance to evaluate the first step in this transport process—i.e. the binding of glucose to its carrier and its dependence on the prevailing Na^+ concentration. Since D-glucose inhibits phlorrhizin binding competitively, the K_i for D-glucose, an indicator of the affinity of D-glucose to its binding site, can be evaluated (8, 9, 76). The most important finding in these studies was that phlorrhizin and D-glucose binding are both Na^+-sensitive (14, 25, 76). The affinity of the receptor to either substrate (phlorrhizin or D-glucose) increased with rising ambient Na^+ concentrations, with a K_{Na} of 13 and 15 mEq l^{-1}, respectively, which is almost identical with K_{Na} for transtubular D-glucose transport. Inhibition studies of phlorrhizin binding (34, 76) have so far given specificity patterns in agreement with the transtubular transport studies, since the actively transported sugars D-glucose, α- and β-methyl-D-glycoside, and D-galactose inhibited phlorrhizin binding, while the nonactively transported sugars D-mannose, D-fructose, D-glucosamine, L-glucose, and D-xylose did not. Furthermore, there is a parallelism between the sequence of the active transport rates (86)—D-glucose > D-galactose > 3-0-methyl-D-glucose— and the potency of the phlorrhizin analog in inhibiting glucose transport— phloretin 2'-glucoside (phlorrhizin) > phloretin 2'-galactoside > phloretin 2'-(3-methoxy-glucoside) (88). On the other hand, it was shown that phloretin-2'-(2-deoxy-D-glucoside) is not bound to the brush-border high-affinity binding site for phlorrhizin (46). These data indicate that the differences in the active transport rates of these sugars were determined by their respective affinities towards the carrier and that the affinity is clearly augmented by the presence of Na^+ ions.

ANALYSIS OF AMINO ACID REABSORPTION IN THE PROXIMAL CONVOLUTION

The methods used to analyze proximal amino acid transport were the same as those used for the analysis of glucose reabsorption. Again, in the doubly perfused proximal tubule the zero net flux transtubular concentration difference of all actively transported amino acids dropped considerably when the perfusion solutions were Na^+-free (87). The same was shown for L-histidine when the perfusates contained ouabain (86). Furthermore, Frömter and co-workers (30, 66–68) observed that L-phenylalanine, L-glutamine, L-asparagine, L-ornithine, L-lysine, L-cysteine, L-methionine, L-arginine, L-proline, L-hydroxyproline, L-glycine, L-aspartate, and L-glutamate added to the luminal perfusate, in the presence of Na^+ depolarize the luminal cell membrane in the same manner as the actively transported hexoses do. These electrophysiological data obtained in the proximal tubule of the rat kidney, however, are at variance with the findings of Hoshi et al (44, 45), obtained in the proximal tubule of the newt kidney, where only the neutral amino acids exert Na^+-dependent depolarization, whilst L-lysine depolarizes Na^+ independently and aspartate does not depolarize at all, although the aspartate transport has been shown to be Na^+-dependent. The explanation for this discrepancy is that in the rat kidney the transport of all amino acids proceeds with a surplus positive charge provided by cotransported Na^+ ions, while in the newt kidney this is only the case for neutral amino acids. In the newt kidney the positively charged L-lysine might be driven through the brush border by its own favorable electrochemical gradient, whereas the negatively charged L-aspartate might cross with just one Na^+ ion in an electroneutral fashion.

When amino acids are offered to the rat proximal tubule from the contraluminal cell side together with Na^+, neither the neutral amino acids phenylalanine, glutamine, and asparagine, nor the dibasic amino acid ornithine show a significant effect on the cell potential (68). However, if glutamate and aspartate are offered from the contraluminal cell side, they depolarize the tubular cells just as if offered from the luminal cell side. The depolarization is not observed when Na^+ in the peritubular perfusion fluid is replaced by choline. With plasma membrane vesicles from the contraluminal cell side, L-glutamate is taken up Na^+-dependently, while L-phenylalanine and L-histidine do not show Na^+-dependence (50). These observations suggest that glutamate and aspartate are taken up into the cell by both cell sides via Na^+-dependent secondary active transport processes. The electrical and vesicle data thus indicate that all tested amino acids except glutamate and aspartate are reabsorbed in accordance with the Na^+-gradient hypothesis: Na^+–amino acid cotransport at the luminal cell side, passive amino acid exit at the contraluminal cell side.

The reabsorption of glutamate and aspartate, however, seems to proceed in a modified manner. The inwardly directed Na^+-glutamate and Na^+-aspartate cotransport at both cell sides in concert with the glutamate formation from glutamine are responsible for the very high intracellular concentration of both amino acids (12). Although L-glutamate and L-aspartate are on the metabolic pathway of NH_3 production and are candidates for gluconeogenesis (90), net transport from the lumen to the interstitium can be achieved if the luminal pump rate is higher and/or the luminal leak rate smaller than their respective rates at the contraluminal cell side.

Amino acid transport into plasma membrane vesicles isolated from either cell side is similar in many ways to glucose transport. Thus, Evers et al (22) could demonstrate that the influx of L-phenylalanine into isolated brush-border membrane vesicles is Na^+-dependent and shows an overshoot phenomenon; the size of the overshoot is dependent on the permeability of the accompanying anions and on the imposed electrical potential difference. Reduction of the sodium concentration in the medium reduces the affinity of the transport system for L-phenylalanine but does not alter the maximum transport rate. Identical conclusions were reached subsequently by Fass et al (23), who worked with L-alanine, L-proline, L-glutamate, and β-alanine. For varying reasons, kinetic data obtained in vesicular uptake studies lack the desired accuracy. Thus, it is difficult to define low and high affinity transport systems when binding is not explicitly excluded (57).

These experiments provide clear evidence that the active transport of the neutral amino acids proceeds as electrogenic cotransport with Na^+ through the brush-border membrane. As can be deduced from L-phenylalanine, L-proline, and L-histidine fluxes into vesicles from basolateral plasma membranes of proximal tubules, the exit from the cell into the interstitium seems to proceed by a Na^+-independent carrier mechanism (22, 50, 77). This does not hold for L-glutamate (50) as already mentioned. It is interesting to note that the amino acid–sodium cotransport systems have, in general, a lower cation specificity than the sugar-sodium cotransport system. In brush-border vesicles, Li^+ in particular is capable of replacing sodium to an appreciable extent (22, 65).

An excellent review (74) covers the specificity of the overall transtubular reabsorption of amino acids. Comprehensive specificity studies on the luminal transport step have been performed recently by Sacktor, Segal, and colleagues (37, 57, 65), who used brush-border membrane vesicles, and by Samarzija & Frömter [(66); I. Samarzija and E. Frömter, in preparation], who analyzed the Na^+-amino acid specific luminal depolarization. In brush-border membrane vesicles a strong mutual inhibition between L-arginine and L-lysine was observed (57, 65). L-glutamate uptake was inhibited by L-aspartate but not by basic, neutral amino nor imino acids (65); and β-alanine uptake was inhibited by taurine, but not by L-α-alanine or other α-amino acids (37). L-proline uptake was inhibited strongly by imino acids only; glycine and other neutral amino acids showed little if any inhibition (57). In contrast, glycine uptake was strongly inhibited both by L-proline and by neutral amino acids (65). With cellular depolarization, a strong mutual interaction was observed within the group of the basic amino acids, the group of acidic amino acids, and within the group of neutral amino acids; but no comparable interaction was seen with amino acids belonging to different groups [(66); I. Samarzija and E. Frömter, in preparation]. Furthermore, within the group of neutral amino acids evidence was obtained for additional separate transport systems for the imino acids and for glycine. Combining all the data, one may propose seven transport systems located within the brush border for: (a) neutral amino acids; (b) acidic amino acids; (c) basic amino acids, the interaction of cystein-cystine with this system being still unclear; (d) imino acids, high affinity; (e) imino acids, low affinity shared by glycine and neutral amino acids; (f) glycine shared by neutral amino acids; (g) β-amino acids.

This specificity is likely to coincide with the specificity of the overall active transtubular amino acid transport since the coupling to the active Na^+ reabsorption occurs in the brush border. Although specificity measurements on contraluminal membrane vesicles are still lacking, one may suggest that the specificity and characteristics of the amino acid exit mechanisms might influence the overall reabsorption rate and might be responsible for mutual interactions. It is therefore not surprising that transport parameters, e.g. K_m, for luminal and overall transport of the same amino acid vary by a factor of more than 10 (66, 73).

Several important findings on the renal transport of D-amino acids have been published in recent years. A net secretion of D-tryptophan was observed, which was proposed to occur as countertransport against the L-enantiomorph (13, 94). In the doubly perfused rat kidney an active reabsorption of D-histidine was observed which was 40% of that of L-histidine, while for D-alanine it was only in the range of 10% of that of the L-isomer (87). Furthermore, in slices of human kidney a concentrative uptake of D-lysine was observed that could be inhibited by L-lysine (63). Similarly Silbernagl & Völkl (75) found that in the case of D-methionine and perhaps also of D-proline, D-serine, and D-phenylalanine, the fractional reabsorption decreased when the luminal perfusate contained high concentrations of the respective L-form. Conversely, it was observed in brush-border vesicles that D-proline inhibits the uptake of L-proline, although only to a small extent (37). In contrast to these findings, Evers et al (22) could detect neither a Na^+-dependence of D-phenylalanine uptake in brush-border vesicles nor a countertransport of D-phenylalanine against L-phenylalanine. Nevertheless, these data taken together support the hypothesis that the D-enantiomorphs use the same transport system as the respective L-enantiomorphs but are transported at a much lower rate.

INTERACTION BETWEEN SUGAR AND AMINO ACID TRANSPORT

A mutual interaction between sugar and amino acid transport was first observed in the intestine (1, 47, 60, 72). The most plausible explanation for this phenomenon was given by Murer et al (60), who argued that the interaction might occur via the common driving force, the electrochemical potential difference for Na^+ ions. Subsequently an inhibition by D-glucose of L-alanine uptake in renal brush-border membrane vesicles was found (23) but only in the presence of a Na^+ gradient. In a comprehensive electrophysiological study on Na^+-dependent amino acid and glucose depolarization of the proximal brush-border membrane, Samarzija & Frömter [manuscript in preparation; (66)] found that the depolarization when D-glucose and L-phenylalanine were applied together was 15% smaller than the sum of the single depolarizations. The same decrease in depolarization was observed when two amino acids were offered that do not share a common transport system. On the contrary, if they use the same system, the depolarization was definitely smaller, caused by additional competitive inhibition. Thus, by quantitative evaluation of the electrical responses it was possible to differentiate between an unspecific inhibition due to a common driving force and a specific inhibition due to use of a common carrier. In kidney cortex slices a mutual inhibition of α-aminoisobutyric acid and α-methyl-D-glycoside uptake was also observed (33), but nothing has been reported on mutual interaction between sugars and the different amino acids in the intact kidney. Also, in the doubly perfused proximal tubule, an attempt to demonstrate mutual inhibition between D-glucose and L-histidine transport was unsuccessful (87). Thus, the discrepancy between mutual interaction at the brush-border entrance step and the missing interaction in steady-state transtubular interaction remains to be clarified.

EFFECT OF SUGARS AND AMINO ACIDS ON NA^+ REABSORPTION

The reabsorption of sugars and amino acids can increase the Na^+ reabsorption in different ways: (a) by contransport with Na^+ ions; (b) by creating a transtubular osmotic pressure difference, with subsequent water movement and Na^+ reabsorption through solvent drag; and (c) by metabolic effects. Assuming a 1:1 cotransport ratio and a luminal sugar concentration of 5.5 mM one can estimate that the Na^+-glucose cotransport might account for approximately 5% of the Na^+ ions reabsorbed in the late proximal convolution (55), and for a value four times as high (i.e. 20%) for the early proximal convolution of rats (10, 29, 30). Furthermore, using the transport parameters of the proximal convolution (83) one can attribute another 3% to sugar-induced solvent drag, at a 5 mosmol concentration difference. Thus it is not surprising that the effect of D-glucose on the sodium reabsorption from the late proximal convolution of the rat has been found to be insignificant (7, 36). In the early parts of isolated rabbit tubule, however, a 20–25% increase in Na^+ reabsorption was observed when 5.5

mM D-glucose or 6 mM L-alanine, respectively, were added to the luminal perfusate (11). The effect of the transported but not metabolized α-methyl D-glycoside or L-cycloleucine seems to be smaller when estimated for the same concentrations. Thus these data, too, agree with expectations from the transport parameters of the *rat* proximal convolution (10, 29, 30, 54). Furthermore, the Na^+-glucose cotransport in the proximal tubule of the rabbit might be somewhat higher than in the rat.

In the rat perfused whole kidney three effects by which sugars stimulated overall Na^+ reabsorption can be discriminated: (*a*) A very small effect of the well-transported but nonmetabolizable α-methyl-D-glycoside, which could be attributed to Na^+ cotransport and solvent drag (26); (*b*) a larger effect of D-glucose, which seems to be metabolic (26, 81); (*c*) an unexplained effect of the nonmetabolizable L-glucose (80), which is not reabsorbed by Na^+ cotransport in the proximal tubule.

THEORY AND CURRENT EXPERIMENTAL APPROACH

The theoretical considerations on Na^+-coupled transport processes have been reviewed by Crane (16), and the recent developments have been summarized by Heinz & Geck (38). In retrospect, one of the first promising descriptions of Na^+–amino acid cotransport was that of Curran et al (20), who proposed a mobile carrier model with the main assumptions that the translocation step was rate-limiting and the association-dissociation reactions at the surface were in equilibrium. Furthermore, they assumed that all forms of the carrier were uncharged or that there was no electrical potential difference across the respective cell membrane, being aware that this was clearly incorrect. Nevertheless, the model described experimental results quite well.

A more extended "transition model" was used by Vidaver & Shepherd (89) to describe the Na^+-dependent glycine transport across pigeon red blood cells and by Goldner et al (35) to describe the Na^+-dependent sugar fluxes across the brush border of the rabbit ileum. These models assumed that ternary complexes were formed of substrate (amino acid or sugar), sodium ion, and a mobile carrier. It was further assumed that the binding of Na^+ will increase either the affinity of the carrier to the substrate and/or the mobility of the ternary complex within the membrane. From such a general model Heinz et al (39) deduced three models in which the possible modification effects of Na^+ are reduced to one each: (*a*) the affinity type, where Na^+ modifies only the affinity of the carrier for the substrate; (*b*) the velocity type, where Na^+ modifies only the mobility of the carrier;

and (c) the mixed type, where Na^+ modifies both the affinity and the velocity.

In another model, proposed by Alvarado & Mahmood (2), the carrier was defined as bifunctional—i.e. as having two separate but functionally related binding sites: one for organic solute, and one for Na^+. Later Geck & Heinz (32) expanded their equations by including the effect of an electrical potential difference (pd). They show that the standard parameters of the overall transport, K_m and V_{max}, respond differently to the introduction of an electrical potential difference, depending on the model. An electrical pd will affect primarily K_m if the loaded carrier is charged, and primarily V_{max} if the empty carrier is charged. From their computer curves it became clear that V_{max} increases with increasing electrochemical potential difference except in an affinity-type model when Δc_{Na} is the driving force. On the other hand, the computer curves show that K_m decreases in all types of models except the velocity-type model when it has a negatively charged empty carrier and is driven by the electrical potential difference.

Another approach to elucidating cotransport phenomena was described by Lagarde (53) on the basis of irreversible thermodynamics. He points out that the phenomenological coefficients describing cotransport depend upon the binding and mobility characteristics and the concentration of the carrier, on the electrical potential difference, and on the concentrations of the co-permeant species, Na^+ and substrate. Furthermore, he gives equations for the coupling coefficient and for the zero net flux concentration ratio of the substrate. If in the latter case the driving force is split into an osmotic component (Δc) and an electrical component ($\Delta\psi$), the resulting equation can be tested experimentally. One has, however, to keep in mind that these models are based on assumptions and that especially those concerning the electric field are uncertain.

A noteworthy attempt to eliminate some parameters experimentally and to get unambiguous results was recently made by Hopfer (42). Working with intestinal brush-border vesicles, he eliminated transmembranal concentration and electrical potential differences and measured simply the exchange diffusion of D-glucose at various Na^+ concentrations equal on both sides of the membrane. In this situation, probably having no empty carrier, he found that Na^+ increases V_{max} and leaves K_m unchanged. Similar experiments with renal brush-border vesicles are urgently needed because the now available but ambiguous data indicate that Na^+ decreases K_m and leaves V_{max} unchanged (86).

An attempt to find out whether the empty glucose carrier is charged or uncharged was made by Tannenbaum et al (78) and by Aronson (3): Imposing a vesicle-inside-negative electrical potential difference on intestinal or renal brush-border vesicles, they found an accelerated initial rate of phlorrhizin binding and suggested that the free carrier might be negatively charged while the glucose-carrier-sodium complex is electroneutral. Thus the electrical potential would regulate the appearance of free carrier at the outer membrane surface.

So far, reliable predictions of the Na^+ concentration and electrical potential profile across the membrane are not possible; but progress is expected from reconstitution experiments, i.e. when sugar and amino acid carriers after isolation are incorporated in artificial lipid membranes. Then, of course, bulk phase concentrations and electrical potentials can be better controlled. Furthermore, the surface charge and lipid composition of the membrane can be changed, and molecular signals from the carrier itself may be obtained. In reconstitution experiments, Crane et al (17, 18, 22a) as well as Kinne & Faust (49) have succeeded in reincorporating Triton X 100 solubilized glucose and alanine carriers into liposomes. These groups dissolved isolated brush-border membranes from rabbit and rat kidney cortex, respectively, and used the 30,000 or 100,000 g supernatant for reincorporation into liposomes prepared from soybean or kidney phospholipids. The membrane extracts and the liposomes were cosonicated and the resulting proteoliposomes harvested by centrifugation. Using these proteoliposomes, transport studies were performed with the Millipore filtration technique in a manner similar to that applied to plasma membrane vesicles. A phlorrhizin-sensitive, Na^+-dependent uptake of D-glucose , and in some preparations an overshoot, was observed (17, 18, 22a, 49). Stimulation of L-alanine and phosphate uptake was larger when NaSCN was the incubation medium than when the medium was KCl (49).

Literature Cited

1. Alvarado, F. 1970. Intestinal transport of sugars and amino acids: independence or federalism. *Am. J. Clin. Nutr.* 23:824–28
2. Alvarado, F., Mahmood, A. 1974. Cotransport of organic solutes and sodium ions in the small intestine: a general model. Amino acid transport. *Biochemistry* 13:2882–90
3. Aronson, P. S. 1977. Electrical dependence of phlorizin binding to isolated rabbit renal cortical brush border membrane vesicles. *Kidney Int.* 12:A548
4. Aronson, P. S., Sacktor, B. 1975. The Na^+ gradient dependent transport of D-glucose in renal brush border membranes. *J. Biol. Chem.* 250:6032–39
5. Barry, R. J. C., Matthews, J., Smyth, D. H., Wright, E. M. 1962. Potential differences and intestinal transport of solutes and water. *J. Physiol. London* 161:17–18P

6. Beck, J. C., Sacktor, B. 1975. Energetics of the Na^+ dependent transport of D-glucose in renal brush border membrane vesicles. *J. Biol. Chem.* 250:8674–80
7. Bishop, J. H. V., Green, R., Thomas, S. 1978. Effects of glucose on water and sodium reabsorption in the proximal convoluted tubule of rat kidney. *J. Physiol. London* 275:481–93
8. Bode, F., Baumann, K., Diedrich, D. F. 1972. Inhibition of ^{3}H-phlorizin binding to isolated kidney brush border membranes by phlorizin-like compounds. *Biochim. Biophys. Acta* 290:134–49
9. Bode, F., Baumann, K., Frasch, W., Kinne, R. 1970. Die Bindung von Phlorrhizin an die Bürstensaumfraktion der Rattenniere. *Pfluegers Arch.* 315:53–65
10. Bode, F., Chan, Y. L., Goldner, A. M., Papavassiliou, F., Wagner, M., Bau-

mann, K. 1975. Reabsorption of D-glucose from various regions of the proximal convoluted tubule: Evidence that the proximal convolution is not homogeneous. In *Biochemical Aspects of Renal Function*, ed. S. Angielski, U. C. Dubach, 4:39–43. Bern: Huber. 242 pp.

11. Burg, M., Patlak, C., Green, N., Villey, D. 1976. Organic solutes in fluid absorption by renal proximal convoluted tubules. *Am. J. Physiol.* 231:627–37

12. Chan, A. W. K., Burch, H. B., Alvey, T. R., Lowry, O. H. 1975. A quantitative histochemical approach to renal transport. I. Aspartate and glutamate. *Am. J. Physiol.* 229:1034–44

13. Chan, Y. L., Huang, K. C. 1973. Renal excretion of D-tryptophan, 5-hydroxytryptamine, and 5-hydroxyindoleacetic acid in rats. *Am. J. Physiol.* 224:140–43

14. Chesney, R., Sacktor, B., Kleinzeller, A. 1974. The binding of phloridzin to the isolated luminal membrane of the proximal renal tubule. *Biochim. Biophys. Acta* 332:263–77

15. Crane, R. K. 1962. Hypothesis of mechanism of intestinal active transport of sugars. *Fed. Proc.* 21:891–95

16. Crane, R. K. 1977. The gradient hypothesis and other models of carrier mediated active transport. *Rev. Physiol. Biochem. Pharmacol.* 78:101–59

17. Crane, R. K., Malathi, P., Preiser, H. 1976. Reconstitution of specific Na$^+$-dependent D-glucose transport in liposomes by Triton-X-100–extracted proteins from purified brush border membranes of rabbit kidney cortex. *FEBS Lett.* 67:214–16

18. Crane, R. K., Malathi, P., Preiser, H., Fairclough, P. 1976. Some characteristics of kidney Na$^+$-dependent glucose carrier reconstituted into sonicated liposomes. *Am. J. Physiol.* 234:E1–5

19. Csáky, T. Z., Thale, M. 1960. Effect of ionic environment on intestinal sugar transport. *J. Physiol. London* 151:59–65

20. Curran, P. F., Schultz, S. G., Chez, R. E., Fuisz, R. E. 1976. Kinetic relations of the Na–amino acid interaction at the mucosal border of intestine. *J. Gen. Physiol.* 50:1261–86

21. Elbrink, J., Bihler, I. 1972. Characteristics of the membrane transport of sugars in the lens of the eye. *Biochim. Biophys. Acta* 282:337–51

22. Evers, J., Murer, H., Kinne, R. 1976. Phenylalanine uptake in isolated renal brush border vesicles. *Biochim. Biophys. Acta* 426:598–615

22a. Fairclough, P. D., Malathi, P., Preiser, H., Crane, R. K. 1978. Glucose transport in renal brush border membranes and reconstituted liposomes. *Proc. 7th Int. Congr. Nephrol., Montreal.* Basel: Karger. pp. 161–66

23. Fass, S. J., Hammerman, M. R., Sacktor, B. 1977. Transport of amino acids in renal brush border membrane vesicles. Uptake of the neutral amino acid L-alanine. *J. Biol. Chem.* 252:583–90

24. Fox, M., Thier, S., Rosenberg, L., Segal, S. 1964. Ionic requirement for amino acid transport in the rat kidney cortex slice. *Biochim. Biophys. Acta* 79:167–76

25. Frasch, W., Frohnert, P. P., Bode, F., Baumann, K., Kinne, R. 1970. Competitive inhibition of phlorizin binding by D-glucose and the influence of sodium: a study on isolated brush border membrane of rat kidney. *Pfluegers Arch.* 320:265–84

26. Frega, N. S., Weinberg, J. M., Ross, B. D., Leaf, A. 1977. Stimulation of sodium transport by glucose in the perfused rat kidney. *Am. J. Physiol.* 233:F235–40

27. Frömter, E. 1974. Der Salz- und Wassertransport im proximalen Tubulus der Niere. *Nieren- und Hochdruckkrankheiten* 6:247–56

28. Frömter, E. 1978. Solute transport across epithelia. *J. Physiol. London.* In press

29. Frömter, E., Gessner, K. 1974. Free-flow potential profile along rat kidney proximal tubule. *Pfluegers Arch.* 351:69–83

30. Frömter, E., Gessner, K. 1974. Active transport potentials, membrane diffusion potentials and streaming potentials across rat kidney proximal tubule. *Pfluegers Arch.* 351:85–98

31. Frömter, E., Lüer, K. 1973. Electrical studies on sugar transport kinetics of rat proximal tubule. *Pfluegers Arch.* 343:R47

32. Geck, P., Heinz, E. 1976. Coupling in secondary transport. Effect of electrical potentials on the kinetics of ion-linked co-transport. *Biochim. Biophys. Acta* 443:49–53

33. Genel, M., Rea, C. F., Segal, S. 1971. Transport interaction of sugars and amino acids in mammalian kidney. *Biochim. Biophys. Acta* 241:779–88

34. Glossmann, H., Neville, D. M. Jr. 1972. Phlorizin receptors in isolated kidney brush border membranes. *J. Biol. Chem.* 247:7779–89

35. Goldner, A. M., Schultz, S. G., Curran, P. F. 1969. Sodium and sugar fluxes across the mucosal border of rabbit ileum. *J. Gen. Physiol.* 53:362–83

36. Green, R., Giebisch, G. 1975. Ionic requirements of proximal tubular sodium transport. I. Bicarbonate and chloride. *Am. J. Physiol.* 229:1205–15

37. Hammerman, M. R., Sacktor, B. 1977. Transport of amino acids in renal brush border membrane vesicles. Uptake of L-proline. *J. Biol. Chem.* 252:591–95

38. Heinz, E., Geck, P. 1978. The electrical potential difference as a driving force in Na⁺-linked cotransport of organic solutes. In *Membrane Transport Processes,* ed. J. F. Hoffman, 1:13–30. New York: Raven. 488 pp.

39. Heinz, E., Geck, P., Wilbrandt, W. 1972. Coupling in secondary active transport. Activation of transport by cotransport and/or countertransport with the fluxes of other solutes. *Biochim. Biophys. Acta* 255:442–61

40. Hillman, R. E., Albrecht, I., Rosenberg, L. E. 1968. Transport of amino acids by isolated rabbit renal tubules. *Biochim. Biophys. Acta* 150:528–30

41. Hillman, R. E., Rosenberg, L. E. 1969. Amino acid transport by isolated mammalian renal tubules. Transport systems for L-proline. *J. Biol. Chem.* 244:4494–98

42. Hopfer, U. 1977. Kinetics of Na⁺-dependent D-glucose transport. *J. Supramol. Struct.* 7:1–13

43. Hopfer, U., Sigrist-Nelson, K., Amman, E., Murer, H. 1976. Differences in neutral amino acid and glucose transport between brush border and basolateral plasma membrane of intestinal epithelial cells. *J. Cell. Physiol.* 89:805–10

44. Hoshi, T. 1976. Electrophysiological studies on amino acid transport across the luminal membrane of the proximal tubular cells of *Triturus* kidney. In *Amino Acid Transport and Uric Acid Transport,* ed. S. Silbernagl, F. Lang, R. Greger, p. 96. Stuttgart: Georg Thieme. 259 pp.

45. Hoshi, T., Sudo, K., Suzuki, Y. 1976. Characteristics of changes in the intracellular potential associated with transport of neutral, dibasic and acidic amino acids in *Triturus* proximal tubule. *Biochim. Biophys. Acta* 448:492–504

46. Keljo, D. J., Kleinzeller, A. 1976. Interaction of phloretin-2'-(2 deoxy-D-glucoside) with renal sugar transport systems. *The Physiologist* 19:250

47. Kimmich, G. A., Randles, J. 1973. Interaction between Na⁺-dependent transtransport systems for sugar and amino acids. Evidence against a role for the

48. Kinne, R. 1976. Properties of the glucose transport system in the renal brush border membrane. In *Current Topics in Membranes and Transport,* ed. F. Bronner, A. Kleinzeller, 8:209–67. New York: Academic. 272 pp.

49. Kinne, R., Faust, R. G. 1978. Incorporation of D-glucose, L-alanine and phosphate transport systems from rat renal brush-border membranes into liposomes. *Biochem. J.* 168:311–14

50. Kinne, R., Murer, H. 1978. Recent advances in the understanding of renal amino acid and sugar transport. *Proc. 7th Int. Congr. Nephrol., Montreal.* Basel: Karger. pp. 601–8

51. Kinne, R., Murer, H., Kinne-Saffran, E., Thees, M., Sachs, G. 1975. Sugar transport by renal plasma membrane vesicles. Characterization of the system in the brush-border microvilli and basal-lateral plasma membranes. *J. Membr. Biol.* 21:375–95

52. Kleinzeller, A., Kolínská, J., Beneš, I. 1967. Transport of glucose and galactose in kidney-cortex cells. *Biochem. J.* 104:843–51

53. Lagarde, A. E. 1976. A non-equilibrium thermodynamics analysis of active transport within the framework of the chemiosmotic theory. *Biochim. Biophys. Acta* 426:198–217

54. Lingard, J., Rumrich, G., Young, J. A. 1973. Reabsorption of L-glutamine and L-histidine from various regions of the rat proximal convolution studied by stationary microperfusion: Evidence that the proximal convolution is not homogeneous. *Pfluegers Arch.* 342:1–11

55. Loeschke, K., Baumann, K., Renschler, H., Ullrich, K. J. 1969. Differenzierung zwischen aktiver und passiver Komponente des D-Glukosetransportes am proximalen Konvolut der Rattenniere. *Pfluegers Arch.* 305:118–38

56. Maruyama, T., Hoshi, T. 1972. The effect of D-glucose on the electrical potential profile across the proximal tubule of newt kidney. *Biochim. Biophys. Acta* 282:214–25

57. McNamara, P. D., Ožegović, B., Pepe, L. M., Segal, S. 1976. Proline and glycine uptake by renal brush-border membrane vesicles. *Proc. Natl. Acad. Sci. USA* 73:4521–25

58. Murer, H., Hopfer, U. 1974. Demonstration of electrogenic Na⁺-dependent D-glucose transport in intestinal brush border membranes. *Proc. Natl. Acad Sci. USA* 71:484–88

59. Murer, H., Hopfer, U., Kinne-Saffran, E., Kinne, R. 1974. Glucose transport in isolated brush border and lateral-basal plasma membrane vesicles from intestinal epithelial cells. *Biochim. Biophys. Acta* 345:170–79

60. Murer, H., Sigrist-Nelson, K., Hopfer, U. 1975. On the mechanism of sugar and amino acid interaction in intestinal transport. *J. Biol. Chem.* 250:7392–96

61. Nathans, D., Tapley, D. F., Ross, J. E. 1960. Intestinal transport of amino acids studied *in vitro* with L-[131I] monoiodotyrosine. *Biochim. Biophys. Acta* 41:271–82

62. Riklis, E., Quastel, J. H. 1958. Effects of cations of sugar absorption by isolated surviving guinea pig intestine. *Can. J. Biochem. Physiol.* 36:347–62

63. Rosenhagen, M., Segal, S. 1974. Stereospecificity of amino acid uptake by rat and human kidney cortex slices. *Am. J. Physiol.* 227:843–47

64. Ruedas, G., Weiss, Ch. 1967. Die Wirkung von Änderungen der Natriumkonzentration im Perfusionsmedium und von Strophanthin auf die Glucoseresorption der isolierten Rattenniere. *Pfluegers Arch.* 298:12–22

65. Sacktor, B. 1977. Transport in membrane vesicles isolated from the mammalian kidney and intestine. *Curr. Top. Bioenerg.* 6:39–81

66. Samarzija, I. 1978. *Experimentelle Untersuchungen zum Aminosäuretransport im proximalen Tubulus der Rattenniere.* PhD thesis, Univ. Frankfurt am Main, Frankfurt, W. Germany

67. Samarzija, I., Frömter, E. 1975. Electrical studies on amino acid transport across brush-border membrane of rat proximal tubule *in vivo. Pfluegers Arch.* 359:R119

68. Samarzija, I., Frömter, E., 1976. Renal transport of glutamate and aspartate. Evidence for Na-dependent uptake from the peritubular surface into proximal tubular cells. *Pfluegers Arch.* 365:R15

69. Schwartzman, L., Blair, A., Segal, S. 1967. Effect of transport inhibitors on dibasic amino acid exchange diffusion in rat kidney cortex. *Biochim. Biophys. Acta* 135:136–45

70. Segal, S., Crawhall, J. C. 1968. Characteristics of cystine and cysteine transport in rat kidney cortex slices. *Proc. Natl. Acad. Sci. USA* 59:231–37

71. Segal, S., Schwartzman, L., Blair, A., Bertoli, D. 1967. Dibasic amino acid transport in rat kidney cortex slices. *Biochim. Biophys. Acta* 135:127–35

72. Semenza, G. 1971. On the mechanism of mutual inhibition among sodium-dependent transport systems in the small intestine. A hypothesis. *Biochim. Biophys. Acta* 241:637–49

73. Silbernagl, S. 1978. Renal handl'ng of aspartate, glutamate, pyroglutamate and of peptides containing these amino acids. *Pfluegers Arch.* 373:R30

74. Silbernagl, S., Foulkes, E. C., Deetjen, P. 1975. Renal transport of amino acids. *Rev. Physiol. Biochem. Pharamacol.* 74:105–67

75. Silbernagl, S., Völkl, H. 1977. Amino acid reabsorption in the proximal tubule of rat kidney. Stereospecificity and passive diffusion studied by continuous microperfusion. *Pfluegers Arch.* 367:221–27

76. Silverman, M., Black, J. 1975. High affinity phlorrizin receptor sites and their relation to glucose transport mechanism in the proximal tubule of dog kidney. *Biochim. Biophys. Acta* 394:10–30

77. Slack, E. N., Liang, C.-C. T., Sacktor, B. 1977. Transport of L-proline and D-glucose in luminal (brush-border) and contraluminal (basal-lateral) membrane vesicles from the renal cortex. *Biochem. Biophys. Res. Commun.* 77:891–97

78. Tannenbaum, C., Toggenburger, G., Kessler, M., Rothstein, A., Semenza, G. 1977. High-affinity phlorizin binding to brush border membranes from small intestine identity with (a part of) the glucose transport system, dependence on the Na⁺-gradient, partial purification. *J. Supramol. Struct.* 6:519–33

79. Thier, S. O., Blair, A., Fox, M., Segal, S. 1967. The effect of extracellular sodium concentration on the kinetics of α-amino-isobutyric acid transport in the rat kidney cortex slice. *Biochim. Biophys. Acta* 135:300–5

80. Trimble, M. E. 1975. Effects of L-glucose on sodium reabsorption in the isolated perfused rat kidney. *Life Sci.* 17:1799–1806

81. Trimble, M. E., Bowman, R. H. 1973. Renal Na⁺ and K⁺ transport: effects of glucose, palmitate and α-bromopalmitate. *Am. J. Physiol.* 225:1057–62

82. Turner, R. J., Silverman, M. 1977. Sugar uptake into brushborder vesicles from normal human kidney. *Proc. Natl. Acad. Sci. USA* 74:2825–29

83. Ullrich, K. J. 1973. Permeability characteristics of the mammalian nephron. In *Handbook of Physiology, Sect. 8,* ed. J. Orloff, R. W. Berliner, pp. 377–98.

Washington DC: Am. Physiol. Soc. 1082 pp.

84. Ullrich, K. J., Capasso, G., Rumrich, G., Papavassiliou, F., Klöss, S. 1977. Coupling between proximal tubular transport processes. Studies with ouabain, SITS and HCO₃ free solutions. *Pfluegers Arch.* 368:245–52

85. Ullrich, K. J., Frömter, E., Hinton, B. T., Rumrich, G., Kleinzeller, A. 1976. Specificity of sugar transport across the brush border of the rat proximal tubule. *Current Probl. Clin. Biochem.* 6:256–61

86. Ullrich, K. J., Rumrich, G., Klöss, S. 1974. Specificity and sodium dependence of the active sugar transport in the proximal convolution of the rat kidney. *Pfluegers Arch.* 351:35–48

87. Ullrich, K. J., Rumrich, G., Klöss, S. 1974. Sodium dependence of the amino acid transport in the proximal convolution of the rat kidney. *Pfluegers Arch.* 351:49–60

88. Vick, H., Diedrich, D. F., Baumann, K. 1973. Reevaluation of renal tubular glucose transport inhibition by phlorrizin analogs. *Am. J. Physiol.* 224:552–57

89. Vidaver, G. A., Shepherd, S. L. 1968. Transport of glycine by hemolyzed and restored pigeon red cells. Symmetry properties, trans effects of sodium ion and glycine and their description by a single rate equation. *J. Biol. Chem.* 243:6140–51

90. Vinay, P., Mapes, J. P., Krebs, H. A. 1978. Fate of glutamine carbon in renal metabolism, *Am. J. Physiol.* 234:F123–29

91. Vogel, G., Kröger, W. 1966. Die Bedeutung des Transportes, der Konzentration und der Darbietungsrichtung von Na⁺ für den tubulären Glucose- und PAH-Transport. *Pfluegers Arch.* 288:342–58

92. Vogel, G., Lauterbach, F., Kröger, W. 1965. Die Bedeutung des Natriums für die renalen Transporte von Glucose und Para-Aminohippursäure. *Pfluegers Arch.* 283:151–59

93. Wilbrandt, W. 1950. Permeabilitätsprobleme. *Arch. Exp. Pathol. Pharmacol.* 212:9–31

94. Williams, W. M., Huang, K. C. 1970. In vitro and in vivo tubular transport of tryptophan derivatives. *Am. J. Physiol.* 219:1468–74

Ann. Rev. Physiol. 1979. 41:197–210

PROTON SECRETION   ♦1214
BY THE KIDNEY

David G. Warnock and Floyd C. Rector, Jr.

Cardiovascular Research Institute, and the Departments of Medicine
and Physiology, University of California, San Francisco, California 94143

INTRODUCTION

Acidification of renal tubular fluid results in reabsorption of filtered bicarbonate and excretion of titratable acid and ammonium into the urine. There is general agreement about the sites of acidification along the nephron and about the relative contributions of the proximal and distal tubule to urinary acidification. However, the detailed mechanisms of bicarbonate reabsorption and proton secretion have remained controversial.

PROXIMAL TUBULE

Figure 1 presents a generally accepted view of acidification in the proximal tubule. Protons secreted into the lumen titrate filtered bicarbonate to form carbonic acid (H_2CO_3). Carbonic anhydrase is postulated to serve two functions. In the cell it catalyzes the hydration of CO_2 to provide a source of protons (from H_2CO_3). In the lumen it catalyzes the dehydration of this acid to form water and carbon dioxide (CO_2) which diffuses back into the cells. This scheme is based upon the demonstration of a "disequilibrium" pH following carbonic anhydrase inhibition in the proximal tubule (38). Recent experimental evidence requires that the specific aspects of this model be reexamined.

CO_2 Diffusion, Gradients, "Disequilibrium" pH, and Carbonic Anhydrase Activity

Previously, studies of proximal acidification have explicitly assumed that the luminal CO_2 tension (P_{CO_2}) was identical to that of the systemic arterial plasma (38). The "disequilibrium" pH was defined as the difference between

197

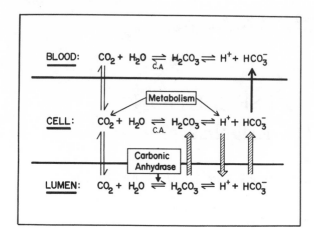

Figure 1 Titration of bicarbonate in the lumen of the proximal tubule. Proton secretion and H_2CO_3 dehydration result in a flow of CO_2 from the lumen into the cell. Bicarbonate reabsorption is completed by the transport of bicarbonate from the cell into the blood of the peritubular capillaries. Carbonic anhydrase activity in the cell cytoplasm and in red blood cells is indicated by the abbreviation C.A.

the pH of luminal fluid measured in situ and that measured in vitro when the sample was equilibrated with the Pco_2 of the animals' arterial plasma. This difference was small in the presence of normal carbonic anhydrase activity, but became significant (0.4–0.85 pH units) when carbonic anhydrase was inhibited. The "disequilibrium" pH was attributed to continued proton secretion during carbonic anhydrase inhibition with the consequent accumulation of H_2CO_3 in the luminal fluid in excess of the equilibrium concentration predicted from the arterial Pco_2 (38). This observation has been the cornerstone for physiologic studies of proton secretion by the proximal tubule. However, Brodsky & Schilb (6) have emphasized that the validity of this approach depends upon the exact knowledge of the luminal in situ Pco_2.

Initial support for the assumption that luminal Pco_2 equalled that of arterial plasma was provided by Malnic & deMello-Aires (29). They observed two components to the rate of luminal acidification of bicarbonate-containing solutions under stopped-flow conditions. The slower phase was attributed to the reabsorption of bicarbonate from the droplet. The faster phase of acidification was due to entry of CO_2 into the droplets. When the droplets were pre-equilibrated with room air, there was a rapid acidification phase due to diffusion of CO_2 into the droplet and formation of H_2CO_3. This rapid phase of acidification was prevented if the droplets were pre-equilibrated with 5% CO_2, suggesting that the luminal Pco_2 was approximately

40 mm in situ (29). A diffusion coefficient for CO_2 can be calculated from the half-time of the "fast" phase of acidification: 19.5×10^{-7} cm^2 sec^{-1}.

Subsequently, Karlmark & Danielson (22) observed that even in the presence of normal carbonic anhydrase activity the in situ luminal pH was approximately 0.15 pH units more acid than would be predicted from the tubular fluid bicarbonate concentration and the arterial blood P_{CO_2}. They attributed this difference to a higher luminal fluid than arterial P_{CO_2}, rather than to excess H_2CO_3. The finding that the luminal P_{CO_2} was elevated was confirmed by direct measurement with a P_{CO_2} microelectrode (42). Karlmark and co-workers (22, 42) proposed that CO_2 exit from the lumen was a rate-limiting step in acidification and that the tubule represented a diffusion barrier to CO_2. They considered the "disequilibrium" pH observed after carbonic anhydrase inhibition to be the result of CO_2 rather than H_2CO_3 accumulation, but still favored the view that proton secretion was the fundamental process in bicarbonate reabsorption. Their observation of elevated luminal P_{CO_2} tensions, and the relatively low CO_2 diffusion coefficient calculated from the kinetic data of Malnic & deMello-Aires (29) represent a marked departure from the classical view that CO_2 diffuses readily across the tubules (41).

Recent studies question the interpretation of the work of Malnic & deMello-Aires (29) and Karlmark and associates (22, 42). DuBose et al (10), also using P_{CO_2} microelectrodes, have found that the P_{CO_2} was elevated throughout the entire renal cortex. Specifically, the P_{CO_2} tension was 65 mm Hg in the proximal and distal tubule, as well as in the peritubular circulation (star-vessels, efferent arterioles). They could not demonstrate any difference in P_{CO_2} between the tubule lumen and the star-vessels, and did not find any decline in P_{CO_2} along the length of the proximal tubule (10). They have interpreted their findings as suggesting that CO_2 is in diffusion equilibrium throughout the renal cortex, in marked contrast to the interpretation of Karlmark and co-workers (22, 42). Both groups have observed a difference in P_{CO_2} tensions between the proximal tubule lumen and the arterial plasma. However, DuBose et al (10) were unable to demonstrate a P_{CO_2} gradient across the proximal tubule. Sohtell, on the other hand, has made preliminary direct measurements and found that the luminal P_{CO_2} was elevated, but the P_{CO_2} in the star-vessels was the same as the systemic arterial value (43). Hopefully, the results of one group or the other can be confirmed in the near future.

Another challenge to the diffusion-barrier hypothesis was provided by studies of the rabbit proximal straight tubule (52) which suggested that the CO_2 permeability coefficient resembled that of an equivalent thickness of water (870×10^{-7} cm^2 sec^{-1}). This result is entirely consistent with the suggestion of DuBose et al (10) that CO_2 is in diffusion equilibrium in the renal cortex, but differs by a factor of 50 from the estimation of CO_2 permeability calculated from the kinetic data of Malnic & deMello-Aires (29). We can account for this discrepancy as follows: Malnic & deMello-Aires (29) calculated the rate of CO_2 entry from the rate of H_2CO_3 generation. However, they neglected the large concentration of carbonate ion in the initial luminal solution that also had to be back-titrated during the initial acidification phase. They probably underestimated the rate of H_2CO_3 generation in the lumen. It may be that the rate-limiting step in H_2CO_3 generation was CO_2 hydration rather than CO_2 diffusion per se. As a result, the CO_2 permeability coefficient may have been greatly underestimated in the studies of Malnic & deMello-Aires (29).

As an illustration of the last point, consider the magnitude of the trans-epithelial CO_2 gradient that would be generated if all proximal bicarbonate reabsorption proceeded as the diffusion of CO_2 following titration of luminal bicarbonate. Recent microperfusion studies have reported that the rate of bicarbonate reabsorption is 23 picomoles $(cm \cdot sec)^{-1}$ for the in vivo rat proximal convoluted tubule (26). [Lower rates have been reported for the in vitro rabbit proximal tubule (8, 33, 50).] If this rate is presumed to represent transepithelial flux of CO_2, then the driving force (CO_2 gradient) can be calculated by dividing the reabsorptive rate by our estimate for the CO_2 permeability coefficient [870×10^{-7} cm^2 sec^{-1}; reference (52)]. Using this coefficient, the calculated CO_2 gradient would be, as a maximal estimate, 8.7 mm Hg. DuBose et al (10) could not demonstrate any P_{CO_2} gradient between the lumen of the proximal tubule and the star-vessels. However, the true gradient may be below or near the limit of resolution for their electrode. These considerations suggest that the proximal tubule is not a major barrier to the movement of CO_2 and that only small CO_2 gradients, if any at all, would exist across it.

With these points in mind we can return to the issue of the "disequilibrium" pH. Clearly, the assumption of equality between luminal P_{CO_2} and arterial P_{CO_2} is wrong (10, 22, 42), and this line of evidence for proton secretion must be reexamined. However, to account for a "disequilibrium" in the proximal tubule of 0.4–0.8 pH units, the luminal P_{CO_2} would have to be elevated 60–400 mm Hg above the arterial P_{CO_2}. DuBose et al (10) found that the luminal P_{CO_2} was only 34 mm Hg above the arterial P_{CO_2} during benzolamide administration. Therefore, there must be some accumulation of H_2CO_3 in the lumen during carbonic anhydrase inhibition since the luminal P_{CO_2} does not account for all of the observed "disequilibrium" pH.

Another approach has been taken by Lang et al (23) to demonstrate a "disequilibrium" pH in the proximal tubule. They continuously recorded the in situ pH in the lumen of the rat proximal tubule, and found that the pH in the early proximal tubule fell by 0.42 ± 0.06 units when benzolamide was administered intravenously. Similar results were obtained when ben-zolamide was microinfused into an early proximal tubule so that a general effect on the renal cortical P_{CO_2} need not be considered. The decrease in luminal pH in the early proximal tubule suggests inhibition of luminal carbonic anhydrase activity with accumulation of H_2CO_3 due to delayed buffering of secreted protons.

The observation that a "disequilibrium" pH occurs in the proximal tubule after inhibition of carbonic anhydrase suggests that the enzyme is functionally accessible to the luminal fluid (38). Maren (32) has challenged this view, arguing that luminal H_2CO_3 can rapidly diffuse back into the cells and be dehydrated by cytoplasmic carbonic anhydrase. According to Maren, inhibition of cytoplasmic carbonic anhydrase would block this process and cause H_2CO_3 to accumulate in both cells and lumen (32). This view ignores the fact that proton secretion into the lumen would consume cellular H_2CO_3 (Figure 1). If only cytoplasmic carbonic anhydrase were inhibited, then the cellular H_2CO_3 concentration would actually fall. Back-diffusion of H_2CO_3 from the lumen would prevent marked alkalinization of the cell, but could not increase the cellular H_2CO_3 concentration above normal levels.

Carbonic anhydrase activity has been localized in the brush border of the proximal tubule by histochemical techniques (25). Activity has also recently been described in brush-border and basal lateral membranes of the rat kidney (53). This membrane-bound activity accounted for 3% of the total carbonic anhydrase activity of the renal cortex, and was less susceptible to inhibition by sulfonamides than the predominant, cytoplasmic enzyme (53). The orientation of the enzyme in the membrane has not been established, but the previous physiologic studies of the intratubular pH (38) would suggest that it is in functional contact with the luminal fluid.

Proton Secretion: Electrogenic and Electroneutral Mechanisms

The view that protons are secreted into the lumen in exchange for sodium was specifically considered for the proximal tubule by Berliner in 1952 (4). This mechanism has recently been demonstrated in brush-border vesicles by Murer, Hopfer & Kinne (37) to be reversible and electrically neutral, and therefore, represented an exchange of one proton for one sodium ion.

Such a system would display a fixed, stoichiometric ratio of unity between the rates of sodium reabsorption and proton secretion. Therefore, inhibition of sodium reabsorption should cause a parallel reduction in the rate of proton secretion. This issue has been studied by McKinney & Burg (33) and Burg & Green (8) in the isolated perfused rabbit proximal tubule. When sodium reabsorption was completely inhibited by a variety of maneuvers, they found an 80–90% reduction in the rate of total CO_2 reabsorption (8,

33). These results are consistent with a coupling ratio of nearly unity between sodium reabsorption and proton secretion in the rabbit proximal convoluted tubule. A small, residual decrease in total CO_2 concentration persisted in the face of complete inhibition of sodium reabsorption, but this only amounted to 10–15% of the control rate of total CO_2 reabsorption.

The coupling between sodium reabsorption and proton secretion appears to be less rigid in the rat proximal convoluted tubule. Some degree of coupling occurs since various buffers all support volume reabsorption and removal of these buffers suppresses volume reabsorption by 75% in the rat proximal convoluted tubule (47). Furthermore, Ullrich and co-workers have found that acetazolamide and furosemide inhibit proton secretion (glycodiazine reabsorption) as well as sodium reabsorption (48). In the same study, replacement of sodium by choline or lithium decreased the generation of a glycodiazine concentration gradient in split-droplets (48). Malnic & deMello-Aires (30) found that proton secretion was reduced when low-sodium perfusion solutions were used. However, proton secretion and sodium reabsorption could be disassociated in a number of conditions. Green & Giebisch (18) found that the ratio of sodium reabsorption to proton secretion can vary from 1 to 6 as a function of the specific buffer in the perfusates. Since the rat is resistant to ouabain, the golden hamster has been used to study the coupling between sodium reabsorption and proton secretion (46). The results showed that sodium transport could be reduced by 80% yet a concentration gradient for glycodiazine could still be generated. In addition, Frömter & Gessner (14) observed a lumen-positive potential difference in the rat proximal convoluted tubule. This potential was abolished by acetazolamide and presumedly represented an uncoupled electrogenic secretion of protons into the lumen. Similar results have not been reported for in vitro rabbit proximal tubules. All of these studies suggest that there is not an obligatory or fixed coupling ratio between proton secretion and sodium reabsorption in the rat.

Hence, there appears to be a genuine species difference between the coupling ratio in rat and rabbit proximal convoluted tubule. Proton secretion in the proximal tubule of the rat and hamster appears to be much less dependent on the presence of sodium than in the rabbit proximal tubule. In addition, another consideration makes the definition of a coupling ratio somewhat problematic. It has been proposed that sodium chloride reabsorption is in part a neutral process in the proximal tubule of the rat and rabbit (51). The thesis is that sodium is reabsorbed by exchange for a proton, and in parallel, chloride is reabsorbed in exchange for hydroxyls. This model operates when the luminal chloride concentration is elevated and is an extension of the demonstration of an anion-exchange mechanism in the brush border of the rat small intestine (24). This mode of transport would have an undefined coupling ratio between sodium reabsorption and proton secretion. Even though sodium is exchanged for a proton on a one-to-one basis, the proton is immediately titrated in the lumen by the base that enters in exchange for chloride. As a result, the coupling ratio between sodium reabsorption and proton secretion becomes undefined (4, 18).

The mechanism by which bicarbonate, which is generated in the cell by proton secretion, is transferred from the cell to blood has only recently received attention. Frömter & Sato (15) found that the peritubular membrane of proximal cells is permeable to potassium and bicarbonate (and/or hydroxyl) but not to sodium and chloride ions. These findings suggest that bicarbonate moves out of the cell via an electrically conductive pathway, driven by its electrochemical gradient. In addition it was observed that acetazolamide decreased the bicarbonate conductance of the peritubular membrane (15). This may represent an effect upon membrane-bound carbonic anhydrase (53), which is involved in the bicarbonate conductance, or even a change in the steady-state cellular concentration of bicarbonate. Recent studies with the isolated rabbit proximal convoluted tubule have also suggested that conductance of bicarbonate across the peritubular membrane must greatly exceed that of chloride (5). The conductive pathway for bicarbonate transport across basolateral membrane of the proximal tubule (46) and of turtle bladder (9, 11) is inhibited by disulfonic stilbenes, agents that also inhibit anion exchange mechanisms. Bicarbonate transport across the peritubular membrane has been shown to alkalinize the blood in the peritubular capillaries (16).

Carbonic Anhydrase–Dependent Bicarbonate Reabsorption

Clearance studies with carbonic anhydrase inhibitors administered intravenously have shown that renal bicarbonate reabsorption is reduced by 50% (31, 32, 38). Micropuncture studies have directly shown that intravenously administered carbonic anhydrase inhibitors reduce, but do not completely inhibit, bicarbonate reabsorption in the proximal tubule (31, 32, 38). The portion of bicarbonate reabsorption that persists after "complete" carbonic anhydrase inhibition in vivo has been attributed to carbonic anhydrase–independent reabsorption of bicarbonate. There is general agreement that the uncatalyzed rate of CO_2 hydration is not sufficient to account for the continuing reabsorption of bicarbonate (31, 32, 38). Rector (38) has proposed that recycling of carbonic acid provides the protons to the cell for their continued secretion into the lumen. Inhibition of carbonic anhydrase causes H_2CO_3 to accumulate in the lumen and to be depleted in the cells. This gradient favors the diffusion of H_2CO_3 from lumen to cell so as to provide a source of protons for continuing acid secretion. This process is depicted by the hatched arrow between luminal and cellular H_2CO_3 in Figure 1.

Maren, on the other hand, favors the direct reabsorption of bicarbonate per se as the explanation for continuing bicarbonate reabsorption in the face of "complete" inhibition of carbonic anhydrase (31, 32). This process is depicted in Figure 1 by the hatched arrow between luminal and cellular bicarbonate.

Recent microperfusion studies have suggested a third explanation for the observation that bicarbonate reabsorption continues in spite of "complete" inhibition of carbonic anhydrase. It is possible that intravenous infusion of acetazolamide does not achieve concentrations of the drug in the lumen of the proximal tubule adequate to inhibit carbonic anhydrase activity totally at that site. Recent studies of proximal bicarbonate reabsorption with in vivo or in vitro microperfusion techniques (8, 26, 33, 50) have precisely measured the total CO_2 content of perfused and collected samples of luminal fluid by microcalorimetry (49). The first study with acetazolamide was published by McKinney & Burg (33). These studies (33) found that the rate of bicarbonate reabsorption was reduced by at least 85% when $10^{-4}M$ acetazolamide was present in bath and perfusate. Similar results have been obtained by Burg & Green (8) for the isolated perfused rabbit proximal convoluted tubule.

It is possible that this marked sensitivity to carbonic anhydrase inhibition is peculiar to bicarbonate reabsorption by the in vitro rabbit proximal tubule. Therefore, these studies were repeated with the in vivo microperfused rat proximal convoluted tubule with various concentrations of acetazolamide added to a luminal perfusion solution, which resembled an ultra-filtrate of plasma. These results are presented as a concentration-response curve of acetazolamide in Figure 2. The control rate of bicarbonate reabsorption was 147 picomoles (mm · min)$^{-1}$, and $10^{-4}M$ acetazolamide completely inhibited the reabsorption of bicarbonate (26). This effect was shown to be specific for carbonic anhydrase inhibition by use of t-butyl acetazolamide. This inactive congener of acetazolamide had no effect on volume reabsorption or total CO_2 reabsorption in maximal concentrations of $8 \times 10^{-4}M$ (26). The I_{50} for inhibition of bicarbonate reabsorption is represented by the dashed lines in Figure 2. This value is 4 μM and represents a 100-fold increment for the I_{50} of carbonic anhydrase inhibition by acetazolamide in whole kidney homogenates. This 100-fold difference between the in vitro inhibition of enzyme activity, and in vivo inhibition of carbonic anhydrase–dependent bicarbonate reabsorption is consistent with the great abundance of the enzyme in the kidney (31, 32, 38).

The results of McKinney & Burg (33), Burg & Green (8), and Lucci, Warnock & Rector (26) demonstrate that nearly all of the reabsorption of bicarbonate is dependent upon carbonic anhydrase activity in the proximal tubule of the rat and rabbit. Luminal acetazolamide ($10^{-4}M$) can nearly completely abolish bicarbonate reabsorption. There may be a small (i.e. less

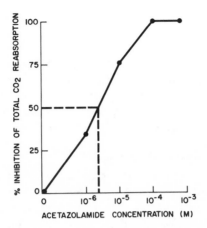

Figure 2   Concentration-response curve for the inhibition of total CO_2 reabsorption by acetazolamide. The studies were conducted in rat proximal convoluted tubules perfused in vivo with a plasma ultrafiltrate-like solution. The control rate of total CO_2 reabsorption was 147 picomoles $(mm \cdot min)^{-1}$, and was determined by microcalorimetry. The tubules were perfused at 13 nl min^{-1}, and the acetazolamide was only present in the luminal perfusate. The dashed line represents the I_{50} for inhibition of total CO_2 reabsorption, and corresponds to 4×10^{-6}M. Reproduced from (26) by permission.

than 10%) component of bicarbonate reabsorption that proceeds independently of carbonic anhydrase activity and represents the uncatalyzed rate of CO_2 hydration. However, it is unnecessary to postulate either recycling of H_2CO_3 or direct bicarbonate reabsorption to account for the reabsorption of bicarbonate in the face of "complete" inhibition of carbonic anhydrase activity.

DISTAL TUBULE

Sites of Acidification

The proton secretory capacity of the distal tubule is much smaller than that of the proximal tubule. It is the site, however, where the final adjustments of urinary pH are made (38).

In contrast to latter segments of the distal tubule, the thick ascending limb probably does not acidify the urine. Free water clearance studies with and without acetazolamide suggest that in the diluting segment of the nephron sodium bicarbonate serves as a nonreabsorbable solute and that there is no specific effect of acetazolamide (39). However, more direct studies utilizing isolated thick ascending limbs are required to establish or exclude the presence of an acidifying mechanism (7).

Classical micropuncture studies have demonstrated a "disequilibrium" pH in the distal tubule, which suggests that protons are secreted into the lumen and that there is not any carbonic anhydrase activity that is functionally accessible to the luminal fluid (38). It is uncertain whether these studies were done on distal convoluted tubules or cortical collecting tubules, since both are accessible for puncture at the cortical surface. Micropuncture studies have also shown that urine can be more acid than the fluid in superficial distal tubules, which suggests that collecting tubules or ducts are the site of final acidification. Studies with isolated cortical collecting tubules have demonstrated the capability of this segment to acidify tubular fluid.

Mechanisms of Distal Acidification

The urinary bladders of the turtle and toad have been useful analogs for investigating transport processes thought to pertain to the distal tubule. The distinction between proton secretion and bicarbonate reabsorption as modes of urinary acidification has been quite controversial (6, 44). In spite of the heat of this debate, the amphibian urinary bladder has served as the prototypic model for proton secretion by the distal tubule. One of the salient features of bladders is their ability to secrete protons even in the absence of sodium (choline replacement) or when sodium transport has been inhibited by ouabain or amiloride (27, 44). Proton secretion under these circumstances is totally uncoupled from sodium transport, and is associated with a lumen-positive transepithelial electrical potential and a "reversed" short-circuit current. Proton secretion depends upon carbonic anhydrase activity, and is inhibited by acetazolamide (27, 44). Two additional lines of evidence also disassociate proton secretion from sodium reabsorption in the turtle bladder. First, the two processes have different specificities for metabolic substrates (2). Second, aldosterone is a well-described stimulus for proton secretion and sodium reabsorption in the toad (28) and turtle bladder (2). Spironolactone, on the other hand, antagonizes the stimulation of sodium transport by aldosterone, but is itself an agonist that can stimulate proton secretion (36).

The mechanism of acidification by the isolated distal convoluted tubule has not yet been studied. Recent work with isolated rabbit cortical collecting tubules has suggested both similarities and differences between the distal tubule and the amphibian bladder. Stoner et al (45) observed a lumen-positive electrical potential when rabbit cortical collecting tubules were exposed to amiloride. They also noted that this potential could be reduced toward zero with acetazolamide (45). They inferred by analogy to the amphibian bladder that the lumen-positive potential difference was due to electrogenic proton secretion, but did not measure rates of bicarbonate reabsorption.

Gross and co-workers (19, 20) found that in cortical collecting tubules from rabbits maintained on a low salt diet there was a lumen-negative potential difference that was reduced towards zero with amiloride but that, in contrast to the results of Stoner et al (45), did not become positive. Gross et al (19) did observe an occasional small lumen-positive potentials in collecting tubules from rabbits maintained on regular or high salt diets, the origin of which was not established. Jacobson et al (21), however, have observed lumen-positive potentials in isolated perfused human collecting tubules that were probably due to electrogenic chloride transport and were inhibited by furosemide.

McKinney & Burg directly examined proton secretion and bicarbonate reabsorption in the rabbit cortical collecting tubule. They found that these tubules absorbed bicarbonate if taken from rabbits given NH_4Cl in vivo (34), and secreted bicarbonate if taken from rabbits given $NaHCO_3$ in vivo (35). Their results are summarized in Figure 3. Tubules that initially secreted bicarbonate are presented on the left, and those that initially absorbed bicarbonate are presented on the right. Bicarbonate reabsorption was increased, regardless of the initial direction of transport, when sodium was replaced by choline. Ouabain had no demonstrable effect on either set of tubules, and acetazolamide greatly reduced both absorption and secretion. Amiloride increased bicarbonate secretion, even in those tubules that initially reabsorbed bicarbonate. Amiloride also caused the potential difference to become positive, similar to to the results of Stoner et al (45). However, the effect of amiloride was clearly to increase bicarbonate secretion (34, 35) rather than to increase luminal acidification as had been proposed by Stoner et al (45).

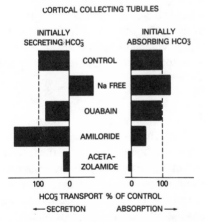

Figure 3 Effects of cations and drugs on bicarbonate transport by cortical collecting tubules. Tubules that were secreting bicarbonate in the control period are compared to tubules that were absorbing bicarbonate during the control period. "Sodium-free" indicates that sodium was replaced by choline in the perfusate and bath. The concentrations of ouabain, amiloride, and acetazolamide were $10^{-5}M$ in the bath, $10^{-5}M$ in the perfusate and $10^{-4}M$ in the perfusate and bath respectively. Reproduced from (35) with permission.

The bicarbonate secretory process in rabbit cortical collecting tubules is quite different from that observed in the turtle bladder (44). Replacement of luminal chloride by nitrate or methylsulfate had no effect on secretion in the collecting tubule (35), similar to the bicarbonate secretory process in the rabbit antral (13) and ileal (40) mucosa. In contrast, exchange of luminal chloride for bicarbonate seems to be the primary mode of bicarbonate secretion in the turtle bladder (44). Furthermore, amiloride increases bicarbonate secretion in the collecting tubule (35) and stimulates "apparent" bicarbonate reabsorption (or H^+ secretion) in the turtle bladder (12).

Another aspect of the results of McKinney & Burg (34, 35) can be compared to findings on proton secretion in amphibian bladder. The transepithelial electrical potential (lumen-negative) has been viewed as an important driving force for proton secretion in the distal tubule (38). The dependence of proton secretion upon the transepithelial potential difference is well documented in the amphibian bladder (1, 54) and reflects the electrogenic nature of proton secretion in these tissues. In contrast, McKinney & Burg (34, 35) observed no apparent relation between the rate of proton secretion (as measured by bicarbonate reabsorption) and the transepithelial potential difference in the cortical collecting tubule.

The contribution to acid-base homeostasis of bicarbonate secretion by the collecting tubule, and the nature of the accompanying cation are presently unknown. McKinney & Burg (35) suggested that bicarbonate secretion may increase the urinary P_{CO_2} by elevating the urinary bicarbonate concentration, in accord with the findings of Arruda et al (3). However, the urinary P_{CO_2} is much less for the rabbit than the dog at the same urinary concentration of bicarbonate (17), which suggests that there are intrinsic differences in the rate of distal proton secretion in these two species.

CONCLUSIONS

Owing to the availability of new, precise microanalytic techniques, the study of urinary acidification has recently undergone a renewed surge of interest. Future studies will focus upon (a) the existence and nature of electrogenic transport mechanisms, (b) the relations between electrically neutral modes of proton transport and the associated anion transport processes, (c) the nature and role of membrane-bound carbonic anhydrase, and (d) the origin of elevated intrarenal CO_2 tensions.

ACKNOWLEDGMENTS

The preparation of this manuscript was supported by grants from the US Public Health Service: Program Projects HL 06285 and AM 19407. We thank Ms. Janette Williams for her assistance.

Literature Cited

1. Al-Awqati, Q., Mueller, A., Steinmetz, P. R. 1977. Transport of H⁺ against electrochemical gradients in turtle urinary bladder. *Am. J. Physiol.* 233: F502-8
2. Al-Awqati, Q., Norby, L. H., Mueller, A., Steinmetz, P. R. 1976. Characteristics of stimulation of H⁺ transport by aldosterone in turtle urinary bladder. *J. Clin. Invest.* 58:351–58
3. Arruda, J. A. L., Nascimento, L., Mehta, P. K., Rademacher, D. R., Sehy, J. T., Westenfelder, C., Kurtzman, N. A. 1977. The critical importance of urinary concentrating ability in the generation of urinary carbon dioxide tension. *J. Clin. Invest.* 60:922–35
4. Berliner, R. W. 1952. Renal secretion of potassium and hydrogen ions. *Fed. Proc.* 11:695–700
5. Berry, C. A., Warnock, D. G., Rector, F. C., Jr. 1978. Ion selectivity and proximal salt reabsorption. *Am. J. Physiol.* 235:F234–45
6. Brodsky, W. A., Schilb, T. P. 1974. The means of distinguishing between hydrogen secretion and bicarbonate reabsorption: theory and applications to the reptilian bladder and mammalian kidney. *Curr. Top. Membr. Transp.,* 5:161–224
7. Burg, M. B. 1976. Mechanism of action of diuretic drugs. In *The Kidney,* ed. B. M. Brenner, F. C. Rector, Jr., 1:737–62. Philadelphia: Saunders. 762 pp.
8. Burg, M., Green, N. 1977. Bicarbonate transport by isolated perfused rabbit proximal convoluted tubules. *Am. J. Physiol.* 233:F307–14
9. Cohen, L. H., Mueller, A., Steinmetz, P. R. 1978. Inhibition of the bicarbonate exit step in urinary acidification by a disulfonic stilbene. *J. Clin. Invest.* 61:981–86
10. DuBose, T. D., Pacacco, L. R., Seldin, D. W., Carter, N. W., Kokko, J. P. 1978. Direct determination of pCO₂ in the rat renal cortex. *J. Clin. Invest.* 62:338–48
11. Ehrenspeck, G., Brodsky, W. A. 1976. Effects of 4-acetamido-4'-isothiocyano-2,2'-disulfonic stilbene on ion transport in turtle bladders. *Biochim. Biophys. Acta* 419:555–58
12. Ehrenspeck, G., Brodsky, W. A., Durham, J. 1977. The effect of amiloride on anion transport. *Physiologist* 20:24 (Abstr.)
13. Fromme, D., Schwartz, J. H., Robertson, R., Fuhro, R. 1976. Ion transport across isolated antral mucosa of the rabbit. *Am. J. Physiol.* 231:1783–89
14. Frömter, E., Gessner, K. 1974. Free-flow potential profile along rat kidney proximal tubule. *Pfluegers Arch.* 351:69–83
15. Frömter, E., Sato, K. 1976. Electrical events in active H⁺/HCO₃⁻ transport across rat kidney proximal tubular epithelium. In *Gastric Hydrogen Ion Secretion,* ed. D. Kasbekar, G. Sachs, W. Rehm, pp. 382–403. New York: Marcel Dekker. 486 pp.
16. Garcia Filho, E. M., Malnic, G. 1976. pH in cortical peritubular capillaries of rat kidney. *Pfluegers Arch.* 363:211–17
17. Giammarco, R. A., Goldstein, M. B., Halperin, J. S., Hammeke, M. D., Richardson, R. M. A., Robson, W. L. M., Stinebaugh, B. J., Halperin, M. L. 1978. Collecting duct hydrogen ion secretion in the rabbit: role of potassium. *J. Lab. Clin. Med.* 91:948–59
18. Green, R., Giebisch, G. 1975. Ionic requirements of proximal tubular sodium transport. II. Hydrogen ion. *Am. J. Physiol.* 229:1216–26
19. Gross, J. B., Imai, M., Kokko, J. P. 1975. A functional comparison of the cortical collecting tubule and the distal convoluted tubule. *J. Clin. Invest.* 55:1284–94
20. Gross, J. B., Kokko, J. P. 1977. Effects of aldosterone and potassium-sparing diuretics on electrical potential differences across the distal nephron. *J. Clin. Invest.* 59:82–89
21. Jacobson, H. R., Gross, J. B., Kawamura, S., Waters, J. D., Kokko, J. P. 1976. Electrophysiologic study of isolated perfused human collecting ducts. Ion dependency of the transepithelial potential difference. *J. Clin. Invest.* 58:1233–39
22. Karlmark, B., Danielson, B. G. 1974. Titratable acid, pCO₂, bicarbonate and ammonia ions along the rat proximal tubule, *Acta Physiol. Scand.* 91:243–58
23. Lang, F., Quehenberger, P., Greger, R., Oberleithner, H. 1978. Effect of benzolamide on luminal pH in proximal convoluted tubules of the rat kidney. *Pfluegers Arch.* 375:39–43
24. Liedtke, C. M., Hopfer, U. 1977. Anion transport in brush-border membrane vesicles isolated from rat small intestine. *Biochem. Biophys. Res. Commun.* 76:579–85
25. Lönnerholm, G. 1971. Histochemical demonstration of carbonic anhydrase activity in the rat kidney. *Acta Physiol. Scand.* 81:433–39
26. Lucci, M. S., Warnock, D. G., Rector, F. C. Jr. 1979. Carbonic anhydrase-

210   WARNOCK & RECTOR

dependent bicarbonate reabsorption in the rat proximal tubule. *Am. J. Physiol.* 236: In press

27. Ludens, J. H., Fanestil, D. D. 1972. Acidification of urine by the isolated urinary bladder of the toad. *Am. J. Physiol.* 223:1338–44

28. Ludens, J. H., Fanestil, D. D. 1974. Aldosterone stimulation of acidification of urine by isolated urinary bladder of the Colombian toad. *Am. J. Physiol.* 226:1321–26

29. Malnic, G., deMello-Aires, M. 1971. Kinetic study of bicarbonate reabsorption in proximal tubule of the rat. *Am. J. Physiol.* 220:1759–67

30. Malnic, G., deMello-Aires, M. 1978. Sodium transport and acidification in renal cortical tubules. In *New Aspects of Renal Function, Sixth Workshop Conference Hoechst,* ed. H. G. Vogel, K. J. Ullrich, 6:58–61. Amsterdam: Exerpta Medica. 221 pp.

31. Maren, T. H. 1967. Carbonic anhydrase: chemistry, physiology and inhibition. *Physiol. Rev.* 47:595–781

32. Maren, T. H. 1974. Chemistry of the renal reabsorption of bicarbonate. *Can. J. Physiol. Pharmacol.* 52:1041–50

33. McKinney, T. D., Burg, M. B. 1977. Bicarbonate and fluid absorption by renal proximal straight tubules. *Kidney Int.* 12:1–8

34. McKinney, T. D., Burg, M. B. 1978. Bicarbonate absorption by rabbit cortical collecting tubules *in vitro. Am. J. Physiol.* 234:F141–45

35. McKinney, T. D., Burg, M. B. 1978. Bicarbonate secretion by rabbit cortical collecting tubules *in vitro. J. Clin. Invest.* 61:1421–27

36. Mueller, A., Steinmetz, P. R. 1978. Spironolactone, an aldosterone agonist in the stimulation of H^+ secretion by turtle urinary bladder. *J. Clin. Invest.* 61:1660–70

37. Murer, H., Hopfer, U., Kinne, R. 1976. Sodium/proton antiport in brush-border membrane vesicles isolated from rat small intestine and kidney. *Biochem. J.* 154:597–604

38. Rector, F. C. Jr. 1973. Acidification of the urine. In *Handbook of Physiology. Renal Physiology,* ed. J. Orloff, R. W. Berliner, pp. 431–54. Washington DC: Am. Physiol. Soc. 1082 pp.

39. Seldin, D. W. 1976. Metabolic alkalosis. See Ref. 7, pp. 661–702

40. Sheerin, H. E., Field, M. 1975. Ileal HCO_3 secretion: relationship to Na and Cl transport and effect of theophylline. *Am. J. Physiol.* 228:1065–74

41. Smith, H. 1937. Acid-base equilibria in plasma and urine. In *Physiology of the*

Kidney, ed. H. Smith, pp. 169–82. New York: Oxford Univ. Press.

42. Sohtell, M., Karlmark, B. 1976. *In vivo* micropuncture pCO_2 measurements. *Pfluegers Arch.* 363:179–80

43. Sohtell, M. 1978. Pco_2 of the proximal tubular fluid and the efferent arteriolar blood in the rat kidney. *Acta Univ. Ups.* 293:V1–V13

44. Steinmetz, P. R. 1974. Cellular mechanisms of urinary acidification. *Physiol. Rev.* 54:890–956

45. Stoner, L. C., Burg, M. B., Orloff, J. 1974. Ion transport in cortical collecting tubule: effect of amiloride. *Am. J. Physiol.* 227:453–59

46. Ullrich, K. J., Capasso, G., Rumrich, G., Papavassiliou, F., Klöss, S. 1977. Coupling between proximal tubular transport processes: studies with ouabain, SITS and HCO_3^--free solutions. *Pfluegers Arch.* 368:245–52

47. Ullrich, K. J., Radtke, H. W., Rumrich, G. 1971. The role of bicarbonate and other buffers on isotonic fluid reabsorption in the proximal convolution of the rat kidney. *Pfluegers Arch.* 330:149–61

48. Ullrich, K. J., Rumrich, G., Baumann, K. 1975. Renal proximal tubule buffer-(Glycodiazine) transport. Inhomogeneity of local transport rate, dependence on sodium, effect of inhibitors and chronic adaptation. *Pfluegers Arch.* 357:149–63

49. Vurek, G. G., Warnock, D. G., Corsey, R. 1975. Measurement of picomole amounts of carbon dioxide by calorimetry. *Anal. Chem.* 47:765–67

50. Warnock, D. G., Burg, M. B. 1977. Urinary acidification: CO_2 transport by the rabbit proximal straight tubule. *Am. J. Physiol.* 233:F20–25

51. Warnock, D. G., Lucci, M. S. 1978. NaCl transport in the proximal tubule. *Proc. Int. Congr. Nephrol., 7th, Montreal,* p. C-8 (Abstr.)

52. Warnock, D. G., Rector, F. C. Jr. 1978. CO_2 permeability and bicarbonate generation by the isolated, perfused, rabbit proximal straight tubule. *Kidney Int.* 11:576a (Abstr.); *Proc. Int. Congr. Nephrol., 7th, Montreal,* p. H-3 (Abstr.)

53. Wistrand, P. J., Kinne, R. 1977. Carbonic anhydrase activity of isolated brush border and basal-lateral membranes of renal tubular cells. *Pfluegers Arch.* 370:121–26

54. Ziegler, R. W., Fanestil, D. D., Ludens, J. H. 1976. Influence of transepithelial potential difference on acidification in the toad urinary bladder. *Kidney Int.* 10:279–86

Ann. Rev. Physiol. 1979. 41:211-27

RHEOGENIC AND PASSIVE ◆1215
NA+ ABSORPTION
BY THE PROXIMAL NEPHRON

James A. Schafer and Thomas E. Andreoli[1]

Nephrology Research and Training Center, Division of Nephrology, Department of Medicine, Department of Physiology & Biophysics, University of Alabama, Birmingham, Alabama 35294

INTRODUCTION

This review summarizes recent considerations germane to the mechanism(s) for NaCl absorption by the mammalian proximal nephron. Most arguments concerning epithelial NaCl transport derive from the hypotheses formulated by H. H. Ussing and his associates in their analysis of Na^+ fluxes in anuran epithelia. Their evocative model derives from three major considerations. Ussing (69) and Ussing & Zerahn (71) demonstrated that net Na^+ transport was identical to the zero-voltage short-circuit current and occurred against an electrochemical gradient. Then Koefoed-Johnsen & Ussing (33) proposed that Na^+ entered cells passively at apical surfaces and was actively transported out of cells at basolateral surfaces via an active Na^+/K^+ exchange pump. Finally, Ussing & Windhager (70) provided strong evidence that dissipative ion transport in epithelia might involve a paracellular route.

The application of Ussing's paradigm to the mammalian proximal renal tubule also requires analysis of certain other factors. Of particular importance in this context are the following:

[1]Address reprint requests to: Department of Medicine, University of Texas Medical School, Houston, Texas 77025.

211

1. *Heterogeneity of the mammalian proximal nephron.* There are morphological differences between convoluted and straight segments of proximal tubules, and cell types within these segments are heterogeneous (77). Thus proximal tubular cell types have been classified as S_1, S_2, or S_3 to denote varying histology and/or axial location (39, 77). This morphologic heterogeneity also correlates with axial changes in function. Differences in rates of isotonic volume absorption, ionic conductance, nonelectrolyte absorption, organic acid secretion, phosphate absorption, and response to parathyroid hormone occur axially among various segments of the superficial proximal mammalian nephron (20, 21, 34, 37, 52, 57, 77). Heterogeneity of proximal tubular function also depends on glomerular location. For example, the permeability ratio P_{Na}/P_{Cl} declines with length in isolated superficial proximal tubules, and this ratio is higher in juxtamedullary than in superficial tubules (7, 29, 30).

2. *Complex modes of Na^+ co-transport at the apical entry step.* Ussing's paradigm proposes a simple passive Na^+ entry step across apical membranes, but a number of different symport or antiport mechanisms may also modulate apical Na^+ entry. There is ample evidence that Na^+ absorption in the proximal nephron involves an antiport mechanism coupled to active H^+ secretion across the brush-border membrane (18, 40, 45, 46). Furthermore, Na^+ absorption may also depend upon Na^+ co-transport with glucose and amino acids (11, 15, 31, 53, 59) or with certain organic anions (11, 53). Finally, others (36, 73) have argued that neutral NaCl entry across apical plasma membranes may provide yet another modality for proximal tubular NaCl absorption.

3. *Role of axial compositional changes.* Fluid absorption in the proximal nephron is accompanied by axial changes in tubular fluid composition at a near-constant osmolality, including an increase in the tubular fluid/plasma (TF/P) Cl^- concentration ratio attendant on tubular fluid acidification. And since axial alterations in transepithelial ionic concentration gradients also modify transepithelial voltages, there exist axial steady-state solute-concentration and voltage profiles that can alter transport rates for Na^+ and other solutes.

4. *Coupling of solvent and NaCl transport.* Depending on the relative distribution of solute and water flows between cellular and paracellular pathways, entrainment of solute and solvent flows through either a cellular or paracellular route may create an appreciable driving force for solute absorption, particularly in view of the high rates of isotonic volume absorption in the mammalian proximal nephron. This issue has been considered in detail by Frömter et al (23) and by Schafer et al (50, 51).

It is evident from these considerations that an evaluation of "simple" Na^+ transport in the proximal nephron, i.e. net Na^+ absorption following the Ussing formulation, requires at a minimum (a) assessment of net Na^+ absorption in the absence of putative symport and/or antiport processes; (b) evaluation of the contribution(s) of axial compositional changes as possible sources for dissipative driving forces for passive NaCl absorption; and (c) analysis of the paracellular pathway as the route for passive ion permeation. These issues are examined in some detail below, following an evaluation of the contribution of diffusion voltages to proximal tubular transepithelial voltages.

DONNAN VOLTAGES AND TRANSEPITHELIAL VOLTAGES

Consider an isolated proximal tubule segment perfused and bathed with isotonic HCO_3^--Krebs-Ringer (KR) solutions, the bath containing approximately 6 gm dl^{-1} albumin. In principle, a Donnan voltage arising from the asymmetrical distribution of protein should occur; yet we (50–52) and others (e.g. 11, 34), working with straight or convoluted segments respectively, have observed that the measured transepithelial voltage is approximately zero when active transport is abolished.

This apparent discrepancy may be rationalized by considering the conditions for measuring transepithelial voltages. As described elsewhere (49–53), agar bridges containing an appropriate salt, generally 150 mM NaCl, are placed in perfusing and bathing solutions. Thus in the absence of active transport processes, the observed transepithelial voltage V_e^o (mV) is:

$$V_e^o = V_{e1 \rightarrow P} + V_D + V_{b \rightarrow e2} \qquad 1.$$

where $V_{e1 \rightarrow P}$ and $V_{b \rightarrow e2}$ are the liquid junction voltages between perfusate-electrode:perfusate and bath:bath-electrode, respectively, and V_D is a transepithelial diffusion voltage. The liquid junction voltages may be computed according to the Henderson equation modified in terms of activities. The ionic diffusion voltage may be expressed as:

$$V_D = \sum_{i=1}^{n} t_i E_i, \qquad 2.$$

where t_i is the transference number of the i-th ion and E_i is the equilibrium voltage for the i-th ion, computed from the Nernst equation and the perfusate:bath-water ion concentration ratios. It follows that, for a Donnan distribution in which the perfusate:bath-water ion concentration ratios for mobile ions are the same, E_i is the same for any of the mobile ions and $V_D \simeq E_i$.

It is evident from equation 1 that V_e^o in the absence of active transport processes will be nearly zero when $(V_{el \to P} + V_{b \to e2})$ is approximately equal in magnitude but opposite in sign to V_D. To test this possibility, Schafer et al (53) computed the values of these parameters when tubules were perfused with simple phosphate-buffered NaCl solutions, bathed with similar solutions containing 6 gm dl^{-1} albumin, and gassed with O_2. The measured bath-water : perfusate concentration ratios for Na^+ and K^+ were 1.073 and 1.062, respectively; and the measured perfusate : bath-water concentration ratio for Cl^- was slightly higher, 1.12, due probably to the presence of unmeasured anions associated with undialyzed albumin (53). The value of V_e^o calculated from the algebraic sum of $(V_{el \to P} + V_{b \to e2})$ and V_D was 0.05 mV, i.e. indistinguishable from zero.

When active transport occurs, the right-hand side of equation 1 will also include a term for V_r, the rheogenic voltage. Thus we may define an actual transepithelial voltage V_e^a as:

$$V_e^a = V_D + V_r = V_e^o - (V_{e1 \to p} + V_{b \to e2}).$$ 3.

When viewed in this context, a rheogenic voltage may represent a lumen-negative displacement from the Donnan equilibrium voltage, rather than an actual lumen-negative value. In this review, transepithelial voltages will be expressed either as V_e^a, when Donnan correction data are available, or as V_e^o, when they are not.

Similar problems due to the presence of variable amounts of unmeasured interstitial protein also complicate measurements of transepithelial voltage during in vivo micropuncture, as discussed by Frömter (18). In such in vivo measurements, the reference electrode is often placed in peritoneal cavity fluid or blood, and there must be a Donnan liquid junction voltage at some point in the circuit.

THE PARACELLULAR SHUNT PATHWAY

Electrical Resistance

It is widely believed that the paracellular route constitutes the pathway for dissipative ion transport in epithelia (19, 22, 50, 52, 56, 70); thus Frömter & Diamond (19) have classified epithelia as "tight" or "leaky" by using transepithelial electrical resistances as indexes of ionic conductances through the paracellular pathway. In the mammalian proximal nephron, transepithelial resistances in the range 4–15 Ω cm^2 have been measured in in vivo proximal convoluted tubules (14, 22), and comparable values have been reported for in vitro proximal tubules (37).

It has been inferred (18, 19, 22, 37) from these data that the paracellular pathway constitutes the route for passive ion transport, since electrical resistances in the range of 10 Ω cm^2 are appreciably less than one expects for two cell membranes in series. This presumption has not been evaluated explicitly in the mammalian proximal tubule, but has been confirmed in amphibian proximal tubules (2, 18, 28). The high ionic conductance of tight junctions in the proximal nephron is also consistent with the observation that lanthanum penetrates the junctional complex of the rat proximal tubule (65).

Ionic Selectivity

A second major consideration in support of the view that passive ion flows in epithelia involve an extracellular route is the observation that transepithelial ionic selectivity patterns differ from those of individual cell membranes. For example, Frömter et al (22) and DeMello et al (14) have shown that rat proximal tubular epithelium exhibits, as a whole, transference numbers for Na$^+$ and K$^+$ that are approximately equal and in excess of that for Cl$^-$; in contrast, the peritubular membrane exhibits much greater Cl$^-$ and K$^+$ than Na$^+$ permeabilities.

Schafer et al (52) evaluated passive ion permeation in isolated superficial rabbit proximal straight tubules by measuring zero-current NaCl dilution potentials at zero volume flow: Active transport was abolished, and voltages were measured when NaCl in either the perfusate or the bath was replaced isosmotically with mannitol. The results, shown in Figure 1, indicate that the salt dilution voltages were equal in magnitude but opposite in sign for a given reduction in the NaCl concentration in either the perfusing or bathing solutions. Thus it seems probable that the salt dilution potentials were expressed across a single symmetrical interface having the same P_{Na}/P_{Cl} ratio on either side. And since the ionic permeability properties of proximal tubular luminal and peritubular membranes differ in various species (8, 18, 25, 28), it was concluded that the salt dilution potentials were expressed across junctional complexes (52). It follows from this argument that the low transepithelial resistance of these tubules is referable to a high ionic conductance of junctional complexes.

Nature of Ionic Barrier in Junctional Complexes

The data shown in Figure 1 indicate that a P_{Na}/P_{Cl} ratio of 0.3 is adequate to describe NaCl dilution potentials produced in the pars recta using external NaCl concentrations in the range 30–130 mM (52). For this nephron segment, one also obtains a P_{Na}/P_{Cl} ratio of 0.3 from unidirectional tracer fluxes measured at zero volume flow with an external Na$^+$ concentration of $\simeq$ 150 mM (52). These results indicate that the P_{Na}/P_{Cl} ratio in proximal straight tubules is independent of ionic concentrations in external solutions.

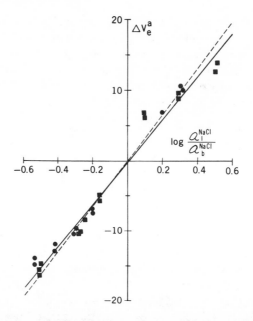

Figure 1.   NaCl dilution potentials in the superficial proximal straight tubule. The change in V_e^a, the transepithelial voltage, is plotted as a function of the log of the NaCl activity ratio (perfusate to bathing solution) according to the Planck-Henderson equation (52). Changes in the NaCl concentrations of up to 90 mM were produced in either the bathing solution (quadrant 1) or the perfusion solution (quadrant 3) by replacing the salt isosmotically with mannitol. The dots denote experiments conducted at 21° C, and the squares denote experiments at 37° C in the presence of 0.1 mM ouabain in the bathing solution. The dashed line represents the theoretical relationship for a P_{Na}/P_{Cl} ratio of 0.3. The solid line represents the least squares linear regression of the data points. Adapted from Schafer et al (52).

But partition into a barrier containing fixed charges occurs in accordance with a Donnan distribution, and depends upon ionic concentrations in the adjacent external solutions (4, 48, 64). Thus the ionic selectivity of a barrier containing fixed-charge sites should depend on the salt concentration in the adjacent bulk solutions. The results discussed above, however, illustrate that in proximal straight tubules [Figure 1; (52)] the ionic selectivity ratio is independent of ion concentrations. Therefore we (52) have argued that, in these tubules, paracellular ion flow may involve junctional complexes containing weakly charged or neutral polar sites, in accord with earlier descriptions of ion permeation pathways in gall bladder (6) and rabbit ileum (16).

It is also important to realize that the Debye lengths calculated for isotonic NaCl solutions, using the dielectric constant of either oil or water, are far less than the length of junctional complexes in mammalian proximal tubules, about 200–400 Å (74). Therefore electroneutrality is required for ion permeation through junctional complexes. And if the latter lack charged sites, electroneutrality obviously requires mobile counter ions.

Diffusion Resistance of Lateral Intercellular Spaces

If one accepts the assumption that passive ion flows in proximal straight tubules involve an extracellular route, then electrical resistance data may be used to compute the diffusion resistance of intercellular spaces exclusive of junctional complexes. The argument is as follows. We may define a dimensionless parameter α as (50):

$$\alpha = \frac{k}{f_m},$$

where k is is a tortuosity factor (the actual length of an intercellular channel with respect to epithelial thickness) and f_m is the fractional area of intercellular channels relative to one cm^2 of luminal membrane area. Thus α represents the ratio of the diffusion resistance of intercellular spaces, exclusive of junctional complexes, in one cm^2 of epithelium relative to the diffusion resistance of a one cm^2 layer of free solution having a thickness equal to that of the epithelium.

No explicit value of α may be computed, but a range of values for α may be set by comparing measured transepithelial resistances with the predicted resistance of a layer of solution having a thickness equal to that of the epithelium (i.e. 7.5 μm for mammalian proximal renal tubules). For example, a 7.5 μm layer of 150 mM NaCl would have a resistance of $\simeq 0.05$ Ω cm^2, while the transepithelial resistances of isolated mammalian proximal renal tubules are about 5 Ω cm^2 (37). Thus we have $1 < \alpha \leqslant 100$, or, in other words, the diffusion resistance of intercellular spaces, exclusive of junctional complexes, in one cm^2 (luminal surface area) of proximal renal tubule is, at a maximum, only 100-fold greater than a 7.5 μm thick layer of 150 mM NaCl having a one cm^2 surface area (50).

The parameter α may therefore be used to compute the contribution of intercellular spaces to total diffusion resistance. If P_D is the diffusional permeability coefficient (μm sec^{-1}) for the i-th species at zero volume flow, the total diffusion resistance for the i-th species ($1/P_D$) may be expressed as (50):

$$\frac{1}{P_D} = \frac{1}{P^j} + \frac{\alpha L}{D^o}, \qquad\qquad 4.$$

where P^j is the diffusional permeability coefficient for the solute across junctional complexes, L (μm) is epithelial thickness, D^o (μm^2 sec^{-1}) is the free diffusion coefficient of the solute, and α has the range of values defined above. Using reported values (see Table 1) of P_D for Na^+, Cl^-, and HCO_3^- in isolated superficial proximal straight or proximal convoluted tubules, it may easily be shown that, even for α values of $\simeq 100$, the

Table 1 Ionic selectivity properties of the proximal nephron[a]

	P_{Na}/P_{Cl}						P_{HCO_3}/P_{Cl}			
	Superficial				Juxta-medullary		Superficial		Juxta-medullary	
Species	Early PCT	Mid PCT	Late PCT	PST	PCT	PST	PCT	PST	PCT	PST
Rabbit	0.6–10.0 (7, 29)	0.5 (29)	0.31 (29)	0.33–0.50* (30, 52, 72)	2.0 (29)	2.0* (30, 72)	0.5 (7)	0.05–0.35 (50, 51, 72)	0.5 (7)	0.53 (72)
Rat	—	~1.6 (14, 22)	—	—	—	—	~0.4 (22)	—	—	—
Dog	—	1.38 (9)	—	—	—	—	0.62 (9)	—	—	—
Necturus	—	0.3–0.6 (1, 3)	—	—	—	—	—	—	—	—

[a] Ionic selectivity ratios were estimated from either single salt dilution potentials or bi-ionic potentials measured either in the presence or in the absence of spontaneous transepithelial voltages in proximal convoluted (PCT) and proximal straight tubules (PST). Mid-PCT values include those obtained from experiments in which the distance of the measurement point along the nephron segment was not specified. The numbers in parentheses indicate the appropriate references.
*An asterisk indicates those studies where P_{Na}/P_{Cl} ratios were confirmed with tracer fluxes.

$\alpha L/D^o$ term in equation 4 is $\leqslant 10\%$ of $1/P_D$. These considerations indicate that, for mammalian proximal renal tubules, lateral intercellular spaces constitute a trivial resistance to transepithelial ionic diffusion (50, 51).

Characteristics of Ionic Discrimination

Table 1 summarizes the relative ionic permeabilities of various regions of the mammalian proximal nephron as estimated from salt dilution voltages (and confirmed in certain instances by unidirectional tracer fluxes). There is heterogeneity of ionic discrimination among various proximal tubular segments; for example, the P_{Na}/P_{Cl} ratio is less than unity in superficial proximal tubules and greater than unity in juxtamedullary nephron segments. It is important to note that Table 1 indicates one common characteristic of all proximal tubule segments: The permeability to Cl^- is greater than the permeability to HCO_3^-. The relevance of the latter observations to proximal tubular fluid absorption is discussed in the section on Passive NaCl Absorption, below.

"SIMPLE" RHEOGENIC Na^+ ABSORPTION

The Ussing model for transepithelial NaCl transport involves passive, conductive Na^+ entry across luminal plasma membranes into a cellular "transport pool," rheogenic Na^+ extrusion across basal-lateral membranes, and passive net Cl^- absorption. The most convincing evidence in favor of active rheogenic Na^+ transport in frog skin was the demonstration of equality between the short-circuit current and the net Na^+ flux (71). However, equivalent techniques are technically difficult in the proximal tubule. Although it has been possible to voltage-clamp short regions of *Necturus* proximal tubule using an axial electrode (62), the variability inherent in current measurements, due to the conductive shunt pathway, has made it extremely difficult to establish an exact relation between electrical currents and ionic fluxes.

A considerable body of alternative evidence, however, suggests that active Na^+ transport mechanisms are involved in proximal tubular salt absorption. Na,K-activated ATPase is distributed uniformly along basal and lateral, but not luminal, cell membranes of proximal tubular epithelial cells (35, 55). Second, Burg & Green (10) showed that, in isolated rabbit proximal convoluted tubules, replacement of Na^+ in the perfusate by choline, or replacement of K^+ in the bath by Na^+, reduced net fluid absorption and transepithelial voltage to zero. Similar results have been obtained with Na^+-replacement experiments in the rat proximal tubule (27). Third, ouabain at 0.01–1.0 mM in the peritubular fluid inhibits all or a significant portion of proximal Na^+ absorption (50, 52, 54). Fourth, a transepithelial Na^+ concentration gradient (lumen < bath) can be established in spite of an opposing electrical gradient, if an impermeant solute is present in the lumen (76).

Finally, net Na^+ absorption in the proximal nephron of *Necturus* is accelerated by adding amphotericin B to luminal solutions, an effect thought to result from an increase in the luminal membrane Na^+ conductance (60, 63). Likewise, organic solutes such as glucose and alanine, by virtue of their electrogenic co-transport with Na^+ across luminal membranes (11, 15, 59), might increase active Na^+ absorption by increasing luminal Na^+ entry into the cell. These latter two observations suggest that apical Na^+ entry may be the rate-controlling step in Na^+ absorption (11, 53, 60, 63).

A major problem in assessing the contribution of "simple" rheogenic Na^+ transport to net Na^+ absorption in the experiments cited above is the fact that proximal tubular Na^+ absorption might be mediated by a number of pathways in parallel with the "simple" rheogenic Na^+ transport system (see the Introduction). In order to exclude the contributions of apical symport and antiport processes to net Na^+ absorption, we (53) recently evaluated net Na^+ absorption in superficial proximal straight tubules exposed to simplified NaCl solutions buffered with 2 mM phosphate to pH 7.4 and gassed with 100% O_2; the other solutes were 5.0 mM KCl, 3 mM $CaCl_2$ and 1 mM $MgCl_2$ in the perfusate, and the same solutes plus 8.3 mM D-glucose, 5.0 mM L-alanine, and 6 g dl^{-1} bovine serum albumin in the bathing solution.

The results, summarized in Table 2, indicate that at 38° C the net rate of fluid absorption was $\simeq 0.20$ nl min^{-1} mm^{-1} and the transepithelial voltage was displaced approximately 1.0 mV lumen-negative from the Donnan

Table 2   An assessment of simple rheogenic Na^+ transport in the proximal straight tubule[a]

Inhibitor	J_v (nl min^{-1} mm^{-1})	V_e^a (mV)	V_D (mV)
None	0.20 ± 0.02	$+1.5 \pm 0.2$	$+2.4$
0.16 mM Ethoxzolamide	0.22 ± 0.03	$+1.7 \pm 0.2$	$+2.4$
0.1 mM Ouabain	-0.02 ± 0.01	$+2.6 \pm 0.2$	$+2.4$

[a]The perfusate and bath were the simple NaCl buffers described in the text, bubbled with 100% O_2 so the system was free of HCO_3^-/CO_2 in the external solutions. V_e^a is the actual transepithelial voltage (cf equation 3); V_D is the Donnan equilibrium voltage. Ouabain or ethoxzolamide was added to the bathing solution only. All measurements were made at 38°C. Adapted from Schafer et al (53).

equilibrium voltage; 10^{-4} M ouabain reduced J_v to approximately zero while V_e^a rose to V_D, the Donnan equilibrium voltage. Table 2 also illustrates that, for these conditions, J_v was not affected by ethoxzolamide; the latter, however, consistently inhibits 50–60% of net fluid absorption when these tubules are bubbled with 95% O_2+5% CO_2 (49). These results indicate that, in proximal straight tubules, "simple" active Na^+ transport constitutes one of the mechanisms for Na^+ absorption.

These results are also consistent with the possibility that the spontaneous negative voltage displacement from Donnan equilibrium illustrated in Table 2 is rheogenic, i.e. provides a major driving force for passive Cl^- absorption. To evaluate this issue quantitatively, we note that, for volume transport under these conditions, Cl^- is the principal anion in an isotonic absorbate and net Cl^- flux may be expressed as (53):

$$J_{Cl} \simeq J_v \cdot [Cl]_p,   5.$$

where J_{Cl} is the net Cl^- flux and $[Cl]_p$ is the Cl^- concentration in the perfusate. Thus for J_v of $\simeq 0.2$ nl min^{-1} mm^{-1} [Table 2; Schafer et al (53)] and $[Cl]_p \simeq 150$ mM, we have $J_{Cl} = 30$ pEq min^{-1} mm^{-1}. And since Cl^- is passively transported in these tubules (50–53), this net J_{Cl} should be accounted for in terms of the expression (23, 42, 50, 51):

$$J_{Cl} = P_{Cl} \left[([Cl]_p - [Cl]_b) - \frac{V_e^a F}{RT} \frac{[Cl]_p + [Cl]_b}{2} \right]$$

$$+ J_v (1 - \sigma_{Cl}) \frac{[Cl]_p + [Cl]_b}{2},   6.$$

where $[Cl]_b$ is the bath Cl^- concentration, F, R, and T have their usual meaning, P_{Cl} is the Cl^- permeability coefficient [0.73 μm sec^{-1} (52)], and σ_{Cl}

is the Cl^- reflection coefficient [for these tubules, $\sigma_{Cl} = 0.65$ (23, 51)].
Inserting these values and the data from Table 2 into equation 6, the
predicted J_{Cl} is 35 $peq\ min^{-1}\ mm^{-1}$, a value in close agreement with the
value computed from equation 5, with approximately 80% of the net Cl^-
flux due to diffusion and the remainder due to solvent drag. These calculations indicate that active Na^+ transport produces a significant electrical
driving force for passive Cl^- absorption, i.e. that "simple" Na^+ transport
is rheogenic.

PASSIVE NaCl TRANSPORT

Axial compositional changes occur during proximal tubular fluid absorption, specifically a rise in the TF/P Cl^- concentration ratio due to tubular
fluid acidification (13, 26, 38, 49, 52); therefore $NaHCO_3$ absorption may
result in a favorable electrochemical gradient for NaCl absorption, an argument first articulated by Rector et al (47). And since maximal TF/P Cl^-
concentration ratios are achieved in terminal regions of the proximal convoluted tubule (13, 26), passive NaCl absorption driven by an electrochemical gradient might reasonably be expected to occur primarily in the pars
recta. Also in accord with this possibility is the fact that a rise in luminal
voltage, which should result in a passive driving force for Na^+ absorption,
occurs in late portions of the in vivo proximal convoluted tubule (5, 9, 14,
20–22, 57).

An in vivo assessment of the relative contributions of active and passive
transport processes to NaCl absorption in the pars recta has not been
carried out because this nephron segment is not accessible to routine micropuncture. Alternatively, Table 3 presents the results of experiments (50,
51) designed to evaluate these issues in superficial proximal straight tubules
microperfused in vitro. The perfusate contained a Cl-KR buffer, pH 6.6,

Table 3 Transport characteristics of the superficial proximal straight tubule: Cl^--KR
perfusate and HCO_3^--KR bath simulating in vivo conditions[a]

Condition	J_v (nl min^{-1} mm^{-1})	V_e^a (mV)	J_{Na} (pmoles min^{-1} mm^{-1}) Observed	Predicted passive	J_{Cl} (pmoles min^{-1} mm^{-1}) Observed	Predicted passive
37°C	0.41 ± 0.05	2.7 ± 0.2	63.9 ± 3.2	21.4	54.1 ± 3.3	50.4
21°C	0.19 ± 0.04	3.6 ± 0.1	28.0 ± 5.9	24.2	29.4 ± 7.4	25.9

[a]Tubules were perfused with a Cl^--KR buffer solution containing ~140 mEq l^{-1}Cl$^-$ and 3.8
mM HCO_3^-; glucose and alanine were replaced by urea. The bathing solution was normal Krebs-
Ringer bicarbonate solution gassed with 95% O_2 + 5% CO_2. The observed Na$^+$ flux was taken
as $J_v \cdot [Na^+]_p$ (equation 5) and the observed Cl^- fluxes were determined directly. Predicted passive fluxes for both ions were derived using equation 6. Adapted from (50, 51).

from which organic solutes had been omitted; and the bath contained a HCO_3-KR buffer, pH 7.4, with organic solutes added; thus the experimental conditions mimicked the in vivo situation for the pars recta. As indicated in Table 3, when proximal straight tubules were cooled to 21° C under these conditions, J_v was inhibited only 60% and V^a rose; identical results obtained when active transport was inhibited at 37° C with ouabain (50). In contrast, when these tubules were perfused and bathed with symmetrical HCO_3-KR solutions, or simplified NaCl solutions [Table 1 of (50)], either ouabain or cooling reduced J_v to values indistinguishable from zero.

Given these observations, the results (Table 3) with a Cl-KR perfusate and an HCO_3-KR bath permit the following general conclusions (50, 51): (a) At 21° C (or at 37° with 10^{-4} M ouabain in the bath), fluid absorption is coupled to passive salt transport. The latter is driven, at least in part, by the lumen-positive transepithelial voltage and the transepithelial Cl^- concentration gradient; and V_e^a for these conditions represents a transepithelial Cl^- diffusion potential. (b) The increase in J_v and the decrease in V_e^a at 37° C in the absence of ouabain (50, 51) depend on active transport processes. According to this view, approximately 60% of net fluid absorption is due to active Na^+ transport. The same conclusion may be reached by comparing the net absorption rates for Na^+ and Cl^- with those computed for the passive components of ion flux by using equation 6. As indicated in Table 3, passive forces account for all net Cl^- absorption both at 37° C and at 21° C; in the case of Na^+, passive flux accounts for approximately one third of Na^+ absorption at 37° C, and for virtually all of Na^- absorption at 21° C.

One other consideration is noteworthy in this regard. The flux comparisons listed in Table 3 indicate that equation 6, which utilizes bulk phase parameters and driving forces, is adequate to describe passive ion absorption. Implicit in this statement is the possibility that ionic concentrations in intercellular spaces are in diffusion equilibrium with bathing solutions. Likewise, as indicated in connection with equation 4, intercellular spaces constitute a trivial resistance to transepithelial passive ion permeation in proximal straight tubules. If this argument is correct, a driving force other than intercellular space hypertonicity is required to account for fluid absorption coupled to salt transport. Solution of the flow-diffusion equations for intercellular ionic concentrations under the conditions listed in Table 3 has indicated (50, 51) that Na^+ concentrations, and hence osmolalities, are either the same as or less than those in external solutions, and that fluid absorption may be accounted for quantitatively in terms of the oppositely directed concentration gradients for Cl^- and HCO_3^-, given the fact that junctional complexes in these tubules are appreciably more permeable to Cl^- than to HCO_3^- [Table 1; (49, 52, 72)].

Finally, it is interesting to calculate the possible contribution of passive Na^+ absorption to net Na^+ absorption in the in vivo kidney. In rabbit kidneys, the average length of the superficial proximal tubule is 8.7 mm, of which 3.4 mm represents proximal straight tubule (77). From Table 3, the net rate of Na^+ absorption in this nephron segment is 64 pEq min^{-1} mm^{-1}, or for a 3.4 mm long superficial proximal straight tubule, 218 pEq min^{-1}. Chonko et al (12), using in vivo micropuncture in rabbits, have found the single-nephron filtration rate to be $20 \cdot 10^{-6}$ cm^3 min^{-1}; thus for a plasma Na^+ concentration of $145 \cdot 10^{-6}$ Eq min^{-1}, the net filtered Na^+ is 2900 pEq min^{-1}. Therefore in an in vivo superficial rabbit nephron, the proximal straight tubule may absorb approximately 7.5% of filtered Na^+, and passive Na^+ absorption by this nephron segment may account for about 2.5% of the filtered Na^+ load.

ACTIVE, ELECTRONEUTRAL NaCl TRANSPORT

The results presented in the preceding sections indicate that Cl^- transport in mammalian proximal straight tubules can be accounted for quantitatively in terms of a dissipative transport process involving the paracellular pathway (23, 24, 42, 43, 50–52, 75). The notion that anion transport processes involve a passive paracellular pathway in mammalian proximal convoluted tubules as well is supported by the observations of Burg & Green (10), who found that the rate of fluid absorption in isolated rabbit convoluted tubules was unaffected when Cl^- in both external solutions was replaced by either nitrate or perchlorate.

On the other hand, there is evidence that, in aquatic and amphibian species, electroneutral NaCl transport may occur across apical membranes. Such a transport event has been implicated in the shark rectal gland (58) and in the flounder small intestine (17); in both of these tissues, the diuretic furosemide may inhibit the process (17, 58). Similarly, Spring & Kimura (61) have suggested a coupled, electroneutral NaCl entry step across apical membranes of *Necturus* proximal tubule, since in that tissue the rate of apical $^{36}Cl^-$ entry into the cellular compartment parallels that for Na^+.

Evidence for a neutral NaCl entry step across apical membranes of mammalian proximal tubules derives largely from analyses of the effects of furosemide or neutral anion-transport inhibitors (32) such as 4-acetamido-4'-isothiocyano-stilbene-2,2'-disulfonic acid (SITS) on rates of fluid absorption. Radtke et al (44) found that 1 mM luminal furosemide inhibited 22% of fluid absorption in rat proximal convolutions in vivo, and attributed this effect to carbonic anhydrase inhibition. But more recently, Lucci et al (36) found that 3.0 mM furosemide inhibited fluid absorption from in vivo rat proximal convolutions to a greater degree than 1.0 mM acetazolamide.

Likewise, Warnock & Lucci (73) found that 3.0 mM furosemide, added both to luminal and peritubular media, produced a 60% inhibition of fluid absorption in rabbit proximal straight tubules in vitro, and either 3 mM furosemide or 0.1 mM SITS also produced a 60% inhibition of net volume absorption when present in the lumen of rat proximal convoluted tubule perfused in vivo.

These investigators (36, 73) have interpreted their findings to indicate the presence of a neutral NaCl luminal-membrane transport system in mammalian proximal tubules that is sensitive to furosemide and similar to that proposed for the small intestine by Frizzell et al (17) and Nellans et al (41). However, two other possibilities could account for the furosemide effect in mammalian proximal tubules: carbonic anhydrase inhibition, and/or inhibition of neutral anion exchange in basolateral membranes by high luminal concentrations of the diuretic.

It is interesting to note in this regard that Ullrich et al (68) found no effect of SITS on fluid absorption in the rat proximal tubule, and moderate inhibition of fluid absorption by SITS in the golden hamster proximal nephron (66, 67). In the latter species, Ullrich et al (66, 67) also found that SITS dramatically inhibited net proton secretion. Since SITS was effective only when added to the peritubular capillary perfusate, these investigators concluded that the agent blocked HCO_3^- exit across basolateral membranes and consequently inhibited Na^+/H^+ antiport at the luminal membrane (66, 67). Obviously, this question requires careful examination and future investigation.

Literature Cited

1. Anagnostopoulos, T. 1973. Bi-ionic potentials in the proximal tubule of *Necturus* kidney. *J. Physiol. London* 233:375–94
2. Anagnostopoulos, T., Velu, E. 1974. Electrical resistance of cell membranes in *Necturus* kidney. *Pfluegers Arch.* 346:327–39
3. Asterita, M. F., Boulpaep, E. L. 1975. Ion selectivity of the paracellular pathway in *Necturus* proximal tubule. *Biophys. J.* 15:228a
4. Baker, P. F., Hodgkin, A. L., Meves, H. 1964. The effect of diluting the internal solution on the external properties of a perfused squid axon. *J. Physiol. London* 170:541–60
5. Barratt, L. J., Rector, F. C., Kokko, J. P., Seldin, D. W. 1974. Factors governing the transepithelial potential difference across the proximal tubule of the rat kidney. *J. Clin. Invest.* 53:454–64

6. Barry, P. H., Diamond, J. M. 1971. A theory of ion permeation through membranes with fixed neutral sites. *J. Memb. Biol.* 4:295–330
7. Berry, C. A., Warnock, D. G., Rector, F. C. 1978. Bicarbonate induced changes in transcellular current flow across proximal convoluted tubules (PCT). *Fed. Proc.* 37:727 (Abstr.)
8. Boulpaep, E. L. 1967. Ion permeability of the peritubular and luminal membrane of the renal tubular cell. In *Transport und Funktion Intercellulärer Elecktrolyte,* ed. F. Krück, pp. 98–125. Munich: Urban and Schwarzenberg
9. Boulpaep, E. L., Seely, J. F. 1971. Electrophysiology of proximal and distal tubules in the autoperfused dog kidney. *Am. J. Physiol.* 221:1084–96
10. Burg, M. B., Green, N. 1976. Role of monovalent ions in the reabsorption of fluid by isolated perfused proximal re-

nal tubules of the rabbit. *Kidney Int.* 10:221–28
11. Burg, M. B., Patlak, C., Green, N., Villey, D. 1976. Organic solutes in fluid absorption by renal proximal convoluted tubules. *Am. J. Physiol.*
12. Chonko, A. M., Osgood, R. W., Nickel, A. E., Ferris, T. F., Stein, J. H. 1975. The measurement of nephron filtration rate and absolute reabsorption in the proximal tubule of the rabbit kidney. *J. Clin. Invest.* 56:232–35
13. Clapp, J. R., Watson, J. F., Berliner, R. W. 1963. Osmolality, bicarbonate concentration, and water reabsorption in proximal tubule of the dog nephron. *Am. J. Physiol.* 205:273–80
14. De Mello, G. B., Lopes, A. G., Malnic, G. 1976. Conductances, diffusion and streaming potentials in the rat proximal tubule. *J. Physiol. London* 260:553–69
15. Evers, J., Murer, H., Kinne, R. 1976. Phenylalanine uptake in isolated renal brush border vesicles. *Biochim. Biophys. Acta* 426:598–615
16. Frizzell, R. A., Schultz, S. G. 1972. Ionic conductances of extracellular shunt pathway in rabbit ileum. Influence of shunt on transmural sodium transport and electrical potential differences. *J. Gen. Physiol.* 59:318–46
17. Frizzell, R. A., Smith, P. L., Field, M. 1978. Coupled NaCl influx across brush border of flounder intestine. *Fed. Proc.* 37:513 (Abstr.)
18. Frömter, E. 1974. Electrophysiology and isotonic fluid absorption of proximal tubules of mammalian kidney. In *MTP International Review of Science. Kidney and Urinary Tract Physiology,* ed. A. C. Guyton, K. Thurau, 6:1–38. London: Butterworths
19. Frömter, E., Diamond, J. 1972. Route of passive ion permeation in epithelia. *Nature New Biol.* 235:9–13
20. Frömter, E., Gessner, K. 1974. Free-flow potential profile along rat kidney proximal tubule. *Pfluegers Arch.* 351:69–83
21. Frömter, E., Gessner, K. 1974. Active transport potentials, membrane diffusion potentials and streaming potentials across rat kidney proximal tubule. *Pfluegers Arch.* 351:85–98
22. Frömter, E., Muller, C. W., Wick, T. 1970. Permeability properties of the proximal tubular epithelium of the rat kidney studied with electrophysiological methods. In *Electrophysiology of Epithelial Cells,* ed. G. Giebisch, pp. 119–42. Stuttgart: Schattauer

23. Frömter, E., Rumrick, G., Ullrich, K. J. 1973. Phenomenologic description of Na^+, Cl^- and HCO_3^- absorption from proximal tubules of the rat kidney. *Pfleugers Arch.* 343:189–220
24. Fujimoto, M., Kubota, T., Kotera, K. 1977. Electrochemical profile of K and Cl ions across the proximal tubule of bullfrog kidneys: a study using double-barreled ion-sensitive microelectrodes. *Contrib. Nephrol.* 6:114–23
25. Giebisch, G. 1968. Some electrical properties of single renal tubule cells. *J. Gen. Physiol.* 51:315a
26. Gottschalk, C. W., Lassiter, W., Mylle, M. 1960. Localization of urine acidification in the mammalian kidney. *Am. J. Physiol.* 198:581–85
27. Green, R., Giebisch, G. 1975. Ionic requirements of proximal tubular sodium transport. I. Bicarbonate and chloride. *Am. J. Physiol.* 229:1205–15
28. Hoski, T., Sakai, F. 1967. A comparison of the electrical resistance of the surface cell membrane and cellular wall in the proximal tubule of the newt kidney. *Jpn. J. Physiol.* 17:627–37
29. Jacobson, H. R., Kokko, J. P. 1976. Intrinsic differences in various segments of the proximal convoluted tubule. *J. Clin. Invest.* 57:818–25
30. Kawamura, S., Imai, M., Seldin, D. W., Kokko, J. P. 1975. Characteristics of salt and water transport in superficial and juxtamedullary straight segments of proximal tubules. *J. Clin. Invest.* 55:1269–77
31. Kinne, R., Murer, H., Kinne-Saffran, E., Thees, M., Sachs, G. 1975. Sugar transport by renal plasma membrane vesicles. Characterization of the systems in the brush border microvillae and basal-lateral plasma membranes. *J. Memb. Biol.* 21:375–95
32. Knauf, P. A., Rothstein, A. 1971. Chemical modification of membranes. I. Effects of sulfhydryl and amino reactive reagents on anion and cation permeability of human red blood cell. *J. Gen. Physiol.* 58:190–210
33. Koefoed-Johnsen, V., Ussing, H. H. 1958. The nature of the frog skin potential. *Acta Physiol. Scand.* 42:298–308
34. Kokko, J. P., Burg, M. B., Orloff, J. 1971. Characteristics of NaCl and water transport in the renal proximal tubule. *J. Clin. Invest.* 50:69–76
35. Kyte, J. 1976. Immunoferritin determination of the distribution of (Na^+ and K^+) ATPase over the plasma membranes of renal convoluted tubules. II.

226 SCHAFER & ANDREOLI

Proximal segment. *J. Cell Biol.* 68: 304–18
36. Lucci, M. S., Rector, F. C., Warnock, D. G. 1977. Dual effects of diuretics on volume reabsorption by the proximal tubule. *Kidney Int.* 12:566 (Abstr.)
37. Lutz, M. D., Cardinal, J., Burg, M. B. 1973. Electrical resistance of renal proximal tubule perfused in vitro. *Am. J. Physiol.* 225:729–34
38. Malnic, G., Enokibara, H., Aires, M. M., Vieira, F. L. 1969. Die Wirkung von Furosemid und NaCl-Belastung auf die Chloridausscheidung im Einzelnephron der Rattenniere. *Pfluegers Arch.* 309:21–27
39. Maunsbach, A. B. 1966. Observations on the segmentation of the proximal tubule in the rat kidney. Comparison of results from phase contrast, fluorescence and electron microscopy. *J. Ultrastr. Res.* 16:239–58
40. Murer, M., Hopfer, U., Kinne, R. 1976. Sodium/proton antiport in brush-border-membrane vesicles isolated from rat small intestine and kidney. *Biochem. J.* 154:597–604
41. Nellans, H. N., Frizzell, R. A., Schultz, S. G. 1973. Coupled sodium-chloride influx across the brush border of rabbit ileum. *Am. J. Physiol.* 225:467–75
42. Neumann, K. H., Rector, F. C. 1976. Mechanism of NaCl and water reabsorption in the proximal convoluted tubule of rat kidney. *J. Clin. Invest.* 58:1110–18
43. Proverbio, F., Whittembury, G. 1975. Cell electrical potentials during enhanced Na⁺ extrusion in guinea pig kidney cortex slices. *J. Physiol. London* 250:559–78
44. Radtke, H. W., Rumrich, G., Kinne-Saffran, E., Ullrich, K. J. 1972. Dual action of acetazolamide and furosemide on proximal volume absorption in the rat kidney. *Kidney Int.* 1:100–5
45. Rector, F. C. Jr. 1976. Renal acidification and ammonia production; chemistry of weak acids and bases. In *The Kidney,* ed. F. C. Rector, B. Brenner, pp. 318–43. Philadelphia: Saunders
46. Rector, F. C., Carter, N. W., Seldin, D. W. 1965. The mechanism of bicarbonate reabsorption in the proximal and distal tubules of the kidney. *J. Clin. Invest.* 44:278–90
47. Rector, F. C., Martinez-Maldonado, M., Brunner, F. P., Seldin, D. W. 1966. Evidence for passive reabsorption of NaCl in proximal tubule of rat kidney. *J. Clin. Invest.* 45:1060 (Abstr.)

48. Sandblom, J. P., Eisenman, G. 1967. Membrane potentials at zero current. The significance of a constant ionic permeability ratio. *Biophys. J.* 7:217–42
49. Schafer, J. A., Andreoli, T. E. 1976. Anion transport processes in the mammalian superficial proximal straight tubule. *J. Clin. Invest.* 58:500–13
50. Schafer, J. A., Patlak, C. S., Andreoli, T. E. 1975. A component of fluid absorption linked to passive ion flows in the superficial pars recta. *J. Gen. Physiol.* 66:445–71
51. Schafer, J. A., Patlak, C. S., Andreoli, T. E. 1977. Fluid absorption and active and passive ion flows in the rabbit superficial pars recta. *Am. J. Physiol.* 233:F154–67
52. Schafer, J. A., Troutman, S. L., Andreoli, T. E. 1974. Volume reabsorption, transepithelial potential differences, and ionic permeability properties in mammalian superficial proximal straight tubules. *J. Gen. Physiol.* 64:582–607
53. Schafer, J. A., Troutman, S. L., Watkins, M. L., Andreoli, T. E. 1978. Volume absorption in the pars recta. I. "Simple" active Na⁺ transport. *Am. J. Physiol.* 234:F332–39
54. Schatzman, H. J., Windhager, E. E., Solomon, A. K. 1958. Single proximal tubules of the *Necturus* kidney. II. Effect of 2,4 dinitrophenol and ouabain on water reabsorption. *Am. J. Physiol.* 195:570–74
55. Schmidt, U., Dubach, U. S. 1969. Activity of (Na⁺-K⁺)-stimulated adenosine-triphosphotase in the rat nephron. *Pfluegers Arch.* 306:219–26
56. Schultz, S. G., Frizzell, R. A., Nellans, H. N. 1974. Ion transport by mammalian small intestine. *Ann. Rev. Physiol.* 36:51–91
57. Seely, J. F., Chirito, E. 1975. Studies of the electrical potential difference in the rat proximal tubule. *Am. J. Physiol.* 229:72–80
58. Silva, P., Stoff, J., Field, M., Fine, L., Forrest, J. N., Epstein, F. H. 1977. Mechanism of active chloride secretion by shark rectal gland: role of Na-K-ATPase in chloride transport. *Am. J. Physiol.* 233:F298–F306
59. Slack, E. N., Liang, C.-C. T., Sacktor, B. 1977. Transport of L-proline and D-glucose in luminal (brush border) and contraluminal (basal-lateral) membrane vesicles from the renal cortex. *Biochem. Biophys. Res. Commun.* 77:891–97
60. Spring, K. R., Giebisch, G. 1977. Kinetics of Na⁺ transport in *Necturus*

proximal tubule. *J. Gen. Physiol.* 70:307–28

61. Spring, K. R., Kimura, G. 1978. Tracer Cl fluxes in *Necturus* proximal tubule. *Fed. Proc.* 37:727 (Abstr.)

62. Spring, K. R., Pagnelli, C. V. 1972. Sodium flux in *Necturus* proximal tubule under voltage clamp. *J. Gen. Physiol.* 60:181–201

63. Stroup, R. F., Weinman, E., Hayslett, J. P., Kashgarian, M. 1974. Effect of luminal permeability on net transport across amphibian proximal tubule. *Am. J. Physiol.* 226:1110–16

64. Teorell, T. 1953. Transport processes and electrical phenomena in ionic membranes. *Prog. Biophys. Biophys. Chem.* 3:305–69

65. Tisher, C. C., Yarger, W. E. 1973. Lanthanum permeability of the tight junction (zonula occludens) in the renal tubule of the rat. *Kidney Int.* 3:238–50

66. Ullrich, K. J., Capasso, G., Rumrich, G., Sato, K. 1977. Effect of p-chloromercuribenzoate (pCMB), ouabain and 4-acetamido-4'-isothiocyamatostilbene-2,2'-disulfonic acid (SITS) on proximal tubular transport processes. *Adv. Exp. Med. Biol.* 84:3–13

67. Ullrich, K. J., Caprasso, G., Rumrich, G., Papavassiliou, F., Klöss, S. 1977. Coupling between proximal tubular transport processes. Studies with ouabain, SITS and HCO₃⁻-free solutions. *Pfluegers Arch.* 368:245–52

68. Ullrich, K. J., Fasold, H., Klöss, S., Rumrich, G. 1973. Effect of SH-, NH₂- and COOH-site group reagents on the transport processes in the proximal convolution of the rat kidney. *Pfluegers Arch.* 344:51–68

69. Ussing, H. H. 1949. The active ion transport through the isolated frog skin in the light of tracer studies. *Acta Physiol. Scand.* 17:1–37

70. Ussing, H. H., Windhager, E. E. 1964. Nature of shunt path and active sodium transport path through frog skin epithelium. *Acta Physiol. Scand.* 61:484–504

71. Ussing, H. H., Zerahn, K. 1951. Active transport of sodium as the source of electric current in the short-circuited isolated frog skin. *Acta Physiol. Scand.* 23:110–27

72. Warnock, D. G., Burg, M. B. 1977. Urinary acidification: CO₂ transport by the rabbit proximal straight tubule. *Am. J. Physiol.* 232:F20–25

73. Warnock, D. G., Lucci, M. S. 1978. NaCl transport in the proximal tubule. *VII Int. Congr. Nephrol, Montreal,* p. C8

74. Welling, L. W., Welling, D. J. 1976. Shape of epithelial cells and intercellular channels in the rabbit proximal nephron. *Kidney Int.* 9:385–94

75. Whittembury, G., Diezi, F., Diezi, J., Spring, K., Giebisch, G. 1975. Some aspects of proximal tubular sodium chloride reabsorption in *Necturus* kidney. *Kidney Int.* 7:293–303

76. Windhager, E. E., Giebisch, G. 1961. Micropuncture study of renal tubular transfer of sodium chloride in the rat. *Am. J. Physiol.* 200:581–90

77. Woodhall, P. B., Tischer, C. C., Simonton, C. A., Robinson, R. R. 1978. Relationship between PAH secretion and cellular morphology in rabbit proximal tubules. *J. Clin. Invest.* 61:1320–29

Ann. Rev. Physiol. 1979. 41:229–40
Copyright © 1979 by Annual Reviews Inc. All rights reserved

RENAL NERVES AND SODIUM EXCRETION

♦1216

Carl W. Gottschalk

Career Investigator, American Heart Association; Department of Medicine and
Physiology, University of North Carolina School of Medicine, Chapel Hill,
North Carolina 27514

INTRODUCTION

Claude Bernard (9) in 1859 was the first to report that unilateral section of
the greater splanchnic nerve in the anesthetized dog resulted in the excretion by the affected kidney of an increased volume of urine with decreased
chloride concentration. These changes were reversible by electrical stimulation of the distal cut end of the nerve. Similar results, termed denervation
diuresis and natriuresis, have been reported repeatedly since the time of
Bernard. An increase in glomerular filtration rate (GFR) has often been
reported following acute denervation, and the increased salt and water
excretion have usually been interpreted as resulting from an increase in
filtered load. The few studies in unanesthetized animals have shown little
or no difference in the function of a unilaterally denervated kidney from that
of the opposite and innervated control kidney. Further, the clinical experience with kidney transplantation in humans has demonstrated that a totally
denervated kidney may provide adequate replacement of the individual's
own kidneys. Thus the prevailing view among renal physiologists has been
that the renal nerves have no important role in the regulation of renal
excretory function under normal conditions. According to this view, any
influences they might exert are present only under such stressful conditions
as anesthesia, surgery, or trauma; they are thus in the realm of pathophysiology, not physiology, and result from changes in renal hemodynamics.

More recent experimental studies, reviewed here, challenge this view.
The concept of a limited but important role of neural influences on renal
excretory function is part of a changing concept about the functional role
of the innervation of visceral organs in general. It is becoming clear that

229

0066-4278/79/0301-0229$01.00

although there may be no changes in basic physiological function following denervation, the adaptive and integrative functional responses of many visceral organs are compromised in the absence of neural mechanisms for exchange of information.

Homer Smith was adamant in his view that the renal nerves are unimportant in the regulation of renal excretory function under normal conditions. In his book *Physiology of the Kidney* (1937) Smith (28) concluded

> In view of the evidence presented by Verney and others it seems necessary to conclude that in the normal, unanesthetized animal renal denervation has no effect upon water excretion, or upon the more involved control thereof. "Denervation diuresis" appears to be a fallacious phenomenon. The long period experiments upon which its existence has been argued are so uncontrolled as to have no meaning, and the acute experiments have been complicated by the fact that the urine volume is very low and the urine very concentrated, due to anesthesia and other abnormal conditions (hemoconcentration, oligemia, et cetera); under these circumstances a transient diuresis may occur in consequence of changes in blood flow, glomerular activity, et cetera. The phenomenon does not occur, nor does it have any bearing on the excretion of water, in the normal, unanesthetized animal.
>
> Several investigators have believed that they have demonstrated the existence of specific secretory fibers in connection with the urinary excretion of various substances other than water, but their experiments have been inadequately controlled and were performed without knowledge of the concomitant changes in blood flow, rate of filtration, etc. For the moment it may be said that substantial evidence of the neural control of either the tubular excretion or reabsorption of any urinary constituent is lacking.

Smith repeated these views in several subsequent publications (21, 29, 30). However, review of the older literature, including the important 1919 experiments of Marshall & Kolls (19), reveals many instances in which an increase in salt and water excretion followed acute renal denervation in anesthetized animals with no apparent change in filtered load of salt and water or renal blood flow. In other words, there has been a residuum of suggestive evidence for a tubular effect of the renal nerves on salt and water excretion.

Recent advances in anatomical knowledge of the distribution of nerve endings in the kidney places this in a different perspective. The rich sympathetic innervation to the kidney and its vasomotor function has been known and repeatedly confirmed since the studies of Bradford, published in 1889 (10). The occasional suggestions of innervation of tubular cells have been largely refuted or ignored. In 1972–73 Barajas & Müller presented for the first time electron microscopic and histochemical evidence for direct innervation of the tubular cells in the cortex of monkey and rat kidneys (1, 20). These investigators demonstrated adrenergic nerve terminals separated from the proximal and distal tubular cells only by basement membrane material. This is identical to the relationship observed between similar vesiculated varicosities and vascular smooth muscle, a site where synaptic transmission is thought to occur. Subsequently, DiBona demonstrated a similar adrenergic innervation of tubular cells in the cortex of the dog kidney (13). These morphological findings provide an anatomic basis for the conclusions of Gill (17) and Schrier & DeWardener (26) that the sympathetic nervous system has a direct effect on tubular sodium reabsorption, as well as for the recent clearance and/or micropuncture findings of Takacs, Benscath, and colleagues (6–8, 32–37), DiBona and colleagues (13–15, 27, 41–43), and those reported from the Chapel Hill Micropuncture Laboratory (3–5, 31).

MICROPUNCTURE AND CLEARANCE EXPERIMENTS

The micropuncture studies of the effects of acute denervation on excretory function performed by Bencsath, Takacs, and associates are in remarkably good agreement with those performed in the Chapel Hill Micropuncture Laboratory. Bencsath, Bonvalet & de Rouffignac (6) were the first to demonstrate by micropuncture a decreased proximal reabsorption of salt and water without change in single nephron (SN) GFR following acute renal denervation by section of the left major splanchnic nerve. In our laboratory Bello-Reuss et al (3) characterized the renal response to acute unilateral renal denervation in an extensive study of sham-denervated and denervated kidneys. Denervation of the left kidney was accomplished by stripping the left renal artery of its adventitia and coating it with a solution of 10% phenol in alcohol. For a variety of reasons the changes observed cannot be attributed to a direct effect of phenol on kidney function: No norepinephrine could be detected in the kidneys several days after denervation; incomplete denervation from splanchnic nerve crushing produced similar but quantitatively smaller effects than the apparently complete chemical denervation, and these effects were reversible by electrical stimulation of the distal end of the splanchnic nerve; coating the artery with lidocaine instead of phenol produced similar, but in this case transitory, effects; and injection of minute amounts of phenol into the renal artery resulted in immediate collapse of the surface tubules, an effect never seen after denervation.

No changes were observed in any function of either kidney of sham-denervated rats. In hydropenic animals urine volume from the denervated kidney increased to about twice its control value, and urinary sodium excretion increased from 332 neq min^{-1} to 1887 neq min^{-1}. There was no change in urine volume or sodium excretion from the innervated right kidney. Glomerular filtration rate (GFR) and renal plasma flow (RPF) remained unchanged in both kidneys after the procedure. After denervation SNGFR remained unchanged. The fluid-to-plasma ratio of inulin decreased from 2.23 to 1.50 (p<0.001) in samples of fluid collected from late proximal tubules of denervated kidneys. Water reabsorption by the proximal tubule decreased from 16.5 to 9.9 nl min^{-1}. F/P inulin ratios were also decreased (6.21 to 3.2) in samples of fluid from early distal and late distal convolutions (16.4 to 8.3) following denervation. The F/P sodium concentration remained unchanged in fluid from early distal convolutions but increased from 0.18 to 0.38 in fluid from late distal convolutions after denervation. Absolute sodium reabsorption after denervation increased in the loop of Henle, distal convolution, and collecting ducts.

Denervation caused no change in estimated glomerular capillary or efferent arteriolar pressure. There were slight increases in hydrostatic pressure in proximal and distal convolutions and in small peritubular capillaries. These increases in pressure were very small; since the intratubular pressure increased more than the peritubular capillary pressure, it is likely that they resulted from the increased tubular flow rate caused by reduction of tubular reabsorption and were not its cause. One might expect that the increased tubular-capillary pressure gradient would tend to increase rather than decrease proximal tubular reabsorption, although the important variable of the renal interstitial pressure remains unknown. Just as there was no change in whole kidney GFR there was no change in single nephron GFR after denervation or sham-denervation. Since there was no change in whole kidney or single nephron GFR and renal plasma flow was unchanged, it is unlikely that there was a change in overall or superficial nephron colloid osmotic pressure or significant redistribution of renal blood flow. It thus appears that the physical factors did not play an important role in the observed changes in tubular reabsorption.

Similar results were observed in animals expanded 10% above their body weight by the infusion of isotonic saline solution (4). There was no change in GFR or RPF in either kidney after unilateral denervation or sham denervation. Urine flow from denervated kidneys increased from 35.2 to 59.2 μl min^{-1} and urinary sodium excretion from 6.9 to 11.8 μeq min^{-1}. The contralateral innervated kidneys showed a simultaneous 45% decrease in urine flow and sodium excretion, so that there was little change in total salt and water excretion. After denervation SNGFR remained unchanged. The F/P inulin ratio in fluid from late proximal tubules decreased from 1.5 to 1.24. The F/P inulin ratio decreased from 3.9 to 2.7 in early distal and from 5.5 to 3.8 in late distal samples. Absolute water reabsorption in the proximal tubule was reduced from 14.7 to 6.4 nl min^{-1} corresponding to a reduction of fractional water reabsorption from 32 to 18%. Absolute sodium reabsorption increased after denervation in the loop of Henle, distal convolution, and collecting ducts.

In another series (3) of experiments in anesthetized volume-expanded rats the natriuresis and diuresis resulting from unilateral crushing of the greater splanchnic nerve was reversed by electrical stimulation of the distal portion of the cut nerve with square wave pulses of 0.5 msec duration, voltage twice threshold, and 1 or 2 Hz frequency. Kidney GFR and RPF and SNGFR remained unchanged during stimulation. Nerve stimulation produced a reduction of approximately 25% in urine flow and sodium excretion due to increased water reabsorption in the proximal tubule. In all animals but one, stimulation at 1 Hz was followed by an increase in proximal F/P inulin ratio, mean values increasing from 1.61 to 1.92. In the one animal in which there was no change in the proximal F/P inulin ratio there was also no consistent change in sodium excretion by the kidney. Apparently, and for unknown reasons, the appropriate fibers were not stimulated. On average the F/P inulin ratio fell after cessation of stimulation to 1.53, a value not significantly different from that in the control period. In all animals subsequent stimulation at 2 Hz sec^{-1} caused an increase in F/P inulin ratio to an average of 2.02. Recordings of the compound action potential of the stimulated nerves indicated that the effect of tubular reabsorption resulted from stimulation of slowly conducting unmyelinated C fibers.

In a small series of nondiuretic and volume-expanded rats Bencsath, Bonvalet & de Rouffignac (6) found no difference in total kidney GFR, SNGFR, or the ratio of superficial to juxtamedullary SNGFR in innervated and denervated kidneys. These data obviously indicate that the diuresis observed following acute denervation resulted from a decrease in tubular reabsorptive activity.

Recent studies both in Budapest and in Chapel Hill demonstrate that the denervation effect is not a transient one that is observed only immediately after denervation, since similar results were observed in chronically denervated kidneys. Takacs, Bencsath & Szalay (37) report that, in dogs in which the left major splanchnic nerve was crushed 3–4 weeks prior to experimentation, the typical denervation effect was observed when the animals were anesthetized with pentobarbital. In rats with unilateral chronic denervation, urine flow from the denervated kidney was increased (3.24 vs 1.79 μl min^{-1}, control kidney), and sodium excretion was enhanced (536 neq min^{-1} vs 162 neq min^{-1}, control kidney). GFR, SNGFR, and renal cortical blood flow determined with radioactive microspheres were the same in denervated and contralateral control kidneys. As after acute denervation, proximal reabsorption was greatly diminished (F/P inulin 1.73 vs 2.57, control kidney). Peritubular hydrostatic pressure and colloid osmotic pressure were no different in denervated and control kidneys.

Spielman, Colindres & Gottschalk (31) report differences between the function of innervated and denervated kidneys in anesthetized rats approximately 2 weeks after unilateral denervation. Urine flow and sodium excretion from the chronically denervated kidney was much greater than from the innervated kidney and resulted from a decrease in fractional and absolute reabsorption in the proximal tubule. Again there was no difference in GFR, RPF, or SNGFR between innervated and denervated kidneys.

Szalay, Bencsath & Takacs (33, 34, 35) have studied other proximal tubular transport systems in chronically denervated kidneys. Very interestingly, all solute systems studied were affected. The glucose threshold was lower and the glucose Tm was diminished in denervated kidneys, and Tm_{PAH} was depressed. There was a significant depression of tubular reabsorption of phosphate at all plasma phosphate levels studied. In dogs loaded with urate, transport rates were decreased on the denervated side at plasma urate levels up to 5 mg% (37). Thus it appears that there is substantial impairment of multiple proximal tubular active transport systems after renal denervation. This suggests that the transport mechanisms are directly affected.

Earlier studies by Szalay, Bencsath & Takacs (32) of the relation between renal sodium reabsorption and oxygen consumption led to the same conclusion. One to two weeks following unilateral splanchnicotomy in dogs, denervation diuresis and natriuresis were present without difference in RBF and GFR between intact and denervated kidneys. The ratio of total tubular reabsorption of sodium to oxygen consumption was no different on the intact and denervated sides before and after extracellular volume expansion with isotonic saline. Nor was the ratio different in innervated and denervated kidneys following administration of furosemide. Thus denervation appears to depress the active tubular transport of sodium without a primary change in cell membrane permeability.

MECHANISM OF NEURAL EFFECT

The denervation and nerve stimulation studies give little insight into whether the neural effect on the tubular transport systems is "direct" (due to the neurotransmitter or electrical events at the nerve ending) or "indirect" (secondary to an effect of change in nerve traffic on the renin-angiotensin, prostaglandin, kallikrein, or other humoral systems). If a humoral substance is involved it does not appear to gain access to the general circulation since a change in sodium excretion by opposite, intact kidneys is not observed.

The experiments of DiBona and colleagues not only give convincing evidence of an effect of renal nerve stimulation on sodium excretion, but also provide useful insight into the mechanism. In the dog they have demonstrated that direct low-level stimulation of the splanchnic nerve or reflex stimulation of high-pressure or low-pressure baroreceptors results in a reduction of sodium excretion without a change in the kidney's GFR or RPF; following cessation of stimulation, sodium excretion returned to control levels (12, 27, 42). Nor did the low-level renal nerve stimulation alter the intrarenal distribution of blood flow as assessed by the radioactive microsphere technique. Very clearly then, the change in sodium excretion results from a change in tubular reabsorption without a change in intrarenal hemodynamics. DiBona et al have established the adrenergic specificity of the antinatriuretic response to low-level electrical stimulation. In paired studies, phenoxybenzamine, an alpha-adrenergic receptor antagonist, or guanethidine, an adrenergic blocking agent, abolished a previously demonstrated antinatriuretic response to low-level nerve stimulation (27, 43).

Since renal nerve stimulation is known to cause release of renin and prostaglandins from the kidney, and since these substances might influence tubular sodium reabsorption, DiBona and colleagues have investigated whether the natriuresis resulting from nerve stimulation might be mediated by these humoral systems. There was no inhibition of the response to low-level nerve stimulation following the administration of Sar 1, Ala-8, angiotensin II, a competitive angiotensin II antagonist, or indomethacin (15, 41). Therefore the response does not appear to be mediated by the intrarenal action of circulating angiotensin II or prostaglandin.

Bencsath et al (7, 8) have demonstrated that the effects of renal nerve stimulation on tubular reabsorption of sodium can be dissociated from those on renin release. Thus their studies also support the concept that denervation natriuresis does not result from a change in activity of the renin-angiotensin system.

In a recent study of isolated tubule fragments from rabbit kidneys Bello-Reuss (2) has demonstrated that the addition of 10^{-6} M l-norepinephrine to the bathing solution results in an approximately 25% increase (1.25 ± 0.05 nl min^{-1} mm^{-1} before and 1.56 ± 0.09 nl min^{-1} mm^{-1} after) in net water reabsorption from perfused segments of proximal convoluted tubules. L-norepinephrine had no effect on isolated fragments of straight portions of the proximal pars recta. These data support the view that the effects observed following change in renal nerve activity are due to a direct effect on the proximal tubular cells of the neurotransmitter released at the nerve endings. Norepinephrine has been shown to stimulate active sodium transport across several isolated tight and leaky epithelia (38, 40).

Studies on isolated tubule fragments could provide information about the direct effect, if any, of norepinephrine and other neurotransmitters and antagonists on salt and water transport in the more distal parts of the nephron. These determinations by in vivo micropuncture studies are difficult because of the inherent responsiveness of tubular salt transport to changes in tubular flow rate.

FUNCTIONAL SIGNIFICANCE

Efferent Nerve Traffic

Although the effect of efferent nerve stimulation on proximal tubular transport of salt, water, and other solutes is now firmly established, its overall significance remains to be elucidated. In theory, the neural pathway provides a rapidly responsive mechanism for regulation of salt and water balance, perhaps on a short-term basis. It may be complementary, for example, to the more slowly activated longer-term salt and water regulation mediated by the renin-aldosterone system or other mechanisms. The circumstances under which the neural mechanism is activated remain to be defined, including a determination of whether they are physiological or pathophysiological. In anesthetized animals, reduced renal sympathetic activity has been observed during distention of the pulmonary vein–left atrial junction or atrium and during intravascular volume expansion (12, 14, 16, 18, 24, 39). Additional studies are specifically required in unanesthetized animals to determine if any efferent renal nerve traffic directly affects sodium excretion under "normal" conditions. Schad & Seller (25) report a decrease in efferent renal sympathetic activity in conscious cats following volume expansion with dextran or isotonic saline solution and suggest this is involved in the renal response to volume expansion. DiBona (13) has discussed possible clinical implications in human disease.

We have been quite interested in the possibility that compensatory adaptive excretory responses of one kidney to changes in excretion by the other kidney are neurally mediated. Many observers have reported that shortly after urine excretion from one kidney is reduced or abolished by such maneuvers as arterial, venous, or ureteral obstruction or uninephrectomy there is an adaptive increase in salt and water excretion by the contralateral kidney. Peters (22) demonstrated that this immediate adaptive response is due to a decrease in fractional salt and water reabsorption with unchanged GFR and RBF and does not depend upon any hemodynamic change such as may occur later. Similar events occur after acute denervation.

Directionally opposite changes were observed in the innervated kidneys following acute unilateral denervation in our studies in volume-expanded rats (4). Coincident with the increase in salt and water excretion by the denervated kidney there was an almost equal decrease in salt and water excretion by the contralateral innervated kidney. There was no measurable change in GFR or RPF in either kidney. In theory the increased fractional reabsorption of salt and water in the contralateral innervated kidney could have resulted from an increase in efferent nerve impulses. To test this hypothesis one kidney was denervated and the rats were studied under pentobarbital anesthesia 2 weeks later during volume expansion (31). Urine flow and sodium excretion from the chronically denervated kidney was much greater than from the innervated kidney. The intact kidney was then acutely denervated. In all instances this led to an increase in salt and water excretion without change in GFR or RPF by the acutely denervated kidney. However, there was no decrease in salt and water excretion by the chronically denervated kidney. This is in sharp contrast to the response of a contralateral innervated kidney.

These results suggest that compensatory adaptive changes in salt and water excretion may involve the renal nerves. Direct recording of renal nerve activity will be required for a definitive answer. We believe this is a potentially important area for further research since adaptive changes in excretory activity are important in maintaining homeostasis in a variety of circumstances. The possibility also exists of an ipsilateral renal reflex.

Afferent Nerve Traffic

The functional significance of the afferent signals that originate from the kidney also requires elucidation. There is strong suggestive evidence that they are involved in cardiovascular regulation (11).

For some time it has been known that there are mechanoreceptors in the kidney that give rise to afferent impulses when stimulated by increases in intrarenal pressure. Recent studies in our laboratory by Recordati, Moss & Waselkov (23) have demonstrated another set of renal receptors that have characteristics of chemoreceptors and that are clearly different from the known mechanoreceptors. These receptors are activated during conditions of markedly impaired renal blood flow such as are produced by clamping of the renal artery, severe hypotension, prolonged renal venous occlusion, or systemic asphyxia. They are not responsive to increases or decreases of arterial pressure or to increases in ureteral or renal venous pressure. The presumed chemical agent(s) responsible for this stimulation has not yet been identified. Recordati & Moss (personal communication) also report the stimulation of afferent impulses from the kidney by intrapelvic perfusion of solutions of selective chemical composition, independent of changes in intrapelvic pressure. The physiological significance of these receptors remains to be determined. The most likely possibilities include participation in cardiovascular reflexes and reno-renal regulation.

CONCLUSION

Recent investigations in several laboratories demonstrate that efferent renal nerve stimuli can cause an increase in salt and water reabsorption and can also affect certain other transport systems in the proximal tubule; any change in GFR that might occur concurrently will only magnify the effects.

The precise mechanism of the tubular effect remains uncertain, but it appears to result from a direct action of the neurotransmitter on the transport systems and does not involve the physical or circulating humoral factors that affect transport. The effect of denervation is not transient but lasts for weeks; it is reversible by nerve stimulation. Additional studies are needed in the absence of the stresses of anesthesia and surgery to further define the circumstances under which these effects occur. There is suggestive evidence that adaptive changes in function of one kidney following change in function of the contralateral kidney may be neurally mediated. The nature and role of the afferent signals that originate from the kidney also require further elucidation, including a determination of the functional significance of the recently described chemoreceptors.

ACKNOWLEDGMENT

The research of the author described in this article was supported by a Grant-in-Aid from the American Heart Association and by National Institutes of Health Grants HLB-02334 and NS-11132.

Literature Cited

1. Barajas, L., Müller, J. 1973. The innervation of the juxtaglomerular apparatus and surrounding tubules: A quantitative analysis by serial section electron microscopy. *J. Ultrastruct. Res.* 43: 107–32
2. Bello-Reuss, E. 1978. The effect of L-norepinephrine on water reabsorption in isolated perfused proximal tubules. *Proc. Fifth Int. Soc. Hypertension, Paris, June 1978* Abstr.)
3. Bello-Reuss, E., Colindres, R. E., Pastoriza-Munoz, E., Mueller, R. A., Gottschalk, C. W. 1975. Effects of acute unilateral renal denervation in the rat. *J. Clin. Invest.* 56:208–17
4. Bello-Reuss, E., Pastoriza-Munoz, E., Colindres, R. E. 1977. Acute unilateral renal denervation in rats with extracellular volume expansion. *Am. J. Physiol.* 232:F26–32
5. Bello-Reuss, E., Trevino, D. L., Gottschalk, C. W. 1976. Effect of renal sympathetic nerve stimulation on proximal water and sodium reabsorption. *J. Clin. Invest.* 57:1104–7
6. Bencsath, P., Bonvalet, J.-P., de Rouffignac, C. 1972. Tubular factors in

denervation diuresis and natriuresis. In *Recent Advances in Renal Physiology. International Symposium on Renal Handling of Sodium,* ed. H. Wirz, F. Spinelli, pp. 96–106. Basel: Karger
7. Bencsath, P., Szalay, L., Debreczeni, L. A., Takacs, L. A., Vajda, L., Fischer, A. 1972. Denervation diuresis and renin secretion in the anaesthetized dog. *Eur. J. Clin. Invest.* 2:422–25
8. Bencsath, P., Szalay, L., Takacs, L. 1976. Natriuresis and renin release by the denervated dog kidney during furosemide administration. *Eur. J. Clin. Invest.* 6:445–48
9. Bernard, C. 1859. *Leçons sur les Proprietes Physiologique des Liquides de l'Organisme.* Paris: Bailliere. pp. 172–73
10. Bradford, J. R. 1889. The innervation of the renal blood vessels. *J. Physiol.* 10:358–407
11. Calaresu, F. R., Stella, A., Zanchetti, A. 1976. Haemodynamic responses and renin release during stimulation of afferent renal nerves in the cat. *J. Physiol.* 255:687–700

12. Clement, D. L., Pelletier, C. L., Shepherd, J. T. 1972. Role of vagal afferents in the control of renal sympathetic nerve activity in the rabbit. *Circ. Res.* 31:824–30

13. DiBona, G. F. 1977. Neurogenic regulation of renal tubular sodium reabsorption. *Am. J. Physiol.* 233:F73–81

14. DiBona, G. F. 1978. Neural control of renal tubular sodium reabsorption in the dog. *Fed. Proc.* 37:1214–17

15. DiBona, G. F., Zambraski, E. J., Aquilera, A. J. Kaloyanides, G. J. 1977. Neurogenic control of renal tubular sodium reabsorption in the dog. *Circ. Res.* 40: (Suppl. I) I-127–30

16. Dieter, E. 1960. Der Einfluss der Kreislauffüllung auf die Aktivität der Nierennerven beim Frosch. *Pfluegers Arch.* 270:215–26

17. Gill, J. R. 1969. The role of the sympathetic nervous system in the regulation of sodium excretion by the kidney. In *Frontiers in Neuroendocrinology.* ed. W. F. Ganong, L. Martini, p. 289. London/Toronto: Oxford Univ. Press

18. Karim, F., Kidd, C., Malpus, C. M., Penna, P. E. 1972. The effects of stimulation of the left atrial receptors on sympathetic efferent nerve activity. *J. Physiol.* 227:243–60

19. Marshall, E. K. Jr., Kolls, A. C. 1919. Studies on the nervous control of the kidney in relation to diuresis and urinary secretion. I. The effect of unilateral excision of the adrenal, section of the splanchnic nerve and section of the renal nerves on the secretion of the kidney. *Am. J. Physiol.* 49:302–16

20. Müller, J., Barajas, L. 1972. Electron microscopic and histochemical evidence for a tubular innervation in the renal cortex of the monkey. *J. Ultrastruct. Res.* 41:533–49

21. Page, L. B., Baxter, C. F., Reem, G. H., Scott-Baker, J. C., Smith, H. W. 1954. Effect of unilateral splanchnic nerve resection on the renal excretion of sodium. *Am. J. Physiol.* 177:194–200

22. Peters, G. 1963. Compensatory adaptation of renal functions in the unanesthetized rat. *Am. J. Physiol.* 205:1042–48

23. Recordati, G. M., Moss, N. G., Waselkov, L. 1978. Renal chemoreceptors in the rat. *Circ. Res.* 43. In press

24. Recordati, G. M., Spielman, W. S. 1977. Effects of fluid volume expansion on renal sympathetic efferent nerve activity in the rat. *Fed. Proc.* 36:487

25. Schad, H., Seller, H. 1976. Reduction of renal nerve activity by volume expansion in conscious cats. *Pfluegers Arch.* 363:155–59

26. Schrier, R. W., De Wardener, H. E. 1971. Tubular reabsorption of sodium ion: Influence of factors other than aldosterone and glomerular filtration rate. *N. Engl. J. Med.* 285:1231–43

27. Slick, G. L., Aquilera, A. J., Zambraski, E. J., DiBona, G. F., Kaloyanides, G. J. 1975. Renal neuroadrenergic transmission. *Am. J. Physiol.* 229:60–65

28. Smith, H. W. 1937. *The Physiology of the Kidney.* New York: Oxford Univ. Press. pp. 245–46

29. Smith, H. W. 1939–40. Physiology of the renal circulation. *Harvey Lect.,* Ser. 35:166–222

30. Smith, H. W., Rovenstine, E. A., Goldring, W., Chasis, H., Ranges, H. A. 1939. The effects of spinal anesthesia on the circulation in normal, unoperated man with reference to the autonomy of the arterioles, and especially those of the renal circulation. *J. Clin. Invest.* 18:319–41

31. Spielman, W. S., Colindres, R. E., Gottschalk, C. W. 1978. Role of the renal nerves in the adaptive response of the kidney to contralateral renal denervation. *Abstr. VIIth Int. Congr. Nephrol., Montreal, June 1978,* p. C-11

32. Szalay, L., Bencsath, P., Takacs, L. 1974. Renal sodium reabsorption and oxygen consumption after unilateral splanchnicotomy in the dog. *Pfluegers Arch.* 349:359–67

33. Szalay, L., Bencsath, P., Takacs, L. 1977. Effect of splanchnicotomy on the renal excretion of inorganic phosphate in the anaesthetized dog. *Pfluegers Arch.* 367:283–86

34. Szalay, L., Bencsath, P., Takacs, L. 1977. Effect of spanchnicotomy on the renal excretion of para-aminohippuric acid in the anaesthetized dog. *Pfluegers Arch.* 367:287–90

35. Szalay, L., Bencsath, P., Takacs, L. 1977. Effect of splanchnicotomy on the renal excretion of d-glucose in the anaesthetized dog. *Pfluegers Arch.* 369:79–84

36. Takacs, L., Bencsath, P., Demeczky, L. 1971. Renal sodium and water excretion after unilateral splanchnicotomy in the dog. *Acta Physiol. Acad. Sci. Hung.* 39:283–91

37. Takacs, L., Bencsath, P., Szalay, L. 1978. Decreased proximal tubular transport capacity after renal sympathectomy. *Proc. VIIth Int. Congr. Nephrol., Montreal, June 1978.* Basel: Karger. pp. 553–58

38. Tomlinson, R. W., Wood, A. W. 1976. Catecholamine-induced changes in ion transport in short-circuited frog skin and the effect of B-blockade. *J. Physiol.* 257:515–30

39. Weaver, L. C. 1977. Cardiopulmonary sympathetic afferent influences on renal nerve activity. *Am. J. Physiol.* 233: H592–99

40. Wood, A. W., Tomlinson, R. 1974. The effect of catecholamines on ion transport in the toad bladder. *Biochim. Biophys. Acta* 367:375–84

41. Zambraski, E. J., DiBona, G. F. 1976. Angiotensin II in antinatriuresis of low-level nerve stimulation. *Am. J. Physiol.* 231:1105–10

42. Zambraski, E. J., DiBona, G. F., Kaloyanides, G. J. 1976. Effect of sympathetic blocking agents on the antinatriuresis of reflex renal nerve stimulation. *J. Pharmacol. Exp. Ther.* 198: 464–72

43. Zambraski, E. J., DiBona, G. F., Kaloyanides, G. J. 1976. Specificity of neural effect on renal tubular sodium reabsorption. *Proc. Soc. Exp. Biol. Med.* 151:543–46

Ann. Rev. Physiol. 1979. 41:241–56

POTASSIUM TRANSPORT IN THE NEPHRON

♦1217

Gerhard Giebisch and Bruce Stanton

Department of Physiology, Yale University School of Medicine,
New Haven, Connecticut 06510

INTRODUCTION

This review focuses on recent studies of single mammalian and amphibian tubules that aim at a delineation both of potassium transport sites and of the electrochemical driving forces across the luminal and peritubular cell membranes that control potassium translocation.

TUBULAR SITES OF POTASSIUM TRANSPORT

Several reviews dealing with the topography of potassium transport and its physiology have appeared (13, 32–40, 42, 43, 61, 83, 100–102). A large body of experimental evidence supports the view that most of the filtered potassium is reabsorbed in the proximal tubule and the loop of Henle. The distal tubule, the collecting tubule, and the papillary collecting duct determine and control the rate of urinary potassium excretion. This control operation consists either of continued reabsorption of that small moiety of potassium that escapes proximal tubular reabsorption, or of secretion, from the peritubular fluid into the lumen, of variable amounts of potassium in response to specific stimuli.

Free-flow micropuncture studies in the amphibian (11, 98), rodent (4, 7, 22, 23, 58, 60, 62–65, 69, 74, 78–80, 103), canine (9), and monkey (8) kidney have demonstrated that the distal convoluted tubule, and to some extent tubular segments downstream from the distal tubule, are key sites of urinary potassium excretion. With some exceptions (to be noted) modifications of potassium transport across the proximal tubular epithelium are much less important in the regulation of renal potassium excretion.

241

Proximal Tubule

Micropuncture studies have firmly established that the accessible portion of the proximal tubule reabsorbs 50 to 70% of the filtered potassium (8, 9, 56, 63, 64). Potassium concentrations in proximal tubular fluid comprise a range of values close to the plasma potassium concentration (8, 9, 20, 55, 58–60, 63, 95). When the potassium activity was measured with potassium-sensitive liquid-ion-exchange microelectrodes, the potassium activity declined by 10% along the proximal tubule (55). Proximal tubular fluid samples have also been analyzed for potassium by electron microprobe X-ray analysis; both a small increase (by 10%) (59) and no change in concentration (6) between early and late proximal tubular collection sites have been reported.

Normally, the rate of reabsorption of potassium along the proximal convoluted tubule appears to be tightly coupled to that of sodium and water (6). Two notable exceptions occur after the administration of acetazolamide (6) and after unilateral nephrectomy (23). In both circumstances, proximal tubular potassium transfer may be regulated independently of sodium and sodium-dependent fluid transport.

Studies on proximal straight tubules by perfusion of isolated segments in vitro have shown net reabsorption of potassium (14), although at a significantly lower rate than across the proximal convoluted tubule.

Loop of Henle

Micropuncture of tubular fluid at the tip of the renal papilla in rodent kidneys has shown a sharp increase in potassium concentration as fluid passes from the end of the proximal convoluted tubule to the hairpin turn of the loop of Henle (5, 21, 52). Jamison and associates have explored this phenomenon in some detail. They observed that the amount of potassium at the hairpin turn of juxtamedullary nephrons may exceed the quantity of potassium filtered (5, 52). The moiety of potassium at the end of the descending limb of Henle's loop fell after addition of furosemide and amiloride but was increased after administration of a carbonic anhydrase inhibitor. Acute or chronic potassium loading also increased the amount of potassium at the end of the descending limb (5). Although the precise source of potassium secreted into the descending limb of Henle's loop is not fully clarified, both the ascending limb of Henle's loop and the medullary collecting ducts have been considered. Two points are noteworthy. First, it is possible that deep juxtamedullary nephrons, in which high potassium concentrations have been demonstrated, deliver a larger fraction of potassium into the early distal tubule than their superficial counterparts. A second point concerns the possible physiological significance of potassium secretion into Henle's loop of juxtamedullary nephrons. Since the terminal segments of the papillary collecting ducts are a site of potential potassium loss from the lumen (22, 51, 79, 80, 88), changes in the potassium concentration of the medullary interstitium could exercise a regulatory influence on transepithelial potassium transfer across the collecting duct. According to this view (5), a high interstitial potassium concentration would curtail diffusional loss from the collecting duct lumen and enhance potassium excretion. The observation that there is a good relationship between medullary interstitial potassium concentration and urinary excretion rate of potassium provides evidence supportive of this thesis. In the loop of Henle of superficial nephrons potassium is vigorously reabsorbed, reducing the amount reaching the early distal tubule to a few percent of the filtered load.

Distal Tubule, Collecting Tubule and Collecting Duct

Most of the regulation of renal potassium excretion takes place along the distal tubule, collecting tubule, and collecting duct. Notable exceptions to this are situations in which fluid and sodium reabsorption are reduced along the proximal tubule by osmotic diuresis (64, 77), extracellular volume expansion (56), and by proximally acting diuretics such as carbonic anhydrase inhibitors (6). Fluid and solute (chloride) reabsorption is also blocked in the thick ascending limb by loop diuretics such as furosemide, ethacrynic acid, and mercurial diuretics (14, 15). As a result of interference with "proximal" fluid, and of sodium and potassium reabsorption, a larger than normal amount of potassium enters the distal tubule. This moiety of potassium may contribute significantly to potassium excretion. Normally, however, the delivery of potassium ions to the early distal tubule is constant and varies between 5 and 10% of the filtered load despite as much as a fifty-fold augmentation of urinary potassium excretion. Therefore, the distal tubule and the collecting duct are the major source of urinary potassium.

The potassium concentration profile along the distal tubule is variable and has been defined in a wide variety of metabolic situations. Potassium concentration increases only moderately and at a rate commensurate with fluid reabsorption in rats on a low potassium (63, 66) or low sodium (74) intake. Potassium secretion may be absent under such conditions and even a moderate degree of net potassium reabsorption has been observed along the distal tubule during severe dietary potassium deprivation (24). Extensive potassium reabsorption also occurs along the distal tubule of *Amphiuma* kidney, which normally elaborates a hypotonic urine (98). Distal tubular potassium secretion can be sharply stimulated by administration of a high-K diet, by carbonic anhydrase inhibitors, or by an exogenous potassium load (66, 87, 103). Other factors that stimulate potassium secretion are acid-base disturbances, such as metabolic alkalosis (62), loop diuretics (24), and adrenal steroids (46). The delivery of increased amounts of fluid into the distal tubule also stimulates distal tubular potassium secretion and results in an augmentation of urinary potassium excretion associated with the elaboration of a sodium-rich urine (56, 57).

With some notable exceptions (4, 7), the amount of potassium secreted by the distal tubule may account for most of the potassium in the final urine. However, some evidence points to the collecting tubule as an additional site of potassium secretion. In rats during potassium adaptation resulting from the exposure to a low-sodium diet (74, 102, 103), or from dramatic reduction of total renal tissue (4, 7), potassium excretion has been found to be significantly augmented by potassium addition beyond superficial distal tubules. Collecting tubule potassium secretion, in these cases, was most dramatic after acute potassium loading. Papillectomy has been reported to impair the ability of rats to excrete an exogenous potassium load (27). This observation also supports the thesis that the collecting duct participates in potassium secretion.

Several in vitro studies have drawn attention to the participation of the cortical collecting duct in the regulation of potassium excretion. Grantham et al (43) first established that isolated cortical collecting tubules actively secrete potassium. More recent investigations by O'Neil & Helman (45, 72) have shown that pretreatment of rabbits with desoxycorticosterone acetate (DOCA) leads to a marked increase in potassium secretion and sodium reabsorption. Furthermore, both amiloride and acidification of the luminal perfusion fluid (12, 90) have been shown to inhibit potassium secretion along cortical collecting tubules in vitro. Stimulation of renal ammonium excretion by infusion of glutamine has been associated with a curtailment of potassium secretion at tubular sites beyond the distal tubule (50).

Net reabsorption of potassium beyond the distal tubular epithelium can easily be demonstrated in the rat; however, it has not been reported in studies of isolated cortical collecting tubules of the rabbit. The comparison of late distal tubular fluid with urinary potassium content (62–64, 74, 79, 80, 88), as well as direct puncture of individual collecting ducts (51) in the rat, has clearly shown that potassium reabsorption is frequently present in the collecting duct. Potassium reabsorption beyond the distal tubule was most apparent in animals maintained on either a low-sodium or a low-potassium diet. Even in animals on a normal potassium intake, significant potassium reabsorption can take place at nephron sites beyond the distal tubule. Such potassium reabsorption is accentuated in hydropenic conditions but often disappears with the delivery of larger fractions of filtrate to the cortical collecting tubules (64, 78).

Reineck, Stein and their associates have compared the fractional delivery of potassium to the late distal tubule with that to the base and tip of the papillary collecting duct of rats after saline loading and amiloride administration (78–80, 88, 89). During saline diuresis they observed net secretion of potassium along the cortical collecting tubule even when significant potassium reabsorption occurred in the papillary collecting duct. Suppression of potassium secretion along cortical collecting tubules by amiloride was also reported (78, 79). From these studies it appears that potassium secretion along the distal tubule and cortical collecting tubule is followed by potassium reabsorption in the papillary collecting duct.

FACTORS AFFECTING THE RATE OF TUBULAR POTASSIUM TRANSFER

Dietary Potassium Intake

Dietary reduction or deletion of potassium leads to a prompt and dramatic fall of urinary potassium excretion (24, 63). Increased alimentary intake of potassium, or an intravenous potassium challenge, stimulate urinary potassium excretion (63, 64, 74, 80, 103). Both responses are due to changes in transepithelial potassium transport along the distal tubule and collecting duct (74, 87, 103).

Modifications of tubular potassium transport are seen after potassium adaptation. Potassium tolerance or adaptation, defined as the ability to survive otherwise lethal acute potassium loads, is produced by chronic potassium loading. The renal tubular response after chronic potassium loading is characterized by accelerated renal secretion of an exogenous potassium load (1, 86, 103). Exposure of a reduced number of nephrons to normal dietary potassium loads has also been shown to accelerate and augment renal secretion of potassium indistinguishable from the response of a normal adapted kidney to an acute potassium load (82, 84). The adaptive increase in potassium excretion in experimental chronic renal insufficiency in the dog occurs despite manipulation of sodium chloride excretion. This adaptive increase could not be related to changes in acid-base parameters or plasma potassium levels, and it occurred in the adrenalectomized state (84).

Distal Tubular Flow Rate, Sodium Delivery, and the Effects of Diuretics

Several reviews on renal potassium excretion have analyzed the critical role of sodium ions in the operation of distal tubule, collecting tubule and collecting duct potassium transport (32, 34, 35, 40, 42, 83, 100–102). Reduction of urinary sodium excretion by a low-sodium diet depressed urinary potassium excretion, mainly by stimulating potassium reabsorption beyond the late distal tubule (22, 64, 74). The potency of adrenal mineralocorticoids to augment potassium excretion also critically depends upon an adequate sodium intake (32, 35). When sodium intake was low, mineralocorticoids failed to stimulate potassium excretion. Again enhanced potassium reabsorption along post-distal tubular sites played a key role in blocking the kaliuresis otherwise observed after mineralocorticoid administration (64). It is possible that the low sodium concentration in the medullary and papillary collecting tubules either directly curtails carrier mediated sodium-potassium exchange (43), or indirectly blocks potassium secretions by lowering the lumen-negative transepithelial potential difference.

The relationship between distal tubular flow rate and luminal potassium concentration has attracted attention in view of the powerful stimulation of distal tubular potassium secretion by increased fluid and sodium delivery into the distal tubule (41, 50, 56, 57). A key observation is the relative insensitivity of distal luminal potassium concentration to changes in luminal flow rate. The potassium concentration in distal tubular samples under nondiuretic conditions is not significantly different from those during stop-flow conditions (63–65). In addition, potassium concentration is either not affected or only moderately reduced by as large as a ten-fold increment in tubular fluid flow rate achieved by the inhibition of sodium chloride and fluid transport upstream (56, 80), or by pump perfusion in vivo (41, 70). Clearly, under such conditions distal tubular secretion of potassium increases proportionately, or nearly so, with flow rate along the distal tubule (56). Enhancement of urine flow rate, and a number of additional kaliuretic factors, does not enhance potassium secretion in sheep (75).

A large number of situations are known in which a flow-dependent increase in potassium secretion has been observed. These include osmotic diuresis by mannitol (64), prolonged states of water diuresis in rats with diabetes insipidus (68), sodium chloride and sodium sulfate diuresis (64), postobstructive diuresis (67), diuresis following contralateral nephrectomy (23), metabolic alkalosis (62), and situations in which metabolic acidosis induces kaliuresis (10, 81). Finally, the increased rate of potassium excretion after furosemide (24), chlorthiazide (18, 28), ouabain [in those species in which this cardiac glycoside inhibits fluid transport upstream of the distal tubule (91)], and after mercurial diuretics (16, 25) is closely associated with the delivery of a larger than normal fraction of fluid into the distal tubule (32).

Acid-Base Balance

Acid-base disturbances exert a powerful effect upon distal tubular potassium secretion. Metabolic alkalosis generally promotes distal tubular potassium secretion (31, 62, 76), while acute metabolic acidosis curtails potassium secretion (31, 62), particularly if care is taken to prevent the increase in distal tubular flow rate often associated with inhibition of proximal tubule fluid reabsorption due to reduced plasma bicarbonate (44, 94). When urine flow rates were comparable in control and acidotic conditions Malnic, deMello-Aires & Giebisch (62) found by micropuncture of distal tubules that potassium secretion was depressed by metabolic acidosis. Lowering the luminal pH of isolated perfused rabbit cortical collecting tubules has also been shown to depress potassium secretion (12). Clearance experiments in dogs during progressive potassium loading confirm that metabolic alkalosis stimulates, whereas metabolic acidosis depresses, the urinary excretion rate of potassium (93). Acute hypocapnia of short duration stimulates potassium secretion, while acute hypercapnia reduces potassium secretion (62). These initial responses to disturbances of acid-base balance of the distal secretory system may be modified during protracted states of acid-base disturbances (31).

A reciprocal relationship exists between renal ammonium and potassium excretion (92). Karlmark, Jaeger & Giebisch (49) have demonstrated that upon acute potassium loading there is no change in ammonium handling in the proximal or distal tubule but ammonium excretion along the collecting tubule is reduced. Hypokalemia stimulates distal ammonium excretion (53), whereas increased ammonium excretion after glutamine administration lowers potassium secretion at sites beyond the late distal tubule (50).

Plasma potassium levels are elevated in acute metabolic and respiratory acidosis and depressed in acute metabolic and respiratory alkalosis (62). These results suggest that potassium moves into cells during alkalosis and out of cell during acidosis. Three experimental observations support this thesis. First, potassium activity of distal tubule cells was elevated in metabolic alkalosis and reduced in metabolic acidosis (54). Second, unidirectional tracer influx of ^{42}K across the peritubular membrane into mammalian distal tubule cells was enhanced in metobolic alkalosis (19). A significant increase in the amount of labeled potassium within cells accompanied stimulation of distal tubular potassium secretion during alkalemia. At the same time, no modifications of luminal transport parameters favoring potassium movement into the tubular lumen were observed. Third, Adler & Fraley (2, 29) have observed that the ratios of K^+INT/K^+EXT and of H^+INT/H^+EXT change frequently together. An increase in extracellular hydrogen ion activity is often accompanied by a smaller but proportional rise in intracellular hydrogen ion activity and hence in a fall in the hydrogen ion ratio across cell membranes. It is likely that such cellular pH changes modulate peritubular potassium uptake.

Peritubular uptake of potassium and alterations in cell potassium are important determinants of transepithelial potassium-concentration differences across the distal tubular epithelium. A second modulating factor of renal potassium excretion is the rate of delivery of fluid and sodium (and the species of accompanying anion) to the distal nephron. Superposition of nonspecific flow effects upon the intrinsic pattern of distal tubular potassium transport can modify the rate of distal potassium secretion. For example, acute metabolic acidosis decreases potassium secretion by the distal tubule [(62); B. Stanton, G. Giebisch, unpublished observations]. However, with continued acidemia and reduction of extracellular bicarbonate concentration, proximal-fluid reabsorption decreases and results in increased fluid delivery to the distal tubule. An increase in potassium excretion follows (10, 81). Therefore, the increase in flow rate to the distal tubule increases potassium secretion despite the initial effect of reduced pH (or bicarbonate) on distal transport of potassium.

Similar considerations are relevant to the proposal of Schwartz, Cohen and associates (85), who have stressed the effect, on potassium secretion, of a time-dependent shift of sodium normally reabsorbed in the proximal nephron to the distal nephron. The essential point of their thesis stipulates that whenever a larger than normal fraction of sodium with an impermeant anion is shifted "downstream" into the distal nephron segment, a proportionally larger moiety of sodium reabsorption will be balanced by the secretory movement of potassium. This effect is even more pronounced if distal avidity for sodium is high. In metabolic alkalosis, it is the replacement of chloride by bicarbonate that results in the delivery of a less permeant anion to the distal tubule. The presence of a larger than normal load of sodium, accompanied by bicarbonate, coupled with a high distal avidity for sodium reabsorption, enhances potassium secretion.

In summary, the effects of acid-base disturbances upon distal potassium transport are mediated either by direct effects of pH (or bicarbonate) upon the distal tubular transport system, by changes in the delivery of sodium and fluid as a result of alterations in anion composition in the filtrate, or as a consequence of bicarbonate-induced alterations in proximal fluid and sodium reabsorption.

Adrenal Mineralocorticoids

The modulation of renal tubular potassium transport by mineralocorticoids has been extensively reviewed (46, 71). In adrenalectomized animals, potassium excretion rises and sodium excretion falls after injection of aldosterone, with a latency period of one to two hours. Lack of mineralocorticoids reduces the ability of the kidney to excrete potassium ions. Augmentation of potassium excretion by mineralocorticoids critically depends upon an adequate sodium supply to the distal nephron.

Mineralocorticoids exert a reciprocal effect upon sodium and potassium transport; however, no fixed relationship exists. The hormone effects on the transport of sodium and potassium may be dissociated in time. Selective effects of mineralocorticoids on either tubular sodium or potassium transport have been demonstrated (46). Also, the potency of the mineralocorticoid effect in stimulating potassium excretion depends on dietary pretreatment. For example, dietary potassium deprivation enhances the effect of mineralocorticoids on potassium excretion (46). Furthermore, persistence of kaliuresis during mineralocorticoid "escape" has been observed (3). Finally, the potentially separate nature of mineralocorticoid effects upon sodium and potassium transport is underscored by the effects of inhibitors of protein synthesis such as actinomycin D, which intereferes with the sodium-retaining effect of aldosterone in adrenalectomized rats but not with the hormonal effect upon potassium transport (26, 46, 47).

Micropuncture and microperfusion studies have localized the main site of mineralocorticoid action on tubular potassium (and sodium) transport at the level of the distal tubule and collecting tubule. Adrenalectomy lowered distal tubule potassium concentration in rats maintained on an elevated sodium intake (48) and in rats treated with dexamethosone (46, 47). In addition to these effects on the distal tubular epithelium in rats, mineralocorticoids also have the ability to stimulate potassium secretion and sodium reabsorption in rabbit isolated cortical collecting tubules (72). It is of interest that in these studies the coupling ratio between sodium and potassium transport rates changed significantly with time.

DISTAL CELLULAR MODELS OF POTASSIUM TRANSPORT

Incisive progress has been made with respect to our understanding of the tubular sites and the mechanism of potassium transport, although important questions remain unresolved. Ultimately, such studies attempt a precise definition of electrochemical driving forces across the luminal and peritubular cell membrane, and the partition of transepithelial secretory and reabsorptive potassium fluxes into transcellular and paracellular routes (34, 37, 40). Based on studies of the electrical and chemical activity differences across the luminal and peritubular cell membranes, some features of potassium transport across distal tubule and collecting tubule epithelium have emerged. It is, however, mandatory to be aware of several uncertainties in the present approach. These have been discussed in detail (37, 61) and concern the unresolved relationship of directional net potassium transport (either secretory or reabsorptive) to the maintenance of cell potassium content, the role of cell compartmentalization of potassium, and the considerable cell heterogeneity of the nephron sites involved in renal tubular potassium transport.

Figure 1 schematically presents possible mechanisms of potassium transport in the distal tubule epithelium. Figure 2 illustrates transport mechanisms thought to be more typical of cortical collecting tubule cells (32, 34–38, 40, 100–102).

Essential features of the cell model of distal tubule potassium transport (Figure 1) include a peritubular sodium-potassium exchange pump. Peritubular potassium uptake is not necessarily coupled to sodium extrusion in a 1:1 ratio. Activation of an electrogenic (rheogenic) mode of operation (sodium-potassium exchange ratio > unity) can be demonstrated when the rate of sodium entry across the luminal cell membrane is suddenly augmented (97). Clearly, such a mode of operation would accelerate potassium uptake across the peritubular cell membrane not only by a carrier-mediated pump mechanism but also by increasing the peritubular, cell-negative, potential. This mechanism is likely to be involved in the stimulation of potassium secretion due to increases in the distal tubular flow rate and sodium deliver.

Several factors have an effect upon the activity of the peritubular sodium-potassium exchange pump. Results from a compartmental analysis of ^{42}K transport across amphibian (98) and mammalian distal tubules (19) have shown that potassium deprivation decreases peritubular potassium uptake. Peritubular potassium uptake is enhanced after diamox, bicarbonate administration, and potassium loading (19, 98). Metabolic alkalosis, therefore, stimulates peritubular potassium uptake. From studies using ion-sensitive microelectrodes, it has been inferred that metabolic acidosis depresses (54) and mineralocorticoids stimulate (96) peritubular potassium uptake.

Active potassium reabsorption normally occurs along the distal tubule of amphibian kidneys (98) and can be demonstrated in mammalian distal tubules during chronic dietary potassium depletion (24). Even in the absence of any net transport of potassium along this nephron segment (4, 63, 74, 103), a component of active potassium reabsorption may be inferred from the negative transepithelial potential difference. Clearly, potassium secretion would be expected to occur were it not for an active reabsorptive transport component. It is certain that the active transport step of potas-

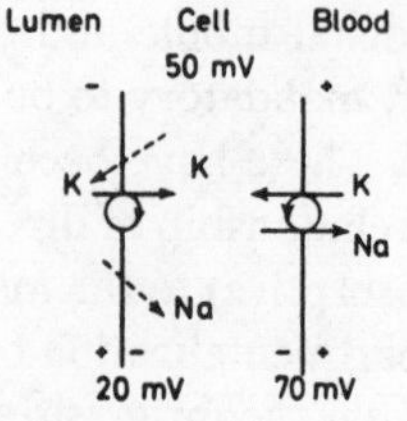

Figure 1 Cellular mechanism of distal tubular potassium transport. From (53,100)

sium reabsorption is located in the luminal cell membrane. In the rat (24) and *Amphiuma* kidney (98), ouabain increases distal tubular potassium concentration, an effect also to be expected from inhibition of a luminal potassium pump.

According to the cell model presented in Figure 1, the main driving force for potassium translocation from cell to lumen is a favorable electrochemical potential gradient across the luminal cell membrane. The importance of the electrochemical gradient across the luminal cell membrane is also implied by observations during microperfusion experiments (41). Increased flow rate in pump-perfused distal tubules stimulated potassium secretion. Late distal luminal potassium concentration fell with increased flow rate favoring cell to lumen movement of potassium. Also relevant is the fact that the luminal transmembrane potential falls along the distal tubule (99). As a consequence, passive potassium efflux from the distal tubule cell into the lumen is favored with progression from the early to the late distal tubule. Nevertheless, there is evidence for an additional active transport component participating in overall potassium secretion across the distal tubular epithelium. In distal tubular segments voltage-clamped at zero potential difference, the tubular-fluid/plasma-potassium ratio exceeded unity (30).

Confirming older observations on the avian kidney (73), the stepwise increase of the systemic potassium concentration during pump perfusion of rat distal tubules in vivo leads to apparent saturation of the secretory mechanism (87). Net secretion rate is dramatically increased in potassium-adapted animals and falls sharply during acute metabolic acidosis (B. Stanton, G. Giebisch, unpublished observations). Most likely these effects are mediated by modifications of peritubular potassium transport.

From the above considerations, several components emerge as important control points of distal tubular potassium secretion: (*a*) peritubular sodium-potassium exchange that primarily regulates the cellular potassium activity, (*b*) electrical and chemical potential differences across the partially depolarized luminal cell membrane, and (*c*) active luminal reabsorption of potassium. Some potassium may also move via a paracellular pathway from the peritubular to the luminal fluid driven by the lumen-negative potential

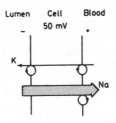

Figure 2 Cellular mechanism of collecting tubular potassium transport. From (53,100)

difference. While the presence of such a mechanism is highly likely, little is known regarding its magnitude and physiological role.

Inspection of Figure 2 indicates one important difference between the transport model of the cortical collecting tubule cell and the transport model of the distal tubule cell depicted in Figure 1. An active transport step has to be postulated in the luminal membrane of the cortical collecting tubule cell. It has been demonstrated in rabbit cortical collecting tubules in vitro that the luminal potassium concentration exceeds that predicted by the electrochemical difference (43). An additional argument supporting an active secretory potassium pump in the luminal cell membrane is the finding of active potassium transport which renders the collecting tubule lumen electrically positive. Reduction of potassium secretion by luminal acidification renders the lumen more negative, an observation consistent with a component of active rheogenic potassium transport (12). The collecting tubule lumen is often electrically negative, and this electronegativity can be accentuated by pretreatment with a low-sodium diet or by administration of DOCA (72).

Little is known about the cellular mechanisms by which potassium transport is modulated at the level of the collecting tubule epithelium. Also, precise measurements of cellular potassium activities and of transmembrane electrical potential differences at different rates of potassium secretion are not available. Removal of sodium from the lumen reduces potassium secretion (43), an observation consistent with some coupling of sodium-potassium exchange in the luminal membrane. The establishment of maximal transepithelial potassium concentration differences is much slower than across the distal tubular epithelium (43). It should be noted that the studies on isolated collecting tubules have been done only at room temperature and are not strictly comparable to those done on distal tubules in vivo. Subsequent to pretreatment with DOCA, the transepithelial conductance of cortical collecting tubules increases sharply and coincides with the increase of potassium secretion (45, 72).

Literature Cited

1. Adam, W. R., Dawborn, J. K. 1972. Potassium tolerance in rats. *Aust. J. Exp. Biol. Med. Sci.* 50:757–63
2. Adler, S., Fraley, D. 1977. Potassium and intracellular pH. *Kidney Int.* 11:433–42
3. August, J. T., Nelson, D. H., Thorn, G. W. 1958. Response of normal subjects to large amounts of aldosterone. *J. Clin. Invest.* 37:1549–53
4. Bank, N., Aynedjian, H. S. 1973. A micropuncture study of potassium excre-

tion by the remnant kidney. *J. Clin. Invest.* 52:1480–90
5. Battilina, C. A., Bhattacharya, F., Lacy, F. B., Dobyan, D. C., Johnstone, P. A., Jamison, R. L. 1978. Effect of chronic potassium loading on potassium secretion by the pars recta or descending limb of the juxtamedullary nephron in the rat. *J. Clin. Invest.* 62: 1093–1103
6. Beck, L. H., Senesky, D., Goldberg, M. 1973. Sodium-independent active potas-

sium reabsorption in proximal tubule of the dog. *J. Clin. Invest.* 52:2641–45

7. Bengele, H. H., Evan, A., McNamara, E. R., Alexander, E. A. 1978. Tubular sites of potassium regulation in the normal and uni-nephrectomized rat. *Am. J. Physiol.* 234:F146–53

8. Bennett, C. M., Brenner, B. M., Berliner, R. W. 1968. Micropuncture study of nephron function in the Rhesus monkey. *J. Clin. Invest.* 47:203–16

9. Bennett, C. M., Clapp, J. R., Berliner, R. W. 1967. Micropuncture study of the proximal and distal tubule in the dog. *Am. J. Physiol.* 213:1254–62

10. Besarab, A., Silva, P., Ross, B., Epstein, F. 1975. Bicarbonate and sodium reabsorption by the isolated perfused kidney. *Am. J. Physiol.* 228:1525–30

11. Bott, P. A. 1962. A micropuncture study of renal excretion of water, K, Na and Cl in *Necturus. Am. J. Physiol.* 203:662–66

12. Boudry, J. F., Stoner, L. C., Burg, M. B. 1976. The effect of lumen pH on potassium transport in renal cortical collecting tubules. *Am. J. Physiol.* 230:239–44

13. Brenner, B. M., Berliner, R. W. 1973. Transport of Potassium. In *Handbook of Physiology,* ed. J. Orloff, R. W. Berliner, Sect. 8:497–520. Washington DC: Am. Physiol. Soc. 1028 pp.

14. Burg, M. B. 1976. The renal handling of sodium chloride. In *The Kidney,* ed. B. M. Brenner, F. C. Rector, Jr., pp. 272–98. Philadelphia: Saunders. 1941 pp.

15. Burg, M. B. 1976. Tubular chloride transport and the mode of action of some diuretics. *Kidney Int.* 9:189–97

16. Clapp, J. R., Robinson, R. R. 1968. Distal sites of action of diuretic drugs in the dog nephron. *Am. J. Physiol.* 215: 228–35

17. Cohen, J. J. 1968. Correction of metabolic alkalosis by the kidney after isometric expansion of extracellular fluid. *J. Clin. Invest.* 47:1181–92

18. Costanzo, L., Windhager, E. E. 1978. Sodium-calcium interaction in the distal convoluted tubule. *Am. J. Physiol.* In press

19. deMello-Aires, M., Giebisch, G., Malnic, G., Curran, P. F. 1973. Kinetics of potassium transport across single distal tubules of rat kidney. *J. Physiol.* 232: 47–70

20. DeRouffignac, C., Lechene, C., Guinnebault, M., Morel, F. Etude par microponction de l'elaboration de l'urine III. Chez le merion non diuretique et en diurese par le manitol. *Nephron* 6:643–66

21. DeRouffignac, C., Morel, F. 1969. Micropuncture study of water, electrolytes, and urea movements along the loops of Henle in *Psammomys. J. Clin. Invest.* 48:474–86

22. Diezi, J., Michoud, P., Aceves, J., Giebisch, G. 1973. Micropuncture study of electrolyte transport across papillary collecting duct of the rat. *Am. J. Physiol.* 224:623–34

23. Diezi, J., Michoud, P., Grandchamp, A., Giebisch, G. 1976. Effects of nephrectomy on renal salt and water transport in the remaining kidney. *Kidney Int.* 10:450–62

24. Duarte, C. G., Chométy, F., Giebisch, G. 1971. Effect of amiloride, ouabain, and furosemide on distal tubular function in the rat. *Am. J. Physiol.* 221: 632–40

25. Evanson, R. L., Lockhart, E. A., Dirks, J. H. 1972. Effect of mercurial diuretics on tubular sodium and potassium transport in the dog. *Am. J. Physiol.* 222: 282–89

26. Fimognari, G. M., Fanestil, D. D., Edelman, I. S. 1967. Induction of RNA and protein synthesis in the action of aldosterone in the rat. *Am. J. Physiol.* 213:954–62

27. Finkelstein, F. O., Hayslett, J. P. 1974. Role of medullary structures in the functional adaptation of renal insufficiency. *Kidney Int.* 6:419–25

28. Foulkes, E. C. 1965. On the mechanism of chlorothiazide-induced kaliuresis in the rabbit. *J. Pharmacol. Exp. Ther.* 150:406–11

29. Fraley, D., Adler, S. 1976. Isohydric regulation of plasma potassium by bicarbonate in the rat. *Kidney Int.* 9:333–43

30. Garcia, E., Malnic, G., Giebisch, G. 1976. Effect of changes in electrical potential difference upon distal tubular potassium concentrations. *Kidney Int.* 10:584 (Abstr.)

31. Gennari, F. J., Cohen, J. J. 1975. The role of the kidney in potassium homeostasis: lessons from acid-base disturbances. *Kidney Int.* 8:1–5

32. Giebisch, G. 1971. Renal potassium excretion. In *The Kidney, Morphology, Biochemistry, Physiology,* ed. C. Rouiller, A. F. Muller, 3:329–82. New York: Academic. 408 pp.

33. Giebisch, G. 1974. Some recent developments in renal electrolyte transport. In *Recent Advances in Renal Physiology and Pharmacology,* ed. L. G. Wesson, G. M. Fanelli, pp. 125–48. Baltimore: University Park Press. 388 pp.

34. Giebisch, G. 1975. Some reflections on the mechanism of renal tubular potassium transport. *Yale J. Biol. Med.* 48:315–36
35. Giebisch, G. 1976. Effects of diuretics on renal transport of potassium. In *Methods in Pharmacology,* ed. M. Martinez-Maldonado, 4A:121–64. New York: Plenum. 387 pp.
36. Giebisch, G. 1978. The distal tubular potassium transport system. In *New Aspects of Renal Function,* ed. H. G. Vogel, K. J. Ullrich, 6:137–46. Amsterdam: Excerpta Medica. 221 pp.
37. Giebisch, G. 1978. Renal potassium transport. In *Transport Across Biological Membranes,* ed. G. Giebisch, D. Tosteson, H. H. Ussing. Berlin: Springer. In press
38. Giebisch, G., Boulpaep, E. L., Whittembury, G., 1971. Electrolyte transport in kidney tubule cells. *Proc. R. Soc. London Ser. B.,* 262:175–96
39. Giebisch, G., Malnic, G. 1969. The regulation of distal tubular potassium transport. In *Renal Transport and Diuretics,* ed. K. Thurau, J. Jahrmaerker, pp. 123–37. Berlin: Springer. 487 pp.
40. Giebisch, G., Windhager, E. E., 1973. Electrolyte transport across renal tubular membranes. See Ref. 13, pp. 315–76
41. Good, D. W., Wright, F. S. 1977. Effects of fluid flow rate and sodium concentration on potassium secretion by renal distal tubule. *Fed. Proc.* 36:628 (Abstr.)
42. Grantham, J. J., 1976. Renal transport and excretion of potassium. See Ref. 14, pp. 299–317
43. Grantham, J. J., Burg, M. B., Orloff, J. 1970. The nature of transtubular Na and K transport in isolated rabbit collecting tubules. *J. Clin. Invest.* 49: 1815–26
44. Green, R., Giebisch, G. 1975. Some ionic requirements of proximal tubular sodium transport. I. The role of bicarbonate and chloride. *Am. J. Physiol.* 229:1205–15
45. Helman, S. I., O'Neil, R. G. 1977. Model of active transepithelial Na and K transport of renal collecting tubules. *Am. J. Physiol.* 233:F559–71
46. Hierholzer, K., Lange, S. 1974. The effects of adrenal steroids on renal function. In: *MTP International Review of Science, Kidney and Urinary Tract Physiology,* ed. K. Thurau, 6:273–334. London: Butterworths. 427 pp.
47. Hierholzer, K., Wiederholt, M. 1976. Some aspects of distal tubular solute

and water transport. *Kidney Int.* 9:198–213
48. Hierholzer, K., Wiederholt, M., Holzgreve, H., Giebisch, G., Klose, R. M., Windhager, E. E. 1965. Micropuncture study of renal transtubular concentration gradients of sodium and potassium in adrenalectomized rats. *Pfluegers Arch.* 285:193–210
49. Jaeger, Ph., Karlmark, B., Giebisch, G. 1977. Micropuncture study of relationship between potassium and tubular acidification. *Kidney Int.* 12:562 (Abstr.)
50. Jaeger, Ph., Karlmark, B., Giebisch, G. 1978. Micropuncture study of the effects of NH_4 on tubular acidification and potassium transport. *Clin. Res.* In press
51. Jamison, R. L., Buerkert, J., Lacy, F. 1971. A micropuncture study of collecting tubule function in rats with hereditary diabetes insipidus. *J. Clin. Invest.* 50:2444–52
52. Jamison, R. L., Lacy, F. B., Pennell, J. P., Sanjana, V. M. 1976. Potassium secretion by the descending limb or pars recta of the juxtamedullary nephron *in vivo. Kidney Int.* 9:323–32
53. Karlmark, B., Jaeger, Ph., Giebisch, G. 1978. Micropuncture study of tubular acidification and NH_3-NH_4 transport during chronic potassium depletion. *Kidney Int.* In press
54. Khuri, R. N., Agulian, S. K., Kalloghlian, A. 1972. Intracellular potassium in cells of the distal tubule. *Pfluegers Arch.* 335:297–307
55. Khuri, R. N., Flannigan, W. J., Oken, D. E. 1966. Potassium in proximal tubule fluid of rats and *Necturus* measured with glass electrodes. *J. Appl. Physiol.* 21:1568–72
56. Khuri, R. N., Strieder, N., Wiederholt, M., Giebisch, G. 1975. The effects of flow rate and potassium intake on distal tubular potassium transfer. *Am. J. Physiol.* 228:1249–61
57. Kunau, R. T., Webb, H. C., Borman, S. C. 1974. Characteristics of the relationship between the flow rate of tubular fluid and potassium transport in the distal tubule of the rat. *J. Clin. Invest.* 54:1488–95
58. Lechène, C., Morel, F., Guinnebault, M., DeRouffignac, C. 1969. Ètude par microponction de l'èlaboration de l'urine I. Chez le Rat dans differents ètats de diurèse. *Nephron* 6:457–77
59. LeGrimellec, C., Roniel, N., Morel, F. 1973. Simultaneous Mg, Ca, P, K, Na and Cl analysis in rat tubular fluid. I. During perfusion of either inulin or fer-

rocyanide. *Pfluegers Arch.* 340:181–96
60. LeGrimellec, C., Roinel, N., Morel, F. 1973. Simultaneous Mg, Ca, P, K, Na, and Cl analysis in rat tubular fluid. II. During acute Mg plasma loading. *Pfluegers Arch.* 340:197–210
61. MacKnight, A. D. C. 1977. Epithelial transport of potassium. *Kidney Int.* 391–414
62. Malnic, G., deMello-Aires, M., Giebisch, G. 1971. Potassium transport across renal distal tubules during acid-base disturbances. *Am. J. Physiol.* 211:1192–1208
63. Malnic, G., Klose, R. M., Giebisch, G. 1964. Micropuncture study of renal potassium excretion in the rat. *Am. J. Physiol.* 206:647–86
64. Malnic, G., Klose, R. M., Giebisch, G. 1966. Micropuncture study of distal tubular potassium and sodium transport in rat nephron. *Am. J. Physiol.* 211:529–47
65. Malnic, G., Klose, R. M., Giebisch, G. 1966. Microperfusion study of distal tubular potassium and sodium transfer in rat kidney. *Am. J. Physiol.* 211:548–59
66. Marsh, D. J., Ullrich, K. F., Rumrich, G. 1963. Micropuncture analysis of the behavior of potassium ions in rat renal cortical tubules. *Pfluegers Arch.* 277: 107–19
67. McDougal, W. S., Wright, F. S. 1972. Defect in proximal and distal sodium transport in post-obstructive diuresis. *Kidney Int.* 2:304–17
68. Möehring, B., Möehring, J., Dauda, G., Haak, D. 1974. Potassium deficiency in rats with hereditary diabetes insipidus. *Am. J. Physiol.* 227:916–20
69. Morel, F., DeRouffignac, C., Marsh, D., Guinnebault, M., Lechene, C. 1969. Etude par microponction de l'elaboration de l'urine II. Chez le *Psammomys* non diuretique. *Nephron* 6:553–70
70. Morgan, T., Berliner, R. W. 1969. A study by continuous microperfusion of water and electrolyte movements in the loop of Henle and distal tubule of the rat. *Nephron* 6:388–405
71. Mulrow, P. J., Forman, B. H. 1972. The tissue effects of mineralocorticoids. *Am. J. Med.* 54:561–72
72. O'Neil, R. G., Helman, S. I. 1977. Transport characteristics of renal collecting tubules: influence of DOCA and diet. *Am. J. Physiol.* 233:F544–58
73. Orloff, J., Davidson, D., Burg, M. 1959. The mechanism of potassium excretion in the chicken. *J. Clin. Invest.* 38:21–30

74. Peterson, L., Wright, F. S. 1977. Effect of sodium intake on renal potassium excretion. *Am. J. Physiol.* 233:F225–34
75. Rabinowitz, L., Gunther, R. A. 1972. Excretion of urea in sheep during urea, mannitol and methylurea osmotic diuresis. *Am. J. Physiol.* 222:807–9
76. Rector, F. C. Jr. 1976. Renal acidification and ammonia production; chemistry of weak acids and bases; buffer mechanisms. See Ref. 14, pp. 318–43
77. Rector, F. C. Jr., Bloomer, H. A., Seldin, D. W. 1964. Proximal tubular reabsorption of potassium during mannitol diuresis in rats. *J. Lab. Clin. Med.* 63:100–5
78. Reineck, H. J., Osgood, R. W., Stein, J. H. 1977. Distal nephron potassium (K) transport in the rat: effect of amiloride. *Clin. Res.* 25:508 (Abstr.)
79. Reineck, H. J., Osgood, R. W., Stein, J. H. 1978. Net potassium addition beyond the superficial distal tubule of the rat. *Am. J. Physiol.* 235:F104–10
80. Reineck, H. J., Asgood, R. W., Stein, J., Ferris, T., 1975. Potassium transport in the distal tubule and collecting duct of the rat. *Am. J. Physiol.* 229:1403–9
81. Rostand, S. G., Watkins, J. B. 1977. Response of the isolated rat kidney to metabolic and respiratory acidosis. *Am. J. Physiol.* 233:F82–88
82. Schon, D. A., Silva, P., Hayslett, J. P. 1974. Mechanism of potassium excretion in renal insufficiency. *Am. J. Physiol.* 277:1323–28
83. Schultze, R. G., 1973. Recent advances in the physiology and pathophysiology of potassium excretion. *Arch. Int. Med.* 113:885–97
84. Schultze, R. G., Taggart, D. D., Shapiro, H., Pennell, J. P., Caglar, S., Bricker, N. S. 1971. On the adaptation in potassium excretion associated with nephron reduction in the dog. *J. Clin. Invest.* 50:1061–68
85. Schwartz, W. B., Cohen, J. J. 1978. The nature of the renal response to disorders of acid-base equilibrium. *Am. J. Med.* 64:417–28
86. Silva, P., Brown, R. S., Epstein, F. 1977. Adaptation to potassium. *Kidney Int.* 11:466–75
87. Stanton, B., Giebisch, G. 1978. In vivo microperfusion study of potassium secretion by the distal convoluted tubule during acute K infusion. *Fed. Proc.* 37:728 (Abstr.)
88. Stein, J. H., Osgood, R. W., Kunau, R. T. 1976. Direct measurement of papillary collecting duct sodium and potassium transport in the rat: Evidence for

heterogeneity of nephron function. *Clin. Res.* 24:469 (Abstr.)

89. Stein, J. H., Reineck, H. J., 1974. The role of the collecting duct in the regulation of excretion of sodium and other electrolytes. *Kidney Int.* 6:1–9

90. Stoner, L. C., Burg, M. B., Orloff, J. 1974. Ion transport in cortical collecting tubule: effect of amiloride. *Am. J. Physiol.* 227:453–59

91. Strieder, N., Khuri, R. N., Wiederholt, M., Giebisch, G. 1974. Studies on the renal action of ouabain in the rat. Effects in the nondiuretic state. *Pfluegers Arch.* 249:91–107

92. Tannen, R. L. 1977. Relationship of renal ammonia production and potassium homeostasis. *Kidney Int.* 11:453–65

93. Toussaint, C., Vereerstraeten, P. 1962. Effects of blood pH changes on potassium excretion in the dog. *Am. J. Physiol.* 202:768–72

94. Ullrich, K. J., Radtke, H. W., Rumrich, G. 1971. The role of bicarbonate and other buffers on isotonic fluid absorption in the proximal convolution of the rat kidney. *Pfluegers Arch.* 330:149–61

95. Watson, J. F., Clapp, J. R., Berliner, R. W. 1964. Micropuncture study of potassium concentration in proximal tubule of dog, rat and *Necturus. J. Clin. Invest.* 43:595–605

96. Wiederholt, M., Agulian, S., Khuri, R. N. 1974. Intracellular potassium in the distal tubule of the adrenalectomized and aldosterone treated rat. *Pfluegers Arch.* 347:117–23

97. Wiederholt, M., Giebisch, G. 1974. Some electrophysiological properties of the distal tubule of *Amphiuma* kidney. *Fed. Proc.* 33:387 (Abstr.)

98. Wiederholt, M.. Sullivan, W. J., Giebisch, G., Solomon, A. K., Curran, P. F. 1971. Transport of potassium and sodium across single distal tubules of *Amphiuma. J. Gen. Physiol.* 57:495–529

99. Wright, F. S. 1971. Increasing magnitude of electrical potential along the renal distal tubule. *Am. J. Physiol.* 220:624–38

100. Wright, F. S., 1974. Potassium transport by the renal tubule. See Ref. 46, pp. 79–106

101. Wright, F. S. 1977. Sites and mechanisms of potassium transport along the renal tubule. *Kidney Int.* 11:415–32

102. Wright, F. S. 1977. Potassium. In *Pathophysiology of the Kidney*, ed. N. A. Kurtzman, M. Martinez-Maldonado, pp. 180–212. Springfield, Ill.: C. Thomas. 1087 pp.

103. Wright, F. S., Strieder, N., Fowler, N., Giebisch, G. 1971. Potassium secretion by distal tubule after potassium adaptation. *Am. J. Physiol.* 221:437–48

Ann. Rev. Physiol. 1979. 41:257–71

RENAL HANDLING OF
PHOSPHATE AND CALCIUM

♦1218

Vincent W. Dennis, William W. Stead, and John L. Myers

Division of Nephrology, Department of Medicine,
Duke University Medical Center, Durham, North Carolina 27710

Three major methodologic advances—electron probe microanalysis, perfusion of nephron segments in vitro, and isolated membrane vesicles—have expanded interest and information regarding the renal handling of phosphate and of calcium. Here we review recent progress and indicate directions of continuing inquiry; our review complements and updates more comprehensive reviews provided by others (11, 26, 53). The renal handling of magnesium was reviewed by Massry in 1977 (51).

PHOSPHATE

Phosphate homeostasis depends primarily on the mechanisms governing renal excretion. Although numerous factors have been described that affect the renal handling of phosphate at the organ level, these descriptions provide only limited insights into the intrinsic renal mechanisms controlling phosphate excretion. Recent efforts have examined phosphate transport directly at the epithelial, cellular, and membrane level; as a result, we now understand more clearly the ultrafilterability of plasma phosphate, the localization of phosphate reabsorption, and, to a limited extent, the transport processes involved in phosphate reabsorption.

Ultrafilterability of Inorganic Phosphate

Walser (78) has summarized considerations regarding the filterability of plasma phosphate. Since whole plasma is only 93% aqueous phase and since the Donnan equilibrium distribution factor for divalent anions is approximately 0.91, complete filterability of plasma phosphate at the glomerulus should result in an ultrafiltrate concentration that is 1.18 times the concen-

257

0066-4278/79/0301-0257$01.00

tration in whole plasma or 1.09 times the concentration in plasma water. Walser's observations regarding the distribution of inorganic phosphate from human plasma across cellophane membranes indicate that only 76% of plasma phosphate is ultrafilterable in this system. Thus a standard practice in micropuncture studies of phosphate transport is to compare the phosphate concentration in tubular fluid to the concentration in an ultrafiltrate of plasma derived from cellophane or noncellulosic (Amicon ®) membranes. These artificial membranes are assumed to approximate adequately the events occurring across the glomerulus in vitro.

This assumption has now been confirmed, with important qualifications, by sampling glomerular ultrafiltrate from the surface glomeruli of Munich-Wistar rats. The data obtained in three studies (29, 30, 49) by two independent laboratories are summarized in Table 1, where they may be compared to similar values derived from artificial membranes (70, 78). The phosphate concentration in glomerular ultrafiltrates (UF) from Munich-Wistar rats averages 94% of that in plasma water (PW), which indicates that (a) under normal conditions UF_{PO_4} derived from cellophane or noncellulosic membranes is a reasonable estimate of glomerular filterability, and (b) approximately 87% of phosphate in plasma (P) is filterable at the glomerulus (0.94 UF/PW $\times$ 0.93 PW/P).

Extensions of these studies examined the possibility that the glomerular ultrafilterability of phosphate might be affected by hypercalcemia. Increasing serum calcium from 5.7 to 9.2 meq l^{-1} reduced the glomerular ultrafilterability of phosphate from 0.98 to 0.78 [(30); Table 1]. Even greater

Table 1 Ultrafilterability of plasma phosphate

Reference	Species	Condition	Membrane	PO_4 UF/PO_4 PW[a]
Walser (78)	Human	Normal	Cellophane	0.82
		Azotemia	Cellophane	0.86
	Dog	Normal	Cellophane	0.85
Strickler (70)	Rat	Normal	Cellophane	0.90
		Phosphate loaded	Cellophane	0.92
LeGrimellec (49)	Rat	Normal	Glomerulus	0.98
Harris (29)	Rat	Normal male	Glomerulus	0.76
		Normal female	Glomerulus	0.95
Harris (30)	Rat	Normal female	Glomerulus	0.98
		Hypercalcemia	Glomerulus	0.78
		Normal plasma	Noncellulose	0.96
		Hypercalcemic plasma	Noncellulose	0.32

[a]UF refers to ultrafiltrate and PW refers to plasma water (generally considered to be 94% of the plasma volume).

reductions occurred across artificial membranes. Thus with hypercalcemia, artificial membranes may tend to overestimate considerably the degree of reduction in glomerular ultrafilterability of phosphate. In this regard, Humes et al (34) demonstrated that hypercalcemia in the presence of parathyroid hormone (PTH) reduces the glomerular capillary ultrafiltration coefficient, although these changes did not occur in the absence of PTH. These observations are useful in understanding the global reductions in glomerular filtration rate (GFR) occasionally observed with acute hypercalcemia (4); and the data show that unlike artificial membranes, the in vivo glomerulus has filtration characteristics that are affected by polypeptide hormones such as PTH (34).

Localization of Phosphate Reabsorption

Under conditions of normal diet and parathyroid activity, the mammalian kidneys reabsorb greater than 80% of the filtered load of phosphate. Where along the nephron does this reabsorption occur?

In 1964, Strickler et al (70) reported the first micropuncture data regarding phosphate handling by the mammalian kidney. Strickler et al (70) sampled free-flowing fluid from both the proximal and distal convolutions of the intact rat. The data from such a classical micropuncture study consist essentially in measurements of inulin and phosphate concentrations in tubular fluid and comparison with corresponding values in plasma or an ultrafiltrate of plasma. From these primary data, various ratios may be derived that estimate what fraction of the filtered load of phosphate has been either delivered to the point of micropuncture or reabsorbed prior to that point. Since these or corresponding observations may be made for fluids sampled from the proximal convolution, the distal convolution, and the final urine, comparisons may be made among the fractions of filtered phosphate delivered to these three sites, and inferences may be drawn regarding what transpired in between.

Using this approach, Strickler et al (70) observed that the fraction of filtered phosphate remaining at the point of proximal micropuncture averaged 24% and was similar to the overall fractional excretion of 22.5%. Accordingly, the major portion of filtered phosphate (76%) was reabsorbed by the proximal tubule, and no further net change in phosphate handling occurred beyond the point of proximal micropuncture. That is, in the presence of PTH there was no evidence for any component of phosphate reabsorption distal to the proximal tubule. As summarized in Table 2, similar observations have been made in other laboratories (5, 12, 28, 44, 50, 70). Only Kuntziger et al (44) demonstrated any significant difference between the fractions delivered to the proximal and distal micropuncture sites. The Kuntziger study was unique in design: Proximal and distal samples

Table 2   Fraction of filtered phosphate remaining at various points along the rat nephron

Reference	Late proximal	Early distal	Urine
Intact Parathyroids			
Strickler (70)	0.24	0.27	0.22
Amiel (5)	0.34	0.41	0.21
LeGrimellec (50)	0.33	0.33	0.23[a]
Kuntziger (44)	0.39	0.32[a]	0.21[a]
Boudry (12)	0.30	0.31	0.17[a]
Greger (28)	0.38	0.37	0.19[a]
Acute Parathyroidectomy			
Amiel (5)	0.34	0.11	0.02
Kuntziger (44)	0.25	0.012	0.002
Greger (28)	0.14	0.04	0.017

[a]Significantly lower than value at preceding site.

were obtained from the same nephron. Since late proximal micropuncture in the rat usually includes most of the superficial convoluted portion of the proximal tubule, Kuntziger's data indicate that additional phosphate reabsorption may occur in the loop of Henle which consists of the straight portion of the proximal tubule and the thin and thick limbs of Henle (74).

The presence of phosphate reabsorption in the loop of Henle may be demonstrated more convincingly in the acute absence of PTH. As shown in Table 2, following acute parathyroidectomy the fraction of filtered phosphate present at the point of distal micropuncture is considerably smaller than the fraction present at the point of late proximal micropuncture; this indicates that reabsorption occurred somewhere along the intervening segments (5, 28, 44). PTH-sensitive phosphate reabsorption by loop structures can also be demonstrated by microinjection techniques. Brunette et al (14) demonstrated that 86% of the radioisotopic phosphate injected into the late proximal tubule is recovered in the urine when PTH is present, while only 50% is recovered when PTH is absent.

Which segments of the loop transport phosphate? Using isolated segments of the rabbit nephron perfused in vitro, Dennis et al (21) demonstrated directly that phosphate reabsorption occurs in the pars recta or straight portion of the proximal tubule, while Rocha et al (64) failed to demonstrate net phosphate transport in either the thin descending, thin ascending, or cortical thick ascending limbs of Henle. Lang et al (46) performed related studies in the thyroparathyroidectomized rat in vivo by infusing a column of fluid into the late proximal tubule, advancing it a short distance downstream, and subsequently withdrawing the fluid and estimating the loss of phosphate. Similarly, a column was advanced upstream through a distal micropuncture site. These stationary microperfusion techniques thus viewed phosphate transport along the descending and ascending portions of the loop, regions generally inaccessible to direct micropuncture. Phosphate transport occurred only in the descending portion, presumably the pars recta of the proximal tubule, and did not occur in the ascending portion, presumably the thick limb and early distal convolutions.

Whether or not significant phosphate reabsorption occurs in distal convoluted and the collecting tubules remains controversial. As shown in Table 2, most micropuncture studies demonstrate that the fraction of phosphate delivered in the final urine (fractional excretion) is less than the fraction delivered to the superficial distal convolution (5, 28, 44). This difference, however, is difficult to interpret since it may represent reabsorption by portions of the terminal nephron or differences between the contributions to the final urine of superficial, micropunctured nephrons and other nephrons not examined directly. Microinjection of radioisotopic phosphate into the accessible distal convolution of intact or parathyroidectomized rats usually results in 100% recovery in the urine (14, 68); recovery of only 95% has been reported when the contribution of upstream phosphate delivery was blocked and injection rates were low (28). This loss of isotopic phosphate may or may not represent actual net transport of phosphate.

Phosphate reabsorption in the distal nephron is demonstrated most clearly by measurement of phosphate delivery in the early and in the late distal convolutions of the same superficial nephrons. Pastoriza-Munoz et al (59) performed such studies in acutely parathyroidectomized rats that were volume expanded to increase distal delivery of phosphate. Under these conditions, the fraction of filtered phosphate present in the early distal convolutions averaged 19 ± 2 (SE)% versus 14 ± 2% in the later convolutions of the same nephrons. This site of phosphate reabsorption was inhibited, although not eliminated, by PTH. Thus a small component of PTH-sensitive phosphate absorption probably occurs also in the distal convoluted tubule. Further phosphate may be reabsorbed in the collecting system, but direct observations in a limited portion of the cortical collecting tubule failed to demonstrate any net phosphate transport (19).

Phosphate reabsorption averaging perhaps 5% of the filtered load may occur in the distal nephron if phosphate delivery to this region is augmented; however, the physiologic impact of this small contribution to the overall rate of phosphate excretion is uncertain. The distal nephron may participate in the almost complete extraction of phosphate from the urine that occurs in the acute absence of PTH (5, 28, 44) or with phosphate depletion (75); but under more physiologic conditions, especially diets, phosphate excretion rates would seem to be determined by the PTH-sensitive, higher capacity phosphate absorptive systems in the convoluted and straight portions of the proximal tubule.

Heterogeneity of Phosphate Reabsorption

Phosphate reabsorptive rates vary along the length of the proximal tubule itself (axial heterogeneity), being three to four times greater in the earlier convolutions than in the later (8, 68, 44). The early, avid component of phosphate reabsorption is not dependent on the composition of the intraluminal fluid and is an intrinsic characteristic of the epithelium (8, 77). Although these differences in reabsorptive rates are demonstrable in the presence (8, 68) or absence of PTH (77), the early, avid component appears to be less responsive to PTH than phosphate transport occurring in the later proximal tubule.

Parathyroid Hormone

Parathyroid hormone increases phosphate excretion by inhibiting phosphate reabsorption in the convoluted (2, 16, 40, 45, 59) and straight portion of the proximal tubule (19) and to a much lesser extent in the distal convoluted tubule (59). The mechanism of inhibition is unknown, but PTH also decreases proximal sodium and bicarbonate reabsorption (2, 3, 5, 18). Reports that PTH may inhibit carbonic anhydrase activity have not been confirmed (24), although carbonic anhydrase inhibitors such as acetazolamide may augment PTH by increasing the intracellular accumulation of cyclic AMP (42). The proximal effects of PTH are clearly associated with increased adenylate cyclase activity and excretion but the exact relationship between these events and changes in phosphate transport is unclear. The hamster (42), rabbit (19), and phosphate-depleted rat (69) are resistant to the phosphaturic effect of PTH, although increases in cyclic AMP do occur (42, 52, 69). Similar events are observed in man with pseudohypoparathyroidism, type 2 (22). This dissociation between the effects of PTH on cyclic AMP and on phosphate transport may be influenced by diet or by some function of pH. In hamsters, the administration of ammonium chloride or acetazolamide (42) or elevation of P_{CO_2} (33) restores events to the traditional relationship. The inference of these studies is that the systemic or perhaps intracellular pH or P_{CO_2} (79) may be an important determinant of the rate of phosphate transport as well as its responsiveness to PTH.

Bank et al (7) and Kaplan et al (37) have recently affirmed increased PTH as a major factor in maintaining phosphate homeostasis as the number of functioning nephrons is reduced. PTH-independent adaptation to renal failure has also been described (72).

Dietary Adaptation

Troehler et al (75) described the renal adaptation to changes in phosphate intake. Absolute renal reabsorption of phosphate is lower in rats maintained for 10 days on a high phosphate diet than in animals maintained on normal or reduced intake. Rats on reduced phosphate intake reabsorb essentially 100% of the filtered load of phosphate and also reabsorb a greater fraction of acute infusions of phosphate than do animals maintained on normal phosphate intake. Thus the capacity of the kidney to reabsorb phosphate increases in response to phosphate restriction and decreases in response to high phosphate diet, an adaptation which is largely independent of PTH and serum calcium.

The mechanism and segmental localization of this renal adaptation to major changes in phosphate intake are unclear. In response to phosphate restriction, phosphate reabsorption increases in the early proximal tubule, but no changes are demonstrable along the micropuncture-accessible portion (54). With phosphate loading, phosphate may be secreted somewhere along the nephron (possibly in the collecting system), since marked differences occur between the fraction of filtered phosphate present in surface distal convolutions and the higher fraction present in the urine (12, 39). Such differences, however, may also be explained by greater contributions to urinary phosphate from sub-surface nephrons than from superficial, micropunctured nephrons (12, 39, 41). Although there is no evidence that net addition of phosphate occurs at any point along the nephron (27), the possibility is entirely reasonable, especially in response to chronic phosphate loading.

Vitamin D

Popovtzer et al (61) noted that phosphate reabsorption increased when either 25-hydroxycholecalciferol (25 HCC) or 1,25-dihydroxycholecalciferol (1,25 DHCC) was infused systemically. These effects required the presence of PTH. Subsequent studies suggested that 25 HCC may inhibit the activation of adenylate cyclase by PTH (60). Puschett et al (63), on the other hand, observed that even in the absence of PTH, 10,000 units of vitamin D_3 or 25 units of 25 HCC increased phosphate reabsorption. This increase was antagonized by PTH, cyclic AMP, thyrocalcitonin, or hypercalcemia (62, 63). Gekle et al (25) had noted earlier that vitamin D_3 caused a transient increase in phosphate reabsorption by the proximal tubule. It seems that vitamin D, possibly in the form of 25 HCC or 1,25 DHCC, increases proximal phosphate reabsorption, but the relationship of PTH and the physiologic significance of this effect are unclear.

Mechanisms of Phosphate Transport

In the proximal convoluted tubule, phosphate reabsorption consists of an influx (lumen to peritubular fluid) averaging approximately 6 pmol mm·min^{-1} in the intact rat in vivo (55) and in the rabbit in vitro (19–21). For comparison, these rates are less than 1% of the rate of unidirectional sodium transport (21). Phosphate reabsorption rates are about three times greater in the proximal convoluted tubule than in the later straight portion (8, 21, 77). For both regions, backflux is insignificant and appears to represent simple diffusion (21). Phosphate reabsorption in the proximal tubule is therefore essentially a unidirectional process, although some movement into phosphate-free perfusates may occur from presumably intracellular sources (67).

Phosphate reabsorption is highly dependent on the presence of sodium transport (8, 20). This dependency is not related to net sodium or volume reabsorption per se, since elimination of net volume flux by adding a nonabsorbable solute such as raffinose to the lumen does not reduce phosphate transport (21). On the other hand, eliminating net sodium transport by inhibiting sodium-potassium ATPase activity either with ouabain or by removal of potassium from the bath does eliminate phosphate reabsorption. Indeed, the progressive replacement of intraluminal sodium with choline results in progressive reductions in phosphate reabsorption rates that are highly correlated with the degree of reduction in sodium transport (20). To a first approximation, little or no detectable phosphate reabsorption occurs in the proximal tubule in the absence of sodium transport (20).

The precise mechanisms whereby sodium and phosphate may interact are unclear. Acidification by the proximal tubule is related to sodium transport, and one model for phosphate reabsorption proposes that movement of hydrogen ions into the lumen and titration of divalent phosphate to the monovalent form may be responsible for net transport (6). LeGrimellec (49) noted that phosphate reabsorption in the rat in vivo appears to correlate with acidification rates. Dennis et al (21) could not confirm this in the rabbit in vitro, however. Replacement of intraluminal bicarbonate with chloride did not increase phosphate reabsorption, although under these conditions increased activity of monovalent phosphate could be expected. Since, in fact, the divalent form of phosphate may be reabsorbed preferentially (9), there is little to support the concept that phosphate reabsorption in the proximal tubule is related directly to acidification.

On the other hand, to suggest that proximal phosphate reabsorption may be explained by simple chemical coupling to sodium transport may also be an oversimplification. The presence of glucose and alanine in the lumen increases sodium transport but reduces phosphate reabsorption (17, 20).

Similarly, phlorizin blocks glucose reabsorption and decreases sodium transport (13) but increases phosphate reabsorption (20). Thus, the movement of phosphate may be "dissociated" from the movement of sodium. These observations may be explained by hypothesizing that electrical as well as chemical coupling may occur between the transport of sodium and of phosphate. In the rabbit proximal tubule, glucose and alanine transport contribute to the transepithelial electrical potential difference (35, 43), presumably by the depolarization of the luminal membrane, and each of these solutes inhibits phosphate reabsorption (20). Bicarbonate reabsorption, on the other hand, is not associated with changes in transepithelial electrical potential difference (15, 43) and does not affect phosphate reabsorption in vitro (20).

Observations using isolated membrane vesicles derived from brush-border material of the rat kidney also indicate that phosphate transport may be related to both the chemical and electrical consequences of sodium transport. Hoffman et al (31) described phosphate transport by isolated membrane vesicles from brush-border or basolateral membrane fractions. Phosphate uptake by brush-border vesicles occurs four times more rapidly in the presence of sodium than of potassium. The sodium-facilitated component of phosphate uptake is saturated at phosphate concentrations above 1 mM and is inhibited by arsenate. Sodium gradients directed inside the vesicles result in transient intravesicular phosphate concentrations that exceed those in the external medium ("overshoot"). These data indicate that the brush-border material contains a component that interacts with sodium and phosphate and facilitates the transfer of phosphate across related membrane structures. Phosphate uptake by vesicles derived largely from basolateral membranes also occurs rapidly but is enhanced only slightly by sodium and does not demonstrate concentrative uptake in the presence of a sodium gradient. Tenenhouse et al (73) noted that membrane vesicles derived from X-linked hypophosphatemic mice have lower phosphate transport rates than vesicles derived from unaffected mice.

A kinetic analysis of the relationship in rat brush-border vesicles between phosphate uptake and sodium concentration suggests that at pH 6.0 (monovalent phosphate), 7.4, and 8.0 (divalent phosphate), two sodium ions interact for each phosphate ion transported. Hoffman et al (31) suggest that the interacting sodium ions are transported and that phosphate transport at pH 6.0 and perhaps at 7.4 would be associated with the translocation of a positive charge. Indeed, at pH 7.4, increasing the estimated negative transmembrane potential by substituting thiocyanate for chloride resulted in a small stimulation of phosphate uptake, qualitatively similar to that observed for glucose uptake (56, 57). Similarly, reducing the presumed electrical potential difference tended to decrease phosphate uptake. These observations may be analogous to the observations in intact proximal renal epithelia which indicate that sodium-dependent glucose transport reduces the inside negative transmembrane electrical potential (58) and also reduces phosphate transport (17, 20). One implication of these observations is that electrical as well as chemical consequences of sodium transport may affect phosphate transport; a second is that the influence of transmembrane electrical potentials on phosphate movements may be modified by the ambient pH. Hopfer (32) has reviewed the limitations of these techniques.

Thus it seems reasonable to propose that proximal phosphate reabsorption is initiated by sodium-dependent interactions between intraluminal phosphate and a brush-border membrane component, and that the mobility and dissociation of this complex may be affected by the electrical as well as chemical gradients across the luminal membrane. These chemical gradients may include not only sodium but also phosphate and possibly hydrogen ions. Completion of transepithelial movement could be accomplished by linkage of metabolically dependent sodium extrusion to the pool of intracellular phosphate available for transport.

CALCIUM

The renal handling of calcium as examined by micropuncture techniques has been reviewed extensively (26, 71). The questions addressed most frequently involve the segmental localization of calcium transport, the effects of PTH, and the relationship of sodium to calcium transport.

Localization of Calcium Transport

It is widely appreciated that only about 60% of the calcium in plasma water is ultrafilterable at the glomerulus (29, 30, 49). This is reduced to approximately 47% by hypercalcemia (30). Approximately 70% of the filtered load of calcium is reabsorbed along the proximal convoluted tubule, and calcium reabsorption in the early proximal tubule occurs at a rate lower than net sodium transport (2, 47, 48). Thus, the intraluminal calcium concentration rises above filtrate levels and then plateaus as calcium transport parallels volume absorption (48). These observations may reflect functional heterogeneity along the proximal tubule or the influence on calcium transport of some intraluminal solute such as bicarbonate or hydrogen ion. Calcium reabsorption also occurs in the loop of Henle (36); direct studies indicate net transport in the pars recta (65) and thick ascending limb but not in the thin descending or ascending limbs (64). Shareghi & Stoner (66) recently demonstrated that net calcium transport also occurs in isolated segments of the distal convoluted tubule as well as the granular portion of the cortical collecting duct. Calcium transport was not demonstrable in the more distal, light portion of the collecting duct. Thus, calcium reabsorption occurs in the proximal convoluted and straight tubules, in the thick ascending limb, and in the distal convoluted and granular cortical collecting tubules.

Parathyroid Hormone

The overall effect of PTH with regard to calcium is to increase its reabsorption (1–3). PTH, however, inhibits calcium reabsorption in the proximal convoluted tubule (2–5), has no direct effect on the thick ascending limb (66), and enhances calcium reabsorption in the distal convoluted tubule and granular cortical collecting duct (66). Thus, the PTH-sensitive regulation of calcium excretion occurs primarily in these two portions of the terminal nephron, although PTH-sensitive adenylate cyclase activity is more widely distributed along the nephron (52).

It is not entirely clear that the effects of PTH on calcium reabsorption are mediated through cyclic AMP. Agus et al (3) failed to demonstrate any effect of cyclic AMP on calcium excretion in the dog, and Kuntziger et al (45) made similar observations in the thyroparathyroidectomized rat. At this time the only clear demonstration that cyclic AMP may mediate the calcium-retaining effects of PTH is that of Burnatowska et al (16) using the hamster.

The effects of PTH on calcium transport in the distal segments occur independent of any changes in sodium or potassium transport. Similarly, furosemide and amiloride inhibit sodium transport in the distal convoluted tubule without affecting calcium reabsorption (66). Chlorothiazide also inhibits distal sodium reabsorption without affecting calcium reabsorption provided diuretic losses are replaced (23). These data indicate clearly that calcium handling by the distal nephron can be dissociated from sodium transport.

Calcium reabsorption in the thick ascending limb of Henle appears to be related directly to the electrochemical gradient established by active chloride reabsorption (66). That is, calcium transport in this segment is passive, and agents such as furosemide that inhibit sodium chloride transport and reduce the transepithelial electrical potential difference also inhibit calcium reabsorption (23, 66).

Mechanism of Calcium Transport

As noted above, calcium transport in the thick ascending limb of Henle is consistent with movement down the electrochemical gradient, but calcium reabsorption by other segments presumably occurs via active processes. In this regard, studies using stopflow microperfusion techniques in the rat indicate that proximal calcium transport is eliminated by replacement of ambient sodium with choline or lithium (76). Ouabain completely inhibits proximal calcium transport in the hamster (76). These observations may be related to the presence of a calcium-stimulated ATPase along the basolateral membranes of the proximal renal tubule (38).

Elimination of bicarbonate or inhibition of proximal carbonic anhydrase activity by acetazolamide had no effect on the active component of proximal calcium reabsorption (76), although other studies demonstrated that acetazolamide reduces proximal sodium and calcium reabsorption (10). These data may be consistent with a significant passive component of proximal calcium transport related perhaps to proximal volume absorption, but otherwise active calcium transport and proximal bicarbonate handling are mutually independent.

Literature Cited

1. Agus, Z. S., Chiu, P. J. S., Goldberg, M. 1977. Regulation of urinary calcium excretion in the rat. *Am. J. Physiol.* 232(6):F545–49
2. Agus, Z. S., Gardner, L. B., Beck, L. H., Goldberg, M. 1973. Effects of parathyroid hormone on renal tubular reabsorption of calcium, sodium, and phosphate. *Am. J. Physiol.* 224(5):1143–48
3. Agus, Z. S., Puschett, J. B., Senesky, D., Goldberg, M. 1971. Mode of action of parathyroid hormone and cyclic adenosine 3',5'-monophosphate on renal tubular phosphate reabsorption in the dog. *J. Clin. Invest.* 50:617–26
4. Amiel, C., Kuntziger, H., Couette, S., Coureau, C., Bergounioux, N. 1976. Evidence for a parathyroid hormone–independent calcium modulation of phosphate transport along the nephron. *J. Clin. Invest.* 57:256–63
5. Amiel, C., Kuntziger, H., Richet, G. 1970. Micropuncture study of handling of phosphate by proximal and distal nephron in normal and parathyroidectomized rat. Evidence for distal reabsorption. *Pfluegers Arch.* 317:93–109
6. Bank, N., Aynedjian, H. S., Weinstein, S. W. 1974. A microperfusion study of phosphate reabsorption by the rat proximal renal tubule. *J. Clin. Invest.* 54:1040–48
7. Bank, N., Su, W.-S., Aynedjian, H. S. 1978. A micropuncture study of renal phosphate transport in rats with chronic renal failure and secondary hyperparathyroidism. *J. Clin. Invest.* 61:884–94
8. Baumann, K., de Rouffignac, C., Roinel, N., Rumrich, G., Ullrich, K. J.

1975. Renal phosphate transport: inhomogeneity of local proximal transport rates and sodium dependence. *Pfleugers Arch.* 356:287–97
9. Baumann, K., Rumrich, G., Papavassiliou, F., Kloss, S. 1975. pH dependence of phosphate reabsorption in the proximal tubule of rat kidney. *Pfluegers Arch.* 360:183–87
10. Beck, L. H., Goldberg, M. 1973. Effects of acetazolamide and parathyroidectomy on renal transport of sodium, calcium and phosphate. *Am. J. Physiol.* 224:1136–42
11. Borle, A. B. 1974. Calcium and phosphate metabolism. *Ann. Rev. Physiol.* 37:361–90
12. Boudry, J.-F., Troehler, U., Touabi, M., Fleisch, H., Bonjour, J.-P. 1975. Secretion of inorganic phosphate in the rat nephron. *Clin. Sci. Mol. Med.* 48:475–89
13. Brazy, P. C., Dennis, V. W. 1978. Characteristics of glucose-phlorizin interactions in isolated proximal tubules. *Am. J. Physiol.* 234:F279–86
14. Brunette, M. G., Taleb, L., Carriere, S. 1973. Effect of parathyroid hormone on phosphate reabsorption along the nephron of the rat. *Am. J. Physiol.* 225:1076–81
15. Burg, M., Green, N. 1977. Bicarbonate transport by isolated perfused rabbit proximal convoluted tubules. *Am. J. Physiol.* 233:F307–14
16. Burnatowska, M. A., Harris, C. A., Sutton, R. A. L., Dirks, J. H. 1977. Effects of PTH and cyclic AMP on renal handling of calcium, magnesium and phos-

phate in the hamster. *Am. J. Physiol.* 233:F514–18

17. DeFronzo, R. A., Goldberg, M., Agus, Z. 1976. The effects of glucose and insulin on renal electrolyte transport. *J. Clin. Invest.* 58:83–90

18. Dennis, V. W. 1976. Influence of bicarbonate on parathyroid hormone–induced changes in fluid absorption by proximal tubule. *Kidney Int.* 10:373–80

19. Dennis, V. W., Bello-Reuss, E., Robinson, R. R. 1977. Response of phosphate transport to parathyroid hormone in segments of rabbit nephron. *Am. J. Physiol.* 233:F29–38

20. Dennis, V. W., Brazy, P. C. 1978. Sodium, phosphate, glucose, bicarbonate and alanine interactions in the isolated proximal convoluted tubule of the rabbit kidney. *J. Clin. Invest.* 62:387–97

21. Dennis, V. W., Woodhall, P. B., Robinson, R. R. 1976. Characteristics of phosphate transport in isolated proximal tubule. *Am. J. Physiol.* 231:979–85

22. Drezner, M., Neelon, F. A., Lebovitz, H. W. 1973. Pseudohypoparathyroidism Type II: A possible defect in the reception of the cyclic AMP signal. *N. Engl. J. Med.* 389:1056–60

23. Edwards, B. R., Baer, P. G., Sutton, R. A. L., Dirks, J. H. 1973. Micropuncture study of diuretic effects on sodium and calcium reabsorption in the dog nephron. *J. Clin. Invest.* 52:2418–27

24. Garg, L. C. 1976. Failure of parathyroid hormone and cyclic AMP to inhibit renal carbonic anhydrase. *Pfluegers Arch.* 367:103–4

25. Gekle, D., Stroder, J., Rostock, D. 1971. The effect of Vitamin D on renal inorganic phosphate reabsorption of normal rats, parathyroidectomized rats, and rats with rickets. *Pediatr. Res.* 5:40–52

26. Goldberg, M., Agus, Z. S., Goldfarb, S. 1976. Renal handling of phosphate, calcium, and magnesium. In *The Kidney,* ed. B. M. Brenner, F. C. Rector, Jr., 1:344–90. Philadelphia: Saunders

27. Greger, R. F., Lang, F. C., Knox, F. G., Lechene, C. P. 1977. Absence of significant secretory flux of phosphate in the proximal convoluted tubule. *Am. J. Physiol.* 232:F235–38

28. Greger, R. F., Lang, F., Marchand, G., Knox, F. G. 1977. Site of renal phosphate reabsorption—micropuncture and microinfusion study. *Pfluegers Arch.* 369:111–18

29. Harris, C. A., Baer, P. G., Chirito, E., Dirks, J. H. 1974. Composition of mammalian glomerular filtrate. *Am. J. Physiol.* 227:972–76

30. Harris, C. A., Sutton, R. A. L., Dirks, J. H. 1977. Effects of hypercalcemia on calcium and phosphate ultrafilterability and tubular reabsorption in the rat. *Am. J. Physiol.* 233:F201–6

31. Hoffman, N., Thees, M., Kinne, R. 1976. Phosphate transport by isolated renal brush-border vesicles. *Pfluegers Arch.* 362:147–56

32. Hopfer, U. 1977. Isolated membrane vesicles as tools for analysis of epithelial transport. *Am. J. Physiol.* 233:E445–49

33. Hoppe, A., Knox, F. G. 1978. Effect of acute acid-base changes on fractional phosphate excretion in thyroparathyroidectomized hamsters. *Clin. Res.* 26:542A (Abstr.)

34. Humes, H. D., Ichikawa, I., Troy, J. L., Brenner, B. M. 1978. Evidence for a parathyroid hormone–dependent influence of calcium on the glomerular ultrafiltration coefficient. *J. Clin. Invest.* 61:32–40

35. Imai, M., Seldin, D. W., Kokko, J. P. 1977. Effect of perfusion rate on the fluxes of water, sodium, chloride and urea across the proximal convoluted tubule. *Kidney Int.* 11:18–27

36. Jamison, R. L., Frey, N. R., Lacy, F. B. 1974. Calcium reabsorption in the thin loop of Henle. *Am. J. Physiol.* 227:745–51

37. Kaplan, M. A., Canterbury, J. M., Gavellas, G., Jaffe, D., Bourgoignie, J. J., Reiss, E., Bricker, N. S. 1978. Interrelations between phosphorus, calcium, parathyroid hormone and renal phosphate excretion in response to an oral phosphate load in normal and uremic dogs. *Kidney Int.* 14:207–14

38. Kinne-Saffran, E., Kinne, R. 1974. Localization of a calcium stimulated ATPase in the basolateral plasma membranes of the proximal tubule of rat kidney cortex. *J. Membr. Biol.* 17:263–74

39. Knox, F. G., Haas, J. A., Berndt, T., Marchand, G. R., Youngberg, S. P. 1977. Phosphate transport in superficial and deep nephrons in phosphate-loaded rats. *Am. J. Physiol.* 233:F150–53

40. Knox, F. G., Lechene, C. 1975. Distal site of action of parathyroid hormone on phosphate reabsorption. *Am. J. Physiol.* 229:1556–60

41. Knox, F. G., Osswald, H., Marchand, G. R., Spielman, W. S., Haas, J. A., Berndt, T., Youngberg, S. P. 1977. Phosphate transport along the nephron. *Am. J. Physiol.* 233:F261–68

42. Knox, F. G., Preiss, J., Kim, J. K., Dousa, T. P. 1977. Mechanism of resistance to the phosphaturic effect of parathyroid hormone in the hamster. *J. Clin. Invest.* 59:675–83

43. Kokko, J. P. 1973. Proximal tubule potential difference: dependence on glucose, HCO_3 and amino acids. *J. Clin. Invest.* 52:1362–67

44. Kuntziger, H., Amiel, C., Gaudebout, C. 1972. Phosphate handling by the rat nephron during saline diuresis. *Kidney Int.* 2:318–23

45. Kuntziger, H., Amiel, C., Roinel, N., Morel, F. 1974. Effects of parathyroidectomy and cyclic AMP on renal transport of phosphate, calcium, and magnesium. *Am. J. Physiol.* 227:905–11

46. Lang, F., Greger, R., Marchand, G. R., Knox, F. G. 1977. Stationary microperfusion study of phosphate reabsorption in proximal and distal nephron segments. *Pfluegers Arch.* 368:45–48

47. Lassiter, W. E., Gottschalk, C. W., Mylle, M. 1963. Micropuncture study of renal tubular reabsorption of calcium in normal rodents. *Am. J. Physiol.* 204:771–75

48. LeGrimellec, C. 1975. Micropuncture study along the proximal convoluted tubule—electrolyte reabsorption in first convolutions. *Pfluegers Arch.* 354: 133–50

49. LeGrimellec, C., Poujeol, P., de Rouffignac, C. 1975. ^{3}H-inulin and electrolyte concentrations in Bowman's capsule in rat kidney. *Pfluegers Arch.* 354:117–31

50. LeGrimellec, C., Roinel, N., Morel, F. 1973. Simultaneous Mg, Ca, P, K, Na and Cl analysis in rat tubular fluid. *Pfluegers Arch.* 340:181–96

51. Massry, S. G. 1977. Pharmacology of magnesium. *Ann. Rev Pharmacol. Toxicol.* 17:67–82

52. Morel, F., Chabardes, D., Imbert, M. 1976. Functional segmentation of the rabbit distal tubule by microdetermination of hormone-dependent adenylate cyclase activity. *Kidney Int.* 9:264–77

53. Mudge, G. H., Berndt, W. O., Valtin, H. 1976. Tubular transport of urea, glucose, phosphate, uric acid, sulfate and thiosulfate. In *Handbook of Physiology: Renal Physiology,* ed. J. Orloff, R. W. Berliner, pp. 587–652. Baltimore: Williams and Wilkins

54. Muhlbauer, R. C., Bonjour, J.-P., Fleisch, H. 1977. Tubular localization of adaptation to dietary phosphate in rats. *Am. J. Physiol.* 233:F342–48

55. Murayama, Y., Morel, F., LeGrimellec, C. 1972. Phosphate, calcium and magnesium transfers in proximal tubules and loops of Henle, as measured by single nephron microperfusion experiments in the rat. *Pfluegers Arch.* 333:1–16

56. Murer, H., Hopfer, U. 1974. Demonstration of electrogenic Na^+-dependent D-glucose transport in intestinal brushborder membranes. *Proc. Natl. Acad. Sci. USA* 71:484–88

57. Murer, H., Sigrist-Nelson, K., Hopfer, U. 1975. On the mechanism of sugar and amino acid interaction in intestinal transport. *J. Biol. Chem.* 250:7392–96

58. Maruyama, T., Hoshi, T. 1972. The effect of D-glucose on the electrical potential profile across the proximal tubule of the newt kidney. *Biophys. Biochim. Acta* 282:214–25

59. Pastoriza-Munoz, E., Colindres, R. E., Lassiter, W. E., Lechene, C. 1978. Effect of PTH on phosphate transport in the rat distal convolution. *Am. J. Physiol.* 235:F321–30

60. Popovtzer, M. M., Robinette, J. B. 1975. Effect of 25(OH)vitamin D_3 on urinary excretion of cyclic adenosine monophosphate. *Am. J. Physiol.* 229: 907–10

61. Popovtzer, M. M., Robinette, J. B., DeLuca, H. F., Holick, M. F. 1974. The acute effect of 25-hydroxycholecalciferol on renal handling of phosphorus. *J. Clin. Invest.* 53:913–21

62. Puschett, J. B., Beck, W. S. Jr., Jelonek, A., Fernandez, P. C. 1974. Study of the renal tubular interactions of thyrocalcitonin, cyclic adenosine 3',5'-monophosphate, 25-hydroxycholecalciferol, and calcium ion. *J. Clin. Invest.* 53:756–67

63. Puschett, J. B., Moranz, J., Kurnick, W. S. 1972. Evidence for a direct action of cholecalciferol and 25-hydroxycholecalciferol on the renal transport of phosphate, sodium, and calcium. *J. Clin. Invest.* 51:373–85

64. Rocha, A. S., Magaldi, J. B., Kokko, J. P. 1977. Calcium and phosphate transport in isolated segments of rabbit Henle's loop. *J. Clin. Invest.* 59:975–83

65. Rouse, D., Suki, W. N. 1978. Calcium transport in the superficial straight proximal tubule. *Clin. Res.* 26:544A (Abstr.)

66. Shareghi, G. R., Stoner, L. C. 1978. Parathyroid hormone sensitive calcium transport by rabbit distal nephron. *Fed. Proc.* 37:728

67. Shirley, D. G., Poujeol, P., LeGrimellec, C. 1976. Phosphate, calcium and magnesium fluxes into the lumen of the rat proximal convoluted tubule. *Pfluegers Arch.* 362:247–54

68. Staum, B. B., Hamburger, R. J., Goldberg, M. 1972. Tracer microinjection study of renal tubular phosphate reabsorption in the rat. *J. Clin. Invest.* 51:2271–76

69. Steele, T. H. 1976. Renal resistance to parathyroid hormone during phosphorus deprivation. *J. Clin. Invest.* 58:1461–64

70. Strickler, J. C., Thompson, D. D., Klose, R. M., Giebisch, G. 1964. Micropuncture study of inorganic phosphate excretion in the rat. *J. Clin. Invest.* 43:1596–1607

71. Sutton, R. A. L., Dirks, J. H. 1975. The renal excretion of calcium: a review of micropuncture data. *Can. J. Physiol. Pharmacol.* 53:979–88

72. Swenson, R. S., Weisinger, J. R., Ruggeri, J. L., Reaven, G. M. 1975. Evidence that parathyroid hormone is not required for phosphate homeostasis in renal failure. *Metabolism* 24:199–204

73. Tenenhouse, H. S., Scriver, C. R., McInnes, R. R., Glorieux, F. H. 1978.

Renal handling of phosphate in vivo and in vitro by the X-linked hypophosphatemic male mouse. Evidence for a defect in the brush-border membrane. *Kidney Int.* 14:236–44

74. Tisher, C. C. 1976. Anatomy of the kidney. See Ref. 26, pp. 3–64.

75. Troehler, U., Bonjour, J.-P., Fleisch, H. 1976. Inorganic phosphate homeostasis: renal adaptation to the dietary intake in intact and thyroparathyroidectomized rats. *J. Clin. Invest.* 57:265–73

76. Ullrich, K. J., Rumrich, G., Kloss, S. 1976. Active Ca^{2+} reabsorption in the proximal tubule of the rat kidney. *Pfluegers Arch.* 364:223–28

77. Ullrich, K. J., Rumrich, G., Kloss, S. 1977. Phosphate transport in the proximal convolution of the rat kidney. *Pfluegers Arch.* 372:269–74

78. Walser, M. 1960. Protein-binding of inorganic phosphate in plasma of normal subjects and patients with renal disease. *J. Clin. Invest.* 39:501–6

79. Webb, R. K., Woodhall, P. B., Tisher, C. C., Glaubiger, G., Neelon, F. A., Robinson, R. R. 1977. Relationship between phosphaturia and acute hypercapnea in the rat. *J. Clin. Invest.* 60:829–37

COMPARATIVE PHYSIOLOGY

Introduction

The assignment of a section of the *Annual Review of Physiology* to comparative physiology allows formal consideration of animals whose functional capabilities differ either quantitatively or qualitatively from those of more conventional experimental subjects. Such consideration contributes to the development of perspective concerning particular processes and assists in placing animal physiology in an evolutionary context. In the present section three major topics are reviewed: natural mammalian hibernation, reproductive endocrinology of lower vertebrates, and avian navigation. The discussions of hibernation summarize the current state of knowledge concerning neural and endocrine correlates of this process and its cellular basis. The two reviews of reproductive endocrinology deal with fish and with amphibians and reptiles, respectively. A number of similarities but some important differences are apparent in these animals in comparison with the endocrine control of reproduction in mammals. A third review on this topic dealing with avian reproductive endocrinology will be included in Volume 42 of the *Annual Review of Physiology*. The last article in the present section deals with current knowledge of avian navigation. A case is made for some impressive sensory capabilities in various birds and for the presence of considerable redundancy in their navigational systems. The reviews comprising the comparative physiology section of this volume provide a cogent reminder of the resourcefulness of nature and of the consequent diversity that can characterize the functional capabilities of animals.

William R. Dawson
Section Editor

Ann. Rev. Physiol. 1979. 41:275–86
Copyright © 1979 by Annual Reviews Inc. All Rights Reserved

HIBERNATION: CELLULAR ASPECTS

♦1219

J. S. Willis

Department of Physiology and Biophysics, University of Illinois,
Urbana, Illinois 61801

INTRODUCTION

The challenges to and involvement of cells in hibernation are as diverse as the phenomenon itself. Seasonal cycles of inanition, inactivity and heterothermy that occur in many species of hibernators require adjustments in metabolic and perhaps neural pathways, in macromolecular synthetic activity, and in cellular work. While some features of such seasonal adjustments may be shared with species that do not hibernate, the short-term cycle of entry into, maintenance in, and arousal from a bout of hibernation presents in the more extreme cases of body cooling a thermal challenge not faced by the cells of the deep "core" of other mammals.

This review focuses on the latter aspect—the problems of cells in the short cycle of hibernation. Many studies, however, have dealt, often unwittingly, with seasonal differences in cells. The most extensive and explicit investigation of metabolic and cellular features of seasonal changes in a hibernator (hedgehog) compared with a nonhibernator (guinea pig) also provides the best review on this subject (28).

Since the principal feature of the short cycle of hibernation is the large span of temperature in which cells must function, this discussion deals mainly with adaptation to cold. It neglects cellular requirements for rewarming during arousal and for suppression of activity during entry. Special adaptations for hibernation in these two categories have not been established, although suppression may be greater than what could be accounted for by ordinary parasympathetic tone and by cooling (32). Recently suggested as factors responsible for such extraordinary metabolic suppression are an increase in relative acidity caused by the shift in the neutral point of water with cooling (32), and a specific hypothalamic neurohumor (47).

275

0066-4278/79/0301-0275$01.00

Turning to the central theme of this review, cold adaptation can be considered from the general physiological viewpoint of the difficulties faced by any cell in surviving and functioning at two widely different temperatures. It can also be considered from the standpoint of peculiar problems and features of specific cells and tissues carrying out differentiated tasks for the whole organism.

GENERAL ASPECTS OF CELL FUNCTION AT LOW TEMPERATURE

Are Cells of Hibernators Intrinsically Cold Adapted?

Hibernating mammals survive for many days at body temperatures (approaching 0°C in some cases) well below those fatal to most mammals. Why do the cold-sensitive mammals die? Is their intolerance of reduced body temperature related to cold sensitivity of cells, to lack of proper coordination, or to failure of a few critical cells? Peripheral nerve conduction in vitro and conduction and beating of isolated perfused hearts were early shown to persist at lower temperatures in preparations from organisms of hibernating species than in those of routinely used nonhibernating ones, although there are exceptions [for references see (52, 55)]. Aside from these two cases and the beating of ciliated epithelia, persistence of differentiated function has not generally been used as a criterion of cold resistance. In terms of cell survival (ion regulation, dye exclusion) or reproductive capacity, other freshly isolated tissues of hibernators tend to show greater cold resistance than those of nonhibernating mammals; exceptions are lens tissue (8) and possibly brain cortical slices (23). Differences between hibernators and nonhibernators persist into primary culture in both differentiated cells [kidney epithelium (65)] and embryonic fibroblasts (3), but are less consistent in longer-term diploid cultures (55, 56). [Aneuploid continuous cultures are cold-resistant regardless of source (24, 55).]

Cold Adaptation of Membrane Function

Regulation of ion gradients (usually K and Na) has frequently been used as a criterion of cell survival because it is essential for maintenance of cell volume and protein synthesis (reviewed in 54) and because it is an indicator of cellular integrity and continued function. It is also part of the differentiated activities that persist at low temperature (see next section). What, then, are the mechanisms underlying the cold adaptation of such regulation? [For detailed reviews and references, see (18, 55, 58, 65).] In principle, cold-sensitive cells lose K at low temperature because the leakage of this ion is less reduced than active accumulation through the Na/K pump. Therefore, maintaining the gradient simply requires keeping that balance. In red blood cells the Na/K pump is less inhibited with cooling in ground squirrels than in guinea pigs. Kinetics of stimulation of the pump by cellular Na and extracellular K change with temperature in red cells of both species, but not in such a way as to account for the differences in net transport (18). In cultured kidney cells of hamsters, guinea pigs, and ground squirrels, there were only minor differences in temperature sensitivity of ouabain-inhibited active transport of K, which has a Q_{10} only slightly greater than 2 in all three species.[1] However, K transport in primary cells of rat kidney is more temperature-sensitive (J. S. Willis, R. F. Foster, unpublished results).

The passive fluxes of K are more reduced by cooling in red cells and kidney cells of ground squirrel and in kidney cells of hamster than in those of guinea pig. Thus by the standard of tissues of ground squirrel, the red cells of guinea pig lose their ion balance both because of reduction of pump activity and because of insufficient reduction of leak, whereas in the kidney cells of guinea pig only the latter (leak) is a problem.

Cold Adaptation of Metabolism

When an energy-dependent activity such as Na/K transport or possibly the maintenance of low cation permeability is lost at low temperature, is the loss due to insufficient energy from metabolism (ATP) or to direct inhibition of the activity? [For reviews, see (12, 35, 45, 55).] One way to answer this question might be to examine the change with temperature in the cellular concentration of ATP (or alternatively the total pool of energy-rich phosphate bonds). In perfused brains of hypothermic rats where precautions were taken against hypoxia and acidosis (35), no decline in ATP or rise in ADP was observed, even though loss of Na/K regulation occurred. In human red cells stored at 5°C, ATP levels decline, but the fall is slow, thanks in part to the regeneration of ATP from a large reservoir of 2,3-diphosphoglycerate. Loss of K is faster and not well correlated with the fall in ATP (61). Energy-rich phosphate reserves decline by 25–40% in erythrocytes of hamsters in vivo during three or four days of hibernation (11).

Levels of ATP, ADP, and inorganic phosphate in cooled perfused hearts of rats and ground squirrels have recently been analyzed (13). At the temperature of failure in rats (below 20°C) the ATP concentration was not significantly lower than at 35°C, but, because of elevated inorganic phosphate concentration, the so-called phosphate potential ($ATP/ADP+P_i$) was decreased. In ground squirrel heart at 6°C (where beating persists) ATP concentration was decreased by about 25% from the value at 35°C, but the phosphate potential was unchanged.

---

[1]Unless otherwise indicated, the term "hamster" in this review refers to the Syrian hamster (*Mesocritus auratus*) and "ground squirrel" to the thirteen-lined ground squirrel (*Citellus tridecemlineatus*).

Attempts to explore temperature sensitivity of metabolic pathways have emphasized mitochondria. Respiration of cardiac mitochondria provided with pyruvate as substrate and with phosphate acceptor show less decrease in respiration with cooling in hibernators than in rats (43). However, when succinate is used as substrate no difference is seen (42). Several studies have involved liver mitochondria, with confusing and conflicting results.

Temperature dependence of glycolysis and (perhaps more important in view of its greater role in hibernation) of fatty acid oxidation have not been investigated extensively. Glycolysis in intact tissue of brain and heart may be less inhibited by cold in ground squirrels than in rats (14). Temperature effects on rate of palmitate oxidation in liver do not differ significantly among rats, hamsters, and ground squirrels (19).

Pyruvate kinase is the only purified enzyme of an energy releasing pathway to have been analyzed intensively for thermal effects on kinetics (5, 6, 9, 37). As a result of altered effects of temperature on the interactions of the various substrates (phosphoenol pyruvate, ADP) and effectors (e.g. fructose diphosphate), the winter form of the enzyme in muscles of bats is less inhibited by cooling over the range of temperature faced by the bat, whereas the winter form in livers of ground squirrels is more inhibited.

Results of metabolic studies at all levels of organization seem ambiguous. As with the issue of balance between pump and leak, the balance between ability to utilize energy and ability to provide utilizable energy probably varies from cell to cell, and in cold-sensitive cells the cause of failure may be variably laid to one or the other category.

Membrane Fluidity

It is widely hypothesized that differences in resistance to low temperature may be due to differences in physical state of the nonpolar interior of membranes, the unusual sensitivity to cold resulting from the membranes undergoing a transition to a less fluid form. Resistant cells are thought to be better able to maintain this fluidity, perhaps in part by possessing more double bonds in their hydrocarbon chains. This hypothesis could account for differences both in mitochondrial respiration (see above) and in plasma membrane–bound enzymes such as Na-K ATPase (see below). It is based upon three lines of evidence: (a) The discontinuities or downward breaks of Arrhenius plots of enzymatic activities observed in sensitive cells and perhaps absent in resistant cells could easily be explained by phase transitions; (b) chemical probes (e.g. fluorescence polarization) show differences in microviscosity of the hydrocarbon region betwen cold-adapted and warm-adapted-cells; (c) increases in unsaturation of hydrocarbon chains of membrane phospholipids and in relative abundance of lyso compounds (i.e. glycerides with only one hydrocarbon chain) have been reported in tissues of hibernating species with onset of the hibernating state [see (15, 55) for references and discussion]. Differences in lipids and in membrane fluidity have so far been compared only seasonally and have not been related to species-specific cold adaptation. In any case breaks in Arrhenius curves also occur in nonmembrane enzymes; and even where differences in membrane fluidity do occur they may be due to differences in proteins, whose structure can affect lipid packing and thermal behavior of membranes (41).

SPECIAL PROBLEMS AND FEATURES OF CELL FUNCTION IN HIBERNATION

Intermediary Metabolism

An issue of long-standing interest has been the source of energy during the course of a single bout of hibernation. Classically lipid metabolism during deep hibernation has been viewed as the dominant source, with carbohydrate metabolism becoming more important during arousal. Originally such a conclusion was based on the respiratory quotient, CO_2/O_2 (0.7 in hibernation, 1.0 during arousal). Findings of depletion of liver glycogen during arousal in hamster tended to confirm the view (31, reviewed in 45). However, two detailed studies (1, 22), both based on changes in concentrations of metabolites, suggest that in garden dormice and arctic ground squirrels lipid continues to be a major energy source even during arousal; this also appears to be the case in bats (20). The fall in R.Q. during warming in these cases may result from release of excess CO_2 held in the blood at low temperature. Glycogen depletion may nevertheless contribute to rewarming (especially the later phases) even in these species and is made good by concurrent and subsequent gluconeogenesis before reentry.

Heart and Skeletal Muscle

With respect to activities of cells that expend energy, perhaps those of muscles most obviously set the deep hibernator apart from other mammals. The beating of the heart not only continues to sustain a viable blood pressure in deep hibernation but also contributes to increased thermogenesis during arousal. Continued contraction of skeletal muscles is required mainly for respiratory movements during deep hibernation, but in rodents it also provides most of the heat for arousal. By contrast, cardiac fibrillation (or blockade) and blocking of respiratory reflexes are two of the more immediate causes of death in forced hypothermia of nonhibernators.

The properties of tension development of cardiac muscle at low temperature have been well studied by South and his associates [for references, see (46)], who found that maximum tension was better sustained at low temperature in ventricular muscle of hamsters than in those of rats and better in ventricular muscle of hibernating hamsters than in those of awake hamsters. Maximum *rate* of tension development at low temperature (allegedly a better function of active state without contribution of elastic elements) was greater at 5°C only in ventricular muscles of hibernating hamsters, muscle from awake hamsters being similar to that of rat. A recent mechanical study of in situ hearts of woodchucks (2) showed that while force development declined during entry into hibernation, maximum force in hibernation was little less than in the waking state and was greatly increased during the early stages of arousal (lowest body temperature was 10°C).

Few attempts have been made to search at a molecular level for any species differences in behavior of molecules involved in contraction. One study (30) showed no difference in temperature sensitivity of Ca-activated myosin ATPase of cardiac muscle between rabbit and woodchuck; another (4) showed no difference in Ca-activated sarcoplasmic reticular ATPase between skeletal muscle of rat and ground squirrel.

Synaptic transmission is peculiarly vulnerable to temperature, and the myoneural junction of the phrenic nerve-diaphragm of rat failed at 10°C even when conduction in nerve and muscle was maintained, whereas in preparations from active and hibernating hamsters no failure occurred at 10°C and 5°, respectively (44). Some of the details of the change with hibernation in this preparation from hamsters have been pursued (34, 38, 50) using only one intermediate temperature. The size of the zone of receptivity and the post-synaptic sensitivity to acetylcholine was found to be greater in the hibernating state. Indirect evidence was also obtained that in hibernation activatable Na channels increase at the expense of activatable K channels.

In skeletal and atrial muscle, the fall in excitability to electrical stimulation (reciprocal of threshold) with declining temperature is less steep for ground squirrels than for rats and rabbits (33, 44). However, in trabecular muscle the decline was actually steeper for hamsters than for rats (46). Resting membrane potentials of atrial fibers—at least active ones—of ground squirrels decrease little down to 6°C, whereas those of rabbit atria decline steeply below 17°C (33); this severe decline accounts for the higher blocking temperature of rabbit atria (33). In contrast, the resting potentials of trabecular muscle decline perhaps as much in hamsters as in rats by 12°C (the lowest temperature tested) (26). The difference in temperature at which block of the trabecular muscle occurs might reflect the greater reduction of action potential in the rat muscle with cooling without any compensatory increase in duration.

In addition to having presumably more stable membrane potentials in the face of changing temperatures, cardiac muscle of hedgehog is also less susceptible to fibrillatory effects of drugs (16, 27). Ground squirrel atria however, are not impervious to arrythmic effects of ouabain (25).

Brain and Peripheral Nerve

Although cold adaptation of peripheral nerve conduction has been demonstrated several times, the cellular basis of the phenomenon has not been examined. In addition, the effects of low temperature on transmitter synthesis and axonal flow must be assessed. In studies of phrenic nerve-diaphragm preparations (34) the kinetics of changes in miniature end-plate potentials suggest that the rate of restoration of transmitter by synthesis is reduced during hibernation. However, measurements with temperature change were not made. Increased synthesis and turnover of 5-hydroxytryptamine is said to increase in brain stem of hamsters just before and during hibernation (40). Axonal transport of labelled proline of isolated nerves of both rats and Richardson's ground squirrels is blocked at 10°C and similar rates are evident for the two species at higher temperatures (7).

Brains of hibernating common dormice perfused in situ maintain cellular regulation of Na and K and prevent swelling better than those of awake dormice (35). In so-called microsomal fractions made from brains of hedgehogs and hamsters, slightly less inhibition of Na-K ATPase with cooling was seen in those preparations from hibernating individuals (see 23). Preparations made from awake individuals of these two species exhibited values no different from those made from rat brains. Charnock (15) did not find evidence for cold adaptation in Na-K ATPase of ground squirrel brains even in preparations made from hibernating individuals. From these bits it would seem that central neurons of hibernators might only be cold resistant, if at all, when the organisms are in a hibernating state. Yet individuals of hibernating species surpass nonhibernators in maintaining function during forced hypothermia [for references see (36)]. During hibernation excitable function and ion regulation are retained at low temperature (23, 36).

Kidney

A priori it might seem that with respect to salt and water balance the kidney faces the same problem at an organ level that the cell membrane faces at the cellular level, namely, having to make good with metabolically dependent (thermally vulnerable) transport processes a loss of material driven by physical forces perhaps less sensitive to temperature. That is, if blood pressure were maintained at normal levels in hibernation driving glomerular filtration, how could tubular reabsorption keep pace? This problem is more apparent than real; because blood pressure is somewhat reduced in hibernation, blood flow to the kidney may be relatively reduced, and resistance to filtration may be increased (49). In any case, urine flow is certainly much reduced in hibernation, and glomerular filtration rate probably is (62).

On the transport side, the most abundant and reliable information concerns the concentration of urine and the maintenance of the corticomedullary (CM) gradient which arises in part from salt reabsorption in distal regions of the nephron. The earliest reports based on urea and Na determinations in slices of kidney of Columbian ground squirrel suggested that the osmotic gradient was abolished in hibernation and restored during arousal (39). A CM gradient of Na is, however, maintained at a reduced level in hibernating hamsters, although it disappears in animals of this species during forced hypothermia (48). There is no CM gradient of urea in either hibernating or hypothermic hamsters (48). A CM gradient of total osmotic concentration was observed in hibernating marmots, and the final concentration of urine produced in hibernation was about twice that of the plasma (63).

Studies based on the "plasma clearance technique" (i.e. without urine collection) seemed to indicate that in hibernating marmots clearance of PAH was about three times that of inulin (62). These results suggested that active secretion of PAH persisted in hibernation, but reexamination of the technique (63) removed the quantitative certainty of this conclusion. PAH secretion probably does occur at low temperature, but because flow is nearly static the gradient is much steeper than usual. In a marmot with body temperature reduced only to 20°C, glucose reabsorption was already considerably impaired (64). Further studies of these issues incorporating urine collection have been hampered by the difficulty of maintaining bladder or ureteral catheters.

Renal cortical K concentration rises greatly during hibernation in hamsters and ground squirrels and during forced hypothermia in hamsters (59). It has been suggested that this may serve to diminish any tendency for a rise in serum K. Renal tissue of hibernators is well able to retain K at low temperature in vitro (55, 58, 65), but the additional accumulation of K to a *higher* steady state under such conditions has not been observed.

The cold adaptation of ion regulation in renal cells has been discussed above. There is roughly a doubling of specific activity of Na-K ATPase in microsomal fraction of hamster kidney cortex during cold exposure prior to hibernation (21), but in hibernating Richardson's ground squirrels specific activity *decreases* by almost two thirds from the level in awake summer squirrels (15). Na-K ATPase in crude fractions of hamster kidney cortex showed measurable activity at 5°C, whereas that of preparations from rat showed none below 10°C (60). On the other hand, the shape of the

Arrhenius plot of Na-K ATPase of renal cortex of Richardson's ground squirrel, when compared with those of rabbit and sheep, did not accord with greater cold resistance (15). However, in the latter study actual data for the low temperatures were not given, and it is also known that ion transport in rabbit kidneys is as cold resistant as that of any hibernator (53). In any case conclusions about temperature adaptation or its absence based on Na-K ATPase may be generally suspect, since the isolated enzyme has been shown to have temperature sensitivity often qualitatively greater than that of the Na-K pump of the intact cells whence it is taken (17, 57).

Applications

Two subjects in which low temperature may provide a useful standard of comparison are hypothermic organ storage and cellular aging. The potential life span of erythrocytes of hamsters (10) and hedgehogs (29) and probably of other hibernators (see 10) is greatly extended during the periods of low body temperature of hibernation. Storage of organs at low temperature reduces the demand for oxygen and the likelihood of autolysis, but it increases damage due to low temperature itself. Tissues and cells of hibernators are better able than those of nonhibernators to withstand long-term storage at low temperature, possibly because of their better regulation of cations (54, 56). Perhaps this will also be the case with whole organs.

Neglected Issues

Several subjects have received virtually no attention with respect to the specializations of hibernators for functioning at low temperature. These include organic molecule transport, either into cells or across cells; kinetics of binding of neural transmitters and of hormones; and turnover (synthesis and degradation) of proteins (but see 51). Cell cycle in tissues of hibernators is blocked at low temperature as in cells of other mammals, but the implications of this and the mechanism of avoiding chromosomal and mitotic damage that usually results from such blockage (55) have not been studied.

CONCLUSION

Within a single bout of hibernation, special cellular problems connected with each phase occur: suppression of activity to permit entry, thermogenic activity to permit arousal, and maintenance of activity at low temperature to permit survival. For the first two of these categories, special adaptations for hibernators have been suggested but not established; for the third their existence is obvious. Most tissues of hibernators maintain minimal function at low temperature in vivo; in many cases this capacity persists in vitro—

in a few instances for several cell generations. Hence cold resistance is variably dependent upon organismic influence.

Nearly all cellular activities are depressed by cooling, and the real problem of the cell hinges upon maintaining *balances* between energy utilization and mobilization of energy and between leakage and pumping of ions. Loss of balance is most likely to occur when temperature-sensitive complex chemical reactions are normally poised against simpler physical forces (e.g. pumping of ions vs their diffusion down a gradient) or where cooling may cause unusually severe effects on molecular order (e.g. fluidity of lipid bilayers, flexibility of regulatory proteins). Not all cells of nonhibernators fail to function at low temperature, and for those that do there is not necessarily a common thermal Achilles heel; each cell type or species may have its own.

Beyond this general problem, differentiated cells face specific challenges. For most of these only the merest description of the status has been provided, and deeper analyses of mechanism are awaited.

Literature Cited

1. Agid, R., Ambid, L. 1969. Effects of corporeal temperature on glucose metabolism in a homeotherm, the rat, and a hibernator, the garden dormouse. In *Depressed Metabolism*, ed. X. J. Musacchia, J. F. Saunders, pp. 119–57. New York: American Elsevier. 630 pp.
2. Armour, J. A., Spurrier, W. A., Dawe, A. R. 1974. Contractility of the *in situ* hibernating marmot ventricle. *Comp. Biochem. Physiol.* 47A:811–20
3. Baudyšová, M. 1977. Cold resistance of cultured cells from hamster and human embryos. *Cryobiology* 14:506–10
4. Becker, J. H., Willis, J. S. 1975. Absence of cold resistance in sarcoplasmic Ca-ATPase in a hibernating mammal. *Comp. Biochem. Physiol.* 52B:533–35
5. Behrisch, H. W. 1974. Temperature and the regulation of enzyme activity in the hibernator. Isoenzymes of liver pyruvate kinase from the hibernating and non-hibernating squirrel. *Can. J. Biochem.* 52:894–902
6. Behrisch, H. W., Johnson, C. E. 1974. Regulatory properties of pyruvate kinase from liver of the summer-active ground squirrel. *Can. J. Biochem.* 52:547–59
7. Bisby, M. A., Jones, D. L. 1978. Temperature sensitivity of axonal transport in hibernators and non-hibernators. *Thermobiology* 3:100
8. Bito, L. Z., Roberts, J. C., Saraff, S. 1972. Maintenance of normal corneal

thickness in the cold *in vivo* (hibernation) as opposed to *in vitro*. *J. Physiol. London* 231:71–86
9. Borgmann, A. I., Moon, T. W. 1976. Enzymes of the normothermic and hibernating bat, *Myotis lucifugus:* temperature as a modulator of pyruvate kinase. *J. Comp. Physiol. B* 107:185–200
10. Brock, M. A. 1960. Production and life span of erythrocytes during hibernation in the golden hamster. *Am. J. Physiol.* 198:1181–86
11. Brock, M. A. 1967. Erythrocyte glycolytic intermediates of control, cold-exposed and hibernating hamsters. In *Mammalian Hibernators III*, ed. K. C. Fisher, A. R. Dawe, C. P. Lyman, E. Schönbaum, F. E. South, pp. 409–20. Edinburgh: Oliver and Boyd. 535 pp.
12. Burlington, R. F. 1972. Recent advances in intermediary metabolism of hibernating mammals. In *Hibernation and Hypothermia, Perspectives and Challenges,* ed. F. E. South, J. P. Hannon, J. S. Willis, E. T. Pengelley, N. R. Alpert, pp. 3–16. Amsterdam: Elsevier. 743 pp.
13. Burlington, R. F., Meininger, G. A., Thurston, J. T. 1976. Effect of low temperature on high energy phosphate compounds in isolated hearts from a hibernator and a non-hibernator. *Comp. Biochem. Physiol.* 55B:403–7
14. Burlington, R. F., Whitten, B. K., Sidel, C. M., Posiviata, M. A., Salkovitz, I. A.

1970. Effect of hypoxia on glycolysis in perfused hearts from rats and ground squirrels (*Citellus lateralis*). *Comp. Bioch. Physiol.* 35:403–14

15. Charnock, J. S. 1978. Membrane lipid phase-transitions: a biological response to hibernation? In *Strategies in Cold: Natural Torpidity and Thermogenesis,* ed. L. Wang, J. W. Hudson, pp. 417–60. NY: Academic

16. Duker, G., Johansson, B. W., Olsson, S.-O. 1978. Differences in resistance to ventricular fibrillation between hibernators and non-hibernators. *Thermobiology* 3:89

17. Ellory, J. C., Willis, J. S. 1976. Temperature dependence of membrane function. Disparity between active potassium transport and (Na+K)-ATPase activity. *Biochim. Biophys. Acta* 443: 301–5

18. Ellory, J. C., Willis, J. S. 1978. Temperature dependence of the cation affinities of the sodium pump in red cells from hibernators and non-hibernators. *J. Physiol. London* 275:62P

19. Entenman, C., Hillyard, L. A., Holloway, R. J., Albright, M. L., Leong, G. F. 1969. Intermediary metabolism in hypothermic rat liver. See Ref. 1, pp. 159–97

20. Esher, R. J., Fleischman, A. I., Leuz, P. H. 1973. Blood and liver lipids in torpid and aroused little brown bats, *Myotis lucifugus. Comp. Biochem. Physiol.* 45A:933–38

21. Fang, L. S. T., Willis, J. S. 1974. Increase of Na–K ATPase activity in renal cortex of hamster (*Mesocricetus auratus*) during prehibernation cold exposure. *Comp. Biochem. Physiol.* 48A:687–98

22. Galster, W., Morrison, P. R. 1975. Gluconeogenesis in arctic ground squirrels between periods of hibernation. *Am. J. Physiol.* 228:325–30

23. Goldman, S. S., Willis, J. S. 1973. Cold resistance of the brain during hibernation. I. K transport in cerebral cortex slices. II. Na–K ATPase. *Cryobiology* 10:212–24

24. Holečková, E., Baudyšová, M., Cinnerová, D. 1965. Adaptation of mammalian cells to cold. Resistance to cold and multiplication of L, Detroit-6 and HeLa cells adapted to low temperature. *Exp. Cell Res.* 40:396–401

25. Illanes, A., Marshall, J. M. 1964. The effects of ouabain on isolated atria of the ground squirrel; comparison with rat and rabbit atria. *Arch. Exp. Pathol. Pharmacol.* 248:15–26

26. Jacobs, H. K., South, F. E. 1976. Effects of temperature on cardiac transmembrane potentials in hibernation. *Am. J. Physiol.* 230:403–9

27. Johansson, B. W. 1963. The effect of aconitine, adrenalin and procaine, and changes in the ionic concentration in the production of ventricular fibrillation in a hibernator (hedgehog) and a nonhibernator (guinea pig) at different temperatures. *Cardiologia* 43:158–69

28. Johansson, B. W., Senturia, J. B., eds. 1972. Seasonal variations in the physiology and biochemistry of the European hedgehog (*Erinaceus europaeus*) including comparisons with non-hibernators, guinea pig and man. *Acta Physiol. Scand. Suppl. 30.* 159 pp.

29. Larsen, B. 1967. Red cell life span in hibernating hedgehogs. *Arch. Univ. Bergen Mat. Naturv. Ser.* 6:1–8

30. Low, R. B., Hamrell, B. B. 1975. Structural and functional comparison of myosin from the rabbit, *Oryctolagus cuniculus,* and the marmot, *Marmota monax. Comp. Biochem. Physiol.* 51B:29–35

31. Lyman, C. P., Leduc, E. H. 1953. Changes in blood sugar and tissue glycogen in the hamster during arousal from hibernation. *J. Cell Comp. Physiol.* 41:471–91

32. Malan, A. 1979. Hibernation as a model for studies on thermogenesis and its control. *Experentia.* In press

33. Marshall, J. M., Willis, J. S. 1962. The effect of temperature on the membrane potentials in isolated atria of the ground squirrel, *Citellus tridecemlineatus. J. Physiol. London* 164:64–76

34. Melichar, I., Brozek, G., Jansky, L., Vyskočil, F. 1973. Effect of hibernation and noradrenaline on acetylcholine release and action at neuromuscular junction of the golden hamster (*Mesocricetus auratus*). *Pfluegers Arch.* 345:107–22

35. Mendler, N., Reuben, H. J., Brendel, W. 1972. Cold swelling and energy metabolism in the hypothermic brain of rats and dogs. See Ref. 12, pp. 167–90

36. Mihailović, L. T. 1972. Cortical and subcortical electrical activity in hibernation and hypothermia. A comparative analysis of the two states. See Ref. 12, pp. 487–534

37. Moon, T. W., Borgmann, A. I. 1976. Enzymes of the normothermic and hibernating bat, *Myotis lucifugus:* metabolites and modulators of pyruvate kinase. *J. Comp. Physiol. B* 107:201–10

38. Moravec, J., Melichar, I., Jansky, L., Vyskočil, F. 1973. Effect of hibernation and noradrenaline on the resting state of neuromuscular junction of golden hamster (*Mesocricetus auratus*). *Pfluegers Arch.* 345:93–106

39. Moy, R. M. 1971. Renal function in the hibernating ground squirrel, *Spermophilus columbianus*. *Am. J. Physiol.* 220:747–53

40. Novotna, R., Jansky, L., Drahota, Z. 1975. Effect of hibernation on serotonin metabolism in the brain stem of the golden hamster (*Mesocricetus auratus*). *Gen. Pharmacol.* 6:23–26

41. Papahadjopoulos, D., Moscarello, M., Eylar, E. H., Isac, T. 1975. Effects of proteins on thermotropic phase transitions of phospholipid membranes. *Biochem. Biophys. Acta* 401:317–35

42. Roberts, J. C., Chaffee, R. R. J. 1973. Effects of cold acclimation, hibernation and temperature on succinoxidase activity of heart homogenates from hamster, rat and squirrel monkey. *Comp. Biochem. Physiol.* 44B:137–44

43. South, F. E. 1960. Hibernation, temperature and rates of oxidative phosphorylation by heart mitochondria. *Am. J. Physiol.* 198:463–66

44. South, F. E. 1961. Phrenic nerve-diaphragm preparations in relation to temperature and hibernation. *Am. J. Physiol.* 200:565–71

45. South, F. E., House, W. A. 1967. Energy metabolism in hibernation. See Ref. 11, pp. 305–24

46. South, F. E., Jacobs, H. K. 1973. Contraction kinetics of ventricular muscle from hibernating and nonhibernating mammals. *Am. J. Physiol.* 225:444–49

47. Swan, H., Schatté, C. 1977. Antimetabolitic extract from the brain of the hibernating ground squirrel, *Citellus tridecemlineatus*. *Science* 195:84–85

48. Tempel, G. E., Musacchia, X. J. 1975. Renal function in the hibernating and hypothermic hamster, *Mesocricetus auratus*. *Am. J. Physiol.* 228:602–7

49. Tempel, G. E., Musacchia, X. J., Jones, S. B. 1977. Mechanisms responsible for decreased glomerular filtration in hibernation and hypothermia. *Am. J. Physiol.* 42:420–25

50. Vyskočil, F. 1976. Miniature end-plate potentials and sensitivity to acetylcholine in the fast and slow muscle limb muscles of hibernating golden hamsters. *Pfluegers Arch.* 361:165–67

51. Whitten, B. K., Schrader, L. E., Huston, R. L., Honold, G. R. 1970. Hepatic polyribosomes and protein synthesis: seasonal changes in a hibernator. *Int. J. Biochem.* 1:406–8

52. Willis, J. S. 1967. Cold adaptation of activities of tissues of hibernating mammals. See Ref. 11, pp. 356–81

53. Willis, J. S. 1968. Cold resistance of kidney cells of mammalian hibernators: cation transport vs respiration. *Am. J. Physiol.* 214:923–28

54. Willis, J. S. 1972. The possible roles of cellular K for survival of cells at low temperature. *Cryobiology* 9:351–66

55. Willis, J. S. 1978. Cold tolerance of mammalian cells: Prevalence and properties. See Ref. 15, pp. 317–415

56. Willis, J. S., Baudyšová, M. 1977. Retention of K+ in relation to cold resistance of cultured cells from hamster and human embryos. *Cryobiology* 14:511–15

57. Willis, J. S., Ellory, J. C., Becker, J. H. 1979. Na–K pump and Na–K ATPase: on the disparity of their temperature sensitivity. *Am. J. Physiol.* (*Cell*). In press

58. Willis, J. S., Fang, L. S. T., Foster, R. F. F. 1972. The significance and analysis of membrane function in hibernation. See Ref. 12, pp. 149–66

59. Willis, J. S., Goldman, S. S., Foster, R. F. 1971. Tissue K concentration in relation to the role of the kidney in hibernation and the cause of periodic arousal. *Comp. Biochem. Physiol.* 39A:437–55

60. Willis, J. S., Li, N. M. 1969. Cold resistance of Na–K ATPase of renal cortex of the hamster, a hibernating mammal. *Am. J. Physiol.* 217:321–26

61. Wood, L., Beutler, E. 1967. Temperature dependence of sodium-potassium activated erythrocyte adenosine triphosphatase. *J. Lab. Clin. Invest.* 70:287–94

62. Zatzman, M. L., South, F. E. 1972. Renal function of the awake and hibernating marmot, *Marmota flaviventris*. *Am. J. Physiol.* 22:1035–39

63. Zatzman, M. L., South, F. E. 1975. Concentration of urine by the hibernating marmot. *Am. J. Physiol.* 228:1336–40

64. Zatzman, M. L., Thompson, E. P., South, F. E. 1971. Influence of hypothermia on renal function of the marmot (*Marmota flaviventris*). *Cryobiology* 8:517–23

65. Zeidler, R. B., Willis, J. S. 1976. Cultured cells from renal cortex of hibernators and non-hibernators. Regulation of cell K at low temperature. *Biochim. Biophys. Acta* 436:628–51

Ann. Rev. Physiol. 1979. 41:287–303

HIBERNATION: ENDOCRINOLOGIC ASPECTS

♦1220

Jack W. Hudson[1]

Section of Ecology and Systematics, Division of Biological Sciences, Cornell University, Ithaca, New York 14853

Lawrence C. H. Wang

Department of Zoology, University of Alberta, Edmonton, Alberta, Canada T6G 2E9

INTRODUCTION

Polyglandular involution of the endocrine system has long been accepted as a necessary stage in preparation for hibernation (48, 62, 64). This view has recently been challenged (8)—in particular, the timing of events (14, 95). For example, in the golden hamster, *Mesocricetus auratus,* involution of thyroid and adrenal cortex occurs in the fall, but hibernation does not occur until spring (14). Recent reviews of hibernation assume that while the nervous system plays a critical role in the induction into, maintenance of, and arousal from hibernation, preparative endocrine changes, which are more than mere consequences of the low body temperature, are also evident (37, 76, 80). Hypothermia (artificial reduction of body temperature) can elicit some of the same endocrine changes observed in dormant hibernators (7): reduction in blood ACTH level and corticosteroid secretion; in the thyroid gland, excessive colloid accumulation, flattened epithelia, and reduced radioiodine uptake. Thus, in attempting to discern the role of the endocrines in hibernation, it is imperative to differentiate between changes due to low body temperature and those that precede the hibernating state

[1]Present address: Department of Biology, University of Alabama, Birmingham, Alabama 35294

287

0066-4278/79/0301-0287$01.00

and have an active, or at least a permissive, role in preparing for hibernation. The contradictions in the literature are innumerable and difficult to resolve. Sometimes they are due to differences between species (37), and sometimes to different methodologies or to an inadequate knowledge of the thermal history of the animal prior to sampling. At the moment, the literature does not appear to provide a really satisfactory basis for determining specific roles in hibernation for particular hormones. Nevertheless, many indications exist that the endocrines are in some way involved in hibernation. The fundamental question addressed in this review is whether specific endocrine glands participate actively or permissively in the regulation of hibernation.

NEUROSECRETORY SYSTEM

The hypothalamus contains neurosecretory cells that synthesize and release neurohormones (releasing factors, oxytocin, and vasopressin). These are transported either by the portal blood vessels surrounding the median eminence to the adenohypophysis or by fibers innervating the neurohypophysis directly. The nucleus supraopticus (NSO) and the nucleus paraventricularis (NPV) contain the cell bodies whose fibers descend via the tractus hypothalamo-hypophyseus towards the hypophysis and form a hypothalamo-hypophyseal neurosecretory system (HHNS) (71). Using Gormori's stain, which stains but does not discriminate different neurohypophyseal hormones or their carriers, the relative abundance of Gormori-positive granules and their advance along the processes of the hypothalamo-hypophyseal tract have been used as indications of activity in the HHNS during hibernation (102).

The size of the cell bodies of the NSO gradually increases as the hedgehog, *Erinaceus europaeus*, prepares for hibernation; this continues during the period of hibernation. The cell bodies become smaller during the "postlethargic period" in April when the animals are still hibernating (93). The density and staining qualities of the fibers running between the NSO and the hypophysis indicate that neurosecretion is slight in summer but intense during hibernation (93). The nuclear size of the cells of the NSO is reported to be larger in more active hedgehogs, decreasing with entry into a single hibernation bout and increasing with arousal. On a seasonal basis, they are smallest in June–July, increase towards fall, decrease in early hibernation, and increase throughout the hibernation period (94). The neurosecretory cells of the bat, *Myotis myotis* (46), garden dormouse, *Eliomys quercinus* (58), and ground squirrels *Citellus* (*Spermophilus*) *erythrogenys* and *C. undulatus* (71, 102) are reported to contain a greater amount of stainable material in hibernation than during their active period (summer), which indicates a lower activity of the HHNS in the hibernating season. Similar conclusions were derived from studies of acid phosphatase in the HHNS of the dormouse, *E. quercinus* (11).

With regard to other hypothalamic neurosecretions, immunocytological techniques indicate an appreciable and progressive increase in LRH and SRIF (somatostatin), in the median eminence of the garden dormouse hibernating at 6°C (83). The increase in LRH is similar to that following continuous illumination at 22°C, although SRIF levels diminish in the latter case after a few weeks (83). A special relationship may exist between some glial cells and the secretory mechanisms of inhibiting and releasing hormones. In the hibernating hedgehog, the percentage of nerve endings comprising the neurohaemal contact zone of the adenohypophysis is only 7% in December—half the number (14%) observed in September. The number of synaptoid contacts between processes of nerve cells and glial cells decreases from September to December (23).

It is almost as true today as it was in 1969 (101) that virtually no studies are available on the functional role of the hypothalamic neurosecretory centers in the regulation of the endocrine systems at any stage of the hibernation cycle.

NEUROHUMORS

The discovery that neurohumors such as 5-hydroxytryptamine (5-HT), norepinephrine (NE), and acetylcholine (ACh) can profoundly affect the hypothalamic control of body temperature raises the question of whether they have a special role in hibernation (45). The 5-HT turnover in the brain stem increases 14 times with the onset of hibernation, and 24 times during hibernation in the golden hamster kept under outdoor conditions (45), which suggests that neurohumors such as 5-HT could function to regulate the endocrine system (45). The 5-HT content is increased in select areas of the brain in the hedgehog during the winter period, either when active or during hibernation, but the NE content decreases (97). In the arctic ground squirrel, *C. undulatus* (22), hypothalamic content of NE was lowest during hibernation and highest during the active period preceding hibernation [although the converse has also been reported (96)], whereas 5-HT was essentially constant throughout the year, with the exception of a slight decline during early arousal. The brain 5-HT level decreases as the golden-mantled ground squirrel, *C. lateralis,* enters hibernation at progressively deeper states; but if 5-HT synthesis is disrupted by parachlorophenylalanine or lesion of the median raphe of the midbrain, hibernation does not occur (91). In the Richardson's ground squirrel, *C. richardsonii,* seasonal differences are apparent in the magnitude of hypothermic responses to intracerebral ventricular injections of 5-HT or harmaline (27). This hypothermia was caused primarily by an increase in heat loss during the nonhibernating season, whereas both an activation of heat loss and a suppression of heat production occurred in the hibernating season, results indicative of a seasonal reorganization of the hypothalamic control of body temperature (27). Brain 5-HT increases two- to four-fold, especially in the hippocampus, when the red-cheeked suslik, *C. erythrogenys,* enters hibernation (75). While in hibernation, 5-HT concentration decreases to between one half and one third the level found during entry, which indicates a probable inhibition of monoamine oxidase during entry, with a subsequent production of a monoamine oxidase that is virtually temperature insensitive during or just prior to hibernation (54, 75). In hibernating garden dormice (19), monoamine oxidase activity increases spontaneously during the middle of winter.

Injection of 5-hydroxytryptophan, a precursor of 5-HT that readily crosses the blood brain barrier, significantly retards the arousal rate of the red-cheeked suslik from hibernation (72). Yet the golden-mantled ground squirrel can be aroused prematurely from hibernation when low doses of 5-HT and NE are injected into the anterior hypothalamus (5) or when ACh is microinjected into the midbrain reticular formation (6). The tyrosine hydroxylase inhibitor (αMpTme or D,L-alpha-methyl-p-tyrosine methyl ester CHL), which inhibits the synthesis of NE, prevented the arousal of 11 out of 13 hibernating golden hamsters (21).

Thus, one finds in the literature examples of conflicting trends in concentrations of 5-HT over the hibernation cycle. 5-HT apparently facilitates entry into hibernation and interferes with arousal, although in small amounts both 5-HT and NE injected directly into the anterior hypothalamus cause arousal. Deciphering the precise role of NE probably awaits further studies using discrete hypothalamic injections which avoid the complications associated with peripheral injections of NE (see the section below on Adrenal Medulla).

PITUITARY

Anterior

Information on the role of the adenohypophysis in hibernation is confined to a few histological observations (33), which depend upon staining procedures to identify cells (2). The pituitary gland of the thirteen-lined ground squirrel, *C. tridecemlineatus,* shows a rapid increase in mass in February–March near the end of hibernation, reaches a maximum mass in April–May after emergence from hibernation and a minimum mass in December–January during the middle of deep hibernation (33). This corresponds with the PAS staining in general, although the most significant change is the marked decline in staining from June to October, with a sharp increase in December and February, a change attributed to an "inherent rhythm" (33). In general, except for the fact that the maximum mass occurred in November instead of spring, the red-cheeked suslik exhibits a similar but less-striking cycle of pituitary mass (51) and a marked pituitary ACTH cycle with the highest levels occurring in the spring. Hedgehogs do not increase their plasma ACTH when exposed to cold in the autumn, and a blocked corticotropic function may be essential for hibernation, although ACTH injections will not cause arousal (34).

Our knowledge concerning the secretory status of the pituitary gland during hibernation is largely derived from the secretory changes of the target glands stimulated by the anterior pituitary. Without direct measurements of pituitary secretions it is convenient to assume that changes in blood levels of target gland hormones reflect changes in pituitary secretory activity.

It has generally been assumed that hibernation cannot occur when the gonads are actively functioning (31). Conflicting data indicated that hibernation occurs at the time the testes of the golden hamster are sufficiently large to be producing spermatozoa (90), but later experiments indicated that hamsters hibernated only if there was gonadal atrophy (88). Cell proliferation does not seem to be affected by hibernation in the golden hamster, although a retardation of cell differentiation occurs (89). However, this retardation of differentiation has been questioned (101). The hazel dormouse, *Muscardinus avellanerius*, exhibits an inhibition of spermatogenesis paralleling a reduced activity of the interstitial cells and the hypothalamic phloxinophile cells (60). The involution of the testes has been taken as an indicator of a marked reduction of pituitary gonadotropic secretion during hibernation (82). Yet glucose-6-phosphate dehydrogenase activity is highest in the diencephalon (hypothalamus) and lowest in the testes of the garden dormouse during hibernation, and the reverse is true at the end of hibernation (59). In the bat, *M. lucifugus,* plasma testosterone level was relatively constant throughout the year, including during hibernation, but increased significantly in mid-August to stimulate the full growth of sex and accessory glands and spermatogenesis (28). Both injection of pituitary gonadotropins in aroused winter bats, *Pipistrellus pipistrellus* (78), and bringing female bats to room temperature after mid-hibernation result in spontaneous ovulation of their persistent follicle, with a direct correlation between proximity to terminal arousal and rapidity of spontaneous ovulation (100).

A pre-hibernal pattern of full spermatogenic regression followed by a partial recovery apparently characterizes hibernating rodents. After the mid-hibernal period, spermatogenic recrudescence occurs, peaking soon after the end of hibernation in most mammals. This pattern indicates that gonadotropic secretions must resume before the termination of hibernation, or at least while arousal periods are becoming more frequent as the hibernation season nears completion (19, 101). In the bats (100), evidence suggests that at least LH, and possibly FSH, secretion occurs during hibernation, for many species of female bats ovulate upon the termination of hibernation.

Posterior

It is generally agreed that during hibernation antidiuretic hormone (ADH) is stored and the NPO and NPV are relatively inactive (94). In general, the storage of ADH is accelerated in autumn by a short photoperiod and cold. ADH is secreted only during arousal, at which time the ability to concentrate urine is reestablished (80). Thus in the garden dormouse the neurohypophysis contains 1.54 IU of ADH before hibernation, 6.35 IU in the middle of hibernation, 4.19 IU shortly before arousal, and 2.10 IU one hour after arousal (58). However, the quantities of neurosecretory material in the neurohypophysis of the hibernating and active mouse-eared bats, *M. myotis,* do not differ (46).

PINEAL GLAND

If mammals cannot hibernate when their pituitary-gonad axis is active, then the role of the pineal gland in the seasonal involution of the reproductive system (81) suggests that changes in the pineal would precede hibernation, rather than vice versa. Golden hamsters pinealectomized (sexually active) and kept for 16 weeks at 8°C with a 2L:22D photoperiod did not hibernate, whereas three of the control animals, which exhibited spontaneous gonadal involution, hibernated (88). When the red-cheeked suslik hibernates, the pineal 5-HT content decreases by 50%, which is coupled with a number of morphological signs indicative that functional depression of the gland occurs (73). However, such studies fail to differentiate simple low-temperature effects due to hibernation from preparatory changes essential for hibernation to occur. If melatonin is the pineal secretion that serves to inhibit the gonads, the increase of hydroxyindole-O-methyl transferase (HIOMT, the enzyme converting 5-HT to melatonin) activity from the breeding season to just prior to onset of hibernation in a natural population of Uinta ground squirrel, *C. armatus,* indicates that pineal suppression of gonadal activity occurs prior to hibernation (20). An annual cycle of both nuclear and nucleolar diameter exists in the bats, *M. lucifugus* and *M. sodalis,* and histological evidence indicates maximum pineal activity in the spring (77). These observations seem inconsistent with the established role of the pineal gland in reproduction. However, it is typical for various species of *Myotis* to exhibit an increase in spermatogenesis, Leydig cell hypertrophy, development of accessory glands, and ovulation at a later date when pinealocyte activity diminishes (101). Thus, in a group of mammals such as bats in which the reproductive cycle is divided and spread out over the year, it may not be unreasonable to expect an unusual cycle of pineal activity in relation to hibernation.

THYROID GLAND

Follicles

None of the various endocrine glands thought to play a role in hibernation has been more thoroughly studied with more conflicting results than the thyroid gland. At present this confusion cannot be resolved; it can merely be reviewed. The consensus, based for the most part on histological studies, has been that the thyroid gland becomes relatively inactive during the summer sometime prior to hibernation; thyroid secretory activity resumes during the hibernation season. These conclusions derive from studies of bats, marmots, ground squirrels, dormice, and hedgehogs (10, 17, 32, 33, 53, 70, 76, 86). The measurement of thyroxine degradation rate (TDR) with radiolabelled thyroxine has given some insight into the rate at which tissues metabolize thyroxine, but the data have been difficult to rationalize when compared to data obtained from other procedures. The TDR (often equated with thyroid secretory rate) measured this way gives relatively short biological half-lives [less than 24 hr for normothermic animals (3)], whereas the rate at which the thyroid gland releases radioiodine is usually measured in terms of days or weeks (3, 38, 40, 43, 95). In the Richardson's ground squirrel TDR is the same during hibernation and normothermia (16); in contrast, the TDR in normothermic thirteen-lined ground squirrels is 900 times greater than in hibernating individuals (3). Some of this discrepancy may be related to striking differences in the serum thyroxine (or PBI) levels. The serum T_4 is between 4 and 6 $\mu g\%$ when the Richardson's ground squirrel is hibernating, but only 1 $\mu g\%$ or less when it is normothermic (15), whereas serum PBI levels (range = 4.4–6.2 $\mu g\%$) do not differ between normothermic and hibernating states in the thirteen-lined ground squirrel (3). The discrepancy may also reflect differences in methodologies and assumptions regarding tissue uptake of thyroxine.

Many investigators have concluded that hibernation does not occur until the thyroid gland becomes inactive (31, 32), that the thyroid can be removed without affecting hibernation (56), or that a summer reduction in activity must reflect preparation for hibernation (10, 56). Hyperthyroidism delays hibernation in several species (56), and evidence of a hypothalamic-pituitary suppression (43) exists for the thirteen-lined ground squirrel.

Others investigators contend that hibernation cannot occur without an active thyroid; that thyroidectomy prevents hibernation and thyroxine restores it; or that, at least, the thyroid is active during hibernation (12, 39, 63). In the golden hamster (95), functional indexes indicate that the thyroid is active preceding hibernation, even though the follicular cells appeared histologically to be inactive. The thyroxine release rate of golden hamsters, which were hibernating 75% of the time, was the same as normothermic animals (4)—evidence that the thyroid is active during hibernation. The round-tailed ground squirrel, *C. tereticaudus*, continued nightly torpor at room temperature even though it received daily injections of L-thyroxine sufficient to double the basal metabolic rate (36).

The ambiguity regarding the role of the thyroid gland in hibernation may reside in interspecific differences reflecting differences in ecology. For example, golden hamsters store energy as food rather than fat (62) and thus may require an active thyroid for the continuous metabolism of food frequently eaten during periodic arousals. Likewise, the garden dormouse, *E. quercinus*, hibernates in relatively unprotected places (55) and may require an active thyroid that fosters sufficient thermogenesis during torpor to prevent body temperature from falling below a critical level that would necessitate arousal. Many hibernators are exposed to low ambient temperatures prior to hibernation, and may need to intensify their thyroid secretory activity as an adaptation to cold prior to dormancy (56, 95). Ground squirrels, which seem to shut down or even to shut off their thyroid secretion for extended periods of time (38), hibernate in underground burrows that are relatively protected from drastic surface temperature fluctuations. Also, these animals are small diurnal mammals. Desert ground squirrels in particular are often exposed to heat loads for which an inactive thyroid and a low endogenous heat production would be adaptive (38).

The functional role of thyroxine in hibernation is presently conjectural. In the garden dormouse the digestive tract undergoes involution in tandem with the involution of the thyroid, and administration of thyroxine accelerates the restoration of the gut accompanied by an augmentation of protein synthesis (1). It has been suggested (41, 42) that the thyroid hormone acts on the membrane to decrease cell tolerance to low temperature by affecting the proportion of saturated to unsaturated fatty acids (41). The percentage of saturated fatty acids in liver mitochondria, heart mitochondria, and microsomes increases with either cold exposure, which intensifies thyroxine secretion, or thyroxine administration (92). In the white rat, thyroidectomy decreases mitochondrial membrane lipid saturation from 39 to 29%, lowers the temperature limit of membrane phase transition, and increases the E_a of succinate oxidase, features reversed within 12 hr after thyroxine treatment (42). With respect to hibernation, it is of interest that the golden-mantled ground squirrel exhibits a shift in membrane phase transition temperature from 23°C during the active season to below 4°C during the hibernating season (79); this decrease can be correlated with seasonal changes in thyroid secretion (38). The proposed hypothesis (41, 42) may also explain why chipmunks do not drop their body temperature much below 5—12°C during hibernation (99): They have relatively high thyroid activity during torpor (39). Ground squirrels, which have an inactive thyroid during most of their pre-hibernation and hibernation periods, can let their body temperatures drop to 0°C (62).

Parafollicular (C) Cells

Calcitonin is secreted by the parafollicular or "C" cells of the thyroid; these cells are more widespread and abundant in the thyroid glands of hibernators than nonhibernators (26, 90). In the bat, *M. lucifugus*, osteoporosis occurs during hibernation and is reversed following arousal (66). Osteoporosis can also be reversed with exogenous calcitonin during hibernation (52). The seasonal variation in the number and morphology of small, dense, smooth, membrane-enclosed granules in bats (29, 98) and other hibernating mammals [*E. quercinus, Centetes ecaudatus, Ericulus ericulus,* and *Paraechinus aethiopicus* (67); *C. tridecemlineatus* (100)] suggests that secretion of calcitonin slows prior to hibernation, ceases during hibernation, and resumes during arousal. The "C" cells contain calcitonin and 5-HT in the same granule (65). The role of 5-HT may be one of stimulating the thyroid gland since calcium acts to regulate "C" cell secretion of calcitonin, and 5-HT is released to act directly on the thyroid follicles to influence the secretion of thyroxine (29). Thus, even if the anterior pituitary were not secreting TSH, the thyroid gland is still regulated but by blood calcium levels acting to affect secretion of 5-HT in conjunction with calcitonin.

PARATHYROIDS

The osteoporosis developing during hibernation implies that the parathyroid gland must be active in the dissolution of bone—a mechanism for keeping the serum calcium up at a time when more calcium is probably being excreted than is taken in. The parathyroids are active throughout the hibernation period (47). Striking ultrastructural changes occur in the parathyroids of the bats, *M. lucifugus* and *P. pipistrellus,* indicating definite intracellular synthesis of secretory material during hibernation (66). This contrasts with the nonhibernating phase of the yearly cycle in which the parathyroid gland of these bats is only moderately active (66).

PANCREAS

Relatively few studies are available concerning the functional roles of the alpha and beta cells, which secrete glucagon and insulin, respectively, in the endocrine pancreas of the hibernator. Most studies have been either histological, dealing with ratios of alpha and beta cells, or involved the measurement of blood glucose, with inferences as to the status of the endocrine pancreas.

Both the free and bound insulin decrease (as detected by radioimmunoassay) during entry into hibernation in the hedgehog, suggesting an adaptive preparation for hibernation in the same way that an increase of serum insulin prior to arousal contributes to metabolic preparation for homeothermia (57). Early in the hibernation season the pancreas hypertrophies and has its peak insulin content (47, 57). This has been taken to indicate that the endocrine pancreas is active during hibernation, but it could merely reflect the lack of secretion during some slow synthesis. A decline in beta cell activity has been described as the cause of the 350% increase in blood sugar levels in the hibernating bats, *Eptisecus fuscus* (30). Whether or not the ratio of alpha to beta cells changes during hibernation in bats is uncertain (30), but the ratio is clearly decreased in the hibernating hedgehog (94). If insulin is significantly lowered during hibernation, apparently its absence does not have a lasting effect, for the in vitro rates of absorption of glucose by the adipose tissue from either active or hibernating ground squirrels, *C. suslicus,* are similar (13).

ADRENAL GLAND

Cortex

An annual rhythm of corticosteroid secretion (cortisone and corticosterone), as well as mass changes in the adrenal gland of the red-cheeked suslik have been described (49). As judged by the nuclear and nucleolar volumes, the adrenal cortex is maximally active in May after hibernation, decreases in July, and is least active in January when *C. erythrogenys* is in deep hibernation (61). The glomerulosa cells exhibit a depressed activity during hibernation in bats (84), yet hedgehogs, common dormice, *Glis glis,* and garden dormice keep their plasma levels of Ca, Na, and K nearly constant during hibernation (35).

Electron-microscopic studies reveal that cells of the fascicular and reticular zones of the adrenal cortex in some bats are active during hibernation (84). In the hibernating suslik, periodic fluctuation in the blood levels of 11-hydroxycorticosteroids occurs in association with arousals (49). The fluctuation is regulated by endogenous rhythms of the pituitary-adrenal system (51) and serves to stimulate the production of gluconeogenic enzymes that can replenish the exhausted carbohydrate reserves during hibernation (49). In the hibernating and aroused garden dormouse and hedgehog, the blood corticosterone and cortisol (17-OH-Cs) levels are virtually the same (9), which suggests that corticosteroid secretion is closely regulated in hibernators. The plasma level of corticosteroids in hibernating dormice and hedgehogs is proportional to the intensity with which reserves are mobilized (9).

Because aminergic neurons innervate the median eminence (24, 25), administration of biogenic amines should affect the control of the hypophyseal-adrenocortical system and, in turn, the output of the adrenal cortex (50, 74). Adrenomimetics, 5-HT, and immobilization with cooling cause a much smaller increase in corticosteroid output in active hibernators (suslik and golden hamster) than the nonhibernators (white rat and guinea pig) (74). In the suslik just before hibernation, adrenalin did not change the level of blood corticosteroids, though this was not due to a loss of sensitivity of the adrenal cortex, for it responded to injections of ACTH. However, in the spring the corticosteroid secretion increased 70% in early May and 30% in June–August when adrenaline was injected subcutaneously (50). Apparently during the time animals prepare for hibernation there occurs either a change in the sensitivity of the receptors to catecholamines or a reduction in the sensitivity or responsiveness of the hypothalamo-hypophyseal-adrenal system. Conclusive evidence on this awaits direct injections of aminergic substances into the hypothalamus, or at least into the third ventricle.

Medulla

An important source of heat for arousal from hibernation is the thermogenesis resulting from NE secreted by the adrenal medulla as well as the sympathetic nervous system, thus bringing the endocrine system and nervous system together in one more way. Ground squirrels, hedgehogs, and hamsters appear to possess an unusually high sensitivity to the effects of NE in comparison with the white rat (44, 69): More thermogenesis results in these hibernators than in rats upon receipt of comparable doses of NE. The increase in metabolism after injection of NE is similar in both cold- and warm-adapted hamsters, which indicates that NE receptors are equally sensitive at all times (44). Whether this is typical for all hibernators remains to be explored.

The mass of the adrenal glands is highest in October–November and lowest in March–May in the hedgehog, with corresponding changes in the catecholamine content (85). The catecholamine content declines during the winter if hedgehogs do not hibernate and remains unchanged if they do (85). The ground squirrel, *C. citellus,* kept at 20–25°C exhibited a doubling of adrenal mass between September and April (68); it is alleged that seasonal variations in catecholamine content of the adrenal gland do not depend on whether the animal hibernates but is a seasonal change per se, and that the European hamster, *Cricetus cricetus,* and the golden hamster do not have such cycles (68). By means of radioactive DOPA a complete standstill of catecholamine turnover was observed 10 hr prior to hibernation in the thirteen-lined ground squirrel, which suggests suppressed activity of the central adrenergic neurons and general reduction of peripheral sympathetic tone (18). In hibernating hedgehogs, the turnover rates of norepinephrine are greatly reduced, which indicates a reduced sympathetic activity (87).

CONCLUSIONS

Progress in understanding the physiology of hibernation has come slowly. This is in part due to the uncertainty of the time of onset of hibernation and to the technical difficulty of systematically following the changes of body temperature in hibernation cycles. The time has come to challenge the longstanding concept of "polyglandular involution" as a requirement for hibernation, a conclusion Mann reached in 1916 (64). We must gain better insight into the functional integration of the nervous system and the endocrine system for hibernation.

ACKNOWLEDGMENTS

The support for writing this review came from NSF Grants PCM74-07798 and PCM77-21799 (J.W.H.), and a NRC (Canada) grant A6455 (L.C.H.W.). We gratefully acknowledge the skillful help from the staff of Mann Library (Cornell), who provided the computer search for the literature using the BIOSIS Previews data base, reviewing all pertinent publications listed in Biological Abstracts and Bioresearch Index from 1970 through February 1, 1978. We also thank Dr. W. K. Kaufman (Alberta) for translating some of the French articles.

Literature Cited

1. Agid, R., Sicart, R. 1969. Role of the thyroid in the involution and restoration of the digestive tube of hibernating animals. *C. R. Acad. Sci. Ser. D* 269(19):1866–69 (In French)
2. Azzali, G. 1971. Cytology of the adenohypophysis of Chiroptera with particular attention to the follicle stimulating hormone, luteinizing hormone ACTH and prolactin cells. *Ateneo Parmense Acta Bio-Med.* 42(3):169–229
3. Bauman, T. R., Anderson, R. R. 1970. Thyroid activity of the squirrel (*Citellus tridecemlineatus*) using a cannula technique. *Gen. Comp. Endocrinol.* 15(3):369–73
4. Bauman, T. R., Anderson, R. R., Turner, C. W. 1969. Thyroid hormone secretion rates and food consumption of the hamster (*Mesocricetus auratus*) at 25.5° and 4.5°. *Gen. Comp. Endocrinol.* 10:92–98
5. Beckman, A. L., Satinoff, E. 1972. Arousal from hibernation by intrahypothalamic injections of biogenic amines in ground squirrels. *Am. J. Physiol.* 222(4):875–79
6. Beckman, A. L., Stanton, T. L., Satinoff, E. 1976. Inhibition of the CNS trigger process for arousal from hibernation. *Am. J. Physiol.* 230(4):1018–25
7. Bigelow, W. G., Sidlofsky, S. 1961. Hormones in hypothermia. *Br. Med. Bull.* 17:56–60
8. Boulouard, R. 1969. Sur le rôle de la fonction corticosurrénalienne chez le mammifère homéotherme permanent soumis au froid et chez le mammifère hibernant au cours du sommeil hivernal. Etude sur le rat, le cobaye, le lerot (*Eliomys quercinus* L.), et le herisson (*Erinaceus europaeus* L.). *Mém. Mus. Natl. Hist. Nat.* 60:77–170
9. Boulouard, R. 1972. Adrenocortical function in two hibernators, the garden dormouse and the hedgehog. In *Proc. Int. Symp. Environ. Physiol., Bioenerget. Temp. Regul.*, ed. R. E. Smith, J. L. Shields, J. P. Hannon, B. A. Horwitz, pp. 108–12. Bethesda, Md: FASEB
10. Braun, A. A., Kurbanova, Sh. 1976. Morphofunctional characteristics of the thyroid glands of several species of Tadzhik-SSR rodents. *Izv. Akad. Nauk Tadzh. SSR Otd. Biol. Nauk* 2:93–97 (In Russian)
11. Burlet, C. 1968. Studies on the acid phosphatase activities of the hypothalamo-neurohypophysial system of *Eliomys quercinus*. *C. R. Assoc. Anat.* 141:625–32 (In French)

12. Canguilhem, B. 1970. Effects of radiothyroidectomy and injections of thyroid hormone on the entry into the state of hibernation of the European hamster *Cricetus cricetus*. *C. R. Seances Soc. Biol. Fil.* 164(6):1366–68 (In French)
13. Daudova, G. M., Sobternova, I. B. 1972. Influence of insulin on the absorption of glucose by adipose tissue of the ground squirrel *Citellus suslicus* during hibernation and arousal. *J. Evol. Biochem. Physiol.* 8(4):399–401 [Transl. from *Zh. Evol. Biokhim. Fiziol.* 8(4):449–51]
14. Deane, H. W., Lyman, C. P. 1954. Body temperature, thyroid and adrenal cortex of hamsters during cold exposure and hibernation, with comparisons to rats. *Endocrinology* 55:300–15
15. Demeneix, B. A., Henderson, N. E. 1978. Serum T_4 and T_3 in active and torpid ground squirrels, *Spermophilus richardsoni*. *Gen. Comp. Endocrinol.* 35:77–85
16. Demeneix, B. A., Henderson, N. E. 1978. Thyroxine metabolism in active and torpid ground squirrels. *Gen. Comp. Endocrinol.* 35:86–92
17. Doerfler, G. V. 1974. The role of the thyroid in the thermoregulation of hibernating Microchiroptera of the species *Myotis myotis* and *Rhinolophus hipposideros*. *Mitt. Hamb. Zool. Mus. Inst.* 70:287–97
18. Draskóczy, P. R., Lyman, C. P. 1967. Turnover of catecholamines in active and hibernating ground squirrels. *J. Pharmacol. Exp. Ther.* 155:101–11
19. Dussart, G., Richoux, J. P. 1973. Regulation of genital function in the garden dormouse. Action of the gonadotropic hormones on the diencephalic monoamine oxidase activities and on the genital glands during hibernation. *Ann. Endocrinol.* 34(2):45–132 (In French)
20. Ellis, L. C., Balph, D. F. 1976. Age and seasonal differences in the synthesis and metabolism of testosterone by testicular tissue and pineal hydroxy indole-O-methyl transferase activity of Uinta ground squirrels, *Spermophilus armatus*. *Gen. Comp. Endocrinol.* 28(1):42–51
21. Feist, D. D. 1970. Blockage of arousal from hibernation by inhibition of norepinephrine synthesis in the golden hamster. *Life Sci.* 9 (Part I):1117–25
22. Feist, D. D., Galster, W. A. 1974. Changes in hypothalamic catecholamines and serotonin during hibernation and arousal in the arctic ground squir-

rel. *Comp. Biochem. Physiol.* 48(4A): 653–62

23. Fleischhauer, K., Wittkowski, W. 1976. Morphological aspects of the formation, transport and secretion of releasing and inhibiting hormones. *Acta Endocrinol. Suppl.* 202:11–12

24. Fuxe, K., Goldstein, M., Hökfelt, T., Jonsson, G., Löfström, A. 1974. New aspects of the catecholamine innervation of the hypothalamus and the limbic system. In *Neurosecretion—The Final Neuroendocrine Pathway,* ed. F. Knowles, L. Vollrath, pp. 223–28. New York-Heidelberg-Berlin: Springer

25. Fuxe, K., Hökfelt, T., Jonsson, G., Löfström, A. 1974. Aminergic mechanisms in neuroendocrine control. See Ref. 24, pp. 266–75

26. Gabe, M., Martoja, M. 1969. Histological data on the calcitonin cells of the thyroid of the garden dormouse, *Eliomys quercinus. Arch. Anat. Microsc. Morphol. Exp.* 58(2):107–22 (In French)

27. Glass, J. D., Wang, L. 1978. Thermoregulatory effects of intracerebroventricular injection of serotonin and a monoamine oxidase inhibitor in a hibernator, *Spermophilus richardsonii. J. Thermal Biol.* 3:92 (Abstr.)

28. Gustafson, A. E., Shemesh, M. 1976. Changes in plasma testosterone levels during the annual reproductive cycle of the hibernating bat *Myotis lucifugus lucifugus* with a survey of plasma testosterone levels in adult male vertebrates. *Biol. Reprod.* 15(1):9–24

29. Haymovits, A., Gershon, M. D., Nunez, E. A. 1976. Calcitonin, serotonin and parafollicular cell granules during hibernation activity cycle in the bat. *Proc. Soc. Exp. Biol. Med.* 153(3): 383–87

30. Hinkley, R. E., Burton, P. R. 1970. Fine structure of the pancreatic islet cells of normal and alloxan treated bats *Eptesicus fuscus. Anat. Rec.* 166(1):67–85

31. Hoffman, R. A. 1964. Terrestrial animals in cold: hibernators. In *Handbook of Physiology,* ed. D. B. Dill, Sec. 4:379–403. Washington, DC: Am. Physiol. Soc.

32. Hoffman, R. A., Zarrow, M. X. 1958. A comparison of seasonal changes and the effect of cold on the thyroid gland of the male rat and ground squirrel (*Citellus tridecemlineatus*). *Acta Endocrinol.* 27:77–84

33. Hoffman, R. A., Zarrow, M. X. 1958. Seasonal changes in the basophilic cells of the pituitary gland of the ground

squirrel (*Citellus tridecemlineatus*). *Anat. Rec.* 131:727

34. Hoo-Paris, R. 1971. Hibernation and ACTH in the hedgehog, *Erinaceus europaeus. Ann. Endocrinol.* 32(6): 743–52 (In French)

35. Hoo-Paris, R., Castex, C., Garcin, H. 1975. Plasma calcium, sodium and potassium evolution during hibernation of hedgehogs, common dormice and garden dormice. *C. R. Seances Soc. Biol. Fil.* 169(4):946–53 (In French)

36. Hudson, J. W. 1968. Ineffectiveness of exogenous L-thyroxine in preventing torpor in *Citellus tereticaudus. Am. Zool.* 8(4). Abstr. 159

37. Hudson, J. W. 1973. Torpidity in mammals. In *Comparative Physiology of Thermoregulation,* Vol. III, ed. G. C. Whittow, pp. 97–165. New York/London: Academic

38. Hudson, J. W., Deavers, D. R. 1976. Thyroid function and basal metabolism in the ground squirrels, *Ammospermophilus leucurus* and *Spermophilus* spp. *Physiol. Zool.* 49(4):425–44

39. Hudson, J. W., Scott, I. 1978. The thyroid and temperature regulation in the prairie vole, *Microtus ochrogaster* and the chipmunk, *Tamias striatus.* Manuscript

40. Hudson, J. W., Wang, L. C. 1969. Thyroid function in desert ground squirrels. In *Physiological Systems in Semiarid Environments,* ed. C. C. Hoff, M. L. Riedesel, pp. 17–33. Albuquerque, NM: Univ. New Mexico Press

41. Hulbert, A. J. 1978. The thyroid hormones: a thesis concerning their action. *J. Theor. Biol.* 73(1):81–100

42. Hulbert, A. J., Augee, M. L., Raison, J. K. 1976. The influence of thyroid hormones on the structure and function of mitochondrial membranes. *Biochim. Biophys. Acta* 455:597–601

43. Hulbert, A. J., Hudson, J. W. 1976. Thyroid function in a hibernator, *Spermophilus tridecemlineatus. Am. J. Physiol.* 230(5):1138–43

44. Jansky, L. 1973. Nonshivering thermogenesis and its thermoregulatory importance. *Biol. Rev.* 48:85–132

45. Jansky, L., Novotná, R. 1976. The role of central aminergic transmission in thermoregulation and hibernation. In *Regulation of Depressed Metabolism and Thermogenesis,* ed. L. Jansky, X. J. Musacchia, pp. 64–80. Springfield, Ill: Thomas

46. Jasinski, A. 1970. Hypothalamic neurosecretion in the bat, *Myotis myotis* Borkhausen, during the period of hiber-

nation and activity. In *Aspects of neuroendocrinology, Vth Int. Symp. Neurosecretion,* ed. W. Bargmann, B. Scharrer, pp. 301–9. Berlin/New York: Springer

47. Kayser, C. 1961. *The Physiology of Natural Hibernation.* New York-Oxford-London-Paris: Pergamon Press. 325 pp.

48. Kayser, Ch., Vincendon, G., Frank, R., Porte, A. 1964. Some external (climatic) and internal (endocrine) factors in relation to production of hibernation. *Ann. Acad. Sci. Fenn. A4* (71/19):271

49. Khabibov, B., Krass, P. M. 1974. Seasonal dynamics of the absolute and relative weight of the adrenals and the level of 11 hydroxy cortico-steroids in the peripheral blood of the red-cheeked suslik *Citellus erythrogenys.* Translated from *Dokl. Akad. Nauk SSSR* 216(6): 1433–35

50. Koryakina, L. A. 1976. Seasonal changes in the response of the hypophyseo-adrenal system of the suslik (*Citellus erythrogenys*) to adrenomimetics. Transl. from *Zh. Evol. Biokhim. Fiziol.* 12(5):444–47

51. Krass, P. M., Khabibov, B. 1975. Seasonal rhythms of functional activity of the adrenocorticotropic function of the pituitary in the red-cheeked suslik. Transl. from *Dokl. Akad. Nauk SSSR Ser. Biol.* 225(2):474–76

52. Krook, L., Wimsatt, W. A., Whalen, J. P., MacIntyre, I., Nunez, E. A. 1977. Calcitonin and hibernation bone loss in the bat (*Myotis lucifugus*). *Cornell Vet.* 67(2):265–71

53. Krupp, P. P., Young, R. A., Frink, R. 1977. The thyroid gland of the woodchuck *Marmota monax:* a morphological study of seasonal variations in the follicular cells. *Anat. Rec.* 187(4):495–513

54. Kudryavtseva, N. N., Popova, N. K. 1973. Serotonin concentration in various parts of the brain during hibernation and waking. Transl. from *Byull. Eksp. Biol. Med.* 75(4):44–47

55. Lachiver, F. 1964. Thyroid activity in the garden dormouse (*Eliomys quercinus* L.) studied from June to November. *Ann. Acad. Sci. Fenn. Ser. A4* 71:285–94

56. Lachiver, F. 1969. Seasonal hormonal effect of states of depressed metabolism. In *Depressed Metabolism,* ed. X. J. Musacchia, J. F. Saunders, pp. 199–230. New York: American Elsevier

57. Lauriла, M., Suomalainen, P. 1974. Studies in the physiology of the hibernating hedgehog, Part 19. The changes

in the insulin level induced by seasons and hibernation cycle. *Ann. Acad. Sci. Fenn. Ser. A4* 201:1–40

58. Legait, E., Burlet, C., Marchetti, J. 1970. Contribution to the study of the hypothalamo-neurohypophyseal system during hibernation. See Ref. 46, pp. 310–21 (In French)

59. Legait, E., Dussart, G., Helas, G. 1971. The glucose and phosphate dehydrogenase activity of the diencephalon and testes in dormice *Eliomys quercinus* during the annual cycle. *C. R. Assoc. Anat.* 151:413–19 (In French)

60. Legait, E., Legait, H., Contet, J., Dussart, G. 1971. Study of the phloxinophilous hypothalamic neurosecretion of the dormouse *Muscardinus avellanarius.* In *Les Entretiens de Chize, Fonction Gonadotrope et Rapports Hypothalamo-Hypophysaires Chez les Animaux Sauvages,* ed. M. Herlant, pp. 143–60. Paris: Masson et Cie. 247 pp. (In French)

61. Lutsenko, N. D., Ginzburg, E. Kh., Kolaeva, S. G., Kolpakov, M. G. 1974. A study of nuclear and nucleolar volumes in the adrenal cortex of the ground squirrel (*Citellus erythrogenys*) in different seasons. *Tsitologiia* 26(2): 198–202 (In Russian)

62. Lyman, C. P., Chatfield, P. O. 1955. Physiology of hibernation in mammals. *Physiol. Rev.* 35:403–42

63. Malan, A., Canguilhem, B. 1971. Thermoregulatory aspects of cold adaptation in a thyroidectomized hibernator, the European hamster. In *Nonshivering Thermogenesis Symp.,* ed. L. Jansky, pp. 147–58. Prague: Academia

64. Mann, F. C. 1916. The ductless glands in hibernation. *Am. J. Physiol.* 41: 173–88

65. Nunez, E. A., Gershon, M. D. 1972. Synthesis and storage of serotonin by parafollicular C cells of the thyroid gland of active pre-hibernating and hibernating bats. *Endocrinology* 90(4): 100–24

66. Nunez, E. A., Whalen, J. P., Krook, L. 1972. An ultrastructural study of the natural secretory cycle of the parathyroid gland of the bat. *Am. J. Anat.* 134(4):459–80

67. Olivereau, M. 1970. Cytological and autoradiographic study of the thyroid gland in some hibernating mammals. Thyroid activity and presence of C cells (calcitonin cells). *Z. Zellforsch. Mikrosk. Anat.* 107(3):374–402 (In French)

68. Petrovic, V. M., Janic, V., Griposis, D., Roffi, J. 1975. Monoamine oxidase ac-

tivity in the brown fat of the ground squirrel. Influence of season on arousal from hibernation and the adrenal cortex. *Comp. Biochem. Physiol.* 51C:101-3

69. Petrovic, V. M., Markovic-Giaja, L. 1973. A comparative study of the calorigenic action of noradrenaline in the rat and ground squirrel adapted to different temperatures. *Experientia* 29(10):1295-96

70. Pinatel, M. C., Durand, N., Girod, C. 1970. Study of the variations in blood iodine and thyroid iodine during the annual cycle in the hedgehog *Erinaceus europaeus* L.: Comparison with thyroid histology. *C. R. Seances Soc. Biol. Fil.* 164(8-9):1719-22 (In French)

71. Polenov, A. L., Yurisova, M. N. 1976. The hypothalamo-hypophyseal system in the ground squirrels *Citellus erythrogenys* and *Citellus undulatus* Part I. Microanatomy and cytomorphology of the Gomori-positive neurosecretory system with special reference to its state during hibernation. *Z. Mikrosk.-Anat. Forsch.* 89(6):991-1014

72. Popova, N. K. 1973. The inhibiting of 5-hydroxytryptophan on temperature regulation during arousal from hibernation. Transl. from *Dokl. Akad. Nauk SSSR Ser. Biol.* 210(2):496-98

73. Popova, N. K., Kolaeva, S. G., Dianova, I. I. 1975. State of the pineal gland during hibernation. Transl. from *Byull. Eksp. Biol. Med.* 79(4):116-17

74. Popova, N. K., Koryakina, L. A., Naumenko, E. V. 1974. A comparison of the functional activity of the hypophyseal-adrenal system of hibernating animals. Transl. from *Zh. Evol. Biokhim. Fiziol.* 10(6):598-602

75. Popova, N. K., Voitenko, N. P. 1974. Serotonin metabolism during hibernation. Transl. from *Dokl. Akad. Nauk SSSR Ser. Biol.* 218(6):1488-90

76. Popovic, V. 1960. Endocrines in hibernation. *Bull. Mus. Comp. Zool.* 124:104-30

77. Quay, W. B. 1976. Seasonal cycle and physiological correlates of pinealocyte nuclear and nucleolar diameters in the bats *Myotis lucifugus* and *Myotis sodalis. Gen. Comp. Endocrinol.* 29(3):369-73

78. Racey, P. A. 1976. Induction of ovulation in the pipistrelle bat, *Pipistrellus pipistrellus. J. Reprod. Fertil.* 46(2):481-83

79. Raison, J. K., Lyon, J. M. 1971. Hibernation: Alteration of mitochondrial membranes as a requisite for metabo-

lism at low temperature. *Proc. Natl. Acad. Sci. USA* 68:2092-94

80. Raths, P., Kulzer, E. 1976. Physiology of hibernation and related lethargic states in mammals and birds. *Bonn. Zool. Monogr.* 9:1-91

81. Reiter, R. J. 1973. Endocrine rhythms associated with pineal gland function. In *Biological Rhythms and Endocrine Function,* ed. L. W. Hedlund, J. M. Franz, A. D. Kenny, pp. 43-78. New York/London: Plenum

82. Reznik-Schueller, H., Reznik, G. 1973. Comparative histometric investigations of the testicular function of European hamsters *Cricetus cricetus* with and without hibernation. *Fertil. Steril.* 24(9):698-705

83. Richoux, J. P., DuBois, M. P. 1976. Immunocytologic detection of peptides immunologically related to luteinizing hormone, releasing hormone and to somatostatin in the dormouse *Eliomys quercinus* under different conditions. *C. R. Seances Soc. Biol. Fil.* 170(4):860-64

84. Romita, G., Montesano, R. 1972. Histochemistry and electron microscopy of the adrenal cortex of Chiroptera during hibernation, awakening and summer. *Ateneo Parmense Acta Bio-Med.* 43(3-4):211-33 (In Italian)

85. Saarikoski, P. L., Suomalainen, P. 1975. Studies in the physiology of the hibernating hedgehog Part 20: The changes in the adrenaline and noradrenaline level induced by seasons and hibernation cycle. *Ann. Acad. Sci. Fenn. Ser. A4* 205:1-9

86. Sadler, W. W., Tyler, W. S. 1960. Thyroidal activity in hibernating Chiroptera. II. Synthesis of radio-iodinated amino acids. *Acta Endocrinol.* 34:597-604

87. Sauerbier, I., Lemmer, B. 1977. Seasonal variations in the turnover of noradrenaline of active and hibernating hedgehogs (*Erinaceus europaeus*). *Comp. Biochem. Physiol.* 57C:61-63

88. Smit-Vis, J. H. 1972. The effect of pinealectomy and of testosterone administration on the occurrence of hibernation in adult male golden hamsters. *Acta Morphol. Neerl.-Scand.* 10(3):269-81

89. Smit-Vis, J. H., Akkerman-Bellaart, M. A. 1967. Spermiogenesis in hibernating golden hamsters. *Experientia* 23:844-46

90. Smit-Vis, J. H., Smit. G. J. 1970. Hibernation and testis activity in the golden hamster. *Neth. J. Zool.* 20(4):502-6

91. Spafford, D. C., Pengelley, E. T. 1971. The influence of the neurohumor serotonin on hibernation in the goldenmantled ground squirrel *Citellus lateralis. Comp. Biochem. Physiol.* 38(2A): 239–50

92. Steffen, D. G., Platner, W. S. 1976. Subcellular membrane fatty acids of rat heart after cold acclimation or thyroxine. *Am. J. Physiol.* 231(2):650–54

93. Suomalainen, P. 1960. Stress and neurosecretion in the hibernating hedgehog. *Bull. Mus. Comp. Zool.* 124:271–83

94. Suomalainen, P., Walin, T. 1972. Studies on the physiology of the hibernating hedgehog 16. Variation in the nuclear sizes of cells of the supraoptic nucleus of hedgehog during circadian, hibernation and annual cycles. *Ann. Acad. Sci. Fenn. Ser. A4* 192:1–5

95. Tashima, L. S. 1965. The effects of cold exposure and hibernation on the thyroidal activity of *Mesocricetus auratus. Gen. Comp. Endocrinol.* 5:267–77

96. Twente, J. W., Cline, W. H. Jr., Twente, J. A. 1970. Distribution of epinephrine and norepinephrine in the brain of *Citellus lateralis* during the hibernating cycle. *Comp. Gen. Pharmacol.* 1(1): 47–53

97. Uuspää, V. J. 1963. The 5-hydroxytryptamine content of the brain and some organs of the hedgehog (*Erinaceus europaeus*) during activity and hibernation. *Experientia* 19(3):156–58

98. Velicky, J., Titlbach, M. 1972. A study of the bat thyroid gland in winter and early spring. II. Electron microscopic observations. *Folia Morphol. (Prague)* 20(4):406–15

99. Wang, L. C.-H., Hudson, J. W. 1971. Temperature regulation in normothermic and hibernating eastern chipmunk, *Tamias striatus. Comp. Biochem. Physiol.* 38(1A):59–90

100. Wimsatt, W. A. 1960. Some problems of reproduction in relation to hibernation in bats. *Bull. Mus. Comp. Zool.* 124:249–70

101. Wimsatt, W. A. 1969. Some interrelations of reproduction and hibernation in mammals. In *Dormancy and Survival, XXIIIrd Symp. Soc. Exp. Biol.,* ed. H. W. Woolhouse, pp. 511–59. Cambridge: Cambridge Univ. Press

102. Yurisova, M. N. 1970. Change of the hypothalamo-hypophyseal neurosecretory system during hibernation of the red-cheeked suslik *Citellus erythrogenys.* Translated from *Zh. Evol. Biokhim. Fiziol.* 6(5):516–22

Ann. Rev. Physiol. 1979. 41:305–21

HIBERNATION: NEURAL ASPECTS

♦1221

H. Craig Heller

Department of Biological Sciences, Stanford University,
Stanford, California 94305

INTRODUCTION

Hibernation involves adaptations at all levels of organization from biochemical to behavioral. It can be studied from many approaches, as is evidenced by this section of the present volume, by earlier reviews (32, 34, 38, 39, 41, 55), and by the proceedings of the five international symposia on hibernation (16, 40, 58, 60, 78). In this paper I emphasize central nervous mechanisms controlling the primary manifestation of hibernation, the periodic lowering of metabolic rate and body temperature.

In no way can this review be considered comprehensive. I have chosen to discuss only those experiments and papers that have been most influential in the formation of my own views about the neural control of hibernation.

REGULATION OF BODY TEMPERATURE DURING HIBERNATION

The hypothalamus plays a major role in the regulation of body temperature (T_b) in mammals. This part of the brain is itself temperature sensitive and receives inputs from temperature sensors in the skin, in the spinal cord, and presumably elsewhere in the body (6, 26). This central regulatory mechanism can be described quantitatively through experiments in which the hypothalamic temperature (T_{hy}) is manipulated while thermoregulatory responses are measured. The relation between a response and T_{hy} can be characterized by a threshold and a proportionality constant. The response of metabolic heat production (MHP), for example, can be described by a threshold T_{hy} (T_{set}) above which MHP remains at a minimal level and

305

independent of T_{hy}, and below which the rate of MHP is inversely proportional to T_{hy}. Changes in such things as spinal temperature or skin temperature influence this relationship between T_{hy} and a thermoregulatory response by shifting the threshold and/or the proportionality constant for that response (26, 27). A hypothalamic thermosensitivity curve, therefore, effectively characterizes the thermoregulatory system under any given set of conditions.

A variety of euthermic hibernators have been shown to possess normal mammalian patterns of hypothalamic thermosensitivity (10, 17, 28, 30, 45, 46, 61, 79, 80). In the smaller species, however, hypothalamic thermosensitivity is quite high, dominating the regulation of T_b (10, 30). High hypothalamic and low peripheral thermosensitivity is probably an adaptation of small body size more than a specific adaptation for hibernation (28). Nevertheless, it may significantly facilitate the drop in T_b during the entrance into hibernation.

The hypothalamus retains its thermosensitivity in deep hibernation. Lowering the temperature of the head of a hibernator with an external heat exchanger, or lowering just T_{hy} by means of internal thermodes causes transient increases in heart rate, respiratory rate, electromyographic activity, and MHP, and also arouses the animal from deep hibernation (17, 18, 29, 33, 42, 43, 46, 61). Applications of these same techniques to hold head temperature or T_{hy} above the level that would stimulate an increase in MHP counteracts the stimulatory effect of very low ambient temperatures in some species (17, 29, 33, 42, 43). However, in the dormouse, *Glis glis*, cooling only the hind feet was effective in stimulating an increase in MHP whether or not head temperature was held constant (43). In cases in which hibernating ground squirrels (*Citellus lateralis*) and marmots (*Marmota flaviventris*) resisted passive equilibrium with ambient temperature (T_a) by periodic bursts of MHP, these bursts were suppressed by slightly elevating T_{hy} (17, 29, 31, 33).

Careful, graded manipulations of T_{hy} in hibernating *C. lateralis* and *M. flaviventris* have shown that increases in MHP proportional to the difference between T_{hy} and a threshold T_{hy} could be elicited without inducing an arousal response (17, 18, 29). Resultant hypothalamic thermosensitivity curves from hibernating ground squirrels and marmots qualitatively resemble hypothalamic thermosensitivity curves from euthermic animals. The fact that the proportionality constant for the MHP response decreased as a function of T_{set} with a Q_{10} around 2.4 suggested the same regulatory mechanism could be operative in both states (17, 29).

Manipulation of T_{hy} of ground squirrels and marmots during entrance into hibernation confirmed the continuity of the regulator of T_b over the range of T_b's experienced by the hibernator (17, 18, 31). The T_{hy} threshold

(T_{set}) for the MHP response declined gradually and continuously from the euthermic level to the level of deep hibernation. Bursts of MHP interrupted entrance whenever T_{hy} fell below T_{set}. Occasionally T_{set} would plateau for several hours at an intermediate level between euthermia and deep hibernation, and T_b would be regulated around this level until the decline in T_{set} resumed. It was possible to determine the proportionality constant for the MHP response in marmots at various T_{set}'s between euthermia and deep hibernation; the result was a smooth exponential curve that projected to the euthermic proportionality constants measured during SWS (see below) (18). Thus hibernation does not seem to be an abandonment or a failure in thermoregulation, but a suite of adaptations that have expanded the range over which hibernators can regulate their T_b.

Changes in hypothalamic thermosensitivity within episodes of hibernation also occur, but descriptions differ even though they concern the same species, the yellow-bellied marmot (*M. flaviventris*). Hypothalamic thermosensitivity was reported to be absent until day 4 of an episode of hibernation in one study (61). In another, it was reported to be present over entire episodes of hibernation, with a gradual decrease throughout the first half and a gradual increase during the second half (17). Perhaps these different results reflect the fact that the former study, like other work from the same laboratory, employed only one thermode whereas two were used routinely in the later study (17). Proportionality constants for the MHP response of euthermic animals in (17) were double those reported in (45, 46), which indicates inequality of the thermal stimuli used by these two groups of workers. A gradual change in hypothalamic thermosensitivity within an episode of hibernation may underlie the phenomenon of progressive irritability during hibernation (4, 72), the determination of the lengths of episodes of hibernation, and therefore the timing of periodic arousals.

A conceptual problem with the proposal of a thermoregulatory mechanism continuously operative over a 40°C range of temperatures was that studies of temperature sensitive preoptic anterior hypothalamic (POAH) neurons showed much narrower ranges of thermosensitivity. The firing rates of most POAH warm-sensitive neurons generally fell to or projected to zero at temperatures above 25°C. Thermosensitivities of POAH neurons in a hibernator and a nonhibernator have been compared, with conflicting results. In one study (7) employing only a moderate range of T_{hy}'s, a comparison of thermosensitive POAH units in the ground squirrel, *Citellus lateralis,* and the white rat revealed no striking interspecific differences. In another (62, 81) comparing the golden hamster and the guinea pig, dramatic differences were found. At euthermic T_{hy}'s the firing rates of warm-sensitive cells were much higher in the hibernator than in the nonhibernator. At lower T_{hy}'s, the warm-sensitive cells of the nonhibernator became silent between about 28° and 34°, but those of the hibernator were active down to 10°–15°. Cooling the skin of the hibernator reduced the slopes of the response curves of the warm-sensitive cells so that they continued to fire at still lower T_{hy}'s (62). Therefore, in at least one species of hibernator the necessary neural components exist for the broad-range thermoregulator revealed by thermal manipulations in the naturally hibernating animal. The unit properties on *C. lateralis* should definitely be investigated further because thermoregulation persists in this species from euthermia to deep hibernation.

ELECTROPHYSIOLOGICAL SIMILARITIES BETWEEN SLEEP AND HIBERNATION

Despite the superficial behavioral similarities between hibernation and sleep, electrophysiological data enabling a comparison of these two phenomena have only recently been obtained. The earliest electrophysiological studies of hibernation emphasized investigation of the activities of the brain at various temperatures, omitting comparison of hibernation and sleep. The first such comparison involved the marmot (*M. flaviventris*); the EMG and the EEG from the cortex, brain stem reticular formation (BSRF), and the hypothalamus were recorded during both euthermic periods and entire episodes of hibernation (59). During euthermic sleep the marmot showed an arousal-state distribution of 80% slow-wave sleep (SWS) and 20% paradoxical sleep (PS), which is typical for mammals. The entrance into hibernation was definitely initiated during sleep and the distribution of sleep states during early entrance was reported to remain at 80% SWS and 20% PS. It was not mentioned whether or not wakefulness occurred during entrance, or whether total sleep time (TST) was 100%. Comparison of the recordings below a T_b of about 25° with ones obtained during euthermia was not possible.

An electrophysiological study of two species of ground squirrels [*Citellus lateralis* and *C. beldingi*] revealed that (*a*) prior to and following an episode of hibernation the ground squirrels showed typical distributions of arousal states for small mammals, about 35% wakefulness, 65% sleep; (*b*) 80% of TST was SWS and 20% was PS; (*c*) during early entrance into hibernation TST increased to 88%, but PS accounted for only 10% of this TST; (*d*) as brain temperature (T_{br}) fell PS progressively decreased and SWS increased correspondingly (77). PS was rarely observed below a T_{br} of 27°C. Brief occurrences of wakefulness during entry were usually accompanied by an increase or plateau in both metabolic rate and T_{br}. As in the marmot study (59), the EEG could not be scored by conventional criteria below a T_{br} of 25°. The exit from hibernation was of course characterized by massive EMG activity. The moderately fast, low voltage cortical EEG resembled that of wakefulness. Brief periods of reduced EMG activity were accompanied by slow-wave EEG activity. Above a T_{br} of 33° EMG was reduced considerably and the EEG was largely that of SWS with intermittent wakefulness (77).

Because of the impossibility of comparing EEGs from hibernating animals with T_{br}'s below 25°C with EEGs from euthermic animals, two subsequent electrophysiological studies were undertaken on animals torpid at T_a's of 22°–25° so that continuous EEG recordings could be scored by conventional criteria for entire episodes of torpor. One of these (77 and unpublished results) concerned the ground squirrel, *C. lateralis;* the other (76) treated a desert species of ground squirrel, *C. tereticaudus*, which enters shallow daily torpor in the summer when deprived of food. During torpor in both species with T_{br} between 25° and 27°C, about 95% of the time was spent in SWS and the remaining 5% was scored as wakefulness; PS was completely absent. In spite of the dramatic decrease in PS during torpor no "PS rebound" occurred immediately following an episode of torpor, and the distribution of arousal states was the same following as it was prior to torpor. The return to euthermia in *C. tereticaudus* calls into question our common use of the word "arousal" for this process, because approximately 60% of it occurred through SWS.

Cortical EEG studies of hibernators indicate that hibernation is continuous with and homologous to sleep; more specifically, it is primarily an extension of SWS.

THERMOREGULATORY SIMILARITIES BETWEEN SLEEP AND HIBERNATION

Given the electrophysiological similarities between hibernation and sleep, it is interesting that body temperature of mammals also declines during sleep. The fall in T_b during sleep is a regulated decline, for it is accompanied by coordinated changes in thermoregulatory responses. At the onset of sleep a cessation or reduction in shivering occurs in a cold environment and an increase in evaporative water loss occurs in a warm environment (reviewed in 32). The onset of sleep is almost invariably a transition from wakefulness to SWS. In contrast, thermoregulatory changes observed during the transition from SWS to PS suggest no consistent direction of shift in the regulated T_b (32, 48, 49). Parmeggiani and co-workers demonstrated that hypothalamic thermosensitivity was retained during SWS but not during PS (48). Quantification of hypothalamic thermosensitivity in kangaroo rats (*Dipodomys* sp.) (19) showed that hypothalamic thermosensitivity during SWS had lower temperature thresholds and proportionality constants than during wakefulness, thus explaining the decrease in regulated T_b during SWS. There was no apparent hypothalamic thermosensitivity during PS.

Similar results have now been obtained for a hibernator, the marmot (M. *flaviventris*) (18).

Since T_b is regulated at a lower level during SWS than during wakefulness, and shallow torpor and hibernation consist predominantly of SWS, mammalian torpor may have evolved as an extension of the thermoregulatory adjustments accompanying SWS (34). However, hibernation is a polyphyletic phenomenon (9), and most of the hibernation studies contributing to this speculation have been performed on species of a single family of rodents, the Sciuridae. The evolution of hibernation in other groups quite independently of thermoregulatory adjustments associated with SWS cannot now be excluded.

Clearly, central nervous mechanisms controlling arousal state have an influence on thermoregulation. I shall now describe experiments that demonstrate the converse relationship—i.e. the influence of the thermoregulatory system on arousal state control. While not performed on hibernators, these experiments do provide evidence for a functional interaction between brain areas, which may be important in the control of hibernation. That warmth promotes sleep, cold interferes with sleep, and changes in skin temperature stimulate arousal are familiar phenomena that have been quantitatively documented through studies of arousal-state distribution in cats and rats held at different T_a's (50, 56, 74). Total sleep time (TST) is greatest at thermoneutral temperatures and decreases below thermoneutrality. In these studies the ratio of PS to SWS is greatest at thermoneutrality and decreases as T_a falls. Comparable data on kangaroo rats (*Dipodomys* sp.) confirmed these findings (20). It is interesting that peripheral stimuli representing a thermal stress decrease the time spent in PS, the sleep state during which thermoregulation is impaired. Yet TST is somewhat buffered by a compensatory increase in SWS during which the thermoregulatory system is functioning.

Is this apparent influence of temperature on brain stem systems controlling arousal state due simply to direct ascending input from peripheral temperature receptors, or is it due to descending input from hypothalamic thermoregulatory mechanisms? Direct influences of peripheral temperature receptors on arousal-state control mechanisms should be independent of thermoregulatory drive; so, at a cold T_a a low TST and a low PS/SWS ratio should exist, even if hypothalamic heating eliminated thermoregulatory drive. On the other hand, if temperature influences on arousal-state control were due to descending input from the thermoregulatory system, manipulating T_{hy} should control the TST and the PS/SWS ratio, regardless of T_a. Arousal-state distributions in kangaroo rats (*Dipodomys* sp.) held at 20° and 30° with and without hypothalamic warming or cooling for the duration of the recording period indicated a different organization of inputs in the control of TST and in the control of the PS/SWS ratio [(20) and unpublished results]. TST was clearly a function of thermoregulatory drive and hence of descending input. TST was the same in experiments at 20°C with hypothalamic warming as in experiments at 30°C with no manipulation of T_{hy}. Similarly, a reduced TST occurred both at 20°C with no manipulation of T_{hy} and at 30°C with sufficient hypothalamic cooling to elevate MHP to the level seen in the 20° run. In contrast, the PS/SWS ratio was influenced by both ascending and descending inputs as cooling either the skin or the hypothalamus reduced the PS/SWS ratio regardless of the level of the other variable. It appears that the generation of an error signal by the hypothalamic regulator of T_b results in an input to the brain-stem systems controlling arousal states; this input interferes with sleep and with the transitions from SWS to PS. Ascending stimuli from peripheral cold receptors also interfere with the transition from SWS to PS independently of the level of thermoregulatory drive. Adequate information does not exist on the influence of high T_a and T_{hy} on TST and the PS/SWS ratio, but the available data indicate that stimuli on the warm and cool sides of thermoneutrality have similar influences (56).

INVOLVEMENT AND INTERACTIONS OF BRAIN AREAS IN THE CONTROL OF HIBERNATION

Hibernation is characterized by regulatory changes in body temperature, food intake, body mass, sleep/wakefulness, and reproductive physiology; therefore, the hypothalamus and the brain stem reticular formation (BSRF) must be involved in its control. Many earlier studies of brain activity during hibernation focused on the electrical activity of the cortex during hibernation (reviewed in 44). These studies established the existence of interspecific differences in the effect of temperature on the electrical activity of the cerebral cortex. Electrophysiological recordings from subcortical structures in ground squirrels, marmots, and hedgehogs have been more instructive about brain mechanisms controlling hibernation. During the entrance into hibernation, the amplitude and regularity of EEG activity in all brain areas are progressively reduced as T_b declines. Electrical activity tends to disappear in a regular sequence: first in the cortex, then in the BSRF, the thalamus, and the limbic system (57, 59). During hibernation at low temperatures the cortex and the BSRF show extended periods of electrical silence, whereas nearly continuous (albeit small amplitude) activity persists in the limbic system and hypothalamus (44, 57, 59, 64).

The electrical silence reported for the BSRF during deep hibernation does not necessarily mean that this area is inactivated by cold, as has been suggested (12). Lightly touching a hibernating ground squirrel (*C. beecheyi*) with a glass rod was a sufficient stimulus to induce activity in the BSRF, which was then followed by an arousal response, increased heart rate, and continuous muscle activity (64). Recordings of hypothalamic EEG have also shown that the decrease in electrical activity of specific brain areas during entrance into hibernation is not simply due to the fall in brain temperature. While T_b was declining, the hypothalamic EEG was mostly desynchronized and of low amplitude. But, over the same range of temperatures, the hypothalamic EEG could show a synchronized, high amplitude pattern during brief arousals. It appears that the small amplitude hypothalamic EEG typical of hibernation is not caused by the T_b decline but precedes it (81).

The reappearance of electrical activity during arousal from hibernation occurs in the reverse order from which it disappeared or declined during entrance. Activity increases first in the limbic system, then hypothalamus, thalamus, BSRF, and lastly the cortex (57). Many studies report an association of limbic system activity with the initiation of the arousal from hibernation (11, 44, 57, 65, 66, 81) and with transient disturbances of the hibernating animal. During incomplete arousals observed in one study (57), electrical activity always appeared first and disappeared last in the hippocampus. In other studies various modes of stimulation such as a puff of smoke (44), movement of electrodes (11), or shivering (63) were followed by bursts of higher-voltage activity originating in the limbic system. A continuous recording of electrical activity in one part of the limbic system, the amygdala, of a ground squirrel (*C. beecheyi*) during deep hibernation revealed periodic increases in activity followed in about 20 min by small increases in brain temperature. Each of these increases in electrical activity was greater than the preceding one until one was followed by full arousal (65). Evidently the limbic system always remains responsive to external and internal stimuli during hibernation.

A brief description of the anatomical relations between the BSRF, the hypothalamus, and the limbic system should be a useful prelude to discussion of their functional interactions and possible roles in the control of hibernation. Somatosensory afferents such as those originating in temperature sensors in the skin and spinal cord ascend to the brain stem in the spinothalamic tracts. These fibers have a wide distribution in the brain stem, some project directly to the thalamus, but most terminate in the BSRF. The BSRF gives rise to thalamocortical projections and also projections to the hypothalamus, the limbic system, and the forebrain. Descending pathways from the limbic system reach the hypothalamus and the BSRF. Descending connections between the hypothalamus and the BSRF also exist. These interconnections among the hypothalamus, limbic system, and BSRF comprise the "limbic system-midbrain circuit" (47), which clearly has important influences on hypothalamic activity and the responsiveness of hypothalamic neurons to sensory stimuli (13, 15).

Observations discussed above that the hypothalamic regulator of T_b operates on a continuum from euthermia to deep hibernation and that hibernation is physiologically homologous with SWS suggest that interactions between the hypothalamus and the BSRF play a central role in the control of hibernation. A variety of studies show functional interactions between these brain areas. Electrical stimulation in the brain stem influences the firing rates of temperature sensitive neurons in the POAH and septum (8, 14). Electrical stimulation of the brain stem has also been shown to induce an increase in metabolic rate mediated by noradrenergic mechanisms in the hypothalamus (67). The changes in hypothalamic thermosensitivity with changes in arousal state and the influences of the thermoregulatory system on distribution of arousal states, as discussed above, also reveal reciprocal interactions between the BSRF and the hypothalamus.

Interactions between the BSRF and the hypothalamus have also been demonstrated during hibernation. Both the POAH and BSRF have been stimulated with microinjections of putative neurotransmitters at different times during episodes of hibernation as well as when the animals were euthermic (1–5). Arousals from hibernation were always triggered by microinjections of acetylcholine (ACh), norepinephrine (NE), or 5-hydoxytryptamine (5-HT) into the POAH. Appropriate control injections into the POAH as well as injections of NE and 5-HT into the nearby extrahypothalamic site, the caudate putamen, did not stimulate arousals. Similar microinjections into the BSRF showed that ACh, but not NE and 5-HT, was effective in inducing arousal. Also, ACh was a less effective arousal stimulus in the BSRF than in the POAH, many injections into the BSRF resulting only in partial arousal responses. Neurons in these two areas are apparently involved in the process of triggering arousal from hibernation. Within an episode of hibernation the sensitivity to ACh in the BSRF increases progressively (4), which is similar to the previously reported progressive irritability of hibernators to peripheral stimuli (72). Combining these results with the facts that arousal from hibernation involves a rapid rise in the hypothalamic threshold for the MHP response (33) and that there seems to be a gradual rise in this threshold toward the end of an episode of hibernation (17, 61), it is reasonable to propose that BSRF neurons trigger arousal by facilitating POAH neurons responsible for generating thermoregulatory threshold temperatures.

The role of the BSRF in controlling sensitivity to peripheral stimuli during hibernation has been recently explored (69, 70) through application of graded, calibrated tactile stimuli to the backs of hibernating ground squirrels (C. lateralis) while muscle action potentials were recorded. This measure of peripheral sensitivity revealed no relationship to T_b or time in hibernation in the intact hibernator, whereas clear relationships were seen in the spinal hibernator or in the hibernator with its BSRF reversibly inactivated by means of cryoprobes. Evidently the BSRF is responsible for the highly variable sensitivity of the hibernating animal to peripheral stimuli. In some experiments multiple unit activity in the BSRF was recorded while measuring peripheral sensitivity. Whenever the BSRF was electrically quiescent the level of sensitivity remained constant, and conversely, electrical activity in the BSRF was associated with shifts in the sensitivity to peripheral stimulation. These results could be explained solely on the basis of BSRF influences on descending supraspinal pathways, but presumably the BSRF also gates ascending information.

Incorporation of the limbic system into a view of hibernation control is more difficult than establishing a reasonable hypothesis about hypothalamic-BSRF interactions. The functions of the limbic system remain controversial (36); nevertheless, evidence exists for interactions between the BSRF and the limbic system, as well as between the thermoregulatory system and the limbic system. Clear correlations between arousal state and hippocampal slow wave activity (the theta rhythm) have long been recognized (37). Direct electrical stimulation of the BSRF can induce the hippocampal theta rhythm (23, 51) and cause most cells in the medial septum (ascending pathway to the hippocampus) to fire in synchrony with the theta rhythm (24, 51, 52). Studies of hippocampal unit responses to BSRF stimulation report either a predominantly inhibitory influence (23), an inhibition followed by excitatory rebound (25), or responses characterized by both excitatory and inhibitory components (21, 22). Conversely, the hippocampus has a descending influence on a large proportion of BSRF cells (40–50%) that is predominantly inhibitory in the "excitatory" areas of the BSRF (i.e. the midbrain RF) and excitatory in the "inhibitory" areas of the BSRF (i.e. the raphe nuclei) (75).

Evidence for functional interactions between the limbic system and the thermoregulatory system is as follows. Thermal stimulation of the skin can induce the hippocampal theta rhythm (35). Temperature sensitive neurons are well represented in the septum as well as in the POAH (8, 14). There are clear projections from the hippocampus to the hypothalamus (47), and electrical stimulation of the hippocampus influences a large percentage of POAH neurons, predominantly those that are temperature sensitive (8, 15, 53). Electrical stimulation of the hippocampus strongly influences the response of hypothalamic neurons to several modalities of sensory stimuli (13, 15).

Certain features of limbic system organization must be kept in mind as its possible role in hibernation is examined. First, hippocampal theta is generated by neurons of the medial septum (24, 51, 52, 68). Theta is thus a measure of the level of afferent input to the hippocampus and may bear little relation to the output of this structure. Second, cells within the hippocampus that fire only during theta activity constitute a very small widely distributed population, whereas the vast majority of hippocampal cells show no simple relation with theta and fire when the hippocampal EEG is desynchronized (54). This finding led to the suggestion that the theta cells are inhibitory interneurons. Third, the descending influence of the hippocampus on the BSRF is largely inhibitory (75).

The above considerations suggest that during sleep, entrance into hibernation, and deep hibernation the hippocampus exerts a tonic suppression on brain stem arousal mechanisms. Arousing stimuli originating in the periphery or perhaps in the hypothalamus (e.g. T_{hy} below T_{set}) ascend to the limbic system via the septum, where they cause the generation of theta activity. The theta cells inhibit hippocampal output resulting in disinhibition of the BSRF. This is a positive feedback loop that would be capable of generating the very rapid reactivation of the brain during arousal from hibernation. Such a positive feedback loop was previously suggested on the basis of thermoregulatory studies (27, 29). Presumably, a major function of the hippocampus in the hibernating animal, as in the euthermic animal, could be the discrimination among stimuli that should or should not stimulate the energetically expensive process of arousal. A mechanism that serves to inhibit arousal from hibernation has been indicated (1, 5); the limbic system may indeed serve this function.

In light of these ideas on limbic system function, reexamination of an observation (63) on the EEG of ground squirrels (*C. beecheyi*) entering hibernation becomes feasible. The entrance was frequently interrupted by bursts of shivering, each of which was preceded and accompanied by a motor cortex discharge and followed by limbic system slow wave activity. This led to postulation that the limbic system and the motor cortex were involved in a mutually inhibitory mechanism controlling shivering. More likely the physical disturbance and consequent tactile sensations caused by the shivering were responsible for generating this limbic slow-wave activity. This activity was only an indication of the level of input to the hippocampus which, presumably, then performed the function of determining whether or not the stimulus was adequate to initiate an arousal.

AN HYPOTHESIS FOR THE NEURAL CONTROL OF HIBERNATION

Figure 1 presents a simple model for the neural control of hibernation based on the information discussed here. It describes a positive feedback loop operating within certain sets of limits. One is imposed by the BSRF and consists of the extremes of the arousal state continuum, fully alert to deep

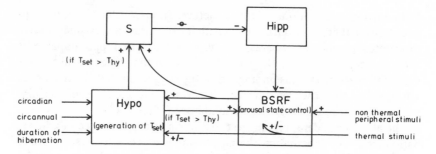

Figure 1 A model of how the brain stem reticular formation (BSRF), the hypothalamus (Hypo), and the limbic system as represented by the septum (S) and the hippocampus (Hipp) might interact to control the daily sleep/wakefulness cycle and the hibernation/euthermia cycle. Excitatory influences are indicated by "+" and inhibitory influences are indicated by "–". T_{set} refers to the hypothalamic temperature threshold for the metabolic heat-production response, and θ represents the activity of theta-rhythm pacemaker cells in the septum. The inputs to the hypothalamic compartment represent influences on the generation of T_{set}.

sleep. Within these limits the positive feedback loop would tend to maintain the animal at one end or the other in the absence of other inputs such as peripheral stimuli or circadian influences. In other words, drowsiness should be a very unstable state and the condition of deep sleep or intense arousal should be self sustaining. Another set of limits is imposed by hypothalamic thermoregulatory mechanisms. There are normally upper and lower limits for thermoregulatory thresholds, regardless of arousal state. These limits may be partially determined by negative feedback from temperature sensors elsewhere in the body. Perhaps tonic levels of activity in some populations of POAH neurons also contribute to limits on the regulated T_b.

Let's travel around the loop conceptually, beginning in the BSRF at the onset of sleep. The arousal-state control function of the BSRF is indicated as an ascending excitatory influence. Decrease in BSRF activity at the onset of sleep would result in a decline in both POAH activity and T_{set}. The latter may reduce thermoregulatory drive and withdraw a source of excitation to the BSRF that would be an internal positive feedback loop in the model. Declining BSRF activity also reduces excitation to the septum, curtailing the activity of the septal theta-generating cells, which in turn produces disinhibition of the hippocampus. Increasing hippocampal inhibition on the BSRF maintains the sleeping state. The loop could be thrown into the opposite mode (awake) by peripheral stimuli or, presumably, by internal influences (e.g. increase in thermoregulatory drive or a circadian input) adequate to excite the BSRF sufficiently to overcome the tonic hippocampal inhibition.

This model requires only one quantitative distinction between normal sleep/wakefulness operation and hibernation/wakefulness operation: the lower limit on T_{set}. What could be different about hibernators that would permit the dramatic drop in T_{set} occurring during hibernation? First, the hibernators we have studied have low extrahypothalamic thermosensitivity. Extrahypothalamic thermosensitivity serves as negative feedback in the thermoregulatory system by raising T_{set} and exciting the BSRF as T_b falls. Second, euthermic hibernators show a greater propensity to sleep during the hibernation season than during the rest of the year (34), which indicates a circannual fluctuation in hippocampal and/or BSRF function. Third, euthermic hibernators show a lower regulated T_b during the hibernation season than during the rest of the year, which indicates a circannual change in POAH activities that generate or place limits on T_{set}. Any or all of these factors could contribute to the lowered lower limit for T_{set} during sleep during hibernation. Such a lowered T_{set} for the MHP response in the model presented is sufficient to effect the transition from normal, euthermic sleep/wakefulness operation to hibernation.

There is an obvious difference between the temporal organizations of the sleep/wakefulness cycle and the hibernation/euthermia cycle. How can our simple model account for this? A decrease in the lower limit of the T_{set} for the MHP response may be responsible for the transition from the normal circadian sleep/wakefulness periodicity to the longer episodes of torpor via a direct thermal effect. Such an effect has been noted in several species; the duration of an individual episode of hibernation is inversely proportional to the T_b during the episode in several species (71, 73). In animals such as the round-tailed ground squirrel, which maintains a distinct circadian organization of its episodes of torpor, the thermal influence due to reduced body temperature is probably overridden by a strong circadian input. But, for deep hibernators a point is presumably reached at which this circadian input can no longer overcome the torpor-prolonging influence of a reduced T_b, and a multiday bout of torpor results.

CONCLUSIONS

Mammalian hibernation is associated with a regulated decline in body temperature rather than a lack of or a failure in thermoregulatory mechanisms. The hibernator, unlike other mammals, can regulate its T_b over an extended range, and apparently the same hypothalamic thermoregulatory mechanism is continuously operative over this broad range. Electrophysiological studies show that hibernation is homologous with sleep, predominantly with slow-wave sleep. The downward resetting of the hypothalamic regulator of T_b during slow-wave sleep suggests that hibernation may have evolved as an adaptive extension of this sleep-regulated thermoregulatory adjustment. Electrophysiological recordings from subcortical structures during hibernation indicate that the limbic system-midbrain circuit plays an important role in the control of hibernation. Evidence has been reviewed for interactions between the components of this circuit: the BSRF, the hypothalamus, the septum, and the hippocampus. A simple model has been proposed showing how this circuit may operate in the control of sleep/ wakefulness and hibernation/wakefulness.

ACKNOWLEDGMENTS

It has been my good fortune to have an excellent group of co-workers to share my interests in thermoregulation, sleep, and hibernation. Much of the work and many of the ideas presented in this paper have resulted from my interactions with R. J. Berger, G. W. Colliver, G. L. Florant, S. F. Glotzbach, H. T. Hammel, S. Sakaguchi, and J. M. Walker. I am grateful to Drs. F. Klussmann, R. Necker, and W. Rautenberg for their kind hospitality while I was writing this paper. Work from my laboratory discussed in this paper has been supported by U.S.N.I.H. grants N.S. 10367 and G.M. 23695.

Literature Cited

1. Beckman, A. L. 1978. Hypothalamic and midbrain function during hibernation. In *Recent Studies of Hypothalamic Function.* Basel: Karger. In press
2. Beckman, A. L., Satinoff, E. 1972. Arousal from hibernation by intrahypothalamic injections of biogenic amines in ground squirrels. *Am. J. Physiol.* 222:875–79
3. Beckman, A. L., Stanton, T. L. 1976. Characterization of midbrain component of the trigger for arousal from hibernation. *Am. J. Physiol.* 230:368–75
4. Beckman, A. L., Stanton, T. L. 1976. Changes in CNS responsiveness during hibernation. *Am. J. Physiol.* 231: 810–16
5. Beckman, A. L., Stanton, T. L., Satinoff, E. 1976. Inhibition of the CNS trigger process for arousal from hibernation. *Am. J. Physiol.* 230:1018–25
6. Bligh, J. 1973. *Temperature Regulation in Mammals and Other Vertebrates.* Amsterdam: North-Holland. 436 pp.
7. Boulant, J. A., Bignall, K. E. 1973. Determinants of hypothalamic thermosensitivity in ground squirrels and rats. *Am. J. Physiol.* 225:306–10

8. Boulant, J. A., Demieville, H. N. 1977. Responses of thermosensitive preoptic and septal neurons to hippocampal and brain stem stimulation. *J. Neurophysiol.* 40:1356–68
9. Cade, T. J. 1964. The evolution of torpidity in rodents. *Ann. Acad. Sci. Fenn. (Biol.)* 71:77–111
10. Chappell, M. A., Calvo, A., Heller, H. C. 1978. Hypothalamic thermosensitivity and adaptations for heat-storage behavior in three species of chipmunks (*Eutamias*) from different thermal environments. *J. Comp. Physiol. B.* 125: 175–84
11. Chatfield, P. O., Lyman, C. P. 1954. Subcortical electrical activity in the golden hamster during arousal from hibernation. *Electroencephalogr. Clin. Neurophysiol.* 6:403–8
12. Chatfield, P. O., Lyman, C. P., Purpura, D. P. 1951. The effects of temperature on the spontaneous and induced electrical activity in the cerebral cortex of the golden hamster. *Electroencephalogr. Clin. Neurophysiol.* 3:225–30
13. Dafny, N., Feldman, S. 1969. Effects of stimulating reticular formation, hippocampus, and septum on single cells in the posterior hypothalamus. *Electro-*

encephalogr. Clin. Neurophysiol. 26: 578–87

14. Eisenman, J. S. 1973. Unit studies of brainstem projections to the preoptic area and hypothalamus. In *Recent Studies of Hypothalamic Function,* ed. K. Lederis, K. E. Cooper, pp. 328–40. Basel: Karger. 434 pp.

15. Feldman, S., Dafny, N. 1970. Effects of extrahypothalamic structures on sensory projections to the hypothalamus. In *The Hypothalamus,* ed. L. Martini, M. Motto, F. Fraschini, pp. 103–114. New York: Academic. 705 pp.

16. Fisher, K. C., Dawe, A. R., Lyman, C. P., Schoenbaum, E., South, F. E., eds. 1967. *Mammalian Hibernation III.* Edinburgh: Oliver and Boyd. 535 pp.

17. Florant, G. L., Heller, H. C. 1977. CNS regulation of body temperature in euthermic and hibernating marmots (*Marmota flaviventris*). *Am. J. Physiol.* 232:R203–8

18. Florant, G. L., Turner, B., Heller, H. C. 1978. Temperature regulation during wakefulness, sleep, and hibernation in marmots (*Marmota flaviventris*). *Am. J. Physiol.* 235:R82–88

19. Glotzbach, S. F., Heller, H. C. 1976. Central nervous regulation of body temperature during sleep. *Science* 194: 537–39

20. Glotzbach, S. F., Sakaguchi, S., Heller, H. C. 1976. Effects of hypothalamic and ambient temperatures on sleep states in the kangaroo rat, *Dipodomys. Sleep Res.* 6:51

21. Grantyn, A. A. 1970. An intracellular study of hippocampal responses to reticular stimulation. *Brain Res.* 22: 409–12

22. Grantyn, R., Grantyn, A. A. 1973. Postsynaptic responses of hippocampal neurons to mesencephalic stimulation: depolarizing potentials and discharge patterns. *Brain Res.* 53:55–69

23. Gogolak, G., Klingberg, F., Otsuka, Y., Stumpf, Ch. 1967. Verhalten von Hippocannus-Pyramidenzellen bei retikulärer Reizung. *Experientia* 23:190–92

24. Gogolak, G., Stumpf, Ch., Petsche, H., Sterc, J. 1968. The firing pattern of septal neurons and the form of the hippocampal theta wave. *Brain Res.* 7:201–7

25. Green, J. D., Maxwell, D. S., Schindler, W. J., Stumpf, Ch. 1960. Rabbit EEG theta rhythm: its anatomical source and relation to activity in single neurons. *J. Neurophysiol.* 23:403–20

26. Hammel, H. T. 1968. Regulation of internal body temperature. *Ann. Rev. Physiol.* 30:641–710

27. Hammel, H. T., Heller, H. C., Sharp, F. R. 1973. Probing the rostral brainstem of anesthetized, unanesthetized, and exercising dogs and of hibernating and euthermic ground squirrels. *Fed. Proc.* 32:1588–96

28. Heller, H. C. 1978. Hypothalamic thermosensitivity in mammals. In *Experientia, Suppl. 32: Effectors of Thermogenesis,* ed. L. Girardier, J. Seydoux. Basel: Birkhäuser. 345 pp.

29. Heller, H. C., Colliver, G. W. 1974. CNS regulation of body temperature during hibernation. *Am. J. Physiol.* 227:583–89

30. Heller, H. C., Colliver, G. W., Anand, P. 1974. CNS regulation of body temperature in euthermic hibernators. *Am. J. Physiol.* 227:576–82

31. Heller, H. C., Colliver, G. W., Beard, J. 1977. Thermoregulation during entrance into hibernation. *Pfluegers Arch.* 369:55–59

32. Heller, H. C., Glotzbach, S. F. 1977. Thermoregulation during sleep and hibernation. *Int. Rev. Physiol.* 15: 147–87

33. Heller, H. C., Hammel, H. T. 1972. CNS control of body temperature during hibernation. *Comp. Biochem. Physiol.* 41A:349–59

34. Heller, H. C., Walker, J. M., Florant, G. L., Glotzbach, S. F., Berger, R. J. 1978. Sleep and hibernation: electrophysiological and thermoregulatory homologies. See Ref. 78, pp. 225–65

35. Horowitz, J. M., Saleh, M. A., Kerem, R. D. 1974. Correlation of hippocampal theta rhythm with changes in cutaneous temperature. *Am. J. Physiol.* 227: 635–42

36. Isaacson, R. L., Pribram, K. H., eds. 1975. *The Hippocampus, Vol. 2: Neurophysiology and Behavior.* New York: Plenum. 445 pp.

37. Jouvet, M. 1967. Neurophysiology of the states of sleep. In *The Neurosciences, A Study Program,* ed. G. C. Quarton, T. Melnechuk, F. O. Schmitt, pp. 529–44. New York: Rockefeller Univ. Press. 962 pp.

38. Kayser, Ch. 1961. *The Physiology of Natural Hibernation.* London: Pergamon. 325 pp.

39. Kayser, Ch., Malan, A. 1963. Central nervous system and hibernation. *Experientia* 19:441–51

40. Lyman, C. P., Dawe, A. R., eds. 1960. Mammalian Hibernation. *Bull. Mus. Comp. Zool. Harvard U.* 124:1–549

41. Lyman, C. P., Chatfield, P. O. 1955. Physiology of hibernation in mammals. *Physiol. Rev.* 35:403–25

42. Lyman, C. P., O'Brien, R. C. 1972. Sensitivity to low temperature in hibernating rodents. *Am. J. Physiol.* 222:864–69

43. Lyman, C. P., O'Brien, R. C. 1974. A comparison of temperature regulation in hibernating rodents. *Am. J. Physiol.* 227:218–23

44. Mihailovic, Lj. T. 1972. Cortical and subcortical electrical activity in hibernation and hypothermia. In *Hibernation and Hypothermia, Perspectives and Challenges*, ed. F. E. South, J. P. Hannon, J. R. Willis, E. T. Pengelley, N. R. Alpert, pp. 487–534. Amsterdam: Elsevier. 743 pp.

45. Mills, S. H., Miller, V. M., South, F. E. 1974. Thermoregulatory responses of a hibernator to hypothalamic and ambient temperature. *Cryobiol.* 11:465–72

46. Mills, S. H., South, F. E. 1972. Central regulation of temperature in hibernation and normothermia. *Cryobiology* 9:393–403

47. Nauta, W. J. H. 1958. Hippocampal projections and related neural pathways to the midbrain in the cat. *Brain* 81:319–40

48. Parmeggiani, P. L., Sabattini, L. 1972. Electromyographic aspects of postural, respiratory, and thermoregulatory mechanisms in sleeping cats. *Electroencephalogr. Clin. Neurophysiol.* 33:1–13

49. Parmeggiani, P. L., Rabini, C. 1967. Shivering and panting during sleep. *Brain Res.* 6:789–91

50. Parmeggiani, P. L., Rabini, C. 1970. Sleep and environmental temperature. *Arch. Ital. Biol.* 108:369–87

51. Petche, H., Gogolak, G., Van Zwieten, P. D. 1965. Rhythmicity of septal cell discharge at various levels of reticular excitation. *Electroencephalogr. Clin. Neurophysiol.* 19:25–33

52. Petche, H., Stumpf, Ch., Gogolak, G. 1962. The significance of the rabbit's septum as a relay station between the midbrain and the hippocampus. 1. The control of hippocampus arousal activity by the septum cells. *Electroencephalogr. Clin. Neurophysiol.* 14:202–11

53. Poletti, C. E., Kinnard, M. H., MacLean, P. D. 1973. Hippocampal influence on unit activity of hypothalamus, preoptic region, and basal forebrain in awake, sitting squirrel monkeys. *J. Neurophysiol.* 36:308–24

54. Ranck, J. B. 1975. Behavioral correlates and firing repertoires of neurons in the dorsal hippocampal formation and septum of unrestrained rats. See Ref. 36, pp. 207–44

55. Satinoff, E. 1970. Hibernation and the central nervous system. *Prog. Physiol. Psychol.* 3:201–36

56. Schmidek, W. R., Hoshino, K., Schmidek, M., Timo-Iara, C. 1972. Influence of environmental temperature on the sleep-wakefulness cycle in the rat. *Physiol. Behav.* 9:363–71

57. Shtark, M. B. 1972. *The Brain of Hibernating Animals,* NASA Tech. Transl. TTF-619. 226 pp.

58. Soumalainen, P., ed. 1964. Mammalian Hibernation. *Ann. Acad. Sci. Fenn. (Biol.)* 71:1–453

59. South, F. E., Breazile, J. E., Dellman, H. D., Epperly, A. D. 1969. Sleep, hibernation and hypothermia in the yellow-bellied marmot (*M. flaviventris*). In *Depressed Metabolism*, ed. X. J. Musacchia, J. F. Saunders, pp. 277–310. New York: Elsevier. 630 pp.

60. South, F. E., Hannon, J. P., Willis, J. S., Pengelley, E. T., Alpert, N. R., eds. 1972. *Hibernation and Hypothermia, Perspectives and Challenges.* Amsterdam: Elsevier. 743 pp.

61. South, F. E., Hartner, W. C., Luecke, R. H. 1975. Responses to preoptic temperature manipulation in the awake and hibernating marmot. *Am. J. Physiol.* 229:150–60

62. Speulda, E., Wünnenberg, W. 1977. Thermosensitivity of preoptic neurones in a hibernator at high and low ambient temperatures. *Pfluegers Arch.* 370:107–9

63. Strumwasser, F. 1959. Thermoregulatory brain and behavioral mechanisms during entrance into hibernation in the squirrel, *Citellus beecheyi. Am. J. Physiol.* 196:15–22

64. Strumwasser, F. 1959. Regulatory mechanisms, brain activity, and behavior during deep hibernation in the squirrel, *Citellus beecheyi. Am. J. Physiol.* 196:23–30

65. Strumwasser, F., Schlechte, F. R., Streeter, J. 1967. The internal rhythms of hibernators. See Ref. 16, pp. 110–139

66. Strumwasser, F., Smith, J., Gilliam, J., Schlechte, F. R. 1963. Identification of active brain regions involved in the process of hibernation. *XVI Int. Congr. Zool.* 2:53–56

67. Szelenyi, Z., Zeisberger, E., Brück, K. 1976. Effects of electrical stimulation in the lower brainstem on temperature regulation in the unanesthetized guinea-pig. *Pfluegers Arch.* 364:123–27

68. Tömböl, T., Petsche, H. 1969. The histological organization of the pacemaker for the hippocampal theta rhythm in the rabbit. *Brain Res.* 12:414–26
69. Toth, D. M. 1977. EMG responses of intact and spinal ground squirrels to tactile stimulation during hibernation, hypothermia, and normothermia. *Comp. Biochem. Physiol.* 57A:167–77
70. Toth, D. M. 1978. Reversible functional blockade of the reticular formation stabilizes level of responsiveness to sensory stimulation and inhibits arousability in hibernating ground squirrels. *Fed. Proc.* 37:250
71. Twente, J. W., Twente, J. A. 1965. Regulation of hibernating periods by temperature. *Proc. Natl. Acad. Sci. USA* 54:1058–61
72. Twente, J. W., Twente, J. A. 1968. Progressive irritability of hibernating *Citellus lateralis. Comp. Biochem. Physiol.* 25:467–74
73. Twente, J. W., Twente, J. A., Moy, R. M. 1977. Regulation of arousal from hibernation by temperature in three species of *Citellus. J. Appl. Physiol.: Respir. Environ. Exercise Physiol.* 42:191–95
74. Valatx, J. L., Roussel, B., Curé, M. 1973. Sommeil et température cérébrale du rat au cours de l'exposition chronique en ambiance chaude. *Brain Res.* 55:107–22

75. Vinogradova, O. S. 1975. Functional organization of the limbic system in the process of registration of information: facts and hypotheses. See Ref. 36, pp. 3–70
76. Walker, J. M., Garber, A., Berger, R. J., Heller, H. C. 1978. Sleep and estivation in the round-tailed ground squirrel (*Citellus tereticaudus*). *Sleep Res.* 7. In press
77. Walker, J. M., Glotzbach, S. F., Berger, R. J., Heller, H. C. 1977. Sleep and hibernation in ground squirrels (*Citellus spp.*): electrophysiological observations. *Am. J. Physiol.* 233:R213–21
78. Wang, L. C., Hudson, J. W., eds. 1978. *Strategies in the Cold: Natural Torpidity and Thermogenesis.* New York: Academic. 715 pp.
79. Williams, B. A., Heath, J. E. 1970. Responses to preoptic heating and cooling in a hibernator *Citellus tridecemlineatus. Am. J. Physiol.* 218:1654–60
80. Williams, B. A., Heath, J. E. 1971. Thermoregulatory responses of a hibernator to preoptic and environmental temperatures. *Am. J. Physiol.* 221:1134–38
81. Wünnenberg, W., Merker, G., Speulda, E. 1976. Thermosensitivity of preoptic neurones and hypothalamic integrative function in hibernators and nonhibernators. See Ref. 78, pp. 267–97

Ann. Rev. Physiol. 1979. 41:323–35

REPRODUCTIVE ENDOCRINOLOGY OF FISHES: Gonadal Cycles and Gonadotropin in Teleosts

♦1222

R. E. Peter

Department of Zoology, University of Alberta, Edmonton T6G 2E9, Canada

L. W. Crim

Marine Sciences Research Laboratory, Memorial University of Newfoundland, St. John's A1C 5S7, Canada

INTRODUCTION

This brief review is restricted to certain aspects of the endocrinology of reproduction of teleost fishes: (*a*) the timing of reproductive cycles and the environmental cues involved; and (*b*) the chemistry and actions of gonadotropin (GtH), its secretory cycles, and the regulation of its secretion.

REPRODUCTIVE CYCLES AND ENVIRONMENTAL CUES

Annual reproductive cycles for many species of teleosts have most frequently been described in terms of seasonal changes in the gonadosomatic index (gonad weight as a percent of total body weight) and/or histological changes in the ovary or testis (31, 33, 35, 36, 42, 74).

Many salmonids spawn in the autumn. Short photoperiods, and acceleration of the cyclic change of increasing and decreasing photoperiods induce earlier gonadal maturity in brook trout, *Salvelinus fontinalis* (50). In rainbow trout, *Salmo gairdneri,* decreasing photoperiods and warm temperature (16°C) accelerate spermatogenesis more than decreasing photoperiod

323

and cold temperature (8°C) (8). These results, among others, indicate that acceleration of the photoperiod cycle, specifically decreasing daylength, induces gonadal maturation in autumn-spawning trout.

The threespine stickleback, *Gasterosteus aculeatus*, spawns in the late spring–early summer; and gonadal recrudescence is regulated by a combination of photoperiod and temperature cues (2). Gonadal recrudescence can be induced in the winter in this species by exposure to a long photoperiod (16 hr light, 8 hr dark) and warm temperatures (20°C), short photoperiods (8 hr light, 16 hr dark) and such temperatures being ineffective. The sensitive period for inducing gonadal maturation in the stickleback is about 12–18 hr after onset of the daily photoperiod. During the spring, long photoperiod induces more rapid gonadal maturation than short photoperiod in both warm and cold. During the summer, after termination of the normal spawning season, long photoperiod and warm conditions do not induce another cycle of gonadal recrudescence. This suggests a refractory period following spawning that terminates reproductive activity and prevents another cycle of gonadal recrudescence in the summer. In another stickleback, *Culea inconstans*, long photoperiod and temperatures of about 14–18°C, but not greater than 19°C, induce reproductive activity (71).

Generally all freshwater temperate zone fishes spawning in the spring or early summer have gonadal recrudescence in the winter or spring in response to long photoperiods and warm temperatures, although there may be more dependence on one factor or the other in different species (31, 35, 42, 46, 49, 56, 74). In these fishes warmth is necessary for final oocyte maturation or spermiogenesis and spawning. However, excessively high temperatures can cause gonadal regression, and additional factors such as vegetation may be necessary for spawning. The catfish, *Heteropneustes fossilis*, has a daily rhythm in photoresponsiveness, with the sensitive phases occurring at between 16–17 hr and 20–21 hr after onset of the daily light period; the catfish, however, responds primarily to warmth for gonadal recrudescence (74). Although a period of postspawning refractoriness probably occurs in most species, it has been demonstrated in only the threespine stickleback (2), the cyprinid *Notropis bifrenatus* (49), the catfish (74), and the medaka, *Oryzias latipes* (42). In the catfish, post-spawning gonadal regression is accelerated by low temperatures (74). Perhaps exposure to low temperatures is necessary to overcome refractoriness for many species, but this has not been investigated. In the cyprinid *Couesius plumbeus*, low temperatures in the winter favor the early stages of spermatogenesis (1); in goldfish, warm temperatures in the autumn inhibit, whereas cold temperatures favor, the early stages of oogenesis (46). Cold temperatures are also favorable to gametogenesis in the cyprinid *Notemigonus crysoleucas* (36). Since many spring-spawning teleosts initiate gametogenesis in the autumn or winter, the role of low temperatures for this process may be more important than is presently realized.

Only a few marine and estuarine temperate-zone teleosts have been investigated. In the viviparous seaperch, *Cymatogaster aggregata*, ovarian recrudescence is enhanced by the warm temperatures and shortening photoperiods of late summer, and final oocyte maturation occurs under cold temperatures (77). Copulation occurs in the summer months, but fertilization of mature oocytes takes place in mid-winter from sperm stored since the summer; parturition occurs in the summer period. In the males, spermatogonia formation occurs under cold conditions, but remaining stages of spermatogenesis are enhanced by warm temperatures and long photoperiods. *Cymatogaster* males and females thus apparently respond to different environmental cues. The marsh killifish, *Fundulus*, spawns in the late spring and apparently resembles many spring-spawning freshwater fishes in that some early stages of gametogenesis are dependent on cold temperatures, whereas rapid gonadal recrudescence and gamete maturation are induced by warm temperatures in the spring (31). For the estuarine gobiid fish, *Gillichthys mirabilis*, the primary environmental cue is temperature (32–34). Gonadal recrudescence occurs under cool temperatures (10–20°C) and is accelerated by short photoperiods; spawning occurs in the winter. Regardless of photoperiod length, gonadal regression occurs only above 22°C in females, 24°C in males. Thus, this species seems to lack an obligatory refractory period following spawning.

It is obvious from the above discussion that regulation of gonadal recrudescence in teleosts involves a complex interaction of temperature and photoperiods. The environmental cues involved in initiating the stages of final oocyte maturation and ovulation, or spermiation, are largely uninvestigated. Social and physical environmental factors, such as courtship and photoperiod in the medaka (42), undoubtedly interact at this stage of the reproductive cycle. However, the cues involved in gonadal recrudescence cannot be viewed in isolation from those involved at other stages of the cycle, because the whole system is physiologically integrated.

GONADOTROPIN

Chemistry and Actions of Gonadotropins (GtH)

Relatively pure GtH has been obtained from carp *Cyprinus carpio* (17), chinook salmon *Oncorhyncus tshawytscha* (14, 39, 40, 70), chum salmon, *O. keta*, (53, 54, 77, 78), rainbow trout (12), and *Tilapia* (43) pituitaries. GtH of these teleosts shares some structural properties with the GtHs of higher vertebrates; it is a glycoprotein (17, 43, 53, 70, 79), a feature used to retain salmon GtH on concanavalin A-Sepharose in some purification procedures (53, 70). Although the amino acid composition of each fish GtH is unique, similarities to mammalian luteinizing hormone (LH) (43, 70, 79) and FSH (79) have been reported. The subunit nature of fish GtH (12, 17, 53, 70) and the ease of dissociation of the native hormone have also been examined (17, 70).

The number of GtHs present in the fish pituitary gland has been debated and is currently unresolved. Biological studies of chinook salmon (SG-G100) (39, 40) and carp (4) GtH preparations showed that complete gametogenesis can be produced in hypophysectomized test animals, favoring the one-hormone hypothesis. However, extensive fractionation of chum (54) and chinook (14) salmon GtH produced preparations with some male or female specificity. The two forms of chinook salmon GtH are chemically very similar and immunologically identical (14), and are qualitatively similar in biological activity (75). *Tilapia* pituitaries were fractionated according to purification procedures for mammalian GtH (43); an "LH-like" preparation with the ability to stimulate in vitro testosterone production in rat Leydig cells was obtained. An "FSH-like" fraction of unspecified activity was also extracted. A glycoprotein GtH obtained from pituitary glands of the American plaice induced oocyte maturation and ovulation (20). Within the fraction lacking affinity for concanavalin A-Sepharose, a nonglycoprotein fraction produced yolk incorporation into the ovary of the winter flounder (19). Extraction of the salmon pituitary has also produced a nonglycoprotein vitellogenic factor that stimulates oocyte uptake of labelled vitellogenin in vitro (18).

GtH apparently regulates some events of oocyte development directly and others indirectly via sex steroid hormones. Maintenance and mitotic division of oogonia, as well as initial oocyte growth through protoplasm synthesis, seem to be independent of GtH requirements. The evidence for GtH action begins with induction of endogenous yolk formation marked by the appearance of multivesicular bodies (75) or intravesicular yolk fragments (59). A major part of oocyte growth is dependent upon uptake of exogenous yolk material (vitellogenin) synthesized in the liver. Synthesis and secretion of vitellogenin is indirectly regulated by the pituitary through the actions of estrogen. Treatment of adult female brown trout, *Salmo trutta*, with crude extracts of the sockeye salmon pituitary gland increased plasma estradiol levels and stimulated yolk accumulation into growing oocytes (24). Treatment of immature female rainbow trout with purified chinook salmon GtH initiated endogenous yolk formation but not incorporation of vitellogenin (75). In contrast, crude sockeye salmon pituitary extract induced both phases of vitellogenesis in the immature brown trout. The evidence for a nonglycoprotein pituitary factor that stimulates vitellogenin uptake by oocytes (18, 20) implies that this phase is directly regulated by the pituitary gland. GtH is responsible for oocyte maturation by stimulation of release of a maturational steroid produced by cells of either the interrenal gland (48) or the ovarian follicular layer (55). Corticosteroid hormone may play a role by sensitization of oocytes to GtH (55). Dissociation of oocyte maturation and ovulation is experimentally possible, and in vitro oocyte studies suggest that a prostaglandin mediates the ovulation process (55).

Fish GtH stimulates complete development of the male gonad (4, 34, 61, 75). Whether GtH acts directly, or indirectly via androgens, or in both ways, is unclear, although high doses of testosterone alone can maintain the testes (61). Full sexual maturation of immature male rainbow trout was produced with the GtH isolated from pituitary glands of either male or female chinook salmon (75). GtH caused hypertrophy of Leydig cells and also stimulated the Sertoli cells surrounding the germinal cysts.

Secretion of Gonadotropin

Spermiating and ovulated pink salmon, *Oncorhynchus gorbuscha,* on spawning grounds had consistently elevated plasma GtH levels (females having the highest levels) compared to fish undergoing gonadal development (25); during gonadal development the plasma GtH levels were frequently undetectable with the radioimmunoassay used. Data for brook trout and sockeye salmon, *O. nerka,* indicate that a small increase in plasma GtH levels generally occurs as the fish progress through gonadal development; during spermiation in males there is usually an increase, and in ovulated females a marked increase, over the levels found during gonadal development (28). However, in female brown trout (24) and male (7) and female (44) rainbow trout plasma GtH levels did not change until the fish had nearly completed gonadal recrudescence, when levels rose slightly. Male parr Atlantic salmon, *Salmo salar,* frequently become precociously sexually mature; in the precocious males the plasma GtH levels increase somewhat during recrudescence and are elevated even more at spermiation (23). Increased levels of plasma GtH were also found in other species at spermiation and ovulation (9, 11). These data generally support the hypothesis of gradual incremental secretion of GtH to stimulate progressive gonadal recrudescence, with a sharp rise in secretion occurring at ovulation and spermiation.

Because teleosts time reproductive cycles by response to environmental cues, it is necessary to know the effects of environmental factors on GtH secretion. Exposure of immature rainbow trout to a decreasing photoperiod (16 hr light to 8 hr light) and to 16°C or 8°C between February and June induced testicular recrudescence through to complete development of spermatozoa (8). In the trout exposed to 16°C plasma GtH levels increased about the middle of the experimental period; at 8°C, however, only a slight rise, if any, occurred. Trout at 16°C had higher plasma GtH levels than at 8°C over the whole experimental period, regardless of the photoperiod imposed. For autumn-spawning rainbow trout, gonadal recrudescence under a decreasing photoperiod is obviously a functional response. However, it is difficult to evaluate the functionality of increased GtH levels at higher temperatures because temperatures normally decrease prior to spawning in the autumn. Experiments on the rainbow trout at the higher temperature did accelerate gonadal recrudescence (8).

Between February and July, 17, 24, and 30°C temperatures induced higher plasma GtH levels in male goldfish than did 10°C or natural pond temperatures for a period of about 3 months; but then GtH levels in the fish in warm temperatures decreased, apparently in association with testicular regression, to levels similar to the other groups (45). Testicular development in the male goldfish at 30°C did not advance beyond the spermatocyte stage, in spite of the high plasma GtH levels. This suggests some sort of temperature block of GtH action on the testes. High temperatures also caused increased plasma GtH levels in male and female goldfish during autumn and winter, but no photoperiodic effects were found (46). In the spring (March to June) exposure to warm temperatures for long periods were associated with ovarian regression, and plasma GtH levels were generally not elevated at higher temperatures. These data suggest that in goldfish warm temperatures stimulate GtH secretion, and regression of the gonad under warm conditions is associated with decreased plasma GtH levels.

Significant daily fluctuation occurs in plasma GtH levels in female goldfish under summer pond conditions (9). Recently (52) significant daily fluctuations in serum GtH levels have been found in female goldfish undergoing ovarian recrudescence (maturing females) and in females with oocytes that have completed vitellogenesis (mature females). However, in goldfish with regressed or relatively inactive gonads, significant daily fluctuations in serum GtH levels are either absent or the fluctuations are smaller than in the maturing and mature females under the same environmental conditions. Under comparable conditions, the lower levels of serum GtH in the maturing and mature fish are similar to those found in the fish with regressed or inactive gonads. In fish at a similar stage of gonadal development, warm temperatures (21°C) caused some elevation in the lower serum GtH levels over that in fish at cold temperatures (12°C). Also, exposure of maturing females to the stimulatory conditions of long photoperiod and warmth caused a large daily fluctuation. The presence of daily cycles of secretion, presumably the presence of peaks in blood GtH, appear to be important in stimulating gonadal activity in female goldfish. Injection of GtH may be effective in *N. crysoleucas* at one time of day and not at another in inducing gonadal development (38). Perhaps the responsiveness of the gonad to GtH varies daily; presumably the daily fluctuations in blood levels of GtH would be related to these changes in gonadal responsiveness to GtH.

Regulation of Gonadotropin Secretion

Pituitary transplantation experiments in various teleosts generally result in regression of the gonads and inactivity of the gonadotroph cells (63). Thus GtH secretion seems to be regulated primarily by a releasing factor (GRF). Lesioning a part of the nucleus lateralis tuberis (NTL) in goldfish blocks gonadal recrudescence and induces regression (62, 65). Interestingly, no significant differences in serum GtH levels were found between NLT-lesioned and control animals (65). However, the effects of NLT lesions may be due to abolition or alteration of the daily cycle of secretion of GtH (R. E. Peter, unpublished). This supports the hypothesis (52) that daily fluctuations in blood GtH levels, specifically the presence of daily peaks in levels, have significance for stimulation of gonadal activity. With the possible exception of the nucleus preopticus (NPO) region, [(65), but cf (62) and R. E. Peter and L. W. Crim, unpublished] lesions in brain regions other than the NLT do not affect gonadal activity. Thus, the results indicate involvement of the NLT in secretion of GRF for regulation of GtH secretion to induce gonadal recrudescence.

Lesions in the NLT of sexually mature female goldfish held in running cold water, conditions under which ovulation would normally never occur, produced ovulation within 2–4 days (66). In addition, serum GtH levels were very markedly increased after 2 days, and after 12 days they were still significantly higher, but reduced to near levels in control fish. There is apparently tonic inhibition of GtH secretion in the sexually mature female goldfish. This inhibition must be abated or abolished to allow the ovulatory surge in GtH secretion. Whether this inhibition involves a GtH release-inhibitory factor (GIF) or some other mechanism is not known. Prostaglandins (PG) $F_{2\alpha}$ and E_2 injected into the third ventricle in sexually mature goldfish suppress serum GtH levels (64), which suggests that PG may be a part of the GIF mechanism. Simultaneous intraventricular injection of PG $F_{2\alpha}$ and synthetic luteinizing hormone–releasing hormone (LHRH) in female goldfish results in an increase in serum GtH levels (R. E. Peter, unpublished), which indicates that the action of PG in blocking GRF action is not at the level of the pituitary. Since lesions in the NLT in goldfish block gonadal recrudescence and cause gonadal regression, whereas similar lesions in mature females cause ovulation, the NLT may be the source of both GRF and GIF. The ovulatory surge in GtH secretion may also in part be due to spontaneous activity of the gonadotrophs after release from inhibition. The brain areas other than the NLT that might be involved in this inhibitory action on GtH secretion have not yet been explored, and there is no information as to whether the inhibitory mechanism is of importance in males.

GRF activity has been claimed in crude hypothalamic extracts from carp (10, 15, 16, 76), rainbow trout (16), goldfish (27) and *N. crysoleucas* (37). Unfortunately, a control brain extract was not used in many of these studies and the conditions of the donor and test animals were not always clear. The GRF activity in carp hypothalamic extract has been shown to be associated with a substance having a molecular weight of less than 5000 (13). Neurohypophysial hormones, epinephrine, norepinephrine, serotonin and dopamine do not have GRF activity on carp pituitaries in vitro (13). However, large doses of LHRH have GtH releasing activity in carp (16, 79), brown trout (22) and goldfish (27), the most responsive period of the reproductive cycle of carp and brown trout being when the fish have mature gonads. Large doses of LHRH also induce ovulation in goldfish (60) and ayu, *Plecoglossus altivelis* (51), and induce gonadal recrudescence in medaka (21). The argument justifying the use of large doses of LHRH is that the native molecule is different from LHRH and that consequently the GRF receptors are not highly responsive to LHRH. LHRH immunohisto-chemical-reactive material has been demonstrated in the neurohypophysial tissue invading the proximal pars distalis in the pituitary (41) and in the area dorsalis pars medialis (Dm) of the telencephalon (47) of rainbow trout. However, destruction of the Dm telencephalon blocks neither ovulation induced by NLT lesions in goldfish (66) nor reproductive activity in other species (30, 73).

Neurosecretory axons directly invade the pars distalis of the pituitary of teleosts. This phenomenon is unique among the vertebrates (67). In the goby (81), goldfish (57), and the black molly, *Poecilia latipinna,* (69) gonado-trophs are directly innervated by neurosecretory endings containing dense-cored granulated vesicles of appearance and size similar to those found in some NLT neurons in these species (68, 69, 80). In the goby one group of NLT neurons shows retrograde degeneration after hypophysectomy (81) and activation following castration (82); the effects of castration are reversed by androgen treatment. In other teleosts investigated either the gonadotrophs are directly innervated by neurosecretory endings supposedly originating from the NLT or the endings are separated from the gonado-trophs by a basement membrane (67). The gonadotrophs of goldfish (57), the black molly (69), and a number of other species (67) are also directly innervated by neurosecretory endings originating from NPO neurons, al-though in many species the NPO endings are separated from the gonado-trophs by a basement membrane (67). While these observations implicate the NLT and NPO regulation of gonadotroph activity, the specific functions are not revealed.

Another means of control of GtH secretion is by the feedback actions of gonadal steroids. Plasma GtH levels increase after castration of rainbow trout at any stage of the testicular cycle, including when the testes are inactive (6, 7); the most pronounced increase occurs after castration of spermiating trout, which indicates that a negative feedback effect by testicular steroids occurs at all gonadal stages in rainbow trout. Sex steroids are taken up in the pituitary, NLT, NPO, nucleus recessus lateralis, and other locations in male paradise fish, *Macropodus opercularis* (29), goldfish (58), and platyfish, *Xiphophorus maculatus* (58), which suggests that a wide variety of sites could serve for feedback actions by sex steroids. Markedly increased serum GtH levels occurred in sexually mature female goldfish following implantation of anti-estrogens in the pituitary; only a small rise occurred due to implantation in the NLT, and no effects occurred as a result of implantation elsewhere (5). These results indicate that the pituitary and the NLT are sites for negative feedback action of estrogens in female goldfish. In vitro studies indicate that the pituitary is a site of negative feedback in the platyfish (72), and in rainbow trout the post-castration rise in plasma GtH levels can be partially blocked by pituitary implantation of 11-ketotestosterone (3). In male and female Atlantic salmon parr, implantation of testosterone in the pituitary and brain, particularly in the NLT region, caused greater levels of pituitary GtH and tended to cause onset of testicular recrudescence (26). These results indicate a positive feedback action by testosterone on the pituitary and brain in the immature parr, and lead to the speculation that positive feedback action by testosterone may be a part of the mechanism of onset of precocious sexual maturity in the males.

CONCLUSION

The information reviewed above is based on very few species in each instance, and information between species is not always consistent. Many previously held assumptions have not been supported by recent investigations. New hypotheses are being presented currently, and exciting developments in this field are anticipated for the near future.

Literature Cited

1. Ahsan, S. N. 1966. Effects of temperature and light on the cyclical changes in the spermatogenetic activity of the lake chub, *Couesius plumbeus. Can. J. Zool.* 44:161–71
2. Baggerman, B. 1972. Photoperiodic responses in the stickleback and their control by a daily rhythm of photosensitivity. *Gen. Comp. Endocrinol.* 3: (Suppl.) 466–76
3. Billard, R. 1978. Testicular feedback on the hypothalamo-pituitary axis in rainbow trout (*Salmo gairdneri* R.). *Ann. Biol. Anim. Biochim. Biophys.* 18: 813–18
4. Billard, R., Escaffre, A. M. 1973. Effects of HCG and carp gonadotropin on the maintenance of spermatogenesis in hypophysectomized goldfish (*Carrasius auratus*). *Int. Res. Commun. Syst.* 73:12–15
5. Billard, R., Peter, R. E. 1977. Gonadotropin release after implantation of antiestrogens in the pituitary and hypothalamus of goldfish, *Carassius auratus. Gen. Comp. Endocrinol.* 32:213–20
6. Billard, R., Richard, M., Breton, B. 1976. Stimulation de la secrétion gonadotrope hypophysaire aprés castration chez la Truite arc-en-ciel; variation de la reponse au cours du cycle reproducteur. *C.R. Acad. Sci. Ser. D* 283:171–74
7. Billard, R., Richard, M., Breton, B. 1977. Stimulation of gonadotropin secretion after castration in rainbow trout. *Gen. Comp. Endocrinol.* 33: 163–65
8. Breton, B., Billard, R. 1977. Effects of photoperiod and temperature on plasma gonadotropin and spermatogenesis in the rainbow trout *Salmo gairdnerii* Richardson. *Ann. Biol. Anim. Biochim. Biophys.* 17:331–40
9. Breton, B., Billard, R., Jalabert, B., Kann, G. 1972. Dosage radioimmunologique des gonadotropines plasmatiques chez *Carassius auratus,* au cours du nycthémère et pendant l'ovulation. *Gen. Comp. Endocrinol.* 18: 463–68
10. Breton, B., Jalabert, B., Billard, R., Weil, C. 1971. Stimulation *in vitro* de la libération d'hormone gonadotrope hypophysaire par un facteur hypothalamique chez la Carpe *Cyprinus carpio* L. *C.R. Acad. Sci. Ser. D* 273:2591–94
11. Breton, B., Jalabert, B., Fostier, A., Billard, R. 1975. Étude sur le cycle reproducteur de la Truite arc-en-ciel et de

la Tanche. Effect de variations expérimentales de la température. *J. Physiol. Paris* 30:561–64
12. Breton, B., Jalabert, B., Reinaud, P. 1976. Purification of gonadotropin from rainbow trout (*Salmo gairdneri* Richardson) pituitary glands. *Ann. Biol. Anim. Biochim. Biophys.* 16:25–36
13. Breton, B., Jalabert, B., Weil, C. 1975. Caracterisation partielle d'un facteur hypothalamique de l'liberation des hormones gonadotropes chez la Carpe (*Cyprinus carpio*). Etude *in vitro. Gen. Comp. Endocrinol.* 25:405–15
14. Breton, B., Prunet, P., Reinaud, P. 1978. Sexual differences in salmon gonadotropin. *Ann. Biol. Anim. Biochim. Biophys.* 18:759–65
15. Breton, B., Weil, C. 1973. Effets du LH/FSH-RH synthétique et d'extraits hypothalamiques de Carpe sur la sécrétion d'hormone gonadotrope *in vivo* chez la Carpe (*Cyprinus carpio* L.). *C.R. Acad. Sci. Ser. D* 277:2061–64
16. Breton, B., Weil, C., Jalabert, B. 1972. Activité réciproque des facteurs hypothalamiques de Bélier (*Ovis aries*) et de poissons téléostéens sur la sécrétion *in vitro* des hormones gonadotropes c-HG et LH respectivement par des hypophyses de Carpe et de Bélier. *C.R. Acad. Sci. Ser. D* 274:2530–33
17. Burzawa-Gerard, E. 1974. A biological and biochemical study of the gonadotropic hormone in a teleost fish, the carp (*Cyprinus carpio* L.). *Mem. Mus. Hist. Nat., Ser. A. Zool.* 86:1–77
18. Campbell, C. M. 1978. *In vitro* stimulation of vitellogenin incorporation into trout oocytes by salmon pituitary extracts. *Ann. Biol. Anim. Biochim. Biophys.* 18:1013–18
19. Campbell, C. M., Idler, D. R. 1976. Hormonal control of vitellogenesis in hypophysectomized winter flounder (*Pseudopleuronectes americanus* Walbaum). *Gen. Comp. Endocrinol.* 28:143–50
20. Campbell, C. M., Idler, D. R. 1977. Oocyte maturation and ovulation induced in hypophysectomized winter flounder (*Pseudopleuronectes americanus*) by preparations from pituitary glands of American plaice (*Hippoglossoides platessoides*). *J. Fish. Res. Bd. Can.* 34:2151–55
21. Chan, K. K.-S. 1977. Effect of synthetic luteinizing hormone–releasing hormone (LH–RH) on ovarian development in Japanese medaka, *Oryzias latipes. Can. J. Zool.* 55:155–60

22. Crim, L. W., Cluett, D. M. 1974. Elevation of plasma gonadotropin concentration in response to mammalian gonadotropin releasing hormone (GRH) treatment of the male brown trout as determined by radioimmunoassay. *Endocrinol. Res. Commun.* 1:101–10

23. Crim, L. W., Evans, D. M. 1978. Seasonal levels of pituitary and plasma gonadotropin in male and female Atlantic salmon parr. *Can. J. Zool.* 56:1550–55

24. Crim, L. W., Idler, D. R. 1978. Plasma gonadotropin, estradiol, and vitellogenin and gonad phosvitin in relation to the seasonal reproductive cycles of female brown trout. *Ann. Biol. Anim. Biochim. Biophys.* 18:1001–5

25. Crim, L. W., Meyer, R. K., Donaldson, E. M. 1973. Radioimmunoassay estimates of plasma gonadotropin levels in spawning pink salmon. *Gen. Comp. Endocrinol.* 21:69–76

26. Crim, L. W., Peter, R. E. 1978. The influence of testosterone implantation in the brain and pituitary on pituitary gonadotropin levels in Atlantic salmon parr. *Ann. Biol. Anim. Biochim. Biophys.* 18:689–94

27. Crim, L. W., Peter, R. E., Billard, R. 1976. Stimulation of gonadotropin secretion by intraventricular injection of hypothalamic extracts in the goldfish, *Carassius auratus. Gen. Comp. Endocrinol.* 30:77–82

28. Crim, L. W., Watts, E. G., Evans, D. M. 1975. The plasma gonadotropin profile during sexual maturation in a variety of salmonid fishes. *Gen. Comp. Endocrinol.* 27:62–70

29. Davis, R. E., Morrell, J. I., Pfaff, D. W. 1977. Autoradiographic localisation of sex steroid concentrating cells in the brain of the teleost *Macropodus opercularis* (Osteichthyes: Belontiidae). *Gen. Comp. Endocrinol.* 33:496–505

30. de Bruin, J. P.-C. 1977. Telencephalic functions in the behaviour of the Siamese fighting fish *Betta splendens* Regan (Pisces, Anabantidae). *Acad. Proefschrift, Univ. van Amsterdam.* 175 pp.

31. de Vlaming, V. L. 1972. Environmental control of teleost reproductive cycles: a brief review. *J. Fish. Biol.* 4:131–40

32. de Vlaming, V. L. 1972. The effects of diurnal thermoperiod treatments on reproductive function in the estuarine gobiid fish, *Gillichys mirabilis* Cooper. *J. Exp. Mar. Biol. Ecol.* 9:155–63

33. de Vlaming, V. L. 1972. The effects of temperature and photoperiod on reproductive cycling in the estuarine gobiid

fish *Gillichthys mirabilis. Fish Bull.* 70:1137–52

34. de Vlaming, V. L. 1972. The role of the endocrine system in temperature-controlled reproductive cycling in the estuarine gobiid fish, *Gillichthys mirabilis. Comp. Biochem. Physiol.* 41A:697–713

35. de Vlaming, V. L. 1974. Environmental and endocrine control of teleost reproduction. In *Control of Sex in Fishes,* ed. C. B. Schreck, pp. 13–83. Blacksburg, Va: Virginia Polytech. Inst. and State Univ. 106 pp.

36. de Vlaming, V. L. 1975. Effects of photoperiod and temperature on gonadal activity in the cyprinid teleost, *Notemigonus crysoleucas. Biol. Bull.* 148:402–15

37. de Vlaming, V. L., Vodicnik, M. J. 1975. Effects of photoperiod-temperature regimes on pituitary gonadotrophs, pituitary gonadotropin potency and hypothalamic gonadotropin releasing activity in the teleost *Notemigonus crysoleucas. J. Therm. Biol.* 1:119–25

38. de Vlaming, V. L., Vodicnik, M. J. 1977. Diurnal variations in pituitary gonadotropin content and in gonadal response to exogenous gonadotropin and prolactin in *Notemigonus crysoleucas. J. Fish. Biol.* 10:371–83

39. Donaldson, E. M. 1973. Reproductive endocrinology in fishes. *Am. Zool.* 13:909–27

40. Donaldson, E. M., Yamazaki, F., Dye, H. M., Philleo, W. W. 1972. Preparation of gonadotropin from salmon (*Oncorhynchus tshawytscha*) pituitary glands. *Gen. Comp. Endocrinol.* 18:469–81

41. Dubois, M. P., Billard, R., Breton, B. 1978. Use of immunofluorescence for localization of the somatostatin-like antigen in the rainbow trout (*Salmo gairdneri*). Comparative distribution of LH-RF and neurophysin. *Ann. Biol. Anim. Biochim. Biophys.* 18:843–50

42. Egami, N., Hosokawa, K. 1973. Responses of gonads to environmental changes in the fish, *Oryzias latipes.* In *Responses of Fish to Environmental Changes,* ed. W. Chavin, pp. 279–301. Springfield, Ill: Charles C. Thomas. 459 pp.

43. Farmer, S. W., Papkoff, H. 1977. A teleost (*Tilapia mossambica*) gonadotropin that resembles luteinizing hormone. *Life Sci.* 20:1227–32

44. Fostier, A., Weil, C., Terqui, M., Breton, B., Jalabert, B. 1978. Plasma estradiol-17β and gonadotropin during ovulation in rainbow trout (*Salmo*

gairdneri R.). *Ann. Biol. Anim. Biochim. Biophys.* 18:929–36

45. Gillet, C., Billard, R., Breton, B. 1977. Effets de la température sur le taux de gonadotropine plasmatique et la spermatogenése du poisson rouge *Carassius auratus. Can. J. Zool.* 55:242–45

46. Gillet, C., Breton, B., Billard, R. 1978. Seasonal effects of exposure to temperature and photoperiod regimes on gonad growth and plasma gonadotropin in goldfish (*Carassius auratus* L.) *Ann. Biol. Anim. Biochim. Biophys.* 18: 1045–49

47. Goos, H. J. Th., Murathanoglu, O. 1977. Localisation of gonadotropin releasing hormone (GRH) in the forebrain and neurohypophysis of the trout (*Salmo gairdneri*). *Cell Tiss. Res.* 181:163–68

48. Goswami, S. V., Sundararaj, B. I., Donaldson, E. M. 1974. In vitro maturation response of oocytes of the catfish *Heteropneustes fossilis* (Bloch) to salmon gonadotropin in ovary-head kidney coculture. *Can. J. Zool.* 52:745–48

49. Harrington, R. W. Jr. 1957. Sexual photoperiodicity of the cyprinid fish, *Notropis bifrenatus* (Cope), in relation to the phases of its annual reproductive cycle. *J. Exp. Zool.* 135:529–53

50. Henderson, N. E. 1963. Influence of light and temperature on the reproductive cycle of the eastern brook trout, *Salvelinus fontinalis* (Mitchill). *J. Fish. Res. Bd. Can.* 20:859–97

51. Hirose, K., Ishida, R. 1974. Induction of ovulation in the ayu, *Plecoglossus altivelis,* with LH-releasing hormone (LH–RH). *Bull. Jpn. Soc. Sci. Fish.* 40:1235–40

52. Hontela, A., Peter, R. E. 1978. Daily cycles in serum gonadotropin levels in the goldfish, *Carassius auratus:* effects of photoperiod, temperature and sexual condition. *Can. J. Zool.* In press

53. Idler, D. R., Bazar, L. S., Hwang, S. J. 1975. Fish gonadotropin(s). II. Isolation of gonadotropin(s) from chum salmon pituitary glands using affinity chromatography. *Endocrinol. Res. Commun.* 2:215–35

54. Idler, D. R., Bazar, L. S., Hwang, S. J. 1975. Fish gonadotropin(s) III. Evidence for more than one gonadotropin in chum salmon pituitary glands. *Endocrinol. Res. Commun.* 2:237–49

55. Jalabert, B. 1976. In vitro oocyte maturation and ovulation in rainbow trout (*Salmo gairdneri*), northern pike (*Esox licius*) and goldfish (*Carassius auratus*). *J. Fish. Res. Bd. Can.* 33: 974–88

56. Kaya, C. M., Hasler, A. D. 1972. Photoperiod and temperature effects on the gonads of green sunfish, *Lepomis cyanellus* (Rafinesque), during the quiescent, winter phase of its annual cycle. *Trans. Am. Fish. Soc.* 101:270–75

57. Kaul, S., Vollrath, L. 1974. The goldfish pituitary. II. Innervation. *Cell Tiss. Res.* 154:231–49

58. Kim, Y. S., Stumpf, W. E., Sar, M., Martinez-Vargas, M. C. 1978. Estrogen and androgen target cells in the brain of fishes, reptiles and birds: phylogeny and ontogeny. *Am. Zool.* In press

59. Korfsmeier, K. H. 1966. The genesis of the yolk system in the oocyte of *Brachydanio rerio:* Autoradiographic studies. *Z. Zellforsch. Mikrosk. Anat.* 71: 283–96 (Sci. Transl. Serv. # 1487)

60. Lam, T. J., Pandey, S., Hoar, W. D. 1975. Induction of ovulation in goldfish by synthetic luteinizing hormone–releasing hormone (LH–RH). *Can. J. Zool.* 53:1189–92

61. Nayyar, S. K., Keshavanath, P., Sundararaj, B. I. 1976. Maintenance of spermatogenesis and seminal vesicles in the hypophysectomized catfish, *Heteropneustes fossilis* (Bloch): effects of ovine and salmon gonadotropin and testosterone. *Can. J. Zool.* 54:285–92

62. Peter, R. E. 1970. Hypothalamic control of thyroid gland activity and gonadal activity in the goldfish, *Carassius auratus. Gen. Comp. Endocrinol.* 14:334–56

63. Peter, R. E. 1973. Neuroendocrinology of teleosts. *Am. Zool.* 13:743–55

64. Peter, R. E., Billard, R. 1976. Effects of third ventricle injection of prostaglandins on gonadotropin secretion in goldfish, *Carassius auratus. Gen. Comp. Endocrinol.* 30:451–56

65. Peter, R. E., Crim, L. W. 1978. Hypothalamic lesions of goldfish: effects on gonadal recrudescence and gonadotropin secretion. *Ann. Biol. Anim. Biochim. Biophys.* 18:819–23

66. Peter, R. E., Crim, L. W., Goos, H. J. Th., Crim, J. W. 1978. Lesioning studies on the gravid female goldfish: neuroendocrine regulation of ovulation. *Gen. Comp. Endocrinol.* 35:391–401

67. Peter, R. E., Fryer, J. N. 1979. Endocrine functions of the hypothalamus of actinopterygians. In *Fish Neurobiology and Behavior,* ed. R. G. Northcutt, R. E. Davis. Ann Arbor, Mich: Univ. Mich. Press. In press

68. Peter, R. E., Nagahama, Y. 1976. A light and electron microscopic study of the structure of the nucleus preopticus

and nucleus lateral tuberis of the goldfish, *Carassius auratus. Can. J. Zool.* 54:1423–37

69. Peute, J., de Bruyn, M. G. A., Seldenryk, R., van Oordt, P. G. W. J. 1976. Cytophysiology and innervation of gonadotropic cells in the pituitary of the black molly (*Poecilia latipinna*). An electron microscopical study. *Cell Tiss. Res.* 174:35–54

70. Pierce, J. G., Faith, M. R., Donaldson, E. M. 1976. Antibodies to reduced s-carboxymethylated alpha subunit of bovine luteinizing hormone and their application to study of the purification of gonadotropin from salmon (*Oncorhynchus tshawytscha*) pituitary glands. *Gen. Comp. Endocrinol.* 30:47–60

71. Reisman, H. M., Cade, T. J. 1967. Physiological and behavioral aspects of reproduction in the brook stickleback, *Culaea inconstans. Am. Midl. Nat.* 77:257–95

72. Sage, M., Bromage, N. R. 1970. The activity of the pituitary cells of the teleost *Poecilia* during the gestation cycle and the control of the gonadotropic cells. *Gen. Comp. Endocrinol.* 14: 127–36

73. Segaar, J. 1965. Behavioural aspects of degeneration and regeneration of fish brain: a comparison with higher vertebrates. *Prog. Brain Res.* 14:143–231

74. Sundararaj, B. I., Vasal, S. 1976. Photoperiod and temperature control in the regulation of reproduction in the female catfish *Heteropneustes fossilis. J. fish. Res. Bd. Can.* 33:959–73

75. Upadhyay, S. N. 1977. *Morphology of immature gonads and experimental*

studies on the induction of *gametogenesis in juvenile rainbow trout* (Salmo gairdneri *R.*). Ph.D. thesis, L'Univ. Pierre et Marie Curie, Paris. 111 pp.

76. Weil, C., Breton, B., Reinaud, P. 1975. Etude de la réponse hypophysaire à l'administration de Gn-RH exogène au cours du cycle reproducteur annuel chez la Carpe *Cyprinus carpio* L. *C.R. Acad. Sci. Ser. D* 280:2469–72

77. Wiebe, J. P. 1968. The effects of temperature and daylength on the reproductive physiology of the viviparous seaperch, *Cymatogaster aggregata* Gibbons. *Can. J. Zool.* 46:1207–19

78. Yoneda, T., Yamazaki, F. 1976. Purification of gonadotropin from chum salmon pituitary glands. *Bull. Jpn. Soc. Sci. Fish.* 42:343–50

79. Yoneda, T., Yamazaki, F., Ishihara, Y. 1977. Amino acid composition of chum salmon gonadotropin. *Bull. Jpn. Soc. Sci. Fish.* 43:1451–54

80. Zambrano, D. 1970. The nucleus lateralis tuberis system of the gobiid fish *Gillichthys mirabilis.* I. Ultrastructural and histochemical characterization of the nucleus. *Z. Zellforsch. Mikrosk. Anat.* 110:9–26

81. Zambrano, D. 1970. The nucleus lateralis tuberis system of the gobiid fish *Gillichthys mirabilis.* II. Innervation of the pituitary. *Z. Zellforsch. Mikrosk. Anat.* 110:496–516

82. Zambrano, D. 1971. The nucleus lateralis tuberis system of the gobiid fish *Gillichthys mirabilis.* III. Functional modifications of the neurons and gonadotropic cells. *Gen. Comp. Endocrinol.* 17:164–82

Ann. Rev. Physiol. 1979. 41:337–51
Copyright © 1970 by Annual Reviews Inc. All rights reserved

REPRODUCTIVE ENDOCRINOLOGY OF REPTILES AND AMPHIBIANS: GONADOTROPINS

♦1223

Paul Licht

Department of Zoology, University of California, Berkeley, California 94720

INTRODUCTION

The components of the reproductive endocrine systems of the Reptilia and Amphibia are similar to those of other vertebrates. Evidence shows that the activities of the gonads are largely dependent upon hormones—gonadotropins—secreted by the pars distalis; secretion of these gonadotropins is regulated by hypothalamic releasing factors; and a feedback relationship exists between gonadotropin secretion and sex steroids produced by the gonads (4, 8, 31, 53, 56). This review focuses on the roles of the gonadotropins in the regulation of testicular and ovarian function. The superficial resemblances in reproductive endocrinology among all tetrapod vertebrates have often led to the assumptions that the nature and function of the nonmammalian hormones are essentially the same as, or reflect the evolutionary stages leading to, the mammalian condition. Recent progress on the biochemistry and physiology of reptilian and amphibian pituitary hormones now permits evaluation of such suppositions.

IDENTIFICATION OF PITUITARY GONADOTROPINS

Two chemically distinct glycoprotein hormones, follicle-stimulating hormone (FSH) and luteinizing hormone (LH), play separate roles in the regulation of gonadal function in eutherian mammals. Until recently, the presence of such a dual hormone system in lower vertebrates was in question. Information on gonadotropin physiology in reptiles and amphibians

337

was indirect (e.g. seasonal asynchrony between different gonadal activities suggested two hormones) or largely derived from the use of heterologous, mammalian hormones. However, there were anomalies (e.g. FSH and LH did not always have the action expected from mammalian studies) and complications in interpreting gonadal responses resulting from poikilothermy (e.g. temperature can modify the hormonal sensitivity of gonads). Consequently, it was postulated that reptiles (31, 47) and amphibians (70) might possess only a single "complete" gonadotropin, but results of direct biochemical investigations on the amphibian and reptilian pituitary hormones did not support this hypothesis.

Fractionation of pituitary hormones from diverse nonmammalian species, including anuran (14, 45) and urodele (49) amphibians and chelonian (44, 50) and crocodilian (50) reptiles, revealed two chemically distinct gonadotropins. The chemical characteristics of these hormones have recently been reviewed in detail (53, 61). Biochemical, immunological, and biological data all indicate a marked structural homology between the two gonadotropins of reptiles and amphibians and the FSH and LH of mammals and birds. Thus these two gonadotropins are probably a primitive feature of the tetrapod vertebrates, but important exceptions to this general pattern may exist. No information on the hormones of caecilian amphibians is available. More importantly, limited data for squamates (snakes and lizards) have failed to demonstrate two distinct gonadotropins (32, 53); this one reptilian order may lack the dual gonadotropin system.

HORMONAL REGULATION OF TESTICULAR AND OVARIAN FUNCTION

The gonads of all vertebrates consist of several types of tissues and perform a number of functions: the production of gametes (spermatogenesis and oogenesis); the release of gametes (spermiation and ovulation); and the secretion of sex steroids (e.g., androgens, estrogens, and progestogens). The mammalian system is frequently used as a model for studying the roles of gonadotropins in comparative studies on reproductive endocrinology. Accordingly, FSH is classically associated with gametogenesis, while LH is clearly important for gamete release (at least ovulation) and many aspects of steroidogenesis (especially testicular androgens and ovarian progesterone). In conjunction with these different functions, there are separate gonadal binding sites (receptors) for each gonadotropin. FSH and LH binding sites tend to be localized on different tissues corresponding to their physiological targets (e.g. FSH receptors on Sertoli and granulosa cells and LH receptors on Leydig and luteal cells); each binding site tends to show a high degree of specificity for one type of gonadotropin.

The apparent antiquity of the FSH- and LH-like gonadotropins certainly suggests a common pattern of gonadotropin regulation of reproduction among tetrapods. However, purified mammalian gonadotropins often fail to have the expected actions when injected into reptiles and amphibians. These discrepancies reflect either an artifact of using heterologous hormones or the existence of phylogenetic variations in the functions of the FSH- and LH-type gonadotropins.

Reproduction in the Male

SPERMATOGENESIS

Amphibia   Although it was commonly assumed that spermatogenesis in anurans was controlled primarily by FSH (56), newer data indicate relatively little gonadotropin specificity for this process. Attempts to accelerate the onset of spermatogenesis in larval or subadult anurans have met with varying success, depending on the developmental pattern of the species. Administration of either mammalian FSH or LH to tadpoles frequently caused a rapid dilation and partial evacuation of the seminiferous tubules without appreciable spermatogenic stimulation (12, 65). When spermatogenesis was initiated in juvenile anurans, mammalian LH was often more potent than FSH (19). In contrast, the few studies on larval urodeles suggest that spermatogenesis is primarily responsive to FSH. In the newt, *Pleurodeles waltii*, ovine FSH, but not LH, promoted complete spermatid production in hypophysectomized animals (3); and ovine FSH was more potent than either ovine LH or the LH-like human chorionic gonadotropin (hCG) in stimulating initiation of spermatogenesis in intact and hypophysectomized larval salamanders, *Ambystoma tigrinum* (57).

Results for adult amphibians are also contradictory. While various studies on adult anurans indicated that mammalian FSH acted primarily on the seminiferous tubules and LH on the steroidogenic interstitial tissues (54, 56), hCG promoted complete spermatogenesis in several species (16, 20, 24). Similarly, ovine FSH and LH had the expected effects on seminiferous tubules and interstitial cells in adult newts, *P. waltii* (2); but in another newt, *Triturus cristatus,* combinations of LH and FSH were most potent in promoting early stages of spermatogenesis, and thereafter, either hormone alone stimulated further maturation of primary spermatocytes (72).

The apparent FSH specificity for spermatogenesis in some amphibians may be an artifact of heterologous hormones, since, in the only study of homologous hormones in a frog, *Rana catesbeiana,* no difference was evident between FSH and LH. Muller (58) found that increases in the number of germ-cell cysts were stimulated either by FSH or LH treatment in adult hypophysectomized bullfrogs. Furthermore, when incubated with ^{3}H-thymidine in vitro, testes from these FSH- and LH-treated frogs showed approximately the same incorporation of counts into acid-precipitable material in spermatogonial cells.

Reptilia In vivo studies on the actions of mammalian gonadotropins in lizards (e.g. 21, 37, 47, 63), snakes (28, 68), and turtles (6, 29) indicated that testis growth and spermatogenesis were highly specific for FSH. In fact, the marked discrepancy in relative potencies of the two gonadotropins suggested that the activity of mammalian LH preparations might be due largely to their contamination with FSH; the testis growth response in lizards was adopted as a relatively specific FSH bioassay. However, subsequent immunoadsorption tests confirmed that both mammalian gonadotropins had intrinsic spermatogenic stimulating activity in lizards (42, 48), and further comparative studies using hormones from a variety of nonmammalian sources confirmed this nonspecificity (reviewed in 53). Potency ratios for different species of FSH and LH varied widely, but both hormones were always active; there was no clear phylogenetic pattern in relative potencies.

The rate of hormonally induced testicular recrudescence in reptiles is highly temperature-dependent; this thermal effect is a property of the testis rather than the gonadotropin, since it is evident with both mammalian and reptilian hormones (22, 33, 47, 68). While temperature may alter the nature of the testis response (e.g. spermatogenesis and steroidogenesis do not show the same thermal sensitivities) there is no indication that activities of the two gonadotropins are differentially affected by temperature. Also, the sensitivity of the testis to gonadotropins may vary with the stage of spermatogenesis [e.g. more hormone is required to initiate than to maintain spermatogenesis (47, 63)], but no differential actions of FSH and LH on certain stages of spermatogenesis have been detected.

It is likely that variations in FSH/LH potency ratios are related in large part to the half-lives of the two gonadotropins, rather than to specificity of gonadal receptors. The potency of gonadotropins in lizards depends on the presence of sialic acid (41, 43), which presumably affects clearance rates; LH preparations with relatively high potencies (e.g. from sea turtle) tend to be the most enriched in this carbohydrate moeity (50). Furthermore, our direct estimates of clearance rates of bullfrog and sea turtle hormones in a lizard (E. Daniels, A. Bona Gallo, P. Licht, unpublished data) correlate well with relative potencies.

Unfortunately, there is no information on the effects of nonmammalian hormones on spermatogenesis in reptiles other than lizards. Since the responses of turtles to mammalian hormones are generally not comparable to those obtained with homologous hormones (see discussions of steroidogenesis), the apparent FSH specificity of spermatogenesis shown with ovine hormones in turtles cannot be generalized.

SPERMIATION   The release of sperm from the testis has been treated as a separate component of testicular activity in anuran amphibians. Interest in the endocrinology of this "reflex" grew out of its application as a bioassay for detection of human pregnancy—the Galli Mainini reaction. Although once considered to be primarily an LH-dependent response, it is now clear that spermiation is essentially nonspecific for the two gonadotropins. Tests in a variety of genera and families (e.g. *Xenopus, Hyla, Rana, Eleuthrodactylus,* and *Bufo*) showed that spermiation could be induced readily with either purified mammalian FSH or LH, even in hypophysectomized animals, and that FSH was usually equal to or more potent than LH (30). Spermiation in a *Rana* and a *Hyla* has also been shown to be nonspecific for FSH and LH derived from several nonmammalian species (44, 45). Moreover, bullfrog FSH and LH were essentially equipotent in stimulating spermiation in the bullfrog (58).

Information on the spermiation response in nonanurans is sparse. Injections of hCG have been used to induce spermatophore deposition in intact salamanders, *A. mexicanum* (66), but no complete comparisons of FSH and LH have been reported. In reptiles, spermiation has not been studied as an independent process, but sperm release into the epididymis has been observed regularly in conjunction with the studies on testis growth and spermatogenesis already discussed, and there is no evidence for a gonadotropin specificity.

TESTICULAR ANDROGEN PRODUCTION   Indirect estimates of androgen secretion, such as histological changes in androgen-dependent target organs or in the interstitial cells thought to be the major site of androgen production, formed the bases of much early research. More recently, additional information has come from direct measurements of in vitro steroid biosynthesis and androgen secretion in vivo. The response of the testes may vary with the source of the gonadotropin in reptiles and amphibians, but there is also good evidence for important interspecific differences in the gonadotropin dependence of testicular steroid secretion.

Amphibia   Amphibians, like mammals, appear to show a relatively high specificity for LH in the regulation of interstitial cell activity and androgen production, although the use of heterologous hormones complicates the picture. Ovine LH has generally been found to be more effective than FSH in stimulating the activity of the interstitial tissue in frogs and salamanders as judged by histological and histochemical criteria (56). However, Wiebe's (74) studies on 3β-dehyroxysteroid dehydrogenase activity in *Xenopus laevis* suggested that ovine FSH was, if anything, more potent than either ovine LH or hCG; a wide range of doses was not examined. Lofts (54) also found that FSH stimulated histochemical changes indicative of steroidogenic activity in the Sertoli cells of frogs, but the nature and importance of the steroids produced by the seminiferous tubules remain undefined. Direct measures of androgen production by amphibian testes also suggest LH specificity. Ovine LH stimulated an elevation in plasma androgen in the salamander *Necturus,* whereas FSH was inactive; but FSH was more potent than LH in stimulating a slight rise in estrogen (8). In the bullfrog, *R. catesbeiana,* the homologous LH, but not FSH, stimulated a rise in plasma androgen (60). The LH specificity of the bullfrog testis was further confirmed by in vitro studies on minced testicular tissues (59); bullfrog LH was 300–1000 times as potent as FSH. Likewise, the testis of a salamander, *A. tigrinum,* was at least 50 times as sensitive to LH as FSH when studied with homologous hormones (58). In vitro studies with *Xenopus* and *Bufo* demonstrated a similar dependency of steroidogenesis on LH, but less distinctly than in assays with homologous hormones. For example, in *Xenopus,* the bullfrog LH was only about 6 times as potent as FSH, and ovine FSH was almost equipotent to LH (58).

Testicular androgen production in both the anurans and urodeles probably follows the classical mammalian pattern in being primarily regulated by LH. However, the gonadotropin specificity of the amphibian testis may be reduced when challenged with heterologous hormones.

Reptilia   Among the most unexpected results of comparative studies on gonadotropin actions in tetrapods are those relating to the regulation of androgen production by the reptilian testis. A variety of approaches have led to the conclusion that reptiles lack the LH specificity characteristic of this component of mammalian and amphibian steroidogenesis (reviewed in 8, 34, 53).

Androgen production in the reptilian testis initially appeared, unlike that of amphibians and mammals, to be regulated by FSH. This conclusion probably resulted from the use of heterologous hormones or inappropriate experimental protocols. In fact, the "peculiarity" of reptiles seems to be their general nonspecificity for FSH or LH. For example, in vivo and in vitro studies with several turtles demonstrated that Leydig cell morphology and androgen production were sensitive only to mammalian FSH (5, 6, 26, 29, 69); but it is now known from tests with other species of hormone, including the homologous ones, that steroidogenesis in turtles can be stimulated with either FSH or LH (26, 69). Other reptiles, including squamates and crocodilians, tend to respond to both FSH and LH from all tetrapods (67, 69). Moreover, the apparent inactivity of some LH preparations in lizards when tested by chronic in vivo injections may have been due to their relatively short half-lives, as discussed above. When tested by acute injection or in vitro, LH preparations are equipotent to, or even more potent than, FSH (53, 67, 69). Finally, immunoadsorption techniques have confirmed that both FSH and LH from several mammalian and nonmammalian species possess intrinsic steroid-stimulating activities in lizards and turtles (69).

The exact source of androgen production in the reptilian testis, and hence the target site for gonadotropin stimulation, is still controversial. Studies of in vitro steroid biosynthesis from labeled precursor (pregnelone) in the cobra led to the postulate that mammalian FSH stimulates the Sertoli cells, whereas LH acts on Leydig cells (55). A similar suggestion came from seasonal in vivo tests with mammalian gonadotropins in a turtle (6); however, such data are difficult to interpret because of the general insensitivity of turtles to mammalian LH. In vitro measurements of androgen production in isolated Leydig cells from a lizard demonstrated that ovine FSH and LH were equipotent; furthermore, androgen production by the Leydig cells was considerably greater than from the seminiferous tubules (67). Thus it is unlikely that the difference between reptiles and mammals in the responsiveness of steroidogenesis to FSH is due only to differences in the primary site of androgen production.

Further evidence for the sensitivity of Leydig cells to FSH in reptiles comes from data on gonadotropin binding sites. Autoradiographic studies with ^{125}I-labeled human FSH demonstrated that, in contrast to the case in mammals, FSH-binding sites are present on both the seminiferous tubules and interstitial cells in lizards, snakes, and turtles (40). Moreover, competitive-inhibition tests showed that these FSH-binding sites were not as hormone specific as they are in mammals (38, 39, 51). Results were in good agreement with physiological studies; turtle testis receptors had specificity for mammalian FSH (38, 51), but not for other species of gonadotropins (39, 51), whereas binding sites on snake and lizard testes displayed nonspecificity for all species of gonadotropins (38, 39, 51).

Reproduction in the Female

The classical view of hormone function in mammals would lead one to predict distinctive roles for FSH and LH in ovarian function: regulation of oocyte development (vitellogensis in the case of the lower tetrapods) for FSH; control of ovulation and the subsequent secretion of progesterone from the post-ovulatory follicles (corpora lutea) for LH. However, data for both amphibians and reptiles do not support these predictions.

OVARIAN GROWTH   The development of ova in reptiles and amphibians is characterized by the large accumulation of yolk in the follicles. The process of vitellogenesis is mediated by steroids (estrogens) that are secreted by the ovaries and act on the liver to induce the synthesis of vitellogenin; this protein is then transported via the circulation to the ovary, where it is taken up by the follicles (15). Gonadotropins probably affect at least two steps of this process: They stimulate the secretion of ovarian steroids and then act directly on the follicle wall to enhance uptake of vitellogenin.

Amphibia   Mammalian FSH may be more potent than LH in stimulating ovarian growth in anurans (56), but hCG is usually the most effective hormone (62, 73). The inactivity of ovine LH compared to hCG has been attributed to the relatively short half-life of the pituitary gonadotropin (62), but the possibility of species specificity was not fully considered. The few studies dealing with the mediation of vitellogenin uptake at the level of the follicle also suggest nonspecificity in gonadotropin dependence. For example, ovine FSH enhanced vitellogenin uptake in estrogen primed *X. laevis* (15), but hCG had the same effect in this and other species (13, 17, 73). Tests of amphibians with nonmammalian hormones, especially homologous ones, remain to be done.

Reptilia   Full ovarian growth and ovulation can be stimulated in hypophysectomized lizards by treatment with purified mammalian or reptilian FSH (23, 27, 35, 37), even after removal of all LH contamination by immunoadsorption (35, 48). Although analyses have not yet been performed to determine whether LH has the same intrinsic activities as FSH on the ovary, this might well be expected in light of the overlap in activities observed in spermatogenesis.

OVULATION

Amphibia   Although ovulation represents the functional counterpart of spermiation, these two processes of gamete release do not appear to share a common hormonal dependence in amphibians. Studies on the ovarian tissues of diverse anurans under defined in vitro conditions have established that ovulation and the preceding stages of oocyte maturation—germinal vesicle breakdown—are highly specific for LH; hormones from a wide array of species, including the homologous one, have been tested (14, 44, 45, 49, 50, 64). The sensitivity to LH may vary depending on the recipient species, and there is little phylogenetic predictability in hormone potency (46); FSH preparations, however, are consistently inactive.

Although few studies have examined the effects of purified hormones on urodele amphibians, members of this order appear to exhibit the same LH specificity for ovulation as do the anurans. Vellano et al (71) found that only purified ovine LH, and not FSH, would induce ovulation in intact newts.

In attempts to develop practical methods for harvesting eggs (18, 25), large doses of crude preparations of both mammalian FSH and LH have been used to induce spawning in intact axolotls, *A. mexicanum.* However, in vitro studies with the related *A. tigrinum,* using purified hormones derived from mammalian, reptilian, and amphibian sources (including the homologous hormone), clearly demonstrated that ovulation was LH-specific (49).

Reptilia Gonadotropin specificity of ovulation in some reptiles may be the opposite to that in amphibians. Mammalian (27, 37, 48) and reptilian (35) FSH were both considerably more potent than the corresponding LH for inducing ovulation in intact and hypophysectomized lizards. Furthermore immunoadsorption of FSH preparations to remove any residual LH contamination had no effect on their ovulating activity (35, 48). Similar tests have not yet been performed to ascertain whether LH possesses intrinsic ovulating activity.

Unfortunately, data for ovulation in other reptiles are sparse. A rise in circulating LH during the ovulatory season was observed in a turtle (4), but data for concomitant changes in FSH titers are not available. The nonspecificity for FSH or LH in other aspects of ovarian function, such as steroid secretion in turtles and other reptiles (see below), suggests either FSH specificity or, more likely, a general lack of gonadotropin specificity.

OVARIAN STEROIDOGENESIS

Amphibia Since follicular growth is probably mediated by ovarian estrogen, nonspecificity for FSH or LH in the regulation of this steroid can be extrapolated from data on ovarian growth. In contrast, the dependence of oocyte maturation and ovulation on progesterone (64) suggests that its secretion is regulated primarily by LH in anurans and urodeles. Such specificity has been confirmed by direct radioimmunological measurements of in vitro progesterone secretion in ovaries of the bullfrog and tiger salamander, using mammalian and homologous hormones in each case (36).

Reptilia Sensitivity of ovarian estrogen secretion to FSH is suggested by the hypertrophy of estrogen-dependent target organs in gonadotropin-treated lizards (23, 27, 35, 48). This action of FSH, at least with hormones derived from turtles (35) and mammals (48), was intrinsic to the molecule and independent of LH. Direct measurements in intact turtles demonstrated a rise of plasma estrogen in response to ovine FSH, whereas LH was relatively inactive; seasonal changes in ovarian sensitivity to gonadotropin were also revealed (4, 8). In vitro results on steroid biosynthesis in turtles conflict, depending on whether production was studied with reference to endogenous or exogenous precursors [cf. (7, 9) vs (10, 36)].

Determination of in vivo progesterone secretion in reptiles is limited to tests with mammalian hormones in turtles: In the season when the ovary is responsive, both ovine FSH and LH were effective (4). Similar results were obtained in several in vitro studies. Progesterone production from endogenous precursors in minced tissues (10, 36) and suspended cells (4) from ovaries of several species of turtle were shown to respond to both mammalian and reptilian FSH, including the hormone from homologous species (36); LH preparations, especially from mammals, were relatively inactive. Furthermore, FSH was able to stimulate progesterone secretion from both pre-ovulatory and post-ovulatory (luteal) tissues in the turtle (10, 36). In parallel in vitro tests with crocodilian ovary (pre-ovulatory), progesterone secretion was found to respond almost equally to FSH and LH of either mammalian or crocodilian origin (36).

Results of studies of progesterone biosynthesis from labeled exogenous precursors (cholesterol and pregnenolone) are not entirely consistent with those described above. In particular, progesterone conversion from labeled precursors appeared to be stimulated predominantly by LH (mammalian or avian); FSH had only minor effects (7, 9). Perhaps the stimulatory effect of FSH on a large pool of endogenous precursors obscures its effect on incorporation of labeled steroid; in contrast, LH may act on only the precursor step (8). Discrepancies between the various types of measurements imply a difference in the actions of the two gonadotropins on the steps of the steroid metabolic pathways. However, in the absence of information on dose-response characteristics, kinetics, and homologous hormones, interpretation of the conversion studies is difficult.

Preliminary information on the localization and characteristics of FSH-binding sites in the reptilian ovary is consistent with physiological studies and supports the conclusion that FSH may have broad effects on steroidogenesis. Autoradiographic studies with ^{125}I-labeled human FSH revealed binding sites on the granulosa cells of the pre-ovulatory follicles in lizards and turtle ovaries, as well as on the post-ovulatory luteal tissues in turtles (40). Moreover, the hormonal specificity of these binding sites determined by competitive inhibition analyses was like that of the reptilian testis. Thus, FSH-binding sites on turtle ovaries were specific for mammalian FSH (1, 38, 51) but not for various nonmammalian gonadotropins (39, 51); squamate ovaries showed little specificity for any species of gonadotropin (38, 39, 51).

CONCLUSIONS

Perhaps the most impressive aspect of the information on hormone function in reptiles and amphibians is the conspicuous variability in results obtained for each type of gonadal function. Thus, even though a pair of pituitary gonadotropins similar to mammalian FSH and LH can be identified within most orders of these two classes, it may be erroneous to assume commonality among all vertebrates in the physiological roles of these hormones. Moreover, it is possible that some reptiles, notably the Squamata, are highly divergent, having lost one gonadotropin. Because absolutely no data currently exist on the gonadotropin biochemistry or physiology of the orders Gymnophiona (Amphibia) and Rhyncocephalia (Reptilia), any generalization about the two classes must be regarded as tentative.

At least two major sources of variability may be identified in comparative studies: the species of hormone employed and the species tested. Because the effects of a particular type of gonadotropin, i.e. FSH or LH, may depend on the species from which it was derived, data based on heterologous hormones are often difficult to interpret. A notable example is the marked insensitivity of steroid production by the turtle testis and ovary to mammalian LH; this lack of LH response is not evidenced in other reptilian orders, nor is it seen when turtles are tested with nonmammalian hormones. The relative potencies of heterologous preparations of FSH and LH in squamates may have little relevance to the endocrinology of these reptiles if indeed they have only a single gonadotropin. Since there is little phylogenetic predictability in the actions of heterologous hormones, they should not be relied upon to define hormone function within a species.

Notwithstanding the problems associated with heterologous hormones, it is clear that the sensitivity of several gonadal functions to FSH vis-à-vis LH is not the same in all species. This variability is most striking when species are tested with homologous hormones, but it occurs to some extent even with heterologous hormones. Comparative data are insufficient to evaluate differences among members of the same order; however, significant divergence in hormone function between Reptilia and Amphibia is evident in several aspects of gonadal physiology, especially ovulation and steroid secretion.

Several components of gonadal physiology, including testicular and ovarian growth, spermiation, and estrogen secretion, seem to exhibit little FSH/LH specificity in either Amphibia or Reptilia. In contrast, ovulation, testicular androgen secretion, and ovarian progesterone secretion tend to be highly LH-dependent in Amphibia, whereas they are either predominantly FSH-sensitive or nonspecific in Reptilia. Comparative studies employing different species of gonadotropins together with information on gonadotropin binding sites indicate that this divergence in hormone action between reptiles and amphibians is probably related more to evolution in gonadal receptors (i.e. their localization and specificity) than to changes in gonadotropin structure. The broader phylogenetic implications of these species differences in gonadotropin physiology have been discussed in detail elsewhere (53). Suffice it to say that neither the Amphibia nor Reptilia show a consistent correspondence to the mammalian model, nor do they represent a simple evolutionary progression to the mammalian condition.

Before the significance of this apparent evolutionary divergence can be appreciated fully it must be recognized that virtually all available information on gonadotropin function deals with the responses to exogenously administered hormones. These data provide insight into the potential actions of each gonadotropin, but they do not rule out the possibility that activities of endogenously secreted hormones may differ. The recent development of sensitive radioimmunoassays that can be used to measure circulatory levels of gonadotropin in reptiles (4, 52) and amphibians (11) will facilitate future explorations into the roles of gonadotropins in reproductive endocrinology.

ACKNOWLEDGMENT

Preparation of this review and unpublished observations were supported by grant BM-75-16138 from the National Science Foundation.

Literature Cited

1. Adachi, T., Ishii, S. 1977. Binding of rat follicle-stimulating hormone to the turtle ovary *in vitro* and inhibition of the binding by gonadotropin preparations of various vertebrates. *Gen. Comp. Endocrinol.* 33:1–7
2. Andrieux, B., Collenot, A. 1970. Hormones gonadotropes et développement testiculaire chez le triton *Pleurodeles waltii* Michah. hypophysectomisé. *Ann. Endocrinol.* (*Paris*) 31:531–37
3. Andrieux, B., Collenot, A., Collenot, G., Pergale, C. 1973. Aspects morphologiques de l'action d'hormones gonadotropes mammaliennes sur l'activite testiculaire du triton *Pleurodeles* mature hypophysectomisé. *Ann. Endocrinol.* (*Paris*) 34:711–12
4. Callard, I. P., Lance, V. 1977. The control of reptilian follicular cycles. In *Reproduction and Evolution,* ed. J. H. Calaby, C. H. Tyndale-Biscoe, pp. 199–210. Canberra City: Australian Acad. Sci.
5. Callard, G. V., Ryan, K. J. 1977. Gonadotropin action and androgen synthesis in enzyme dispersed testicular cells of the turtle (*Chrysemys picta*). *Gen. Comp. Endocrinol.* 31:414–21
6. Callard, I. P., Callard, G. V., Lance, V., Eccles, S. 1976. Seasonal changes in testicular structure and function and the effects of gonadotropins in the freshwater turtle, *Chrysemys picta. Gen. Comp. Endocrinol.* 30:347–56
7. Callard, I. P., McChesney, I., Scanes, C., Callard, G. V. 1976. The influence of mammalian and avian gonadotropins on *in vitro* ovarian steroid synthesis in the turtle (*Chrysemys picta*). *Gen. Comp. Endocrinol.* 28:2–9
8. Callard, I. P., Callard, G. V., Lance, V., Bolaffi, J. L., Rosset, J. S. 1978. Testicular regulation in nonmammalian vertebrates. *Biol. Reprod.* 18:16–43
9. Chan, S. W. C., Callard, I. P. 1974. Reptilian ovarian steroidogenesis and the influence of mammalian gonadotrophins (follicle-stimulating hormone and luteinizing hormone) *in vitro. J. Endocrinol.* 62:267–75
10. Crews, D., Licht, P. 1975. Stimulation of *in vitro* steroid production in turtle ovarian tissue by reptilian, amphibian and mammalian gonadotropins. *Gen. Comp. Endocrinol.* 27:71–83
11. Daniels, E., Licht, P., Farmer, S. W., Papkoff, H. 1977. Immunochemical studies on the pituitary gonadotropins (FSH and LH) from the bullfrog, *Rana catesbeiana. Gen. Comp. Endocrinol.* 32:146–57
12. Delsol, M., Burzawa-Gerard, E., Flatin, J., Fontaine, Y. A., Leray, C. 1970. Nouvelles observations sur le test de dosage de hormones gonadotropes utilisant le têtard *Alytes obstetricans.* Essais réalises avec des substances purifées LH et FSH (N.I.H.). *Ann. Endocrinol.* (*Paris*) 31:481–84

13. Emmersen, B., Kjaer, K. 1974. Seasonal and hormonally induced changes in the serum level of the precursor protein vitellogenin in relation to ovarian vitellogenic growth in the toad *Bufo bufo bufo* (L.). *Gen. Comp. Endocrinol.* 22:261–67

14. Farmer, S. W., Licht, P., Papkoff, H., Daniels, E. 1977. Purification of gonadotropins in the leopard frog (*Rana pipiens*). *Gen. Comp. Endocrinol.* 32:158–62

15. Follett, B. K., Redshaw, M. R. 1974. The physiology of vittelogenesis. In *Physiology of the Amphibia,* ed. B. Lofts, pp. 219–309. London: Academic

16. Guha, K. K., Jorgensen, C. B. 1978. Effects of hypophysectomy on structure and function of testes in adult toads, *Bufo bufo bufo* (L.). *Gen. Comp. Endocrinol.* 34:201–10

17. Holland, C. A., Dumont, J. N. 1975. Oogenesis in *Xenopus laevis* (*Daudin*). IV. Effects of gonadotropin, estrogen and starvation on endocytosis in developing oocytes. *Cell Tiss. Res.* 162:177–84

18. Humphrey, R. R. 1977. Factors influencing ovulation in the Mexican axolotl as revealed by inducing spawnings. *J. Exp. Zool.* 199:209–14

19. Iwasawa, H. 1978. Spermatogonial responsiveness to mammalian gonadotropins in subadult *Rana nigromaculata.* *Gen. Comp. Endocrinol.* 34:1–5

20. Iwasawa, H., Michibata, H., Satoh, N. 1973. Effects of exogenous gonadotropins on spermatogenetic activity in summer and autumn frogs. *Sci. Rep. Niigata Univ., Ser. D.* 10:71–78

21. Jalali, S., Arslan, M., Qazi, M. H. 1975. Effect of mammalian gonadotropins (FSH, LH and PMSG) on the testes of the spiny-tailed lizard, *Uromastix hardwicki. Islamabad J. Sci.* 2:10–14

22. Jalali, S., Arslan, M., Qureshi, S., Qazi, M. H. 1976. Effect of temperature and pregnant mare's serum gonadotropin on testicular function in the spiny-tailed lizard, *Uromastix hardwicki. Gen. Comp. Endocrinol.* 30:162–70

23. Jones, R. E. 1969. Effect of mammalian gonadotropins on the ovaries and oviducts of the lizard, *Lygosoma laterale. J. Exp. Zool.* 171:217–22

24. Kasinathan, S., Basu, S. L. 1973. Effect of hormones on spermatogenesis in hypophysectomized *Rana hexadactyla* (Lesson). *Acta Morphol. Acad. Sci. Hung.* 21:249–59

25. Ketterer, D., Forbes, W. R. 1972. Induction of spawning in the Mexican axolotl (*Ambystoma mexicanum*) by luteinizing hormone. *J. Endocrinol.* 55:457–58

26. Lance, V., Scanes, C., Callard, I. P. 1977. Plasma testosterone levels in male turtles, *Chrysemys picta,* following single injections of mammalian, avian and teleostean gonadotropins. *Gen. Comp. Endocrinol.* 31:435–41

27. Licht, P. 1970. Effects of mammalian gonadotropins (ovine FSH and LH) in female lizards. *Gen. Comp. Endocrinol.* 14:98–106

28. Licht, P. 1972. Action of mammalian pituitary gonadotropins (FSH and LH) in reptiles. I. Male snakes. *Gen. Comp. Endocrinol.* 19:273–81

29. Licht, P. 1972. Action of mammalian pituitary gonadotropins (FSH and LH) in reptiles. II. Turtles. *Gen. Comp. Endocrinol.* 19:282–89

30. Licht, P. 1973. Induction of spermation in anurans by mammalian gonadotropins and their subunits. *Gen. Comp. Endocrinol.* 20:522–29

31. Licht, P. 1974. Endocrinology of Reptilia—the pituitary system. *Chem. Zool.* 9:399–448

32. Licht, P. 1974. Luteinizing hormone (LH) in the reptilian pituitary gland. *Gen. Comp. Endocrinol.* 22:463–69

33. Licht, P. 1975. Temperature dependence of the actions of mammalian and reptilian gonadotropins in a lizard. *Comp. Biochem. Physiol.* 50A:221–22

34. Licht, P. 1977. Evolution in the roles of gonadotropins in the regulation of the tetrapod testes. See Ref. 4, pp. 101–10

35. Licht, P., Crews, D. 1975. Stimulation of ovarian and oviducal growth and ovulation in female lizards by reptilian (turtle) gonadotropins. *Gen. Comp. Endocrinol.* 25:467–71

36. Licht, P., Crews, D. 1976. Gonadotropic stimulation of *in vitro* progesterone production in reptilian and amphibian ovaries. *Gen. Comp. Endocrinol.* 29:141–51

37. Licht, P., Hartree, S. 1971. Actions of mammalian, avian and piscine gonadotropins in the lizard. *J. Endocrinol.* 53:329–49

38. Licht, P., Midgley, A. R. Jr. 1976. *In vitro* binding of radioiodinated human follicle-stimulating hormone to reptilian and avian gonads: radioligand studies with mammalian hormones. *Biol. Reprod.* 15:195–205

39. Licht, P., Midgley, A. R. Jr. 1976. Competition for the *in vitro* binding of radioiodinated human follicle-stimulating hormone in reptilian, avian and

mammalian gonads by nonmammalian gonadtropins. *Gen. Comp. Endocrinol.* 30:364–71

40. Licht, P., Midgley, A. R. Jr. 1977. Autoradiographic localization of binding sites for human follicle-stimulating hormone in reptilian testes and ovaries. *Biol. Reprod.* 16:117–21

41. Licht, P., Papkoff, H. 1972. Relationship of sialic acid to the biological activity of vertebrate gonadotropins. *Gen. Comp. Endocrinol.* 19:102–14

42. Licht, P., Papkoff, H. 1973. Evidence for an intrinsic gonadotropic activity of ovine LH in the lizard. *Gen. Comp. Endocrinol.* 20:172–76

43. Licht, P., Papkoff, H. 1974. Phylogenetic survey of the neuraminidase sensitivity of reptilian gonadotropin. *Gen. Comp. Endocrinol.* 23:415–20

44. Licht, P., Papkoff, H. 1974. Separation of two distinct gonadotropins from the pituitary gland of the snapping turtle (*Chelydra serpentina*). *Gen. Comp. Endocrinol.* 22:218–37

45. Licht, P., Papkoff, H. 1974. Separation of two distinct gonadotropins from the pituitary gland of the bullfrog *Rana catesbeiana*. *Endocrinology* 94:1587–94

46. Licht, P., Papkoff, H. 1976. Species specificity in the response of an *in vitro* amphibian (*Xenopus laevis*) ovulation assay to mammalian luteinizing hormone. *Gen. Comp. Endocrinol.* 29:552–55

47. Licht, P., Pearson, A. K. 1969. Effects of mammalian gonadotropins (FSH and LH) on the testis of the lizard *Anolis carolinensis. Gen. Comp. Endocrinol.* 13:367–81

48. Licht, P., Tsui, H. W. 1975. Evidence for the intrinsic activity of ovine FSH on spermatogenesis, ovarian growth, steroidogenesis and ovulation in lizards. *Biol. Reprod.* 12:346–50

49. Licht, P., Farmer, S. W., Papkoff, H. 1975. The nature of the pituitary gonadotropins and their role in ovulation in a urodele amphibian (*Ambystoma tigrinum*). *Life Sci.* 17:1049–54

50. Licht, P., Farmer, S. W., Papkoff, H. 1976. Further studies on the chemical nature of reptilian pituitary gonadotropins: FSH and LH in the American alligator and green sea turtle. *Biol. Reprod.* 14:222–32

51. Licht, P., Bona Gallo, A., Daniels, E. L. 1977. *In vitro* binding of radioiodinated sea turtle (*Chelonia mydas*) follicle-stimulating hormone to reptilian gonadal tissues. *Gen. Comp. Endocrinol.* 33:226–30

52. Licht, P., MacKenzie, D. S., Papkoff, H., Farmer, S. W. 1977. Immunological studies with the gonadotropins and their subunits from the green sea turtle *Chelonia mydas. Gen. Comp. Endocrinol.* 33:231–41

53. Licht, P., Papkoff, H., Farmer, S. W., Muller, C. H., Tsui, H. W., Crews, D. 1977. Evolution of gonadotropin structure and function. *Rec. Prog. Horm. Res.* 33:169–248

54. Lofts, B. 1961. The effects of follicle-stimulating hormone and luteinizing hormone on the testis of hypophysectomized frogs (*Rana temporaria*). *Gen. Comp. Endocrinol.* 1:179–89

55. Lofts, B. 1972. The Sertoli cell. *Gen. Comp. Endocrinol.*, Suppl. 3, 636–48

56. Lofts, B. 1974. Reproduction. See Ref. 15, pp. 107–218

57. Moore, F. L. 1975. Spermatogenesis in larval *Ambystoma tigrinum:* positive and negative interactions of FSH and testosterone. *Gen. Comp. Endocrinol.* 26:525–33

58. Muller, C. H. 1976. *Steroidogenesis and spermatogenesis in the male bullfrog,* Rana catesbeiana: *Regulation by purified bullfrog gonadotropins.* Ph.D. thesis, Univ. California, Berkeley. 156 pp.

59. Muller, C. H. 1977. *In vitro* stimulation of 5α-dihydrotestosterone and testosterone secretion from bullfrog testis by nonmammalian and mammalian gonadotropins. *Gen. Comp. Endocrinol.* 33:109–21

60. Muller, C. H. 1977. Plasma 5α-dihydrotestosterone and testosterone in the bullfrog, *Rana catesbeiana:* stimulation by bullfrog LH. *Gen. Comp. Endocrinol.* 33:122–32

61. Papkoff, H., Farmer, S. W., Licht, P. 1977. Biochemical aspects of the evolution of the pituitary gonadotropins. *Excerpta Med. Found. Int. Congr. Ser.* 403:77–81

62. Roos, J., Jorgensen, C. B. 1974. Rates of disappearance from blood and biological potencies of mammalian gonadotropins (hCG and ovine LH) in the toad *Bufo bufo bufo* (L.). *Gen. Comp. Endocrinol.* 23:432–37

63. Reddy, P. R. K., Prasad, M. R. N. 1970. Effect of gonadotropins and testosterone on the initiation of spermatogenesis in hypophysectomized Indian house lizard, *Hemidactylus flaviviridis* Ruppell. *J. Exp. Zool.* 174:205–14

64. Schuetz, A. W. 1974. Role of hormones in oocyte maturation. *Biol. Reprod.* 10:150–78

65. Simon, N., Reinboth, R. 1966. Juvenile Anuren als Testobjekte für gonadotropische Hormone. *Verh. Dtch. Zool. Ges.* (Suppl.) 30:254–64

66. Trottier, T. M., Armstrong, J. B. 1975. Hormonal stimulation as an aid to artificial insemination in *Ambystoma tigrinum. Can. J. Biol.* 53:171–73

67. Tsui, H. W. 1976. Stimulation of androgen production by the lizard testes: site of action of ovine FSH and LH. *Gen. Comp. Endocrinol.* 28:386–94

68. Tsui, H. W., Licht, P. 1974. Pituitary independence of sperm storage in male snakes. *Gen. Comp. Endocrinol.* 22:277–79

69. Tsui, H. W., Licht, P. 1977. Gonadotropin regulation of *in vitro* androgen production by reptilian testes. *Gen. Comp. Endocrinol.* 31:422–34

70. Van Oordt, P. G. W. J. 1974. Cytology of the adenohypophyses. See Ref. 15, pp. 53–106

71. Vellano, C., Lodi, G., Bona, A., Mazzi, V. 1974. Endocrine determinism of ovulation in the crested newt: effects of mammalian gonadotropins (LH and FSH) and ACTH. *Monit. Zool. Ital.* 8:221–26

72. Vellano, C., Sacerdote, M., Mazzi, V. 1974. Effects of mammalian gonadotropins (FSH and LH) on spermatogenesis in the crested newt under different temperature conditions. *Monit. Zool. Ital.* 8:177–88

73. Wallace, R. A., Jared, D. W., Nelson, B. L. 1970. Protein incorporation by isolated amphibian oocytes. 1. Preliminary studies. *J. Exp. Zool.* 175:259–70

74. Wiebe, J. P. 1970. The mechanism of action of gonadotropic hormones in amphibians: The stimulation of Δ5-3β-hydroxysteroid dehydrogenase activity in testes of *Xenopus laevis* Dandin. *J. Endocrinol.* 47:439–50

Ann. Rev. Physiol. 1979. 41:353–66
Copyright © 1979 by Annual Reviews Inc. All rights reserved

AVIAN ORIENTATION AND NAVIGATION

♦1224

William T. Keeton

Section of Neurobiology and Behavior, Cornell University,
Ithaca, New York 14853

INTRODUCTION

The last decade has witnessed intensified attention to the question of how birds find their way across hundreds or even thousands of miles of often unfamiliar territory. Although no comprehensive answer can yet be given, many new and exciting aspects of avian orientation and navigation have been discovered. Here I review some of the principal topics under investigation in recent years; for more comprehensive (though now somewhat dated) reviews, see (18) and (11). Several shorter discussions are also available (8, 19, 20, 51).

Avian navigation systems are amazingly flexible. Birds utilize multiple cues, some of them redundant, and integrate them in many different ways, depending both on the birds' age, experience, and species, and on the weather conditions and the season of the year. The old hope that one simple avian orientation system would be found seems no longer tenable.

VISUAL CUES

Early investigations of avian orientation focused on the visual cues birds might use. It soon became apparent that terrestrial visual landmarks usually play only a very minor role (11, 18). Thus, for example, pigeons wearing frosted contact lenses that eliminate image vision beyond two or three meters can orient accurately toward home from distant locations, and can even tell when they have arrived at their goal (47, 49). Celestial visual cues, however, were found to be very important. Though bicoordinate celestial navigation as proposed by Matthews (41) does not seem to be used, birds do rely on so-called compass information derived from viewing the sun or

353

0066-4278/79/0301-0353$01.00

the stars. The literature on the sun and star compasses is much too extensive to be covered here, but a few major ideas may be mentioned.

The Sun Compass

During the 1950s, Kramer and his students established that birds tested in circular cages can obtain compass information from the sun (26), a process that requires time compensation because of the sun's changing azimuth throughout the day (14, 26). Schmidt-Koenig (48) extended these findings by showing that pigeons whose internal clocks (i.e. circadian rhythms) have been phase-shifted 6 hr from true sun time misread the sun compass and choose initial bearings roughly 90° different from control birds when released for homing flights from distant sites; in other words, a clock-shift of a quarter of a day results in a deflection of the bearings by a quarter of a circle (Figure 1a). Even at release sites within a mile from home, which should be completely familiar to the birds from their daily exercise flights around the loft, clock-shifted pigeons usually choose deflected bearings (Figure 1b) (13, 18).

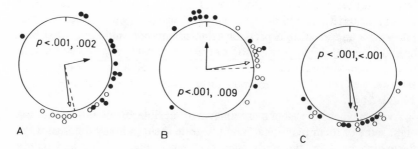

Figure 1 Vanishing bearings of pigeons that have been clock-shifted 6 hr fast. A: Experienced pigeons released on a sunny day at a distant site. The mean bearing of the clock-shifted birds is roughly 90° to the left of that of the controls. B: Experienced pigeons released on a sunny day at a site less than a mile from home, where the landscape should be completely familiar. Again, the mean bearing of the clock-shifted birds is roughly 90° to the left of that of the controls. C: Experienced pigeons released on a totally overcast day at a distant unfamiliar site. Both the clock-shifted and the control birds are homeward oriented, and there is no indication of a difference between them, which suggests that, in the absence of the sun compass, the pigeons use orientational cues that do not require time compensation. [In this and later figures showing bearings, north is indicated by a small line at the top of the circle, and the home direction by a dashed line reaching the perimeter of the circle. The bearing of each bird is shown as a small dot outside the circle; where two treatments are included on a single circle, the bearings of the controls are shown as open dots and the bearings of the experimental birds as filled dots. The mean vectors are shown as arrows (with open or filled heads, respectively), whose length is drawn proportional to the tightness of clumping of the bearings (i.e. the longer the vector—at maximum reaching the perimeter of the circle—the better-oriented the sample of bearings). The uniform probability under the Rayleigh test is given inside the circle; the first value is for the controls and the second for the experimentals.]

Studies of the ontogeny of the sun compass in pigeons have revealed that the coupling of times, directions, and solar azimuths is not inherited. Thus when young pigeons are raised under 6-hr-slow clock-shifted conditions, they orient normally, with no trace of the deflection seen in ordinary clock-shift tests; the birds have learned that the "morning" sun is in the south, the "noon" sun in the west, etc (60). In short, the sun compass must be calibrated, which suggests that there may be a more fundamental directional cue that functions as the reference for calibration. Attempts are underway to identify that reference cue.

Because of the geometric relationship between the position of the observer, the polarization of sunlight, and the position of the sun, it is possible to derive the sun's position if the polarization can be detected. Recent evidence indicates that homing pigeons can detect the polarization of light (7, 31); like honeybees, they can probably continue to use the sun compass on partially overcast days, when the sun's disk is hidden from view but some blue sky remains. The very recent discovery that homing pigeons can also see ultraviolet light (at roughly 350 nM) (28, 29) raises the question whether, like honeybees, they perform their analysis of polarization in the ultraviolet wavelengths.

Thus the sun compass is a preferred orientational cue for pigeons (and probably for other diurnal birds). Such special sensory capabilities as detection of polarized light probably evolved as an aid in reading the sun compass. Very young pigeons reieased for their first homing flight appear to require the sun compass for orientation; if they are released under heavy total overcast they depart randomly (22). However, convincing evidence suggests that experienced pigeons can use other cues on heavily overcast days, cues that do not require time compensation (Figure 1c) (16). And even first-flight youngsters, if raised without having seen the sun, can orient under total overcast; having never learned to use the sun compass, they are not bothered by its absence (W. Wiltschko, R. Wiltschko, A. I. Brown, and W. T. Keeton, unpublished).

The Star Compass

Since the early demonstration by Sauer (46) that European warblers (*Sylvia* sp.) can derive directional information from the stars, use of stellar cues has been demonstrated in a variety of nocturnal migrants [for summary, see (11)]. The most thorough studies of the star compass have been carried out by Emlen (8, 12), using indigo buntings (*Passerina cyanea*) tested in circular cages both in the field and in a planetarium. He has shown that the buntings use star patterns to determine directions, a process that, contrary to Sauer's expectation, does not require time compensation (Figure 2). Thus the manner of reading the star compass differs fundamentally from that of the sun compass.

Having found that his buntings relied primarily on stars in the northern circumpolar area of the sky, within 35° of Polaris (8), Emlen pursued the question whether the seasonal differences in the temporal positions of these stars determine southward orientation in autumn and northward orientation in spring, or whether the differences in orientation result from corresponding differences in the physiological condition of the bird. By manipulating photoperiods, he contrived to bring one group of male buntings into autumnal physiological condition at the same time that another group was in spring condition (9). He could then test both groups simultaneously under a spring sky in the planetarium. The birds in autumnal condition oriented southward, whereas the birds in spring condition oriented northward (Figure 3). Since the two groups saw identical star patterns, Emlen concluded that their orientations were due to their physiological condition, not to the environmental stimuli. He predicted that the important factor would be found to be hormonal. Later studies by Martin & Meier (39) supported his prediction by showing that the orientation of white-throated sparrows (*Zonotrichia albicollis*) in circular cages could be reversed by altering the temporal pattern of administration of prolactin and corticosterone. Thus birds given injections of prolactin 4 hr after injections of corticosterone oriented southward, whereas birds given the prolactin 12 hr after corticosterone oriented northward.

In a series of studies on the ontogeny of stellar orientation, Emlen (10) found that there is a critical period during which young buntings learn to read the star compass. Thus buntings that have had a view of the starry sky during the weeks preceding the start of their first autumnal migration season can orient properly when tested under a starry sky, but buntings that have not seen the night sky until after that first migration season has begun never learn to use the star compass, no matter how often they see the sky thereafter.

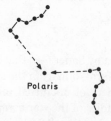

Polaris

Figure 2   An example of how north can be located by star patterns. An arrow running through two particular stars in the cup of the big dipper (Ursa Major) points toward Polaris. Although the positions of the constellations change during the night (two positions are shown here), the same stars always determine an arrow pointing toward Polaris (i.e. toward north, or the pole of the celestial rotation); hence, directions can be determined without time compensation. Many different star patterns could be used for direction finding in this way.

Spring   "Autumn"

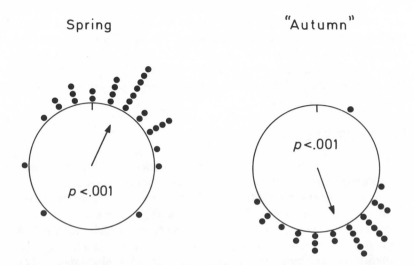

Figure 3   The orientation under a spring planetarium sky of indigo buntings in spring and "autumnal" physiological condition. The birds in spring condition oriented north-northeastward, the usual direction for this species. The birds brought artificially into autumnal condition oriented south-southeastward. [Redrawn from data in (11)]

Emlen (10) also showed that young buntings respond initially to the apparent rotation of the starry sky during the night. The axis of this rotation is, of course, north-south, and thus it can provide compass information. But the birds do not long depend on the axis of rotation per se; rather they learn star patterns that will indicate where the axis is, and thereafter they rely exclusively on those patterns. The axis of rotation functions in ontogeny as the reference system against which the star compass is initially calibrated. Thus when Emlen exposed hand-reared young buntings to a planetarium sky rotating around an incorrect axis—one for which Betelgeuse was the pole star—they learned to use the stars in the 35° circum-Betelgeuse area of the sky; consequently, they oriented in an inappropriate direction when later tested under a normal sky. When retested a year later, after extensive exposure to the normal sky, they had not corrected their orientation; what they had learned during the critical period in their early life still dominated their behavior. As we shall see below, however, it is not yet clear how far these results from buntings can be generalized to other species, for Wiltschko & Wiltschko have reported that adults of several species of European migrants calibrate their star compass relative to the earth's magnetic field and can recalibrate repeatedly (58).

During the last decade, evidence has accumulated [especially from radar studies (11)] that nocturnal migrants can continue oriented flight under heavy overcast, when the stars are no longer visible. Thus, as in the case of the sun compass in pigeons, there must be alternative cues the birds can use. Moreover, Kramer (27) early pointed out that since solar and stellar cues apparently provide only compass information, and since a compass alone cannot tell a bird where it is or which direction it should choose in order to reach its goal, other environmental cues must provide map information.

MAGNETIC CUES

Early suggestions that birds might derive directional information from the earth's magnetic field—indeed, that any organism could detect a magnetic field as weak as the earth's (about 0.5 G)—were not convincing. Reports by Brown and his colleagues [summarized in (5)] that a variety of invertebrates respond to weak magnetic fields were not widely accepted. But beginning in the mid-1960s and continuing to the present, a group at Frankfurt, led first by F. Merkel and then by W. Wiltschko, reported (e.g. 57) that the migratory orientation of European robins (*Erithacus rubecula*) and several species of warblers (*Sylvia*) in circular test cages can be altered predictably by changing the magnetic field in the cages, using Helmholtz coils. Shortly thereafter, Southern (50) found evidence that magnetic cues may be used by ring-billed gulls, and Keeton (17) reported an effect of magnets on the homeward orientation of pigeons. At roughly the same time, Lindauer & Martin (38) found convincing evidence that the orientation of the dance of scout honeybees is influenced by the earth's magnetic field. More recently, orientational responses to weak magnetic fields have been reported for a host of different organisms, including magnetotactic bacteria (3), various kinds of insects (e.g. 1, 55), amphibians (45), and elasmobranch fishes (15).

Following up his earlier work, Wiltschko (58) reported that birds apparently do not respond to the polarity of the magnetic field, but rather, in the northern hemisphere, take north as that direction in which the magnetic and gravity vectors form the most acute angle (Figure 4). In short, their manner of reading the magnetic compass is very different from our own. The Wiltschkos (59) have reported evidence that their birds periodically use the magnetic field to recalibrate their star compass, and then may orient by the stars for a day or so before again taking a magnetic reading. A person might use a similar process: After consulting his magnetic compass, he would walk toward a mountain peak in the desired direction; he might not take another magnetic bearing until he needed to recheck the visual marker.

A magnetic effect on pigeon homing was suggested by my own studies. After showing that pigeons could orient under total overcast (16), I found (17) that bar magnets attached to experienced birds' backs often caused

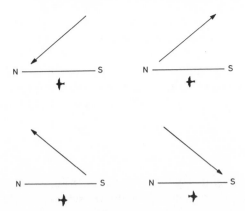

Figure 4   The magnetic compass of the European robin. Top: The birds orient northward in spring, whether the magnetic field vector points north and down (which is the normal condition) or south and up. Bottom: The same birds change their orientation to southward if the magnetic vector points north and up or south and down. It appears to be the alignment of the magnetic vector, not its polarity, that determines the birds' behavior.

disorientation under overcast, whereas the bars had little effect on sunny days. Thus emerged the concept that the magnetic field provides compass information that experienced pigeons use primarily when the sun compass is unavailable [magnets sometimes have a weak effect even on sunny days (17, 52)]; young first-flight pigeons appear to rely more heavily on magnetic cues (17). An important advance came when Walcott & Green (54), using Helmholtz coils on the pigeons' head and neck, were able to change the direction of the birds' orientation under overcast.

Further investigations confirmed not only that a variety of organisms can detect magnetic fields as weak as that of the earth but also that they can detect very tiny changes in such fields. Thus the orientation of honeybees (40), gull chicks (50), pigeons (24, 35), and migrating birds (42) seems to be affected by naturally occurring fluctuations in the earth's field (caused mainly by events on the sun, such as solar flares). Such fluctuations are often considerably smaller than 10^{-3} G; animals may be able to sense changes as small as 10^{-4} or even 10^{-5} G. Recent evidence shows that the initial orientation of pigeons is influenced by natural geomagnetic anomalies (53) and that migratory birds respond to the weak low-frequency alternating fields produced by the test antenna for the US Navy's proposed Project Seafarer (34).

Although there are now reasonable models to explain magnetic detection in both bacteria and elasmobranch fishes (15, 62), the mechanism of detection in birds and insects remains unknown. Several hypotheses (e.g. 6, 37) have been advanced but remain inadequately evaluated. Indeed, until very recently no one had succeeded in training animals to magnetic stimuli in the laboratory (as opposed to recording spontaneous responses) (32). Animals may require several minutes (sometimes even hours) to read a magnetic stimulus; movement may play a part, either in the detection process itself or in making the animals attend to the stimuli. In 1977, Bookman (4) reported the successful training of pigeons in a two-choice test allowing more time than previous conditioning attempts and permitting flight within the test field.

GRAVITY CUES

Impressed by the fact that in many studies when animals had shown responsiveness to magnetic stimuli they had been simultaneously responding to gravity (as in the negative geotactic runs of *Drosophila* or in the gravitationally oriented waggle dance of honeybees) (38, 55, 58), Larkin and I (36) sought to determine whether gravitational cues might play a role in pigeon homing. Unable to alter gravity in a laboratory test of orientation, we looked for an influence of the natural monthly gravitational cycle caused by the changing relative positions of the earth, sun, and moon. In six series of test releases conducted during four years at three locations, we found a significant correlation between the pigeons' mean vanishing bearings and the day of the lunar synodic month. Suggestive as these results may be, however, they do not prove a direct effect of gravitational changes on orientation because many other environmental variables are also related to the lunar cycle.

Gravitational cues could be useful in navigation; due to the geographic variation in the strength of the gravitational field, they could provide an additional topography. Moreover, if a bird could use the north-south gravitational gradient to determine true north, then magnetic declination (the deviation of magnetic north from true north) might be readable. Declination is one of the very few environmental parameters that vary as a rough analog of longitude, and hence its usefulness would be very great indeed. It is important to emphasize, however, that no evidence is yet available that birds can detect such very tiny differences in gravity ($<$ 10 gal) as would be necessary to permit use of gravitational cues in long-distance navigation; this is a subject on which research has only just begun.

OLFACTORY CUES

In 1972, Papi and his colleagues (43) proposed that olfactory cues might provide the basis for the navigational map of birds. According to their hypothesis, young pigeons at their home loft would learn to associate particular odors with winds from certain directions. Thus odor *A* might arrive primarily on winds from the north, odor B on winds from the east, etc. A bird released at a distance from home, say north of home, would detect a strong odor of A and thus determine its position to be north of home. The bird would then use one of its compass systems to locate south and begin its homeward flight.

Papi and his colleagues have performed a long series of ingenious experiments designed to test their hypothesis [for summary, see (44)] and have reported consistently positive results. These experiments have included unilateral and bilateral sectioning of the olfactory nerves, painting strongly odorous chemicals on the birds' noses just before release, transporting the birds to release sites under altered olfactory conditions, exposing young pigeons to altered olfactory stimuli at the home loft, etc. Unfortunately, our own attempts to repeat most of these experiments have yielded either negative results (e.g. 21, 23) or somewhat ambiguous results (43a). Much more work on this interesting topic is needed.

In one set of experiments, however, Papi's results have been clearly replicated, both in the US (43a) and in Germany (25). In these experiments, young pigeons are raised in specially designed lofts (Figure 5) where the walls allow free flow of air (2). Birds in the control loft receive winds—and the odors they are presumed to carry—from the proper directions. Birds in two experimental lofts receive winds deflected either clockwise or counterclockwise. When tested at distant release sites, pigeons from the control loft choose homeward-oriented initial bearings, but pigeons from the experimental lofts choose bearings to the right or left of those of the controls, as predicted by the olfactory hypothesis. These dramatic results may well indicate that olfactory cues provide another important source of orientational information for birds. A firmer conclusion awaits experiments that control for other cues (e.g. the polarization of light, the apparent position of the sun, acoustic signals) that were altered by the wind deflectors.

I think it reasonable that olfaction provides one of the many cues orienting birds can use, but I doubt that it will be found to play as essential a role in the navigation process as Papi and his colleagues have suggested. Indeed, I'm not convinced that any single cue so far known is essential; there seems to be sufficient redundancy in the avian navigation system so that experienced birds can orient themselves even when only a few of the many possible cues are available.

INFRASONIC CUES

The recent discovery (61) that homing pigeons can detect infrasound raises an intriguing new orientational possibility. Because attenuation is proportional to the square of frequency, infrasonic frequencies as low as those

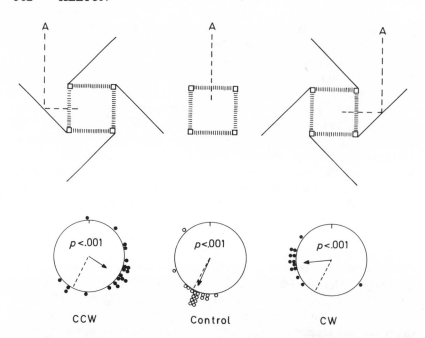

Figure 5 The deflector loft experiments. Top: All three lofts (control loft in center, lofts with deflectors on each side) have walls that allow free flow of air. Winds from the north, presumably carrying odor *A*, enter the control loft from the north, but they enter the other lofts from the east and west because of the deflectors. Bottom: Bearings of pigeons released north-northeast of home. The control birds, which had earlier experienced normal air flow (i.e. *A* winds from the north) oriented properly south-southwest, toward home. By contrast, the CW birds, which had experienced *A* winds from the east, oriented more westerly, and the CCW birds, which had experienced *A* winds from the west, oriented easterly. [Redrawn from (2)]

the birds can detect [down at least to 0.05 Hz (33)] travel hundreds or even thousands of miles with little energy loss. Pigeons might therefore be able to monitor distant infrasonic sound sources, such as ocean breakers or winds whistling around mountains, and use these as a rough system of beacons for determining position.

The question arises whether the pigeons can determine the directions from which the infrasounds come. At such low frequencies, the wavelengths are so very long (over 3 km at 0.1 Hz) that binaural comparisons would be impossible. However, birds can discriminate frequency in the infrasonic range well enough to detect the Doppler shifts that would occur between flights toward and then away from a sound (33). Thus pigeons may be able to get directional information from infrasound during flight, even if they cannot do so while perching; field experiments to evaluate this possibility are now in progress at Cornell University. Tests of infrasound detection by species other than pigeons have not yet been conducted.

METEOROLOGICAL CUES

The last decade has witnessed many surveillance-radar studies of avian migratory flights (for summary, see 11). The wind and weather conditions in which flights in north-temperate latitudes are most likely to begin can now be specified: on the east side of a high-pressure cell following passage of a cold front in autumn; on the west side of a high pressure area ahead of an advancing cold front in spring. Birds are remarkably good meteorologists, and can predict in the late afternoon or early evening, while they are still on the ground, what the conditions aloft will be later that night. Their meteorological abilities may depend, at least in part, on their newly discovered remarkable sensitivity to barometric pressure changes (30).

The importance of correctly predicting the weather, especially the winds aloft, is apparent when one realizes that mortality can be extremely heavy if migrants encounter very unfavorable conditions while in flight. This is particularly true of the many small song birds that depart in an east-southeasterly direction from Nova Scotia and Cape Cod in autumn; they fly well out over the Atlantic until they encounter the southwesterly trade winds, which they then ride nonstop to South America, sometimes flying as high as 20,000 ft (56).

Though most attention to meteorological factors has been directed at their role in determining the intensity of avian migratory movements or in influencing the bioenergetic cost of migration, there has been considerable recent interest in the possibility that wind directions, patterns of air turbulence, pressure patterns in the atmosphere, or other such aspects of the weather might also be used as orientational cues. This is an important new area of active research.

CONCLUDING REMARKS

It has become increasingly apparent in recent years that avian navigation systems are extremely complex. Birds probably use not only the more traditionally studied cues of sun and stars, along with such previously known but largely ignored cues as odors, but also a host of cues they were previously not known to detect, such as the earth's magnetic field, barometric pressure, ultraviolet light, the polarization of light, and infrasound.

Much of the current research in this field is devoted to determining how the many cues are integrated. One promising approach has been to study the ontogeny of orientation behavior in order to see how the various cues become incorporated into the system originally. Very young birds are still flexible enough that they can often be induced to adopt an atypical cue-weighting scheme, thereby exposing to experimental manipulation cues that would normally be difficult to study. Another valuable approach has been to pit two or more cues against each other to see how (or whether) the birds will resolve the conflict. Whatever the approach, research on the ever-perplexing puzzle of how birds find their way seems sure to yield further contributions to our knowledge of animal behavior, sensory physiology, development, and other areas of biology.

Acknowledgment

The author's work was supported by NSF grant BMS 75–18905 A02.

Literature Cited

1. Arendse, M. C., Vrins, J. C. M. 1975. Magnetic orientation and its relation to photic orientation in *Tenebrio molitor* L. (Coleoptera, Tenebrionidae). *Neth. J. Zool.* 25:407–37
2. Baldaccini, N. E., Benvenuti, S., Fiaschi, V., Papi, F. 1975. Pigeon navigation: Effects of wind deflection at home cage on homing behaviour. *J. Comp. Physiol.* 99:177–86
3. Blakemore, R. 1975. Magnetotactic bacteria. *Science* 190:377–79
4. Bookman, M. A. 1977. Sensitivity of the homing pigeon to an earth-strength magnetic field. *Nature* 267:340–42
5. Brown, F. A. 1971. Some orientational influences of nonvisual terrestrial electromagnetic fields. *Ann. NY Acad. Sci.* 188:224–41
6. Cope, F. W. 1973. Biological sensitivity to weak magnetic fields due to biological superconductive Josephson junctions? *Physiol. Chem. Phys.* 5:173–76
7. Delius, J. D., Perchard, R. J., Emmerton, J. 1976. Polarized light discrimination by pigeons and an electroretinographic correlate. *J. Comp. Physiol. Psychol.* 90:560–71
8. Emlen, S. T. 1967. Migratory orientation of the indigo bunting, *Passerina cyanea. Auk* 84:309–42; 463–89
9. Emlen, S. T. 1969. Bird migration: Influence of physiological state upon celestial orientation. *Science* 165:716–18
10. Emlen, S. T. 1972. The ontogenetic development of orientation capabilities. In *Animal Orientation and Navigation,* ed. S. R. Galler, K. Schmidt-Koenig, G. J. Jacobs, R. E. Belleville, pp. 191–210. Washington DC: NASA SP-262, US GPO. 606 pp.
11. Emlen, S. T. 1975. Migration: Orientation and navigation. In *Avian Biology,* ed. D. S. Farner, J. R. King, 5:129–219. New York: Academic. 523 pp.
12. Emlen, S. T. 1975. The stellar-orientation system of a migratory bird. *Sci. Am.* 233(2):102–11
13. Graue, L. C. 1963. The effect of phase shifts in the day-night cycle on pigeon homing at distances of less than one mile. *Ohio J. Sci.* 63:214–17
14. Hoffmann, K. 1960. Experimental manipulation of the orientational clock in birds. *Cold Spring Harbor Symp. Quant. Biol.* 25:379–87
15. Kalmijn, A. 1978. Experimental evidence of geomagnetic orientation in elasmobranch fishes. In *Animal Migration, Navigation and Homing,* ed. K. Schmidt-Koenig, W. T. Keeton, pp. 347–53. Heidelberg: Springer. 467 pp.
16. Keeton, W. T. 1969. Orientation by pigeons: Is the sun necessary? *Science* 165:922–28
17. Keeton, W. T. 1971. Magnets interfere with pigeon homing. *Proc. Natl. Acad. Sci. USA* 68:102–6
18. Keeton, W. T. 1974. The orientational and navigational basis of homing in birds. *Adv. Study Behav.* 5:47–132
19. Keeton, W. T. 1974. The mystery of pigeon homing. *Sci. Am.* 231(6):96–107
20. Keeton, W. T. 1978. Pigeon navigation. In *Neural Mechanisms of Behavior in the Pigeon,* edited by A. M. Granda, J. H. Maxwell. New York: Plenum Press.
21. Keeton, W. T., Brown, A. I. 1976. Homing behavior of pigeons not disturbed by application of an olfactory stimulus. *J. Comp. Physiol.* 105:259–66
22. Keeton, W. T., Gobert, A. 1970. Orientation by untrained pigeons requires the sun. *Proc. Natl. Acad. Sci. USA* 65:853–56
23. Keeton, W. T., Kreithen, M. L., Hermayer, K. L. 1977. Orientation by pigeons deprived of olfaction by nasal tubes. *J. Comp. Physiol.* 114:289–99
24. Keeton, W. T., Larkin, T. S., Windsor, D. M. 1974. Normal fluctuations in the earth's magnetic field influence pigeon

orientation. *J. Comp. Physiol.* 95:95–103
25. Kiepenheuer, J. 1978. Pigeon homing: A repetition of the deflector loft experiment. *Behav. Ecol. Sociobiol.* 3: In press
26. Kramer, G. 1952. Experiments on bird orientation. *Ibis* 94:265–85
27. Kramer, G. 1953. Die Sonnenorientierung der Vögel. *Verh. Dtsch. Zool. Ges.* 1952:72–84
28. Kreithen, M. L. 1978. The sensory world of the homing pigeon. See Ref. 20
29. Kreithen, M. L., Eisner, T. 1978. Detection of ultraviolet light by the homing pigeon. *Nature* 272:347–48
30. Kreithen, M. L., Keeton, W. T. 1974. Detection of changes in atmospheric pressure by the homing pigeon, *Columba livia. J. Comp. Physiol.* 89: 73–82
31. Kreithen, M. L., Keeton, W. T. 1974. Detection of polarized light by the homing pigeon, *Columba livia. J. Comp. Physiol.* 89:83–92
32. Kreithen, M. L., Keeton, W. T. 1974. Attempts to condition homing pigeons to magnetic stimuli. *J. Comp. Physiol.* 91:355–62
33. Kreithen, M. L., Quine, D. 1979. Infrasound detection by the homing pigeon: A behavioral audiogram. *J. Comp. Physiol.* In press
34. Larkin, R. P., Sutherland, P. J. 1977. Migrating birds react to Project Seafarer's electromagnetic field. *Science* 195:777–79
35. Larkin, T. S., Keeton, W. T. 1976. Bar magnets mask the effect of normal magnetic disturbances on pigeon orientation. *J. Comp. Physiol.* 110:227–31
36. Larkin, T. S., Keeton, W. T. 1978. An apparent lunar rhythm in the day-to-day variations in the initial bearings of homing pigeons. See Ref. 15, pp. 92–106
37. Leask, M. J. M. 1977. A physico-chemical mechanism for magnetic field detection by migratory birds and homing pigeons. *Nature* 267:144–45
38. Lindauer, M., Martin, H. 1968. Die Schwereorientierung der Bienen unter dem Einfluss des Erdmagnetfeldes. *Z. Vergl. Physiol.* 60:219–43
39. Martin, D. D., Meier, A. H. 1973. Temporal synergism of corticosterone and prolactin in regulating orientation in the migratory white-throated sparrow (*Zonotrichia albicollis*). *Condor* 75:369–74
40. Martin, H., Lindauer, M. 1977. Der Einfluss des Erdmagnetfeldes auf die Schwereorientierung der Honigbiene

(*Apis mellifica*). *J. Comp. Physiol.* 122: 145–87
41. Matthews, G. V. T. 1955. *Bird Navigation.* London: Cambridge Univ. Press. 141 pp.
42. Moore, F. R. 1977. Geomagnetic disturbance and the orientation of nocturnally migrating birds. *Science* 196: 682–84
43. Papi, F., Fiore, L., Fiaschi, V., Benvenuti, S. 1972. Olfaction and homing in pigeons. *Monit. Zool. Ital. (N.S.)* 6:85–95
43a. Papi, F., Keeton, W. T., Benvenuti, S., Brown, A. I. 1978. Do American and Italian pigeons rely on different homing devices? *J. Comp. Physiol.* In press
44. Papi, F. 1976. The olfactory navigation system of the homing pigeon. *Verh. Dtsch. Zool. Ges.* 1976:184–205
45. Phillips, J. B. 1977. Use of the earth's magnetic field by orienting cave salamanders (*Eurycea lucifuga*). *J. Comp. Physiol.* 121:273–88
46. Sauer, E. G. F. 1957. Die Sternenorientierung nächtlich ziehender Grasmücken (*Sylvia atricapilla, borin* and *curruca*). *Z. Tierpsychol.* 14:29–70
47. Schlichte, H. J. 1973. *Untersuchungen über die Bedeutung optischer Parameter für das Heimkehrverhalten der Brieftaube. Z. Tierpsychol.* 32:257–80
48. Schmidt-Koenig, K. 1960. Internal clocks and homing. *Cold Spring Harbor Symp. Quant. Biol.* 25:389–93
49. Schmidt-Koenig, K., Schlichte, H. J. 1972. Homing in pigeons with reduced vision. *Proc. Natl. Acad. Sci. USA* 69:2446–47
50. Southern, W. E. 1972. Influence of disturbances in the earth's magnetic field on ring-billed gull orientation. *Condor* 74:102–5
51. Walcott, C. 1974. The homing of pigeons. *Am. Sci.* 62:542–52
52. Walcott, C. 1977. Magnetic fields and the orientation of homing pigeons under sun. *J. Exp. Biol.* 70:105–23
53. Walcott, C. 1978. Anomalies in the earth's magnetic field increase the scatter of pigeons' vanishing bearings. See Ref. 15, pp. 143–51
54. Walcott, C., Green, R. 1974. Orientation of homing pigeons altered by a change in the direction of an applied magnetic field. *Science* 184:180–82
54a. Waldvogel, J., Benvenuti, S., Keeton, W. T., Papi, F. 1978. Homing pigeon orientation influenced by deflected winds at home loft. *J. Comp. Physiol.* In press

55. Wehner, R., Labhart, T. 1970. Perception of the geomagnetic field in the fly *Drosophila melanogaster*. *Experientia* 26:967–68
56. Williams, T. C., Williams, J. M. 1978. The orientation of transatlantic migrants. See Ref. 15, pp. 239–51
57. Wiltschko, W. 1968. Über den Einfluss statischer Magnetfelder auf die Zugorientierung der Rotkehlchen (*Erithacus rubecula*). *Z. Tierpsychol.* 25: 537–58
58. Wiltschko, W. 1972. The influence of magnetic total intensity and inclination on directions preferred by migrating European robins (*Erithacus rubecula*). See Ref. 10, pp. 569–78

59. Wiltschko, W., Wiltschko, R. 1975. The interaction of stars and magnetic field in the orientation system of night migrating birds. *Z. Tierpsychol.* 37:337–55; 39:265–82
60. Wiltschko, W., Wiltschko, R., Keeton, W. T. 1976. Effects of a "permanent" clock-shift on the orientation of young homing pigeons. *Behav. Ecol. Sociobiol.* 1:229–43
61. Yodlowski, M. L., Kreithen, M. L., Keeton, W. T. 1977. Detection of atmospheric infrasound by homing pigeons. *Nature* 265:725–26
62. Kalmijn, A., Blakemore, R. P. 1978. The magnetic behavior of mud bacteria. See Ref. 15, pp. 354–55

RESPIRATORY AND CARDIOVASCULAR PHYSIOLOGY

Introduction

Cardiovascular physiology is readily divided into subsections, such as 1. functional cardiac morphology and development; 2. electrophysiology of the heart; 3. mechanisms of cardiac contraction; 4. hemodynamics; 5. neural and hormonal regulation of the heart; 6. cardiac energetics and metabolism; 7. regulation of the peripheral circulation; 8. capacitance and resistance vessels; 9. special circulations; 10. the microcirculation; 11. vascular smooth muscle, and a host of other classifications that involve two or more of the more conventional categories and also deal with abnormalities and dysfunction of segments of the cardiovascular system. It is our intent to cover two or three specific areas in depth each year. We anticipate covering all of the major aspects of the cardiovascular system over a span of 3 to 4 years. Obviously, shifts in coverage and emphasis will be made to keep in step with major research developments and breakthroughs.

In this volume of the *Annual Review of Physiology*—the first to employ the new format—respiration has been handled by the Section Editor for cardiovascular physiology. In subsequent volumes respiration will be treated in a separate section with its own editor. Here only two chapters on respiration have been included; no attempt has been made to unify them around a central theme. In contrast, the chapters on the cardiovascular system have been divided into two main categories: electrophysiology of the heart and cardiac contraction. The introductory chapter on the sodium pump provides a broad characterization of the present state of our knowledge about sodium-potassium ATPase, the enzyme responsible for movement of these ions across the membrane. The second chapter deals with the inward currents in the heart, namely, the fast sodium current that is sensitive to tetrodotoxin (TTX) and the TTX-insensitive slow current mostly carried by calcium. This leads naturally into the next chapter, a discussion of the action potential plateau and the various factors that influence it; the

367

electrogenesis of the pacemaker potential is also discussed in this chapter. Next follows a chapter on divergent concepts of impulse propagation, followed by a chapter on the current ideas of the mechanisms involved in the development of various cardiac arrhythmias.

The subject of cardiac contraction is introduced by a chapter on the role of calcium in excitation-contraction coupling. This review is followed by one on the function of mitochondria in the heart and the various regulatory mechanisms involved in the supply of energy (in the form of ATP) for cardiac contractions. The subsequent chapter deals with cardiac heat; it describes cardiac energy expenditures throughout the cardiac cycle and expresses them in terms of ATPase activities. In the next article, the mechanics of cardiac contraction—such as force development, velocity of contraction, and compliance—are discussed at the molecular level with respect to the factors involved in crossbridge interaction and filament behavior. Finally, as in the section on cardiac electrophysiology, the section on cardiac contraction concludes with a foray into abnormal physiology: a chapter on cardiac hypertrophy. The review approaches this subject from a fundamental mechanistic point of view and indicates both the limits of our knowledge of this important pathophysiological process and the direction of future research.

We anticipate that this new format for the *Annual Review of Physiology* will greatly enhance its usefulness to the reader and will provide a readily accessible source of current material on the subject.

Robert M. Berne
Section Editor

Ann. Rev. Physiol. 1979. 41:369–81
Copyright © 1979 by Annual Reviews Inc. All rights reserved

CONTROL OF MUCUS SECRETION AND ION TRANSPORT IN AIRWAYS

♦1225

Jay A. Nadel, Brian Davis, and Roger J. Phipps

Cardiovascular Research Institute and Departments of Medicine
and Physiology, University of California, San Francisco, California 94143

INTRODUCTION

Mucus and water combine in a complex way to form the respiratory tract secretions. Electron micrographs (33) indicate that vesicles in the mucous and serous cells of the submucosal glands and in the goblet and serous cells of the airway epithelia discharge granules of mucus into the gland ducts and into the airway lumen, respectively. These granules are hydrated, in some unknown way, and form a coating of secretion over the ciliated epithelium of the airways. This secretion consists of an upper gel (38, 78) and a lower, more fluid sol in which the cilia can beat freely and sweep the gel, with its trapped inhaled particles, up the airway to be swallowed.

Excellent reviews of the comparative anatomy of airways (12), chemistry of mucus (44), rheology of airway mucus secretion (36, 65), mechanisms of ciliary beating (63), and mucociliary clearance from the lungs (73) and the nose (61) give detailed information about these aspects of the structure and function of airways. In this review we discuss recent advances in the regulation of mucoprotein secretion and the possible role of ion transport in the regulation of water secretion into the airway lumen. New techniques allow the functions of the submucosal glands to be separated from those of the surface epithelial cells. Therefore, as far as possible, we discuss the physiology of these subunits independently. Although the role of ion transport in the movement of fluid across most other mammalian epithelia has been studied extensively, the investigation of ion transport in airway epithelia was initiated only recently and promises to provide important new information about the physiology of the airways.

369

0066-4278/79/0301-0369$01.00

MUCUS SECRETION

Studies of tracheobronchial mucus secretion are hampered by the small volume of secretions normally produced, by the relative inaccessibility of the sources of these secretions, and by the limited sensitivity of techniques available to analyze the small amounts of glycoproteins collected. Many studies have involved the collection of sputum, but because sputum is contaminated with both saliva and nasal mucus its study gives little information about the normal control of airway secretions. Since mucus is transported toward the mouth, methods have been employed to collect the total secretions at a given level of the airway (e.g. in the trachea) (1, 55). However, these techniques are limited because it is not known where the collected secretions originate, and because these methods are likely to stimulate mucus secretion by local irritation and reflex mechanisms. Nevertheless, the use of tracheal segments in vivo (20, 23), explants of trachea and bronchi (9, 68), isolated pieces of trachea mounted in chambers (57), and micropipettes to obtain secretions from specific structures (e.g. submucosal gland duct openings) (51) have provided useful information about the various sources of airway mucus.

Submucosal Glands

These are found in the trachea and bronchi, but not in bronchioles. They are numerous in several species, including humans (70), cats (20, 23), and pigs (7); infrequent or nonexistent in some species, including rabbits and guinea pigs (45); and nonexistent in other species, including geese (59) and chickens (72). Each gland is comprised of four distinct regions: (*a*) a short, funnel-shaped ciliated duct that is a continuation of the surface epithelium; (*b*) a nonciliated collecting duct; (*c*) mucous tubules, lined with mucous secretory cells, opening into the collecting duct; and (*d*) serous tubules, lined with serous secretory cells, opening into mucous tubules (49) (Figure 1). Both mucous and serous cells produce glycoproteins; in addition, the serous cells probably also produce other proteins (44). Myoepithelial cells closely related to the secretory cells (8, 48) may aid the passage of secretion along the tubules by contracting and squeezing the cells.

The evidence for parasympathetic efferent innervation of the submucosal glands is strong. Electron-microscopic studies in humans show nerve fibers that contain agranular vesicles near mucous and serous cells, which suggests the presence of postganglionic cholinergic efferent nerve endings (8, 48). Anatomic studies using a specific acetylcholinesterase stain confirm the presence of a cholinergic innervation of submucosal glands (19, 40, 74). Stimulation of the efferent parasympathetic nerve supply to the airways increases both the volume of the secretions (20, 50) and the output of

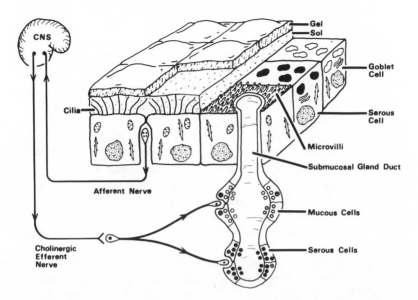

Figure 1   Diagram of secretory cells in airway. Serous (●) and mucous (○) secretions from the appropriate cells in the submucosal gland combine with water to form the submucosal gland secretion, which is discharged via the gland duct onto the airway luminal surface. This secretion mixes with the mucous and serous secretions from the epithelial goblet and serous cells to coat the epithelial surface with an upper gel and a lower more fluid sol in which the cilia beat and propel the gel toward the mouth. The apical surfaces of some cells are covered by microvilli whose function is unknown. Golgi apparatus (≋) of the secretory epithelial cells, and nuclei (◉), endoplasmic reticulum (⌇), and mitochondria (⬭) in the other surface cells are shown. Endings of cholinergic afferent nerves in the lateral intercellular spaces close to the junctions between epithelial cells send impulses to the central nervous system and reflexly stimulate secretion from the serous and mucous cells of the submucosal glands via cholinergic efferent nerves.

radiolabelled glycoprotein (23). These effects are cholinergic since they are mimicked by cholinergic agonists, and both nerve and drug effects can be blocked by muscarinic antagonists. There is no direct evidence for a para-sympathetic nervous effect in human airway submucosal glands, but cholinergic agonists stimulate glycoprotein secretion in humans in vitro (9, 68), as they do in other species (13). The evidence that these cholinergic effects are, at least in part, due to glandular secretions derives from two sources. First, histologic studies following vagal stimulation show a decrease in glycoprotein primarily in the submucosal glands (both mucous and serous cells) (20, 23). Second, using a new technique that we have developed to visualize secretions from gland duct openings in vivo, we showed that stimulation of the efferent vagus nerves causes localized fluid accumulation above the gland ducts (52).

Stimulation of cough receptors in the trachea and bronchi with ammonia increases tracheal mucus output reflexly via parasympathetic efferent pathways, but stimulation of irritant receptors in peripheral airways does not (58). It is postulated that stimulation of the cough reflex has the following reflex components: (a) expulsive expiration; (b) narrowing of large bronchi and trachea, perhaps increasing shear rates in airways during cough; and (c) mucus secretion, thus increasing the mucus barrier and perhaps also increasing the effectiveness of removal of the foreign irritant during cough (58). It is interesting that cough receptors, submucosal glands, and sites of airway compression during cough have a similar distribution! Stimulation of other pulmonary receptors has no apparent effect on tracheal mucus secretion (58). In cats, irritation of the nose, pharynx, or larynx also reflexly increases mucus secretion, partly via parasympathetic efferent nerves (58). Chemicals given to the stomach increase the output of respiratory tract fluid, but the efferent pathways are not known (55).

Direct sympathetic nervous regulation of submucosal glands is less certain. The presence of dense-cored vesicles in nerve fibers near human submucosal gland cells is suggestive of an efferent adrenergic innervation (48), but the evidence concerning the existence of these fibers is conflicting (8). No adrenergic effect on airway mucus secretion could be shown in several species (11, 13, 59, 68), but some of these findings may be due to inadequate knowledge of anatomy or to species variations. Thus, the lack of an effect of electrical stimulation of the cervical sympathetic nerves on tracheal mucus in rabbits and guinea pigs could be due to the fact that the main sympathetic nerve supply to the trachea usually derives from the stellate ganglia; or it could be due to the fact that these species contain little "mucus-secreting tissue" (11). In cats, electrical stimulation of the stellate ganglia increases tracheal mucus secretion via a β-adrenergic action (23). Irritation of the nose, pharynx, or larynx also increases tracheal mucus secretion in cats, partly via sympathetic pathways (58). Similarly, adrenergic agonists stimulate mucus secretion in cats in vivo via a β-adrenergic action (23), while in vitro studies suggest an additional α-adrenergic action (B. Davis, R. J. Phipps, J. A. Nadel, unpublished). It may be that specific adrenergic agonists stimulate receptors in different cells, some responsible for volume secretion and others for the secretion of concentrated mucoproteins. This could explain the finding that a specific β_2-agonist produced secretions with normal viscosity, whereas other β-agonists produced secretions with increased viscosity (47). Could the higher death rate in asthmatic patients associated with the use of high doses of nonspecific β-agonists have been caused by the production of viscid mucus, with subsequent plugging of airways (56, 66)?

Epithelial Cells

Two epithelial cell types in the airway are sources of glycoproteins: goblet cells and epithelial serous cells. The goblet cells resemble the goblet cells of the intestine and the mucous cells of the airway submucosal glands. They are found mainly in the trachea and bronchi, decrease in number toward the periphery, and are infrequent in bronchioles. Goblet cells are numerous in several species, including humans (76), cats (20, 23), pigs (6), and geese (59), but are sparse in other species, such as rabbits, guinea pigs (45) and healthy rats (32).

Epithelial serous cells resemble serous cells of the airway submucosal glands. Their distribution is similar to that of goblet cells, and they have so far been found in the airway of humans (33), cats (30), and geese (59). A third secretory cell type, the Clara cell, is found in several species, mainly in the bronchioles (12). Whether they secrete lipid or protein is unclear. They may have the capacity to produce either lipid or glycoprotein depending upon environmental conditions: Airway irritation with smoke or SO_2 induces transitions of Clara cells to goblet cells and stimulates the production of glycoprotein by these cells (33). A sulfated glycoprotein has been shown to line the luminal surface of airway ciliated cells, including the cilia, in humans and dogs (67), and in cats and geese (30, 56). Its chemical composition is different from that of submucosal gland glycoproteins; it is probably secreted from epithelial cells (22, 24).

Evidence for an innervation of epithelial secretory cells is conflicting, and there is probably much species variation. Specific acetylcholinesterase staining shows cholinergic efferent fibers in the epithelia of pigs (40): Specific immunofluorescent staining shows adrenergic efferent fibers in the epithelia of pigs (40) and rats (79). Efferent nerve profiles have been observed in the airway epithelia of rats (31) and geese (59): In both these species fibers containing agranular vesicles and fibers containing dense-cored vesicles were found. Some of these fibers in both species were observed near secretory cells. The presence of a cholinergic innervation of epithelial secretory cells in geese (a species with only epithelial secretory cells and no submucosal glands) is confirmed by the finding that tracheal mucus secretion increased following parasympathetic nerve stimulation (59).

Effects of Irritants

Acute administration of irritant agents to the airways, including organic vapors (10), ammonia, cigarette smoke, and CS solution (0-chlorobenzilidine malononitrile) (62), increases airway mucus secretion. Inhaled ammonia vapor and cigarette smoke stimulate secretion from both epithelial secretory cells and submucosal glands, and cause release of a surface muco-substance (30, 56). These irritants act partly through reflex neural pathways (perhaps involving stimulation of cough receptors) and partly through a direct effect: The reflex stimulation probably causes secretion from the submucosal glands, and the direct stimulation probably causes secretion from the mucosal cells (56, 62). The mechanism of this direct effect is not clear, but it may involve prostaglandins as intermediaries (62). Chronic administration of SO_2 (32) or cigarette smoke (34) to the airways increases airway mucus secretion and produces goblet cell hyperplasia, transformation of epithelial cells, and enlargement of submucosal glands.

Effects of Drugs

Various pharmacologic mediators affect mucus secretion. Histamine, a putative mediator in asthma, stimulated mucus secretion in cats and geese in vivo (62), but had no effect in vitro either in dogs (13) or in humans (68). The discrepancies could be due to species differences. Local application of prostaglandin $(PG)E_1$ stimulated mucus secretion in various airways of cats (62) and rats (29); also, $PGF_{2\alpha}$ when given locally stimulated mucus secretion in cats (62), and when inhaled as an aerosol induced sputum production in healthy humans (37). $PGF_{2\alpha}$ stimulates cough receptors, and since part of the effect of this drug on bronchomotor tone is mediated by cholinergic efferent pathways (75), the secretory effects of $PGF_{2\alpha}$ could similarly be mediated partly via cholinergic efferent pathways, although a direct effect cannot be excluded. Tissue inflammation causes local PG release, and such release could account for the increase in mucus secretion found in inflammatory airway diseases. Basic polypeptides (including kallidin and substance P) increased tracheal glycoprotein secretion in dogs in vitro, while a kalladin antagonist (hexadrimethrine) decreased it (5). Local application of the anesthetic lidocaine to the tracheas of cats or geese not only blocked the responses to known secretogogues, but also stimulated glycoprotein secretion directly (56, 59). The mechanisms of these actions are unknown but may involve the displacement of calcium ions from extra- and intracellular binding sites (56).

ACTIVE ION TRANSPORT

Since water plays such an important role in the formation of the respiratory tract secretions, we hypothesized that the regulation of water movement into the airway lumen might be important in determining the physical properties of the mucus layer and the rate of its movement up the airway by the cilia (51). Therefore, we sought methods for the study of water movement across the airway epithelium. It is generally accepted (28) that water crosses absorptive (14, 17, 64) and secretory (18, 69) epithelia as a result of local osmotic gradients created by active ion transport. To investigate ionic fluxes in airway epithelia, we used Ussing's short-circuit current method (71) and pieces of epithelium from the posterior membranous part of dog tracheas. We found a net flux of Cl^- toward the lumen and a smaller net flux of Na^+ toward the submucosa; these net fluxes accounted for the measured short-circuit current (53). Therefore, Cl^- and Na^+ are actively transported across tracheal epithelium and may be the only actively transported ions. Our findings have been confirmed subsequently in dogs (2), and suggestive evidence has been provided that Cl^- and Na^+ are transported similarly in rabbits (46) and cats (57) and that Cl^- is actively transported toward the lumen in rats (39). Evidence presented for active K^+ transport in rabbits (46) is unconvincing.

Submucosal gland cells and surface epithelial cells may both be involved in active ion transport. However, since rabbits have no tracheal submucosal glands but their tracheas actively transport Cl^- and Na^+, the sites of active ion movement in this species must be in the surface epithelial cells. Active secretion of Cl^- may be a property of all epithelial tissues derived from the primitive foregut, since it occurs in the amphibian (27) and mammalian (35) stomach, the mammalian esophagus (60), and the amphibian (25) and mammalian (54) lung.

Furosemide reduced net Cl^- movement toward the lumen when added to the submucosal side, but not when added to the luminal side of the tracheal epithelium (16). Ouabain was bound to more sites on the submucosal membrane than on the luminal membrane of the tracheal epithelium (77); this binding is presumably to Na^+-K^+ATPase (4, 77), the sodium pump. These findings suggest that active Cl^- and active Na^+ transport occur at the submucosal membrane. Cl^- and Na^+ transport are interdependent, since net Cl^- movement is greatly reduced by replacement of Na^+ in the bathing solution [(2, 43); J. H. Widdicombe, personal communication], and by adding ouabain, an inhibitor of sodium pumps, to the submucosal bathing solution (2, 77). In one experimental model for the link between Na^+ and Cl^- movement, Cl^- enters the cells by a Na^+-linked system across the submucosal membranes, the transmembrane Na^+ gradient providing the energy for active accumulation of Cl^- by the cells. The Na^+ entering with the Cl^- is pumped back to the submucosa by basolaterally placed Na^+ pumps, while the Cl^- diffuses down an electrochemical gradient across the luminal surfaces of the cells. The energy for Cl^- secretion is thus provided by the transmembrane Na^+ gradient and ultimately therefore by the Na^+ pump (J. H. Widdicombe, personal communication).

The electrical resistances and the spontaneous electrical potential differences across epithelia correlate well with physical parameters such as permeability to electrolytes, hydraulic conductivity, and the ability of epithelia to maintain an osmotic gradient (21). Airway epithelia of different species have electrical resistances about 300 ohm cm^2 and a range of spontaneous electrical potential differences between 20 and 60 mV. This classifies them as "tight junction" epithelia and implies that, relative to "leaky junction" epithelia (e.g. rat jejunum), they are less permeable to electrolytes, are poor conductors of water, and can maintain large transepithelial osmotic gradients.

Two patterns of electrical potential differences across the luminal and submucosal membranes of rabbit tracheal epithelial cells have been observed from intracellular recordings. One group found some cells with the inside negative to both the luminal surface and the submucosal surface, and other cells with the inside positive to the luminal surface and negative to the submucosal surface (26). Another group found only cells with the inside negative to both the luminal surface and the submucosal surface, and they attributed the potential differences to the following differences in the permeabilities of each cell membrane to electrolytes: In the luminal membrane the permeability to $Cl^- > SO_4^{2-} > Na^+ > K^+$, and in the submucosal membrane the permeability to $K^+ > Na^+ > Cl^- > SO_4^{2-}$ (46). Further studies of the intracellular distribution of ions and the associated electrical potentials should help to determine the role of active ion transport in transmembrane water movement.

We studied the effects of drugs that mimic the actions of the autonomic nervous system, and the effects of mediators on active ion transport across pieces of tracheal epithelium mounted in Ussing chambers. Acetylcholine increased net movement of Cl^- and Na^+ toward the canine tracheal lumen. The electrical resistance of the tissue was unchanged, and most of the increase of ion movement was electrically neutral. The effect was prevented by small concentrations of atropine (41). Terbutaline, a specific β_2-adrenergic agonist, increased net movement of Cl^-, but not of Na^+, toward the tracheal lumen in dogs (15) and cats (57). The electrical potential difference increased despite a fall in electrical resistance of the tissue. Propranolol prevented the effects in dogs. The effects of epinephrine (3) were similar to those of terbutaline. Also, terbutaline given intravenously to dogs increased the potential difference between a fluid-filled tracheal segment in situ and the paratracheal fascia (B. Davis, M. G. Marin, J. A. Nadel, unpublished). Phenylephrine, a specific α-adrenergic agonist, increased net movement of Cl^- and Na^+ toward the tracheal lumen in cats (B. Davis, R. J. Phipps, J. A. Nadel, unpublished). The major effect was stimulation of Na^+ secretion into the lumen, which was measured under open-circuit conditions. Since phenylephrine had no effect on the electrical properties of the posterior membranous part of tracheal epithelium in dogs (B. Davis, M. G. Marin,

J. A. Nadel, unpublished), the marked effect on the anterior portion of tracheal epithelium in cats may indicate either a species difference or an effect on submucosal glands, which are abundant in the anterior part of cat tracheas and sparse in the posterior membranous part of dog tracheas.

Histamine increased net movement of Cl^- and Na^+ toward the tracheal lumen. The increase in total ion transport was dose-related and could be prevented by an H_1-antagonist, but not by an H_2-antagonist (42). The electrical potential difference was increased despite a small decrease in tissue resistance. Thus, the effects of autonomic agonists and mediators on the output of respiratory tract secretions could be due in part to their effects on ion transport.

SUMMARY

The output of secretions from the airway submucosal glands is regulated by vagal efferent nerves. Stimulation of cough receptors increases mucus output reflexly via the vagus nerves. Adrenergic agonists increase submucosal gland secretions in some species, which indicates that adrenergic receptors are present in these cells. However, evidence for adrenergic nervous pathways to the glands is limited. Irritants and drugs stimulate secretion from epithelial cells by direct effects. There is also evidence that the secretion of epithelial cells can be stimulated by parasympathetic nervous pathways in birds but not in mammals. Active ion transport of Cl^- toward the lumen and of Na^+ toward the submucosa results in net ion movement toward the airway lumen in unstimulated tracheal epithelia. Drugs and mediators increase the net movement of ions toward the lumen. No agents have yet been found that increase net ion movement toward the submucosa. The link between ion transport and water secretion in airway epithelia, although speculative, seems likely in view of the evidence from other epithelia. Since airway epithelium is a "tight junction" epithelium, modification of the tight junctions may alter the transepithelial movement of water and ions. We suggest that the depth and consistency of the periciliary layer of airway secretions determine the ability of the cilia to propel the mucoprotein gel and thereby modify mucociliary transport. To achieve this, secretion of mucus must be controlled separately from the secretion of water. Studies are needed to determine which of the specialized functions of the epithelial cells interact to regulate the clearance of secretions from the airway. Is the sol maintained by secretion and reabsorption of fluid across the epithelium? Does the sol move with the gel by ciliary action or does it remain stationary? Do changes in the epithelial tight junctions influence net water movement and thus indirectly alter the depth of the sol layer? To answer these questions, techniques are needed to study subunits of the airway, including isolated surface cells and submucosal glands; and sensitive methods are required to analyze the very small samples of secretions for glycoprotein and electrolyte content. Intracellular measurements of electrolyte concentrations and electrical potentials may help to elucidate the mechanisms of transepithelial ion and water movement.

The control system for the production and removal of respiratory tract secretions may be altered in disease. For instance, chronic stimulation of cough receptors causes reflex secretion and may be the cause of the hyperplasia of submucosal glands and of the abnormal secretions that occur in chronic bronchitis and asthma (50, 58). The abnormally viscid mucus in cystic fibrosis may be due to a defect in Cl⁻ transport, which provides too little water for both the gel and sol layers. These speculations are intended to identify areas for further research, which hopefully will reduce the morbidity and mortality in these common lung diseases.

ACKNOWLEDGMENTS

We thank Ms. Linda Morehead and Mrs. Beth Cost for typing and preparation of the manuscript, and Mr. Robert W. Surface for medical illustration. During the preparation of this review, Dr. Davis was supported by Young Investigator Research Award HL-21150 from the National Heart, Lung and Blood Institute. Some of the reported studies were supported by grants from the U.S. Public Health Service: Program Project HL-06285 and Pulmonary SCOR Grant HL-19156, and in part by a grant from the Cystic Fibrosis Foundation.

Literature Cited

1. Adams, G. K., Aharonson, E. F., Reasor, M. J., Proctor, D. F. 1976. Collection of normal canine tracheobronchial secretions. *J. Appl. Physiol.* 40:247–49
2. Al-Bazzaz, F., Al-Awqati, Q. 1977. Characteristics of ion transport in canine tracheal epithelia. *Fed. Proc.* 36(3):479 (Abstr.)
3. Al-Bazzaz, F. J., Khan, A., Cheng, E. 1977. Stimulation of chloride secretion across canine tracheal epithelia by theophylline and epinephrine. *Clin. Res.* 25:414A (Abstr.)
4. Al-Bazzaz, F. J., Westenfelder, C., Earnest, W., Kurtzman, N. 1977. Characterization of canine tracheal epithelium Na-K-ATPase. *Clin. Res.* 25:413A (Abstr.)
5. Baker, A. P., Hillegass, L. M., Holden, D. A., Smith, W. J. 1977. Effect of kallidin, substance P, and other basic polypeptides on the production of respiratory macromolecules. *Am. Rev. Resp. Dis.* 115:811–17
6. Baskerville, A. 1970. Ultrastructure of the bronchial epithelium of the pig. *Zentralbl. Vet. Med.* 17:796–802
7. Baskerville, A. 1976. Animal model of human disease: chronic bronchitis. *Am. J. Pathol.* 82:237–40
8. Bensch, K. G., Gordon, G. B., Miller, L. R. 1965. Studies on the bronchial counterpart of the Kulchitsky (argentaffin) cell and innervation of bronchial glands. *J. Ultrastruct. Res.* 12:668–86
9. Boat, T. F., Kleinerman, J. I. 1975. Human respiratory tract secretions. 2. Effect of cholinergic and adrenergic agents on in vitro release of protein and mucous glycoprotein. *Chest* 67:(2 Suppl.) 32S–34S
10. Boyd, E. M. 1972. *Respiratory Tract Fluid,* Springfield, Ill.: Charles C. Thomas. 321 pp.

11. Boyd, E. M., Jackson, S., Ronan, M. 1943. The effect of sympathomimetic amines upon the output of respiratory tract fluid in rabbits. *Am. J. Physiol.* 138:565–68

12. Breeze, R. G., Wheeldon, E. B. 1977. The cells of the pulmonary airways. *Am. Rev. Resp. Dis.* 116:705–77

13. Chakrin, L. W., Baker, A. P., Christian, P., Wardell, J. R. 1973. Effect of cholinergic stimulation on the release of macromolecules by canine trachea *in vitro. Am. Rev. Resp. Dis.* 108:69–76

14. Curran, P. F., MacIntosh, J. R. 1962. A model system for biological water transport. *Nature* 193:347–48

15. Davis, B., Marin, M. G., Nadel, J. A. 1975. β-adrenergic receptor in canine tracheal epithelium. *Am. Rev. Resp. Dis.* 111:947 (Abstr.)

16. Davis, B., Marin, M. G., Ueki, I., Nadel, J. A. 1977. Effect of furosemide on chloride ion transport and electrical properties of canine tracheal epithelium. *Clin. Res.* 25:132 (Abstr.)

17. Diamond, J. M., Bossert, W. H. 1967. Standing gradient osmotic flow: A mechanism for coupling of water and solute transport in epithelia. *J. Gen. Physiol.* 50:2061–83

18. Diamond, J. M., Bossert, W. H. 1968. Functional consequences of ultrastructural geometry in "backwards" fluid-transporting epithelia. *J. Cell Biol.* 37:694–702

19. El-Bermani, Al-W. I., Grant, M. 1975. Acetylcholinesterase-positive nerves of the rhesus monkey bronchial tree. *Thorax* 30:162–70

20. Florey, H., Carleton, H. M., Wells, A. Q. 1932. Mucus secretion in the trachea. *Br. J. Exp. Pathol.* 13:269–84

21. Frömter, E., Diamond, J. 1972. Route of passive ion permeation in epithelia. *Nature New Biol.* 235:9–13

22. Gallagher, J. T., Hall, R. L., Jeffery, P. K., Phipps, R. J., Richardson, P. S. 1977. The nature and origin of tracheal secretions released in response to pilocarpine and ammonia. *J. Physiol. London* 275:36–37P (Abstr.)

23. Gallagher, J. T., Kent, P. W., Passatore, M., Phipps, R. J., Richardson, P. S. 1975. The composition of tracheal mucus, and the nervous control of its secretion in the cat. *Proc. R. Soc. London Ser. B.* 192:49–76

24. Gallagher, J. T., Kent, P. W., Phipps, R. J., Richardson, P. S. 1977. Influence of pilocarpine and ammonia vapor on the secretion and structure of cat tracheal mucins: differentiation of goblet and submucosal gland cell secretions. In *Mucus in Health and Disease,* ed. M. Elstein, D. V. Parke, pp. 91–102. London: Plenum. 558 pp.

25. Gatzy, J. T. 1975. Ion transport across the excised bullfrog lung. *Am. J. Physiol.* 228:1162–71

26. Hakansson, C. H., Toremalm, N. G. 1966. Studies on the physiology of the trachea. II. Electrical potential gradients within the tracheal wall. *Ann. Otol. Rhinol. Laryngol.* 75:33–47

27. Hogben, C. A. M. 1955. Active transport of chloride by isolated frog gastric epithelium. Origin of the gastric mucosal potential. *Am. J. Physiol.* 180:641–49

28. House, C. R. 1974. *Water Transport in Cells and Tissues.* London: Edward Arnold. 562 pp.

29. Iravani, J., Melville, G. N. 1975. Mucociliary activity in the respiratory tract as influenced by prostaglandin E_1. *Respiration* 32:305–15

30. Jeffery, P. K. 1978. Structure and function of mucus-secreting cells of cat and goose airway epithelium. In *CIBA Symposium Respiratory Tract Mucus,* pp. 5–23. Amsterdam: Elsevier. 334 pp.

31. Jeffery, P. K., Reid, L. 1973. Intra-epithelial nerves in normal rat airways: a quantitative electron microscopic study. *J. Anat.* 114:35–45

32. Jeffery, P. K., Reid, L. 1975. New observations of rat airway epithelium: a quantitative and electron microscopic study. *J. Anat.* 120:295–320

33. Jeffery, P. K., Reid, L. 1977. The respiratory mucous membrane. In *Respiratory Defense Mechanisms,* ed. J. D. Brain, D. F. Proctor, L. Reid, pp. 193–245. New York: Marcel Dekker. 488 pp.

34. Jones, R., Bolduc, P., Reid, L. 1973. Goblet cell glycoprotein and tracheal gland hypertrophy in rat airways: the effect of tobacco smoke with or without the anti-inflammatory agent phenylmethyloxadiazole. *Br. J. Exp. Pathol.* 54:229–39

35. Kitahara, S. 1967. Active transport of Na^+ and Cl^- by *in vitro* nonsecreting cat gastric mucosa. *Am. J. Physiol.* 213:819–23

36. Litt, M. 1973. Basic concepts of mucus rheology. *Bull. Physio-Pathol. Resp.* 9:33–46

37. Lopez-Vidriero, M. T., Reid, L. 1978. Bronchial mucus in health and disease. *Br. Med. Bull.* 34:63–74

38. Lucas, M. A., Douglas, L. C. 1934. Principles underlying ciliary activity in

the respiratory tract. II. A comparison of nasal clearance in man, monkey and other mammals. *Arch. Otolaryngol.* 20:518–41

39. Mangos, J. A. 1976. Fluxes of electrolytes and water in rat trachea. *Cystic Fibrosis* 15:17 (Abstr.)

40. Mann, S. P. 1971. The innervation of mammalian bronchial smooth muscle: the localization of catecholamines and cholinesterases. *Histochem. J.* 3:319–31

41. Marin, M. G., Davis, B., Nadel, J. A. 1976. Effect of acetylcholine on Cl⁻ and Na⁺ fluxes across dog tracheal epithelium *in vitro. Am. J. Physiol.* 231: 1546–49

42. Marin, M. G., Davis, B., Nadel, J. A. 1977. Effect of histamine on electrical and ion transport properties of tracheal epithelium. *Am. J. Physiol.* 42:735–38

43. Marin, M. G., Zaremba, M. M. 1978. Influence of Na⁺ on stimulation of net Cl⁻ flux by acetylcholine and terbutaline in dog tracheal epithelium. *Fed. Proc.* 37(3):514 (Abstr.)

44. Masson, P. L., Heremans, J. F. 1973. Sputum proteins. In *Sputum, Fundamentals and Clinical Pathology,* ed. M. Dulfano, pp. 412–75. Springfield, Ill.: Charles C. Thomas. 632 pp.

45. Mawdsley-Thomas, L. E., Healey, P., Barry, D. H. 1971. Experimental bronchitis in animals due to sulphur dioxide and cigarette smoke. An automated quantitative study. In *Inhaled Particles III* Vols. 1, 2, ed. W. H. Walton, pp. 509–26. London: Unwin. 1090 pp.

46. Melon, J. 1968. Activité sécrétoire de la muqueuse nasale. *Acta Otorhinolaryngol. Belg.* 22:11–244

47. Melville, G. N., Horstmann, G., Iravani, J. 1976. Adrenergic compounds and the respiratory tract. A physiological and electron-microscopical study. *Respiration* 33:261–69

48. Meyrick, B., Reid, L. 1970. Ultrastructure of cells in the human bronchial submucosal glands. *J. Anat.* 107:281–99

49. Meyrick, B., Sturgess, J. M., Reid, L. 1969. A reconstruction of the duct system and secretory tubules of the human bronchial submucosal gland. *Thorax* 24:729–36

50. Nadel, J. A. 1977. Autonomic control of airway smooth muscle and airway secretions. *Am. Rev. Resp. Dis.* 115: (Suppl.) 117–26

51. Nadel, J. A., Davis, B. 1977. Autonomic regulation of mucus secretion and ion transport in airways. In *Asthma II,* ed. K. F. Austen, L. M. Lichten-

stein, pp. 197–210. New York: Academic. 414 pp.

52. Nadel, J. A., Davis, B. 1978. Regulation of Na and Cl transport and mucous gland secretion in airway epithelium. See Ref. 30, pp. 133–47

53. Olver, R. E., Davis, B., Marin, M. G., Nadel, J. A. 1975. Active transport of Na⁺ and Cl⁻ across the canine tracheal epithelium *in vitro. Am. Rev. Resp. Dis.* 112:811–15

54. Olver, R. E., Strang, L. B. 1974. Ion fluxes across the pulmonary epithelium and the secretion of lung liquid in the foetal lamb. *J. Physiol. London* 241: 327–57

55. Perry, W. F., Boyd, E. M. 1941. A method for studying expectorant action in animals by direct measurement of the output of respiratory tract fluids. *J. Pharmacol. Exp. Ther.* 73:65–67

56. Phipps, R. J. 1977. *The control of tracheal mucin secretion.* Ph D Thesis, London Univ., England. 341 pp.

57. Phipps, R., Davis, B., Nadel, J. A. 1978. Effect of terbutaline on mucin secretion in cat airway using a new *in vitro* method. *Fed. Proc.* 37(3):221 (Abstr.)

58. Phipps, R. J., Richardson, P. S. 1976. The effects of irritation at various levels of the airway upon tracheal mucus secretion in the cat. *J. Physiol. London* 261:563–81

59. Phipps, R. J., Richardson, P. S., Corfield, A., Gallagher, J. T., Jeffery, P. K., Kent, P. W., Passatore, M. 1977. A physiological, biochemical and histological study of goose tracheal mucin and its secretion. *Philos. Trans. R. Soc. London Ser. B.* 279:513–43

60. Powell, D. W., Morris, S. M., Boyd, D. D. 1975. Water and electrolyte transport by rabbit esophagus. *Am. J. Physiol.* 229:438–43

61. Proctor, D. F. 1977. The upper airway, I. Nasal physiology and defense of the lungs. *Am. Rev. Resp. Dis.* 115:97–129

62. Richardson, P. S., Phipps, R. J., Balfre, K., Hall, R. 1978. The roles of mediators, irritants and allergens in causing mucin secretion from the trachea. See Ref. 30, pp. 111–31

63. Satir, P. 1974. The present status of the sliding microtubule model of ciliary motion. In *Cilia and Flagella,* ed. M. A. Sleigh, pp. 131–42. London and New York: Academic 500 pp.

64. Schultz, S. G. 1977. The role of paracellular pathways in isotonic fluid transport. *Yale J. Biol. Med.* 50:99–113

65. Silberberg, A., Meyer, F. A., Gilboa, A., Gelman, R. A. 1977. Function and

properties of epithelial mucus. See Ref. 24 pp. 171–80

66. Speizer, F. E., Doll, R., Heaf, P., Strang, L. B. 1968. Investigation into use of drugs preceding death in asthma. Br. Med. J. 1:335–39

67. Spicer, S. S., Chakrin, L. W., Wardell, J. R., Kendrick, W. 1971. Histochemistry of mucosubstances in the canine and human respiratory tract. Lab. Invest. 25:483–90

68. Sturgess, J., Reid, L. 1972. An organ culture study of the effect of drugs on the secretory activity of the human bronchial submucosal gland. Clin. Sci. 43:533–43

69. Swanson, C. H. 1977. Isotonic water transport in secretory epithelia. Yale J. Biol. Med. 50:153–63

70. Thurlbeck, W. M., Benjamin, B., Reid, L. 1961. Development and distribution of mucous glands in the foetal human trachea. Br. J. Dis. Chest 55:54–64

71. Ussing, H. H., Zerahn, K. 1951. Active transport of sodium as the source of electric current in the short-circuited isolated frog skin. Acta Physiol. Scand. 23:110–27

72. Walsh, C., McLelland, J. 1974. The ultrastructure of the avian extrapulmo-

nary respiratory epithelium. Acta Anat. 89:412–22

73. Wanner, A. 1977. Clinical aspects of mucociliary transport. Am. Rev. Resp. Dis. 116:73–125

74. Wardell, J. R. Jr., Chakrin, L. W., Payne, B. J. 1970. The canine tracheal pouch: a model for use in respiratory mucus research. Am. Rev. Resp. Dis. 101:741–54

75. Wasserman, M. A. 1975. Bronchopulmonary responses to prostaglandin $F_{2\alpha}$, histamine and acetylcholine in the dog. Eur. J. Pharmacol. 32:146–55

76. Watson, J. H. L., Brinkman, G. L. 1964. Electron microscopy of the epithelial cells of normal and bronchitic human bronchus. Am. Rev. Resp. Dis. 90:851–66

77. Widdicombe, J. H., Yee, J. Y., Nadel, J. A. 1978. Site of Na-pumps in dog tracheal epithelium. Fed. Proc. 37(3):221 (Abstr.)

78. Yoneda, K. 1976. Mucous blanket of rat bronchus: an ultrastructural study. Am. Rev. Resp. Dis. 114:837–42

79. Zussman, W. V. 1966. Fluorescent localization of catecholamine stores in the rat lung. Anat. Rec. 156:19–30

Ann. Rev. Physiol. 1979. 41:383–95
Copyright © 1979 by Annual Reviews Inc. All rights reserved

FETAL AND NEONATAL PULMONARY CIRCULATION

♦1226

Abraham M. Rudolph

Cardiovascular Research Institute and the Departments of Pediatrics,
Physiology, and Obstetrics, Gynecology, and Reproductive Sciences,
University of California, San Francisco, California 94143

During fetal life, gas exchange is carried out in the placenta. The lung does not have a physiological role, apart from possible metabolic functions which include secretion of hormones, enzymatic conversion of inactive substances to functional hormones, and degradation of active materials to inactive metabolites. Blood flow through the lungs is quite low during fetal life; most of the systemic and umbilical venous blood returning to the heart is shunted through the foramen ovale to the left atrium and left ventricle, or through the ductus arteriosus directly from the pulmonary trunk to the descending aorta. About 85–90% of the blood ejected by the right ventricle is diverted from the lungs through the ductus arteriosus (48). Because the right ventricle ejects about 66% of the combined ventricular output of the fetal heart, about 60% of the total output of the heart passes through the ductus arteriosus and thus does not enter the lungs. Should this volume of blood pass through the pulmonary circulation and return to the left ventricle, there would be an unnecessary increase in the volume of work placed on the heart.

The low fetal pulmonary blood flow has been explained on the basis of a high pulmonary vascular resistance. After birth, however, a marked increase in pulmonary blood flow is necessary to permit adequate gas exchange. This review considers: (*a*) pulmonary arterial pressures and flows in utero and changes during gestation; (*b*) patterns of fetal pulmonary blood flow; (*c*) factors that influence fetal pulmonary vascular responses; and (*d*) mechanisms responsible for the postnatal decrease in pulmonary vascular resistance.

383

0066-4278/79/0301-0383$01.00

GESTATIONAL CHANGES

Until recently, measurements of fetal pulmonary arterial blood pressure and flow were obtained acutely in exteriorized fetal lambs or goats, after extensive surgical procedures and often under general anesthesia (3, 4). These measurements could not be considered to represent pressures and flows in undisturbed fetuses, particularly since the fetal pulmonary circulation is very labile. The authors reported that pulmonary arterial pressure was consistently higher than aortic pressure, with a systolic pressure difference of 10–15 mm Hg. In studies in chronically catheterized fetal lambs of 0.7–1.0 gestation, pulmonary arterial and aortic pressure levels were almost identical (40). It is reasonable to assume that these pressures are equal in younger fetal animals. Mean pulmonary arterial and aortic pressures increase progressively with gestational age; with amniotic cavity pressure as zero reference, pressures increased from approximately 30 mm Hg at 0.4 gestation to about 50 mm Hg at term (Figure 1) (40, 49). These pressures are considerably lower than those reported in acutely exteriorized fetal lambs (20).

Pulmonary blood flow has been measured by the radionuclide labeled microsphere technique (25, 50, 51) and by electromagnetic flowmeters in chronically instrumented fetal lambs (25, 40). Actual pulmonary blood flow increases from about 4 ml min^{-1} at 0.4 gestation to about 160 ml min^{-1} at

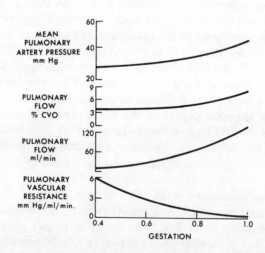

Figure 1 Diagrammatic representation of the changes in mean pulmonary arterial pressure, proportion of combined ventricular output (CVO) distributed to the lungs, actual pulmonary blood flow, and calculated pulmonary vascular resistance, in fetal lambs during gestational development from 0.4–1.0 gestation. [From (49)]

term (Figure 1). The combined ventricular output of the fetal lamb parallels changes in weight with intrauterine growth, and from 0.4–1.0 gestation, mean combined ventricular output is about 475 ml min^{-1} kg^{-1}. The proportion of cardiac output distributed to the lung is 3–4% from 0.4–0.7 gestation, but it increases progressively to 8–10% at term (51). Calculated pulmonary vascular resistance is extremely high at 6 mm Hg min^{-1} ml^{-1} at 0.4 gestation and falls progressively to 0.3–0.35 mm Hg min^{-1} ml^{-1} at term (Figure 1). This decrease in pulmonary vascular resistance represents a 17–20-fold increase in the cross-sectional area of the pulmonary vascular bed. It could result from a decrease in resting vascular constriction, or from an increase in individual vessel diameter, but probably is largely related to growth of new vessels, as discussed below.

PATTERNS OF PULMONARY FLOW

The velocity profiles of blood in the pulmonary trunk and pulmonary arteries have been recorded by chronically implanted cuff-type electromagnetic flow transducers (40, 53). The profile in the pulmonary trunk is similar to that seen in the main pulmonary artery after birth. Velocity rises rapidly in association with the rise of pulmonary arterial pressure, and, after reaching a peak, falls to reach zero coincident with the dicrotic notch; no flow is recorded during diastole. Flow in the pulmonary arteries commences with the rapid rise of pulmonary arterial pressure, reaches a peak early in systole, and then falls to zero in about the middle of systole. A pronounced reverse flow occurs in late systole and early diastole, after which there is zero flow to the onset of the next systole (Figure 2). The velocity pattern in the fetal pulmonary artery has been explained on the high (relative to systemic) pulmonary vascular resistance and the presence of the ductus arteriosus. During early systole, when blood is ejected at high velocity, blood flows through the large pulmonary arteries and through the peripheral pulmonary vessels. As velocity falls, blood flows preferentially through the ductus arteriosus to the descending aorta; since peripheral pulmonary vascular resistance is high, reverse flow is recorded as blood flows from the large pulmonary arteries through the ductus arteriosus in association with elastic recoil of these vessels (49). This concept is supported by observations of the effects of changing pulmonary vascular resistance (40). When pulmonary vascular resistance is increased by inducing fetal hypoxia by administering low-oxygen gas mixtures to the ewe, the forward flow phase decreases and the magnitude and duration of recorded backflow increases. Conversely, when pulmonary vascular resistance is reduced by infusion of acetylcholine, forward flow increases in magnitude and extends throughout systole, whereas backflow is greatly reduced.

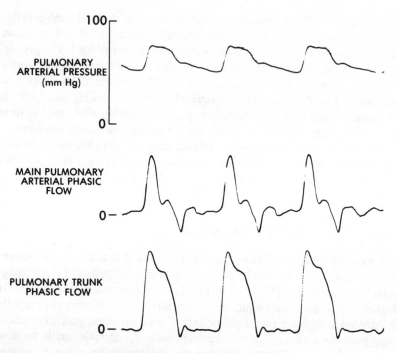

Figure 2 Recording of pulmonary arterial pressure, pulmonary arterial flow contour, and pulmonary trunk flow pattern in a fetal lamb with chronically implanted intravascular catheters and electromagnetic flow transducers. Forward flow occurs only in the early part of systole in the pulmonary artery, followed by rapid return to zero flow and then a pronounced backflow. In pulmonary trunk, representing right ventricular outflow, there is continuous forward flow throughout the whole of systole.

MORPHOLOGICAL FEATURES

The high pulmonary vascular resistance during fetal life and the greater vasomotor responsiveness in the lung as compared with adult animals have been explained by the greater muscularity of the arteries (16, 47). Earlier studies suggested that there was an extension of muscle into more distal pulmonary arteries as gestation advanced (47, 62) and that the area of muscle in the walls of vessels less than 50 μm diameter increased in the latter half of gestation (44). Recently, in fetal lungs in which the pulmonary circulation was distended to achieve pressures similar to those present during fetal life, it has been shown that there is no change in the thickness of the medial muscular layers in the small pulmonary arteries in human (28) or lamb (39). In the lamb lungs, there is a marked increase in the wall thickness as a percentage of vessel diameter at the fifth and sixth generation, designating the left and right main branches as second generation vessels. The external diameter of these vessels ranges from 20–50 μm, and the medial layer is constituted almost entirely of smooth muscle; they appear to account for the major resistance to flow through the lungs. The thickness of the muscle layers in small fetal pulmonary arteries is increased by prolonged hypoxia of maternal rats (24). In fetal lambs, systemic arterial hypertension (resulting from either unilateral renal constriction or umbilical arterial constriction), and pulmonary arterial hypertension (produced by constriction of the ductus arteriosus) are also associated with increased thickness of smooth muscle in resistance vessels of the lung (38). Ingestion of prostaglandin synthetase inhibitors by pregnant women has been reported to be associated with the presence of increased pulmonary vascular smooth muscle development (37). It has been suggested that this may be due to constriction of the ductus arteriosus in the fetus, which results in pulmonary arterial hypertension (26), but a direct effect on pulmonary vessels cannot be excluded.

The pulmonary vessels rapidly lose the medial smooth muscle layer after birth (19, 61, 62). However, the muscle-layer thickness in the small vessels may increase again with pulmonary hypertension. Exposure of rats to a decreased oxygen environment for two weeks resulted in an increase in vessel-wall thickness (29). Furthermore, there is evidence that new muscle may develop in peripheral nonmuscular vessels as the result of differentiation of cells that are normally present in the vessel wall—the *pericytes* of nonmuscular arteries—and intermediate cells of partially muscular arteries (43). After return to normal oxygen levels, the vessel thickness decreased, but there was also a reduction in the total number of small vessels in the lung (30). It has been suggested that there may be a permanent reduction in the number of small vessels with a restricted cross-sectional area of the pulmonary vascular bed.

FACTORS AFFECTING FETAL PULMONARY CIRCULATION

Although the high pulmonary vascular resistance during fetal life has been ascribed to the muscularity of the small pulmonary arteries, the mechanisms that maintain vasoconstriction in utero and permit rapid vasodilatation after birth are not fully understood. The pulmonary vasoconstriction in the fetal lung has been related to the low P_{O_2} of blood perfusing the lungs, to autonomic nervous influences, and to circulating hormones.

Effects of P_{O_2} and pH

The fetal pulmonary arterioles are exposed to the P_{O_2} of blood perfusing the lungs. Lung metabolism presumably results in some oxygen consumption so that the P_{O_2} influencing the small pulmonary vessels may be somewhat lower than that in pulmonary arterial blood. In the normal fetal lamb, with the ewe breathing room air, pulmonary arterial P_{O_2} is 18–21 torr as compared with a descending aortic P_{O_2} of 21–24 torr (52). Earlier studies showed that fetal hypoxia induced by umbilical cord compression or maternal hypoxia resulted in pulmonary vasoconstriction (10, 11, 18, 21, 58). The lambs were exteriorized and anesthetized in most studies; the pulmonary vasculature responses thus may have been altered markedly in these experimental circumstances. In a study in fetal lambs in utero, pulmonary blood flow, measured by the radioactive microsphere technique, fell to 50% of resting levels when aortic P_{O_2} was reduced to 12–24 torr (17). Since pulmonary arterial pressure also rose, this reflected an increase in pulmonary vascular resistance.

A more detailed study of the effects of hypoxia was made in fetal lambs with chronically implanted flow transducers around the pulmonary artery, distal to the pulmonary trunk. Fetal arterial P_{O_2} was reduced progressively by lowering the oxygen concentration in gas inspired by the ewe (40). Pulmonary vascular resistance increased with reduction in P_{O_2}, in a curvilinear fashion, with a progressively greater rise as P_{O_2} fell. Of great interest was the finding that the response to hypoxia increased in magnitude with advancing gestation; the curve became much steeper, so that small reductions of P_{O_2} resulted in more marked increases of pulmonary vascular resistance.

As mentioned above, there is no change in the morphology of the fifth and sixth generation resistance vessels over the latter half of gestation in fetal lambs. Since there was a greater percentage increase of pulmonary vascular resistance over control levels with hypoxia (40), it was suggested that the sensitivity of pulmonary vascular smooth muscle to hypoxia increases with advancing gestation.

PARASYMPATHETIC REGULATION   Injection or infusion of acetylcholine into the fetal pulmonary circulation results in dramatic vasodilatation (21), as does electrical stimulation of the cut end of the vagus nerve (18). In perfused lungs of fetal lambs with gestational ages of about 120 days (0.8) and 75–90 days (0.5–0.6) similar responses of pulmonary vascular resistance were noted (13, 14). With increasing gestation of fetal lambs in utero, however, a progressively greater reduction of pulmonary vascular resistance occurs with comparable doses of acetylcholine [based on fetal body weight (40)]. Similarly, a progressively greater fall in pulmonary arterial pressure with increasing fetal age was observed after acetylcholine injection (1).

Although cholinergic stimulation of the pulmonary vasculature has a dramatic effect in the fetus, parasympathetic nerves do not exert a significant effect on the fetus in utero. In exteriorized lambs, bilateral cervical vagotomy or atropine injection did not alter resting pulmonary vascular resistance (18), and atropine had no effect on the pulmonary circulation of fetal lambs in utero (40, 52).

SYMPATHETIC REGULATION Stimulation of both alpha- and beta-adrenergic receptor activity in fetal lambs results in pulmonary vascular responses. Methoxamine, an alpha stimulator, and norepinephrine, a predominantly alpha stimulator, increase pulmonary vascular resistance (5, 13, 14). Pulmonary vasoconstriction also results from electrical stimulation of the peripheral end of the cut thoracic sympathetic chain in fetal lambs (18). Isoproterenol, a beta stimulator, has a potent pulmonary vasodilator effect in exteriorized (13, 14, 57) as well as chronically instrumented fetal lambs (A. M. Rudolph, M. A. Heymann, unpublished observations). It does not appear, however, that the sympathetic nerves have a significant tonic effect on the resting fetal pulmonary circulation since administration of the beta-adrenergic blocker propranolol, or the alpha-adrenergic blockers phentolamine or dibenzyline, does not alter pulmonary vascular resistance (40).

Role of Hormones

The renin-angiotensin system is well developed in the fetus at an early period of gestation (56). Administration of angiotensin II results in general vasoconstriction, including the umbilical vessels (8), the peripheral circulation, and the pulmonary circulation (31). It had been demonstrated in isolated perfused rodent lungs that the presence of angiotensin II was necessary to elicit a vasoconstrictor response to hypoxia (7). This suggested the possibility that the high pulmonary vascular resistance in the fetus might result from potentiation of the response to the low pulmonary arterial P_{O_2} by local conversion of renin to angiotensin II in the lung. However, infusion of Saralasin, a competitive blocker of angiotensin II, in amounts that prevent the effects of infused angiotensin II, does not affect the pulmonary vascular resistance of fetal lambs in utero (31). Furthermore, it does not influence the pulmonary vasoconstrictor response to hypoxia.

Mechanisms of Pulmonary Vascular Response to Changes of P_{O_2}

Although it had been shown that fetal hypoxia results in pulmonary vasoconstriction, it was not clear whether this occurred exclusively as the direct effect of the low P_{O_2} in the lung or whether a reflex response resulting from chemoreceptor stimulation was also involved, or an hormonal response from circulating catecholamines. Vagotomy and thoracic sympathectomy did not inhibit hypoxic pulmonary vasoconstriction (18). Studies in twin lamb fetuses with cross-perfusion of the lung, however, suggested that the role of the sympathetic nervous system is related to gestational age (10, 11). When hypoxia was induced in the fetus whose lung was being infused from its twin, pulmonary vasoconstriction was not elicited in immature lambs (0.6 gestation) but did occur in mature lambs; the effect was abolished by section of the sympathetic nerves to the lung or by administering hexamethonium. These studies were performed acutely in anesthetized, exteriorized fetuses and are not borne out by observations in lambs in utero. Administration of phenoxybenzamine or phentolamine in doses that produce complete alpha-adrenergic blockade does not have any effect on the pulmonary vascular response to hypoxia (40). Similarly, the hypoxic response was not affected by beta-adrenergic blockade with propranolol or by parasympathetic blockade with atropine. It was also concluded that the sympathetic nervous system is not involved in hypoxic pulmonary vasoconstriction in newborn calves since pretreatment with reserpine did not affect the response (55).

MECHANISMS RESPONSIBLE FOR POSTNATAL PULMONARY VASODILATATION

Several studies have demonstrated conclusively that ventilation of the lungs with air results in a dramatic decrease in pulmonary vascular resistance. This work has been reviewed extensively (20, 54). In summary, it was shown that physical expansion of the lungs with gas produces a small drop in vascular resistance, but the main effect is related to the increased Po_2. An increase in Po_2 without the associated lung expansion was produced in two studies by placing the ewe in a hyperbaric oxygen environment. In one study pulmonary blood flow, as measured by electromagnetic flowmeter in acutely exteriorized lambs, increased (2); in the other, flows were measured in lambs in utero with the microsphere method and a marked drop in pulmonary vascular resistance was noted (27).

It is not known whether oxygen produces its dilator effect directly on the pulmonary vascular smooth muscle, or if it stimulates the release of a chemical mediator. Because kinin levels are high in the fetal circulation after birth, the possibility that kinins may be involved in the decrease in pulmonary vascular resistance after birth has been investigated in lambs (27). These studies were stimulated by the finding that bradykinin is a potent pulmonary vasodilator in the fetal lamb (12). When Po_2 was increased by ventilating the lungs of mature fetal lambs with oxygen, levels of kininogen, a bradykinin precursor, decreased and levels of bradykinin increased in blood that had passed through the lungs. The release of bradykinin in the lungs was not the result of physical expansion of the lungs alone, as ventilation of the lungs with nitrogen did not influence kininogen or kinin levels. A similar increase in kinin levels in fetal blood was noted when ewes were exposed to hyperbaric oxygen. Although kinins may be involved in the immediate pulmonary vasodilatation after birth, they do not appear to be important in maintaining the lowered pulmonary vascular resistance since blood kinin levels rapidly fall within the first hour after ventilation of fetal lambs. Kinin release may be a supplementary mechanism, in addition to direct vascular effects of oxygen or other mediators, in establishing pulmonary circulation in the immediate neonatal period.

PROSTAGLANDINS AND PERINATAL PULMONARY CIRCULATION

Prostaglandins of the E and F series have been shown to produce marked cardiovascular responses when injected into the circulation of animals or humans. E-series prostaglandins generally produce vasodilatation, whereas F-series prostaglandins tend to be vasoconstrictors (6, 9, 32–35). In the pulmonary circulation PGE_1 consistently results in a small decrease in pulmonary vascular resistance (32, 33), but PGE_2 has produced conflicting effects (35, 41, 45).

In acutely exteriorized fetal goats, infusion of PGE_1 consistently produced a marked decrease in pulmonary vascular resistance of the perfused left lower lobe by about 50% (15). In a similar experimental preparation in which the lungs were ventilated, PGE_1 produced a lesser effect on the pulmonary circulation of the ventilated newborn goat breathing room air, but when pulmonary vasoconstriction was induced by ventilation with an hypoxia-producing gas mixture, PGE_1 resulted in a marked fall in vascular resistance (60). When PGE_1 was infused before hypoxia was induced, the rise in pulmonary vascular resistance was almost completely prevented.

PGE_2 produced similar but considerably less dramatic effects (59, 60). In these studies, systemic vasodilatation was observed only when large amounts of PGE_1 were infused into the pulmonary artery. It was suggested that this was due to the degradation of the PGE_1 in its passage through the lung. In adults, almost all prostaglandins are metabolized as blood passes through the lung (23), and the fetal lung also has a high capacity to degrade prostaglandins (46). Infusion of PGE_1 into a peripheral pulmonary artery in fetal lambs in utero resulted in a 50% reduction of pulmonary vascular resistance but, as infusion rates were increased, the PGE_1 passed through the lungs and resulted in umbilical vasoconstriction. In newborn lambs in which the ductus had been ligated, PGE_1 had insignificant effects on the pulmonary vascular resistance during normoxia but produced pulmonary vasodilatation during hypoxia. The dose of PGE_1 required to produce this effect, however, consistently resulted in systemic vasodilatation (M. E. Tripp and associates, unpublished observations). The differences in these results could be explained by the type of experimental preparation, but it is possible that the fetal and neonatal lung does not have the degrading capability of the adult lung.

$PGF_{2\alpha}$ is a vasoconstrictor in the perfused lung of the fetal and neonatal goat (59). Infusion of the prostaglandin precursors arachidonic and diho-mo-γ-linolenic acid also produces pulmonary vasoconstriction, and this effect is blocked by prostaglandin synthetase inhibitors. The authors suggest that the pulmonary vascular response could not be explained by singular formation of E or F series prostaglandins because the pulmonary vasocon-striction is associated with systemic vasodilatation.

Distension of the lungs of adult animals results in release of prostaglan-dins (22), and the lungs produce E-series prostaglandins predominantly (42). The possibility that PGE_1 may be involved in the fall in pulmonary vascular resistance after birth has been examined in fetal and neonatal goats. In the acutely exteriorized fetal goat in which the left lower lobe pulmonary artery was perfused, administration of indomethacin, a prosta-glandin synthetase inhibitor, resulted in no change in pulmonary vascular resistance (36). The decrease in pulmonary vascular resistance following ventilation, however, was influenced. Two phases of pulmonary arterial pressure reduction were noted following ventilation. The initial rapid fall in pulmonary vascular resistance occurred within 30 seconds, and this result was not affected by indomethacin. The slower decline over the next 10–20 minutes was impaired by indomethacin; this effect was only slight in mature animals, but it was more pronounced in immature animals of less than 0.9 gestation. It was suggested that prostaglandin release was impor-tant in the pulmonary vasodilatation associated with ventilation of the fetal lungs with air.

Acknowledgment

The work reported from Dr. Rudolph's laboratory was supported by a grant from the U.S. Public Health Service: Program Project Grant HL-06285.

Literature Cited

1. Assali, N. S., Brinkman, C. R. III, Woods, J. R. Jr., Dandavino, A., Nuwayhid, B. 1977. Development of neurohumoral control of fetal, neonatal, and adult cardiovascular functions. *Am. J. Obstet. Gynecol.* 129:748–59

2. Assali, N. S., Kirschbaum, T. M., Dilts, P. V. Jr. 1968. Effects of hyperbaric oxygen on uteroplacental and fetal circulation. *Circ. Res.* 22:573–88

3. Assali, N. S., Morris, J. A., Smith, R. W., Munson, W. A. 1963. Studies on ductus arteriosus circulation. *Circ. Res.* 13:478–89

4. Assali, N. S., Selogal, N., Marable, S. 1962. Pulmonary and ductus arteriosus circulation in the fetal lamb before and after birth. *Am. J. Physiol.* 202:536–40

5. Barrett, C. T., Heymann, M. A., Rudolph, A. M. 1972. Alpha and beta adrenergic receptor activity in fetal sheep. *Am. J. Obstet. Gynecol.* 112:1114–21

6. Bergstrom, S., Carlson, L. A., Ekelund, L. G., Oro, L. 1965. Cardiovascular and metabolic response to infusion of prostaglandin E_1 and to simultaneous infusions of noradrenaline and prostaglandin E_1 in man. *Acta Physiol. Scand.* 64:332–39

7. Berkov, S. 1974. Hypoxic pulmonary vasoconstriction in the rat: The necessary role of angiotensin II. *Circ. Res.* 35:256–61

8. Berman, W. Jr., Goodlin, R. C., Heymann, M. A., Rudolph, A. M. 1978. Effects of pharmacologic agents on umbilical blood flow in fetal lambs in utero. *Biol. Neonate* 33(5–6):225–35

9. Bloor, C. M., White, F. C., Sobel, B. E. 1973. Coronary and systemic thermodynamic effects of prostaglandins in unanesthetized dog. *Cardiovasc. Res.* 7:156–66

10. Campbell, A. G. M., Cockburn, F., Dawes, G. S., Milligan, J. E. 1967. Pulmonary vasoconstriction in asphyxia during cross-circulation between twin foetal lambs. *J. Physiol. London* 192:111–21

11. Campbell, A. G. M., Dawes, G. S., Fishman, A. P., Hyman, A. I. 1967. Pulmonary vasconstriction and changes in heart rate during asphyxia in immature foetal lambs. *J. Physiol. London* 192:93–110

12. Campbell, A. G. M., Dawes, G. S., Fishman, A. P., Hyman, A. I., Perks, A. M. 1968. Release of a bradykinin-like pulmonary vasodilator substance in

foetal and newborn lambs. *J. Physiol. London* 195:83–96

13. Cassin, S., Dawes, G. S., Mott, J. C., Ross, B. B., Strang, L. B. 1964. The vascular resistance of the foetal and newly ventilated lung of the lamb. *J. Physiol. London* 171:61–79

14. Cassin, S., Dawes, G. S., Ross, B. B. 1964. Pulmonary blood flow and vascular resistance in immature foetal lambs. *J. Physiol. London* 171:80–89

15. Cassin, S., Tyler, T., Wallis, R. 1975. The effects of prostaglandin E_1 on fetal pulmonary vascular resistance (38588). *Proc. Soc. Exp. Biol. Med.* 148:584–87

16. Civin, W. R., Edwards, J. E. 1951. The postnatal structural changes in the intrapulmonary arteries and arterioles. *Arch. Pathol.* 51:192–200

17. Cohn, H. E., Sacks, E. J., Heymann, M. A., Rudolph, A. M. 1972. Cardiovascular responses to hypoxemia and acidemia in unanesthetized fetal lambs. *Am. J. Obstet. Gynecol.* 120(6):817–24

18. Colebatch, H. J. H., Dawes, G. S., Goodwin, J. W., Nadeau, R. A. 1965. The nervous control of the circulation in the foetal and newly expanded lungs of the lamb. *J. Physiol. London* 178:544–62

19. Davies, G., Reid, L. 1970. Growth of the alveoli and pulmonary arteries in childhood. *Thorax* 25:669–81

20. Dawes, G. 1968. *Fetal and Neonatal Physiology.* Chicago, Ill: Year Book Medical Publishers. p. 98

21. Dawes, G. S., Mott, J. C. 1962. The vascular tone of the foetal lung. *J. Physiol. London* 164:465–77

22. Edmonds, J. R., Berry, E., Wyllie, J. H. 1969. Release of prostaglandins caused by distension of the lungs. *Brit. J. Surg.* 56:622–23

23. Ferreira, S. H., Vane, J. R. 1967. Prostaglandins: their disappearance from and release into the circulation. *Nature* 216:868–73

24. Goldberg, S. J., Levy, R. A., Siassi, B., Betten, J. 1971. Effects of maternal hypoxia and hyperoxia upon the neonatal pulmonary vasculature. *Pediatrics* 48:528–33

25. Heymann, M. A., Creasy, R. K., Rudolph, A. M. 1973. Quantitation of blood flow pattern in the foetal lamb in utero. In *Proceedings of the Sir Joseph Barcroft Centenary Symposium: Foetal and Neonatal Physiology,* pp. 129–35. Cambridge, England: Cambridge University Press. 641 pp.

26. Heymann, M. A., Rudolph, A. M. 1976. Effects of acetylsalicylic acid on the ductus arteriosus and circulation in fetal lambs in utero. *Circ. Res.* 38: 418–22

27. Heymann, M. A., Rudolph, A. M., Nies, A. S., Melmon, K. L. 1969. Bradykinin production associated with oxygenation of the fetal lamb. *Circ. Res.* 25:521–34

28. Hislop, A., Reid, L. 1972. Intra-pulmonary arterial development during fetal life—branching pattern and structure. *J. Anat.* 113:35–48

29. Hislop, A., Reid, L. 1976. New findings in pulmonary arteries of rats with hypoxia-induced pulmonary hypertension. *Br. J. Exp. Pathol.* 57:542–54

30. Hislop, A., Reid, L. 1978. Changes in the pulmonary arteries of the rat during recovery from hypoxia-induced pulmonary hypertension. *Brit. J. Exp. Pathol.* In press

31. Hyman, A., Heymann, M. A., Levin, D. L., Rudolph, A. M. 1975. Angiotensin is not the mediator of hypoxia-induced pulmonary vasoconstriction in fetal lambs. *Circulation* 52:II–132 (Abstr.)

32. Kadowitz, P. J., Joiner, P. D., Hyman, A. L. 1974. Effects of prostaglandins E_1 and $F_{2\alpha}$ in the swine pulmonary circulation. *Proc. Soc. Exp. Biol. Med.* 145:53–56

33. Kadowitz, P. J., Joiner, P. D., Hyman, A. L. 1974. Influence of prostaglandins E_1 and $F_{2\alpha}$ on pulmonary vascular resistance in the sheep. *Proc. Soc. Exp. Biol. Med.* 145:1258–61

34. Kadowitz, P. J., Joiner, P. D., Hyman, A. L. 1975. Physiological and pharmacological roles of prostaglandins. *Ann. Rev. Pharmacol.* 15:255–306

35. Kadowitz, P. J., Joiner, P. D., Hyman, A. L. 1975. Effect of prostaglandin E_2 on pulmonary vascular resistance in intact dog, swine, and lamb. *Eur. J. Pharmacol.* 31:72–80

36. Leffler, C. W., Tyler, T. L., Cassin, S. 1978. Effect of indomethacin on pulmonary vascular response to ventilation of fetal goats. *Am. J. Physiol.* 234(4): H346–51

37. Levin, D., Fixler, D., Morriss, F. C., Tyson, J. 1978. Morphologic analysis of the pulmonary vascular bed in infants exposed in utero to prostaglandin synthetase inhibitors. *J. Pediatr.* 92:478

38. Levin, D. L., Hyman, A. I., Heymann, M. A., Rudolph, A. M. 1978. Fetal hypertension and the development of increased pulmonary vascular smooth

muscle: A possible mechanism for persistent pulmonary hypertension of the newborn infant. *J. Pediatr.* 92:265–69

39. Levin, D. L., Rudolph, A. M., Heymann, M. A., Phibbs, R. H. 1976. Morphological development of the pulmonary vascular bed in fetal lambs. *Circulation* 53:144–51

40. Lewis, A. B., Heymann, M. A., Rudolph, A. M. 1976. Gestational changes in pulmonary vascular responses in fetal lambs in utero. *Circ. Res.* 39:536–41

41. Mathews, C. S., Hyman, A. L., Joiner, P. D., Kadowitz, P. J. 1975. Effect of prostaglandin E_2 on pulmonary vascular resistance in the intact dog, swine, and lamb. *Clin. Res.* 23:54A (Abstr.)

42. McGiff, J. C., Itskovitz, H. D., Terragno, N. A. 1975. The actions of bradykinin and eledoisin in the canine isolated kidney: Relationships to prostaglandins. *Clin. Sci. Mol. Med.* 49: 125–31

43. Meyrick, B., Reid, L. 1978. The effect of continued hypoxia on rat pulmonary arterial circulation: An ultrastructural study. *Lab. Invest.* 38:188–200

44. Naeye, R. L. 1961. Arterial changes during the perinatal period. *Arch. Pathol.* 71:121–28

45. Okpako, D. T. 1972. The actions of histamine and prostaglandins $F_{2\alpha}$ and E_2 on pulmonary vascular resistance of the lung of the guinea pig. *J. Pharm. Pharmacol.* 24:40–46

46. Olley, P. M., Coceani, F., Kent, G. 1974. Inactivation of prostaglandin E_1 by lungs of the foetal lamb. *Experientia* 30:58–59

47. O'Neal, R. M., Ahlvin, R. C., Bauer, W. C., Thomas, W. A. 1957. Development of foetal pulmonary arterioles. *Arch. Pathol.* 63:309–15

48. Rudolph, A. M. 1974. *Congenital Diseases of the Heart: Clinical-Physiologic Considerations in Diagnosis and Management.* Chicago, Ill.: Yearbook Medical Publishers. 646 pp.

49. Rudolph, A. M. 1977. Fetal and neonatal pulmonary circulation. *Am. Rev. Resp. Dis.* 115:11–18

50. Rudolph, A. M., Heymann, M. A. 1967. The circulation of the fetus in utero. *Circ. Res.* 21:163–84

51. Rudolph, A. M., Heymann, M. A. 1970. Circulatory changes with growth in the fetal lamb. *Circ. Res.* 26:289–99

52. Rudolph, A. M., Heymann, M. A. 1972. Pulmonary circulation in fetal lambs. *Pediatr. Res.* 6:341 (Abstr.)

53. Rudolph, A. M., Heymann, M. A.

1973. Control of the foetal circulation. See Ref. 24, pp. 89–111

54. Rudolph, A. M., Heymann, M. A., Lewis, A. B. 1977. Physiology and pharmacology of the pulmonary circulation in the fetus and newborn. In *Lung Biology in Health and Disease. The Development of the Lung,* ed. W. A. Hodson, pp. 497–523. New York: Marcel Dekker. 646 pp.

55. Silove, E. D., Grover, R. F. 1968. Effects of alpha adrenergic blockade and tissue catecholamine depletion on pulmonary vascular responses to hypoxia. *J. Clin. Invest.* 47:274–85

56. Smith, F. G. Jr., Lupu, A. N., Barajas, L., Bauer, R., Bashore, R. A. 1974. The renin-angiotensin system in the fetal lamb. *Pediatr. Res.* 8:611–20

57. Smith, R. W., Morris, J. A., Assali, N. S. 1964. Effects of chemical mediators on the pulmonary and ductus arteriosus circulation in the fetal lamb. *Am. J. Obstet. Gynecol.* 89:252–60

58. Stahlman, M., Shepard, F., Gray, J., Young, W. 1964. The effects of hypoxia and hypercapnia on the circulation in newborn lambs. *J. Pediatr.* 65:1091–92 (Abstr.)

59. Tyler, T. L., Leffler, C. W., Cassin, S. 1977. Effects of prostaglandin precursors, prostaglandins, and prostaglandin metabolites on pulmonary circulation of perinatal goats. *Chest* 71S:271S–73S

60. Tyler, T., Leffler, C., Wallis, R., Cassin, S. 1975. Effects of prostaglandins of the E-series on pulmonary and systemic circulations of newborn goats during normoxia and hypoxia. *Prostaglandins* 10:963–70

61. Wagenvoort, C. A., Neufeld, H. N., Edwards, J. E. 1961. The structure of the pulmonary arterial tree in fetal and early postnatal life. *Lab. Invest.* 10:751–61

62. Wagenvoort, C. A., Wagenvoort, N. 1965. The pulmonary vascular bed in the normal fetus and newborn. In *International Symposium on the Heart and Circulation in the Newborn and Infant,* ed. D. E. Cassels, p. 201. New York: Grune & Stratton. 426 pp.

Ann. Rev. Physiol. 1979. 41:397–411

BIOCHEMICAL MECHANISM OF THE SODIUM PUMP

♦1227

Earl T. Wallick, Lois K. Lane, and Arnold Schwartz

Department of Pharmacology and Cell Biophysics, University of Cincinnati College of Medicine, Cincinnati, Ohio 45267

INTRODUCTION

For several years it has been widely accepted that the membrane-bound Na,K-ATPase is the enzymatic machinery for the active transport of Na^+ and K^+ across the cell membrane. The recent demonstration that ouabain-inhibitable, ATP-dependent Na^+ and K^+ transport can be measured in vesicles reconstituted from purified Na,K-ATPase and phospholipids provided direct evidence that Na,K-ATPase is, in fact, the sodium pump. Since the last review in this series, numerous papers have appeared that bear on the nature and mechanism of the pump. We still do not know, however, how the hydrolysis of ATP is coupled to the movement of Na^+ and K^+ across the plasma membrane, or how the inhibition of Na,K-ATPase by cardiac glycosides leads to an increased force of myocardial contraction. One of the obstacles to unraveling this puzzle is that neither the minimum molecular constituents nor the organization of these constituents in the Na,K-ATPase is known. We have therefore chosen to concentrate on the structure of the enzyme and on the biochemical mechanism of the fragmented enzyme. The reader is also referred to earlier reviews of the sodium pump (23, 41, 79).

Structural Aspects of the Na,K-ATPase

PROTEINS   The Na,K-ATPase has thus far been purified from the outer medulla of dog, sheep, rabbit, and pig kidneys (39, 51, 54, 55), shark rectal gland (33), eel electroplax (70), and duck salt gland (34). Despite the variety of isolation techniques, tissues, and species used, all of the purified Na,K-ATPase fractions reported to date are similar. They consist primarily of a $M_r = 90,000–100,000$ catalytic protein that is phosphorylated from

397

0066-4278/79/0301-0397$01.00

$(\gamma\text{-}^{32}P)ATP$ in the presence of Mg^{2+} and Na^+ at the β-carboxyl group of an aspartic acid residue (68, 72). It has been reported recently (30, 76) that cardiac glycoside analogs also bind to this protein, which suggests that at least a portion of the digitalis binding site is located on this subunit. Since cardiac glycosides are known to have their effect at the extracellular surface of the plasma membrane, whereas ATP hydrolysis occurs at the interior surface, this indicates that the catalytic subunit of the Na,K-ATPase spans the plasma membrane. The recent studies of Giotta (21) and Jørgensen (42–44) on the effects of limited tryptic digestion of Na,K-ATPase in the presence of Na^+ or K^+, together with the earlier reports of differential sulfhydryl group labeling by Titus & Hart (83), indicate that the catalytic subunit undergoes conformational changes during the reaction cycle of the enzyme.

The second protein present in the purified Na,K-ATPase preparations is a glycoprotein with an apparent molecular weight of about 45,000 (40, 52, 55). At the present time there is no compelling evidence that the glycoprotein has a functional role in the Na,K-ATPase. It is thought to be a constituent of the enzyme because (a) it is present in all of the purified fractions, (b) it can be covalently crosslinked to the catalytic subunit (52), and (c) antiserum raised against purified glycoprotein partially inhibits Na,K-ATPase activity (37, 38, 73).

There is not complete agreement on either the molecular weights or the molar ratio of these two proteins in the Na,K-ATPase. This is due primarily to the technical difficulties encountered in quantifying these proteins on coomassie blue-stained polyacrylamide gels and in determining the molecular weights via gel electrophoresis and gel filtration in detergents. The crosslinking studies of Kyte (52, 53) and Giotta (22) suggest that the Na,K-ATPase is a dimer, with each monomer consisting of one catalytic and one glycoprotein subunit. Assuming molecular weights of 95,000 and 45,000 for the two proteins, the molecular weight of the Na,K-ATPase dimer is 280,000. This value is in good agreement with the reported functional molecular weights of the Na,K-ATPase determined by radiation inactivation (48) and calculated from levels of steady-state phosphorylation and ouabain binding (33, 40, 55).

LIPIDS   It is widely accepted that lipids perform an essential role in the functioning of the Na,K-ATPase. Exactly what this role is and whether specific lipids are required for enzymic activity is not yet known. It has been reported that phosphatidylserine is absolutely required for Na,K-ATPase activity in erythrocyte ghosts (75), but not in brain (11). Recently, Mandersloot et al (60) identified phosphatidylinositol as the endogenous activator of Na,K-ATPase in rabbit kidney microsomes. De Pont et al (12), however, concluded that there is no absolute requirement for a specific phospholipid in a purified Na,K-ATPase from the same tissue. There does appear to be general agreement that negatively charged phospholipids are required for Na,K-ATPase activity (12, 60). This requirement can also be satisfied by phosphatidylethanolamine or phosphatidylcholine if cholate is present (60). There is some evidence suggesting that cholesterol may increase the selectivity of the sodium pump in erythrocytes for internal Na$^+$ (8). It has also been suggested that the primary role of cholesterol is via control of membrane fluidity (49).

RECONSTITUTION   Several investigators have now demonstrated that purified Na,K-ATPase is capable of catalyzing ATP-dependent and ouabain-inhibitable coupled Na$^+$–K$^+$ transport when reconstituted into phospholipid vesicles (3, 24, 32). These reconstitution experiments have provided the first direct evidence that the Na,K-ATPase is, in fact, the sodium pump. In an earlier paper, it was suggested (25) that the mammalian kidney Na,K-ATPase, unlike the enzyme in brain and shark rectal gland, catalyzed the transport of Na$^+$ and Cl$^-$, rather than Na$^+$ and K$^+$. It has since been shown that Na,K-ATPase from both lamb (3) and dog (24) kidney medulla does, in fact, catalyze coupled Na$^+$–K$^+$ transport. Using a highly efficient in vitro transport system, Goldin (24) has shown that the active transport of Na$^+$ and K$^+$ is coupled to ATP hydrolysis in approximately a $3:2:1$ ratio.

ULTRASTRUCTURE   Electron microscopy of purified Na,K-ATPase preparations after negative staining or freeze-fracturing reveals that the enzyme purified without solubilization is in the form of flat or cup-shaped membrane fragments or discs (9, 87), whereas enzyme purified by solubilization with lubrol or deoxycholate is in the form of vesicles (86) or vesicles plus rods and fragments (33). Freeze-fracturing has revealed a substructure of intramembranous particles with diameters of 80–120 Å (9, 86, 87), and negative staining has shown surface particles with approximate diameters of 45–70 Å (86), 50 Å (87), or 20–30 Å (9). The relationship between the observed particles and the protein components of the Na,K-ATPase is however, not yet clear. Deguchi et al (9) have proposed that the surface particle represents the $M_r = 140,000$ monomer, and that the intramembrane particle represents an oligomer of two or more monomers. Vogel et al (87) have suggested that their protoplasmic surface particle is the catalytic center of the $M_r = 95,000$ subunit and that the "fuzzy coat" on the exterior surface is glycoprotein.

IDENTIFICATION OF REACTIVE AMINO ACIDS   Evidence for an essential tyrosine at the active site of Na,K-ATPase has been obtained from studies on the reaction of 7-chloro-4-nitrobenzo-2-oxa-1,3-diazole (NBD-

CL) with 2 tyrosine residues per mole of purified Na,K-ATPase (6). Although modification of a single tyrosine results in the complete inhibition of the Na,K-ATPase activity, both tyrosines must be modified for complete inhibition of p-nitrophenylphosphatase activity. Inhibition can be partially reversed by 2-mercaptoethanol. The rate of tyrosine modification is increased by Na^+, retarded by K^+, and the more reactive tyrosine is protected by ATP. The modified tyrosines appear to be located on the 95,000-dalton polypeptide chain.

Reaction of Na,K-ATPase with butanedione leads to reversible inhibition of Na,K-ATPase activity (10). Kinetic studies suggested that inactivation was due to the modification of a single amino acid residue, most likely arginine. ATP protected against inactivation. Formation of phosphoenzyme was inhibited to the same degree as Na,K-ATPase activity, but p-nitrophenylphosphatase activity was much less inhibited; this suggested that an arginine residue is present in the nucleotide binding center of the enzyme.

Evidence for a sulfhydryl group in the ATP binding site comes from the reaction of 5,5'dithio-bis(2-nitrobenzoate) and several "protein reactive" ATP analogs with the enzyme (69). Similar to the effect of N-ethylmaleimide, the modification affected primarily the Na^+-dependent phosphorylation reaction, and was protected by low concentrations of ATP.

Reports of studies on the reaction of N-ethylmaleimide (NEM) with Na,K-ATPase continue to appear (31, 78, 89). Schoot et al (78) treated a purified rabbit kidney Na,K-ATPase with NEM and observed parallel inhibition of Na,K-ATPase activity, p-nitrophenylphosphatase, and phosphorylation by ATP. Both ATP and p-nitrophenylphosphate protected against inhibition of hydrolytic activity. These results are in contrast to those of earlier workers, who found that NEM treatment inhibited hydrolysis of ATP, with little effect on phosphorylation from ATP. These previous reports provided much of the early evidence for the existence of the ADP-sensitive E_1 form of the phosphoenzyme (reviewed in 23).

Schoot et al (78) offer two explanations for the differences in their results and the results of previous workers. They suggest that the impure Na,K-ATPase preparations previously used to study the effects of NEM were contaminated by other proteins that caused appreciable errors. They further suggest that purified preparations might differ from crude preparations with respect to the accessibility of groups reacting with NEM. Wallick et al (89) have examined the effects of NEM on sheep kidney Na,K-ATPase at several stages of purification (250–1100 μmol P_i mg^{-1} hr^{-1}), and found that the effects of NEM treatment were independent of the stage of purification. ATP hydrolysis was inhibited faster than phosphorylation was inhibited in both impure and pure Na,K-ATPase fractions. These results suggest that it is the ligands present during the reaction of the enzyme with NEM, rather than the purity of Na,K-ATPase, that is responsible for variable effects. We observed that the inclusion of ATP is necessary in order to produce a modified enzyme that forms a high level of ADP-sensitive phosphoenzyme and that has a low level of hydrolytic activity. We agree, however, that NEM treatment yields a heterogeneous preparation, consisting of several different species of modified Na,K-ATPase.

Jørgensen and Klodos (44) have examined the effect of partial tryptic digestion of purified Na,K-ATPase in the presence of Na^+. Although tryptic digestion inhibited Na,K-ATPase activity by 40%, it had little effect on ATP binding and/or the steady-state level of phosphorylation. Trypsin digestion increased the rate of ATP exchange by 50% and reduced K^+-phosphatase activity 80–85%. The fraction of ADP-sensitive phosphoenzyme was increased 2–3-fold. The authors suggest that the partial tryptic digestion selectively affects protein areas involved both in the transformation of the phosphoenzyme from an ADP-sensitive to an ADP-insensitive form and in the stimulation by K^+ of the dephosphorylation process and the K^+-phosphatase activity.

Sweadner (82) reported that monofunctional imidoesters such as ethyl acetimidate induce crosslinking of the subunits of Na,K-ATPase. The crosslinked enzyme consisted of equal quantities of the two subunits, suggesting that the crosslinking caused by bifunctional imidoesters is probably not due to the formation of a bisamidine derivative. The author proposed that a favorably positioned amino group on one subunit displaces the amidino group on the other, forming a covalent diamidino crosslink between the two subunits. The reaction with the imidoesters inhibited Na,K-ATPase and reduced the sensitivity of the phosphoenzyme to K^+.

CONFORMATIONAL PROBES   An electron spin probe study of Na,K-ATPase-containing membranes using a spin-labeled derivative of stearic acid suggested the existence of two lipid domains, one of which is closely associated with the enzyme (2). Further evidence for the existence of boundary lipids comes from a fluorescent probe study in which dansyl phosphatidylethanolamine (DPE) was incorporated into purified Na,K-ATPase (26). Energy transfer from tryptophans of the protein to the phospholipid probe was observed. Further, addition of Ca^{2+} and Mg^{2+} to the labeled enzyme increased the intensity of fluorescence in a saturable manner. The apparent dissociation constant (0.12 mM) estimated from the change in fluorescence is consistent with dissociation constants (0.10 mM) estimated from binding of ^{45}Ca to the lipid moiety of Na,K-ATPase previously reported (20). The enhancement of intensity and the blue shift of DPE fluorescence caused by the divalent cations suggests an increase in rigidity of the lipids. This increase in rigidity may result in a general exposure of "buried" amino acid residues to the aqueous medium, since magnesium has been reported to increase the reactivity of several different amino acid residues to group-specific reagents (78, 90). The interaction of anthroylouabain, a fluorescent derivative of ouabain, with Na,K-ATPase suggests that the ouabain binding site is either hydrophobic or is viscous and shielded from water (14). The fluorescent sulfhydryl reagent, S-mecuric-N-dansyl cysteine, has been used to label a purified preparation of Na,K-ATPase (28). All the labeling occurred in the 95,000-dalton catalytic subunit. Na,K-ATPase and p-nitrophenylphosphatase activity were inhibited, but formation of the phosphorylated intermediate was not. The fluorescence of the labeled enzyme increased dramatically (100%) when ligands (Mg^{2+} + ATP + Na^+ or Mg^{2+} + P_i) were added, suggesting that there were conformational changes associated with phosphorylation of the enzyme.

ANTIBODIES   There is considerable variability in the reported effects of antibodies to the Na,K–ATPase on the measurable reactions of Na,K-ATPase and Na^+-transport. It has been reported, for example, that antibodies to the holoenzyme have variable or have no effects on ATP binding, ouabain binding, phosphorylation, and ATP hydrolysis. Kyte (53) reported that antibodies to the catalytic subunit bind at the intracellular surface of the enzyme, but do not inhibit ATP hydrolysis or ouabain binding. Jean & Albers (37, 38) found that antiserum raised to the catalytic subunit partially inhibits ATP hydrolysis and phosphorylation but not ouabain binding, while antiserum to the glycoprotein inhibits ouabain binding but not phosphorylation. Rhee & Hokin (73, 74), on the other hand, reported that antibodies raised against the holoenzyme or the catalytic subunit partially inhibit ATP hydrolysis and ouabain binding, while antibodies to the glycoprotein have no effect on the binding of ouabain to the Na,K-ATPase. McCans et al (64, 65) found that antibodies to the holoenzyme could be further fractionated into two populations; one that inhibited the binding of ouabain to the Na,K-ATPase without affecting ATP hydrolysis, and a second that inhibited ATP hydrolysis but not ouabain binding. These results indicate that even a purified antibody fraction contains multiple populations of antibodies. Since it is generally accepted that there are numerous antigenic sites on the enzyme, it is reasonable to expect that a number of different antibodies, specific to different regions of the protein, can be raised. The recent work of Michael et al (67) underscores some of the difficulties encountered using heterogeneous antibody fractions. It was reported that two antisera fractions raised against the same purified Na,K-ATPase had markedly different effects on the inhibition of ATP hydrolysis and ouabain binding. These differences, some of which depend on the ligands and on the ratio of antibody to enzyme, were still evident even after purification of the antibody fractions by elution from the Na,K-ATPase.

In view of these difficulties, the contradictory reports of Jean & Albers (37, 38) and Rhee & Hokin (73, 74) are not surprising, particularly since whole globulin fractions rather than purified antibodies were used in some of the studies. Considering that the effects of these antibodies are dependent on (*a*) the purity, specificity, and affinity of the antibodies, (*b*) the ratio of antibody to Na,K-ATPase, and (*c*) the ligand conditions (67), any conclusions about the molecular organization of the Na,K-ATPase arising from such studies are, at best, speculative.

Mechanistic Aspects of the Na,K-ATPase

KINETIC STUDIES   The detailed reaction mechanism of Na,K-ATPase has not yet been elucidated. It has been suggested (80) that the hydrolysis of ATP by Na,K-ATPase may proceed without the formation of a phosphoenzyme. While this concept is interesting, in that it has certain similarities to the proposed reaction mechanism for the Mg^{2+}-dependent myosin ATPase, there is little direct experimental evidence that it applies to the Na,K-ATPase. On the other hand, the evidence for a phosphoenzyme intermediate in the turnover cycle is rather compelling (23). The next question is whether there is more than one form of phosphoenzyme. Rapid mixing techniques have recently been used to study the transient-state kinetics of Na,K-ATPase (16, 58, 61, 62). All of these studies show that in the presence of Na^+ and K^+, phosphate production can be resolved into two phases, an initial burst and a later steady-state phase. The initial burst of phosphate production coincides with a transient decay in the level of phosphoenzyme. Although the data from the different laboratories appear to be similar, different mechanisms are postulated in order to explain the transient overshoot of phosphoenzyme. Froehlich et al (16) suggest that the acid-stable phosphoenzyme, $E{\sim}P$, rapidly breaks down to an acid-labile, phosphate-containing noncovalent intermediate ($E{\cdot}P$) as shown below.

$$E + ATP \rightleftharpoons E{\cdot}ATP \rightleftharpoons E{\sim}P \rightleftharpoons E{\cdot}P \rightleftharpoons E + P_i \qquad 1.$$

A similar mechanism has been suggested to explain the kinetics of the Ca^{2+}-ATPase of sarcoplasmic reticulum (17). It is of interest in this regard that the "site" of phosphorylation, a β-carboxyl of an aspartic acid residue, is the same in Na,K- and Ca^{2+}-ATPase. Lowe & Smart (58) fit their data by nonlinear least squares regression to the following scheme:

$$E_1 + ATP \rightleftharpoons E_1{\cdot}ATP \rightleftharpoons E_2{\sim}P \rightleftharpoons E_2 + P_i \rightleftharpoons E_1 \qquad 2.$$

The authors claim that the postulation of an $E{\cdot}P_i$ type of intermediate is not necessary to explain the early burst of phosphate but they admit that their rate constants (derived from phosphate release experiments) do not predict the overshoot of phosphoenzyme and underestimate the amount of phosphoenzyme formed during early stages of the reaction. They conclude that their kinetic model is probably too simple. The addition of a second phosphoenzyme to the scheme did not improve the fit, but the authors state that a second E·ATP complex, as suggested earlier (46), might explain the discrepancy. Märdh has performed a series of transient-state experiments, which are summarized in (61). He fit his data by computer simulation to a reaction mechanism identical to that originally proposed by Albers and co-workers (13).

$$E_1 + ATP \rightleftharpoons E_1{\sim}P \rightleftharpoons E_2{\sim}P \rightleftharpoons E_2 + P_i \qquad 3.$$

A good fit of the experimental data to a simpler model of hydrolysis that included one phosphoenzyme form and two dephosphoenzyme forms was also obtained. This model, however, failed to predict correctly the steady-state rate of ATP hydrolysis. It appears that at least four enzyme species, one of which is a phosphoenzyme, are required to explain the results. It is obvious from the mechanisms shown above and from those proposed by earlier workers (reviewed in 23) that a number of different mechanisms can account for the data. Furthermore, it is quite likely that more than four active enzyme species lie along the reaction pathway. For example, none of the mechanisms shown above includes the E·ADP species suggested by Kanazawa et al (46) and Fukushima & Tonomura (18).

Steady-state kinetic studies also suggest a larger number of active enzyme species. Wang et al (93), studying the steady-state hydrolysis of ATP in the presence of various concentrations of Mg^{2+}, ATP, Na^+, and K^+, conclude that the models best fitting their data contain up to fourteen active enzyme species. The results are consistent with a simultaneous model rather than a consecutive model. The authors also suggest that more than one enzyme complex decomposes to yield products. Complexes of the type $E{\cdot}Na_x{}^+K_y{}^+$ where $x=2$ or 3 and $y = 1$ or 2, could coexist, depending upon the concentrations of Na^+ and K^+. The enzyme does not require the binding of three Na^+ and two K^+ simultaneously in order to hydrolyze ATP.

CATION BINDING   Another approach to determining whether Na^+ and K^+ bind simultaneously to the enzyme is the direct measurement of cation binding. Kaniike et al (47) reported specific sodium-22 binding to purified Na,K-ATPase. Two classes of Na^+ binding sites were revealed. The higher affinity site ($K_D = 0.2$ mM) binds 6–7 nmol Na^+ per mg of protein (3 Na^+ sites per phosphorylation site) and is blocked by pretreatment of the enzyme with ouabain. Neither heat-denatured enzyme nor phospholipids extracted from the enzyme contain the ouabain-inhibitable, higher-affinity Na^+ binding site. Matsui et al (63) used a similar method to examine the interaction of potassium-42 with Na,K-ATPase. A portion of the K^+ binding was ouabain-sensitive and of a relatively high affinity ($K_D \simeq 50~\mu M$). The ratio of K^+ binding to ouabain binding was $2:1$. Scatchard-plot analysis revealed a complicated nonlinear relationship, which suggested to the authors that the two K^+ sites might be nonequivalent. Using ion-selective electrodes, Hastings (29) measured K^+ binding to Na,K-ATPase and determined a K_D of $42~\mu M$. Furthermore, he found a binding level of 7.3 nmol mg^{-1}, which agrees closely with the level of 6.2 nmol mg^{-1} of ouabain-inhibitable binding reported by Matsui. Hastings used a differential titration technique, in which K^+ binding to denatured protein was automatically subtracted, and obtained a linear Scatchard plot, which suggests that the two K^+ sites are equivalent. This technique for measuring cation binding appears to be capable of accurate and precise measurements. However, it should be noted that Hastings' measurements were made at room temperature, whereas Matsui's were made at 0°C. The $K_D \simeq 50~\mu M$ estimated for K^+ binding in these two studies is similar to the K_D previously reported for the cation site that modulates ouabain binding (57, 91).

INHIBITION BY VANADATE Cantley [see (7,45) for references] has found that an impurity in ATP derived from muscle sources is a potent inhibitor of Na,K-ATPase. This inhibitor, which can be derived directly from striated muscle, has been identified as orthovanadate ion. The inhibition by vanadate ($K_i \simeq 40$ nM) is completely reversed by high concentrations of norepinephrine. Vanadate does not inhibit Ca^{2+}-activated ATPase derived from sarcoplasmic reticulum, mitochondrial ATPase, or actomyosin ATPase. The inhibitor is not present in synthetic ATP derived from nonmuscle sources (35). Experiments with red blood cells indicate that vanadate inhibits Na,K-ATPase by interacting with the cytoplasmic side of the cell membranes, and probably binds to a site on the enzyme specific for phosphate (7). The binding of vanadate to the internal surface of the pump alters the response of the pump to external K^+ (4). Since vanadate occurs in muscle tissue at concentrations of 10^{-6}–10^{-7}M, it is possible that it serves as a physiological modulator of sodium-pump activity.

INTERACTION WITH CARDIAC GLYCOSIDES The mechanism by which cardiac glycosides bind to and inhibit Na,K-ATPase is not completely understood (reviewed in 1, 56, 88). It is clear that physiological concentrations of ligands change the affinity of the enzyme for cardiac glycosides, primarily by altering the association rate. Ouabain can bind to the enzyme even in the absence of ligands (59), indicating that phosphorylation of the enzyme is not a prerequisite for ouabain binding. However, conditions that lead to phosphorylation are also the conditions in which the enzyme has the highest affinity for ouabain. The number of ouabain binding sites is approximately equal to the number of phosphorylation sites. The number of classes of ouabain binding sites on the Na,K-ATPase is controversial. Fricke & Klaus (15), for example, claim that two different classes of ouabain sites exist. They suggest that Na^+ modulates the number of sites in each class of sites and that the two different sites are on the E_1P and E_2P forms of the enzyme. Earlier kinetic evidence also suggested two ouabain binding sites modulated by Na^+, which might represent two different conformations for ouabain binding (36). Schoner et al (77) also suggest the existence of interconvertible low- and high-affinity ouabain binding sites. Van Alstyne et al (85) detected two populations of ouabain binding species in cardiac membrane vesicles. Based on the nonlinearity of Scatchard plots, Hansen (27) has also detected two or more populations of enzymes with different affinities for substrates and ligands which affect cardiac glycoside binding. Others, however, have found for the most part linear Scatchard plots, (59, 88, 94). The interpretation of nonlinear Scatchard plots is difficult. As has been pointed out (27, 88), if sites of different affinities are in equilibrium, Scatchard plots and kinetic plots will appear linear, and the apparent affinity or rate constant for the cardiac glycosides derived from the plots will lie between the absolute affinities or rates of the two sites. The postulated reaction mechanisms of ouabain binding that invoke two species of receptors (such as E_1P or E_2P) in a state of equilibrium or steady-state do not account for the nonlinearity of the Scatchard plots.

The existence of two noninterconvertible populations of enzymes will lead to nonlinear plots. Alternatively, the nonlinearity could be an artifact of the experimental protocol. If these two possibilities are eliminated, then the nonlinearity represents a cooperative effect that can only occur if the enzyme exists as a dimer (or higher oligomer) as has been suggested (81).

It now seems reasonably certain that the pharmacological effect of cardiac glycosides on the heart is a result of the binding of cardiac glycosides to the plasma membrane Na,K-ATPase. Three groups have shown a good correlation between occupation of the receptors (i.e. Na,K-ATPase) and inotropy (19, 50, 92). Further, it has been demonstrated that the lack of an inotropic effect in skeletal muscle is not due to the insensitivity of Na,K-ATPase derived from skeletal muscle to ouabain (71).

The issue of stimulation of the Na,K-ATPase by low concentrations of cardiac glycosides has surfaced again, based chiefly on the electrophysiological studies of Noble, Tsien, and their colleagues (5, 84). The data, however, are derived from conducting tissue preparations and their interpretation is complex. Attempts to demonstrate stimulation of isolated Na,K-ATPase by low concentrations of cardiac glycosides have been unsuccessful (66). Therefore, it is diffucult to envision such a role for cardiac glycosides in the mechanism of the inotropic effect.

ACKNOWLEDGMENTS

The original studies reported in this review were generously supported by grants from the National Institutes of Health (HL 22109–01, HL 22039–01, HL 07283–01, and HL 22619–01) and the University of Cincinnati College of Medicine. The authors gratefully acknowledge the assistance of Misses Juanita Hamler, Cynthia Edelbrock, and Linda Miner in the preparation of this manuscript.

Literature Cited

1. Akera, T. 1977. Membrane adenosine-triphosphatase: a digitalis receptor? *Science* 198:569–74
2. Almeida, A. F., Charnock, J. S. 1977. An electron spin probe study of Na,K-ATPase containing membranes. *Biochim. Biophys. Acta* 467:19–28
3. Anner, B. M., Lane, L. K., Schwartz, A., Pitts, B. J. R. 1977. A reconstituted Na^++K^+ pump in liposomes containing purified Na,K-ATPase from kidney medulla. *Biochim. Biophys. Acta* 467: 340–45
4. Beauge, L. A., Glynn, I. M. 1978. Commercial ATP containing traces of vanadate alters the response of Na,K-ATPase to external potassium. *Nature* 272:551–52
5. Blood, B. E., Noble, D. 1978. Two mechanisms for the inotropic action of ouabain on sheep cardiac Purkinje fiber contractility. In *Biophysical Aspects of Cardiac Muscle*, ed. M. Morad. New York: Academic. In Press
6. Cantley, L. C. Jr., Gelles, G., Josephson, L. 1978. Reaction of Na,K-ATPase with 7-Chloro-4-nitrobenzo-2-oxa-1,3-diazole. Evidence for an essential tyrosine at the active site. *Biochemistry* 17:418–25
7. Cantley, L. C. Jr., Resh, M. D., Guidotti, G. 1978. Vanadate inhibits the red cell Na,K-ATPase from the cytoplasmic side. *Nature* 272:552–54
8. Claret, M., Garay, R., Giraud, F. 1978. The effect of membrane cholesterol on the sodium pump in red blood cells. *J. Physiol. London* 274:247–63
9. Deguchi, N., Jørgensen, P. L., Maunsbach, A. B. 1977. Ultrastructure of the sodium pump. Comparison of thin sectioning, negative staining and freeze-fracture of purified, membrane-bound Na,K-ATPase. *J. Cell Biol.* 75:619–34
10. DePont, J. J. H. H. M., Schoot, B. M., Van Prooijen–Van Eeden, A., Bonting, S. L. 1977. An essential arginine residue in the ATP-binding centre of

Na,K-ATPase. *Biochim. Biophys. Acta* 482:213–27
11. DePont, J. J. H. H. M., Van Prooijen–Van Eeden, A., Bonting, S. L. 1973. Studies on Na^+-K^+-activated ATPase XXXIV. Phosphatidylserine not essential for Na,K-ATPase activity. *Biochim. Biophys. Acta* 323:487–94
12. DePont, J. J. H. H. M., Van Prooijen–Van Eeden, A., Bonting, S. L. 1978. Role of negatively charged phospholipids in highly purified Na,K-ATPase from rabbit kidney outer medulla. *Biochim. Biophys. Acta* 508:464–77
13. Fahn, S., Koval, G. J., Albers, R. W. 1966. Sodium-potassium activated adenosine triphosphatase of *Electrophorus* electric organ. *J. Biol. Chem.* 241:1882–89
14. Fortes, P. A. G. 1977. Anthroylouabain: A specific fluorescent probe for the cardiac glycoside receptor of the Na,K-ATPase. *J. Biochem.* 16:531–40
15. Fricke, V., Klaus, W. 1977. Evidence for two different Na^+-dependent [^3H]ouabain binding sites of a Na,K-ATPase of guinea pig hearts. *Br. J. Pharmacol.* 61:423–28
16. Froehlich, J. P., Albers, R. W., Koval, G. J., Goebel, R., Berman, M. 1976. Evidence for a new intermediate state in the mechanism of Na^+,K^+-adenosine triphosphatase. *J. Biol. Chem.* 251: 2186–88
17. Froehlich, J. P., Taylor, E. W. 1976. Transient state kinetic effects of calcium ion on sarcoplasmic reticulum adenosine triphosphatase. *J. Biol. Chem.* 251:2307–15
18. Fukushima, Y., Tonomura, Y. 1973. Two kinds of high energy phosphorylation intermediate, with and without bound ADP, in the reaction of Na^+-K^+-dependent ATPase. *J. Biochem.* 74:135–42
19. Gelbart, A., Goldman, R. H. 1977. Correlation between microsomal Na,K-

408   WALLICK, LANE & SCHWARTZ

ATPase activity and ^{3}H ouabain binding to heart tissue homogenates. *Biochim. Biophys. Acta* 481:689–94

20. Gervais, A., Lane, L. K., Anner, B. M., Lindenmayer, G. E., Schwartz, A. 1977. A possible molecular mechanism of the action of digitalis. Ouabain action on calcium binding to sites associated with a purified sodium-potassium-activated adenosine triphosphatase from kidney. *Circ. Res.* 40:8–14

21. Giotta, G. J. 1975. Native Na$^+$+K$^+$ dependent adenosine triphosphatase has two trypsin-sensitive sites. *J. Biol. Chem.* 250:5159–64

22. Giotta, G. J. 1976. Quaternary structure of Na$^+$+K$^+$ dependent adenosine triphosphatase. *J. Biol. Chem.* 251:1247–52

23. Glynn, I. M., Karlish, S. J. D. 1975. The sodium pump. *Ann. Rev. Physiol.* 37:13–55

24. Goldin, S. M. 1977. Active transport of sodium and potassium ions by the sodium and potassium ion-activated adenosine triphosphatase from renal medulla. *J. Biol. Chem.* 252:5630–42

25. Goldin, S. M., Tong, S. W. 1975. Reconstitution of active transport catalyzed by the purified sodium and potassium ion-stimulated adenosine triphosphatase from canine renal medulla. *J. Biol. Chem.* 249:5907–15

26. Gupte, S. S., Lane, L. K., Johnson, J. D., Wallick, E. T. 1978. Effect of divalent cations on sheep-kidney Na,K-ATPase: lipid bound fluorescent probe study. *Fed. Proc.* 37(6):1817 (Abstr.)

27. Hansen, O. 1976. Non-uniform populations of G-strophanthin binding sites of Na$^+$+K$^+$-activated ATPase. Apparent conversion to uniformity by K$^+$. *Biochim. Biophys. Acta* 433:383–92

28. Harris, W. E., Stahl, W. L. 1977. Conformational changes of purified Na,K-ATPase detected by a sulfhydryl fluorescence probe. *Biochim. Biophys. Acta* 485:203–14

29. Hastings, D. F. 1977. Differential titration of potassium binding to membrane proteins using ion selective electrodes. *Anal. Biochem.* 83:416–32

30. Hegyvary, C. 1975. Covalent labeling of the digitalis-binding compartment of plasma membranes. *Mol. Pharmacol.* 11:588–94

31. Hegyvary, C. 1976. Ouabain-binding and phosphorylation of Na,K-ATPase treated with N-ethylmaleimide or oligomycin. *Biochim. Biophys. Acta* 422:365–79

32. Hilden, S., Hokin, L. 1976. Coupled Na$^+$-K$^+$ transport in vesicles containing a purified Na,K-ATPase and only phosphatidylcholine. *Biochem. Biophys. Res. Commun.* 69:521–27

33. Hokin, L. E., Dahl, J. L., Deupree, J. D., Dixon, J. F., Hackney, J. F., Perdue, J. F. 1973. Studies on the characterization of the sodium-potassium transport adenosine triphosphatase. X. Purification of the enzyme from the rectal gland of *Squalus acanthias*. *J. Biol. Chem.* 248:2593–2605

34. Hopkins, B. E., Wagner, H. Jr., Smith, J. W. 1976. Sodium and potassium activated adenosine triphosphatase of the nasal salt gland of the duck (*Anas platyrhynchos*). *J. Biol. Chem.* 251:4365–71

35. Hudgins, P. M., Bond, G. H. 1977. (Mg^{2+}+K$^+$)-dependent inhibition of Na,K-ATPase due to a contaminant in equine muscle ATP. *Biochem. Biophys. Res. Commun.* 77:1024–29

36. Inagaki, C., Lindenmayer, G. E., Schwartz, A. S. 1974. Effects of sodium and potassium on binding of ouabain to the transport adenosine triphosphatase. *J. Biol. Chem.* 249:5135–40

37. Jean, D. H., Albers, R. W., Koval, G. 1975. Sodium-potassium-activated adenosine triphosphatase of *Electrophorus* electric organ. X. Immunochemical properties of the lubrolsolubilized enzyme and its constituent polypeptides. *J. Biol. Chem.* 250:1035–40

38. Jean, D. H., Albers, R. W. 1977. Molecular organization of subunits of electroplax (sodium plus potassium) activated adenosine triphosphatase. *J. Biol. Chem.* 252:2450–51

39. Jørgensen, P. L. 1974. Purification and characterization of Na,K-ATPase. III. Purification from outer medulla of mammalian kidney after selective removal of membrane components by sodium dodecylsulfate. *Biochim. Biophys. Acta* 356:36–52

40. Jørgensen, P. L. 1974. Purification and characterization of Na,K-ATPase. IV. Estimation of the purity of the molecular weight and polypeptide content per enzyme unit in preparations from the outer medulla of rabbit kidney. *Biochim. Biophys. Acta.* 356:53–67

41. Jørgensen, P. L. 1975. Isolation and characterization of the components of the sodium pump. *Q. Rev. Biophys.* 7:239–74

42. Jørgensen, P. L. 1975. Purification and characterization of Na,K-ATPase. V. Conformational changes in the enzyme.

Transitions between the Na$^+$ form and the K$^+$ form studied with tryptic digestion as a tool. *Biochim. Biophys. Acta* 401:399–415

43. Jørgensen, P. L. 1977. Purification and characterization of Na,K-ATPase. VI. Differential tryptic modification of catalytic functions of the purified enzyme in presence of NaCl and KCl. *Biochim. Biophys. Acta* 466:97–108

44. Jørgensen, P. L., Klodos, I. 1978. Purification and characterization of Na,K-ATPase. VII. Tryptic degradation of the Na form of the enzyme protein resulting in selective modification of dephosphorylation reactions of the Na,K-ATPase. *Biochim. Biophys. Acta* 507:8–16

45. Josephson, L., Cantley, L. C. Jr. 1977. Isolation of a potent Na,K-ATPase inhibitor from striated muscle. *Biochemistry* 16:4572–78

46. Kanazawa, T., Saito, M., Tonomura, Y. 1970. Formation and decomposition of a phosphorylated intermediate in the reaction of Na$^+$,K$^+$-dependent ATPase. *J. Biochem. Tokyo* 67:693–711

47. Kaniike, K., Lindenmayer, G. E., Wallick, E. T., Lane, L. K., Schwartz, A. 1976. Specific sodium-22 binding to a purified sodium + potassium adenosine triphosphatase. *J. Biol. Chem.* 251:4794–95

48. Kepner, G. R., Macey, R. I. 1968. Membrane enzyme systems. Molecular size determinations by radiation inactivation. *Biochim. Biophys. Acta* 163:188–203

49. Kimelberg, H. K., Papahadjopoulos, D. 1974. Effects of phospholipid acyl chain fluidity, phase transitions, and cholesterol on Na$^+$+K$^+$-stimulated adenosine triphosphatase. *J. Biol. Chem.* 249:1071–80

50. Ku, D., Akera, T., Pew, C. L., Brody, T. M. 1974. Cardiac glycosides: correlations among Na,K-ATPase, sodium pump and contractility in the guinea pig heart. *Naunyn - Schmeideberg's Arch. Pharmacol.* 285:185–200

51. Kyte, J. 1971. Purification of the sodium-and-potassium-dependent adenosine triphosphatase from canine renal medulla. *J. Biol. Chem.* 246:4157–65

52. Kyte, J. 1972. Properties of the two polypeptides of sodium-and-potassium-dependent adenosine triphosphatase. *J. Biol. Chem.* 247:7642–49

53. Kyte, J. 1975. Structural studies of sodium and potassium ion-activated adenosine triphosphatase. *J. Biol. Chem.* 250:7443–49

54. Lane, L. K., Anner, B. M., Wallick, E. T., Ray, M. V., Schwartz, A. 1978. Effect of phospholipase. A treatment on the partial reactions of, and ouabain binding to, a purified sodium and potassium activated adenosine triphosphatase. *Biochem. Pharmacol.* 27:225–31

55. Lane, L. K., Copenhaver, J. H. Jr., Lindenmayer, G. E., Schwartz, A. 1973. Purification and characterization of and ^{3}H ouabain binding to the transport adenosine triphosphatase from outer medulla of canine kidney. *J. Biol. Chem.* 248:7197–7200

56. Lindenmayer, G. E. 1976. Mechanism of action of digitalis glycoside at the subcellular level. *Pharmacol. Ther.* 2:843–61

57. Lindenmayer, G. E., Schwartz, A. 1973. Nature of the transport ATPase glycoside complex. IV. Evidence that sodium and potassium competition for a common site modulates the rate of glycoside interaction. *J. Biol. Chem.* 248:1291–1300

58. Lowe, A. G., Smart, J. W. 1977. The pre-steady-state hydrolysis of ATP by porcine brain Na$^+$+K$^+$-dependent ATPase. *Biochim. Biophys. Acta* 481:695–705

59. Mandel, F., Wallick, E. T., Schwartz, A. 1977. Mg-stimulated ouabain binding to purified Na,K-ATPase from lamb kidney. *Fed. Proc.* 36:(3):274 (Abstr.)

60. Mandersloot, J. G., Roelofsen, B., DeGier, J. 1978. Phosphatidylinositol as the endogenous activator of the Na,K-ATPase in microsomes of rabbit kidney. *Biochim. Biophys. Acta* 508:478–85

61. Märdh, S., Lindahl, S. 1977. On the mechanism of sodium and potassium activated adenosine triphosphatase. *J. Biol. Chem.* 252:8058–61

62. Märdh, S., Post, R. L. 1977. Phosphorylation from adenosine triphosphate of sodium and potassium-activated adenosine triphosphatase. *J. Biol. Chem.* 252:633–38

63. Matsui, H., Hayashi, Y., Homaredo, H., Kimimura, M. 1977. Ouabain-sensitive ^{42}K binding to Na,K-ATPase purified from canine kidney outer medulla. *Biochem. Biophys. Res. Commun.* 75:373–80

64. McCans, J. L., Lindenmayer, G. E., Pitts, B. J. R., Ray, M. V., Raynor, B. D., Butler, V. P. Jr., Schwartz, A. 1975. Antigenic differences in Na,K-ATPase preparations isolated from various organs and species. *J. Biol. Chem.* 250:7257–65

65. McCans, J. L., Lane, L. K., Linden-mayer, G. E., Butler, V. P. Jr., Schwartz, A. 1974. Effects of an antibody to a highly purified Na,K-ATPase from canine renal medulla: separation of the "holoenzyme antibody" into catalytic and cardiac glycoside receptor–specific components. *Proc. Natl. Acad. Sci. USA* 71:2449–52

66. Michael, L., Pitts, B. J. R., Schwartz, A. 1978. Is pump stimulation associated with positive inotropy of the heart? *Science* 200:1287–89

67. Michael, L., Wallick, E. T., Schwartz, A. 1977. Modification of Na,K-ATPase function by purified antibodies to the holoenzyme. Effects on enzyme activity and [³H]ouabain binding. *J. Biol. Chem.* 252:8476–80

68. Nishigaki, I., Chen, F. T., Hokin, L. E. 1974. Studies on the characterization of the sodium-potassium transport adenosine triphosphatase. XV. Direct chemical characterization of the acyl phosphate in the enzyme as an aspartyl B-phosphate residue. *J. Biol. Chem.* 249:4911–16

69. Patzelt-Wenczler, R., Pauls, H., Erdmann, E., Schoner, W. 1975. Evidences for a sulfhydryl group in the ATP-binding site of Na⁺+K⁺-activated ATPase. *Eur. J. Biochem.* 53:301–11

70. Perrone, J. R., Hackney, J. F., Dixon, J. F., Hokin, L. E. 1975. Molecular properties of purified sodium + potassium–activated adenosine triphosphatases and their subunits from the rectal gland of *Squalus acanthias* and the electric organ of *Electrophorus electricus*. *J. Biol. Chem.* 250:4178–84

71. Pitts, B. J. R., Wallick, E. T., Van Winkle, W. B., Allen, J. C., Schwartz, A. 1977. On the lack of inotropy of cardiac glycosides on skeletal muscle: A comparison of Na,K-ATPase from skeletal and cardiac muscle. *Arch. Biochem. Biophys.* 184:431–40

72. Post, R. L., Kume, S. 1973. Evidence for an aspartyl phosphate residue at the active site of sodium and potassium ion transport adenosine triphosphatase. *J. Biol. Chem.* 248:6993–7000

73. Rhee, H. M., Hokin, L. E. 1975. Inhibition of the purified sodium-potassium activated adenosinetriphosphatase from the rectal gland of *Squalus acanthias* by antibody against the glycoprotein subunit. *Biochem. Biophys. Res. Commun.* 63:1139–45

74. Rhee, H. M., Hokin, L. E. 1976. Inhibition of ³H-ouabain binding to purified Na,K-ATPase by antibodies raised against the holoenzyme and its catalytic subunit. *Fed. Proc.* 35(3):425 (Abstr.)

75. Roelofsen, B., Van Deenen, L. L. M. 1973. Lipid requirement of membrane bound ATPase. Studies on human erythrocyte ghosts. *Eur. J. Biochem.* 40:245–57

76. Ruoho, A., Kyte, J. 1974. Photoaffinity labeling of the ouabain-binding site on Na⁺+K⁺ adenosine triphosphatase. *Proc. Natl. Acad. Sci. USA* 71:2352–56

77. Schoner, W., Pauls, H., Patzelt-Wenczler, R. 1977. *Myocardial Failure*, ed. G. Rieker, A. Weber, J. Goodwin, pp. 104–119. Berlin: Springer-Verlag

78. Schoot, B. M., Schoots, A. F. M., De-Pont, J. J. H. H. M., Schuurmans Stekhoven, F. M. A. H., Bonting, S. L. 1977. Studies on Na⁺+K⁺ activated ATPase. XLI. Effects of N-ethylmaleimide on overall and partial reactions. *Biochim. Biophys. Acta* 483:181–92

79. Schwartz, A., Lindenmayer, G. E., Allen, J. C. 1975. The sodium-potassium adenosine triphosphatase: pharmacological, physiological, and biochemical aspects. *Pharmacol. Rev.* 27:3–134

80. Skou, J. C. 1965. Enzymatic basis for active transport of Na⁺ and K⁺ across cell membrane. *Physiol. Rev.* 45:596–617

81. Stein, W. D., Lieb, W. R., Karlish, S. J. D., Eilam, Y. 1973. A model for the active transport of sodium and potassium ions as mediated by a tetrameric enzyme. *Proc. Natl. Acad. Sci. USA* 70:275–78

82. Sweadner, K. J. 1977. Crosslinking and modification of Na,K-ATPase by ethyl acetimidate. *Biochem. Biophys. Res. Commun.* 78:962–69

83. Titus, E. O., Hart, W. M. Jr., 1974. The use of sulfhydryl reagents to identify proteins undergoing ligand-dependent conformational changes associated with the function of (Na⁺+K⁺)-ATPase. *Ann. N.Y. Acad. Sci.* 242:246–53

84. Tsien, R. W., Carpenter, D. O. 1978. Ionic mechanisms of pacemaker activity in cardiac Purkinje fibers. *Fed. Proc.* 34:2127–31

85. Van Alstyne, E., Bartschat, D. K., Poe, S. L., Lindenmayer, G. E. 1978. Cardiac membrane vesicles enriched in ouabain sites. *Fed. Proc.* 37(3):779 (Abstr.)

86. Van Winkle, W. B., Lane, L. K., Schwartz, A. 1976. The subunit fine structure of isolated, purified Na⁺,K⁺-adenosine triphosphatase. Freeze-fracture study. *Exp. Cell Res.* 100:291–96

87. Vogel, F., Meyer, H. W., Grosse, R., Repke, K. R. H. 1977. Electron micro-

scopic visualization of the arrangement of the two protein components of (Na$^+$ +K$^+$)-ATPase. *Biochim. Biophys. Acta* 470:497–502

88. Wallick, E. T., Lindenmayer, G. E., Lane, L. K., Allen, J. C., Pitts, B. J. R., Schwartz, A. 1977. Recent advances in cardiac glycoside–Na$^+$,K$^+$-ATPase interaction. *Fed. Proc.* 36:2214–18

89. Wallick, E. T., Ray, M. V., Anner, B. M., Leuchter, A. F., Schwartz, A. 1975. ^{3}H-ouabain binding to highly purified Na$^+$,K-ATPase: The E conformation as a site of action. *Fed. Proc.* 34(3):249 (Abstr.)

90. Wallick, E. T., Ray, M. V., Leuchter, A. F., Schwartz, A. 1976. Chemical modification of purified Na,K-ATPase. *Fed. Proc.* 35(7):1663 (Abstr.)

91. Wallick, E. T., Schwartz, A. 1974. Thermodynamics of the rate of binding of ouabain to the sodium, potassium-

adenosine triphosphatase. *J. Biol. Chem.* 249:5141–47

92. Wallick, E. T., Schwartz, A., Michael, L. H., Huggins, R. A. 1977. Ouabain binding to heart muscle and inotropy. *Fed. Proc.* 36(3):972 (Abstr.)

93. Wang, T., Lindenmayer, G. E., Schwartz, A. 1977. Steady-state kinetic study of magnesium and ATP effects on ligand affinity and catalytic activity of sheep kidney sodium, potassium-adenosinetriphosphatase. *Biochim. Biophys. Acta* 484:140–60

94. Yoda, A., Yoda, S. 1977. Association and dissociation rate constants of the complexes between various cardiac aglycones and sodium-and-potassium-dependent adenosine triphosphatase formed in the presence of magnesium and phosphate. *Mol. Pharmacol.* 13:352–61

Ann. Rev. Physiol. 1979. 41:413–24
Copyright © 1979 by Annual Reviews Inc. All rights reserved

PROPERTIES OF TWO INWARD MEMBRANE CURRENTS IN THE HEART

♦1228

Harald Reuter

Department of Pharmacology, University of Berne, 3010 Berne, Switzerland.

INTRODUCTION

During the last 12 years impressive experimental evidence has accumulated that two distinct inward membrane currents are responsible for excitation of the heart. The first inward current (I_{Na}) is abolished by removal of external Na ions or by tetrodotoxin (TTX) and, at least qualitatively, resembles Na currents in nerve or skeletal muscle (78). I_{Na} is responsible for the fast upstroke velocity ($\dot{V}_{max}$) of the cardiac action potential (AP). $\dot{V}_{max}$ is an important factor in impulse conduction velocity in myocardial tissue (38, 60). The much smaller secondary inward current (I_{si}) is very sensitive to variation in the external Ca ion concentration and has many features in common with Ca currents in other excitable tissues (29, 65). I_{si} is important for the characteristic plateau phase of the cardiac AP (8, 53) and for excitation-contraction coupling (reviewed in 17, 51, 79).

Some physiological and pharmacological properties of these inward currents are described in this review. Since the length of this article is limited, I can discuss only a few of the numerous papers that lead to the concept of two distinct inward membrane currents in cardiac muscle. The literature until about 1974 has been reviewed in several major articles and books (13, 60, 65, 75). Several articles in the Annual Review series have dealt with certain aspects of this subject (17, 40, 51, 79, 81). This review emphasizes voltage-clamp results and includes a brief discussion of methodological limitations.

413

0066-4278/79/0301-0413$01.00

METHODOLOGICAL LIMITATIONS

There can be little doubt that multicellular preparations, like strands of cardiac muscle, are much less suitable for voltage clamping (VC) than the classical single cell preparation, the squid axon. This view has been emphasized forcefully by Johnson & Lieberman (40). Since then several theoretical and experimental papers have been published dealing with the problems of various VC methods for multicellular preparations (reviewed in 2, 5, 18, 38).

Resistances in series (R_s) with the membranes within a fiber bundle limit quantitative experimental evaluation of membrane currents (6, 39, 47, 66). A major fraction of R_s is most likely located in clefts between individual cells or cell strands and hence cannot be compensated (2, 5, 39). The problem of narrow clefts and consequently of radial voltage non-uniformities (and of ion accumulation and depletion) is probably more severe in ungulate Purkinje fibers and frog heart than in working myocardial fibers from larger mammals (2, 40, 66). However, in all preparations VC is obviously impossible when the membrane resistance approaches the value of the (distributed) R_s, e.g. during the flow of I_{Na} (2, 6, 47). Though more severe, the problem of R_s is not confined to multicellular preparations like cardiac muscle; it also holds true for single cell preparations, particularly if their membranes are folded or have narrow invaginations (neuron somata, skeletal muscle fibers). A search in the literature showed that in most preparations (including squid axon) the ratio between measured R_s and the negative slope resistance of the membrane during the flow of inward currents ($R_s/-R_{slope}$) is between 1/2 and 1/15. In mammalian cardiac muscle this ratio for I_{si} is at least 1/10 [Figure 1B; (54, 66)], which is acceptable; but the ratio becomes larger than 1 during the flow of I_{Na}, which means that the membrane potential is no longer under control (6, 47).

With sucrose-gap methods one is faced with additional problems due to (a) shunt current across the gaps, and (b) mixing of sucrose solution with saline solution (Ringer, Tyrode, etc) within the bundle (2, 56). The shunt current depends on the ratio of the internal and external resistances of the bundle in the sucrose gap (R_i/R_o). R_i can be kept relatively constant for some time (1–2 hr) if a small concentration (10^{-5}–10^{-4} M) of $CaCl_2$ is added to the sucrose solution (45, 54, 66), although this reduces R_o. Under favorable conditions R_i/R_o is smaller than 0.1 (54, 66), but even then the shunt current is not negligible. Goldman & Morad (24) suggest that a "guard gap" added to the single sucrose-gap arrangement is effective in trapping a large portion of the shunt current. The problem of interdiffusion of sucrose and saline solutions in the muscle bundle can be reduced (70) by using rubber membranes with holes small enough to squeeze the bundle at the solution interface (6, 24, 54, 56, 66).

A promising new approach is the application of the modified three-microelectrode VC technique of Adrian et al (1) to mammalian ventricular preparations (42, 66). This method makes use of the voltage drop along the internal resistance during current flow in a cable-like structure. The voltage gradient between two intracellular microelectrodes is proportional to the current flowing across the membrane. Current can be applied either through a third intracellular microelectrode (1, 42) or through a sucrose gap (66). So far this method has been used successfully in cardiac preparations in the evaluation of I_{si} (42, 66), but it may also be suitable for measurements of I_{Na}.

Generally one may conclude that VC analysis of cardiac membrane currents, though difficult, can be done with a reasonable degree of reliability, provided the necessary experimental precautions are taken and the investigated membrane conductances are small compared to $1/R_s$. Our knowledge of the plateau phase of the AP, of pacemaker activity, of "slow responses," of mechanisms of drug actions, and of excitation-contraction coupling would be much less advanced without this technique, despite its problems.

Since I_{Na} cannot at present be adequately measured in cardiac muscle by VC methods, the upstroke velocity ($\dot{V}_{max}$) of the membrane AP is often used as a measure of I_{Na} [$\dot{V}_{max} = -I_m/C_m$, where I_m is ionic membrane current ($I_{in} + I_{out}$), and C_m is membrane capacity]. From model computations of the squid axon AP it has recently been argued (12) that $\dot{V}_{max}$ is a nonlinear and highly unreliable measure not only of the limiting Na conductance, $\overline{G}_{Na}$, but also of I_{Na}, since $\dot{V}_{max} = 0$ if $I_{out} = I_{Na}$. However, in squid axon, total I_{out} *increases* steeply during depolarization, while this is not true in cardiac muscle where I_{out} *falls* during depolarization (inward-going rectification). $\dot{V}_{max}$ is reached around -20 mV (68), and at this potential the contribution of I_{out} to I_m is only a few percent. Even in the absence of I_{Na}, e.g. from a reduced resting potential, the much smaller I_{si} can still produce APs. Computations of the cardiac AP show an excellent correlation between I_{Na}, $\overline{G}_{Na}$, and $\dot{V}_{max}$ (32), although this may be a feature of the particular AP model (8) used. As pointed out by Strichartz & Cohen (73a), in squid axon the relation between $\dot{V}_{max}$ and $\overline{G}_{Na}$ is still nonlinear even in the absence of any outward conductance. Therefore, the exact relation between I_{Na}, $\overline{G}_{Na}$, and $\dot{V}_{max}$ in cardiac muscle can only be resolved by a complete experimental analysis.

SODIUM CURRENT (I_{Na})

Several attempts have been made to analyze I_{Na} of different cardiac preparations by VC methods (reviewed in 40, 60, 75, 81). Unfortunately, all studies suffer from the lack of membrane-potential control during the flow of I_{Na}

and from other methodological difficulties. The only conclusions that can be drawn are the following: I_{Na} depends on the external Na concentration and is sensitive to TTX, albeit at rather high concentrations; I_{Na} is a large and rapid inward current lasting for only a few msec; the current inactivates upon depolarization from -90 to -50 mV; recovery from inactivation may be slower than inactivation. Beyond this nothing can be said about the kinetic properties of this inward current. However, the data are not inconsistent with the view that I_{Na} in cardiac muscle is similar to that in nerve and skeletal muscle (60, 78). This assumption was made for modelling $\dot{V}_{max}$ in two computer reconstructions of cardiac APs, one for Purkinje fibers (53) and the other for ventricular myocardial fibers (8).

$\dot{V}_{max}$ of the AP is often used as a measure of I_{Na}. Weidmann (80) showed that after an AP during which I_{Na} is inactivated, $\dot{V}_{max}$ recovers within a few msec at membrane potentials (V_m) between -106 and -80 mV. This finding has been confirmed (20), but it has also been shown that at less-negative V_m the recovery of I_{Na} and $\dot{V}_{max}$ is considerably prolonged and becomes much slower than the inactivation rate of I_{Na} (20, 28, 83). A similar feature of the Na system has been reported for other excitable tissues and has been explained in terms of coupled activation-inactivation kinetics of Na channels (23). In the heart the steep potential dependence of the recovery kinetics of $\dot{V}_{max}$ (20) may cause large inhomogeneities in impulse conduction between normal and slightly depolarized tissue regions, e.g. near infarcted areas.

Membrane potential also affects the potency of some drugs acting on the Na system (33). The effects of quinidine and lidocaine (11, 30, 83), two important antiarrhythmic and local anesthetic drugs, strongly depend on the electrical activity of the cardiac cell membrane. If quinidine is applied during a long period of rest, $\dot{V}_{max}$ of the first post-rest AP is virtually unaffected. However, during continuous stimulation there is a very rapid reduction of $\dot{V}_{max}$, which recovers slowly when the rate of stimulation is reduced (30). Similarly, lidocaine strongly delays the rate of recovery of $\dot{V}_{max}$ after a preceding depolarization (11, 83). Both drugs shift the $\dot{V}_{max}$-V_m relationship (inactivation) towards more negative potentials. Since these drugs interact with receptors linked to the Na channels, the voltage-dependent states of these channels (resting, open, inactivated), and hence V_m, may influence the drug-receptor interaction (31, 33). Kinetic analyses of the action of local anesthetic drugs on I_{Na} in nerve fibers (31) have indeed shown a strong voltage dependence of the action of these drugs, depolarization causing a larger receptor occupancy than hyperpolarization. The phenomena observed in heart muscle (11, 30, 33, 83) agree, at least qualitatively, with the more rigorous data available from myelinated nerves (31).

Surprisingly, in mammalian cardiac muscle the TTX effect on $\dot{V}_{max}$ not only occurs at more than a thousand times higher concentrations than in nerve and skeletal muscle, but it is also strongly voltage-dependent (3, 68). A 18–20 mV depolarization from a resting potential of about –90 mV causes a large shift of the concentration-response curve with a ten-fold increase in the apparent affinity. Moreover, the toxin effect depends on the rate of stimulation, the recovery kinetics of $\dot{V}_{max}$ are greatly prolonged, and the $\dot{V}_{max}$-V_m relationship is shifted towards more negative potentials. These and other results led to the suggestion (3, 68) that TTX dissociates much less readily from inactivated than from resting Na channels, a hypothesis similar to that proposed for the action of local anesthetics (31, 33).

Various toxins (batrachotoxin, grayanotoxin, *Anemonia sulcata* toxin, veratrine, germitrine) increase the Na permeability in cardiac muscle (34–36, 50, 63), as in other excitable tissues (57). One of the most interesting aspects of these studies is that an increase in the Na permeability of the membrane is associated with an increase in force of contraction. This is most likely due to the Na-Ca exchange system in the membrane, which promotes Ca influx when the internal Na concentration is raised (16, 22).

SLOW INWARD CURRENT (I_{si})

Initial evidence for Ca-dependent I_{si} came from VC results in Purkinje fibers (64). I_{si} has since been shown to occur in all cardiac tissues investigated so far (65, 75), although its analysis is sometimes complicated by the overlap of other current components (37, 72). I_{si} not only determines the plateau phase of cardiac APs [Figure 1A; (8, 53)][1] but it is also the primary inward current during spontaneous activity of the sinus node (9, 61). When V_m is depolarized, I_{si} generates repetitive activity in atrial (10) and ventricular (8, 26, 65) fibers. The evidence that I_{si} is an inward current distinct from the fast I_{Na} has been obtained from kinetic data, from ion substitution, and from pharmacological experiments (7, 20, 41, 54, 64–66, 69, 75).

I_{si} can be described (8, 65) as $I_{si} = \bar{G}_{si} \cdot d(V,t) \cdot f(V,t) \cdot (V_m-V_o)$. The voltage ranges of steady-state activation (d_∞, Figure 1C) and inactivation (f_∞, Figure 1C) of I_{si} are different from I_{Na} (20, 54, 65, 66, 76). I_{si} can be activated from holding potentials (V_H) at which I_{Na} is completely inactivated (Figure 1 A–C), and it is still recorded after Na removal or in the presence of TTX (7, 64, 65, 69, 75). During VC steps I_{si} reaches a peak in the range –15 to 0 mV [Figure 1B; (54, 65, 66, 75)]. Inactivation is not always complete

---

[1]In contrast to suggestions by Goldman & Morad (25), "linear" instantaneous current-voltage relations with little decrease in slope [i.e. very positive "rotation potential" (25)] during the plateau of the AP are quite compatible with the concept (8, 53) of independent ion channels for I_{si} and I_{out} (G. W. Beeler, unpublished computations).

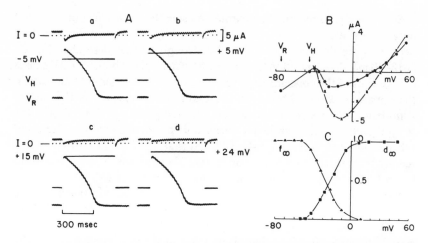

Figure 1   (A) Relation between I_{si} (upper traces) and APs (lower traces). Resting potential (V_R) –75 mV; I = 0 corresponds to V_R. VC steps (middle traces) from a holding potential (V_H) of –45 mV, at which I_{Na} is inactivated, to –5, +5, +15, and +24 mV (a–d) produce inward currents that partially inactivate during the 500 msec steps; net membrane current is zero at peak of action potential (+15 mV). (B) Current-voltage relations (ordinate μA; abscissa mV) of peak inward or outward currents 10–20 msec after beginning of VC steps (X) and currents at the end of the 500 msec VC steps (●); I = 0 at V_H. (C) Voltage range of steady-state activation (d∞) and inactivation (f∞). Experimental results from a cow ventricular trabecula; C_m = 1.6 μF; R_s = 360 Ω. [H. Reuter, unpublished experiment; for method see (66)].

during prolonged depolarization (Figure 1A). This is partly, but not exclusively (43), due to the crossover of d_∞ and f_∞ (Figure 1C; 66, 76). While the time constants of activation (τ_d) reach a maximum around –20 mV (8), the time constants of inactivation (τ_f) seem to increase continuously in the range –70 to +30 mV (8, 54, 66, 76). It is still unsettled whether the rates of inactivation and of recovery from inactivation of I_{si} are different (20, 54, 66, 76). Furthermore, since there are considerable differences in AP configuration, not only between different species but even between different parts of the same ventricle, it is not surprising that the absolute kinetic values of I_{si} (and of other currents) are somewhat variable.

Systematic ion-substitution experiments indicate that I_{si} is largely, but not exclusively, carried by Ca ions. The reversal potential, V_0, of I_{si} is considerably more negative than the Ca equilibrium potential calculated from the Nernst equation (54, 65, 66, 75). However, V_0 could be fitted by the constant field equation (66). The membrane ion channels carrying I_{si} have been estimated as being at least one hundred times more selective for Ca than for Na or K ions (66), which justifies the term "Ca channels." Since Na and K ions are much more concentrated than Ca ions in both the external medium and in the cytoplasm of the cell, some fraction of I_{si} is carried by these ions. This explains (66) why I_{si} does not decrease proportionally to the reduction in the external Ca concentration, $[Ca]_o$, and why Na ions are the predominant charge carriers when $[Ca]_o$ is low or absent (19, 25). With high $[Ca]_o$, Ca channels seem to saturate (29, 65), indicating deviation from the independence principle (29, 78). Furthermore, the influence of intracellular electrolyte composition on ion permeabilities and selectivities of Ca channels (48, 49) is unknown in cardiac muscle.

Intracellular Ca injection in Purkinje fibers seems to increase I_{si} in the range −65 to −35 mV (37), an effect opposite to that seen in snail neurons (49). Such an effect could arise from an involvement of the sarcoplasmic reticulum (37), but more likely from a negative shift of d_∞ and f_∞ along the voltage axis, or from changes in the ion permeabilities of the channels.

Most significantly, adrenergic and cholinergic transmitters have a strong effect on I_{si}. β-Adrenergic drugs increase I_{si} (64; reviewed in 10, 65, 77), while muscarinic agonists reduce it (21, 74). A recent analysis of the epinephrine effect on I_{si} (67) indicates that neither the kinetics of I_{si} nor the selectivity of the corresponding conductance channels are altered by the drug. However, the limiting conductance, $\overline{G}_{si}$, is greatly increased. This has been interpreted as caused by an increase in the number of functional Ca channels (67). The same conclusion has been reached on the basis of more indirect results (59). Figure 2 shows a hypothetical scheme involving cell metabolism for the regulation of the availability of Ca channels (46, 67, 73). Catecholamines may increase the availability of functional channels by a cAMP-dependent phosphorylation reaction (27, 59, 67, 73, 77), while ace-

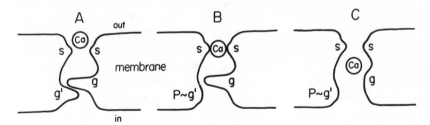

Figure 2 Hypothetical scheme for regulation of Ca channels in cardiac muscle. The channel contains a filter (s) determining its Ca selectivity (78), and two gates (g and g'); g is the voltage-dependent d,f gate [assuming coupled activation - inactivation reactions (23,78)]; g' is a phosphorylation-dependent, voltage-independent gate. Phosphorylation of g' may be due to a cAMP-dependent proteinkinase reaction (27); dephosphorylation may depend on a phosphatase. (A) Without phosphorylation g' is closed and hence channels are not available. (B) Channels are available but nonconducting when g' is phosphorylated (P~g') but g is closed. (C) Phosphorylated channels conduct when g opens upon depolarization of the membrane.

tylcholine could reduce the availability by dephosphorylation of the channels, possibly either by a decrease in cAMP or by an increase in cGMP (71). This implies that the respective ratios cAMP/cGMP could regulate the number of functional channels and thereby also the contractility of the heart (15).

It would be highly desirable to have specific inhibitors for Ca channels, like TTX for Na channels. Although verapamil and its methoxy derivative, D 600, have been proposed as such inhibitors (14), they unfortunately lack the desired specificity. In addition to the reduction of I_{si}, they alter its kinetics (58) and have considerable depressant effects on I_{Na} [$\dot{V}_{max}$, (4)] and I_{out} (41), although the action of these drugs on I_{si}, particularly of the (−)isomers (4), is somewhat more potent. Similarly, La, Mn, and related ions must be used with caution as Ca channel blockers, since they also have effects on I_{out} (41). Moreover, Mn ions are themselves quite permeable (62).

Both an increase (82) and a reduction (55) of I_{si} by nontoxic concentrations of cardiac glycosides have been reported. A novel, transient, inward current (TI), partly carried by Na ions, has been described as occurring during toxic concentrations of these drugs (44, 52). TI is responsible for certain digitalis-induced arrhythmias in Purkinje fibers (52). It resembles neither I_{Na} nor I_{si} but may depend on shifts of intracellular Ca. Binding of Ca to the inner surface of the membrane could open rather nonspecific ion channels, thus inducing TI (44).

Slow APs can be generated from a depolarized membrane potential (around −50 mV) at which I_{Na} is inactivated. They are often called "slow responses" or "Ca action potentials" since they depend on I_{si} (8, 13, 65). The literature on these APs is vast (13) and cannot be reviewed in this article. However, since slow responses are often used as indicators for I_{si}, particularly in pharmacological studies, a word of caution may be in order. In most instances it is very difficult to decide without VC analysis, whether external conditions and drugs have altered I_{si}, or I_{out}, or both. Since I_{out} is not negligible during the flow of I_{si}, slow responses, their $\dot{V}_{max}$, and their amplitudes can be altered by changes in either current component.

CONCLUSIONS

The existence of two separate inward membrane currents, I_{Na} and I_{si}, in cardiac cell membranes is well established. Although up to now technical limitations of the VC method have not permitted a quantitative evaluation of I_{Na}, there are sufficient data to conclude that I_{Na} in cardiac muscle is probably similar to that in other excitable cells. While I_{Na} is responsible for the rapid rising phase of the AP, I_{si} is activated by this depolarization and generates the plateau of the AP. Under normal conditions I_{si} is carried primarily by Ca ions and can be described by Hodgkin-Huxley kinetics. An intriguing feature of I_{si} is its modulation by adrenergic and cholinergic transmitters. The number of functional Ca channels may be regulated by cyclic nucleotides in the cell (chemical gating). Embryonic development of cardiac cells, a topic that could not be covered in this review, may provide an unique model for further investigation of channel regulation.

ACKNOWLEDGMENT

Support by the Swiss National Science Foundation is gratefully acknowledged.

Literature Cited

1. Adrian, R. H., Chandler, W. K., Hodgkin, A. L. 1970. Voltage clamp experiments in striated muscle fibres. *J. Physiol. London* 208:607–44
2. Attwell, D., Cohen, I. 1977. The voltage clamp of multicellular preparations. *Prog. Biophys. Mol. Biol.* 31:201–45
3. Baer, M., Best, P. M., Reuter, H. 1976. Voltage-dependent action of tetrodotoxin in mammalian cardiac muscle. *Nature* 263:344–45
4. Bayer, R., Kalusche, D., Kaufmann, R., Mannhold, R. 1975. Inotropic and electrophysiological actions of verapamil and D 600 in mammalian myocardium. III. Effects of optical isomers on transmembrane action potentials. *Naunyn-Schmiedeberg's Arch. Pharmacol.* 290:81–97
5. Beeler, G. W., McGuigan, J. A. S. 1978. Voltage clamping of multicellular cardiac preparations; capabilities and limitations of existing methods. *Prog. Biophys. Mol. Biol.* In press
6. Beeler, G. W. Jr., Reuter, H. 1970. Voltage clamp experiments on ventricular myocardium fibres. *J. Physiol. London* 207:165–90
7. Beeler, G. W. Jr., Reuter, H. 1970. Membrane calcium current in ventricular myocardium fibres. *J. Physiol. London* 207:191–209
8. Beeler, G. W., Reuter, H. 1977. Reconstruction of the action potential of ventricular myocardial fibres. *J. Physiol. London* 268:177–210
9. Brown, H. F., Giles, W., Noble, S. J. 1977. Membrane currents underlying activity in frog sinus venosus. *J. Physiol. London* 271:783–816
10. Brown, H. F., McNaughton, P. A., Noble, D., Noble, S. J. 1975. Adrenergic control of pacemaker currents. *Philos. Trans. R. Soc. Lond. Ser. B.* 270:527–37

11. Chen, C.-M., Gettes, L. S., Katzung, B. G. 1975. Effect of lidocaine and quinidine on steady-state characteristics and recovery kinetics of $(dV/dt)_{max}$ in guinea pig ventricular myocardium. *Circ. Res.* 37:20–29
12. Cohen, I. S., Strichartz, G. R. 1977. On the voltage-dependent action of tetrodotoxin. *Biophys. J.* 17:275–79
13. Cranefield, P. F. 1975. *The Conduction of the Cardiac Impulse.* Mount Kisco, NY: Futura. 404 pp.
14. Fleckenstein, A. 1977. Specific pharmacology of calcium in myocardium, cardiac pacemaker, and vascular smooth muscle. *Ann. Rev. Pharmacol. Toxicol.* 17:149–66
15. Flitney, F. W., Lamb, J. F., Singh, J. 1978. Intracellular cyclic nucleotides and contractility of the hypodynamic frog ventricle. *J. Physiol. London* 276:38–39P
16. Fosset, M., De Barry, J., Lenoir, M.-C., Lazdunski, M. 1977. Analysis of molecular aspects of Na^+ and Ca^{2+} uptakes by embryonic cardiac cells in culture. *J. Biol. Chem.* 252:6112–17
17. Fozzard, H. A. 1977. Heart: excitation-contraction coupling. *Ann. Rev. Physiol.* 39:201–20
18. Fozzard, H. A., Beeler, G. W. 1975. The voltage clamp and cardiac electrophysiology. *Circ. Res.* 37:403–13
19. Garnier, D., Rougier, O., Gargouil, Y. M., Coraboeuf, E. 1969. Analyse électrophysiologique du plateau des réponses myocardiques, mise en évidence d'un courant lent entrant en absence d'ions bivalents. *Pfluegers Arch.* 313:321–42
20. Gettes, L. S., Reuter, H. 1974. Slow recovery from inactivation of inward currents in mammalian myocardial fibres. *J. Physiol. London* 240:703–24

21. Giles, W., Noble, S. J. 1976. Changes in membrane currents in bullfrog atrium produced by acetylcholine. *J. Physiol. London* 261:103–23

22. Glitsch, H. G., Reuter, H., Scholz, H. 1970. The effect of the internal sodium concentration on calcium fluxes in isolated guinea-pig auricles. *J. Physiol. London* 209:25–43

23. Goldman, L. 1976. Kinetics of channel gating in excitable membranes. *Q. Rev. Biophys.* 9:491–526

24. Goldman, Y., Morad, M. 1977. Measurement of transmembrane potential and current in cardiac muscle: a new voltage clamp method. *J. Physiol. London* 268:613–54

25. Goldman, Y., Morad, M. 1977. Ionic membrane conductance during the time course of the cardiac action potential. *J. Physiol. London* 268:655–95

26. Grant, A. O., Katzung, B. G. 1976. The effects of quinidine and verapamil on electrically induced automaticity in the ventricular myocardium of guinea pig. *J. Pharmacol. Exp. Ther.* 196:407–19

27. Greengard, P. 1976. Possible role for cyclic nucleotides and phosphorylated membrane proteins in postsynaptic actions of neurotransmitters. *Nature* 260:101–8

28. Haas, H. G., Kern, R., Einwächter, H. M., Tarr, M. 1971. Kinetics of Na inactivation in frog atria. *Pfluegers Arch.* 323:141–57

29. Hagiwara, S. 1973. Ca spike. *Adv. Biophys.* 4:71–102

30. Heistracher, P. 1971. Mechanism of action of antifibrillatory drugs. *Naunyn-Schmiedeberg's Arch. Pharmacol.* 269:199–219

31. Hille, B. 1977. Local anesthetics: hydrophilic and hydrophobic pathways for the drug-receptor reaction. *J. Gen. Physiol.* 69:497–515

32. Hondeghem, L. M. 1978. Validity of $\dot{V}_{max}$ as a measure of the sodium current in cardiac and nervous tissues. *Biophys. J.* 23:147–52

33. Hondeghem, L. M., Katzung, B. G. 1977. Time- and voltage-dependent interactions of antiarrhythmic drugs with cardiac sodium channels. *Biochim. Biophys. Acta* 472:373–98

34. Honerjäger, P., Reiter, M. 1977. The cardiotoxic effect of batrachotoxin. *Naunyn-Schmiedeberg's Arch. Pharmacol.* 299:239–52

35. Honerjäger, P., Reiter, M. 1977. Sarcolemmal sodium permeability and contractile force of guinea pig papillary muscle: effects of germitrine. *Circ. Res.* 40:90–98

36. Horackova, M., Vassort, G. 1974. Excitation-contraction coupling in frog heart. Effect of veratrine. *Pfluegers Arch.* 352:291–302

37. Isenberg, G. 1977. Cardiac Purkinje fibres. The slow inward current component under the influence of modified $[Ca^{2+}]_i$. *Pfluegers Arch.* 371:61–69

38. Jack, J. J. B., Noble, D., Tsien, R. W. 1975. *Electric Current Flow in Excitable Cells.* Oxford: Clarendon Press. 502 pp.

39. Jakobsson, E., Barr, L., Connor, J. A. 1975. An equivalent circuit for small atrial trabeculae of frog. *Biophys. J.* 15:1069–85

40. Johnson, E. A., Lieberman, M. 1971. Heart: excitation and contraction. *Ann. Rev. Physiol.* 33:479–532

41. Kass, R. S., Tsien, R. W. 1975. Multiple effects of calcium antagonists on plateau currents in cardiac Purkinje fibers. *J. Gen. Physiol.* 66:169–92

42. Kass, R. S., Tsien, R. W. 1975. Analysis of the three-microelectrode method as applied to inward currents in cardiac Purkinje fibers. *Biophys. J.* 15:257a

43. Kass, R. S., Siegelbaum, S., Tsien, R. W. 1976. Incomplete inactivation of the slow inward current in cardiac Purkinje fibres. *J. Physiol. London* 263:127–28P

44. Kass, R. S., Tsien, R. W., Weingart, R. 1978. Ionic basis of transient inward current induced by strophanthidin in cardiac Purkinje fibres. *J. Physiol. London* 281:209–26

45. Kléber, A. G. 1973. Effects of sucrose solution on the longitudinal tissue resistivity of trabecular muscle from mammalian heart. *Pfluegers Arch.* 345:195–205

46. Kohlhardt, M., Kübler, M. 1975. The influence of metabolic inhibitors upon the transmembrane slow inward current in the mammalian ventricular myocardium. *Naunyn-Schmiedeberg's Arch. Pharmacol.* 290:265–74

47. Kootsey, J. M., Johnson, E. A. 1972. Voltage clamp of cardiac muscle. A theoretical analysis of early currents in the single sucrose gap. *Biophys. J.* 12:1496–1508

48. Kostyuk, P. G., Krishtal, O. A. 1977. Separation of sodium and calcium currents in the somatic membrane of mollusc neurones. *J. Physiol. London* 270:545–68

49. Kostyuk, P. G., Krishtal, O. A. 1977. Effects of calcium and calcium-chelating agents on the inward and outward current in the membrane of mollusc

neurones. *J. Physiol. London* 270: 569–80
50. Ku, D. A., Akera, T., Frank, M., Brody, T. M., Iwasa, J. 1977. The effects of grayanotoxin I and α-dihydrograyanotoxin II on guinea pig myocardium. *J. Pharmacol. Exp. Ther.* 200:363–72
51. Langer, G. A. 1973. Heart: excitation-contraction coupling. *Ann. Rev. Physiol.* 35:55–86
52. Lederer, W. J., Tsien, R. W. 1976. Transient inward current underlying arrhythmogenic effects of cardiotonic steroids in Purkinje fibres. *J. Physiol. London* 263:73–100
53. McAllister, R. E., Noble, D., Tsien, R. W. 1975. Reconstruction of the electrical activity of cardiac Purkinje fibres. *J. Physiol. London* 251:1–59
54. McDonald, T. F., Trautwein, W. 1978. Membrane currents in cat myocardium: separation of inward and outward components. *J. Physiol. London* 274:193–216
55. McDonald, T. F., Nawrath, H., Trautwein, W. 1975. Membrane currents and tension in cat ventricular muscle treated with cardiac glycosides. *Circ. Res.* 37:674–82
56. McGuigan, J. A. S. 1974. Some limitations of the double sucrose gap, and its use in a study of the slow outward current in mammalian ventricular muscle. *J. Physiol. London* 240:775–806
57. Narahashi, T. 1974. Chemicals as tools in the study of excitable membranes. *Physiol. Rev.* 54:813–89
58. Nawrath, H., Ten Eick, R. E., McDonald, T. F., Trautwein, W. 1977. On the mechanism underlying the action of D-600 on slow inward current and tension in mammalian myocardium. *Circ. Res.* 40:408–14
59. Niedergerke, R., Page, S. 1977. Analysis of catecholamine effects in single atrial trabeculae of the frog heart. *Proc. R. Soc. Lond. Ser. B.* 197:333–62
60. Noble, D. 1975. *The Initiation of the Heart Beat.* Oxford: Clarendon Press. 156 pp.
61. Noma, A., Irisawa, H. 1976. Membrane currents in the rabbit sinoatrial node cell as studied by the double microelectrode method. *Pfluegers Arch.* 364:45–52
62. Ochi, R. 1976. Manganese-dependent propagated action potentials and their depression by electrical stimulation in guinea-pig myocardium perfused by sodium-free media. *J. Physiol. London* 263:139–56

63. Ravens, U. 1976. Electromechanical studies of an *Anemonia sulcata* toxin in mammalian cardiac muscle. *Naunyn-Schmiedeberg's Arch. Pharmacol.* 269: 73–78
64. Reuter, H. 1967. The dependence of slow inward current in Purkinje fibres on the extracellular calcium-concentration. *J. Physiol. London* 192:479–92
65. Reuter, H. 1973. Divalent cations as charge carriers in excitable membranes. *Prog. Biophys. Mol. Biol.* 26:1–43
66. Reuter, H., Scholz, H. 1977. A study of the ion selectivity and the kinetic properties of the calcium-dependent slow inward current in mammalian cardiac muscle. *J. Physiol. London* 264:17–47
67. Reuter, H., Scholz, H. 1977. The regulation of the Ca conductance of cardiac muscle by adrenaline. *J. Physiol. London* 264:49–62
68. Reuter, H., Baer, M., Best, P. M. 1978. Voltage dependence of tetrodotoxin action in mammalian cardiac muscle. In *Biophysical Aspects of Cardiac Muscle,* ed. M. Morad. New York: Academic.
69. Rougier, O., Vassort, G., Garnier, D., Gargouil, Y. M., Coraboeuf, E. 1969. Existence and role of a slow inward current during the frog atrial action potential. *Pfluegers Arch.* 308:91–110
70. Salama, G., Morad, M. 1977. Use of fluorescent dyes to evaluate single sucrose gap voltage clamp technique in frog heart. *Biophys. J.* 17:5a
71. Sandoval, I. V., Cuatrecasas, P. 1976. Opposing effects of cyclic AMP and cyclic GMP on protein phosphorylation in tubulin preparations. *Nature* 262: 511–13
72. Siegelbaum, S. A., Tsien, R. W., Kass, R. S. 1977. Role of intracellular calcium in the transient outward current of calf Purkinje fibres. *Nature* 269:611–13
73. Sperelakis, N., Schneider, J. A. 1976. A metabolic control mechanism for calcium ion influx that may protect the ventricular myocardial cell. *Am. J. Cardiol.* 37:1079–85
73a. Strichartz, G., Cohen, I. 1978. $\dot{V}_{max}$ as a measure of $\bar{G}_{Na}$ in nerve and cardiac membranes. *Biophys. J.* 23:153–56
74. Ten Eick, R., Nawrath, H., McDonald, T. F., Trautwein, W. 1976. On the mechanism of the negative inotropic effect of acetylcholine. *Pfluegers Arch.* 361:207–13
75. Trautwein, W. 1973. Membrane currents in cardiac muscle fibers. *Physiol. Rev.* 53:793–835
76. Trautwein, W., McDonald, T. F., Tripathi, O. 1975. Calcium conduc-

tance and tension in mammalian ventricular muscle. *Pfluegers Arch.* 354: 55–74

77. Tsien, R. W. 1977. Cyclic AMP and contractile activity in heart. *Adv. Cyclic Nucleotide Res.* 8:363–420

78. Ulbricht, W. 1977. Ionic channels and gating currents in excitable membranes. *Ann. Rev. Biophys. Bioeng.* 6:7–31

79. Van Winkle, W. B., Schwartz, A. 1976. Ions and inotropy. *Ann. Rev. Physiol.* 38:247–72

80. Weidmann, S. 1955. The effect of the cardiac membrane potential on the rapid availability of the sodium carrying system. *J. Physiol. London* 127:213–24

81. Weidmann, S. 1974. Heart: electrophysiology. *Ann. Rev. Physiol.* 36: 155–69

82. Weingart, R., Kass, R. S., Tsien, R. W. 1978. Is digitalis inotropy associated with enhanced slow inward calcium current? *Nature* 273:389–92

83. Weld, F. M., Bigger, J. T. Jr. 1975. Effect of lidocaine on the early inward transient current in cardiac Purkinje fibers. *Circ. Res.* 37:630–39

Ann. Rev. Physiol. 1979. 41:425–40
Copyright © 1979 by Annual Reviews Inc. All rights reserved

ELECTROGENESIS OF THE ♦1229
PLATEAU AND PACEMAKER
POTENTIAL

Mario Vassalle

Department of Physiology, State University of New York
Downstate Medical Center, Brooklyn, New York 11203

INTRODUCTION

The long duration of cardiac action potentials is caused mostly by a slow phase of repolarization (plateau) interposed between a fast initial depolarization (upstroke) and a final phase of a relatively fast repolarization. Also, some cardiac cells show a diastolic depolarization that is responsible for pacemaker activity. This review presents evidence concerning the events underlying the plateau and pacemaker potential as they are presently understood. Since the literature on this subject is extensive and the space available here limited, several other reviews may be consulted on different aspects of cardiac electrophysiology (11, 12, 13, 67, 81, 82, 86, 88, 94–96, 104, 105).

ELECTROGENESIS OF THE PLATEAU

The process underlying the plateau is illustrated in detail for Purkinje fibers; differences in other tissues are then pointed out.

The experiments of Weidmann have shown that the fast sodium current is inactivated within a few milliseconds (103), the potassium channel displays an inward-going (anomalous) rectification (102), and the membrane resistance during the plateau is higher than at rest (101). Therefore, it seems likely that the plateau is due to a balance of small (not large) inward and outward currents.

The introduction of a voltage clamp method by Deck, Kern & Trautwein (15) opened the way to an intensive analysis of the ionic mechanisms

425

responsible for the plateau. The method has limitations (11, 23) as discussed by Reuter in this volume (82). Furthermore, the analysis of the individual currents flowing during a clamp requires manipulations such as ion substitution, use of pharmacological agents, and exploitation of the different kinetic properties of the currents. None of these methods is without flaws: The substitution of an ion often markedly affects the movements of others, pharmacological agents are often nonspecific in their action, and use of the different kinetic properties does not eliminate overlaps in all instances. Furthermore, ionic shifts may occur during the clamping procedures (1, 5).

The Early Outward Current

In Purkinje fibers the initial spike is followed by a relatively fast repolarization (phase 1) to the beginning of the plateau. The early outward current responsible for this effect is little affected by large changes in $[K]_o$ (19) but is drastically reduced when chloride is substituted by less permeant anions (19, 24, 80). Thus the early outward current has been attributed to a voltage- and time-dependent inward flow of chloride ions. During an action potential, the current is activated at potentials positive to −30 mV, attains its maximal value some 20 msec after the upstroke, and declines in about 30 msec to a low value, mostly because of repolarization-induced deactivation. The current is frequency-dependent and is inactivated by a preconditioning depolarization to −50 mV (80). Because of the long repriming time (removal of inactivation), this current may not be important for a fiber depolarizing at a rate of 90 min^{-1} (80). Peper & Trautwein (76) showed that the currents flowing during ("positive dynamic current" = early outward current) and after short depolarizing pulses ("negative dynamic current" = inward current tails) have the same time course and are both decreased by repetitive stimulation or preconditioning depolarization. Subsequent work of Vitek & Trautwein (99) demonstrated that the early outward component could be clearly separated from the inward tails, the first being caused by inward chloride movement and the second by inward movement of sodium and calcium. The time courses of activation and inactivation of the early outward current are markedly voltage-dependent (24).

One unexplained feature is that the reversal potential of the early outward current does not change with the omission of chloride (24, 76). Doubts have arisen recently that chloride is responsible for the early outward current. Kenyon & Gibbons (53) have shown that many chloride substitutes decrease calcium activity in the solution and induce junction potentials. Correction of these sources of error demonstrated that low chloride solutions had little effect on the action potential (53). The large outward current still present in the absence of chloride is eliminated by agents (tetraethylammonium and 4-aminopiridine) that decrease potassium conductance (J. L.

Kenyon & W. R. Gibbons, personal communication). An additional com-
plication in evaluating the effect of chloride withdrawal is that the absence
of Cl reduces potassium conductance (9). The slow inward calcium current
may control the early outward current since the latter varies with $[Ca]_o$,
D600, Mn, and recovers in a parallel fashion with the twitch (85). It must
be noted that the early outward current is not found in myocardial fibers
(see 88). An additional factor in the fast repolarization during phase 1 must
be the rapid inactivation of the fast sodium current.

The Slow Inward Current

This current is reviewed in detail by Reuter in this volume; it is discussed
here only briefly (see 82, 88). The slow inward current has a threshold of
about -55 mV, attains its maximal value at about -10 mV in about 20 msec,
and activates and inactivates as a function of voltage and time. The slow
inward current can be carried by both Na and Ca, although in some tissues
the current is carried mostly by calcium. It has a relatively long repriming
time (27, 99), which is voltage-dependent (26). The slow inward current is
not due to a residual fast conductance since it increases to a peak over
several milliseconds (76, 99) and inward tails in Na-free solution are suppressed by Mn (99). At the plateau level there is a substantial steady-state
slow inward current (see 82).

The study of the plateau has been fostered by the use of compounds
(verapamil, its methoxy-derivative D600, nifedipine, etc) that block the
slow channel as first demonstrated in the laboratory of Fleckenstein (22).
Verapamil blocks the slow inward current, shortens the plateau, and
abolishes the force of contraction of cardiac muscle. The slow channel is
nonspecific: It admits strontium and barium, while nickel, cobalt, and
manganese antagonize the slow inward current by competing with Ca. The
selectivity of several of these compounds is unsatisfactory. Mn, La, and
D600 block the slow inward current but also affect the fast inward current
and the pacemaker current (Mn and La); they decrease the activation of the
slow outward current i_{x1} and increase net time-independent outward current (49; but see 83). Manganese shifts the plateau to more negative values,
shortens it (49, 99), and at the same time increases the slope of diastolic
depolarization (49). The slow inward current (54) and the slow response
(84) are depressed by metabolic inhibitors, possibly through an increase in
intracellular Ca and/or Na (55).

The slow inward current contributes to the plateau in Purkinje fibers, in
atrial and ventricular muscle fibers (see 11, 82, 88, 94), and is the excitatory
current in the slow response recorded from these tissues under depolarized
conditions (see 12). The slow inward current is responsible also for the
excitation of the sinoatrial and atrioventricular nodes. In the sinus node, it

is possible that both Na and Ca carry the excitatory current through the slow channel. The maximum rate of rise of the sinus node action potential depends on $[Na]_o$ and on the take-off potential (70). Yet the sinus-node action potential and the slow inward current (5) are insensitive to tetrodotoxin (TTX) on one hand, and on the other are inhibited by Mn (see 4, 12). Calcium has been shown to modify the kinetic parameters of the sodium conductance and to increase the overshoot (72). The inward current in the sinus node has been separated into a fast and a slow component, both of which are abolished in Na-free solution. Therefore it has been proposed that the excitation in the sinus node is caused by entry of Na through a slow channel (74). In subsidiary sinus-node pacemakers the elimination of a fast component with TTX does not lead to quiescence because the fast component is substituted by a slow component (59). Furthermore, it appears that Na entry may be predominantly responsible for the fast component while Ca entry may cause the slow component (60).

The Slow Outward Potassium Current

The slow outward current was first demonstrated by Noble & Tsien (69): In a fiber kept at a depolarized level (–30 mV), a depolarizing clamp caused the flow of an outward current that increased progressively with time. The slow outward current has been dissected into two components, i_{x1} and i_{x2}. Only i_{x1} is activated fast enough to play a role in the configuration of normal action potential. The threshold of this current is about –40 mV and in the steady state is fully activated at +20 mV. At plateau levels, it activates with a time constant of about 500 msec and shows inward-going rectification. The reversal potential is less negative than E_K and therefore other ions contribute to this current (69).

Several workers failed to find the delayed rectification due to i_{x1}. Part of the discrepancy may be due to the masking of i_{x1} by the early outward current when depolarizing clamps are applied from the resting potential. In fact, Reuter (80) found that when the early outward current was abolished by repeated pulses, a slowly increasing outward current became apparent. However, part of the discrepancy arises because a slow outward current is present in the tissue of one species but is absent or very small in the same tissue of other species (see 94). The difference in importance of potassium currents to various tissues is underlined by the fact that the increase in potassium movements with activity is far larger in Purkinje than in ventricular muscle fibers (77).

Background Currents

There are several inward and outward background currents. The finding that on depolarization the membrane resistance increases (102) in the presence and in the absence of sodium (7, 16, 21) has been attributed to the anomalous (inward-going) rectification of a time-independent background potassium channel that shows a negative slope in the current-voltage relation (21). Such a decrease is also shown by potassium efflux measured as a function of clamps to different potentials (34). The reversal potential of this current is shifted in a depolarizing direction by an increase in $[K]_o$ and the rectification disappears when K is omitted from the solution (21).

A sodium background current in Purkinje fibers is certainly present, since the resting potential is less negative than the potassium equilibrium potential (68, 76, 92). Substitution of Na with choline often increases the resting potential (18, 92), although hyperpolarization is not always found since choline may enter the fibers (3). The marked shortening of the action potential (18) and the reduction of the steady-state inward current [(20); see (88), p. 819] in Na-free solutions may indicate that the background Na current is important at the plateau as well. A background chloride current especially large at depolarized levels is demonstrated by the results of Carmeliet (7) and by the decrease in steady-state outward current when Cl is omitted (16, 19, but see 9).

Electrogenic Sodium Pump

Several examples show that sodium extrusion is electrogenic following hypothermia or overdrive (see 95). When the sinus node is returned from a K-free solution to normal-K solution (71), or Purkinje fibers perfused in Na-free solution are exposed to a small concentration of sodium (106), a hyperpolarization occurs that is abolished by interfering with the sodium pump. Also, an electrogenic sodium current has been shown to contribute to the plateau of Purkinje fibers (48).

Possible Relation Between Calcium and Outward Currents

Calcium appears to influence several outward currents. Increasing $[Ca]_o$ shortens the action potential through an increase in the background potassium current (50) while the slow outward current is actually decreased (49). High calcium shifts the activation curves and the reversal potential of both the slow outward current and the pacemaker current (17). It may inhibit the Na-K pump and thus cause a local accumulation of potassium which, in turn, increases the potassium background current (17). Intracellular injection of calcium in cardiac Purkinje fibers shortens the action potential and causes a transient hyperpolarization through an increase in potassium conductance of the time-independent and of the pacemaker channels (46, 47). Calcium increases radioactive potassium movements in active but not in quiescent fibers; this effect is larger when the rate of stimulation is low (65).

Effect of Neurotransmitters and Autonomic Agents on the Plateau Duration

Acetylcholine markedly shortens the action potential of atrial fibers through an increase in potassium conductance (see 58) and a reduction in the slow inward current (28, 29, 43, 87). In low concentrations, acetylcholine decreases potassium movements (62), and this action is brought about by the stimulation of a nicotinic receptor (63, 58).

Catecholamines shift the plateau in a depolarizing direction and shorten the action potential (79). Catecholamines increase the slow inward current [(78, 98); whether carried by calcium or sodium (33, 83, 98)], which explains the more positive plateau; they increase the slow outward current, which accounts for the shorter action potential (89). The stimulation of an electrogenic sodium-potassium pump (see 94, 95, 96) may contribute to the shortening of the plateau, to the more negative maximum diastolic depolarization, and to the repolarization of cardiac fibers with a low resting potential (25). Catecholamines increase the amplitude and duration of the slow response in cardiac Purkinje fibers, an effect that is blocked by Mn and beta blocker antagonists (10, see 12).

Effect of the Heart Rate on Plateau Duration

The effects of a change in heart rate on the plateau are rather complex (see 8). Only the changes occurring in Purkinje fibers are considered here. With an increase in rate, phase 1 is slowed, the notch disappears, and the plateau becomes shorter. A shorter diastole curtails the repriming of the early outward (24) and slow inward (27, 99) currents, which are therefore smaller during the following action potential—hence the slowing of phase 1 and the more negative plateau. For the same reason, the slow outward current is only partially deactivated and contributes to the shortening of the next action potential (39). An incomplete repriming of the fast sodium channel (35) will reduce the rate of rise and the amplitude of the upstroke with a smaller activation of the early outward current. In addition, an increase in rate temporarily increases $[K]_o$ as shown by measurement of coronary sinus potassium (56) and extracellular K (57), and by electrical recordings (93). As the cell loses K and gains Na, the Na-K pump is stimulated and an electrogenic sodium extrusion increases the maximum diastolic potential with long drives (93). With repeated stimulation, calcium may accumulate in the fiber, thereby increasing K conductance (46, 47). In fact, the increase in K movements with stimulation (77) are more pronounced in the presence of high calcium (65).

Prolongation of the Plateau

Agents that increase the inward currents or decrease the outward currents increase the plateau duration. Veratridine increases the amplitude and duration of the plateau by markedly slowing the inactivation of the fast sodium current (42). These results resemble those obtained with aconitine, which also increases the sodium current and modifies the kinetics of the fast sodium channel (75).

The plateau is increased by agents that increase the slow inward current. Fluoride increases the contractile force, prolongs the action potential, and elicits slow responses when the fast channel has been inactivated. Since the slow responses induced by fluoride are eliminated by Mn and D600, it was concluded that fluoride increases the density of the slow channels (100). Tetraethylammonium markedly prolongs the action potential of Purkinje and ventricular muscle fibers, probably by slowing delayed rectification (36). A lower $[K]_o$ decreases potassium conductance (7, 91), and this prolongs the plateau (91). Barium decreases potassium conductance and therefore induces depolarization (41, 51).

Computer Reconstruction of the Action Potential of Purkinje Fibers

In a computer reconstruction of the action potential (66) the upstroke is brought about by sodium entry. The upstroke activates the early outward current, which brings about the initial repolarization (phase 1). The early outward current is deactivated by this initial repolarization, and the onset of the slow inward current provokes a secondary depolarization (the notch). The activation of the slow outward current together with the time-dependent inactivation of the slow inward current eventually brings the potential to a value where the steady-state current–voltage relationship is outward and the plateau is terminated.

The earlier a short hyperpolarizing clamp is applied during the plateau (92), the more negative is the threshold for all-or-none repolarization (14, 101). The finding supports the above description of events during the plateau (66). The initial predominance of the slow inward current, the gradual growth of the slow outward current, and the removal of anomalous rectification at more negative potentials cause the instantaneous current–voltage relation to be N-shaped and to shift with time in an outward direction. A pulse negative to the threshold is followed by a repolarization to the maximum diastolic potential because the net current is outward. Later the instantaneous voltage–current relation moves in an outward direction, and therefore the threshold shifts to more positive values. At the beginning of phase 3, the speed of repolarization is determined by the membrane capacity and the magnitude of the steady-state outward current.

In frog ventricles there is a threshold for repolarization with long (30–50 msec) pulses (but not with pulses shorter than 20 msec), and the threshold shifts to more positive values during the plateau. On the basis of these and several other findings, Goldman & Morad (31–33) conclude that the quasi-instantaneous current–voltage relation during the plateau is linear. During repolarizing pulses of long duration (>30 msec), the sodium conductance is deactivated and K conductance is activated sufficiently for the current voltage relation to *become* N-shaped. If the repolarizing pulse is long enough, the net current is outward at the end of the pulse, and repolarization to the resting potential follows. These experiments suggest that the electrogenesis of the plateau is likely to be different in different tissues.

THE ELECTROGENESIS OF THE PACEMAKER POTENTIALS

A pacemaker potential (diastolic depolarization) is present in various cardiac tissues.

Pacemaker Potential in Purkinje Fibers

The use of voltage-clamp methods has substantially advanced our understanding of the diastolic depolarization. In a first approach, Deck & Trautwein (16) clamped Purkinje fibers at the plateau and found that, on clamping back to the resting potential, a brief inward current is followed by an outward current due to a delayed increase in K conductance. The outward current declined with a time constant of 250–300 msec and reversed its polarity at potentials negative to E_K. The outward-current tail appeared with repolarizations more negative than –50 mV, and this value was taken as the threshold for the activation of the pacemaker current. Deck & Trautwein (16) concluded that diastolic depolarization is due to a time-dependent fall of a potassium conductance that was triggered by sufficiently large repolarizations. In a different approach, Vassalle (92) allowed the preparations to develop spontaneous action potentials and clamped the potential at the maximum diastolic value: An inward current was recorded that increased with a time constant of about 1.5 sec and would have caused diastolic depolarization in the absence of clamp. This could be ascertained because the potential was either allowed to follow its "natural" time course or was kept constant while the current underlying the process of diastolic depolarization was measured [see (92), Figures 1–3]. Thus, diastolic depolarization and the ionic current underlying it could be directly related. In such an approach all other currents flowing during the action potential have their usual value at the beginning of diastolic depolarization; therefore these currents either do not contribute to the pacemaker current or else would contribute to both the pacemaker potential and the recorded pacemaker current. That previous depolarization at the plateau is not required for the presence of a pacemaker current was demonstrated by clamping the resting potential of quiescent fibers to more negative values: An inward current flows that increases with time toward a steady value. If the potential is clamped back to the resting potential, a tail of decreasing inward current follows due to the reactivation of the pacemaker current. Thus, the pacemaker current is already (partially) activated at the resting potential. The reversal of this current with more negative clamps and the increase in membrane resistance during the clamp allowed the conclusion that diastolic depolarization is due to a time-dependent fall in potassium conductance (92).

Noble & Tsien (68) investigated the kinetic and rectifier properties of the pacemaker current, which they labelled i_{K2}. In the steady state, the current is deactivated at -90 mV and fully activated at -50 mV. On depolarization, the pacemaker current activates rapidly but shows inward-going (anomalous) rectification with a negative slope (68), so that at zero potential the current becomes very small (40). Because of these characteristics the pacemaker current contributes little to the time-dependent changes occurring during the plateau. As the gating variable s attains its maximal value during the plateau and the effects of inward-going rectification are removed on repolarization, the membrane reaches the maximum diastolic potential. As discussed above, the pacemaker channel then begins to deactivate with a time constant typical of that negative potential. As the pacemaker current becomes smaller, the inward-going rectification of i_{K1}, i_{K2} (68), and possibly a sodium component (66) allow the attainment of threshold.

Pacemaker Potential in the Sinus Node

Voltage clamping in the sinus node is made more difficult by the histological characteristics of this tissue. Irisawa (45) found that diastolic depolarization in the sinus node is due to a slow deactivation of a potassium current, a finding confirmed since (5, 73). Noma & Irisawa (73) showed that in the steady state the pacemaker current is deactivated below -50 mV and is fully activated at $+20$ mV. A reversal potential is observed only at $[K]_o$ higher than usual (see also 5) and shifts by 58 mV for a ten-fold increase in $[K]_o$. The difference between the resting and the reversal potential increases at low $[K]_o$ due to a large background current. Inward-going rectification (with no negative slope) persists in the absence of Cl or Na. The pacemaker current in the sinus node resembles the slow outward current i_{x1} in Purkinje fibers but is carried selectively by K ions (73).

The frog sinus venosus has two time-dependent outward currents (5): A selective K current has a threshold at about -70 mV, a maximal activation at about 0 mV, and decays slowly; the other current has an activation curve between -40 and $+10$ mV and decays rapidly. Both components participate in the repolarization and deactivate during diastolic depolarization. A third current is activated at more negative potentials and does not show reversal. The slow inward current contributes to the latter part of pacemaker potential (5).

The pacemaker potential in both sinus node and Purkinje fibers is due to a time-dependent fall in potassium conductance. In the presence of an inward background current, the decay of the outward potassium current leads to diastolic depolarization. The conditioning role of the background inward current in diastolic depolarization is due to the fact that in the absence of a background inward current the potential would be at a value (E_K) where a decrease in time-dependent potassium conductance would fail to depolarize.

The importance of calcium as a carrier of the inward current in the sinus node is stressed by the fact that an increase in $[Ca]_o$ increases the sinus rate (see 4). Also, calcium antagonists suppress sinus-node and atrioventricular-node pacemaker activity by flattening diastolic depolarization and by reducing the rate of rise and the amplitude of the action potential. However, sodium-channel antagonists like lidocaine and procaine in high doses also reduce the activity of the sinus node (see 22).

Pacemaker Potential in Myocardial Fibers

Pacemaker activity can also be demonstrated in myocardial fibers by applying long depolarizing pulses (44, 51, 52). After an action potential and during clamps at values positive to the resting potential there is a tail of outward current that reverses during clamps at potentials more negative than the resting potential. The reversal potential is close to the calculated potassium equilibrium potential and varies 60 mV with a ten-fold change in external $[K]_o$. The range of activation is -30 to $+20$ mV, and it decays at -90 mV with a time constant of 100 msec (52). This form of the pacemaker activity is also recorded in other myocardial tissues and is due to the deactivation of the slow outward current i_{x1} during diastole. In Purkinje fibers depolarized at -60 mV or less, the pacemaker current is fully activated, and pacemaker activity is also brought about by a decay of the slow outward current (38). Pacemaker activity of this type and special (triggered) activity have been extensively reviewed by Cranefield [(12, 13), this volume].

Effect of Neuromediators

As reported above, the mechanism of the inhibitory action of acetylcholine includes an increase in potassium conductance and a decrease in calcium influx in the sinus node and atrial tissues. The mechanism by which acetylcholine decreases inward calcium current may be related to an increase in cyclic GMP: Intracellular injection of this nucleotide also reduces this current (43) and decreases diastolic depolarization (90). In contrast to its effect in the sinus node, acetylcholine has but a small stimulatory effect on potassium uptake in Purkinje fibers (64).

The mechanism of the acceleratory action of catecholamines is different in the atrial pacemakers and in Purkinje fibers. In atrial fibers made automatic by depolarizing pulses, epinephrine induces an increase in both the slow inward current and the slow outward current i_{x1} (6). These changes explain the increase in amplitude of the overshoot and of the maximum diastolic depolarization. The enhanced diastolic depolarization is probably due to an increase in the inward current. In Purkinje fibers, instead, the steepening of diastolic depolarization is due to a shift in a depolarizing direction of the activation curve of the pacemaker current i_{K2}. This factor and a decrease in the time constant of decay increase the slope of diastolic depolarization (37). As mentioned above, catecholamines also stimulate the sodium-potassium pump with electrogenic characteristics, and this may be responsible for the increase in maximum diastolic potential (see 94, 95). In low concentrations, catecholamines decrease potassium uptake in Purkinje fibers; this response seems to be mediated by an alpha receptor (2, 78).

Overdrive Suppression

Driving cardiac pacemakers at a rate higher than their spontaneous rate is followed by a period of quiescence ("overdrive suppression"). The phenomenon has been recently reviewed (95) and is therefore only outlined here.

In Purkinje fibers with a fast drive there is a decrease (depolarization) followed by an increase (hyperpolarization) of maximum diastolic potential with respect to pre-drive value. The initial depolarization has been attributed to an accumulation of K on the basis of electrical measurements (93) and measurement of coronary sinus potassium (56). Measurements with a K^+ liquid ion-exchange microelectrode reveal that an increase in rate induces a transient increase in $[K]_o$ that is larger when the rate is faster (57). The hyperpolarization has been attributed to the activation of a sodium-potassium pump with electrogenic characteristics (see 95). An active sodium extrusion would cause suppression by keeping the membrane potential negative to the threshold. During a prolonged drive, the coronary sinus potassium (95) and the extra-cellular K (57) return to control value in about one minute and transiently decrease below control after the end of the drive. The decline of K accumulation (57) and the hyperpolarization (95) during and after drive are reduced or suppressed by interventions that block the pump or its metabolic supply. Overdrive-induced depolarization and hyperpolarization have been found also in atrial muscle fibers and are caused by similar mechanisms (30). For relatively short periods of drive, K accumulation may contribute to the following suppression. For longer periods of drive, an increase in metabolic outward current appears more important. Other factors, such as a decreased inward driving force for Na, may also contribute to the suppression. In atrial pacemakers, overdrive suppression and subsequent acceleration are mostly due to release of acetylcholine and catecholamines, respectively (61). Some suppression may be due to other factors, such as K accumulation (61, see 4).

Suppression of Automaticity By Potassium

Purkinje-fiber automaticity is suppressed by a small increase in $[K]_o$ due to a flattening of diastolic depolarization [see (94) Figure 7]. An increase in $[K]_o$ increases the potassium conductance (7, 91) and the potassium current (21), and therefore the potential is kept negative to the threshold. The resistance of the sinus node to high K seems in part related to the abundant sympathetic innervation (97) and in part to the fact that if the subsidiary pacemakers in the sinus node are depolarized somewhat by high $[K]_o$ activity is maintained by switching from a relative fast to a slow channel activation (59). An additional factor could be the increase in K conductance that may partly offset the depolarizing effect of high K.

Depolarization-induced automaticity in myocardial fibers (44, 52) is abolished by high K, in part because the reversal potential is shifted to more positive values and in part because membrane conductance increases and the potential is moved within the range of the activation curve (52).

Agents that reduce K conductance accelerate the pacemaker discharge. For example, reduction of K conductance by barium either depolarizes ventricular muscle enough to induce spontaneous activity or reduces the magnitude of depolarizing pulses needed to induce automaticity (51).

CONCLUDING REMARKS

The analysis of the ionic events underlying the electrical activity of the heart is still incomplete, but the concept is clearly emerging that there are substantial differences among different cardiac tissues and different species. The inward-going rectification of the potassium channels as well as the small magnitude of the currents flowing during the plateau have a general application. However, several currents (fast sodium current, early outward current, slow outward current, slow inward calcium current) are present in certain tissues or species but are small or absent in others. The ion species carrying some of the currents are still not clearly defined or vary with different tissues. The specificity of most of the channels is still to be established. The pacemaker potential is caused by the decay of time-dependent potassium currents that are different in different tissues.

ACKNOWLEDGMENTS

Original work reported in this paper was supported by NIH and New York Heart grants.

Literature Cited

1. Baumgarten, C. M., Isenberg, G., McDonald, T. F., Ten Eick, R. E. 1977. Depletion and accumulation of potassium in the extracellular clefts of cardiac Purkinje fibers during voltage clamp hyperpolarization and depolarization. *J. Gen. Physiol.* 70:149–69
2. Borasio, P. G., Vassalle, M. 1975. Inhibition of potassium uptake by low concentrations of norepinephrine and dibutyryl cyclic AMP. *Arch. Int. Physiol. Biochim.* 83:79–97
3. Boulpaep, E. 1963. Permeability of heart muscle to choline. *Arch. Int. Physiol.* 71:623–25
4. Brooks, C. McC., Lu, H.-H. 1972. *The Sinoatrial Pacemaker of the Heart.* Springfield, Ill.: Charles C. Thomas
5. Brown, H. F., Giles, W., Noble, S. J. 1977. Membrane currents underlying activity in frog sinus venosus. *J. Physiol. London* 271:783–816
6. Brown, H. F., Noble, S. J. 1974. Effect of adrenaline on membrane currents underlying pacemaker activity in frog atrial muscle. *J. Physiol. London* 238:51P–53P
7. Carmeliet, E. E. 1961. *Chloride and Potassium Permeability in Cardiac Purkinje Fibres.* Bruxelles: Arscia S. A./Presses Académiques Européennes
8. Carmeliet, E. E. 1977. Repolarization and frequency in cardiac cells. *J. Physiol. Paris* 73:903–23
9. Carmeliet, E. E., Verdonck, F. 1977. Reduction of potassium permeability by chloride substitution in cardiac cells. *J. Physiol. London* 265:193–206
10. Carmeliet, E. E., Vereecke, J. 1969. Adrenaline and the plateau phase of the cardiac action potential. *Pfluegers Arch.* 313:300–15
11. Coraboeuf, E. 1978. Ionic basis of electrical activity in cardiac tissues. *Am. J. Physiol.* 234:H101–16
12. Cranefield, P. F. 1975 *The Conduction of the Cardiac Impulse.* New York: Futura
13. Cranefield, P. F. 1977. Action potentials, afterpotentials, and arrhythmias. *Circ. Res.* 41:415–23
14. Cranefield, P. F., Hoffman, B. F. 1958. Propagated repolarization in heart muscle. *J. Gen. Physiol.* 41:633–49
15. Deck, K. A., Kern, R., Trautwein, W. 1964. Voltage clamp technique in mammalian cardiac fibres. *Pfluegers Arch.* 280:50–62
16. Deck, K. A., Trautwein, W. 1964. Ionic currents in cardiac excitation. *Pfluegers Arch.* 280:63–80

17. Di Francesco, D., McNaughton, P. A. 1977. The effects of calcium on outward membrane currents in Purkinje fibres from sheep hearts. *J. Physiol. London* 270:47P–48P
18. Draper, M. H., Weidmann, S. 1951. Cardiac resting and action potentials recorded with an intracellular electrode. *J. Physiol. London* 115:74–94
19. Dudel, J., Peper, K., Rüdel, R., Trautwein, W. 1967. The dynamic chloride component of membrane current in Purkinje fibers. *Pfluegers Arch.* 295:197–212
20. Dudel, J., Peper, K., Rüdel, R., Trautwein, W. 1967. The effect of tetrodotoxin on the membrane current in cardiac muscle (Purkinje fibers). *Pfluegers Arch.* 295:213–26
21. Dudel, J., Peper, K., Rüdel, R., Trautwein, W. 1967. The potassium component of membrane current in Purkinje fibers. *Pfluegers Arch.* 296:308–27
22. Fleckenstein, A. 1977. Specific pharmacology of calcium in myocardium, cardiac pacemakers, and vascular smooth muscle. *Ann. Rev. Pharmacol. Toxicol.* 17:149–66
23. Fozzard, H. A., Beeler, G. W. Jr. 1975. The voltage clamp and cardiac electrophysiology. *Circ. Res.* 37:403–13
24. Fozzard, H. A., Hiraoka, M. 1973. The positive dynamic current and its inactivation properties in cardiac Purkinje fibres. *J. Physiol. London* 234:569–86
25. Gelband, H., Rosen, M. R., Myerburg, R. J., Bush, H. L., Bassett, A. L., Hoffman, B. F. 1977. Restorative effect of epinephrine on the electrophysiologic properties of depressed human atrial tissue. *J. Electrocardiol.* 10:313–20
26. Gettes, L. S., Reuter, H. 1974. Slow recovery from inactivation of inward currents in mammalian myocardial fibres. *J. Physiol. London* 240:703–24
27. Gibbons, W. R., Fozzard, H. A. 1975. Slow inward current and contraction of sheep cardiac Purkinje fibers. *J. Gen. Physiol.* 65:367–84
29. Giles, W., Tsien, R. W. 1975. Effects of in membrane currents in bullfrog atrium produced by acetylcholine. *J. Physiol. London* 261:103–23
29. Giles, W., Tsien, W. 1975. Effects of acetylcholine on membrane currents in frog atrial muscle. *J. Physiol. London* 246:64P–66P
30. Glitsch, H. G. 1973. An effect of the electrogenic sodium pump on the membrane potential in beating guinea-pig atria. *Pfluegers Arch.* 344:169–80

31. Goldman, Y., Morad, M. 1977. Regenerative repolarization of the frog ventricular action potential: a time and voltage-dependent phenomenon. *J. Physiol. London* 268:575–611
32. Goldman, Y., Morad, M. 1977. Measurements of transmembrane potential and current in cardiac muscle: a new voltage clamp method. *J. Physiol. London* 268:613–54
33. Goldman, Y., Morad, M. 1977. Ionic membrane conductance during the time course of the cardiac action potential. *J. Physiol. London* 268:655–95
34. Haas, H. G., Kern, R. 1966. Potassium fluxes in voltage clamped Purkinje fibres. *Pfluegers Arch.* 291:69–84
35. Haas, H. G., Kern, R., Einwächter, H. M., Tarr, M. 1971. Kinetics of Na inactivation in frog atria. *Pfluegers Arch.* 323:141–57
36. Haldimann, C. 1963. Effet du tétraéthylammonium sur les potentiels de repos et d'action du coeur de mouton. *Arch. Int. Pharmacodyn.* 146:1–9
37. Hauswirth, O., Noble, D., Tsien, R. W. 1968. Adrenaline: mechanism of action on the pacemaker potential in cardiac Purkinje fibers. *Science* 162:916–17
38. Hauswirth, O., Noble, D., Tsien, R. W. 1969. The mechanism of oscillatory activity at low membrane potentials in cardiac Purkinje fibres. *J. Physiol. London* 200:255–65
39. Hauswirth, O., Noble, D., Tsien, R. W. 1972. The dependence of plateau currents in cardiac Purkinje fibres on the interval between action potentials. *J. Physiol. London* 222:27–49
40. Hauswirth, O., Noble, D., Tsien, R. W. 1972. Separation of the pacemaker and plateau components of delayed rectification in cardiac Purkinje fibres. *J. Physiol. London* 225:211–35
41. Hermsmeyer, K., Sperelakis, N. 1970. Decrease in K^+ conductance and depolarization of frog cardiac muscle produced by Ba^{++}. *Am. J. Physiol.* 219:1108–14
42. Horackova, M., Vassort, G. 1974. Excitation-contraction coupling in frog heart. Effect of veratrine. *Pfluegers Arch.* 352:291–302
43. Ikemoto, Y., Goto, M. 1978. Effects of acetylcholine and cyclic nucleotides on the bullfrog atrial muscle. In *Recent Advances in Studies on Cardiac Structure and Metabolism: Heart Function and Metabolism*, ed. T. Kobayashi, T. Sano, N. S. Dhalla, 11:57–61. Baltimore: University Park Press

44. Imanishi, S., Surawicz, B. 1976. Automatic activity in depolarized guinea pig ventricular myocardium. Characteristics and mechanisms. *Circ. Res.* 39:751–59
45. Irisawa, H. 1972. Electrical activity of rabbit sino-atrial node as studied by a double sucrose gap method. In *Prod. Satel. Symp. XXVth Int. Cong. Physiol. Sci.: The Electrical Field of the Heart*, ed. P. Rijlant, pp. 242–48. Bruxelles: Presses Académiques Européennes
46. Isenberg, G. 1975. Is potassium conductance of cardiac Purkinje fibres controlled by $[Ca^{2+}]_i$? *Nature* 253:273–74
47. Isenberg, G. 1977. Cardiac Purkinje fibres. $[Ca^{2+}]_i$ controls the potassium permeability via the conductance components g_{K1} and $\bar{g}_{K2}$. *Pfluegers Arch.* 371:77–85
48. Isenberg, G., Trautwein, W. 1974. The effect of dihydro-ouabain and lithium ions on the outward current in cardiac Purkinje fibers. *Pfluegers Arch.* 350:41–54
49. Kass, R. S., Tsien, R. W. 1975. Multiple effects of calcium antagonists on plateau currents in cardiac Purkinje fibers. *J. Gen. Physiol.* 66:169–92
50. Kass, R. S., Tsien, R. W. 1976. Control of action potential duration by calcium ions in cardiac Purkinje fibers. *J. Gen. Physiol.* 67:599–617
51. Katzung, B. G., Morgenstern, J. 1976. The effects of potassium and barium on ventricular automaticity and the pacemaker current. *Proc. West. Pharmacol. Soc.* 19:299–302
52. Katzung, B. G., Morgenstern, J. A. 1977. Effects of extracellular potassium on ventricular automaticity and evidence for a pacemaker current in mammalian ventricular myocardium. *Circ. Res.* 40:105–11
53. Kenyon, J. L., Gibbons, W. R. 1977. Effects of low-chloride solutions on action potentials of sheep cardiac Purkinje fibers. *J. Gen. Physiol.* 70:635–60
54. Kohlhardt, M., Kübler, M. 1975. The influence of metabolic inhibitors upon the transmembrane slow inward current in the mammalian ventricular myocardium. *Naunyn-Schmiedeberg's Arch. Pharmacol.* 290:265–74
55. Kohlhardt, M., Mnich, Z., Maier, G. 1977. Alterations of the excitation process of the sinoatrial pacemaker cell in the presence of anoxia and metabolic inhibitors. *J. Mol. Cell. Cardiol.* 9:477–88
56. Krellenstein, D. J., Pliam, M. B., Brooks, C. McC., Vassalle, M. 1978.

Factors affecting overdrive suppression of idioventricular pacemakers and associated potassium shifts. *J. Electrocardiol.* 11:3–10

57. Kunze, D. L. 1977. Rate-dependent changes in extracellular potassium in the rabbit atrium. *Circ. Res.* 41:122–27

58. Lipsius, S. L., Vassalle, M. 1977. Effects of acetylcholine on potassium movements in the guinea-pig sinus node. *J. Pharmacol. Exp. Ther.* 201:669–77

59. Lipsius, S. L., Vassalle, M. 1978. Dual excitatory channels in the sinus node. *J. Mol. Cell. Cardiol.* 10:753–67

60. Lipsius, S. L., Vassalle, M. 1978. Characterization of a two-component upstroke in the sinus node subsidiary pacemakers. In *The Sinus Node: Structure, Function and Clinical Relevance,* ed. F. I. M. Bonke, pp. 232–44. The Hague: M. Nijhoff.

61. Lu, H. H., Lange, G., Brooks, C. McC. 1965. Factors controlling pacemaker action in cells of the sinoatrial node. *Circ. Res.* 17:460–71

62. Musso, E., Vassalle, M. 1975. Inhibitory action of acetylcholine on potassium uptake of the sinus node. *Cardiovasc. Res.* 9:490–97

63. Musso, E., Vassalle, M. 1977. Evidence for a nicotinic receptor in the sinus node. *Eur. J. Pharmacol.* 46:1–8

64. Musso, E., Vassalle, M. 1977. The action of theophylline on potassium uptake in cardiac Purkinje fibers. *Cardiology* 62:322–31

65. Musso, E., Vassalle, M. 1978. Effects of norepinephrine, calcium, and rate of discharge on ^{42}K movements in canine cardiac Purkinje fibers. *Circ. Res.* 42:276–84

66. Mc Allister, R. E., Noble, D., Tsien, R. W. 1975. Reconstruction of the electrical activity of cardiac Purkinje fibres. *J. Physiol. London* 251:1–59

67. Noble, D. 1975. *The Initiation of the Heartbeat.* Oxford: Clarendon Press.

68. Noble, D., Tsien, R. W. 1968. The kinetic and rectifier properties of the slow potassium current in cardiac Purkinje fibres. *J. Physiol. London* 195:185–214

69. Noble, D., Tsien, R. W. 1969. Outward membrane currents activated in the plateau range of potentials in cardiac Purkinje fibres. *J. Physiol. London* 200:205–31

70. Noma, A., Irisawa, H. 1974. The effect of sodium in the initial phase of the sinoatrial pacemaker action potentials in rabbits. *Jpn. J. Physiol.* 24:617–32

71. Noma, A., Irisawa, H. 1974. Electro-genic sodium pump in rabbit sinoatrial node cell. *Pfluegers Arch.* 351:177–82

72. Noma, A., Irisawa, H. 1976. Effects of calcium ion on the rising phase of the action potential in rabbit sinoatrial node cells. *Jpn. J. Physiol.* 26:93–99

73. Noma, A., Irisawa, H. 1976. A time- and voltage-dependent potassium current in the rabbit sinoatrial node cell. *Pfluegers Arch.* 366:251–58

74. Noma, A., Yanagihara, K., Irisawa, H. 1977. Inward current of the rabbit sinoatrial node cell. *Pfluegers Arch.* 372:43–51

75. Peper, K., Trautwein, W. 1967. The effect of aconitine on the membrane current in cardiac muscle. *Pfluegers Arch.* 296:328–36

76. Peper, K., Trautwein, W. 1968. A membrane current related to the plateau of the action potential of Purkinje fibers. *Pfluegers Arch.* 303:108–23

77. Polimeni, P. I., Vassalle, M. 1970. Potassium fluxes in Purkinje and ventricular muscle fibers during rest and activity. *Am. J. Physiol.* 218:1381–88

78. Posner, P., Vassalle, M. 1971. The inhibitory action of norepinephrine on potassium uptake in cardiac Purkinje fibers. *TIT J. Life Sci.* 1:67–78

79. Reuter, H. 1967. The dependence of slow inward current in Purkinje fibres on the extracellular calcium concentration. *J. Physiol. London* 192:479–92

80. Reuter, H. 1968. Slow inactivation of currents in cardiac Purkinje fibres. *J. Physiol. London* 197:233–53

81. Reuter, H. 1973. Divalent cations as charge carriers in excitable membranes. *Prog. Biophys. Mol. Biol.* 26:1–43

82. Reuter, H. 1979. Properties of two inward membrane currents in the heart. *Ann. Rev. Physiol.* 41:413–24

83. Robinson, R. B., Sleator, W. W. 1977. Effects of Ca^{2+} and catecholamines on the guinea pig atrium action potential plateau. *Am. J. Physiol.* 233:H203–10

84. Schneider, J. A., Sperelakis, N. 1975. Slow Ca^{2+} and Na^+ responses induced by isoproterenol and methylxanthines in isolated perfused guinea pig hearts exposed to elevated K^+. *J. Mol. Cell. Cardiol.* 7:249–73

85. Siegelbaum, S. A., Tsien, R. W., Kass, R. S. 1977. Role of intracellular calcium in the transient outward current of calf Purkinje fibres. *Nature* 269:611–13

86. Sperelakis, N., Shigenobu, K., McLean, M. J. 1975. Membrane cation channels. Changes in developing hearts, in cell culture, and in organ culture. In *Developmental and Physiological Correlates*

of Cardiac Muscle: Perspectives in Cardiovascular Research, ed. M. Lieberman, T. Sano, 1:209–34. New York: Raven

87. Ten Eick, R., Nawrath, H., McDonald, T. F., Trautwein, W. 1976. On the mechanism of the negative inotropic effect of acetylcholine. Pfluegers Arch. 361:207–13

88. Trautwein, W. 1973. Membrane currents in cardiac muscle fibers. Physiol. Rev. 53:793–835

89. Tsien, R. W., Giles, W., Greengard, P. 1972. Cyclic AMP mediates the action of adrenaline on cardiac Purkinje fibres. Nature New Biol. 240:181–83

90. Tuganowski, W., Kopec, P., Kopyta, M., Wezowska, J. 1977. Iontophoretic application of autonomic mediators and cyclic nucleotides in the sinus node cells. Naunyn-Schmiedeberg's Arch. Pharmacol. 299:65–67

91. Vassalle, M. 1965. Cardiac pacemaker potentials at different extra- and intracellular K concentrations. Am. J. Physiol. 208:770–75

92. Vassalle, M. 1966. Analysis of cardiac pacemaker potential using a "voltage clamp" technique. Am. J. Physiol. 210:1335–41

93. Vassalle, M. 1970. Electrogenic suppression of automaticity in sheep and dog Purkinje fibers. Circ. Res. 27: 361–77

94. Vassalle, M. 1977. Generation and conduction of impulses in the heart under physiological and pathological conditions. Pharmacol. Ther. B. 3:1–39

95. Vassalle, M. 1977. The relationship among cardiac pacemakers: overdrive suppression. Circ. Res. 41:269–77

96. Vassalle, M. 1977. Cardiac automaticity and its control. Am. J. Physiol. 233:H625–34

97. Vassalle, M., Greineder, J. K., Stuckey, J. H. 1973. Role of the sympathetic nervous system in the sinus node resistance to high potassium. Circ. Res. 22:348–55

98. Vassort, G., Rougier, O., Garnier, D., Sauviat, M. P., Coraboeuf, E., Gargouïl, Y. M. 1969. Effects of adrenaline on membrane inward currents during the cardiac action potential. Pfluegers Arch. 309:70–81

99. Vitek, M., Trautwein, W. 1971. Slow inward current and action potential in cardiac Purkinje fibres. Pfluegers Arch. 323:204–18

100. Vogel, S., Sperelakis, N., Josephson, I., Brooker, G. 1977. Fluoride stimulation of slow Ca²⁺ current in cardiac muscle. J. Mol. Cell. Cardiol. 9:461–75

101. Weidmann, S. 1951. Effect of current flow on the membrane potential of cardiac muscle. J. Physiol. London 115:227–36

102. Weidmann, S. 1955. Rectifier properties of Purkinje fibers. Am. J. Physiol. 183:671P

103. Weidmann, S. 1955. The effect of the cardiac membrane potential on the rapid availability of the sodium-carrying system. J. Physiol. London 127:213–24

104. Weidmann, S. 1974. Heart: Electrophysiology. Ann. Rev. Physiol. 36: 155–69

105. West, T. C. 1972. Electrophysiology of the sinoatrial node. In Electrical Phenomena in the Heart, ed. W. C. DeMello, pp. 191–217. New York: Academic

106. Wiggins, J. R., Cranefield, P. F. 1974. Effect on membrane potential and electrical activity of adding sodium to sodium-depleted cardiac Purkinje fibers. J. Gen. Physiol. 64:473–93

Ann Rev. Physiol. 1979. 41:441–57

PROPAGATION MECHANISMS IN HEART ♦1230

Nick Sperelakis

Department of Physiology, School of Medicine, University of Virginia, Charlottesville, Virginia 22901

INTRODUCTION

The myocardium is composed of an assembly of short cells, separated at their ends by the intercalated disks (IDs). The fluid in the ID cleft gap is continuous with the bulk interstitial fluid (ISF), and the width of the gap averages about 200 Å. Regions where the two membranes come into closer proximity are termed the gap junctions. The ID gap width is increased by conditions that depress propagation (59, 60); a step on the rising phase of the action potential, resembling a postjunctional potential, then becomes prominent. The cell-to-cell transmission process is labile, often failing. Transmission is normally bi-directional. Contiguous cells become functionally disconnected at the IDs following focal injury (9, 11). When the myocardial cells are dissociated by proteolytic enzymes, the cells separate at the IDs (see 55).

Cardiac muscle normally behaves as a functional syncytium, i.e. stimulation of one region leads to a rapid spread of excitation to all regions. However, the mechanism(s) for the transfer of excitation between contiguous myocardial cells is not universally agreed upon. Here I review some of the most relevant facts concerning the transfer of excitation between myocardial cells and examine the major possibilities for the mechanism(s) of the transfer: (*a*) electrical, (*b*) chemical, and (*c*) mechanical. (Electrical transmission may be subdivided into three major subtypes: low-resistance coupling, capacitive coupling, and electric field coupling. All three of these subtypes are purely electrical in nature, and therefore transmission should be fast.)

0066-4278/79/0301-0441$01.00

MECHANICAL TRANSMISSION

In mechanical transmission, it is presumed that contraction of the pre-cell stretches or otherwise deforms the cell membrane of the post-cell and depolarizes it. For example, it is well known that mechanical deformation of the membrane produces depolarization in some smooth muscles and in some neurons. It has been suggested that mechanical transmission may be important between cardiac nodal cells, which conduct slowly (49). However, it is unlikely that mechanical transmission is an important mechanism in the transfer of excitation between myocardial cells because the electromechanical latency period is considerably longer than the maximum time available for transmission from one cell to the next, and propagation continues at about a normal velocity during nearly complete uncoupling of contraction from excitation.

CHEMICAL TRANSMISSION

Synaptic Transmitters

Chemical transmission requires a chemical substance, rapidly released from the prejunctional membrane during the rising phase of the action potential, that is capable of depolarizing the post-membrane. The chemical substance could be a specially synthesized compound. However, electron micrographs provide no evidence for the presence of typical synaptic vesicles.

K^+ Accumulation

A normal cell constituent such as K^+ ion could serve as a chemical messenger. During depolarization, the electrochemical driving force for net outward K^+ current increases instantaneously. Therefore, efflux of K^+ across all surfaces of the cell will suddenly increase during the rising phase of the action potential, if K^+ conductance (g_K) remains constant. The K^+ effluxing across the surface sarcolemma will tend to diffuse rapidly into and mix with the bulk ISF. However, the K^+ effluxing into the narrow ID cleft will accumulate and tend to depolarize the post-membrane. A theoretical analysis (39) indicated that the K^+ concentration in the ID cleft would increase from a baseline level of 4 mM to about 10 mM within 1 msec. Such a K^+ accumulation is sufficient to decrease E_K across the post-membrane by about 20 mV. K^+ accumulation may be at least a contributory factor in the transmission process (39).

Page & McCallister (48) proposed that transient ion accumulations occurring in the ID cleft might be electrophysiologically important. By use of K^+-sensitive microelectrodes, Kline & Morad (34) demonstrated that a K^+ accumulation of 1–2 mM occurs in the ISF of frog ventricular strips during each action potential; they suggested that much greater K^+ accumulations may occur in narrow clefts.

Consistent with the view that K^+ accumulation in the ID cleft may be important in the transfer of the signal are the observations that propagation velocity (a) increases (to a maximum) when $[K]_0$ is elevated two- to three-fold (12, 60), and (b) decreases to about 50% when cardiac muscle bundles are equilibrated in two-fold hypertonic solution [to increase the cleft volume (60); the effects were much smaller in skeletal muscle (60)].

ELECTRICAL TRANSMISSION

Low-Resistance Coupling

The simplest mechanism for cell-to-cell transmission is probably that of low-resistance connections between cells. If myocardial cells formed connections with low enough resistance, then local-circuit current could readily pass from one cell to the next and thereby spread excitation. There is a general agreement that the maximum allowable value for resistivity of the ID, if local-circuit current is to be sufficient to account for the transfer of excitation, is about 5 Ω cm^2 if the standard shunting-gap model is used (55, 67, 72, 74). The low-resistance connections are thought to occur at the gap junction (or "nexus") by means of small-diameter (10–20Å) tunnels between adjacent cells—i.e. protoplasmic continuity. The evidence in favor of this hypothesis is summarized in (68), the evidence against it in (55).

LONGITUDINAL RESISTIVITY OF THE BUNDLE   To determine whether or not there are low-resistance connections between myocardial cells, the longitudinal resistivity of muscle bundles bathed in Ringer solution was compared to that in a high-resistance solution (e.g. a mixture of 10% Ringer solution and 90% isosmotic sucrose solution). If the bundle is considered to contain two parallel current paths, an extracellular path (r_{isf}) in parallel with an intracellular path (r_{cell}), then increasing the resistance of the extracellular path should have differing effects on the resistivity of the tissue, depending on whether the cell pathway is of high or low resistance. If r_{cell} is low in resistance because the cells have low-resistance connections, then increasing r_{isf} should have a relatively small effect on longitudinal tissue resistivity (ρ_1). In contrast, if r_{cell} is high in resistance, then increasing r_{isf} should have a large effect on ρ_1.

In such experiments, Sperelakis & Hoshiko (56) found that, for cat trabeculae and papillary muscles, ρ_1 was 268 Ω cm in Ringer solution and 1876 Ω cm in high-resistance solution, a seven-fold increase (the high-resistance solution had a resistivity 8.5 times that of the normal Ringer solution). In skeletal muscle, ρ_1 increased only 1.6-fold in the high-resistance solution, thus indicating that much more of the current passes through the cell pathway in this tissue (composed of long cables). The ratio of resistivities of the cell path (R_{cell}) to ISF path (R_{isf}) for cardiac muscle was 33.5 (ratio of 0.65 expected if the IDs had zero resistance). Because the longitudinal current path through the cells was much higher in resistance than that through the ISF, it was suggested that the resistance of the ID membranes (R_{mj}) is high (calculated resistivity, corrected for ID convolutions, of 864 Ω cm^2). In related experiments, Sperelakis & Macdonald (57) found that ρ_l increased 6.3-fold in the high-resistance solution (from 296 to 1865 Ω cm), and they calculated an R_{cell}/R_{isf} ratio of 19.8 (6140 Ω cm/311 Ω cm) and an R_{mj} of 576 Ω cm^2. By use of a different technique, Weidmann (69) reported that the ratio of intracellular to extracellular longitudinal resistance in sheep and calf ventricular trabeculae was only 3.5. Clerc (5) reported a value of 3.6 for the absolute resistances and a ratio of 8.4 for the resistivities (402 Ω cm/48 Ω cm).

LENGTH CONSTANT   The argument most often used to support the concept of low-resistance connections is that the length constant (λ') measured for a cardiac muscle bundle by the method of extracellular application of current is generally between 0.5 mm and 2 mm (e.g. see 67, 69). For example, by applying constant-current pulses across the ends of ventricular trabeculae (sheep and calf) with extracellular electrodes and recording the transmembrane potential as a function of distance along the length of the bundle, Weidmann (69) obtained a length constant of 880 μm. Since λ' is at least the length of several cells, he concluded that there are low-resistance pathways between cells. Sperelakis (55) has presented several arguments relevant to the interpretation of measurements of length constant by extracellular application of current, and has cautioned that such measurements may not distinguish between low-resistance and high-resistance junctions (cf 38). In addition, it was demonstrated that the resistivity of cardiac muscle bundles was actually much higher in the transverse direction than in the longitudinal direction (5, 57).

ELECTRICAL ANISOTROPY OF CARDIAC MUSCLE

Transverse vs longitudinal resistivities   Cardiac muscle is electrically anisotropic; the tissue resistivity is greater in the direction transverse to the fiber axis than in the parallel (summarized in 57). Sperelakis & Macdonald (57) measured the transverse (ρ_t) and longitudinal (ρ_l) resistivities of isolated cat cardiac muscle bundles composed of parallel fibers (papillary muscles and ventricular trabeculae). The ratio of ρ_t/ρ_l averaged 11.3 (3351 Ω cm/296 Ω cm), compared to a ratio of 21 for frog sartorius muscle. The ratio of

ρ_t/ρ_1 was greatly reduced in high-resistance solution (10% Ringer, 90% isosmotic sucrose); ρ_1 increased without much change in ρ_t. It was concluded that the much larger tissue resistivity in the transverse direction causes the muscle bundle itself to act as a cable.

Using the method of Weidmann (69) on calf ventricular trabeculae at 25° C, Clerc (5) measured intracellular resistivities of 402 Ω cm in the longitudinal direction versus 3620 Ω cm in the transverse direction, thus giving a ratio of 9.0. The ratio for the extracellular resistivities (transverse to longitudinal) was 2.7 (127 Ω cm/48 Ω cm). The ratio of resistivities, intracellular to extracellular, was 8.4 (402 Ω cm/48 Ω cm) longitudinally, and 28.5 (3620 Ω cm/127 Ω cm) transversely (absolute resistance ratio was 12.7). These results are relevant to the question of whether or not there are low-resistance connections between cells lying side by side (e.g. 49, 69, 72).

Transverse vs longitudinal propagation velocities   The velocity of propagation is also markedly different in the two directions. Transverse spread of excitation in the myocardium (e.g. from endocardial to epicardial surface) has been demonstrated. For example, Sano et al (52) reported that the velocity in dog heart was 2–5 times slower in the transverse than in the longitudinal direction. Clerc (5) reported a transverse/longitudinal ratio of 1/3 in isolated ventricular trabeculae. Joyner et al (31) computed the potential profile for a two-dimensional sheet of myocardial cells connected by low-resistance pathways (simulating the atrium). By making the coupling resistance in the transverse direction 9.0-fold higher than that in the longitudinal direction, they showed that the velocity in the transverse direction would be 3.8-fold slower, thus giving an approximately elliptical wavefront. Directional differences in velocities are probably affected also by the differences in tissue resistivities in the two directions (5, 57) and by the geometry of the cells, the cells being many times longer than they are wide. A dove-tailing model of the ID has been proposed (72) in which the end of one cell makes functional contact with two or more cells, so that lateral and longitudinal spread occur simultaneously.

LONGITUDINAL MOVEMENT OF RADIOACTIVE COMPOUNDS AND DYES   Weidmann (67) originated a two-compartment method to study the longitudinal movement of radioactive material in sheep ventricular trabeculae (pulled through a tight-fitting hole in a partition). One compartment was continuously exposed to a ^{42}K Ringer solution; the other was continuously washed. After 6 hr (to allow steady-state distribution of ^{42}K), the muscles were blotted, frozen, and cut into pieces (0.5 mm each). The ^{42}K concentration decline had an average length constant of 1.55 mm. The calculated apparent diffusion coefficient of K^+ through the IDs was 7.9 $\times$ 10^{-6} cm^2

sec^{-1}, giving a P_{disk} of 6.3×10^{-4} cm sec^{-1} (assuming a cell length of 125 μm) and an ID resistivity of 3 Ω cm^2. Weidmann calculated that the length constant would be 0.60 mm if the ratio of extracellular diffusion coefficients in the radial to longitudinal direction (D_r/D_l) were 1/10; however, from ^{42}K efflux experiments he estimated that D_r/D_l was actually about 1/2. The length constant for ^{82}Br distribution (used as a predominantly extracellular tracer) was about 0.5 mm. Weidmann concluded that the longitudinal movement of the ^{42}K is not through the ISF or nonmyocardial cells, and that myocardial cells are connected by low-resistance pathways.

Using the two-compartment "cut-and-seal" method of Imanaga (26), the longitudinal movement of other radioactive substances has also been studied. Weingart (70) examined the movement of ^{14}C-tetraethylammonium ion (TEA$^+$) in sheep and calf ventricular trabeculae. The calculated longitudinal diffusion coefficient was 2×10^{-6} cm^2 sec^{-1} and the permeability of the cell junctions to TEA$^+$ was 1.27×10^{-3} cm sec^{-1}. Weingart concluded that there are low-resistance pathways between myocardial cells, and he estimated that the pore diameter must be at least 7.5 Å. The longitudinal movement of [^3H]-cyclic AMP had an average effective longitudinal diffusion coefficient of 0.84×10^{-6} cm^2 sec^{-1} (for 30 min and 180 min diffusion periods) (66).

Imanaga (26) studied the longitudinal movement of Procion Yellow (mol wt 697) along sheep and calf Purkinje fibers by pulling the strands through a hole in a rubber membrane. One end was cut and exposed to a solution containing Procion Yellow (in zero Ca^{2+}) for 15 min to allow the dye to enter the cells; then the cut ends were sealed by applying Ca^{2+}. After 3–4 hr, the tissue was frozen and sectioned, and the distribution of dye was measured. The length constant was about 0.4 mm, and the longitudinal diffusion coefficient for the dye was about 0.03 that for dye in an agar gel. Because another dye, Chicago Blue (mol wt $\sim$ 1000), did not move beyond 100–200 μm, Imanaga postulated that there was a critical pore size for movement across the IDs. He concluded that the Purkinje cells are coupled by low-resistance pathways.

Pollack (49) micro-iontophoresed fluorescein (mol wt 332) intracellularly in rabbit heart and observed the spread by video microscopy. By assuming that the cell borders occurred wherever there was a sharp spatial discontinuity of light intensity, he reported that, in myocardial cells and Purkinje fibers, the dye was able to spread into the contiguous cells on either end of the injected cell by 1 min after injection (faint light intensity detected and gradual diminution of light intensity in the injected cell). In many cases some dye also spread into the laterally contiguous cells. Pollack concluded that the cells are electrically coupled.

In the nodal (N) cells of the atrio-ventricular node, Pollack (49) could not detect passage of the dye into neighboring cells; hence, he concluded that the nodal cells are not sufficiently coupled by low-resistance connections to permit propagation through the AV node by intercellular current alone.

INPUT RESISTANCE   Input resistance (r_{in}) measurements are also relevant to the question of whether or not low-resistance coupling occurs. By definition, r_{in} is the ΔV at the site of current injection ($x = 0$) divided by the applied current ($\Delta V_o/I_o$). A low r_{in} suggests that the injected current passes into many neighboring cells. In a three-dimensional array of cells, all interconnected by low-resistance pathways, r_{in} should be very low. For a discussion of the input resistance expected in a branching closed-loop syncytium, see (14, 27). Woodbury & Crill (72) reported a low value (30 KΩ) for the input resistance of rat atrial cells, and Johnson & Tille (29) reported a value of 47 KΩ for rabbit ventricular cells.

Sperelakis and his colleagues reported r_{in} values ranging between 3.0 and 13 MΩ for various preparations (see 55). Other investigators have also reported high values (summary in 55). Johnson & Sommer (28) reported values of 0.5–1.0 MΩ for rabbit ventricular cells. Hermsmeyer & Sperelakis (24) showed that the r_{in} of frog ventricular cells increased from an average of 7 MΩ to about 30 MΩ upon addition of Ba^{2+} (to decrease K^+ permeability). DeMello (10) used a bridge circuit to measure r_{in} in dog Purkinje strands and obtained a value of about 3 MΩ; r_{in} increased several fold (to over 7 MΩ) when he injected Ca^{2+} ions to decouple the cells. DeFelice & DeHaan (7) found an r_{in} of 4 MΩ for cultured heart cell reaggregates. The higher the r_{in}, the greater the likelihood that the IDs are high in resistance, because it suggests that most of the current injected intracellularly exits into the ISF close to the site of injection. However a high r_{in} of 5 MΩ cannot distinguish whether or not contiguous cells lying end to end are connected by low-resistance paths unless R_m and radius are precisely known (see 55). But a high r_{in} indicates that if low-resistance connections exist in the lateral directions to form a three-dimensional system, R_m would have to be extraordinarily high.

With a balanced bridge circuit, the current-injecting electrode can be used to record potential also (63). However, balance of the bridge outside a cell does not insure that the bridge will remain balanced after impalement (55). There is also a theoretical problem because of the point injection of current. These and other problems are discussed in (14, 27, 53, 55, 63).

DEGREE OF INTERACTION

Adult cardiac muscle   Another method of determining whether current can spread easily from one myocardial cell to another is to inject current in one cell and to record the simultaneous potential change (steady-state) in that cell (ΔV_1) and in a neighboring cell (ΔV_2). If the ratio $\Delta V_2/\Delta V_1$ approaches 1.0, the two cells are almost perfectly coupled, i.e. the cell junctions are very low in resistance. If $\Delta V_2/\Delta_1$ approaches 0, the two cells are almost completely insulated from one another. (When very large currents are injected, one would expect to see a small potential change in all nearby cells even if the cells are not interconnected by pathways low in resistance.) In such an experiment, Tarr & Sperelakis (63) observed that electrical interaction never occurred when the electrodes were more than 60 μm apart. When the interelectrode distance was short (e.g. 7 or 11 μm), they obtained large interactions in some impalements and almost none in others. The probability of obtaining substantial interactions increased as the interelectrode distance was decreased. These data suggest that when the two electrodes impaled the same cell, the interaction was large, whereas when the two electrodes were in neighboring cells, the interaction was very low. Similar results were obtained by other investigators [references in (55)]. For example, Sakamoto (51) was unable to detect electrotonic potentials in any cell at a distance of more than 15 μm from the cell impaled with a current-injecting microelectrode.

Cultured heart cells   Investigation on electrotonic spread of current in cultured myocardial cells has yielded a spectrum of results. For example, Lehmkuhl & Sperelakis (36) found that in a tight packing ("pavement") of monolayer cells (from embryonic chick ventricle), there was little or no interaction between nearby cells; in contrast, in some thick strands there were long apparent length constants of about 1 mm. Hyde et al (25), Jongsma & van Rijn (30), and Lieberman (37) reported length constants over 1 mm for both monolayer cells and strands. Using spherical reaggregates (100–400 μm in diameter) of embryonic chick myocardial cells, De-Hann & Fozzard (8) reported that the cells were isopotential (i.e. the reaggregate behaved electrotonically like one large cell) and that therefore all cells were interconnected by low-resistance pathways. In contrast, McLean & Sperelakis (unpublished observations) found that highly differentiated myocardial cells in reaggregate cultures were not electrotonically coupled (although propagation occurred). However, reaggregates composed of less-differentiated (or reverted) cells (i.e. lower resting potential and slower rate of rise of the action potentials) showed a moderate or strong degree of DC coupling in about half of the double impalements, which suggested that the degree of electrotonic coupling is a function of the state of differentiation.

In cultured reaggregates, DeFelice & DeHaan (7) have made a case for using autocorrelation and cross-correlation analysis of the "noise" (random voltage fluctuations of about 50–500 μV) recorded by two intracellular microelectrodes to determine whether or not the two cells impaled are electrically coupled. It was reported that the beating of mouse myocardial cells in culture may be synchronized by nonmuscle cells by means of the formation of low-resistance junctions between the different cell types (19).

ULTRASTRUCTURE OF THE JUNCTIONS

Interdigitation of cells; effect of hypertonicity   In hearts of higher vertebrates, the IDs are usually stepped. The two abutting cells interdigitate extensively (one cell may abut on more than one cell at each end), so that the area of the ID membrane is much greater, because of such folding, than it would be if each cell ended as a simple flat surface. In cat ventricular muscle, Sperelakis & Rubio (59) measured a folding factor of 6.4 in isotonic solution and 11 in two-fold hypertonic solution. A folding factor of 12.2 was obtained for guinea pig ventricle. Page & McCallister (48) measured a folding factor of 9 for rat ventricular cells and pointed out that numerous investigators had not taken folding into account in their calculations. Thus, the true resistivity of the ID would be 6–12 times greater than the values calculated without taking the folding into account. The ultrastructure of sheep Purkinje strands, including the clefts between the cells, has been studied in detail (22).

Hypertonicity has rapid effects on the ultrastructure of the IDs. For example, the cleft gap widened from an average of 190 Å in isotonic solution to 310 Å in two-fold hypertonic solution (59). The frequency of occurrence of the gap junctions decreased to about 18% of the control value; those gap junctions that were not pulled apart appeared normal. Propagation velocity decreases markedly in hypertonic solution; this effect was attributed to the ultrastructural changes at the IDs (60). Hypertonicity sometimes affected certain cells more selectively; in such cases, the ID always acted as the sharp boundary between the affected and the unaffected cells (59). Sharp differences in sarcomere lengths sometimes can be seen across the IDs (61).

Gap junctions   The IDs of higher vertebrates (mammals and birds) contain specialized regions known as gap junctions ("close" junctions or "nexuses"). These structures are generally presumed to be the morphological correlate of low-resistance connections between myocardial cells (3, 15). Gap junctions have been thought to be absent or rare in the hearts of lower vertebrates (see 16). More recently, however, it has been reported (32, 43) that frog myocardial cells contain small punctate membrane appositions that resemble the typical gap junctions of mammalian hearts. For example, junctions in three amphibian hearts containing particles in linear rows, circles, and clusters were observed (43); the length of the membrane appositions was only about 160 Å (32). Short regions of the ID that resembled gap junctions (but were sparse) were also reported for fish and turtle ventricles (41). During embryonic development of mouse heart, the frequency and size of the gap junctions increases (21).

True tight junctions (i.e. fusion of the contiguous membranes, with no gap between them) do not exist in cardiac and smooth muscles; there is a gap of 20–40 Å (50). For a review of the literature and description of the ultrastructure of the gap junction see (35, 45). Freeze-fracture studies have revealed that the gap junctions are composed of globular subunits arranged in various patterns [e.g. honeycombs (50)]. The subunits are thought to make bridges between the two cells, with a 10–20 Å pore in the center of each junctional particle (44, 45, 50). It has been estimated that there are about 6.7×10^5 subunits per ID in rat ventricular cells (42).

In rat ventricular cells, it was reported that the gap junctions occupied 12% (48) or 7.5% (42) of the ID area. If there are water-filled pores connecting two myocardial cells and if certain assumptions are made (including a pore diameter of 10 Å), the calculated resistivity of the ID is less than 0.2 Ω cm^2 (42).

Since gap junctions and low-resistance coupling occur between many cell types that do not propagate action potentials (reviewed in 45), it has been suggested that the gap junction also serves as a pathway for the exchange of larger molecules between cells in the interest of metabolic cooperation (45, 49).

Significant differences may exist in the number and total area of gap junctions between two synchronously beating groups of cultured heart cells (aggregates and monolayers) and between two asynchronous groups (20). Inhibitors of protein synthesis prevented the normal acquisition of synchrony in beating between the groups. Baldwin (1, 2) did not observe any ultrastructural change in the gap junctions between myocardial cells and Purkinje cells that presumably were uncoupled.

CAPACITANCE OF THE INTERCALATED DISKS   Fozzard (17) and Dudel et al (13) found two time constants for Purkinje fibers and attributed the second to a shunting transverse tubular system. Freygang & Trautwein (18) also found two time constants in sheep Purkinje strands, but they attributed the lower one of 0.07 msec to the IDs (on the basis of the T-tubular system's being poorly developed in Purkinje cells). If the capacitance of the ID is assumed to be the same as that for the myocardial surface membrane, namely 0.7 μF cm^{-2} (69), the calculated resistivity of the ID is 100 Ω cm^2. Sperelakis & Hoshiko (56) demonstrated that the longitudinal impedance of cardiac muscle bundles was frequency-dependent, consistent with a substantial capacitance in the transverse ID membranes. The ratio of impedance at 10,000 Hz to that at 10 Hz was 0.75 in Ringer solution and 0.48 in an isosmotic sucrose solution. In agreement, Tarr & Trank (64) found that the transgap (double sucrose gap) impedance of frog atrial trabeculae had a ratio at 1000 Hz to 10 Hz of 0.63.

Capacitative Coupling

In capacitative coupling, a capacitative current flows through a capacitance that acts to couple the two cells together (62). That is, the coupling current is capacitative, not resistive. Since the action potential is effectively an AC signal, it might be possible for sufficient capacitative current to flow into the post-cell through the post-membrane to depolarize the surface membrane to threshold. (The voltage change in the post-cell would be proportional to the first time derivative of the action potential in the pre-cell.) If the coupling capacitance (C_j) were assumed to be 1 μF cm^{-2}, calculations indicate that sufficient capacitative current would flow into the post-cell to depolarize it to threshold. However, capacitative coupling may not work for the following reasons: (a) The junctional coupling capacitance would be decreased by a factor of 2 (two capacitors in series). (b) If only a small fraction of the ID were involved in the capacitative coupling, the total capacitance would be proportionately smaller (capacitance is proportional to area of the plates). (c) If the two junctional membranes are not very close to one another and there is a sizeable shunt pathway to ground, then the effectiveness of the capacitative coupling would be greatly reduced; the capacitative (and resistive) current from the pre-cell would be shunted to ground. Thus, it appears doubtful whether capacitative coupling can result in a viable mechanism for the transfer of excitation in a situation where there is a junctional gap. However, the degree of capacitative coupling is difficult to assess in cardiac muscle. The cells are short; because the two intracellular microelectrodes must be relatively close, electromagnetic radiation can readily occur between the current-injecting and voltage-recording electrodes.

Electric Field Coupling

Recently, Sperelakis & Mann (58) presented a new model that would allow an electrical transmission process to occur at the IDs but that requires neither low-resistance connections between the cells nor a very large capacitance between the cells.[1] They analyzed the electric field that would develop in the narrow cleft between two myocardial cells, with the assumption that the pre-membrane was an ordinary excitable membrane, by building an

---

[1]Electric field coupling is not the same as "ephaptic" transmission, which, as generally used, involves local-circuit passage through the neighboring cell to achieve excitation, e. g. as in cross-talk between neurons.

electrical analog and by doing a theoretical analysis with the aid of a computer. When the pre-membrane fired an action potential, the cleft between the cells became negative with respect to ground (ISF), and this potential acted to depolarize the post-membrane to its threshold (although its inner surface remained at nearly constant potential with respect to ground). Firing of an action potential in the post-membrane brought the surface membrane of the post-cell to threshold. However, for the successful transfer of excitation, the pre-membrane had to fire a fraction of a millisecond before the adjacent surface membrane. This was made possible either by lowering the threshold of the junctional membranes slightly or by allowing K^+ to accumulate in the cleft. Transmission was facilitated by decreasing the junctional membrane capacitances (or time constant) by only about a factor of 2 below the prorated value (relative to that of the surface membrane) (J. E. Mann, N. Sperelakis, unpublished observations).

Mann et al (40) expanded the ID cleft into a 3-dimensional grid of discrete resistors to study the voltage profile through the cleft. The potential profile (assuming that current entering the cleft is uniformly distributed) was bullet-shaped, the voltage being maximum in the center of the cleft and zero at the edges. The resistance profile (a single node measured at a time) was flatter in shape, the resistance changing most sharply at the edges. There was no difference in potential across the thickness of the cleft. The results obtained were similar to those based on continuously distributed models by Heppner & Plonsey (23), and Woodbury & Crill (73).

DECOUPLING

The longitudinal resistance of bundles of cardiac muscle increases under a variety of experimental conditions. This resistance increase has usually been interpreted to reflect mainly an increase in resistance of the cell junctions, i.e. cell decoupling. Pathological decoupling could result in slowing of conduction and block (68). Slow conduction and undirectional block are important elements in the development of circus movement (see 6), and can be experimentally produced in frog cardiac muscle (55). Thus, the mechanism(s) of propagation from cell to cell has important implications with respect to the genesis of arrhythmias, fibrillation, and heart block.

Injury

The injury potential of cardiac muscle slowly declines over a period of 5–30 min (1, 9, 10, 11). This decline has been used as an index of uncoupling of the myocardial cells, on the assumption that injury potentials depend on the existence of low-resistance connections between the injured and uninjured myocardial cells. Since intracellular injection of Ca^{2+} or Sr^{2+} ions affects the degree of cell coupling (10), the uncoupling may be caused by a rise in $[Ca]_i$, which somehow decreases the permeability of the cell junctions to ions. Baldwin (1, 2) reported that the gap junctions between bullfrog atrial myocardial cells and between sheep Purkinje strands were unaffected morphologically at a time when the injury potential had dissipated (tissues were cut and allowed to heal over) and the cells were presumed to be uncoupled; she concluded that gap junctions do not insure electrical coupling.

Ca^{2+}, Sr^{2+}, and Na^+ Injection; Ouabain

DeMello (10) showed that intracellular injection of Ca^{2+} or Sr^{2+} into dog Purkinje cells produced electrical uncoupling, and that the uncoupling was spontaneously reversed (presumably as the divalent cation was pumped out of the myoplasm). Uncoupling was determined by reduction in amplitude and disappearance of the electrotonic potential recorded from an adjacent cell when depolarizing current pulses of 70–180 nA were applied in one cell. During uncoupling, r_{in} increased from 3 MΩ to about 7 MΩ. (For an r_{in} of 3 MΩ and an applied current of 100 nA, the calculated potential change in the injected cell is 300 mV; since the voltage change in the second cell was only a few millivolts, there was a large potential difference between the two cells.) It is thought that a rise in $[Ca]_i$ in some way increases the resistance of the cell junctions. Intracellular injection of Na^+ also produced uncoupling, presumably by causing a rise in $[Ca]_i$ indirectly by means of the Ca_o-Na_i exchange reaction.

Ouabain also produces uncoupling, presumably by blocking the Na-K pump and allowing $[Na]_i$ to rise (71). For example, Weingart (71) reported that 2×10^{-6} M ouabain (but not doses lower than 5×10^{-7}M) caused the internal longitudinal resistance of isolated bovine ventricular trabeculae to increase gradually (irreversibly) two- to four-fold over a period of 160 min. Concomitantly, conduction velocity decreased, rate of rise of the action potential decreased, and contracture occurred. Weingart suggested that an increase in $[Ca]_i$ was the cause of the uncoupling.

Hypertonicity; Stretch

Hypertonic solutions have pronounced effects on cardiac muscle. For example, some myocardial cells became electrically isolated from their neighbors when frog hearts were perfused with Ringer solution made two-fold hypertonic by addition of sucrose (55). Propagation across a sucrose gap was blocked, presumably due to separation of the nexal junctions, when the sucrose solution was made hyperosmotic (3). The ID cleft width increased over 50% and the frequency of occurrence of gap junctions greatly decreased in two-fold hypertonic solution (59); propagation velocity also decreased to about 50% (60). Two-fold hypertonic solution raised the longitudinal tissue resistivity by only 29% (57), contrary to what would be expected if the cells were coupled in isotonic solution and then decoupled in hypertonic solution. It has been reported that stretch can induce propagation disturbances in rat papillary muscle (54).

Isosmotic Sucrose Solution

Equilibration of cat papillary muscle in isosmotic sucrose solution caused a large rise in longitudinal tissue resistivity (56). This was interpreted to indicate that the cell-to-cell pathway through the muscle was high in resistance. New & Trautwein (46) observed a gradual rise in longitudinal resistance (over 30–60 min) in their sucrose-gap voltage-clamp experiments, and they suggested that this reflected an irreversible uncoupling of the cells; addition of 10^{-5} M Ca^{2+} to the sucrose solution prevented the increase in resistance. Kléber (33) found that the longitudinal resistivity of isolated trabeculae (single sucrose gap) increased ten-fold after 4 hr in isosmotic sucrose solution; this change was also prevented by addition of 10^{-4} M Ca^{2+}. The K^+ loss from the cells was not great enough to account for the increase in resistance, and therefore Kléber interpreted his data in terms of a slowly progressing and partially reversible uncoupling of the myocardial cells in ion-free sucrose solution.

NODAL CELLS

Bonke (4) used a large extracellular suction electrode for applying polarizing current (1–7 μA) in rabbit SA node and an intracellular microelectrode for measuring the potential change in the cells at various distances. He reported that the node behaved as a one-dimensional cable (rather than three-dimensional), with an average length constant of 465 μm. The magnitude of the potential change, however, was very small (e.g. 2 mV) even very close (e.g. 100 μm) to the current electrode. Bonke reported that in some cases the polarizing current affected the frequency of discharge but that in other cases even stronger currents did not. He concluded that the nodal cells are connected by low-resistance pathways, but that electrotonic spread is not "strong enough" to synchronize all fibers within the node. As mentioned previously, Pollack (49) concluded from dye injection studies that the rabbit AV nodal cells were not connected by low-resistance pathways.

However, Noma & Irisawa (47) demonstrated that ligation of the isolated rabbit SA node into short strips (e.g. 0.3 mm by 0.3 mm) caused good electrotonic coupling to occur between two microelectrodes 50–300 μm apart (current applied through a third electrode) and caused r_{in} to increase by a factor of 6 (to a mean of 1.4 or 2.2 MΩ). They concluded that the cells were well coupled.

ACKNOWLEDGMENT

The unpublished observations of the author quoted in this article were supported by a research grant from the National Institutes of Health (HL-18711).

Literature Cited

1. Baldwin, K. M. 1970. The fine structure and electrophysiology of heart muscle cell injury. *J. Cell Biol.* 46:455–76
2. Baldwin, K. M. 1977. The fine structure of healing over in mammalian cardiac muscle. *J. Mol. Cell. Cardiol.* 9:959–66
3. Barr, L., Dewey, M. M., Berger, W. 1965. Propagation of action potentials and the structure of the nexus in cardiac muscle. *J. Gen. Physiol.* 48:797–823
4. Bonke, F. I. M. 1973. Electrotonic spread in the sinoatrial node of the rabbit heart. *Pfluegers Arch.* 339:17–23
5. Clerc, L. 1976. Directional differences of impulse spread in trabecular muscle from mammalian heart. *J. Physiol. London* 255:335–46
6. Cranefield, P. F. 1975. *The Conduction of the Cardiac Impulse.* Mount Kisco, NY: Futura
7. DeFelice, L. J., DeHaan, R. L. 1977. Membrane noise and intercellular communication. *Proc. IEEE Special Issue Biol. Signals* 65:896–99
8. DeHaan, R. L., Fozzard, H. A. 1975. Membrane response to current pulses in spheroidal aggregates of embryonic heart cells. *J. Gen. Physiol.* 65:207–22
9. Délèze, J. 1970. The recovery of resting potential and input resistance in sheep heart injured by knife or laser. *J. Physiol. London* 208:547–62
10. DeMello, W. C. 1975. Effect of intracellular injection of calcium and strontium on cell communication in heart. *J. Physiol. London* 250:231–45
11. DeMello, W. C., Motta, G. E., Chapeau, M. 1969. A study of the healing-over of myocardial cells of toads. *Circ. Res.* 24:475–87
12. Dominguez, G., Fozzard, H. A. 1970. Influence of extracellular K^+ concentration on cable properties and excitability of sheep cardiac Purkinje fibers. *Circ. Res.* 26:565–74
13. Dudel, J., Peper, K., Rüdel, R., Trautwein, W. 1966. Excitatory membrane current in heart muscle (Purkinje fibers). *Pfluegers Arch.* 292:255–73
14. Eisenberg, R. S., Johnson, E. A. 1970. Three-dimensional electrical field problems in physiology. *Prog. Biophys. Mol. Biol.* 20:1–65
15. Fawcett, D., McNutt, N. S. 1969. The ultrastructure of the cat myocardium. I. Ventricular papillary muscle. *J. Cell Biol.* 42:1–45
16. Forbes, M. S., Sperelakis, N. 1971. Ultrastructure of lizard ventricular muscle. *J. Ultrastruct. Res.* 34:439–51
17. Fozzard, H. A. 1966. Membrane capacity of the cardiac Purkinje fibre. *J. Physiol. London* 182:255–67
18. Freygang, W. H., Trautwein, W. 1970. The structural implications of the linear electrical properties of cardiac Purkinje strands. *J. Gen. Physiol.* 55:524–47
19. Goshima, K. 1975. Beating of myocardial cells in culture. In *Developmental and Physiological Correlates of Cardiac Muscle,* ed. M. Lieberman, T. Sano pp. 197–208. NY: Raven
20. Griep, E. B., Peacock, J. H., Bernfield, M. R., Revel, J.-P. 1978. Morphological and functional correlates of synchronous beating between embryonic heart cell aggregates and layers. *Exp. Cell Res.* 113:273–82
21. Gros, D., Challice, C. E. 1976. Early development of gap junctions between the mouse embryonic myocardial cells. A freeze-etching study. *Experientia* 32:996–98
22. Hellam, D. C., Studt, J. W. 1974. A core-conductor model of the cardiac Purkinje fibre based on structural analysis. *J. Physiol. London* 243:637–60
23. Heppner, D. B., Plonsey, R. 1970. Simulation of electrical interaction of cardiac cells. *Biophys. J.* 10:1057–75
24. Hermsmeyer, K., Sperelakis, N. 1970. Decrease in K^+ conductance and depolarization of frog cardiac muscle produced by Ba^{++}. *Am. J. Physiol.* 219:952–63
25. Hyde, A., Blondel, B., Matter, A., Cheneval, J. P., Filloux, B., Girardier, L. 1969. Homo- and heterocellular junctions in cell cultures: an electrophysiological and morphological study. *Prog. Brain Res.* 31:283–311
26. Imanaga, I. 1974. Cell-to-cell diffusion of Procion Yellow in sheep and calf

456   SPERELAKIS

Purkinje fibers. *J. Memb. Biol.* 16:381–88

27. Jack, J. J. B., Noble, D., Tsien, R. W. 1975. *Electric Current Flow in Excitable Cells.* Oxford: Clarendon Press

28. Johnson, E. A., Sommer, J. R. 1967. A strand of cardiac muscle: its ultrastructure and the electrophysiological implications of its geometry. *J. Cell Biol.* 33:C103–29

29. Johnson, E. A., Tille, J. 1961. Investigation of the electrical properties of cardiac muscle fibers with the aid of intracellular double-barrelled electrodes. *J. Gen. Physiol.* 44:443–67

30. Jongsma, H. J., van Rijn, H. E. 1972. Electrotonic spread of current in monolayer cultures of neonatal rat heart cells. *J. Memb. Biol.* 9:341–60

31. Joyner, R. W., Ramón, F., Moore, J. W. 1975. Simulation of action potential propagation in an inhomogeneous sheet of coupled excitable cells. *Circ. Res.* 36:654–61

32. Kensler, R. W., Brink, P., Dewey, M. M. 1977. Nexus of frog ventricle. *J. Cell Biol.* 73:768–81

33. Kléber, A. 1973. Effects of sucrose solution on the longitudinal tissue resistivity of trabecular muscle from mammalian heart. *Pfluegers Arch* 345:195–205

34. Kline, R., Morad, M. 1976. Potassium efflux and accumulation in heart muscle. *Biophys. J.* 16:367–72

35. Larsen, W. J. 1977. Structural diversity of gap junctions: a review. *Tissue and Cell* 9:373–94

36. Lehmkuhl, D., Sperelakis, N. 1965. Electrotonic spread of current in cultured chick heart cells. *J. Cell. Comp. Physiol.* 66:119–33

37. Lieberman, M. 1973. Electrophysiological studies of a synthetic strand of cardiac muscle. *Physiologist* 16:551–63

38. Macdonald, R. L., Mann, J. E. Jr., Sperelakis, N. 1974. Derivation of general equations describing tracer diffusion in any two-compartment tissue, with application to diffusion in cylindrical muscle bundles. *J. Theor. Biol.* 45:107–31

39. Macdonald, R. L., Hsu, D., Mann, J. E., Sperelakis, N. 1975. An analysis of the problem of K^+ accumulation in the intercalated disk clefts of cardiac muscle. *J. Theor. Biol.* 52:455–74

40. Mann, J. E. Jr., Foley, E., Sperelakis, N. 1977. Resistance and potential profiles in the cleft between two myocardial cells: electrical analog and computer simulations. *J. Theor. Biol.* 68:1–15

41. Martínez-Palomo, A., Mendez, R. 1971. Presence of gap junctions between cardiac cells in the heart of nonmammalian species. *J. Ultrastruct. Res.* 37:592–600

42. Matter, A. 1973. A morphometric study on the nexus of rat cardiac muscle. *J. Cell Biol.* 56:690–96

43. Mazet, F. 1977. Freeze-fracture studies of gap junctions in the developing and adult amphibian cardiac muscle. *Devel. Biol.* 60:139–52

44. McNutt, N. S., Weinstein, R. S. 1970. The ultrastructure of the nexus. *J. Cell Biol.* 47:666–88

45. McNutt, N. S., Weinstein, R. S. 1973. Membrane ultrastructure at mammalian intercellular junctions. *Prog. Biophys.* 26:45–101

46. New, W., Trautwein, W. 1972. Inward membrane currents in mammalian myocardium. *Pfluegers Arch.* 334:1–23

47. Noma, A., Irisawa, H. 1976. Membrane currents in the rabbit sinoatrial node cell as studied by the double microelectrode method. *Pfluegers. Arch.* 364:45–52

48. Page, E., McCallister, L. P. 1973. Studies on the intercalated disk of rat left ventricular myocardial cells. *J. Ultrastruct. Res.* 43:388–411

49. Pollack, G. H. 1976. Intercellular coupling in the atrioventricular node and other tissues of the rabbit heart. *J. Physiol. London* 255:275–98

50. Revel, J. P., Karnovsky, M. J. 1967. Hexagonal array of subunits in intercellular junctions of mouse heart and liver. *J. Cell Biol.* 33:C7–12

51. Sakamoto, Y. 1969. Membrane characteristics of the canine papillary muscle fiber. *J. Gen. Physiol.* 54:765–81

52. Sano, T., Takayama, N., Shimamoto, T. 1959. Directional difference of conduction velocity in the cardiac ventricular syncytium studied by microelectrodes. *Circ. Res.* 7:262–67

53. Schanne, O., Ceretti, E. R. P. 1978. *Impedance Measurement in Biological Cells.* NY: Wiley, 430 pp.

54. Spear, J. F., Moore, E. N. 1971. A comparison of alternation in myocardial action potentials and contractility. *Am. J. Physiol.* 220:1708–16

55. Sperelakis, N. 1969. Lack of electrical coupling between contiguous myocardial cells in vertebrate hearts. In *Comparative Physiology of the Heart: Current Trends,* ed. F. V. McCann. Basel: Birkhäuser

56. Sperelakis, N., Hoshiko, T. 1961. Elec-

trical impedance of cardiac muscle. *Circ. Res.* 9:1280–83

57. Sperelakis, N., Macdonald, R. L. 1974. Ratio of transverse to longitudinal resistivities of isolated cardiac muscle fiber bundles. *J. Electrocardiol.* 7:301–14

58. Sperelakis, N., Mann, J. E. Jr. 1977. Evaluation of electric field changes in the cleft between excitable cells. *J. Theor. Biol.* 64:71–96

59. Sperelakis, N., Rubio, R. 1971. Ultrastructural changes produced by hypertonicity in cat cardiac muscle. *J. Mol. Cell. Cardiol.* 3:139–56

60. Sperelakis, N., Mayer, G., Macdonald, R. 1970. Velocity of propagation in vertebrate cardiac muscles as functions of tonicity and $[K^+]_o$. *Am. J. Physiol.* 219:952–63

61. Sperelakis, N., Rubio, R., Redick, J. 1970. Sharp discontinuity in sarcomere lengths across intercalated disks of fibrillating cat hearts. *J. Ultrastruct. Res.* 30:503–32

62. Stibitz, G. R., McCann, F. V. 1974. Studies of impedance in cardiac tissue using sucrose gap and computer techniques. II. Circuit simulation of passive electrical properties and cell-to-cell transmission. *Biophys. J.* 14:75–98

63. Tarr, M., Sperelakis, N. 1964. Weak electronic interaction between contiguous cardiac cells. *Am. J. Physiol.* 207:691–700

64. Tarr, M., Trank, J. W. 1974. An assessment of the double sucrose-gap voltage clamp technique as applied to frog atrial muscle. *Biophys. J.* 14:627–43

65. Trautwein, W. 1973. Membrane currents in cardiac muscle fibers. *Physiol. Rev.* 53:793–835

66. Tsien, R. W., Weingart, R. 1976. Inotropic effect of cyclic AMP in calf ventricular muscle studied by a cut end method. *J. Physiol. London* 260:117–41

67. Weidmann, S. 1966. The diffusion of radiopotassium across intercalated disks of mammalian cardiac muscle. *J. Physiol. London* 187:323–42

68. Weidmann, S. 1969. Electrical coupling between myocardial cells. *Prog. Brain Res.* 31:275–81

69. Weidmann, S. 1970. Electrical constants of trabecular muscle from mammalian heart. *J. Physiol. London* 210:1040–54

70. Weingart, R. 1974. The permeability to tetraethylammonium ions of the surface membrane and the intercalated disks of sheep and calf myocardium. *J. Physiol. London* 240:741–62

71. Weingart, R. 1977. The actions of ouabain on intercellular coupling and conduction velocity in mammalian ventricular muscle. *J. Physiol. London* 264:341–65

72. Woodbury, J. W., Crill, W. E. 1961. On the problem of impulse conduction in the atrium. In *Nervous Inhibition*, ed. E. Florey, pp. 124–35. London: Pergamon

73. Woodbury, J. W., Crill, W. E. 1970. The potential in the gap between two abutting cardiac muscle cells. A closed solution. *Biophys. J.* 10:1076–83

74. Woodbury, J. W., Gordon, A. M. 1965. The electrical equivalent circuit of heart muscle. *J. Cell. Comp. Physiol.* 66:35–40

Ann. Rev. Physiol. 1979. 41:459–72
Copyright © 1979 by Annual Reviews Inc. All rights reserved

CARDIAC ARRHYTHMIAS   ♦1231

Paul F. Cranefield and Andrew L. Wit

The Rockefeller University, New York, N.Y. 10021

The literature on arrhythmias is extensive and well reviewed (5, 16, 17, 21, 27, 35, 38, 74, 76, 78, 79, 82, 86, 90, 95); the present review is necessarily selective and largely excludes recent clinical investigations.

REENTRY

Reentry in the Atria

Unequivocal evidence of circulating excitation waves in the intact atria has not yet been obtained (61) but circus movement has been demonstrated in isolated rabbit atria (1–3). Repetitive activity was induced by a single premature stimulus and records from some 300 sites determined the sequence of atrial activation. The premature impulse that initiated repetitive activity blocked in one direction in fibers with long refractory periods, conducted in fibers with shorter refractory periods, and could return to the initial point of block and circulate repeatedly in a pathway of circumference as small as 6–8 mm. The spread of activity from the circulating vortex toward its center excited fibers in the center of the vortex twice during each revolution of the impulse, creating slow conduction, collision of impulses, and refractoriness that prevented the impulses from conducting across the circle. An analysis of atrial activation during atrial arrhythmias in the in situ dog heart has found activation sequences compatible with reentry during atrial flutter (9). Atrial flutter in the canine heart can be induced more easily by rapid stimulation of the left atrial insertion of Bachman's bundle than by stimulation of the body of the right atrium (63). Elevating plasma K^+ concentration to 9.5 mM l^{-1} caused total inactivation of atrial myocardium without suppressing flutter waves recorded from the vicinity of the internodal path-

0066-4308/79/0201-0459$01.00

ways. Section of the middle and posterior internodal pathways prevented the establishment of flutter.

Human atrial myocardium removed during cardiac surgery has very low resting potentials, action potentials of low amplitude and slow upstrokes, and areas of inexcitability (47, 72); all of these changes might predispose to reentry in diseased myocardium.

Reentry in the AV Node

Watanabe & Dreifus (81) demonstrated inhomogenous activation of nodal cells during reciprocal rhythms with microelectrode techniques. The classic study of Mendez & Moe (60) did much to establish the role in nodal reentry of functional longitudinal dissociation occurring in the upper region of the rabbit AV node. Wit et al (93) suggested that reentry in the isolated rabbit AV node could cause in that preparation an arrhythmia that resembled paroxysmal supraventricular tachycardia. Janse et al (52) mapped the sequence of nodal activation during reciprocating nodal tachycardia in isolated rabbit AV node and atrium by using a 10 microelectrode "brush," recording nodal potentials sequentially from 54 cells. During the tachycardia the sequence of activation of these cells agreed with that expected in circus movement; but most of the impaled fibers appeared to be part of the returning pathway, and potentials were recorded from only two cells in the antegrade pathway. The major limitation of microelectrode studies of AV nodal reentry is still the difficulty of recording from a large number of cells during reentry. The complete pathway through which the impulse propagates has yet to be traced.

Preexcitation

Supraventricular tachycardia in patients with the preexcitation syndrome is perhaps the best-documented example of reentry in the in situ heart. Activation sequences of atria and ventricle often serve to identify an accessory AV connection that, with the normal AV connection, completes the circuit around which sustained reentry occurs. Severing that accessory pathway often abolishes the tachycardia (27, 35, 85, 86).

Reentry in the Ventricles

For reentry to occur in short loops composed of terminal branches of the peripheral Purkinje system (71) or in short parallel bundles of myocardial fibers the impulse must conduct very slowly. Exposing segments of canine Purkinje bundles to elevated potassium markedly reduced the resting potential, and caused action potentials with very slow upstrokes to appear (16, 19–21). Conduction velocity was as low as 0.05–0.1 m sec^{-1}, which is slow enough to permit reentry in small twigs of the conducting system. Further studies demonstrated reentry in small loops of the canine and bovine conducting systems exposed to high K^+ and epinephrine (91, 94). Cutting the loop abolished the repetitive responses, and unidirectional conduction block was shown to persist at strategic sites in the loop after it was cut (91). Slow conduction was attributed to the local replacement of the normal action potential by a slow response in which the upstroke depends on current flowing through the slow channel (16), but reentry might occur in Purkinje fiber bundles in which the fast inward Na^+ current is only partially inactivated (12). Action potentials with slow upstrokes, arising from low membrane potentials and presumably capable of causing reentry, are seen in preparations isolated from canine hearts after coronary artery occlusion (32, 56, 57, 67). The action potentials of Purkinje fibers surviving infarction may be very long and have correspondingly long refractory periods (32, 56). Early premature impulses might block in regions with long refractory periods but return slowly through regions with shorter refractory periods to their point of origin. Nonstimulated and probably reentrant impulses can occur because of marked local reduction in the refractory periods of Purkinje fibers that appear after two or three early premature activations (68). Reentry in peripheral Purkinje fibers in situ has yet to be demonstrated.

Electrograms recorded from a fresh infarct rapidly decrease in amplitude and increase in duration, eventually becoming "fragmented," at which time ventricular extrasystoles occur (10, 24, 69, 70, 80). The "fragmented" activity may well reflect slowed conduction in the ischemic region (23). After coronary occlusion, areas of unidirectional block and islands of inexcitable tissue may appear, and the impulse may conduct slowly through the ischemic region, reemerging to reexcite the ventricles. If reentry occurs in an infarct, continuous electrical activity should be recorded from the time the impulse enters the infarct until it reemerges to cause reexcitation of the ventricles (40). Such activity appears on the epicardial surface of the canine heart within 10 minutes of coronary artery ligation (80), and continuous electrical activity on the epicardium is associated with ventricular extrasystoles in 3–7-day old infarcts (25, 26). The presence in the ischemic zone of multiple asynchronous spikes was attributed to delayed conduction. The number of multiple asynchronous spikes could often be increased by increasing the heart rate; when this was done, activity was seen during the entire diastolic interval and was associated with the appearance of ventricular extrasystoles and tachycardia. In the cat heart, in infarcts several weeks to several months old there are muscle fibers that generate low-amplitude action potentials with slow upstrokes (62); chronic arrhythmias had been present in these cats.

AUTOMATICITY

Automaticity is seen in cells of the sinoatrial (SA) node (13, 74), "plateau" atrial fibers (44), cardiac fibers in the atrioventricular (AV) valves (8, 92), and around the coronary sinus orifice (89), AV junctional fibers, and Purkinje fibers (43). The intrinsic rate of the sinus node normally is faster than that of other automatic cells, which are thus normally inhibited by overdrive suppression (76–78). If the sinus node fails to activate the heart a subsidiary pacemaker may "escape" and initiate impulses. If there is block of conduction into an ectopic pacemaker, that pacemaker will not be subjected to the inhibitory influences of the sinus node and may become a parasystolic focus, able to excite the rest of the heart whenever it is not surrounded by exit block. The view that parasystole can be diagnosed electrocardiographically when the ectopic impulses are simple multiples of the presumed rate in the focus has been challenged because electrotonic interaction between the sinus impulse and that of the ectopic focus can prolong or curtail the cycle length of the focus by as much as 40% (51). Electrotonic interaction across the region of exit or entry block can also cause parasystolic impulses to arise with fixed coupling to the dominant rhythm (51).

An increase in the rate of an ectopic automatic focus causes the pacemaker to move from the SA node to that site; this may occur as the result of a local release of catecholamines (8, 43, 44, 75, 92). Sympathetic stimulation in situ often causes shifts of the pacemaker from the sinus node to other regions of the heart; such sympathetic activation may have a selective effect on localized regions (4, 36, 39).

Pathological events may increase the automaticity of latent pacemakers or cause fibers not normally automatic to become automatic. Purkinje fibers on the endocardial surface of a recent (24 hr) infarct possess an enhanced automaticity that causes the ventricular arrhythmias that occur in situ at this time (33, 46, 56, 67, 69). Many of the arrhythmias of myocardial infarction may arise in subendocardial Purkinje fibers (33, 46, 48, 73), which have very low maximum diastolic potentials that may cause their automaticity (7, 49); alternatively the activity may be triggered (see below).

Apparently automatic activity has been found in partially depolarized atrial fibers in atrial myocardium obtained from diseased human hearts (47, 72). Normal human "plateau" atrial fibers can be automatic (37), but normal working atrial myocardial cells are not. Working myocardial cells might become automatic following a decrease in membrane potential (14) since reduction of membrane potential of guinea pig and cat papillary muscle to less than –40 mV causes rhythmic activity (50, 53, 55). Automaticity in depolarized ventricular muscle has not yet been shown to cause arrhythmias, but ventricular muscle fibers may be depolarized by the current of injury caused by ischemia (54).

TRIGGERED ACTIVITY

Activity sustained by afterdepolarizations is called "triggered" because a quiescent but triggerable fiber will remain quiescent until driven either by a locally evoked action potential or by an action potential that propagates into the fiber from a distant site; by definition an automatic fiber cannot remain forever quiescent (16, 17).

Acetylstrophanthidin or ouabain can cause delayed afterdepolarizations in cardiac Purkinje fibers (22, 28, 30, 31, 65). The maximum diastolic potential decreases to between -70 and -80 mV and repolarization carries the membrane potential to a level more negative than that seen later in diastole, i.e. an afterhyperpolarization appears. The afterhyperpolarization is followed by a transient diastolic depolarization (31) or, in our terminology, a delayed afterdepolarization (16). The amplitude of the afterdepolarization can be increased by driving the fibers more rapidly; this may bring the afterdepolarization to threshold, causing one or a burst of nondriven impulses—i.e. triggered activity. The rapid drive that increases the amplitude of the afterdepolarizations also causes a gradual decrease in the maximum diastolic potential of the fibers. Ferrier (29) has recently found that decreasing the membrane potential of Purkinje fibers exposed to digitalis increases the amplitude of the afterdepolarization. The amplitude of the delayed afterdepolarization seen in canine Purkinje fibers exposed to acetylstrophanthidin increases with increasing $[Ca^{2+}]_o$, increases with decreasing $[K^+]_o$, and is depressed by Mn^{2+} (30) and by the slow-channel blocking drug verapamil (64); but this does not prove that the slow inward current is involved in the genesis of the delayed afterdepolarization. Moreover, afterdepolarizations can be seen at membrane potentials well negative to the threshold of the slow response. Tsien and his coworkers have shown that depolarizing pulses are followed by a transient inward current. That current appeared superimposed on the decay of the pacemaker (i_{K2}) current, but could be dissociated from it and therefore seems to be caused by a different mechanism (58). Weingart, Kass & Tsien (84) suggest that the inward current responsible for the delayed afterdepolarization in Purkinje fibers exposed to strophanthidin may result from a "phasic release of Ca^{2+} from an internal store" and that such an increase in Ca_i might change the permeability of background or leak channels to Na^+, K^+, or to both. Delayed afterdepolarizations caused by acetylstrophanthidin have also been observed in specialized atrial fibers (41).

Canine Purkinje fibers exposed to Na-free, Ca-rich solutions (6) can be quiescent at either of two levels of resting potential (87) (see below) and are triggerable at the lower level of resting potential (18). Delayed afterdepolarizations that can be brought to threshold by increased drive rate or premature stimulation occur in atrial fibers in the simian mitral valve (88) and in the canine coronary sinus (89) exposed to normal Tyrode's solution to which catecholamines are added. In the absence of catecholamines the action potentials in the mitral valve arise from low resting potentials (−60 to −50 mV), have slow upstrokes (<20 V sec^{-1}) and are followed by a small afterhyperpolarization. When catecholamines are added the magnitude of the afterhyperpolarization increases and a delayed afterdepolarization appears (88). If catecholamines are added in the absence of electrical stimulation, the fibers will remain quiescent until driven at least once. Afterdepolarizations and triggering in mitral valve fibers are prevented by verapamil (88). Atrial fibers in the coronary sinus that have resting potentials of −80 mV can easily be driven (89) and have action potentials with an upstroke velocity exceeding 50 V sec^{-1}. In some preparations fibers within the sinus show a resting potential positive to −70 mV and are difficult to excite. When norepinephrine is added, the resting potential of the formerly inexcitable fibers increases by 10–15 mV, the fibers become excitable, respond to atrial drive, develop afterdepolarizations, and can be triggered (89).

The addition of catecholamines causes the appearance of delayed afterdepolarizations in tissue obtained from the right atrial free wall of humans at the time of surgery (59). In this tissue the resting potential was low (<65 mV) and the action potentials were slow responses. The afterdepolarizations, their response to changes in rate, and the characteristics of the triggered activity are similar to those of mitral valve fibers. The action potentials and effects of catecholamines on afterdepolarizations in left atrial free wall tissue from cats with spontaneous cardiomyopathy are identical to those seen in diseased human atria (11). These observations suggest that cardiac diseases may cause afterdepolarizations and triggering.

That the presence of catecholamines is not always necessary for triggering in atrial fibers has been shown in rabbit right atrial preparations. Typical action potentials recorded from some fibers in the upper pectinate muscle and in the pectinate muscle along the crista terminalis were followed by afterdepolarizations. The amplitude of the afterdepolarizations increased as the stimulus rate increased and triggering occurred (66).

It has not been shown that triggered activity can cause atrial arrhythmias in the in situ heart; but if it does, those arrhythmias probably can be started and stopped by stimulation so that differentiation of reentry from triggering in situ is not easy (96).

RESTING POTENTIAL

Canine cardiac Purkinje fibers exposed to Na-free, Ca-rich solutions (87) or to normal or Cl-free Tyrode's solution can show two levels of resting potential, at about −40 to −50 mV and at −90 mV. In normal Tyrode's solution, when $[K]_o$ is between 1 and 4 mM, the resting potential can be switched from either level to the other by current pulses. The potassium conductance (g_k) is low at the low level of resting potential and high at the high level; the steady-state current-voltage relationship of such fibers is "N" shaped and intersects the zero-current axis at three points, two of which correspond to stable resting potentials (34).

The significance of these findings for the genesis of arrhythmias remains largely unexplored, but the fiber at the low level of membrane potential can show rhythmic activity very like that of the SA node, with upstrokes dependent on the slow inward current (7, 16, 17, 49, 50, 53), and can presumably also be a locus of slow conduction of the kind needed to sustain circus movement. Exposure of part of a bundle of ventricular fibers to very high $[K]_o$ can induce a marked depolarization and rhythmic activity in adjacent fibers exposed to normal levels of $[K]_o$ (54, 55). Since such rhythmic activity or such slow conduction can be abolished by shifting the membrane to the high resting potential, and since such a shift can be caused by a transient increase in $[K]_o$, by enhanced electrogenic sodium extrusion, by the application of acetylcholine, or by lidocaine, it is clear that fibers at the low level of resting potential may cause arrhythmias and that agents that favor a shift to the high level may be antiarrhythmic [cf Figure VIII-IA in (16)].

EXCITATORY CURRENT IN PARTIALLY DEPOLARIZED FIBERS

The existence of two levels of resting potential suggest that the action potentials that arise at each of the levels may differ not only electrophysiologically but also in their response to drugs (34). A fiber that has been depolarized to −50 mV by elevation of $[K]_o$ has properties very different from those of a fiber that is at the low (−50 mV) resting potential when exposed to 4 mM K. The fiber exposed to high $[K]_o$ has a much lower membrane resistance and presumably a much higher potassium permeability than has the fiber exposed to 4 mM $[K]_o$, even though the resting potential of each is −50 mV. If the upstroke of an action potential depends on an increase in conductance that is small compared with the increase in conductance that accompanies the fast upstroke, that action potential will be markedly affected by the level of g_K and will be less likely to occur when

g_K is high than when it is low. Two factors thus may facilitate the appearance of action potentials in depolarized fibers: enhancement of the inward current and the presence of a low g_K. With these facts in mind one may offer a classification of the sorts of excitatory activity one might see in Purkinje fibers (and perhaps in other types of fibers), and with it a tentative classification of the modes of action of certain antiarrhythmic drugs. [That lidocaine acts by binding to inactivated fast channels (12, 15, 42, 45) is assumed throughout the following discussion.]

High g_K, Unenhanced Slow Inward Current

Such fibers are presumably inexcitable if the resting potential is low enough to cause substantial inactivation because the unenhanced slow inward current cannot sustain an action potential against a high g_K. This is discussed in more detail in the next paragraph.

High g_K, Enhanced Slow Inward Current

A Purkinje fiber exposed to elevated external $[K]_o$, say 18–20 mM, has a resting potential of about –55 mV, has its sodium channels largely inactivated, has a high g_K, and is inexcitable. If such a fiber is exposed to norepinephrine it regains excitability without an increase in resting potential. The resulting action potential has a slow upstroke (5 V sec^{-1}), a low conduction velocity (0.1 m sec^{-1} or less) and is a "slow response," i.e. it is blocked by verapamil and by Mn^{2+} but neither by TTX nor by lidocaine, and it has a threshold potential positive to –50 mV (16). Such fibers can be made excitable by an agent that increases the density of the slow inward current (such as norepinephrine); since g_K is high, an increase in the conductance of the slow channel is needed to permit regenerative depolarization.

Low g_K, Unenhanced Slow Inward Current

A Purkinje fiber exposed to a normal or Cl-free Tyrode's solution containing 4 mM K$^+$ can exhibit resting potential of about –90 mV or about –40 mV. At a resting potential of –40 mV the fast sodium channels are presumably virtually totally inactivated (83) yet the fiber is excitable even if no agent is added to increase the slow inward current. The action potentials that arise in such fibers have not been studied extensively; they may depend on the slow inward current since our unpublished studies show that they have slow upstrokes and are sensitive to verapamil. These action potentials can arise without enhancement of the slow inward current because g_K is low so that a moderate increase in the conductance of the slow channel is sufficient to sustain regenerative depolarization.

Low g_K, Enhanced Slow Inward Current

This combination is seen under the artificial conditions of zero Na_o, 128 mM tetraethylammonium chloride and 16 mM Ca_o (6). The action potentials arise at a threshold potential of about -40 mV and are slow responses since they have a slow upstroke and a low conduction velocity and are sensitive to Mn^{2+} and verapamil but insensitive to lidocaine, quinidine, and TTX. In certain disease states or as the result of congenital abnormalities there may be fibers in the atrium or ventricle or conducting system that always have a low resting potential and a low g_K but can develop slow response action potentials provided the conductance of the slow channel is enhanced by norepinephrine (11, 47). If so, the action potentials of those fibers should have the same pharmacological sensitivities as the Ca-spikes seen in Na-free solutions.

High g_K, Partially Inactivated Fast Channel Current

If a fiber is depolarized to about -50 mV by elevation of $[K]_o$ it is inexcitable (see above), which suggests that the density of noninactivated fast channels in such a fiber is too low to sustain a regenerative depolarization against the background of a high g_K. If the $[K]_o$ is only 10–12 mM, Purkinje fibers *can* develop action potentials the upstrokes of which appear to depend on excitatory current flowing through fast channels; at any rate those action potentials are sensitive to quinidine, lidocaine, and TTX but are not particularly sensitive to verapamil (12, 15, 42, 45).

Low g_K, Substantially Inactivated Fast Channel Current

Little consideration has been given to the possibility that a fiber at a resting potential low enough to inactivate the fast channel almost completely might possess a low g_K so that the few remaining fast channels might sustain regenerative depolarization. Such a regenerative depolarization might give rise to an action potential that could propagate over a fairly long distance (but with decrement), and these action potentials could not easily be distinguished from propagating slow responses. Such action potentials could be blocked by TTX or lidocaine. Alternatively, the fast-channel current, although insufficient to sustain even decremental conduction, might cause a local response sufficient to depolarize the membrane to the threshold of the slow channel, thereby evoking a propagated slow response. The appearance of such a response might be prevented by TTX or lidocaine acting solely on the fast-channel dependent local response; but the propagated slow response could, of course, be blocked by verapamil. Under such circumstances relatively small changes in resting potential (e.g. of a kind that might be caused by changes in the rate of electrogenic sodium extrusion) might markedly change the character of the action potential by causing an increase or decrease in fast-channel current. One can even envision blocking an arrhythmia that arises in such a fiber by use of lidocaine only to have a subsequent depolarization (caused, for example, by digitalis toxicity) bring the fiber to the potential at which lidocaine-insensitive slow responses would appear and become arrhythmogenic.

High g_K, Large Fast Channel Current

This set of circumstances refers to the fiber exposed to physiological concentrations of K_o that is at the high level of resting potential and has a high g_K. In such a fiber there is very little inactivation so that the conductance of the fast channel can easily increase sufficiently to produce the familiar "normal" rapid upstroke. The classification might for the sake of completeness include an entry under the heading low g_K and large fast channel current but it is not easy to envision Purkinje fiber with a markedly low g_K remaining at a high resting potential, although ventricular fibers exposed to low K_o might do so.

One of us has suggested (16) that many arrhythmias result from a loss of resting potential that leads to replacement of the normal action potential by a slow response. To that possibility we would now add the replacement of a normal action potential by an action potential in which the upstroke depends on current carried via the largely inactivated fast channel. We would also emphasize the importance of g_K and again point out that the delayed afterdepolarizations responsible for triggered activity can arise at membrane potentials well negative to the threshold of the slow response.

ACKNOWLEDGMENT

The authors were supported in part by USPHS Grant HL 14899.

Literature Cited

1. Allessie, M. A., Bonke, F. I. M., Schopman, F. 1973. Circus movement in rabbit atrial muscle as a mechanism of tachycardia. *Circ. Res.* 33:54–62
2. Allessie, M. A., Bonke, F. I. M., Schopman, F. J. G. 1976. Circus movement in rabbit atrial muscle as a mechanism of tachycardia. II. Role of nonuniform recovery of excitability in the occurrence of unidirectional block, as studied with multiple microelectrodes. *Circ. Res.* 39:168–78
3. Allessie, M. A., Bonke, F. I. M., Schopman, F. J. G. 1977. Circus movement in rabbit atrial muscle as a mechanism of tachycardia. III. The "Leading Circle" concept: A new model of circus movement in cardiac tissue without the involvement of an anatomical obstacle. *Circ. Res.* 41:9–18
4. Armour, J. A., Hageman, G. R., Randall, W. C. 1972. Arrhythmias induced by local cardiac nerve stimulation. *Am. J. Physiol.* 223:1068–75
5. Arnsdorf, M. F. 1977. Membrane factors in arrhythmogenesis: Concepts and definitions. *Prog. Cardiovasc. Dis.* 19:413–29

6. Aronson, R. S., Cranefield, P. F. 1973. The electrical activity of canine cardiac Purkinje fibers in sodium-free, calcium-rich solutions. *J. Gen. Physiol.* 61:786–808

7. Aronson, R. S., Cranefield, P. F. 1974. The effect of resting potential on the electrical activity of canine cardiac Purkinje fibers exposed to Na-free solution or to ouabain. *Pfluegers Arch.* 347: 101–16

8. Bassett, A. L., Fenoglio, J. J. Jr., Wit, A. L., Myerburg, R. J., Gelband, H. 1976. Electrophysiological and ultrastructural characteristics of the canine tricuspid valve. *Am. J. Physiol.* 230: 1366–73

9. Boineau, J. P., Mooney, C. R., Hudson, R. D., Hughes, D. C., Erdin, R. A., Wylds, A. C. 1977. Observations on reentrant excitation pathways and refractory period distribution in spontaneous and experimental atrial flutter in the dog. In *Reentrant Arrhythmias; Mechanisms and Treatment,* ed. H. E. Kulbertus, pp. 72–98. Lancaster, England: MTP Press.

10. Boineau, J. P., Cox, J. L. 1973. Slow ventricular activation in acute myocardial infarction. A source of reentrant premature ventricular contractions. *Circulation* 48:703–13

11. Boyden, P. A., Tilley, L. P., Lui, S. K., Wit, A. L. 1977. Effects of atrial dilatation on atrial cellular electrophysiology: Studies on cats with spontaneous cardiomyopathy. *Circulation* 56:III–48

12. Brennan, F. J., Cranefield, P. F., Wit, A. L. 1978. Effects of lidocaine on slow response and depressed fast response action potentials of canine cardiac Purkinje fibers. *J. Pharmacol. Exp. Ther.* 204:312–24

13. Brooks, C. McC., Lu, H. H. 1972. *The Sinoatrial Pacemaker of the Heart.* Springfield, Ill.: Charles C. Thomas. pp. 68–117

14. Brown, H. F., Noble, S. J. 1969. Membrane currents underlying rectification and pace-maker activity in frog atrial muscle. *J. Physiol. London* 204:717–36

15. Chen, C. M., Gettes, L. S., Katzung, B. G. 1975. Effect of lidocaine and quinidine on steady-state characteristics and recovery kinetics of $(dV/dT)_{max}$ in guinea pig ventricular myocardium. *Circ. Res.* 37:20–29

16. Cranefield, P. F. 1975. *The Conduction of the Cardiac Impulse: The Slow Response and Cardiac Arrhythmias.* Mount Kisco, N.Y.: Futura.

17. Cranefield, P. F. 1977. Action potentials, afterpotentials and arrhythmias. *Circ. Res.* 41:415–23

18. Cranefield, P. F., Aronson, R. S. 1974. Initiation of sustained rhythmic activity by single propagated action potentials in canine cardiac Purkinje fibers exposed to sodium-free solution or to ouabain. *Circ. Res.* 34:477–81

19. Cranefield, P. F., Hoffman, B. F. 1971. Conduction of the cardiac impulse. II. Summation and inhibition. *Circ. Res.* 28:220–33

20. Cranefield, P. F., Klein, H. O., Hoffman, B. F. 1971. Conduction of the cardiac impulse. I: Delay, block and one-way block in depressed Purkinje fibers. *Circ. Res.* 28:199–219

21. Cranefield, P. F., Wit, A. L., Hoffman, B. F. 1973. Genesis of cardiac arrhythmias. *Circulation* 47:190–204

22. Davis, L. D. 1973. Effect of changes in cycle length on diastolic depolarization produced by ouabain in canine Purkinje fibers. *Circ. Res.* 32:206–14

23. Downar, E., Janse, M. J., Durrer, D. 1977. Effect of acute coronary artery occlusion on subepicardial transmembrane potentials in the intact porcine heart. *Circulation* 56:217–24

24. Durrer, D., Van Dam, R. T., Freud, G. E., Janse, M. J. 1971. Reentry and ventricular arrhythmias in local ischemia and infarction of the intact dog heart. *Proc. K. Ned. Acad. Wet. Biol. Med.* 74:321–30

25. El-Sherif, N., Hope, R. R., Scherlag, B. J., Lazzara, R. 1977. Reentrant ventricular arrhythmias in the late myocardial infarction period: 1. Conduction characteristics in the infarction zone. *Circulation* 55:686–702

26. El-Sherif, N., Hope, R. R., Scherlag, B. J., Lazzara, R. 1977. Reentrant ventricular arrhythmias in the late myocardial infarction period: 2. Patterns of initiation and termination of reentry. *Circulation* 55:702–18

27. Ferrer, M. I. 1976. *Pre-excitation Including the Wolff-Parkinson-White and other Related Syndromes.* Mount Kisco, N.Y.: Futura

28. Ferrier, G. R. 1977. Relation between acetylstrophanthidin-induced aftercontractions and the strength of contraction of canine ventricular myocardium. *Circ. Res.* 41:622–29

29. Ferrier, G. R. 1978. Effects of transmembrane potential on oscillatory afterpotentials induced by acetylstrophanthidin in canine ventricular tissues. *Fed. Proc.* 37:419

30. Ferrier, G. R., Moe, G. K. 1973. Effect of calcium on acetylstrophanthidin-induced transient depolarizations in canine Purkinje tissue. *Circ. Res.* 33: 508–15

31. Ferrier, G. R., Saunders, J. H., Mendez, C. 1973. A cellular mechanism for the generation of ventricular arrhythmias by acetylstrophanthidin. *Circ. Res.* 32: 600–9

32. Friedman, P. L., Stewart, J. R., Fenoglio, J. J., Wit, A. L. 1973. Survival of subendocardial Purkinje fibers after extensive myocardial infarction in dogs. In vitro and in vivo correlations. *Circ. Res.* 33:597–611

33. Friedman, P. L., Stewart, J. R., Wit, A. L. 1973. Spontaneous and induced cardiac arrhythmias in subendocardial Purkinje fibers surviving extensive myocardial infarction in dogs. *Circ. Res.* 33:612–26

34. Gadsby, D. C., Cranefield, P. F. 1977. Two levels of resting potential in cardiac Purkinje fibers. *J. Gen. Physiol.* 70:725–46

35. Gallagher, J. J., Gilbert, M., Svenson, R. H., Sealy, W. C., Kasell, J., Wallace, A. G. 1975. Wolff-Parkinson-White Syndrome: The problem, evaluation and surgical correction. *Circulation* 51:767–85

36. Geesbreght, J. M., Randall, W. C. 1971. Area localization of shifting cardiac pacemakers during sympathetic stimulation. *Am. J. Physiol.* 220:1522–27

37. Gelband, H., Bush, H. L., Rosen, M. R., Myerburg, R. J., Hoffman, B. F. 1972. Electrophysiologic properties of isolated preparations of human atrial myocardium. *Circ. Res.* 30:293–300

38. Gettes, L. S. 1976. Possible role of ionic changes in the appearance of arrhythmias. *Pharmacol. Ther. B.* 2:787–810

39. Hageman, G. R., Goldberg, J. M., Armour, J. A., Randall, W. C. 1973. Cardiac dysrhythmias induced by autonomic nerve stimulation. *Am. J. Cardiol.* 32:823–30

40. Harris, A. S., Rojas, A. G. 1943. The initiation of ventricular fibrillation due to coronary occlusion. *Exp. Med. Surg.* 1:105–11

41. Hashimoto, K., Moe, G. K. 1973. Transient depolarizations induced by acetylstrophanthidin in specialized tissue of dog atrium and ventricle. *Circ. Res.* 32:618–24

42. Hille, B. 1977. Local anesthetics: hydrophilic and hydrophobic pathways for the drug-receptor interaction. *J. Gen. Physiol.* 69:497–515

43. Hoffman, B. F., Cranefield, P. F. 1960. *Electrophysiology of the Heart.* New York: McGraw Hill

44. Hogan, P. M., Davis, L. D. 1968. Evidence for specialized fibers in the canine atrium. *Circ. Res.* 23:387–96

45. Hondeghem, L. M., Katzung, B. G. 1977. Time- and voltage-dependent interactions of antiarrhythmic drugs with cardiac sodium channels. *Biochim. Biophys. Acta* 472:373–98

46. Hope, R. R., Scherlag, B. J., El-Sherif, N., Lazzara, R. 1976. Hierarchy of ventricular pacemakers. *Circ. Res.* 39: 883–88

47. Hordof, A. J., Edie, R., Malm, J. R., Hoffman, B. F., Rosen, M. R. 1976. Electrophysiologic properties and response to pharmacologic agents of fibers from diseased atria. *Circulation* 54: 774–79

48. Horowitz, L. N., Spear, J. F., Moore, E. N. 1975. Subendocardial origin of ventricular arrhythmias in 24-hour-old experimental myocardial infarction. *Circulation* 53:56–63

49. Imanishi, S. 1971. Calcium sensitive discharges in canine Purkinje fibers. *Jpn. J. Physiol.* 21:443–63

50. Imanishi, S., Surawicz, B. 1976. Automatic activity in depolarized guinea pig ventricular myocardium: characteristics and mechanisms. *Circ. Res.* 39: 751–59

51. Jalife, J., Moe, G. K. 1976. Effect of electrotonic potentials on pacemaker activity of canine Purkinje fibers in relation to parasystole. *Circ. Res.* 39:801–8

52. Janse, M. J., van Capelle, F. J. L., Freud, G. E., Durrer, D. 1971. Circus movement within the AV node. *Circ. Res.* 28:403–14

53. Katzung, B. G. 1975. Effects of extracellular calcium and sodium on depolarization-induced automaticity in guinea pig papillary muscle. *Circ. Res.* 37:118–27

54. Katzung, B. G., Hondeghem, L. M., Grant, A. O. 1973. Cardiac ventricular automaticity induced by current of injury. *Pfluegers Arch.* 360:193–97

55. Katzung, B. G., Morgenstern, J. A. 1977. Effects of extracellular potassium on ventricular automaticity and evidence for a pacemaker current in mammalian ventricular myocardium. *Circ. Res.* 40:105–11

56. Lazzara, R., El-Sherif, N., Scherlag, B. J. 1973. Electrophysiological properties of canine Purkinje cells in one-day-old myocardial infarction. *Circ. Res.* 33: 722–34

57. Lazzara, R., El-Sherif, N., Scherlag, B. J. 1975. Disorders of cellular electrophysiology produced by ischemia of the canine His bundle. *Circ. Res.* 36:444–54

58. Lederer, W. J., Tsien, R. W. 1976. Transient inward current underlying arrhythmogenic effects of cardiotonic steroids in Purkinje fibres. *J. Physiol. (London)* 263:73–100

59. Mary-Rabine, L., Rosen, M. R. 1977. Sustained rhythmic activity in human atria. *Circulation* 56:III–48

60. Mendez, C., Moe, G. K. 1966. Demonstration of a dual A-V nodal conduction system in the isolated rabbit heart. *Circ. Res.* 29:378–92

61. Moe, G. K. 1962. On the multiple wavelet hypothesis of atrial fibrillation. *Arch. Int. Pharmacodyn.* 140:183–88

62. Myerburg, R. J., Gelband, H., Nilsson, K., Sung, R. J., Thurer, R. J., Morales, A. R., Bassett, A. L. 1977. Long term electrophysiological abnormalities resulting from experimental myocardial infarction in cats. *Circ. Res.* 41:73–84

63. Pastelin, G., Mendez, R., Moe, G. K. 1978. Participation of atrial specialized conduction pathways in atrial flutter. *Circ. Res.* 42:386–93

64. Rosen, M., Ilvento, J., Gelband, H., Merker, C. 1974. Effects of verapamil on electrophysiologic properties of canine cardiac Purkinje fibers. *J. Pharmacol. Exp. Ther.* 189:414–22

65. Rosen, M. R., Gelband, H., Hoffman, B. F. 1973. Correlation between effects of ouabain on the canine electrocardiogram and transmembrane potentials of isolated Purkinje fibers. *Circulation* 47:65–72

66. Saito, T., Otoguro, M., Matsubara, T. 1978. Electrophysiological studies on the mechanism of electrically induced sustained rhythmic activity in the rabbit right atrium. *Circ. Res.* 42:199–205

67. Sasyniuk, B. I., Kus, T., 1973. Alterations in electrophysiological properties of cells from infarcted ventricular tissue. *Pharmacologist* 15:178

68. Sasyniuk, B. I., Mendez, C. 1973. A mechanism for reentry in canine ventricular tissue. *Circ. Res.* 28:3–15

69. Scherlag, B. J., El-Sherif, N., Hope, R. R., Lazzara, R. 1974. Characterization and localization of ventricular arrhythmias resulting from myocardial ischemia and infarction. *Circ. Res.* 35:372–83

70. Scherlag, B. J., Helfant, R. H., Haft, J. I., Damato, A. N. 1970. Electrophysiology underlying ventricular arrhythmias due to coronary ligation. *Am. J. Physiol.* 219:1665–71

71. Schmitt, F. O., Erlanger, J. 1928. Directional differences in the conduction of the impulse through heart muscle and their possible relation to extrasystolic and fibrillary contractions. *Am. J. Physiol.* 87:326–47

72. Singer, D. H., Ten Eick, R. E., DeBoer, A. 1973. Electrophysiological correlates of human atrial tachyarrhythmias. In *Cardiac Arrhythmias*, ed. L. S. Dreifus, W. Likoff, pp. 97–111. New York: Grune and Stratton

73. Spear, J. F., Michelson, E. L., Spielman, S. R., Moore, E. N. 1977. The origin of ventricular arrhythmias 24 hours following experimental anterior septal coronary artery occlusion. *Circulation* 55:844–52

74. Strauss, H. C., Prystowsky, E. N., Scheinman, M. M. 1977. Sino-atrial and atrial electrogenesis. *Prog. Cardiovasc. Dis.* 19:385–404

75. Tsien, R. W. 1974. Effects of epinephrine on the pacemaker potassium current of cardiac Purkinje fibers. *J. Gen. Physiol.* 64:293–319

76. Vassalle, M. 1971. Automaticity and automatic rhythms. *Am. J. Cardiol.* 28:245–52

77. Vassalle, M. 1977. Cardiac automaticity and its control. *Am. J. Physiol.* 233:H625–34

78. Vassalle, M. 1977. The relationship among cardiac pacemakers: Overdrive suppression. *Circ. Res.* 41:269–77

79. Vassalle, M. 1977. Generation and conduction of impulses in the heart under physiological and pathological conditions. *Pharmacol. Ther. B.* 3:1–39

80. Waldo, A. L., Kaiser, G. A. 1973. Study of ventricular arrhythmias associated with acute myocardial infarction in the canine heart. *Circulation* 47:1222–28

81. Watanabe, J., Dreifus, L. S. 1965. Inhomogeneous conduction in the AV node. *Am. Heart J.* 70:505–14

82. Weidmann, S. 1974. Heart: electrophysiology. *Ann. Rev. Physiol.* 36:155–70

83. Weidmann, S. 1956. *Electrophysiologie der Herzmuskelfaser.* Bern: Huber. pp. 71–75

84. Weingart, R., Kass, R. S., Tsien, R. W. 1977. Roles of calcium and sodium ions in the transient inward current induced by strophanthidin in cardiac Purkinje fibers *Biophys. J.* 17:3A (Abstr)

85. Wellens, H. J. J. 1976. The electrophysiologic properties of the accessory pathway in the Wolff-Parkinson-White

Syndrome. In *The Conduction System of the Heart,* ed. H. J. J. Wellens, K. I. Lie, M. J. Janse, pp. 567–87. Philadelphia: Lea & Febiger

86. Wellens, H. J. J., Lie, K. I., Janse, M. J., eds. 1976. *The Conduction System of the Heart: Structure, Function and Clinical Implication.* Philadelphia: Lea and Febiger.

87. Wiggins, J. R., Cranefield, P. F. 1976. Two levels of resting potential in canine cardiac Purkinje fibers exposed to sodium-free solutions. *Circ. Res.* 39:466–74

88. Wit, A. L., Cranefield, P. F. 1976. Triggered activity in cardiac muscle fibers of the simian mitral valve. *Circ. Res.* 38:85–98

89. Wit, A. L., Cranefield, P. F. 1977. Triggered and automatic activity in the canine coronary sinus. *Circ. Res.* 41:435–45

90. Wit, A. L., Cranefield, P. F. 1978. Reentrant excitation as a cause of cardiac arrhythmias. *Am. J. Physiol.* 235:H1–17

91. Wit, A. L., Cranefield, P. F., Hoffman, B. F. 1972. Slow conduction and reentry in the ventricular conducting system. II. Single and sustained circus movement in networks of canine and bovine Purkinje fibers. *Circ. Res.* 30:11–22

92. Wit, A. L., Fenoglio, J. J., Wagner, B. M., Bassett, A. L. 1973. Electrophysiological properties of cardiac muscle in the anterior mitral valve leaflet and the adjacent atrium in the dog. Possible implications for the genesis of atrial dysrhythmias. *Circ. Res.* 32:731–45

93. Wit, A. L., Goldreyer, B. N., Damato, A. N. 1971. In vitro model of paroxysmal supraventricular tachycardia. *Circulation* 43:862–75

94. Wit, A. L., Hoffman, B. F., Cranefield, P. F. 1972. Slow conduction and reentry in the ventricular conducting system. I. Return extra-systole in canine Purkinje fibers. *Circ. Res.* 30:1–10

95. Wit, A. L., Rosen, M. R., Hoffman, B. F. 1974. Electrophysiology and pharmacology of cardiac arrhythmias. II. Relationship of normal and abnormal electrical activity of cardiac fibers to the genesis of arrhythmias. A. Automaticity. *Am. Heart. J.* 88:515–24

96. Wit, A. L., Wiggins, J. R., Cranefield, P. F. 1976. Some effects of electrical stimulation on impulse initiation in cardiac fibers: its relevance for the determination of the mechanisms of clinical cardiac arrhythmias. See Ref. 86, pp. 163–81

Ann. Rev. Physiol. 1979. 41:473–84

CALCIUM AND CARDIAC EXCITATION-CONTRACTION COUPLING

♦1232

Alexandre Fabiato and Françoise Fabiato

Department of Physiology, Medical College of Virginia,
Richmond, Virginia 23298

INTRODUCTION

That an increase of myoplasmic free Ca^{2+} concentration ([free Ca^{2+}]) precedes contraction has been shown in skeletal muscle cells injected with various Ca^{2+}-sensitive probes, including aequorin (9). For approximately ten years Blinks maintained that no steadfast reason precluded such a demonstration in heart muscle (e.g. 8). During these ten years he and his collaborators carefully characterized the relation between [free Ca^{2+}] and aequorin bioluminescence and applied this method to progressively smaller cells (8, 9). It is encouraging to know that he and Allen have finally succeeded in obtaining records of aequorin bioluminescence from multicellular preparations of cardiac muscle (2). This exemplifies the patient experimental work required for progress in the complex field of cardiac excitation-contraction coupling and explains why this field has progressed slowly since the time of the excellent review by Fozzard (22). Recent studies on the role of the sarcolemma and the sarcoplasmic reticulum (SR) in the beat-to-beat Ca^{2+} regulation and of other organelles in slower Ca^{2+} movements are discussed here in order to indicate some of the alternative hypotheses for the mechanism of cardiac excitation-contraction coupling that are currently being tested. [See (53) for a justification of this approach.]

CALCIUM INFLUX AND EFFLUX ACROSS THE SARCOLEMMA

The data supporting the demonstration of an inward Ca^{2+} current during the plateau of the cardiac action potential are reviewed in this volume by

473

Reuter (56), who suggests that this current is the major if not the unique route of transsarcolemmal net influx of Ca^{2+} for the beat-to-beat Ca^{2+} regulation (55). Langer proposed that in addition to this Ca^{2+} current, a carrier-mediated $Na^+ : Ca^{2+}$ exchange across the sarcolemma could contribute to the beat-to-beat contractile activation (39, 40). Indeed, ionic flux studies suggest that following membrane depolarization the increase of intracellular $[Na^+]$ (while the intracellular $[Ca^{2+}]$ is low) should increase the (unidirectional) Ca^{2+} influx (25, 72). But that this mechanism results in a net Ca^{2+} influx sufficient to contribute significantly to the beat-to-beat Ca^{2+} regulation is still uncertain (a) because the ionic flux studies (72) do not indicate at which phase of the cardiac cycle the influx of Ca^{2+} takes place, and (b) because of the difficulties caused by the presence in the mammalian myocardial preparations used by Langer (39, 40) of at least three potential mechanisms for increasing the myoplasmic $[Ca^{2+}]$ during activation: Ca^{2+} current and $Na^+ : Ca^{2+}$ exchange across the sarcolemma plus Ca^{2+} release from the SR. To distinguish among these three mechanisms Langer used two simplifications: first, the assumption that the SR does not release Ca^{2+} into the mammalian cardiac myoplasm, which is suggested by his compartmental analysis of the ionic flux data (39) but is so controversial (21, 22, 55, 71) that it should be tested more directly before being used as a premise for a demonstration; second, a perhaps excessive (31, 56, 71) confidence in the specificity with which some drugs (verapamil) or ions (La^{3+}, Mn^{2+}) inhibit the Ca^{2+} current or displace Ca^{2+} from extracellular binding sites. The refutation of these assumptions would render insufficient the present demonstration by Langer of two routes of transsarcolemmal influx of Ca^{2+} for the beat-to-beat contractile activation but would not eliminate this elegant hypothesis.

The evidence in favor of a net influx of Ca^{2+} by $Na^+ : Ca^{2+}$ exchange recently proposed by Anderson, Hirsch & Kavaler (4) for the frog ventricle is more direct than that offered by Langer because: (a) the contractile modifications were induced by changes of the extracellular $[Na^+]$ and $[Ca^{2+}]$ during a single contraction; (b) experimental evidence, which will be reviewed later, suggests that the SR may not participate in the beat-to-beat activation in the frog ventricle; and (c) no reliance on the specificity of any pharmacological tool was required for the demonstration. Unfortunately, the demonstration proposed by Anderson, Hirsch & Kavaler for Langer's second route of transsarcolemmal influx of Ca^{2+} ($Na^+ : Ca^{2+}$ exchange) implies the negation of the first route (Ca^{2+} current), as will be shown.

Anderson, Hirsch & Kavaler (4) provided evidence that the contractile activation of the frog ventricle is brought about by a transsarcolemmal net influx of Ca^{2+}, which is enhanced by an increase of extracellular $[Ca^{2+}]$ or a decrease of extracellular $[Na^+]$ or an increase of positive electrical polarization of the membrane even above the assumed equilibrium potential for a pure Ca^{2+} current (4). If, as proposed (4), this net Ca^{2+} influx is caused by a carrier-mediated $Na^+ : Ca^{2+}$ exchange, an explanation must be sought for its membrane-potential dependence since under a number of experimental conditions, including K^+-induced depolarization (28), the apparent stoichiometry of the $Na^+ : Ca^{2+}$ exchange in cardiac muscle is approximately two Na^+ ions for one Ca^{2+} (5, 28, 47, 58). Kavaler suggested to us that the key to this explanation may be a change of the relative dissociation constants of the carrier for the two competitive ions induced by the electrical field (7). This would not change the stoichiometry or driving force but would modify the permeability and the net influx of Ca^{2+} (59). Such an hypothesis may provide an alternative interpretation for the data supporting a slow inward channel competitively used by Ca^{2+} and Na^+ (56, 57).

Conversely, the data of Anderson, Hirsch & Kavaler (4) could still be compatible with the hypothesis of a Ca^{2+} current in the frog ventricle that was first suggested by Niedergerke & Orkand (50), but only if the actual positive potential applied to the membrane did not, in fact, exceed the equilibrium potential for Ca^{2+}. This would require the assumptions of an imperfect voltage control of the preparations used in (4) and of a large negative surface charge outside the membrane, especially in the presence of a low $[Ca^{2+}]$ (57). Then it could be argued that the effect of the decrease of driving force for Ca^{2+} induced by a more positive polarization may have been cancelled out by the increased selectivity for Ca^{2+} over Na^+ of a nonspecific slow inward channel because the equilibrium potential was less positive for the latter ion (57). Accordingly, the slightly different phrases used in Figure 1 to define the transsarcolemmal influx of Ca^{2+} for the frog and mammalian ventricles reflect a difference in available data and do not imply a true difference between the two tissues.

Contrasting with the uncertainty of its exact role in a carrier-mediated net Ca^{2+} influx, the role of the $Na^+ : Ca^{2+}$ exchange in Ca^{2+} extrusion from the cell has been comprehensively described by Reuter and his collaborators (25, 58). In mammalian cardiac muscle the $Na^+ : Ca^{2+}$ exchange probably only backs up the Ca^{2+} accumulation by the SR (28). In contrast, recent experiments suggest that the $Na^+ : Ca^{2+}$ exchange alone could insure the beat-to-beat relaxation in frog myocardium without the requirement of any intervention of the SR (26, 36).

A suggested alternative for the net Ca^{2+} efflux across the sarcolemma through a $Na^+ : Ca^{2+}$ exchange would be a metabolic Ca^{2+} pump. St. Louis & Sulakhe (66) have shown that purified preparations of isolated sarcolemmal vesicles contain a Ca^{2+} ATPase sensitive to free Ca^{2+} in the 10^{-5} M range in the presence of Mg^{2+}. Yet even in preparations of sarcolemma purer than those used by St. Louis & Sulakhe (higher Na^+-K^+ATPase content), Besch et al (6) and Jones et al (27) found a large contamination by SR vesicles. Since the "sarcolemmal Ca^{2+} ATPase" of St. Louis & Sulakhe has many characteristics in common with the SR Ca^{2+} ATPase (27), the possibility that it might be, in fact, a SR ATPase is not excluded.

CALCIUM RELEASE FROM, AND ACCUMULATION BY, THE SARCOPLASMIC RETICULUM

Data from intact frog ventricular muscle suggest that both activation and relaxation are entirely dependent upon Ca^{2+} movements across the sarcolemma (4, 36, 37, 49). Consistently, experiments in single skinned cardiac cells (sarcolemma removed) and in partly skinned preparations (subsarcolemmal SR present) show no evidence of rapid Ca^{2+}-induced release of Ca^{2+} or rapid Ca^{2+} accumulation by the SR of the frog ventricle (21). In addition, evidence has been presented that the small diameter of the frog ventricular cells may permit a Ca^{2+} diffusion from the extracellular space to the central myofilaments compatible with the rate of tension development observed in the intact frog ventricle (21). However, the SR of the frog ventricle accumulates and releases Ca^{2+} (73), but it may do so slowly, giving to the sparse SR of the frog ventricle (51) the role of a Ca^{2+} buffer. This intracellular buffering by the SR could explain some of the observations made in the intact frog ventricle (4, 49). Yet the scheme proposed in Figure 1 for the frog ventricle may still be an oversimplification (74 but see 21).

In the adult mammalian cardiac muscle there is evidence that the SR participates in the beat-to-beat contractile activation and relaxation (22, 71). One possible mechanism linking the net Ca^{2+} influx across the sarcolemma and Ca^{2+} release from the SR is that the former would not activate the myofilaments directly but would induce a release of Ca^{2+} from the SR that would activate the myofilaments. It seems to us that experiments in adult mammalian skinned cardiac cells indicate that this Ca^{2+}-induced release of Ca^{2+} operates in these preparations (21). But a major problem is whether the methods used for skinned cardiac cells could induce in the SR properties that it does not have in the intact cardiac muscle. This hypothesis has been tested directly by correcting known abnormal conditions of skinned cardiac cells and indirectly by comparing Ca^{2+}-induced release of Ca^{2+} in skinned cardiac cells from different animal species and at different developmental stages to the excitation-contraction coupling of the intact cardiac muscles of the same animal species and at the same developmental stages. Until now, none of these studies has eliminated the possibility that Ca^{2+}-induced release of Ca^{2+} can be a physiological process (17, 21), despite what we have been quoted as demonstrating (39).

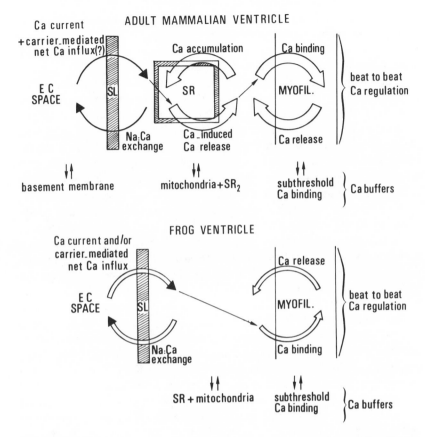

Figure 1   Possible Ca^{2+} movements during cardiac excitation-contraction coupling. See text for discussion.

Another way to eliminate, modify, or support the hypothesis of a Ca^{2+}-induced release of Ca^{2+} is to investigate its weakest point, namely its unknown mechanism. Experiments in skinned cardiac cells suggest only two possible leads: (*a*) that the Ca^{2+}-induced release of Ca^{2+} is facilitated (lower [free Ca^{2+}] threshold) by the experimental conditions that increase the rate of Ca^{2+} accumulation in the SR (20, 21), which suggests that Ca^{2+} release may use part of the mechanism involved in Ca^{2+} accumulation; and (*b*) that Ca^{2+} release induced by Ca^{2+} or caffeine is accompanied by an increased absorption of light in skinned cells stained with a potential-sensitive dye (18). This optical signal has been interpreted tentatively as indicating a decrease of the absolute value of the potential across the SR membrane (18). The accumulation of Ca^{2+} in the SR is accompanied by an optical signal in the direction opposite to that observed during Ca^{2+} release

(19). These preliminary data (18, 19) do not indicate whether the possible change of membrane potential could be the mechanism causing the partial reversal of the Ca^{2+} accumulation process or the consequence of an electrogenic translocation of Ca^{2+} across the SR membrane.

Recent studies by Katz et al (32–35) on the isolated skeletal muscle SR suggest that Ca^{2+}-induced efflux of Ca^{2+} may use part of the mechanism used for Ca^{2+} influx and that the apparent Ca^{2+} permeability of the SR (defined by the ratio: Efflux/intravesicular $[Ca^{2+}]$) is dependent upon both intravesicular $[Ca^{2+}]$ and extravesicular $[Ca^{2+}]$. The rationale of the experiments leading to these conclusions was the presumption that a calcium-precipitating anion, such as oxalate, "clamped" the intravesicular $[Ca^{2+}]$ at a level determined solely by the solubility product of the calcium-anion crystal. Whether or not this concept holds true under the changing conditions inside the vesicles during active calcium accumulation needs to be determined. In fact, the increase in rate of Ca^{2+} transport (32–35) or accumulation by the SR (21) that oxalate causes can be explained by mechanisms other than a precipitation of calcium oxalate within the vesicles. For instance, oxalate could stimulate the Ca^{2+} transport ATPase of the SR by inhibiting a protein phosphatase activity (29, 30). In addition, the slow rate of Ca^{2+} release and the high extravesicular $[Ca^{2+}]$ required to induce it in isolated skeletal muscle SR render it unlikely that these experiments are representative of the observations made in skinned cardiac cells. Thus, despite the great interest generated by the data of Katz et al (32–35), the mechanism of Ca^{2+}-induced release of Ca^{2+} remains unknown.

The preceding discussion shows that the hypothesis of a Ca^{2+}-induced release of Ca^{2+} is still too vague to discourage the search for alternative or additional mechanisms of Ca^{2+} release from the SR. Space does not permit us to review again the evidence against a Ca^{2+} release induced by variations of pH (20) or by an increase of intracellular $[Na^+]$ (17). Focusing the discussion on the strongest alternative hypothesis, that the Ca^{2+} release may be induced by the depolarization of the sarcolemma or the transverse tubules (13, 22), obliges us to review comparatively data on skeletal muscle excitation-contraction coupling.

A first approach consists of proposing that excitation-contraction coupling may be simpler (more rudimentary) in mammalian cardiac muscle than in skeletal muscle simply because the cells have a smaller diameter in the former tissue. Cardiac muscle needs extracellular Ca^{2+} to contract (39), and even the tight correlation between Ca^{2+} conductance and tension observed during voltage clamp experiments (68) does not require any explanation other than a Ca^{2+}-induced release of Ca^{2+} from the SR since this process is not all-or-none but graded with the [free Ca^{2+}] that induces it (20, 21). In contrast, skeletal muscle contracts in the absence of rapidly exchangeable extracellular Ca^{2+} (60). This suggests that a process not requiring extracellular Ca^{2+} initiates Ca^{2+} release from skeletal muscle SR and that this process could be bypassed in mammalian cardiac muscle. In skeletal muscle Ca^{2+}-induced release could be a secondary process amplifying the release of Ca^{2+} from the SR initiated by this other process (65). However, Endo (16) finds this hypothesis unlikely because, in contrast to the findings in skinned cardiac cells (17, 20, 21), a [free Ca^{2+}] higher than sufficient to saturate the myofilaments is needed to induce Ca^{2+} release from the SR of skinned skeletal muscle fibers. Yet the [free Ca^{2+}] requirement for Ca^{2+}-induced release of Ca^{2+} may have been very high because the change of [free Ca^{2+}] in the vicinity of the SR was unphysiologically slow under Endo's experimental conditions (48). In addition, the [free Ca^{2+}] requirement may decrease once the SR membrane has been modified by the process that initiates the Ca^{2+} release.

An opposite and more often used (22) approach consists of assuming that the presumably non-Ca^{2+} process that initiates Ca^{2+} release from skeletal muscle SR may also play a role in cardiac muscle. But this process initiating Ca^{2+} release in skeletal muscle is still unknown, despite the relative optimism that was prevalent two years ago (13). It seems unlikely, now, that the contractions induced by replacing an impermeant anion by Cl^- in skinned skeletal muscle fibers (16) correspond to a depolarization-induced release of Ca^{2+} of physiological relevance (46, 64; but see 45). Some of the optical signals recorded in intact skeletal muscle fibers that could have corresponded to a depolarization of the SR (13) have now been claimed to correspond to an event subsequent to the Ca^{2+} release from the SR (67). Finally, the electrical properties of intact skeletal muscle fibers [linear: e.g. (69, 70); nonlinear: e.g. (10, 11)] can be well described by models that do not include the SR (15, 44). All these negative findings render tempting the elegant hypothesis of Chandler, Rakowski & Schneider (11) that reconciles a possible absence of electrical coupling between SR and transverse tubules and the tight control of contractile activation by imposed changes in surface membrane potential (12). This hypothesis proposes that mechanical links, which probably correspond to the foot processes in the SR transverse tubule junction observed under electron microscopy (24), could couple the charges from the transverse tubules to sites that are "plugged" in the SR membrane. The depolarization-induced movement of charges of the transverse tubules would then unplug a channel in the SR membrane through which Ca^{2+} would flow into the myoplasm (11). The foot processes exist at the level of all junctions between SR and transverse tubules in skeletal (24) and cardiac muscle (3), but they are also present in cardiac muscle of some birds at the level of "extended junctional SR" that does not face either surface membrane or transverse tubules (3).

The hypothesis of Chandler, Rakowski & Schneider, however, is not yet supported by sufficient experimental evidence to warrant the rejection of alternative hypotheses for the non-Ca^{2+} process that initiates the Ca^{2+} release from skeletal muscle SR. Accordingly, we are most grateful to R. S. Eisenberg for pointing out to us that current might spread from the transverse tubular system into the SR in a manner that would have escaped notice during previous investigations by himself (15, 44, 69, 70) and others (e.g. 10, 11). For instance, R. T. Mathias, R. Levis, and R. S. Eisenberg (in preparation) have investigated two electrical models that allow the spread of potential from the transverse tubular system into the SR without significantly altering the measured linear electrical properties of muscle fibers (15, 44, 69, 70). In one model the space between the transverse tubular system membrane and the nearest membrane of the SR is isolated from the sarcoplasm by a large linear resistance. In such a model substantial potentials can exist across the membranes in the junctional region of the SR without noticeable effect on the previously measured electrical properties (15, 44, 69, 70). There is no morphological evidence for the existence of such a large resistance (14, 23), but it is somewhat difficult to determine the value of an electrical resistance with morphological techniques. In the other model a channel is placed between the transverse tubular system and the SR (54, 63). It has been shown that such a model need not seriously modify the observed electrical properties (43). Arbitrary nonlinear membrane properties have been included in both models, but the number of possibilities precludes systematic investigation. Specific nonlinear properties will need to be determined experimentally before these models can be pursued. Yet the hypothesis of electrical coupling between the transverse tubular system and the SR of skeletal muscle that was first proposed by Peachey & Porter (52) cannot be rejected. Accordingly, it is not possible at the present time to reject the hypothesis of a control of the Ca^{2+} release from the SR by the depolarization of the surface membrane and the transverse tubules in cardiac muscle in addition to or instead of the Ca^{2+}-induced process.

The role of the SR in inducing relaxation by accumulating Ca^{2+} is less problematic than its role in Ca^{2+} release. Data on isolated cardiac SR indicate that the SR may accumulate enough Ca^{2+} to permit relaxation (61). The rate of relaxation observed in skinned cardiac cells is comparable with that observed in the intact cardiac tissue (21). Yet Ca^{2+}-induced release of Ca^{2+} occurs repetitively in skinned cardiac cells unless the myoplasmic [free Ca^{2+}] is decreased during or just after contraction by the same small amount used to trigger Ca^{2+} release (21). This suggests the requirement of a transsarcolemmal back-up mechanism that may be represented in the intact tissue by the $Na^{+}:Ca^{2+}$ exchange (28). For this reason, beat-to-beat Ca^{2+} activation is represented in Figure 1 by Ca^{2+} movements in three compartments, with the Ca^{2+} movements in each compartment triggering (without an all-or-none implication) and backing up the Ca^{2+} movements in the next compartment.

CELLULAR AND EXTRACELLULAR CALCIUM BUFFERS

In addition to the beat-to-beat Ca^{2+} regulation by the sarcolemma and the SR, cellular or extracellular buffers in each compartment cause slow Ca^{2+} shifts that may play a role, for instance, in the force-frequency relationships.

In the myofilament space the binding of Ca^{2+} to troponin or other proteins below the threshold for the contraction but above the threshold for Ca^{2+} transport by the SR (62) may represent a Ca^{2+} buffer (21).

In the intermediary compartment the mitochondria might play a role as a Ca^{2+} buffer under unphysiological conditions that increase the myoplasmic [free Ca^{2+}] (17, 21, 28, 38). They have a very large capacity for Ca^{2+} (73) but a low affinity [see (21) for references]; the changes of myoplasmic [free Ca^{2+}] that they can generate are slow (73). However, a more important role for the mitochondria is not yet excluded (1), and it must be recognized that most of the experiments done in intact or skinned cardiac cells do not meet the methodological standards used for isolated mitochondria (1). In addition to or instead of the mitochondria, a slow component of the Ca^{2+} transport by the SR (SR_2 in Figure 1) in mammalian cardiac muscle, and perhaps the whole SR in frog heart, may play the role of a Ca^{2+} buffer in the intermediary compartment [see (21) for references].

For the extracellular compartment Langer has convincingly demonstrated only that the basement membrane of the mammalian myocardium controls the permeability of the sarcolemma to Ca^{2+} (41, 42). Experiments in partially skinned cardiac cells suggest, in addition, that the basement membrane binds Ca^{2+} and could be a low-affinity Ca^{2+} buffer at the outer face of the sarcolemma (21). Finally, internally consistent but indirect evidence suggests to Langer that the basement membrane represents a Ca^{2+} sink (39–41). In the frog ventricle there is no basement membrane, but the endothelial layer that encloses the bundles of cardiac cells (51) might play the same role. The approach used for the present review (53) prevented us from giving to Langer's theory the space that it deserves. Langer's most recent review (40) provides a very fair and thorough discussion of not only his work but also a number of recent studies in intact cardiac muscle that we did not discuss.

Obviously, the present review proposes no conclusion, and Figure 1 represents only one of several alternative hypotheses for the mechanism of cardiac excitation-contraction coupling.

ACKNOWLEDGMENTS

The authors are supported by an Established Investigatorship (73–186) and grants-in-aid (75–783 and 78–1137) from the American Heart Association and by a research grant (1 R01 HL 19138–03) from the National Heart, Lung, and Blood Institute.

Literature Cited

1. Affolter, H., Chiesi, M., Dabrowska, R., Carafoli, E. 1976. Calcium regulation in heart cells: the interaction of mitochondrial and sarcoplasmic reticulum with troponin-bound calcium. *Eur. J. Biochem.* 67:389–96
2. Allen, D. G., Blinks, J. R. 1978. Calcium transients in aequorin-injected frog cardiac muscle. *Nature* 273:509–13
3. Anderson, P. A. W., Manring, A., Sommer, J. R., Johnson, E. A. 1976. Cardiac muscle: an attempt to relate structure to function. *J. Mol. Cell. Cardiol.* 8:123–43
4. Anderson, T. W., Hirsch, C., Kavaler, F. 1977. Mechanism of activation of contraction in frog ventricular muscle. *Circ. Res.* 41:472–80
5. Benninger, C., Einwächter, H. M., Haas, H. G., Kern, R. 1976. Calcium-sodium antagonism on the frog's heart: a voltage-clamp study. *J. Physiol. London* 259:617–45
6. Besch, H. R. Jr., Jones, L. R., Fleming, J. W., Watanabe, A. M. 1977. Parallel unmasking of latent adenylate cyclase and (Na$^+$,K$^+$)-ATPase activities in cardiac sarcolemmal vesicles. *J. Biol. Chem.* 252:7905–8
7. Bianchi, C. P., Lakshminarayanaiah, N. 1969. A model for the regulation of calcium binding in the directly coupled muscle membrane. *Fed. Proc.* 28:1627–28
8. Blinks, J. R. 1973. Calcium transients in striated muscle cells. *Eur. J. Cardiol.* 1:135–42
9. Blinks, J. R., Prendergast, F. G., Allen, D. G. 1976. Photoproteins as biological calcium indicators. *Pharmacol. Rev.* 28:1–93
10. Chandler, W. K., Rakowski, R. F., Schneider, M. F. 1976. A non-linear voltage dependent charge movement in frog skeletal muscle. *J. Physiol. London* 254:245–83
11. Chandler, W. K., Rakowski, R. F., Schneider, M. F. 1976. Effects of glycerol treatment and maintained depolarization on charge movement in skeletal muscle. *J. Physiol. London* 254:285–316

12. Costantin, L. L., Taylor, S. R. 1973. Graded activation in frog muscle fibers. *J. Gen. Physiol.* 61:424–43
13. Ebashi, S. 1976. Excitation-contraction coupling. *Ann. Rev. Physiol.* 38:293–313
14. Eisenberg, B. R., Mathias, R. T., Gilai, A. 1978. The intracellular localization of markers within intact or cut frog muscle fibers. *Am. J. Physiol.* In press
15. Eisenberg, R. S., Mathias, R. T., Rae, J. S. 1977. Measurement, modeling, and analysis of the linear electrical properties of cells. *Ann. NY Acad. Sci.* 303:342–54
16. Endo, M. 1977. Calcium release from the sarcoplasmic reticulum. *Physiol. Rev.* 57:71–108
17. Fabiato, A., Fabiato, F. 1973. Activation of skinned cardiac cells: subcellular effects of cardioactive drugs. *Eur. J. Cardiol.* 1:143–55
18. Fabiato, A., Fabiato, F. 1977. Variations of the membrane potential of the sarcoplasmic reticulum of skinned cells from cardiac and skeletal muscle detected with a potential-sensitive dye. *J. Gen. Physiol.* 70:6a (Abstr.)
19. Fabiato, A., Fabiato, F. 1978. Optical recordings during Ca^{2+} accumulation in and release from the sarcoplasmic reticulum in skinned skeletal and cardiac muscle cells stained with a potential-sensitive dye or with chlorotetracycline. *Proc. VIth Int. Biophys. Congr. Kyoto, Japan.* 233 (Abstr.)
20. Fabiato, A., Fabiato, F. 1978. Effects of pH on the myofilaments and the sarcoplasmic reticulum of skinned cells from cardiac and skeletal muscles. *J. Physiol. London* 276:233–55
21. Fabiato, A., Fabiato, F. 1978. Calcium-induced release of calcium from the sarcoplasmic reticulum of skinned cells from adult human, dog, cat, rabbit, rat, and frog hearts and from fetal and newborn rat ventricles. *Ann. NY Acad. Sci.* 307:491–522
22. Fozzard, H. A. 1977. Heart: excitation-contraction coupling. *Ann. Rev. Physiol.* 39:201–20

23. Franzini-Armstrong, C. 1971. Studies of the triad. II. Penetration of tracers into the junctional gap. *J. Cell Biol.* 49:196–203
24. Franzini-Armstrong, C. 1975. Membrane particles and transmission at the triad. *Fed. Proc.* 34:1382–89
25. Glitsch, H. G., Reuter, H., Scholz, H. 1970. The effect of the internal sodium concentration on calcium fluxes in isolated guinea-pig auricles. *J. Physiol. London* 209:25–43
26. Goto, M., Kimoto, Y., Saito, M., Wada, Y. 1972. Tension fall after contraction of bullfrog atrial muscle examined with the voltage clamp technique. *Jpn. J. Physiol.* 22:637–50
27. Jones, L. R., Besch, H. R. Jr., Fleming, J. W., McConnaughey, M. M., Watanabe, A. M. 1978. Separation of vesicles of cardiac sarcolemma from vesicles of cardiac sarcoplasmic reticulum: comparative biochemical analysis of component activities. *J. Biol. Chem.* In press
28. Jundt, H., Porzig, H., Reuter, H., Stucki, J. W. 1975. The effect of substances releasing intracellular calcium ions on sodium-dependent calcium efflux from guinea-pig auricles. *J. Physiol. London* 246:229–53
29. Hörl, W. H., Heilmeyer, L. M. G. Jr. 1978. Evidence for the participation of a Ca^{2+}-dependent protein kinase and protein phosphatase in the regulation of the Ca^{2+} transport ATPase of the sarcoplasmic reticulum. 2. Effect of phosphorylase kinase and the phosphorylase phosphatase. *Biochemistry* 17:766–72
30. Hörl, W. H., Jennissen, H. P., Heilmeyer, L. M. G. Jr. 1978. Evidence for the participation of a Ca^{2+}-dependent protein kinase and a protein phosphatase in the regulation of the Ca^{2+} transport ATPase of the sarcoplasmic reticulum. 1. Effect of inhibitors of the Ca^{2+}-dependent protein kinase and protein phosphatase. *Biochemistry* 17:759–66
31. Kass, R. S., Tsien, R. W. 1975. Multiple effects of calcium antagonists on plateau currents in cardiac Purkinje fibers. *J. Gen. Physiol.* 66:169–92
32. Katz, A. M., Dunnett, J., Repke, D. I., Hasselbach, W. 1976. Control of calcium permeability in the sarcoplasmic reticulum. *FEBS Lett.* 67:207–8
33. Katz, A. M., Repke, D. I., Dunnett, J., Hasselbach, W. 1977. Dependence of calcium permeability of sarcoplasmic reticulum vesicles on external and internal calcium ion concentrations. *J. Biol. Chem.* 252:1950–56
34. Katz, A. M., Repke, D. I., Fudyma, G., Shigekawa, M. 1977. Control of calcium efflux from sarcoplasmic reticulum vesicles by external calcium. *J. Biol. Chem.* 252:4210–14
35. Katz, A. M., Repke, D. I., Hasselbach, W. 1977. Dependence of ionophore- and caffeine-induced calcium release from sarcoplasmic reticulum vesicles on external and internal calcium ion concentrations. *J. Biol. Chem.* 252:1938–49
36. Kavaler, F., Anderson, T. W. 1978. Indirect evidence that calcium activation causes relaxation of frog ventricular muscle. *Fed. Proc.* 37:300 (Abstr.)
37. Kavaler, F., Anderson, T. W., Fisher, V. J. 1978. Sarcolemmal site of caffeine's inotropic action on ventricular muscle of the frog. *Circ. Res.* 42:285–90
38. Kitazawa, T. 1976. Physiological significance of Ca uptake by mitochondria in the heart in comparison with that by cardiac sarcoplasmic reticulum. *J. Biochem. Tokyo* 80:1129–47
39. Langer, G. A. 1976. Events at the cardiac sarcolemma: localization and movement of contractile-dependent calcium. *Fed. Proc.* 35:1274–78
40. Langer, G. A. 1977. Ionic basis of myocardial contractility. *Ann. Rev. Med.* 28:13–20
41. Langer, G. A. 1978. The structure and function of the myocardial cell surface. *Am. J. Physiol.* In press
42. Langer, G. A., Frank, J. S., Nudd, L. M., Seraydarian, K. 1976. Sialic acid: effect of removal on calcium exchangeability of cultured heart cells. *Science* 193:1013–15
43. Mathias, R. T. 1978. An analysis of the consequences of electrical continuity between the t-system and sarcoplasmic reticulum. Appendix to Neville, M. C. 1978. The extracellular compartments of frog skeletal muscle. *J. Physiol. London.* In press
44. Mathias, R. T., Eisenberg, R. S., Valdiosera, R. 1977. Electrical properties of frog skeletal muscle fibers interpreted with a mesh model of the tubular system. *Biophys. J.* 17:57–93
45. Matsubara, S., Hashizume, T., Hashizume, K. 1977. Chloride-induced contraction in a skinned fiber of toad striated muscle. *Jpn. J. Physiol.* 27:501–9
46. Meissner, G., McKinley, D. 1976. Permeability of sarcoplasmic reticulum membrane: the effect of changed ionic environments on Ca^{2+} release. *J. Membr. Biol.* 30:79–98
47. Miller, D. J., Moisescu, D. G. 1976. The effects of very low external calcium and

sodium concentrations on cardiac contractile strength and calcium-sodium antagonism. *J. Physiol. London* 259:283–308

48. Miller, D. J., Thieleczek, R. 1977. Calcium release by caffeine and other methylxanthines in skinned skeletal muscle fibres. *J. Physiol. London* 273:67P–68P (Abstr.)

49. Niedergerke, R., Ogden, D. C., Page, S. 1976. Contractile activation and calcium movements in heart cells. *Symp. Soc. Exp. Biol.* 30:381–95

50. Niedergerke, R., Orkand, R. K. 1966. The dual effect of calcium on the action potential of the frog's heart. *J. Physiol. London* 184:291–311

51. Page, S. G., Niedergerke, R. 1972. Structures of physiological interest in the frog heart ventricle. *J. Cell Sci.* 11:179–203

52. Peachey, L. D., Porter, K. R. 1959. Intracellular impulse conduction in muscle cells. *Science* 129:721–22

53. Platt, J. R. 1964. Strong inference: certain systematic methods of scientific thinking may produce much more rapid progress than others. *Science* 146:347–53

54. Rakowski, R. F. 1978. Recovery of linear capacitance in skeletal muscle fibers. *Biophys. J.* 21:167a (Abstr.)

55. Reuter, H. 1973. Divalent cations as charge carriers in excitable membranes. *Prog. Biophys. Mol. Biol.* 26:1–43

56. Reuter, H. 1979. Properties of two membrane inward currents in the heart. *Ann. Rev. Physiol.* 41:413–24

57. Reuter, H., Scholz, H. 1977. A study of the ion selectivity and the kinetic properties of the calcium dependent slow inward current in mammalian cardiac muscle. *J. Physiol. London* 264:17–47

58. Reuter, H., Seitz, N. 1968. The dependence of calcium efflux from cardiac muscle on temperature and external ion composition. *J. Physiol. London* 195:451–70

59. Rosenberg, T., Wilbrandt, W. 1957. Uphill transport induced by counterflow. *J. Gen. Physiol.* 41:289–96

60. Sandow, A., Pagala, M. K. D., Sphicas, E. C. 1975. Excitation-contraction coupling: effects of "zero"-Ca^{2+} medium. *Biochim. Biophys. Acta* 404:157–63

61. Solaro, R. J., Briggs, F. N. 1974. Estimating the functional capabilities of sarcoplasmic reticulum in cardiac muscle: calcium binding. *Circ. Res.* 34:531–40

62. Solaro, R. J., Wise, R. M., Shiner, J. S., Briggs, F. N. 1974. Calcium requirements for cardiac myofibrillar activation. *Circ. Res.* 34:525–30

63. Somlyo, A. V. 1978. Membrane bridges across the triadic gap after tannic acid fixation. *Biophys. J.* 21:56a (Abstr.)

64. Somlyo, A. V., Shuman, H., Somlyo, A. P. 1977. Composition of sarcoplasmic reticulum *in situ* by electron probe X-ray microanalysis. *Nature* 268:556–58

65. Stephenson, E. W., Podolsky, R. J. 1977. Influence of magnesium on chloride-induced calcium release in skinned muscle fibers. *J. Gen. Physiol.* 69:17–35

66. St. Louis, P. J., Sulakhe, P. V. 1976. Adenosine triphosphate-dependent calcium binding and accumulation by guinea pig cardiac sarcolemma. *Can. J. Biochem.* 54:946–56

67. Suarez-Kurtz, G., Parker, I. 1977. Birefringence signals and calcium transients in skeletal muscle. *Nature* 270:746–48

68. Trautwein, W., McDonald, T. F., Tripathi, O. 1975. Calcium conductance and tension in mammalian ventricular muscle. *Pfluegers Arch.* 354:55–74

69. Valdiosera, R., Clausen, C., Eisenberg, R. S. 1974. Circuit models of the passive electrical properties of frog skeletal muscle fibers. *J. Gen. Physiol.* 63:432–59

70. Valdiosera, R., Clausen, C., Eisenberg, R. S. 1974. Impedance of frog skeletal muscle fibers in various solutions. *J. Gen. Physiol.* 63:460–91

71. Van Winkle, W. B., Schwartz, A. 1976. Ions and inotropy. *Ann. Rev. Physiol.* 38:247–72

72. Wendt, I. R., Langer, G. A. 1977. The sodium-calcium relationship in mammalian myocardium: effect of sodium deficient perfusion on calcium fluxes. *J. Mol. Cell. Cardiol.* 9:551–64

73. Winegrad, S. 1973. Intracellular calcium binding and release in frog heart. *J. Gen. Physiol.* 62:693–706

74. Winegrad, S. 1976. Spontaneous mechanical activity in depolarized frog ventricle. *J. Gen. Physiol.* 68:145–57

Ann. Rev. Physiol. 1979. 41:485–506

MITOCHONDRIAL FUNCTION
IN THE HEART

♦1233

John R. Williamson

Department of Biochemistry and Biophysics, University of Pennsylvania, Philadelphia, Pennsylvania 19104

INTRODUCTION

The primary function of heart mitochondria is the production of ATP to support rhythmic contraction and ion pumping reactions of the myocardium. The heart can almost instantaneously modulate its rate of ATP production and oxygen consumption over at least a 5-fold range in response to different work loads with only relatively minor changes in the concentration of the various intermediates involved in the oxidative pathways. The mechanisms for the control of respiration and substrate oxidation reside almost entirely within the mitochondria, and have been elucidated mainly from studies with either isolated mitochondria or purified enzymes from heart and other organs. Work with intact cardiac muscle, notably the isolated perfused working rat heart model pioneered by Neely et al (33), has added valuable information concerning the regulation of mitochondrial function, which in general confirms and complements the in vitro studies. In this review I focus on control of respiration and on the feedback regulation of acetyl-CoA production and its utilization by the citric acid cycle. Reviews are available that describe the basic biochemistry of the metabolic processes and factors regulating the supply and relative fuel utilization by the myocardium under different hormonal, dietary, and work states (23, 34, 35, 43, 68, 71, 73).

CONTROL OF RESPIRATION

Basically, the rate of mitochondrial oxygen uptake is regulated by the state of phosphorylation of the extramitochondrial adenine nucleotides. Enzymes and respiratory carriers of the electron transport chain, succinate

485

0066-4308/79/0201-0485$01.00

dehydrogenase, and the oligomycin-sensitive ATPase are structurally associated with the inner mitochondrial membrane. Several enzymes of importance in energy metabolism, notably adenylate kinase, are associated with the outer mitochondrial membrane or the intermembrane space; but these, like the mitochondrial creatine phosphokinase, react functionally with substrates in the extramitochondrial space. The oxidized coenzymes NAD^+ and FAD are reduced in the mitochondrial matrix by substrate dehydrogenases located in the matrix space. Energy for ATP synthesis is provided by the free energy change associated with the transport of electrons from NADH and $FADH_2$ through the enzymes of the respiratory chain to molecular oxygen, which is thereby reduced to water. Figure 1 shows an abbreviated scheme of the mitochondrial electron transport chain and location of the energy coupling sites. According to the generally accepted chemiosmotic coupling hypothesis (32), the respiratory carriers are arranged spatially in the membrane such that electron transport is associated with proton efflux from the mitochondrial matrix and the generation of a proton electrochemical gradient ($\Delta \bar{\mu} H^+$). This establishes an electrical potential, $\Delta \Psi$ (negative inside), and a pH gradient (alkaline inside) across

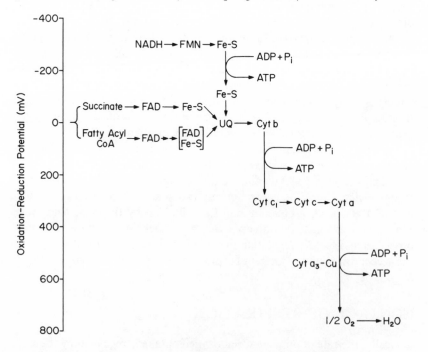

Figure 1 Scheme of mitochondrial electron transport. Approximate oxidation-reduction potentials of the components are shown by the scale on the lefthand side.

the inner mitochondrial membrane, with the overall protonmotive force (Δp) being defined by the relationship:

$$\Delta p = \Delta \bar{\mu} H^+ / F = \Delta \Psi - (2.3\ RT/F)\ \Delta pH, \qquad 1.$$

where R is the gas constant (8.314 joules/°K·mole), F is the Faraday constant (96,490 coulombs/mol equiv. electrons), and T is the absolute temperature.

The proton electrochemical gradient provides a back pressure to the driving force produced by the oxidation-reduction reactions of electron transport and thus regulates forward electron transport and the respiratory rate. Electron flow occurs when a proton circuit is established by inward proton transport. During ATP synthesis, inward movement of protons is channeled through the vectorial ATPase, which spans the mitochondrial inner membrane; ATP is formed from ADP and inorganic phosphate (Pi) in the matrix space. ATP is subsequently transported out of the mitochondria in exchange for ADP on the adenine nucleotide translocator during ADP-stimulated respiration (state 3), and respiration slows to the controlled state-4 rate when the extramitochondrial adenine nucleotide phosphorylation potential achieves equilibrium with the protonmotive force. Energy invested in the maintenance of $\Delta \bar{\mu} H^+$ can also be used to support an electrophoretic influx of cations such as Ca^{2+}, or net efflux of negative charge associated with anion transport, as in the electrogenic exchange of ADP^{3-} with ATP^{4-} (26). Consequently during ion-transport respiration is not associated with ATP synthesis. On the other hand, increased proton-permeability of the mitochondrial membrane dissipates $\Delta \bar{\mu} H^+$, so that respiration and ATP synthesis become uncoupled, as after addition of uncoupling agents (proton ionophores), or during thermogenesis in brown adipose tissue (37).

Free energy is released in the oxidation-reduction reactions of the electron transport chain by movement of reducing equivalents or electrons from a high electrochemical pressure (negative redox potential) to a lower electrochemical pressure (more positive redox potential). Redox potentials (E_h) are calculated from the relationship:

$$E_h = E'_m + 2.3\ RT/nF\ \log\ (ox/red), \qquad 2.$$

where E'_m is the midpoint (or half-reduction) potential of the couple under the prevailing conditions (pH, ionic strength, temperature) and n is the number of electrons transferred (7). Under state-4 conditions the redox potentials of the respiratory chain components fall into three isopotential groups (due primarily to differences of their midpoint potentials), with each span separated by about 300 mV (12). These correspond to the three phosphorylation sites from the NAD couple (–300 mV) to cytochrome b, from cytochrome b to cytochrome c, and from cytochrome c to oxygen (Figure 1). Although the overall redox span from cytochrome c to oxygen (with a redox potential of about 800 mV) is greater than 300 mV, part of the free energy change in the terminal step from cytochrome a_3 to oxygen is unavailable for energy transduction (54). In principle, the free energy change $\Delta G_{ox/red}$ available from electron transport can be calculated from the difference between the E_h values (ΔE_h) for respiratory components spanning one, two, or three phosphorylation sites, using the relationship $\Delta G = -nF\Delta E$. In practice this can presently be measured satisfactorily only for the span between NAD and cytochrome c (12) because of uncertainties of the E'_m values for the components of the cytochrome aa_3–Cu complex (64). The ΔE_h per site may not in fact be the same for the three sites.

The chemical free energy required for the synthesis of extramitochondrial ATP, $(\Delta G_{ATP})_c$, is comprised of the energy required to synthesize ATP in the matrix of the mitochondria, $(\Delta G_{ATP})_m$, plus that required to transport ATP across the mitochondrial membrane. The energy requirements for ATP synthesis in kcal/mole are calculated according to the general equation:

$$\Delta G_{ATP} = \Delta G'_0 + 2.3 \ RT \ \log[ATP]/[ADP][Pi], \qquad 3.$$

where ΔG_{ATP} is the ATP phosphorylation potential, $\Delta G'_0$ is the standard free energy for ATP synthesis under prevailing conditions for the particular adenine nucleotide compartment, and the terms in square brackets refer to molar concentrations of ATP, ADP, and inorganic phosphate. When the mitochondrial electron transport flux is zero in the presence of oxidizable substrates, extramitochondrial adenine nucleotides, and oxygen (i.e. with no proton leak or ion-transport), the driving force, ΔE_h, per phosphorylation site should equal the back pressure exerted by the ATP phosphorylation potential, $(\Delta G_{ATP})_c$. Under these conditions no work is performed, and the system behaves as if it is in thermodynamic equilibrium. Mitochondria in state 4 represent the closest practical approximation to this condition (12, 32, 54).

Since the protonmotive force is postulated to be the energy transducing intermediate between the respiratory chain and the proton-translocating ATPase, it should be stoichiometrically related to the overall ΔE_h and $(\Delta G_{ATP})_c$, when expressed in appropriate units, as follows:

$$2 \ \Delta E_h = (\Delta G_{ATP})_c = n_1 \ \Delta p \qquad 4.$$

$$(\Delta G_{ATP})_m = n_2 \ \Delta p, \qquad 5.$$

where n_1 is the number of protons transported out of the mitochondrial matrix per phosphorylation site ($H^+/2e^-$ ratio) and n_2 is the number of protons entering the mitochondria per ATP formed in the mitochondrial matrix (H^+/ATP ratio). It follows that the energy required for ATP translocation from the matrix to the extramitochondrial space, $(\Delta G_{ATP})_T$, is given by:

$$(\Delta G_{ATP})_T = (\Delta G_{ATP})_c - (\Delta G_{ATP})_m = (n_1-n_2)\, \Delta p. \qquad\qquad 6.$$

Since influx of one H^+ is coupled to the influx of one P_i and one ADP^{3-} and efflux of one ATP^{4-}, it follows that $n_1-n_2 = 1$. Furthermore, since

$$\log(Pi)_m/(Pi)_c = \Delta pH, \qquad\qquad 7.$$

where the subscripts m and c refer to the mitochondrial and extramitochondrial spaces, it follows from equations 1, 3, and 6 that

$$\Delta\Psi = 2.3\ RT/F\ \log\ [(ATP/ADP)_c/(ATP/ADP)_m]. \qquad\qquad 8.$$

Although the chemiosmotic coupling hypothesis as formulated by Mitchell (32) requires both the $H^+/2e^-$ and H^+/ATP stoichiometries to be equal to 2, other studies (e.g. 3, 46) have obtained $H^+/2e^-$ values of 3 or 4. The exact value for the stoichiometry of $H^+/2e^-$ at each of the three phosphorylation sites is at present controversial, but data correlating Δp, ΔE_h and $(\Delta G_{ATP})_c$ in studies with isolated mitochondria under state-4 conditions indicate a value for the $(\Delta G_{ATP})_c/\Delta p$ ratio close to 3 (1, 24, 37). Evidence is accumulating to indicate that the $H^+/2e^-$ value may not be the same at each site, possibly being 3, 2, and 4, giving an average value of 3.0. If so, then equations 4 and 5 require slight modification when applied to each site. Also, if the H^+/ATP ratio is invariant, as seems likely, the P/O ratios at each site will not be the same. Typical values observed with isolated mitochondria in state 4 are: 150 mV for $\Delta\Psi$, 210 mV for Δp, 1 unit for ΔpH, 14 kcal/mole for $(\Delta G_{ATP})_c$, 10 kcal/mole for $(\Delta G_{ATP})_m$, and 310 mV for $\Delta E_h/2e^-$ (1, 11, 12, 27, 36, 54). There is enough variation and uncertainty in the experimentally determined values, however, to accommodate a $H^+/2e^-$ ratio of 4 and a H^+/ATP ratio of 3. Equation 8 has also been verified experimentally with rat liver mitochondria (26).

With increased respiration, the poise of the near equilibrium between the free energy produced by the redox reactions of electron transport and that required for ATP synthesis is disturbed. On the basis of treatments developed from the principles of irreversible thermodynamics (48, 59a), flux should be proportional to the displacement from equilibrium as found experimentally with rat hepatocytes (60). Operationally, ΔE_h, Δp, and $(\Delta G_{ATP})_c$ all decrease with increased respiration, while $(\Delta G_{ATP})_m$ appears to remain almost constant (11, 12, 36). In the rather special case of brown fat mitochondria, which have low ATPase and ATP translocase activities, the respiratory rate doubled for a 30 mV fall of the proton electrochemical gradient (37). In liver mitochondria, the matrix ATP/ADP ratio is almost independent of the decrease in external ATP/ADP ratio, and the adenine nucleotide translocase deviates from equilibrium with $\Delta\Psi$, according to equation 8, by about 2 kcal/mole during a state-4 to state-3 transition [data from (11, 36, 54)]; but here also respiratory rate is proportional to Δp over a limited range (2, 36). Possible disequilibrium between ΔE_h and Δp or between Δp and $(\Delta G_{ATP})_c$ with increasing respiratory activity has not yet been satisfactorily resolved (1, 2, 24, 36, 37, 59a, 64). However, at nonlimiting phosphate concentrations the rate of respiration has been found to be linearly related to the extramitochondrial ATP/ADP ratio [(10), contrast (19)], suggesting a kinetic regulation by the adenine nucleotide translocator.

In summary, respiratory control is determined by relatively small differences between the chemical energy produced by the redox reactions of electron transport and utilization of the proton electrochemical gradient for synthesis and translocation of ATP. From presently available data, it is difficult to determine whether the respiratory rate is regulated by the proton electrochemical potential solely through a kinetic regulation exerted at the adenine nucleotide translocator step or by additional interactions at other sites. This uncertainty relates primarily to the unresolved possibility that the mitochondrial ATPase and the adenine nucleotide translocator may be functionally coupled (61). If a compartmentalized pool of ATP and ADP adjacent to the ATPase exists, near equilibrium of $(\Delta G_{ATP})_T$ with $\Delta\Psi$ may be maintained during active respiration. The above description of respiratory control based on the principles of the chemiosmotic coupling mechanism is incompatible with the concept of maintenance of the thermodynamic equilibrium between the external adenine nucleotide phosphorylation potential and electron transport through the first two phosphorylation sites (13). Further criticism of the views of Erecinska et al (12, 13) have been made by Van der Meer et al (60).

REGULATION OF ACETYL-CoA PRODUCTION

The two major sources of acetyl-CoA for the citric acid cycle in the heart in vivo are from β-oxidation of fatty acids and from pyruvate oxidation. Unlike liver, where ketone body production provides a means of disposing of excess acetyl-CoA, the rate of acetyl-CoA production in heart is strictly coordinated with the rate of acetyl-CoA utilization by the citric acid cycle. Furthermore, since maximal ATP generation by glycolysis is only 5–10% of the total ATP production in aerobic hearts, the rate of myocardial oxygen consumption is proportional to flux in the citric acid cycle.

Acetyl-CoA from β-Oxidation

Activation of free fatty acids to the long chain acyl-CoA derivatives occurs by a highly exergonic reaction in the extramitochondrial compartment of the cell whereby ATP is converted to AMP and pyrophosphate. Extramitochondrial fatty acyl-CoA is not directly accessible to the β-oxidation enzyme system on the matrix side of the inner mitochondrial membrane. It requires conversion first to the fatty acylcarnitine derivative by palmitylcarnitine transferase I situated on the outer face of the inner mitochondrial membrane, followed by transport of the fatty acylcarnitine across the mitochondrial membrane in exchange with free carnitine (39, 40). Intramitochondrial fatty acyl-CoA as the primary substrate for the β-oxidation complex is then generated by interaction of fatty acylcarnitine and free CoASH in the mitochondrial matrix with palmitylcarnitine transferase II located on the inside of the inner mitochondrial membrane (20). Short-chain fatty acids up to C-8 can be activated to the CoA derivative directly in mitochondria.

At low long-chain fatty-acid:albumin molar ratios (e.g. below 0.5) uptake and oxidation of palmitate by the perfused rat heart is proportional to its concentration, and the tissue contents of fatty acyl-CoA and fatty acylcarnitine derivatives remain almost unchanged (38). Even at low concentrations, exogenous fatty acids compete effectively with endogenous fatty acids and other fuels for oxidation, and utilization appears limited by the permeability barriers of the capillary and sarcolemma membranes (47). At higher fatty acid concentrations, tissue contents of acetyl-CoA, acetylcarnitine, fatty acyl-CoA, and fatty acylcarnitine were found to increase while free CoASH and carnitine contents decreased (38). Further studies by Idell-Wenger et al (21) indicated that about 95% of the total CoA (acyl and free) in the heart is located in the mitochondria, while most of the carnitine is cytosolic. Uptake and activation of fatty acids thus become limited by an increased intracellular free fatty acid concentration and a lack of CoASH and carnitine in the cytosol, while β-oxidation flux is probably regulated by the negative feedback effects due to the highly reduced state of the mitochondrial pyridine nucleotides and flavins, and a low mitochondrial CoASH concentration. Fatty acid metabolism at nonlimiting fatty-acid: albumin molar ratios is therefore primarily regulated by the rate of acetyl-CoA oxidation in the citric acid cycle.

When cardiac work of the perfused rat heart was increased with glucose and palmitate as substrates, palmitate uptake and oxygen consumption increased. The tissue contents of free fatty acids, fatty acyl-CoA, acetyl-CoA and acetyl-carnitine decreased, while fatty acylcarnitine, CoASH, and carnitine levels increased (38). Since the fatty acylcarnitine is mainly extramitochondrial while the fatty acyl-CoA is mainly intramitochondrial, these data suggest that fatty acid oxidation becomes limited either by the translocation of fatty acyl groups through the mitochondrial membrane or by the activity of palmitylcarnitine transferase II. This conclusion is supported by the fact that with octanoate as respiratory fuel, which does not require carnitine, acetyl-CoA levels remained elevated at both high and low work loads. However, due to lack of more precise knowledge of the compartmentation of CoA and carnitine derivatives across the mitochondrial membrane, the redox state of the mitochondrial NAD, and particularly the redox states of flavin and iron-sulfur proteins associated with β-oxidation in the intact heart, details of the regulatory interactions are lacking.

Decreased oxygen delivery to the heart, as in ischemia, results in a fall in the tissue contents of acetyl-CoA, acetyl-carnitine, CoASH, and carnitine and a rise in the contents of fatty acyl-CoA and fatty acylcarnitine, indicating that β-oxidation becomes limiting under these conditions (62). In severely ischemic hearts the tissue contents of fatty acylcarnitine and fatty acyl-CoA reach values of 4.4 and 0.35 μmol/g dry wt, respectively. The detergent properties or direct inhibitory effects of fatty acyl-CoA or fatty acylcarnitine derivatives on the adenine nucleotide translocator (6, 52) or the Na^+,K^+-ATPase (75) may contribute to the development of irreversible loss of mechanical and metabolic function after ischemic episodes (see also 53).

Acetoacetate and β-hydroxybutyrate are readily oxidized by cardiac tissue; like fatty acids, they suppress glucose oxidation (72). The metabolism of ketone bodies has been reviewed (65). Acetoacetate is activated to acetoacetyl-CoA by interaction with succinyl-CoA via acetoacetate succinyl-CoA transferase in the mitochondria, while acetoacetyl-CoA is subsequently converted to acetyl-CoA by acetyl-CoA acetyltransferase. Acetyl-CoA levels are elevated in heart during acetoacetate metabolism, and feedback regulation is presumably exerted by the mitochondrial acetyl-CoA/CoASH ratio. Because of the rapid oxidation of acetoacetate by heart muscle, equilibrium of the β-hydroxybutyrate/acetoacetate ratio with the mitochondrial free NADH/NAD ratio is not established; thus the β-hydroxybutyrate dehydrogenase substrate couple cannot be used for measurement of the mitochondrial NAD redox state in heart (18, 63). Acetate is activated directly to acetyl-CoA in the mitochondria by the short-chain acyl-CoA thiokinase. It is readily oxidized by perfused hearts and causes an elevation of acetyl-CoA levels (34). As a physiological fuel it is only important during ethanol metabolism by the liver, where acetate is an end product.

Acetyl-CoA from Pyruvate

Pyruvate at relatively high concentrations (1 mM or above) is an excellent respiratory fuel for the heart (22, 67), whereas lactate is less readily oxidized except in hyperthyroid rats (49, 66). Glucose uptake and oxidation are regulated mainly at the sites of the plasma membrane and phosphofructokinase (34, 43), but regulation of the conversion of pyruvate to acetyl-CoA by pyruvate dehydrogenase also exerts an important selective effect on the relative rates of carbohydrate and fatty acid oxidation by the heart. Inhibition of pyruvate oxidation is revealed by excess lactate production, which may be distinguished from accelerated anaerobic glycolysis by the lower lactate/pyruvate ratio. The activity of the enzyme and flux through pyruvate dehydrogenase is enhanced by high pyruvate concentrations and is inhibited by long- or short-chain fatty acids, by ketone bodies, and by alterations in the metabolic state due to starvation and diabetes (25, 43, 63). The pyruvate dehydrogenase complex contains three enzymes: pyruvate decarboxylase, dihydrolipoyl acetyl transferase and dihydrolipoyl dehydrogenase, which are bound together in a single complex and require Mg^{2+}, thiamine pyrophosphate, NAD^+, and FAD as cofactors. Coordination of the enzymes in the complex is effected by lipoate bound covalently to the acetyl transferase core, which successively becomes acetylated, deacetylated, and oxidized by interaction with the active sites of the three enzymes (44). In addition to the above three enzymes, a MgATP-dependent kinase, pyruvate dehydrogenase kinase, is tightly bound to the complex through the acetyl transferase, while pyruvate dehydrogenase phosphatase is loosely associated with the complex.

The structure, properties, and regulation of the pyruvate dehydrogenase complex have been very actively investigated; regulation, in particular, appears to be remarkably similar in different organs and species (31). Basically, the overall reaction:

$$\text{pyruvate} + NAD^+ + CoASH \rightarrow \text{acetyl-CoA} \qquad \qquad$$
$$+ NADH + H^+ + CO_2 \qquad \qquad 9.$$

appears to be regulated by two different but interdependent mechanisms. End product inhibition by NADH (competitive with NAD^+) and by acetyl-CoA (competitive with CoASH) has been known for some time (4). More recently, regulation by phosphorylation of the α-subunit of pyruvate decarboxylase in the complex has been elucidated (45). Phosphorylation is accompanied by inactivation of pyruvate dehydrogenase [to $(PHD)_b$], and dephosphorylation induces reactivation [to $(PDH)_a$]. The degree of enzyme phosphorylation, and hence the percentage of total enzyme as PDH_a in the steady state, is determined mainly by modification of the activity of PDH_a kinase by various effectors (see 43). NADH and acetyl-CoA are activators of PDH_a kinase, while ADP, NAD^+, CoASH, and pyruvate are inhibitors. In addition, PDH_b phosphatase activity is stimulated by Mg^{2+} and Ca^{2+} ions, which also inhibit PDH_a kinase (41). Regulation by product feedback inhibition and by interconversion between PDH_a and PDH_b operate in the same sense, with overall activity of pyruvate dehydrogenase being inhibited by increases in the ratios of $NADH/NAD^+$, acetyl-CoA/CoASH, and ATP/ADP, and vice versa. The detailed regulation of pyruvate dehydrogenase interconversion between active and inactive forms by modulation of PDH_a kinase activity is complex and not fully understood, particularly with regard to the relative strengths of effects induced by changes of the $NADH/NAD^+$ and acetyl-CoA/CoASH ratios. An interesting unifying mechanism recently advanced to explain the effects of different modulators on PDH_a kinase activity is that direct interaction with the enzyme is mediated by the form of the lipoyl moiety bound to the transacetylase, with acetylhydrolipoate being a stronger activator of PDH_a kinase than dihydrolipoate (5).

Regulation of the flux and the activity of pyruvate dehydrogenase has been studied in isolated heart mitochondria and perfused hearts. Control by alterations of the ratios of ATP/ADP, $NADH/NAD^+$, and acetyl-CoA/CoASH has been clearly demonstrated (14, 15, 18, 25, 63). In hearts from normal, fed rats, about 20% of total pyruvate dehydrogenase activity is in the active nonphosphorylated form. This percentage is decreased to 1–7% by starvation, in alloxan diabetes, or by perfusion of hearts with fatty acids or ketone bodies, in accordance with a decreased rate of oxidation of pyruvate. The percentage of active pyruvate dehydrogenase is increased by elevating the pyruvate concentration, by addition of dichloroacetate, and by an increase of cardiac work, or vice versa (18, 25, 43). The intramitochondrial ATP/ADP ratio is likely to change very little with different nutritional and activity states of the heart; hence feedback regulation from the citric acid cycle and the respiratory chain to pyruvate dehydrogenase is determined principally by alterations of the intramitochondrial $NADH/NAD^+$ and acetyl-CoA/CoASH ratios acting either separately or in concert.

REGULATION OF ACETYL-CoA UTILIZATION
BY THE CITRIC ACID CYCLE

The major role of the citric acid cycle in heart is to accomplish the oxidation of the acetyl group of acetyl-CoA to CO_2 and water. Reducing equivalents are thereby produced in the mitochondria, their reoxidation by the enzymes of the electron transport chain being coupled to ATP synthesis. Intermediates of the citric acid cycle are used catalytically; except for brief intervals during transition states, the citric acid cycle enzymes act as a functional unit, flux being proportional to oxygen consumption. Regulation of the citric acid cycle is therefore associated with feedback interactions that allow flux through the cycle to keep pace with the energy expenditure by the heart. Whether the enzymes of the citric acid cycle are combined physically as a multienzyme is uncertain (55). With the exception of oxalacetate, the matrix citric acid cycle enzymes appear to react with a single pool of intermediates and coenzymes in the matrix space of the mitochondria, this pool being confined by the inner mitochondrial membrane. The volume of the matrix space is about 0.8 μl/mg mitochondrial protein, while the total mitochondrial content is close to 250 mg/g dry wt (21); thus the mitochondrial matrix volume is 0.2 ml/g dry wt compared with a cytosolic volume of about 2.0 ml/g dry wt. Most of the oxalacetate in the mitochondrial matrix appears to be protein-bound, and calculations based on assayed values for citric acid cycle intermediates in the matrix space of isolated heart mitochondria (74) suggest that two different pools of oxalacetate are available to citrate synthase and aspartate aminotransferase. Elucidation of the specific channeling of metabolites through different pathways at bifurcation points by direct enzyme-enzyme or enzyme-translocator interactions awaits future research (56). More detailed discussions are given elsewhere for the regulation of flux through the citric acid cycle under different substrate conditions, based on studies with isolated heart mitochondria (16, 28, 30, 69, 74) and perfused hearts (22, 34, 35, 42, 43, 51, 71, 73).

Heart muscle lacks the ability to carboxylate pyruvate to oxalacetate via pyruvate carboxylase; but when acetyl-CoA levels are elevated, the total contents of intermediates of the citric acid cycle can increase several fold as a consequence of transamination of part of the large aspartate pool to oxalacetate (9, 42, 50). Under such conditions (e.g. with high rates of delivery of fatty acids, ketone bodies, or pyruvate) the citrate content of the heart can increase up to 10-fold. The increased citrate levels have an important feedback effect of inhibiting pyruvate production from glycolysis as a consequence of the inhibition of phosphofructokinase by citrate (see 43).

Interpretation of changes in the total tissue contents of intermediates of the citric acid cycle requires some knowledge of their distribution within the intracellular compartments. The principles underlying the equilibrium distribution of anions across the mitochondrial membrane have been discussed elsewhere (70). With the exception of ATP, ADP, and aspartate, which are transported by electrogenic mechanisms, other carboxylic acid intermediates of the citric acid cycle (i.e. pyruvate, malate, citrate, isocitrate, α-ketoglutarate, succinate, and glutamate) are transported by specific carrier-mediated electroneutral exchange reactions. Since the energization of the mitochondrial membrane maintains a more alkaline environment in the mitochondrial matrix than in the cytosol, permeant anions are concentrated in the mitochondria; at equilibrium, the anion gradient will be equal to the nth power of the proton gradient, where n is the charge on the anion. In the presence of physiological concentrations of phosphate and bicarbonate ions, the ΔpH with isolated mitochondria is less than 0.5 pH units. A ΔpH of 0.4 has been measured for mitochondria in isolated rat liver cells (8, 58). Assuming that a similar pH gradient exists across the mitochondrial membrane in the intact heart, the equilibrium gradients for mono-, di-, and tricarboxylic acids will be 2.5, 6.3, and 15.6, respectively. Since the ratio of the volume of cytosol to mitochondrial matrix space is about 10:1, the amounts of intermediates of the citric acid cycle other than those for citrate and isocitrate are likely to be greater in the cytosol than in the mito-chondria. However, several factors will tend to disturb the equilibrium concentration gradients. Influx of malate into mitochondria in exchange with α-ketoglutarate, which is required during operation of the malate-aspartate cycle for transport of glycolytic reducing equivalents from cytosol to mitochondria (see 49, 73), requires that the α-ketoglutarate gradient be greater than the malate gradient since the exchange is electroneutral. Transport of citrate (in exchange with malate) has a low activity in heart, hence equilibrium across the mitochondrial membrane may not be maintained. Nevertheless, changes in the tissue contents of all the citric acid cycle intermediates except oxalacetate, but including CoASH and acetyl-CoA, are likely to reflect changes in the mitochondrial compartment and therefore may be used to identify regulatory sites.

It is more difficult to identify sites of regulation in a cyclic than in a linear enzyme sequence. Disequilibrium enzymes of the citric acid cycle, and hence the most likely sites for regulation, have been identified as citrate synthase, NAD-linked isocitrate dehydrogenase, and α-ketoglutarate dehy-drogenase (69, 74). Studies with isolated heart mitochondria incubated under various respiratory states (16, 28, 30) and with perfused rat hearts subjected to metabolic transitions (22, 35, 42, 50, 51, 71), together with knowledge of the kinetics of individual enzymes of the citric acid cycle, permit a number of basic conclusions. In fact, the metabolite changes observed in the intact heart with increased work are in general very similar to those observed in the matrix of isolated mitochondria for a state-4 to state-3 transition.

The most important factor in coordinating the activity of the citric acid cycle with flux in the electron transport chain appears to be the oxidation-reduction state of the mitochondrial nicotinamide nucleotides. Regulation of acetyl-CoA entry into the cycle is achieved by interactions at malate dehydrogenase, citrate synthase, and isocitrate dehydrogenase. For conve-nience of reference, an abbreviated scheme of the citric acid cycle and its interrelationship with the malate-aspartate cycle is given in Figure 2. Transport of metabolites across the mitochondrial membrane involved in the malate-aspartate cycle are shown by dotted lines. The transition from low to high work in perfused hearts with a concomitant increase of respiration is associated with a decrease of the mitochondrial $NADH/NAD^+$ ratio irrespective of the nature of the substrate being oxidized (17, 35, 51, 71). This will tend to increase oxalacetate levels provided the redox effect is not offset by a sufficiently large fall of malate or alteration of the disequilibrium poise of malate dehydrogenase. Total tissue oxalacetate levels have been observed to rise (35) or fall (51) with increased work, depending on the nature of the substrate. The site initially most sensitive to regulation by the lowered $NADH/NAD^+$ ratio appears to be NAD-linked isocitrate dehydrogenase, which is strongly inhibited by NADH (as well as activated by ADP). Citrate levels invariably fall immediately after a transition to increased work, which indicates an activational interaction at isocitrate dehydrogenase. The fall of citrate levels has an important feedback effect on citrate synthase since it is inhibited by citrate (the inhibition being competitive with oxalacetate). Consequently, when acetyl-CoA levels remain constant (or above the Km region), flux through citrate synthase will increase when citrate levels fall even though the oxalacetate concentration in the

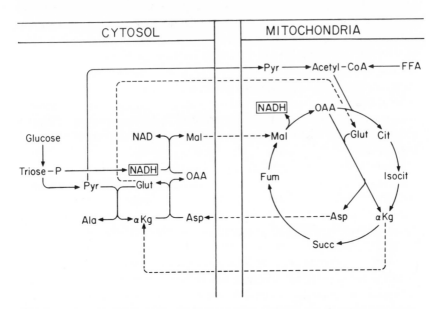

Figure 2 Metabolic scheme showing major reactions of the citric acid cycle and transport of NADH from the cytosol to mitochondria by the malate-aspartate cycle. Abbreviations used: Pyr, pyruvate; Ala, alanine; Glut, glutamate; αKg, α-ketoglutarate; Mal, malate; OAA, oxalacetate; Asp, aspartate; Fum, fumarate; Succ, succinate; Cit, citrate; Isocit, isocitrate.

mitochondria may not change. With glucose as substrate, acetyl-CoA levels are very low—probably within the operational Km region for citrate synthase. Under these conditions, increased work produced an increase of acetyl-CoA levels presumably because of activation of pyruvate dehydrogenase, thereby contributing to the flux increase through citrate synthase (51). In contrast, respiratory acidosis in perfused rat hearts with glucose as substrate in the presence of insulin caused a decrease of cycle flux, associated with a fall of citrate levels, an increase of acetyl-CoA levels, and an oxidation of the mitochondrial nicotinamide nucleotides. This suggested a direct inhibitory effect of H^+ on citrate synthase (51).

Depending on the respiratory substrate, tissue α-ketoglutarate levels may either rise (35), fall (22), or remain unchanged (51) with increased work in the perfused heart. However, since α-ketoglutarate dehydrogenase is strongly product-inhibited, activation occurs when the $NADH/NAD^+$ ratio decreases; at the new NAD redox state, flux from α-ketoglutarate to malate will depend on the matrix α-ketoglutarate concentration and on the succinyl-CoA/CoASH ratio (30). Coordination of flux between α-ketoglutarate dehydrogenase and citrate synthase is achieved (*a*) by the effect of flux through α-ketoglutarate dehydrogenase on the malate (and hence oxalacetate) levels, and (*b*) by the inhibitory effect of succinyl-CoA (competitive with acetyl-CoA) on citrate synthase (28). When the malate-aspartate cycle is operating (see Figure 2 and below), α-ketoglutarate is formed in the mitochondrial matrix not only from isocitrate dehydrogenase but also as a product of transamination between oxalacetate and glutamate. There is thus a competition for α-ketoglutarate between further oxidation in the citric acid cycle and efflux to the cytosol in exchange with malate on the α-ketoglutarate carrier. α-Ketoglutarate efflux is activated by the cytosolic malate concentration; net flux is determined by the relative concentration gradients of α-ketoglutarate and malate across the mitochondrial membrane (73).

The relative importance of the NAD- and NADP-linked isocitrate dehydrogenases in contributing to the citric acid cycle flux is not known. Since the NADP-linked isocitrate dehydrogenase is probably a near-equilibrium enzyme regulated by the $NADPH/NADP^+$ ratio, while there is no obvious mitochondrial NADPH utilizing enzyme in heart other than the energy-linked transhydrogenase acting in reverse, flux through the NADP pathway is probably negligible under normal conditions. In heart as in liver (57), the $NADP^+$ redox potential probably has as low a value (about -400 mV) in the cytosol as in the mitochondria, and reductive carboxylation of α-ketoglutarate by cytosolic NADP-linked isocitrate dehydrogenase may contribute to the observed citrate accumulation in heart with pyruvate or fatty acids as substrate (73).

MITOCHONDRIAL-CYTOSOLIC INTERACTIONS

Experiments in which the respiratory fuel of perfused rat hearts was switched from glucose to acetate or fatty acids (35, 42, 71), or from endogenous fatty acids to glucose (50), have been useful in delineating control mechanisms in the citric acid cycle and interactions with transamination enzymes in the cytosol. Under these conditions ATP turnover changes slightly, but the pool sizes of the cycle intermediates change markedly along with the tissue contents of glutamate, asparate, and alanine. These transitions involve changes in the rate of glycolysis, and hence the rate of transport of reducing equivalents into mitochondria. Since NADH cannot directly penetrate the mitochondrial membrane in mammalian mitochondria, indirect transport shuttles are used. The predominant shuttle in heart appears to be the malate-aspartate cycle, as discussed in detail elsewhere (49, 50, 73). In this cycle (see Figure 2), cytosolic oxalacetate is reduced to malate which enters the mitochondria where it is reoxidized to oxalacetate with release of NADH for reoxidation by the respiratory chain. Efflux of oxalacetate from the mitochondria is kinetically limited, so that oxalacetate is preferentially transaminated with glutamate to yield aspartate and α-ketoglutarate. α-Ketoglutarate leaves the mitochondria by a carrier mediated exchange with malate, while aspartate efflux is coupled with glutamate influx to complete the cycle. The latter exchange, being electrogenic, is energy consuming and provides directionality to the malate-aspartate cycle since aspartate entry into mitochondria is very slow against the membrane potential (29). In addition, since aspartate is an inhibitor of glutamate entry (59), the glutamate-aspartate translocator is kinetically controlled by the glutamate/aspartate ratio in the cytosol. Factors that have not yet been completely elucidated are also probably involved—e.g. a functional complex between malate dehydrogenase and aspartate aminotransferase or between the latter enzyme and the aspartate translocator.

With an increased rate of glycolysis, as in the transition from substrate-free to glucose-plus-insulin perfusion (50), acetyl-CoA levels rise because of increased pyruvate availability to pyruvate dehydrogenase; calculated flux through citrate synthase initially increases. Citrate levels also increase. Simultaneously, increased production of NADH from glyceraldehyde-3-P dehydrogenase causes increased reduction of oxalacetate to malate, which enters the mitochondria to fulfill the co-substrate requirements of citrate synthase. Tissue oxalacetate levels fall rapidly and displace the near-equilibrium of aspartate aminotransferase in the cytosol. Aspartate levels also fall rapidly, and glutamate levels rise. The requirement for α-ketoglutarate to transaminate with aspartate in the cytosol causes efflux of α-ketoglutarate from the mitochondria and a postulated depletion of mitochondrial α-

ketoglutarate, which, together with inhibition of α-ketoglutarate dehydrogenase by increased NADH and succinyl-CoA levels, produces an initial fall of flux through this enzyme step. The transition phase is thus associated with an unspanning of flux in the citric acid cycle, with an increased flux from malate to α-ketoglutarate and decreased flux from α-ketoglutarate to malate. About 1 min after glucose addition, when the cytosolic glutamate/aspartate ratio has risen sufficiently, glutamate enters the mitochondria at an accelerated rate and competes with citrate synthase for oxalacetate. This results in decreased flux through citrate synthase and increased flux through α-ketoglutarate dehydrogenase as a consequence of the increased rate of production of α-ketoglutarate. After 3 min, cycle flux is uniform at a rate only slightly higher than that prior to glucose addition, and transport of reducing equivalents from mitochondria is established at a rate approximately equivalent to twice the glycolytic flux.

A similar unspanning of flux in the citric acid cycle is seen after acetate or fatty acid addition to glucose perfused hearts where there is overproduction of acetyl-CoA. A relatively enhanced flux through citrate synthase and accumulation of citrate is seen, with the required oxalacetate being derived from the aspartate pool (35, 42). Initially, both isocitrate dehydrogenase and α-ketoglutarate dehydrogenase are inhibited by the increased NADH/NAD+ ratio and require an increase of substrate concentration (i.e. isocitrate and α-ketoglutarate, respectively) before a uniform flux in the citric acid cycle is reestablished. Glycolysis and pyruvate oxidation are inhibited, resulting in diminished flux of reducing equivalents into the mitochondria. The fact that the glutamate/aspartate ratio is also elevated suggests that control of the malate-aspartate cycle flux under these conditions is not regulated solely by the kinetic effects of cytosolic glutamate and aspartate concentrations on the glutamate-aspartate translocator. However, decreased cardiac work and glycolytic flux induced by respiratory acidosis with glucose or lactate as substrate correlated well with a fall of the glutamate/aspartate ratio (51).

CONCLUSIONS

The feedback regulatory mechanisms responsible for the coordination of ATP production by the respiratory chain to the ATP utilizing systems outside the mitochondria are very efficiently coupled in heart. Increased respiration in response to increased cardiac work is achieved with only minor variations of the total tissue contents of adenine nucleotides and citric acid cycle intermediates. Creatine phosphate, by near equilibrium of creatine phosphokinase, buffers the cytosol against changes of ATP concentration during intervals of intermittent ATP utilization caused by the heart beat. A high phosphorylation potential and a high ATP/ADP ratio is maintained in the cytosol under low work conditions (71). With increased work, the cytosolic ATP/ADP ratio falls and the inorganic phosphate concentration increases at the expense of creatine phosphate. The concentration of free ADP in the cytosol in probably maintained within the operational Km region for the adenine nucleotide translocator because of binding to actin and other proteins and by chelation with Mg^{2+}. An increased ADP concentration in the cytosol will thus stimulate ADP entry into mitochondria in exchange with ATP from the mitochondrial matrix. Although not experimentally determined, this is expected to cause a transient fall of the matrix ATP/ADP ratio, at least in the environment of the mitochondrial ATPase, and a diminished difference of the phosophorylation potentials between the cytosol and the mitochondrial matrix.

On the basis of the postulate that the proton electrochemical potential $(\Delta \bar{\mu} H^{+})$ provides a back pressure to transport of electrons through the respiratory chain and is the energy transducing intermediate between oxidation and phosphorylation, it follows that a fall of the intramitochondrial phosphorylation potential will cause a fall of $\Delta \bar{\mu} H^{+}$. This will produce a stimulation of respiration, which will tend also to diminish the redox span in the electron transport chain used for energy conservation. This explanation implies that both ΔE_{h} and the mitochondrial phosphorylation potential remain close to thermodynamic equilibrium with $\Delta \bar{\mu} H^{+}$. Electron transport flux should be directly proportional to the deviation from equilibrium between the driving force of the oxidation-reduction reactions and the extramitochondrial phosphorylation potential. Disequilibrium between $(\Delta G_{ATP})_{c}$ and $(\Delta G_{ATP})_{m}$ is considered more likely than between ΔE_{h} and $\Delta \bar{\mu} H^{+}$ or between $\Delta \bar{\mu} H^{+}$ and $(\Delta G_{ATP})_{m}$ on the basis of available data. The back pressure which $(\Delta G_{ATP})_{c}$ normally exerts on $(\Delta_{ATP})_{m}$ in state-4 conditions is diminished when $(\Delta G_{ATP})_{c}$ falls, so that electron transport, proton flux, and ADP : ATP exchange are initiated in an attempt to reestablish the extramitochondrial ATP/ADP ratio. However, the gradient of the ATP/ADP ratios across the mitochondrial membrane is not maintained in equilibrium with the $\Delta \Psi$ component of the $\Delta \bar{\mu} H^{+}$ because of the kinetic regulation of the adenine nucleotide translocator by the concentrations of external free ADP and internal free ATP. Consequently, the intramitochondrial ATP/ADP ratio is maintained relatively constant by the activity of the mitochondrial ATPase, while $\Delta \bar{\mu} H^{+}$ remains depressed. The diminished back pressure exerted by $\Delta \bar{\mu} H^{+}$ increases the rate of NADH oxidation by NADH dehydrogenase, which results in an oxidation of the $NADH/NAD^{+}$ couple. The mitochondrial NAD-linked substrate dehydrogenases are mostly irreversible enzymes that are kinetically regulated by the $NADH/NAD^{+}$ ratio. Hence each steady-state increase of flux is associated with a new, more oxidized NAD redox potential. The absolute NAD^+ redox potential for a given flux will, however, depend on the concentration and nature of the substrate supply to the mitochondria, since the different NAD-substrate dehydrogenases are inhibited with different sensitivities by the $NADH/NAD^+$ ratio as well as being regulated by other factors. Thus, for instance, the mitochondrial nicotinamide nucleotides are more oxidized in hearts perfused with glucose as substrate compared with pyruvate, lactate, or fatty acids as substrate at similar rates of oxygen consumption.

If near-equilibrium is maintained between $\Delta\bar{\mu}H^+$ and ΔE_h across the three phosphorylation sites, a fall of $\Delta\bar{\mu}H^+$ will be associated with a fall of ΔE_h. Thus the redox state of each respiratory component of the electron transport chain will change by an amount dependent on the E_h of the $NAD^+/NADH$ redox couple and the respiratory rate. Considering only the first two phosphorylation sites, if the contraction of the redox span ΔE_h is greater than the change of E_h for the $NAD^+/NADH$ couple as respiration increases, the E_h for cytochrome c will become more reduced, as observed experimentally with perfused cardiac muscle (17, 46a) and isolated mitochondria under suitable conditions. The special case of blowfly flight-muscle mitochondria with pyruvate as substrate (24), where the redox states of both NAD^+ and cytochrome c become more reduced after a state-4 to state-3 transition, is interesting because it illustrates the specific effects of activation of the NAD-linked isocitrate dehydrogenase by a fall of the ATP/ADP ratio.

The mechanism of energy coupling at the third phosphorylation site between cytochrome c and oxygen is less well understood and may involve a direct allosteric effect of the membrane potential on the midpoint potential of cytochrome a_3 (64). However, increased reduction of cytochrome c is likely to result in an increased reduction of cytochrome a_3; the terminal irreversible step of the electron transport chain is regulated by the level of reduced cytochrome a_3 and is therefore dependent on the effects exerted by $\Delta\bar{\mu}H^+$ on ΔE_h between NADH and cytochrome c.

It should be stressed that the above résumé, although based on experimental findings, requires further experimental verification and should be considered as a working hypothesis. I have tried to provide a coherent picture of the regulation of mitochondrial substrate oxidation and electron transport, identifying the key control sites and effector molecules: When respiration changes, the primary control signal is the cytosolic ATP/ADP ratio; this transmits its effects via changes of the transmembrane proton electrochemical potential and the mitochondrial $NADH/NAD^+$ ratio to the substrate dehydrogenases and the respiratory carriers. Complex and multiple-effector regulation of pyruvate dehydrogenase by covalent modification and by the $NADH/NAD^+$, ATP/ADP, and acetyl-CoA/CoASH ratios is required in order to provide a flexible selection of fuel for oxidation by the citric acid cycle. Since the activity of the citric acid cycle itself is strictly coordinated with the rate of oxidative phosphorylation in heart, detailed regulation of flux relatively independent of the substrate supply is achieved by feedback at several sites. Thus, although primary control is exerted by the effects of mitochondrial NADH/NAD$^+$ redox state (a) on citrate synthase activity mediated by oxalacetate and (b) directly at isocitrate dehydrogenase, separate effects are exerted by changes of the acetyl-CoA/CoASH ratio at citrate synthase and of the succinyl-CoA/CoASH ratio at citrate synthase and α-ketoglutarate dehydrogenase. One of the most intriguing areas for future work concerns elucidation of the significance of intracellular heterogeneity on metabolic regulation.

ACKNOWLEDGMENT

This work was supported by NIH Grants AM-15120, HL-14461, and HL-18708.

Literature Cited

1. Azzone, G. F., Pozzan, T., Massari, S. 1978. Proton electrochemical gradient and phosphate potential in mitochondria. *Biochim. Biophys. Acta.* 501:307–16
2. Azzone, G. F., Pozzan, T., Massari, S., Bragadin, M. 1978. Proton electrochemical gradient and rate of controlled respiration in mitochondria. *Biochim. Biophys. Acta.* 501:296–306
3. Brand, M. D., Reynafarje, B., Lehninger, A. L. 1976. Re-evaluation of the H$^+$/site ratio of mitochondrial electron transport with the oxygen pulse technique. *J. Biol. Chem.* 251:5670–79
4. Bremer, J. 1969. Pyruvate dehydrogenase, substrate specificity and product inhibition. *Eur. J. Biochem.* 8:535–40
5. Cate, R. L., Roche, T. E. 1978. A unifying mechanism for stimulation of mammalian pyruvate dehydrogenase kinase by reduced nicotinamide adenine dinucleotide, dihydrolipoamide, acetyl-CoA or pyruvate. *J. Biol. Chem.* 253:496–503
6. Chua, B. H., Shrago, E. 1977. Reversible inhibition of adenine nucleotide translocation by long chain acyl-CoA esters in bovine heart mitochondria and inverted submitochondria particles. *J. Biol. Chem.* 252:6711–16
7. Clark, W. M. 1960. *Oxidation-Reduction Potentials of Organic Systems.* Baltimore: Williams and Wilkins. 584 pp.

8. Cohen, S., Ogawa, S., Rottenberg, H., Glynn, P., Yamane, T., Brown, T. R., Shulman, R. G., Williamson, J. R. 1978. ^{31}P Nuclear magnetic resonance studies of isolated rat liver cells. *Nature* 273:554–56
9. Davis, E. J., Bremer, J. 1973. Studies with isolated surviving rat hearts: Interdependence of free amino acid levels and citric acid cycle intermediates. *Eur. J. Biochem.* 38:86–97
10. Davis, E. J., Davis-van Thienen, W. I. A. 1978. Control of mitochondrial metabolism by the ATP/ADP ratio. *Biochem. Biophys. Res. Commun.* 83:1260–66
11. Davis, E. J., Lumeng, L. 1975. Relationships between phosphorylation potentials generated by liver mitochondria and respiratory state under conditions of adenosine diphosphate control. *J. Biol. Chem.* 250:2275–82
12. Erecinska, M., Veech, R. L., Wilson, D. F. 1974. Thermodynamic relationships between the oxidation-reduction reactions and the ATP synthesis in suspensions of isolated pigeon heart mitochondria. *Arch. Biochem. Biophys.* 160:412–21
13. Erecinska, M., Wilson, D. F., Nishiki, K. 1978. Homeostatic regulation of cellular energy metabolism: experimental characterization in vivo and fit to a model. *Am. J. Physiol.* 234:C82–C89

14. Hansford, R. G. 1976. Studies on the effects of CoASH: Acetyl-CoA, nicotinamide adenine dinucleotide: reduced nicotinamide adenine dinucleotide, and adenosine diphosphate: adenosine triphosphate ratios on the interconversion of active and inactive pyruvate dehydrogenase in isolated rat heart mitochondria. *J. Biol. Chem.* 251:5483–89

15. Hansford, R. G. 1977. Studies on inactivation of pyruvate dehydrogenase by palmitoylcarnitine oxidation in isolated rat heart mitochondria. *J. Biol. Chem.* 252:1552–60

16. Hansford, R. G., Johnson, R. N. 1975. The steady state concentrations of Coenzyme A and Coenzyme A thioester, citrate and isocitrate during tricarboxylate cycle oxidation in rabbit heart mitochondria. *J. Biol. Chem.* 250:8361–75

17. Hassinen, I. E., Hiltunen, K. 1975. Respiratory control in isolated perfused rat heart. Role of the equilibrium relations between the mitochondrial electron carriers and the adenylate system. *Biochim. Biophys. Acta.* 408:319–30

18. Hiltunen, J. K., Hassinen, I. E. 1976. Energy-linked regulation of glucose and pyruvate oxidation in isolated perfused rat heart: role of pyruvate dehydrogenase. *Biochim. Biophys. Acta.* 44: 377–90

19. Holian, A., Owen, C. S., Wilson, D. F. 1977. Control of respiration in isolated mitochondria: quantitative evaluation of the dependence of respiratory rates on [ATP], [ADP], and [Pi]. *Arch. Biochem. Biophys.* 181:164–71

20. Hoppel, C. L. 1976. Carnitine palmityltransferase and transport of fatty acids. In *The Enzymes of Biological Membranes*, ed. A. Martonosi, 2:119–43. New York: Plenum

21. Idell-Wenger, J. A., Grotyohann, L. W., Neely, J. R. 1978. Coenzyme A and carnitine distribution in normal and ischemic hearts. *J. Biol. Chem.* 253: 4310–18

22. Illingworth, J. A., Ford, W. C. L., Kobayashi, K., Williamson, J. R. 1975. Regulation of myocardial energy metabolism. In *Recent Advances in Studies of Cardiac Structure and Metabolism*, ed. P. E. Roy, E. Harris, 8:271–90. Baltimore: University Park Press

23. Jöbsis, F. F. 1964. Basic processes in cellular respiration. In *Handbook of Physiology, Respiration*, Sect. 3, Vol. 1, ed. W. O. Fenn, H. Rahn, pp. 63–124. Washington DC: Am. Physiol. Soc.

24. Johnson, R. N., Hansford, R. G. 1977. The nature of controlled respiration and its relationship to protonmotive force and proton conductance in blowfly flight muscle mitochondria. *Biochem. J.* 164:305–22

25. Kerbey, A. L., Randle, P. J., Cooper, R. H., Whitehouse, S., Pask, H. T., Denton, R. M. 1976. Regulation of pyruvate dehydrogenase in rat heart. *Biochem J.* 154:327–48

26. Klingenberg, M., Rottenberg, H. 1977. Relationship between the gradient of the ATP/ADP ratio and the membrane potential across the mitochondrial membrane. *Eur. J. Biochem.* 73:125–30

27. Kuster, U., Bohnensack, R., Kunz, W. 1976. Control of oxidative phosphorylation by the extramitochondrial ATP/ADP ratio. *Biochim. Biophys. Acta.* 440:391–402

28. LaNoue, K. F., Bryla, J., Williamson, J. R. 1972. Feedback interactions in the control of citric acid cycle activity in rat heart mitochondria. *J. Biol. Chem.* 247:667–79

29. LaNoue, K. F., Tischler, M. E. 1974. Electrogenic characteristics of the mitochondrial glutamate-aspartate antiporter. *J. Biol. Chem.* 249:7522–28

30. LaNoue, K. F., Walajtys, E. I., Williamson, J. R. 1973. Regulation of glutamate metabolism and interactions with the citric acid cycle in rat heart mitochondria. *J. Biol. Chem.* 248: 7171–83

31. Linn, T. C., Pettit, F. H., Hucho, F., Reed, L. J. 1969. Comparative studies of regulatory properties of the pyruvate dehydrogenase complexes from kidney, heart, and liver mitochondria. *Proc. Natl. Acad. Sci. USA* 64:227–34

32. Mitchell, P. 1976. Vectorial chemistry and the molecular mechanics of chemiosmotic coupling: power transmission by proticity. *Biochem. Soc. Trans.* 4:399–430

33. Neely, J. R., Leibermeister, H., Battersby, E. J., Morgan, H. E. 1967. Effect of pressure development on oxygen consumption by isolated rat heart. *Am. J. Physiol.* 212:804–14

34. Neely, J. R., Morgan, H. E. 1974. Substrate and energy metabolism of heart. *Ann. Rev. Physiol.* 36:413–59

35. Neely, J. R., Whitmer, K. M., Mochizuki, S. 1976. Effects of mechanical activity and hormones on myocardial glucose and fatty acid utilization. *Circ. Res.* 38: (Suppl. I) 22–29

36. Nicholls, D. G. 1974. The influence of respiration and ATP hydrolysis on the proton-electrochemical gradient across the inner membrane of rat liver mito-

chondria as determined by ion distribution. *Eur. J. Biochem.* 50:305–15

37. Nicholls, D. G., Bernson, V. S. M. 1977. Interrelationships between proton electrochemical gradient, adenine nucleotide phosphorylation potential and respiration, during substrate level and oxidative phosphorylation by mitochondria from brown adipose tissue of cold-adapted guinea-pigs. *Eur. J. Biochem.* 75:601–12

38. Oram, J. F., Bennetch, S. L., Neely, J. R. 1973. Regulation of fatty acid utilization in isolated perfused rat hearts. *J. Biol. Chem.* 248:5299–309

39. Pande, S. V., Parvin, R. 1976. Characterization of carnitine acylcarnitine translocase system of heart mitochondria. *J. Biol. Chem.* 251:6683–91

40. Ramsay, R. R., Tubbs, P. K. 1976. The effects of temperature and some inhibitors on the carnitine exchange system of heart mitochondria. *Eur. J. Biochem.* 69:299–303

41. Randle, P. J., Denton, R. M., Pask, H. T., Severson, D. L. 1974. Calcium ions and the regulation of pyruvate dehydrogenase. *Biochem. Soc. Symp.* 39: 75–87

42. Randle, P. J., England, P. J., Denton, R. M. 1970. Control of the tricarboxylate cycle and its interactions with glycolysis during acetate utilization in rat heart. *Biochem J.* 117:677–95

43. Randle, P. J., Tubbs, P. K. 1978. Carbohydrate and fatty acid metabolism. In *Handbook of Physiology, Circulation,* Sect. 2, Vol. 1, ed. R. M. Berne. Washington DC: Am. Physiol. Soc.

44. Reed, L. J. 1969. Multienzyme complexes. *Curr. Top. Cell. Regul.* 1:233–42

45. Reed, L. J., Pettit, F. H., Roche, T. E., Butterworth, P. J., Barrera, C. R., Tsai, C. S. 1974. Structure, function, and regulation of the mammalian pyruvate dehydrogenase complex. In *Metabolic Interconversions of Enzymes,* ed. E. H. Fischer, E. G. Krebs, H. Neurath, E. R. Stadtman, pp. 99–106. New York: Springer

46. Reynafarje, B., Brand, M. D., Lehninger, A. L. 1976. Evaluation of the H^+/site ratio of mitochondrial electron transport from rate measurements. *J. Biol. Chem.* 251:7442–51

46a. Rich, T. L., Williamson, J. R. 1978. Correlation of isometric tension and redox state in perfused interventricular septum. In *Frontiers of Biological Energetics,* ed. L. Dutton, J. Leigh, A. Scarpa. New York: Academic. In press

47. Rose, C. P., Goresky, C. A. 1977. Constraints on the uptake of labeled palmitate by the heart. *Circ. Res.* 41:534–45

48. Rottenberg, H. 1978. An irreversible thermodynamic approach to energy coupling in mitochondria and chloroplasts. In *Progress in Surface and Membrane Science,* Vol. 12, ed. J. F. Danielli, A. Kadenhead, M. D. Rosenberg. New York: Academic. In press

49. Safer, B., Smith, C. M., Williamson, J. R. 1971. Control of the transport of reducing equivalents across the mitochondrial membrane in perfused rat heart. *J. Mol. Cell. Cardiol.* 2:111–24

50. Safer, B., Williamson, J. R. 1973. Mitochondrial-cytosolic interactions in perfused rat heart. Role of coupled transamination in repletion of citric acid cycle intermediates. *J. Biol. Chem.* 248: 2570–79

51. Schaffer, S. W., Safer, B., Ford, C., Illingworth, J., Williamson, J. R. 1978. Respiratory acidosis and its reversibility in perfused rat heart: regulation of citric acid cycle activity. *Am. J. Physiol.* 234:H40–H51

52. Shug, A. L., Shrago, E., Bittar, N., Folts, J. D., Koke, J. R. 1975. Acyl-CoA inhibition of adenine nucleotide translocation in ischemic myocardium. *Am. J. Physiol.* 228:689–92

53. Shug, A. L., Thomsen, J. H., Folts, J. D., Bittar, N., Klein, M. I., Koke, J. R., Huth, P. J. 1978. Changes in tissue levels of carnitine and other metabolites during myocardial ischemia and anoxia. *Arch. Biochem. Biophys.* 187:25–33

54. Slater, E. C., Rosing, J., Mol, A. 1973. The phosphorylation potential generated by respiring mitochondria. *Biochim. Biophys. Acta.* 292:534–53

55. Srere, P. A. 1972. Is there an organization of Krebs Cycle enzymes in the mitochondrial matrix? In *Energy Metabolism and the Regulation of Metabolic Processes in Mitochondria,* ed. M. A. Mehlman, R. W. Hanson, pp. 79–91. New York: Academic

56. Srere, P. A., Halper, L. A., Finkelstein, M. B. 1978. Interaction of citrate synthase and malate dehydrogenase. In *Microenvironments and Metabolic Compartmentation,* ed. P. A. Srere, R. W. Estabrook. New York: Academic. In press

57. Tischler, M. E., Friedricks, D., Coll, K., Williamson, J. R. 1977. Pyridine nucleotide distributions and enzyme mass action ratios in hepatocytes from fed and starved rats. *Arch. Biochem. Biophys.* 184:222–36

58. Tischler, M. E., Hecht, P., Williamson, J. R. 1977. Determination of mitochondrial/cytosolic metabolite gradients in isolated liver cells by cell disruption. *Arch. Biochem. Biophys.* 181:278–92

59. Tischler, M. E., Pachence, J., Williamson, J. R., LaNoue, K. F. 1976. Mechanism of glutamate-aspartate translocation across the mitochondrial inner membrane. *Arch. Biochem. Biophys.* 173:448–62

59a. Van Dam, K., Westerhoff, H. V. 1977. A description of oxidative phosphorylation in terms of irreversible thermodynamics. In *Structure and Function of Energy-Transducing Membranes,* Vol. 14, ed. K. Van Dam, B. F. Gelder, pp. 157–67. Amsterdam: Elsevier

60. Van der Meer, R., Akerboom, T. P. M., Groen, A. K., Tager, J. M. 1978. Relationship between oxygen uptake of perfused rat liver cells and the cytosolic phosphorylation state calculated from indicator metabolites and a redetermined equilibrium constant. *Eur. J. Biochem.* 84:421–28

61. Vignais, P. V. 1976. Molecular and physiological aspects of adenine nucleotide transport in mitochondria. *Biochim. Biophys. Acta.* 456:1–38

62. Whitmer, J. T., Idell-Wenger, J. A., Rovetto, M. J., Neely, J. R. 1978. Control of fatty acid metabolism in ischemic and hypoxic hearts. *J. Biol. Chem.* 253:4305–9

63. Wieland, O. H., V. Funcke, H., Löffler, G. 1971. Interconversion of pyruvate dehydrogenase in rat heart muscle upon perfusion with fatty acids or ketone bodies. *FEBS Lett.* 15:295–98

64. Wikström, M. K. F., Saari, H. T. 1975. Conformational changes in cytochrome aa_3 and ATP synthetase of the mitochondrial membrane and their role in mitochondrial energy transduction. *Mol. Cell. Biochem.* 11:17–33

65. Williamson, D. H., Hems, R. 1970. Metabolism and function of ketone bodies. In *Essays in Cell Metabolism,* ed. W.

Bartley, H. L. Kornberg, J. R. Quale, pp. 257–81. London: Wiley

66. Williamson, J. R. 1962. Effects of insulin and diet on the metabolism of L(+) lactate and glucose by the perfused rat heart. *Biochem. J.* 83:377–83

67. Williamson, J. R. 1974. Effects of insulin and starvation on the metabolism of acetate and pyruvate by the perfused rat heart. *Biochem. J.* 93:97–106

68. Williamson, J. R. 1975. Effects of epinephrine on glycogenolysis and myocardial contractility. In *Handbook of Physiology,* ed. H. Blaschko, A. D. Smith, 6:605–36. Washington DC: Am. Physiol. Soc.

69. Williamson, J. R. 1976. Mitochondrial metabolism and cell regulation. In *Mitochondria,* ed. L. Packer, A. Gómez-Puyon, pp. 79–107. New York: Academic

70. Williamson, J. R. 1976. Role of anion transport in the regulation of metabolism. In *Gluconeogenesis,* ed. R. W. Hanson, M. A. Mehlman, pp. 165–220. New York: Wiley

71. Williamson, J. R., Ford, C., Illingworth, J., Safer, B. 1976. Coordination of citric acid cycle activity with electron transport flux. *Circ. Res.* 38: (Suppl. I) 39–48

72. Williamson, J. R., Krebs, H. A. 1961. Acetoacetate as fuel of respiration in perfused rat heart. *Biochem. J.* 80: 540–47

73. Williamson, J. R., Safer, B., LaNoue, K. F., Smith, C. M., Walajtys, E. 1973. Mitochondrial-cytosolic interactions in cardiac tissue. *Soc. Exp. Biol. Symp.* 27:241–81

74. Williamson, J. R., Smith, C. M., La-Noue, K. F., Bryla, J. 1972. Feedback control of the citric acid cycle. See Ref. 55, pp. 185–210

75. Wood, J. M., Bush, B., Pitts, B. J. R., Schwartz, A. 1977. Inhibition of bovine heart Na^+,K^+-ATPase by palmitylcarnitine and palmityl-CoA. *Biochem. Biophys. Res. Commun.* 74:677–84

Ann. Rev. Physiol. 1979. 41:507–19

CARDIAC HEAT PRODUCTION ♦1234

Colin L. Gibbs and J. Brian Chapman

Department of Physiology, Monash University, Clayton,
Victoria 3168, Australia

INTRODUCTION

Before the mid-1960s there was no literature on cardiac heat. Even now few publications have documented the heat production of whole hearts. However a considerable body of literature reports the heat production of isolated mammalian papillary muscles, and a recent technological advance (48) holds promise of significant expansion of the myothermic technique to other cardiac preparations.

The interpretative basis for present cardiac heat measurements derives mainly from the myothermic studies of amphibian skeletal muscle classically performed by A. V. Hill and his colleagues and documented in Hill's *Trails and Trials in Physiology* (37). Several important reviews reflect the continuing interest in the biochemistry and physiology of skeletal muscle contraction (1, 46, 62, 63). However, the considerable differences between many of the properties of cardiac and skeletal muscle should be sufficient warning to cardiac physiologists against the hazards of too slavish a reliance on the skeletal muscle literature. We have recently published two articles that deal specifically with cardiac energetics. One (27) gives the thermodynamic background to heat measurements with a somewhat different approach from that of the definitive exposition for skeletal muscle by Wilkie (62). It also describes oxygen consumption data from whole hearts, attempts to find correlations between oxygen consumption measurements and myothermic measurements, and seeks to relate the experimental findings in vitro to cardiac oxygen consumption in man. Our other article (26) embraces additional topics relating to cardiac mechanics, the problems of energy balance, and the imperfection of current mechanical and energetic models of muscle.

While the present review concentrates on the heat production of mammalian papillary muscles it also considers information on cardiac energetics

507

0066-4278/79/0301-0507$01.00

obtained by other techniques and with other preparations. Indeed, at the outset we would draw attention to an important result obtained recently by Coulson, who measured oxygen consumption and heat production simultaneously in the isolated beating rabbit heart (18). Not only do Coulson's data agree with the separate measurements of either oxygen consumption or heat production in papillary muscles, but his simultaneous measurements yield a calorific equivalent for oxygen consumption by the beating heart of 20.5 mJ ml^{-1} O_2 at 25°C with pyruvate as substrate—a result in agreement with classical biochemical predictions.

THERMODYNAMICS

It is customary to treat isolated muscles mounted on thermopiles as closed thermodynamic systems exchanging energy, but not matter, with their environment. This approximation is justified by the fact that the thermal consequences of respiratory gas exchange are negligible (27). Hence, by the first law, one can equate measured enthalpy production to equivalent quantities of associated chemical reactions such as oxygen consumption or the splitting of adenosine triphosphate (ATP). For detailed expositions relating thermodynamics to the interpretation of myothermic data, see (27) and (62).

METHODS OF HEAT MEASUREMENT

Most myothermic measurements in cardiac muscle have been made on isolated papillary muscles or trabeculae carneae mounted on thermopiles constructed from electroplated silver-constantan junctions (53). The detailed experimental findings from such preparations are in general agreement with the more limited information obtainable from calorimetric studies of isolated perfused whole hearts (18, 45, 49, 54) or from thermometric monitoring in the coronary sinus and ascending aorta of the anaesthetized dog (2). A new development in thermopile technology involves vaccum deposition of antimony and bismuth onto thin mica sheets (48). This new approach is described in detail and should allow the use of smaller preparations since these thermopiles have almost an order of magnitude lower thermal capacity. Their low electrical resistance allows them to be used with galvanometers.

RESTING HEAT RATE

Right ventricular papillary muscles from the rabbit have a resting heat rate of about 1.8 mW per gram of muscle at 20°C in the presence of glucose as exogenous metabolic substrate (32). This rate can be increased by stretch or by replacing glucose with pyruvate (7, 32). The physiological basis of the resting heat has not been identified; active transport of sodium probably accounts for less than 10% of it (27).

While the effect of pyruvate on resting heat rate is associated with a positive inotropic effect on contractility (37), there is no general correlation between resting heat rate and contractility. Neither calcium ion, caffeine, epinephrine, nor ouabain has any significant influence on the resting heat rate (23, 24, 28, 33).

Large variations in resting heat rate are found between different mammalian species (31), and there is an unexplained decline in this rate with time; a parallel decline occurs in the basal oxygen consumption of whole hearts [documented in a recent review (26)]. It seems likely that the high resting heat rates reflect in part the energy cost of protein synthesis: Calculations based on measured protein turnover rates of 6–15% per day (19b) and a likely energy cost of 5.9 kJ g^{-1} protein synthesized (45a) give heat production rates that would account for about 30% of the measured basal values. This estimate is probably conservative and it is interesting that there seems to be good correlation between basal heat rates and protein turnover rates across species (19a). Several authors have shown in vivo that increased mechanical stress upon the heart leads to a rapid increase in protein synthesis associated with cardiac hypertrophy (19b, 52); such effects may be expected to increase basal metabolism (17).

INITIAL AND RECOVERY HEAT

The clear temporal distinction between initial heat evolved within a few seconds of contraction and the subsequent recovery heat evolved over the next twenty minutes, classically described for amphibian skeletal muscle at 0°C (35), is totally lacking in mammalian cardiac muscle at room temperature or above. At room temperature there is a rapid phase of heat production associated with each contraction, followed immediately by a slower phase that evolves over the next 20–30 seconds. The slower phase is about 0.2–0.3 times the magnitude of the rapid phase, depending on the metabolic substrate and the arbitrary choice of demarcation between the rapid and slow phases (7, 25, 32).

The smallness of the slower phase does not appear to be due to any insufficiency of the metabolic processes underlying recovery from a single contraction. Fluorometric measurement of pyridine nucleotide fluorescence from a rabbit papillary muscle indicates that the metabolic recovery response to a single contraction is fully developed in proportion to the response to a series of contractions (4). The fluorometric response proceeds more rapidly with pyruvate as substrate than with glucose (4) in agreement with similar effects on the rate of evolution of the slow phase of heat production. Of the substrates tested, pyruvate yields the most rapid evolution of slow or recovery heat, followed by lactate, acetate, and glucose (7). However, it is evident from the fluorometric studies that a large measure of the recovery metabolic response is activated during the time course of the mechanical event. Thus a temporal justification for the terms "initial" and "recovery" in relation to the two phases of cardiac heat production is lacking. The possible enzymatic basis for the initial and recovery processes and reasons for the temporal integration of the two phases in cardiac muscle have been considered recently (26, 27).

COMPONENTS OF ACTIVE ENERGY PRODUCTION

The total energy of a cardiac contraction is influenced by many factors, particularly those that affect myocardial contractility (see next section). However, in common with skeletal muscle contraction, the energy consumed by a cardiac twitch for a given inotropic state and rest length depends on the mechanical conditions under which the contraction occurs —i.e. there is mechanical feedback regulation of energy output. For a particular set of physiological conditions the energy output varies with load, as illustrated in Figure 1. This shows the energy per contraction (in mJ per gram of muscle) plotted against the load or tension expressed as a fraction of the maximum isometric tension, P_0. The top curve shows the variation in total energy consumption during afterloaded isotonic contractions under various loads. The curve below this is the total heat production obtained for such contractions after subtraction of the mechanical work performed in lifting the load. The next curve down shows the heat production recorded from isometric contractions in which the heat and tension were varied by pre-shortening the rest length of the muscle below the normal rest length, l_0. For more detail as to how these curves are obtained experimentally, see (27, 29, 32).

Shortening Heat

The horizontally hatched area in Figure 1, representing the difference between the heat production of isotonic and isometric contractions, has traditionally been referred to as the shortening heat (32, 46), as if it were analogous to the extra heat associated with shortening as classically described by A. V. Hill (36) for amphibian skeletal muscle at 0°C. However, most of this area should correspond to the recovery counterpart of the work component, thus leaving little room for a significant quantity of shortening heat. This conclusion is critically dependent upon the accuracy of the calibration procedure, which is more suspect for the small preparations used (approximately 5 mg); the newer thermopiles (48) may be able to cope with this problem more satisfactorily.

Nevertheless, it has yet to be demonstrated myothermically that cardiac muscle releases energy at a higher rate during shortening than during isometric contraction (29); thus, even the phenomenological manifestation of "shortening heat" as originally described by A. V. Hill in amphibian skeletal muscle (36) has not been shown for mammalian cardiac muscle.

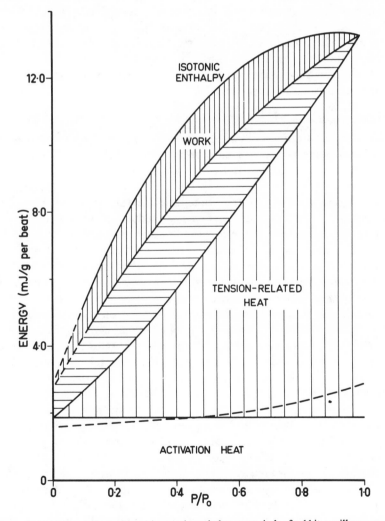

Figure 1   Variation in isotonic and isometric enthalpy per twitch of rabbit papillary muscle at 20°C. Load or force expressed as a fraction of maximum isometric force, P_0. Subdivisions of energy components are explained in text.

However, attention should be focused on the high series compliance (42) and non-uniform force distribution (50) of papillary muscle preparations and of cardiac tissue in general. It is possible that, even in isometric contractions, there is considerable internal shortening at high velocity, much more than would take place in skeletal muscle (44, 58). Therefore, we are reluctant to conclude dogmatically that the molecular mechanism underlying shortening-heat production in skeletal muscle (36) is absent in cardiac muscle, even though a recent study of oxygen consumption in isolated servo-controlled canine hearts has shown a negligible influence of fiber shortening (61). Perhaps the classical myothermic preparations and protocols for skeletal muscles (frog and toad sartorius muscles at low temperatures with the necessity for long rest periods to establish a reference baseline) have produced results that cannot be extrapolated to repetitively activated mammalian myocardium.

Tension-Related Heat

Linear or curvilinear relations between energy production and active development of force or pressure have been reported in skeletal, smooth, and cardiac muscle by authors using a variety of techniques (26, 27). Several other related mechanical parameters have been shown to correlate well with energy usage. Some of these (e.g. force-time integral, maximum rate of force development) are good indexes of energy production, whereas others (e.g. contractile element work) are restricted in their range of applicability (12, 26, 29). A more detailed account of these mechanical indexes and their applicability under various physiological conditions may be found in (26).

The tension-related component of heat production should reflect myofibrillar ATPase activity—i.e. crossbridge activity (see the section below regarding the Rationale for Separate Energetic components). There are considerable species differences in the biochemical activity of actomyosin ATPase (19), and this should lead to quite different rates of energy expenditure across species. For detection of these differences the myothermic technique is possibly the only one possessing the required speed of response. If the actual heat production or oxygen consumption per contraction is examined at comparable inotropic levels across species the differences are slight. This is because a high rate of energy expenditure in a species such as rat is usually offset by the longer duration of contraction (systole) in larger species such as cat. If pharmacological interventions are used to allow tetanization of cardiac muscle (21) then the biochemical predictions can be strikingly confirmed myothermically, with some species having surprisingly high heat rates (31). In these tetanic experiments there is good correlation between energy production measured polarographically and myothermically (15, 31).

Work and Efficiency

As evidenced in Figure 1, the work output per beat depends on the load; the bell-shaped relation is similar to that obtained with all types of muscle. [This may not be immediately apparent from the way Figure 1 is drawn, but see (29) and (32).] The mechanical efficiency of cardiac contractions, defined as work/active enthalpy (resting heat production not included in denominator), appears to be quite high although the actual values obtained (10–25%) depend very much upon the intrinsic level of contractility (10, 28, 30). Because ethalpy production falls dramatically at the lower load range, the efficiency versus load curve is more skewed than in skeletal muscle and maximum efficiency is usually reached in the 0.2–0.4 P_0 load range. The problems associated with measuring internal and external work and with extrapolating results from isolated tissues to the heart in vivo have been discussed elsewhere (26).

Rationale for Separate Energetic Components

The whole rationale for compartmentalizing the energy associated with mechanical parameters (tension, work, shortening) has been questioned (6), and now it seems likely that the only proper subdivision of muscle energy consumption should be an enzymatic one that distinguishes between the ATPases of active transport and the ATPase of the myofilaments or mechanical transducer (5, 26, 27, 38, 56). According to this view, the upper curves of Figure 1 represent the variation of heat and work obtained from the splitting of ATP by a single enzyme, the actomyosin ATPase. The remaining component of heat production, designated activation heat, is thought to arise from the splitting of ATP by the Ca^{2+}-ATPase of the sarcoreticular Ca^{2+} pump (59) and the Na^+, K^+-ATPase of the sarcolemma (8).

Activation Heat

Because the activation or tension-independent heat in cardiac muscle is measured by pre-shortening the muscle to eliminate detectable development of tension, it is probable (a) that some residual contamination from myofibrillar ATPase occurs during internal shortening, and (b) that there is some length-dependent deactivation of the normal calcium release (39, 40, 43). The dashed curve superimposed on the horizontal activation heat line of Figure 1 is drawn in recognition of these possible complexities. However, the magnitude of the activation heat measured in the above fashion is generally less than half the upper limit (about 4 mJ g^{-1}) that has been calculated for the possible contribution per twitch in maximally activated myocardium (27). These upper limits include the recovery heat, as do the curves illustrated in Figure 1 (27). Not only may the extent of calcium release be modified by muscle length, but inotrophic agents (catecholamines, glycosides, calcium levels) significantly increase its magnitude (23, 28, 30). Indeed, some combination of drugs can render the size of this component so large that active mechanical efficiency (defined above) falls in spite of maximum work output per beat (10).

The Fenn Effect

Several authors have concluded that there is a Fenn effect present in cardiac muscle (14, 32), but, since maximum enthalpy output at a particular length always occurs under isometric or near isometric conditions, it is necessary to employ a somewhat different definition from that originally used by Fenn (20). Undoubtedly the energy flux of cardiac muscle is regulated in some way by the mechanical constraints under which it contracts (47). Possibly the length-dependency of activation and the varying affinity of myofibrillar protein, particularly troponin, for calcium ions (22, 60) may influence the shape of the isotonic-enthalpy: load relation.

ENTHALPY: LOAD RELATIONS

Several groups of workers using chemical, fluorometric, and polarographic techniques have obtained isotonic energy versus load curves similar to those shown in Figure 1 (9, 12, 51). It cannot be emphasized too often that such a relation is not static: Both axes will expand or contract depending upon the prevailing level of contractility and upon the length (end-diastolic volume for the whole heart) from which contraction is initiated (27). Length-dependency results from a complex interaction between the geometric consequences of myofilament overlap (41) and length-dependent activation (40). Without considering such pathological situations as ischemia, anoxia, and hypertrophy, the more common factors that change the enthalpy: load relation by affecting contractility are the pattern and history of stimulation, autonomic outflow, and humoral or pharmacological agents.

The data usually obtained from papillary muscles are static in the sense that they only relate to a particular preload length and to a fixed set of physiological conditions. The system in vivo is considerably more complex. The most obvious difference is that, prior to excitation, chamber volume at the end of diastole is actually increasing. It seems likely that such an effect occurs for papillary muscles in situ (55). Coleman (12) has shown that increases in the preload, i.e. initial fibre length, increase cardiac oxygen consumption and work output while the general shape of the relation between energy production and load is maintained. [See (27), Figure 4, for a fuller discussion of the experimental consequences of altered preload.]

Agents or procedures that increase force development per beat (e.g. lowering temperature, raising extracellular calcium) also raise energy output while maintaining the usual shape of the enthalpy:load relation (10, 28, 30). This effect has not only been found myothermically but has also been reported in several oxygen-consumption studies (11, 13, 14). Whether there is any increase in the mechanical efficiency depends upon several other factors. Unless preparations are hypodynamic to start with, it is not possible to show any significant improvement in mechanical efficiency, even with agents such as the cardiac glycosides (28). High concentrations of catecholamines or mixtures of caffeine and catecholamines, which greatly increase the magnitude of the activation heat component, can actually reduce cardiac efficiency (10). From myothermic studies it has been concluded that all positive inotropic agents or procedures operate by increasing the amount of calcium delivered to the contractile proteins; up to the present, there is no evidence that such agents act by altering the efficiency of either the mechanochemical transduction mechanism or the calcium pump (28, 30). This statement may not hold for pressure-overload hypertrophy (see below). The magnitude of the activation heat increases with all these interventions, but the slope of the heat:force relation in short-term experiments has never been shown to be significantly different from the control (28, 30). Substantially similar data have been obtained in experiments measuring oxygen consumption versus load in papillary muscles (11, 14), but there continues to be a difference in interpretation. In the myothermic studies the increased energy output has been attributed to an increment in the activation heat (i.e. calcium release) whereas in polarographic studies the energy difference has been attributed to an increase in the intrinsic shortening velocity (V_{max}) of the contractile element (14, 57).

HYPERTROPHY

During the last 5 years some interesting studies on the oxygen consumption of papillary muscles from normal and hypertrophied cat right ventricle have been published (16, 17, 34). In pressure-overload hypertrophy it was shown that the papillary muscles had depressed force-velocity and length-tension curves, and that their resting oxygen consumption was approximately double the normal value. Although the oxygen cost of afterloaded isotonic contractions was reported to be about normal, the slope of the oxygen-consumption:force relation was significantly higher than in the controls (34) which has led to speculation that decreased isotonic work output and shortening compensated for the higher cost of tension development. The authors suggest that, in such hypertrophy, there is abnormal mitochondrial respiration and an increase in nonphosphorylating respiration associated with disturbances in calcium transport. When the same type of mechanical and energetic analysis was made on papillary muscles from cat right ventricles with volume-overload hypertrophy there were no abnormalities despite about a 50% increase in cell diameter; this suggests that increased size per se does not result in diminished contractility or metabolic abnormalities.

Recently, some myothermic studies have been carried out (3) with papillary muscles from pressure-overloaded rabbit right ventricles. V_{max} and the rate of tension development were depressed, but peak tension development was reported to be near the control values. In contradistinction to results from the oxygen consumption studies (34), energy production of the hypertrophic muscles was about half normal, which implies a decrease in the slope of the energy: tension relation. Both the tension-dependent and tension-independent heat components were reduced, as were the rates of heat evolution. The data were interpreted in terms of disturbances in excitation-contraction coupling, and were correlated with the measured depression of the actin-activated myosin ATPase. The authors refer to initial heat production only, but the criterion for the initial heat partition is not stated (see the section above on Initial and Recovery Heat). Obviously there is an unexplained discrepancy between the data obtained by the two groups.

SUMMARY

The energy production (heat + work) of cardiac muscle must be interpreted in terms of the major ATPases underwriting cardiac contraction; these are the Ca^{2+} and Na^+-K^+ transport ATPases and actomyosin ATPase. It is possible to apply the classical phenomenological subdivisions to cardiac energy production; when this is done, certain properties immediately distinguish cardiac muscle from skeletal muscle. Little or no temporal distinction exists between initial (anaerobic) and recovery (oxidative) metabolism. Even at temperatures as low as 20°C most of the recovery heat is released within the time course of a single contraction. Cardiac muscle is characterized by a high resting heat rate, the magnitude of which varies between species and depends on the metabolic substrate. In isometric contractions there is a slightly curvilinear relationship between developed force and heat production. There is a tension-independent or activation component, the magnitude of which reflects the prevailing level of contractility and is probably associated with calcium release and retrieval.

In isotonic contractions energy production is maximal when the muscle is heavily loaded but falls steeply when the size of the load is reduced. The enthalpy: load relation is probably similar to that found in twitch contractions of skeletal muscle working at room temperature or above; but, unlike for skeletal muscle, there are families of such curves: At any instant of time the relation depends upon the prevailing physiological conditions (e.g. stimulus rate, substrate supply, humoral agents, extracellular ionic concentrations, initial length).

Cardiac energy production can be estimated by a variety of other techniques (such as high-energy phosphate utilization, oxygen consumption, and changes in tissue fluorescence related to pyridine nucleotide oxidation levels). At the present time there is considerable agreement between heat measurements and results obtained with these different techniques.

We should like to conclude on a cautionary note. First, there is considerable variability in the properties of cardiac muscle from different species. Significant variations occur at nearly all levels of cellular function—e.g. shape of action potential, electrical and mechanical dependence upon stimulus history, mechanisms of excitation-contraction coupling, actomyosin ATPase activity, metabolic regulation, and differential sensitivity to anoxia or ischemia. Second, the types of contractions readily studied in isolated papillary muscles (i.e. isometric or isotonic twitches) may not necessarily be the best mechanical paradigms for understanding myocardial energetics in vivo. The particular geometric demands of individual research techniques require the use of a wide variety of myocardial preparations from a wide variety of species. This necessarily produces a pastiche view of cardiac muscle rather than an integrated picture of some hypothetically typical mammalian myocardium.

ACKNOWLEDGMENT

The authors' myothermic and fluorometric studies of papillary muscles reported in this review were supported by the National Heart Foundation of Australia.

Literature Cited

1. Abbott, B. C., Howarth, J. V. 1973. Heat studies in excitable tissues. *Physiol. Rev.* 53:120–58
2. Afonso, S., Rowe, G. G., Lugo, J. E., Crumpton, C. W. 1965. Left ventricle heat production in intact anesthetized dogs. *Am. J. Physiol.* 208:946–53
3. Alpert, N. R., Mulieri, L. A. 1977. The partitioning of altered mechanics in hypertrophied heart muscle between the sarcoplasmic reticulum and the contractile apparatus by means of myothermal measurements. *Basic Res. Cardiol.* 72:153–59
4. Chapman, J. B. 1972. Fluorometric studies of oxidative metabolism in iso-

lated papillary muscle of the rabbit. *J. Gen. Physiol.* 59:135–54
5. Chapman, J. B., Gibbs, C. L. 1972. An energetic model of muscle contraction. *Biophys. J.* 12:227–36
6. Chapman, J. B., Gibbs, C. L. 1972. Energetics of isometric and isotonic twitches in toad sartorius. *Biophys. J.* 12:215–26
7. Chapman, J. B., Gibbs, C. L. 1974. The effect of metabolic substrate on mechanical activity and heat production in papillary muscle. *Cardiovasc. Res.* 8:656–67
8. Chapman, J. B., Gibbs, C. L., Gibson, W. R. 1970. Effects of calcium and sodium on cardiac contractility and

heat production in rabbit papillary muscle. *Circ. Res.* 27:601–10

9. Chapman, J. B., Gibbs, C. L., Gibson, W. R. 1976. Heat and fluorescence changes in cardiac muscle: effects of substrate and calcium. *J. Mol. Cell. Cardiol.* 8:545–58

10. Chapman, J. B., Gibbs, C. L., Loiselle, D. S. 1977. Simultaneous heat and fluorescence changes in cardiac muscle at high rates of energy expenditure. *J. Mol. Cell. Cardiol.* 9:715–32

11. Coleman, H. N. 1967. Role of acetylstrophanthidin in augmenting myocardial oxygen consumption. Relation of increased O_2 consumption to changes in velocity of contraction. *Circ. Res.* 21:487–95

12. Coleman, H. N. 1968. Effect of alterations in shortening and external work on oxygen consumption of cat papillary muscle. *Am. J. Physiol.* 214:100–6

13. Coleman, H. N., Sonnenblick, E. H., Braunwald, E. 1969. Myocardial oxygen consumption associated with external work: the Fenn effect. *Am. J. Physiol.* 217:291–96

14. Coleman, H. N., Sonnenblick, E. H., Braunwald, E. 1971. Mechanism of norepinephrine-induced stimulation of myocardial oxygen consumption. *Am. J. Physiol.* 221:778–83

15. Cooper, G. 1976. The myocardial energetic active state. Oxygen consumption during tetanus of cat papillary muscle. *Circ. Res.* 39:695–704

16. Cooper, G., Puga, F. J., Zujko, K. J., Harrison, C. E., Coleman, H. N. 1973. Normal myocardial function and energetics in volume-overload hypertrophy in the cat. *Circ. Res.* 32:140–48

17. Cooper, G., Satava, R. M., Harrison, C. E., Coleman, H. N. 1973. Mechanism for the abnormal energetics of pressure-induced hypertrophy of cat myocardium. *Circ. Res.* 33:213–23

18. Coulson, R. L. 1976. Energetics of isovolumic contractions of the isolated rabbit heart. *J. Physiol. London* 260: 45–53

19. Delcayre, C., Swynghedauw, B. 1975. A comparative study of heart myosin ATPase and light subunits from different species. *Pfluegers Arch.* 355:39–47

19a. Earl, C. A., Laurent, G. J., Everett, A. W., Bonnin, C. M., Sparrow, M. P. 1978. Turnover rates of muscle protein in cardiac and skeletal muscles of dog, fowl, rat and mouse: turnover rate related to muscle function. *Aust. J. Exp. Biol. Med. Sci.* In press

19b. Everett, A. W., Taylor, R. R., Sparrow, M. P. 1977. Protein synthesis during right ventricular hypertrophy after pulmonary-artery stenosis in the dog. *Biochem. J.* 166:315–21

20. Fenn, W. O. 1923. A quantitative comparison between the energy liberated and the work performed by the isolated sartorius of the frog. *J. Physiol. London* 58:175–203

21. Forman, R., Ford, L. E., Sonnenblick, E. H. 1972. Effect of muscle length on the force-velocity relationship of tetanized cardiac muscle. *Circ. Res.* 31: 195–206

22. Fuchs, F. 1974. Striated muscle. *Ann. Rev. Physiol.* 36:461–502

23. Gibbs, C. L. 1967. Changes in cardiac heat production with agents that alter contractility. *Aust. J. Exp. Biol. Med. Sci.* 45:379–92

24. Gibbs, C. L., 1967. Role of catecholamines in heat production in the myocardium. *Circ. Res.* 21: (Suppl. 3) 223–30

25. Gibbs, C. L. 1969. The energy output of normal and anoxic cardiac muscle. In *Comparative Physiology of the Heart: Current Trends,* ed. F. V. McCann, pp. 78–92. Basel: Birkauser Verlag

26. Gibbs, C. L. 1978. Cardiac energetics. *Physiol. Rev.* 58:174–254

27. Gibbs, C. L., Chapman, J. B. 1979. Cardiac energetics. In *Handbook of Physiology. Circulation.* Washington DC: Am. Physiol. Soc. In press

28. Gibbs, C. L., Gibson, W. R. 1969. Effect of ouabain on the energy output of rabbit cardiac muscle. *Circ. Res.* 24:951–67

29. Gibbs, C. L., Gibson, W. R. 1970. Energy production in cardiac isotonic contractions. *J. Gen. Physiol.* 56:732–50

30. Gibbs, C. L., Gibson, W. R. 1972. Isoprenaline, propranolol and the energy output of rabbit cardiac muscle. *Cardiovasc. Res.* 6:508–15

31. Gibbs, C. L., Loiselle, D. S. 1978. The energy output of tetanized cardiac muscle: species differences. *Pfluegers Arch.* 373:31–38

32. Gibbs, C. L., Mommaerts, W. F. H. M., Ricchiuti, N. V. 1967. Energetics of cardiac contractions. *J. Physiol. London* 191:25–46

33. Gibbs, C. L., Vaughan, P. 1968. The effect of calcium depletion upon the tension-independent component of cardiac heat production. *J. Gen. Physiol.* 52:532–49

34. Gunning, J. F., Coleman, H. N. 1973. Myocardial oxygen consumption during experimental hypertrophy and con-

gestive heart failure. *J. Mol. Cell. Cardiol.* 5:25–38

35. Hartree, W., Hill, A. V. 1922. The recovery heat production of muscle. *J. Physiol. London* 56:367–81

36. Hill, A. V. 1938. The heat of shortening and the dynamic constants of muscle. *Proc. R. Soc. London Ser. B.* 126: 136–95

37. Hill, A. V. 1965. *Trails and Trials in Physiology.* London: Arnold. 374 pp.

38. Homsher, E., Mommaerts, W. F. H. M., Ricchiuti, N. V., Wallner, A. 1972. Activation heat, activation metabolism and tension-related heat in frog semitendinosus muscles. *J. Physiol. London* 220:601–25

39. Huntsman, L. L., Stewart, D. K. 1977. Length-dependent calcium inotropism in cat papillary muscle. *Circ. Res.* 40:366–71

40. Jewell, B. R. 1977. A reexamination of the influence of muscle length on myocardial performance. *Circulation* 40:221–30

41. Julian, F. J., Sollins, M. R. 1975. Sarcomere length-tension relations in living rat papillary muscle. *Circ. Res.* 37:299–308

42. Krueger, J. W., Pollack, G. D. 1975. Myocardial sarcomere dynamics during isometric contraction. *J. Physiol. London* 251:627–43

43. Lakatta, E. G., Jewell, B. R. 1977. Length-dependent activation. Its effect on the length-tension relation in cat ventricular muscle. *Circ. Res.* 40: 251–57

44. Manring, A., Nassar, R., Johnson, E. A. 1977. Light diffraction of cardiac muscle: an analysis of sarcomere shortening and muscle tension. *J. Mol. Cell. Cardiol.* 9:441–59

45. McDonald, R. H. Jr. 1971. Myocardial heat production: its relationship to tension development. *Am. J. Physiol.* 220:894–900

45a. Millward, D. J., Garlick, P. J., James, W. P. T., Sender, P., Waterlow, J. C. 1976. Protein turnover. In *Protein Metabolism and Nutrition: Proceedings,* ed. D. J. A. Cole, K. N. Boorman, P. J. Buttery, D. Lewis, R. J. Neale, H. Swan, pp. 49–69. London: Butterworths

46. Mommaerts, W. F. H. M. 1969. Energetics of muscular contraction. *Physiol. Rev.* 49:427–508

47. Mommaerts, W. F. H. M. 1970. What is the Fenn effect: Muscle is a regulatory engine the energy output of which is governed by the load. *Naturwissenschaften* 57:326–30

48. Mulieri, L. A., Luhr, G., Trefry, J., Alpert, N. R. 1977. Metal-film thermopiles for use with rabbit right ventricular papillary muscles. *Am. J. Physiol.* 233:146–56

49. Neill, W. A., Huckabee, N. W. 1966. Anaerobic heat production by the heart. *J. Clin. Invest.* 45:1412–20

50. Pinto, J. G., Win, R. 1977. Nonuniform strain distribution in papillary muscles. *Am. J. Physiol.* 233:H410–16

51. Pool, P. E., Chandler, B. M., Seagren, S. C., Sonnenblick, E. H. 1968. Mechanochemistry of cardiac muscle. II. The isotonic contraction. *Cir. Res.* 22:465–72

52. Rabinowitz, M. 1971. Control of metabolism and synthesis of macromolecules in normal and ischaemic heart. *J. Mol. Cell. Cardiol.* 2:277–92

53. Ricchiuti, N. V., Mommaerts, W. F. H. M. 1965. Technique for myothermic measurements. *Physiologist* 8:259

54. Rusy, B. F., Coulson, R. L. 1973. Energy consumption in the isolated rabbit heart. *Anesthesiology* 39:428–34

55. Semafuko, W. E. B., Bowie, W. C. 1975. Papillary muscle dynamics: in situ function and responses of the papillary muscle. *Am. J. Physiol.* 228:1800–7

56. Smith, I. C. H. 1972. Energetics of activation in frog and toad muscle. *J. Physiol. London* 220:583–99

57. Sonnenblick, E. H., Ross, J. Jr., Covell, J. W., Kaiser, G. A., Braunwald, E. 1965. Velocity of contraction as a determinant of myocardial oxygen consumption. *Am. J. Physiol.* 209:919–27

58. Takanji, M., Honig, C. R. 1972. Shortening and ATPase activities of single cardiac fibrils of normal sarcomere length. *Am. J. Physiol.* 222:1–9

59. Weber, A., Herz, R., Reiss, I. 1966. Study of the kinetics of calcium transport by isolated fragmented sarcoplasmic reticulum. *Biochem. Z.* 345:329–69

60. Weber, A., Murray, J. M. 1973. Molecular control mechanisms in muscle contraction. *Physiol. Rev.* 53:612–73

61. Weber, K. T., Janicki, J. S. 1977. Myocardial oxygen consumption: the role of wall force and shortening. *Am. J. Physiol.* 233:H421–30

62. Wilkie, D. R. 1960. Thermodynamics and the interpretation of biological heat measurements. *Prog. Biophys. Biophys. Chem.* 10:260–98

63. Woledge, R. C. 1971. Heat production and chemical change in muscle. *Prog. Biophys. Mol. Biol.* 22:39–74

Ann. Rev. Physiol. 1979. 41:521–37

HEART MUSCLE MECHANICS ♦1235

Norman R. Alpert, Burt B. Hamrell and Louis A. Mulieri

Department of Physiology and Biophysics, University of Vermont
College of Medicine, Burlington, Vermont 05405

INTRODUCTION

Selected experimental studies are reviewed that deal directly with force generation, shortening velocity, and compliance in heart muscle. The first detailed description of force, velocity, and compliance of heart muscle was presented by Abbott & Mommaerts (1) about 20 years ago. They used papillary muscle and trabeculae carneae preparations comparable to those developed by Cattell & Gold (16) and Ullrich & Whitehorn (69). By applying the methods that had been used for discovering the mechanical properties of skeletal muscle (31, 32, 53, 70), they described the following: (*a*) the staircase phenomenon; (*b*) the length-tension diagram; (*c*) the series elastic component; (*d*) the duration of the active state; (*e*) the force-velocity relation; and (*f*) the effect of quick stretch. Later work refined the methods and the data and fit them into the evolving concepts of muscle contraction. The general approach was based on the rationale worked out for skeletal muscle. That trend has continued, and thus data from skeletal muscle work will be discussed in this review where they are important for understanding heart muscle experiments.

Working with heart muscle involves certain difficulties. Compliance is large, which means considerable internal movement occurs. Furthermore, during a normal contraction-relaxation cycle, internal Ca^{2+} levels continuously change. Two new techniques, which were developed using skeletal muscle, help deal with these problems. The first is the important advance of visualizing the sarcomeres during activity and describing or controlling their length. The second concerns making the sarcolemma of intact or fragmented heart muscle freely permeable to ions and small molecules.

521

0066-4278/79/0301-0521$01.00

ISOMETRIC FORCE GENERATION

Highly Permeable Preparations

During a normal contraction and relaxation cycle and over a period of long-term activity, free Ca^{2+}, Mg^{2+}, $MgATP^{2-}$, and H^+ are known to change and to influence the force generated. Removal of the barrier presented to small ions and molecules by the myocardial sarcolemma permits the environment immediately surrounding the contractile elements to be kept constant and controlled. In these preparations the function of the plasma membrane may be changed by either (a) removal of the membrane (20), (b) treatment with EDTA (72), (c) glycerination (30), or (d) a combination of chemical treatment and mechanical disruption of the muscle (5, 40). The preparations consist of single cells or multicellular fragments.

When the free calcium ion concentration is increased from 10^{-7} to 10^{-4} M, these preparations manifest a sigmoid increase in force as a function of the Ca^{2+} concentration. The sensitivity of the contractile system to calcium can be expressed in terms of the pCa (pCa = $-log[Ca^{2+}]$) at which half maximal activation occurs (pCa 50%). The effect of Mg^{2+} and $MgATP^{2-}$ on pCa 50% is seen in Table 1. As the pMg^{2+} or $pMgATP^{2-}$ is increased, the pCa 50%, and therefore the sensitivity of the contractile system, is increased in skinned single-fiber preparations (21) and ventricular bundles (4). At a $pMgATP^{2-}$ of 5.5, even with low free calcium levels (pCa > 9.0), substantial tension is developed in skinned rat cardiac cells (21). Analogous data are seen in guinea pig ventricular bundles in a $pMgATP^{2-}$ of 2.69 and a pMg^{2+} of 3.30. At moderate and high levels of free calcium these bundles develop greater isometric force in the absence of an ATP regenerating system [creatine phosphate (CP) and creatine phosphokinase (CPK)] than in its presence. This presumably results from a high $pMgATP^{2-}$ in the core

Table 1 The effect of Mg^{2+} and $MgATP^{2-}$ on sensitivity of the myocardium to Ca^{2+}

Preparation	pMg^{2+}	$pMgATP^{2-}$	pCa 50%	Reference
Skinned fragments	2.5	1.8	5.58	Fabiato & Fabiato,
rat (single fibers)	2.5	2.5	5.66	1975 (21)
	3.5	2.5	6.00	
	4.5	2.5	6.08	
	4.5	3.5	6.16	
Disrupted bundles	4.3	4.5	5.8	Best, Donaldson
rat	3.0	4.5	5.4	& Kerrick, 1977
	4.3	4.0	5.3	(4)
	3.0	4.0	5.0	
	4.3	2.4	5.5	
	3.0	2.4	5.1	

of the bundle and is consistent with the observed increase of velocity of shortening at a P/P_0 [active force (P) relative to maximal active force (P_0)] of 0.2 in the presence of CP and CPK (47). In contrast, skinned cardiac cells do not respond to CP and CPK under comparable conditions, which indicates ample $MgATP^{2-}$ in the core of those preparations. The effect of high $pMgATP^{2-}$ is explained in terms of the removal of substrate inhibition (60) or the cooperative interaction of actin and myosin leading to the development of rigor complexes as the low affinity sites of troponin change into high affinity sites in the presence of low concentrations of $MgATP^{2-}$ (7). Hydrogen ion concentration also has a profound effect on calcium sensitivity. Reducing the pH from 7.2 to 6.4 increases by a factor of five the free calcium required for 50% tension development in skinned cardiac cells (23).

Internal Shortening

Julian & Sollins (38), using a photomicrographic approach, report a 3–6% decrease in average sarcomere length during the muscle isometric twitch of rat right ventricular papillary muscles, while Krueger & Pollack (42), using laser diffraction patterns and microsphere movement, observed a 7% decrease. Pollack & Krueger (58) control the internal shortening by stretching the muscle to an extent and with a time course that keeps average sarcomere length constant to within 1–2% during much of the muscle twitch. The rate of rise of tension is fast; isometric peak tension occurs within one half to two thirds of the time required for a conventional isometric twitch to reach peak value. The maximum sarcomere isometric twitch tension is almost double muscle isometric twitch tension. These findings suggest that activation occurs promptly following electrical stimulation ($24~min^{-1}$) of isolated cardiac muscle at 26° (58). Internal shortening changes the time course and intensity of the twitch because of the force-velocity relation and motion-dependent inactivation.

The Length–Tension Relationship

If sarcomere shortening is eliminated by servo-controlled stretch, the length–active tension relationship has a steep ascending limb with no plateau region in contrast to the plateau seen when only the external muscle length is fixed (39). Julian et al (39) propose that factors other than myofilament overlap (e.g. length-dependent activation) may have to be considered to explain the data. It is also important to consider the observation that thin-filament length in frog atrial trabeculae, rat atrial trabeculae, and rat papillary muscles varies by as much as 0.6 μm (61). Thus the broad distribution of actin and myosin overlap might also contribute to the absence of a force-length plateau in the heart muscle (39).

Pollack & Huntsman (57) report that the resting sarcomere length does not vary in proportion to resting muscle length in rat right ventricular trabecular or papillary muscles. They propose that end-compliance resulting from damage and the inter-muscle variability of that compliance account in part for the poor coupling between external resting muscle length and sarcomere length. In contrast Winegrad (71) observes that in frog atrial trabeculae there is evidence for tight mechanical coupling between fibers in series but little coupling of fibers in parallel. He notes 10–15% sarcomere shortening when the external length of the frog atrial trabeculae are held fixed; this amount of internal shortening is greater than the 7% observed by Krueger & Pollack (42), Wohlfart et al (74), Grimm & Wohlfart (26), and Grimm (25), or the 3–6% observed by Julian & Sollins (38); it may reflect a species difference or a difference between atrial and ventricular tissue.

In a detailed and insightful review of the length–tension relationship, Jewell recently (35) pointed out that the slope and shape of the ascending limb of the length-tension curve is modulated by (a) factors that contribute to internal resistance—e.g. double overlap of the thin filaments at sarcomere lengths of 1.95 μm or less, and buckling of the thick filaments at sarcomere lengths of 1.6 μm or less; and (b) the length effects on activation such as length-dependent intensity or duration of activation and the inactivation caused by sarcomere shortening. Pertinent to (a) above, Grimm et al (25) find no change in sarcomere length when resting muscle length is reduced below 85% L_{max} where sarcomere length is 1.94 μm. This is similar to the 1.89 μm value observed by Winegrad (71) as the smallest frog atrial sarcomere length attained in the unrestrained resting preparation. Information concerning the contribution of internal resistance and length-dependent activation is obtained by comparing length-tension measurements in skinned or disrupted fibers with those made on intact papillary muscles. The decrease in tension as length is decreased from L_{max} is much more rapid in intact preparations (38) than in skinned single fibers (22) (Table 2, Numbers 1 and 2). The decline is even more striking when the Julian & Sollins (38) data are analyzed in terms of the Voigt rather than the Maxwell model so that the total rather than the active tension is used in the analysis (Table 2, Number 3). The difference between the intact and skinned preparations has been attributed to length-dependent activation phenomena (35). Fabiato & Fabiato (22) address another potential difference between preparations, namely the swelling in the skinned preparation that occurs in the normal incubating milieu. When polyvinylpyrrolidone (PVP) is added to the preparation the diameter of the cell shrinks back to normal dimensions and restores the in vivo filament distances. Under these circumstances the decline in tension as length is decreased falls between the skinned and intact

Table 2 The length–tension relationship for heart—skinned fibers, disrupted bundles and papillary muscles

No.	$L/L_{max}\%^a$	90	80	70	60	Preparation	Reference
1	P/Po%	96	90	83	69	Rat ventricle skinned cells	Fabiato & Fabiato (22)
2	P/Po%	96	92	56	0	Rat papillary muscle (Maxwell model)	Julian & Sollins (38)
3	P/Po%	84	67	41	0	Rat papillary muscle (Voigt model)	Julian & Sollins (38)
4	P/Po%	96	90	77	45	Rat ventricle skinned cells (100 mg ml^{-1} PVP)	Fabiato & Fabiato (22)
5	P/Po%	96^b	27			Guinea pig ventricular bundle (pCa = 4)	Maughan, Low & Alpert (47)
6	P/Po%	20	0			Guinea pig ventricular bundle (pCa = 5.4)	Maughan, Low & Alpert (47)

[a] Calculated from graphs in original papers.
[b] Assumed to be 96% for purposes of comparison.

preparations (Table 2, Number 4). Maughan et al (47) derive the length-tension relation in disrupted guinea pig bundles (Table 2, Numbers 5 and 6) by measuring the length to which the fully or partially activated muscle shortens isotonically following a quick release to a specific load. The decline in force as a function of length in this preparation is greater than in the intact preparation and even more precipitous when the calcium level is low (Table 2, Number 6). Although the abrupt decline in the force as a function of length in the intact preparation certainly is related to length-dependent activation phenomena, internal resistance to shortening must also play a role. Under circumstances where activation is controlled, skinned single fibers behave differently in the presence and absence of PVP; their behavior is also different from that of disrupted guinea pig fiber bundles where the sarcolemma is left in place. The possible contribution of the internal hindrance to force development may be seen in the low and high calcium experiments (Table 2, Numbers 5 and 6) where at partial activation the decline in force as length decreases is greatest of all. If one assumes that the internal hindrance is constant at high and low calcium levels, the relative contribution of hindrance to the slope of the length-tension curve is greatest in the case of partial activation.

Relaxation

The relaxation of cardiac muscle, i.e. the return from peak active tension development to the baseline, is difficult to interpret because tension levels during this phase of the twitch are the resultant of the level of internal free Ca^{2+} during activation, the kinetics of the Ca^{2+}–troponin interaction, the dynamics of crossbridge detachment, and the rate and extent of Ca^{2+} binding and uptake by the sarcoplasmic reticulum. Understanding the molecular basis of relaxation in isolated heart tissue is important because normal pump function of the ventricle depends on adequate ventricular filling, which is affected by the rate and extent of relaxation, particularly at high heart rates.

An arterially perfused canine papillary muscle that is allowed to shorten against varying loads and is then length-clamped at the peak of isotonic shortening exhibits a rate of tension decline directly and linearly related to the load (64). The maximal rate of tension fall is increased by positive and decreased by negative inotropic interventions (62, 64). The magnitude of the preload or final shortened length has relatively little effect on relaxation parameters (64). The authors propose that the maximal rate of tension fall divided by the total load is a useful index of relaxation since it is independent of the amount of muscle shortening.

Morad & Rolette (51) studied the role of catecholamines in relaxation of right ventricular papillary muscles or thin trabeculae obtained from adult or neonatal cats, or rabbits. The addition of 2 $\mu g\ ml^{-1}$ of epinephrine results in an increase in isometric twitch height, a decrease in contraction time, and more rapid relaxation that is independent of the duration of the action potential. When the ventricular preparations develop contracture following the addition of 137 mM KCl, catecholamines enhance relaxation. Furthermore, the presence of catecholamines is required for full relaxation where calcium level or the twitch frequency is high (51). The effectiveness of catecholamines in facilitating relaxation decreases as the temperature is increased. The authors conclude that "catecholamines exert their relaxant effect independent of their positive inotropic effect by stimulating the sequestering system (sarcoplasmic reticulum, mitochondria or sarcolemma) for calcium" (51).

Relaxation has also been studied by the introduction of stimuli during the downslope of the muscle isometric twitch where the rate of development and amplitude of the second twitch are considered an index of the free Ca^{2+} remaining during relaxation (3). The rate of rise of tension development in responses evoked during relaxation increases abruptly as the stimulus interval is increased from immediately after peak tension to a maximum at about one half relaxation. It dips following this point and rises again late in the relaxation period. These interesting changes may be related to fluctuations in the internal calcium level or to inhomogeneous length changes in the sarcomeres.

Krueger & Pollack (47) note that diffraction patterns during muscle isometric relaxation in rat right ventricular papillary muscles exhibit multiple peaks on the first order line, thus indicating the complex relation between tension decline and sarcomere motion. Krueger (41), in a preliminary report, describes twitches in which sarcomere length during relaxation in rat right ventricular papillary muscles is held constant. The rate of tension decrease is constant throughout relaxation as compared with an exponential fall of tension noted when sarcomere motion is permitted. In addition, the rate of sarcomere isometric tension decline is more rapid when sarcomere motion is prevented and is independent of initial resting sarcomere length (41).

Part of the fall in tension during isometric relaxation may be related to internal restoring forces. In skinned single-fiber preparations when the pCa is lowered from 9 to 6.5 the preparation contracts from 1.97 to 1.57 μm, the point at which the thick filaments are in contact with the Z-line structure (22). Decreasing the pCa to 6.0 causes an additional length decrease to 1.10 μm. When the muscle is returned to relaxing solution there is a rapid phase of lengthening of sarcomeres from 1.10 to 1.57 μm (6 sec) and a slow phase from 1.57 to 1.91 μm (43 sec). Skinned cardiac cells behave like isolated myofibrils, i.e. they do not extend beyond 1.57 μm when the sarcoplasmic reticulum is destroyed with Brij 58. Thus there appear to be two types of restoring forces: (a) the straightening of the crumpled thick filaments; and (b) a force related to an intact sarcoplasmic reticulum. Both probably contribute to relaxation as well as to the slope of the ascending limb of the length-tension curve.

SHORTENING

The shape of the force-velocity curve has been extensively studied in the past. In this review we concentrate on the effects of length and activation on the unloaded velocity of shortening (V_{max}).

Dependence of V_{max} on Muscle and Sarcomere Length

In an examination of several analog models for the analysis of force-velocity data, Parmley et al (56) use isotonic afterloads from zero to two thirds of peak tension to measure the force-velocity relation in cat right ventricular papillary muscles at lengths from 92 to 100% of L_{max}. V_{max} is inversely related to initial muscle length from 100% to 97% L_{max} and is constant from 97% to 92%. This interesting finding is at variance with the studies noted below.

Brutsaert et al (10) impose sudden changes in load on isotonically contracting cat right ventricular papillary muscles, causing instantaneous changes in shortening and shortening velocity. The velocity of shortening in these experiments is related to the total load and the muscle length and is independent of the history of load and length changes prior to the measurement (10). These experiments are an extension of earlier experiments using a quick-release technique to study shortening velocity at various times in the onset of an isometric twitch over a range of initial muscle lengths but at a constant total load (13). The velocity-length curves become superimposable at peak velocity and during the subsequent velocity decline. Consequently the time course of shortening velocity is not dependent on initial muscle length (13). In another study a spot-follower feedback technique is used to remove the preload continuously during shortening (11). The velocity of shortening under these circumstances is very close to V_{max}, and is independent of initial muscle length between about 95% and 100% L_{max} (11). In accord with these studies (10, 11, 13) V_{max} estimated by extrapolation from force-velocity data obtained with quick releases early in the twitch in rabbit right ventricular papillary muscles is independent of initial muscle length between 96% and 100% L_{max} (28).

In contrast with the above studies several investigators observe a direct dependence of V_{max} on initial muscle length. In rabbit right ventricular papillary muscles studied with optimally damped quick releases at the peak of the isometric twitch, V_{max} is estimated with a linearized form of the Hill hyperbola and P_0 is peak active twitch tension (54). As initial muscle length is reduced from the longest length to 93% of that length, V_{max} and P_0 are decreased to the same extent. Gulch & Jacob (24) report that in cat right ventricular papillary muscles V_{max} is directly dependent on length; force-velocity data are obtained late in the twitch at 75% of peak force. In the latter two studies (24, 54) the stimulus frequency is 30 min^{-1}. Donald et al (18) report a direct dependence of V_{max} on initial muscle length based on measurements of isotonic afterloaded twitches in cat right ventricular papillary muscles at initial lengths of 90–100% L_{max}.

The differences in the above experiments may be related to differences in experimental conditions, namely: stimulus frequency [30 min^{-1}, Nilsson (54); 12 min^{-1}, Brutsaert (10, 11, 13) and Hamrell (28)] and the time during the twitch when the muscle is studied [late, Nilsson (54) and Gulch & Jacob (24); combination of late and early, Donald et al (18); early, Brutsaert (10, 11, 13) and Hamrell & Alpert (28)]. Consequently, a decrease in V_{max} as length is decreased below L_{max} may be a phenomenon uniquely related to measurements made late in the twitch.

Dependence of V_{max} on Level of Activation

Brutsaert et al (9) studied the effect of external calcium levels on unloaded shortening velocity of cat right ventricular papillary muscles at L_{max}. P_0 and V_{max} increase when the external calcium level is changed from 2.5 to 7.5 mM (56) or 2.5 to 5.0 mM (2). In contrast, Hamrell using rabbits found no effect of raising the calcium level from 2.5 to 11 mM on V_{max} at 15 and 30% time-to-peak-tension (27).

Hamrell (27) analyzed V_{max} and P_0, obtained by an extrapolation technique using the linearized form of the Hill force-velocity relation, at various times early in the twitch (6). V_{max} reaches a steady level at 10% and remains stable to 30% of time-to-peak-tension; P_0 rises rapidly during this interval. Similar results regarding the time-independence of unloaded shortening velocity have been reported by Brutsaert et al (8, 11, 14, 15) and Henderson et al (29), although in the latter studies shortening velocity did not reach a steady state until 16–20% of time-to-peak-tension.

Experimental perturbations of the muscle preparation must be taken into consideration when evaluating shortening. Jewell & Rovell (36) find, in cat right ventricular papillary muscles contracting isometrically at 24 min^{-1}, that an interposed quick release or simple afterloaded isotonic twitch results in potentiation of the succeeding isometric twitch, and that a total of 10 consecutive isometric twitches are required to return to the steady-state level. Brutsaert & Sonnenblick (11) quickly release cat right ventricular papillary muscles with no afterload at a number of instants through the course of an isometric twitch. The velocity-length relation of quick-release contractions is depressed below that of the isotonic beat (no release perturbation) for releases later than about the first one third of time-to-peak tension. Consequently force-velocity data obtained late in the twitch have the potentially confounding effect of shortening inactivation. It may be that inactivation can be ameliorated by critical damping (19, 46, 54), particularly that component of inactivation attributable to oscillations occurring during a release (19).

The direct effect of free calcium on the velocity of shortening is difficult to evaluate in intact hearts and papillary muscle preparations. The free calcium level changes dramatically during the contraction-relaxation cycle and is not monotonically related to the calcium concentration in the external medium. Thus measurements made at different times in the twitch are difficult to compare. Similarly temperature and the type of release affect the internal calcium level.

Shortening studies carried out on disrupted fibers make it possible to evaluate the direct effect of free calcium concentration on velocity of shortening. Thus at 10^{-5} and 4×10^{-6} M Ca^{2+} velocity at 0.2 P_0 decreases to 87 and 64%, respectively, of that obtained at 10^{-4} M Ca^{2+} (47). DeClerck et al (17) studied contraction in single rat ventricular cells activated by calcium released by iontophoresis in an EGTA buffered solution. Although the Ca^{2+} concentration is not directly measured, peak force and velocity of shortening increased with the amount of calcium ejected from the microelectrode. Analogous changes in skeletal muscle have been explained by the direct effect of calcium on myosin crossbridge kinetics (37, 73). In contrast Thames et al (68) suggest the presence of abnormal crossbridges linking myosin to actin (present even at low Ca^{2+} concentrations and sensitive to ionic strength) that retard the sliding of filaments. Decreased velocity of shortening at lower calcium levels thus reflects a lower ratio of normal to abnormal crossbridge links. The internal load (abnormal crossbridges) necessary to explain the results presented above would be about $0.6\ P_0$ for the guinea pig preparation and $0.3\ P_0$ for the single rat ventricular cells discussed above. At present it is not possible to say whether the restoring forces or the internal hindrance to shortening are of this magnitude. Thus the mechanism to account for the calcium effect on the velocity of shortening is still undecided.

ACTIVE AND PASSIVE STIFFNESS OF ISOLATED MUSCLE

Stiffness measurements have been made on isolated cardiac muscle preparations in order to evaluate various muscle models and to elucidate the role of myocardial stiffness in determining ventricular diastolic pressure. The bulk of recent research has been directed at testing the expectation of the Huxley-Simmons crossbridge model (34) that active stiffness is proportional to the number of active crossbridges or contractile force.

Active Stiffness vs Tension

Using cat right ventricular papillary muscle Templeton et al (66) apply a sinusoidal length perturbation (0.6% L_{max}) throughout the contraction and relaxation phase of isometric twitches. They find dynamic stiffness to be linearly related to mean instantaneous tension throughout contraction and relaxation. Furthermore, changes in peak twitch tension caused by alterations in stimulation rate or elevation of extracellular calcium concentration have no effect on the stiffness-tension relation. Loeffler & Sagawa (43) evaluate a three-component model for active cat papillary muscle using sinusoidal length perturbation analysis. The stiffness of the components corresponding to the elastic elements vary linearly with active force during a twitch. Meiss & Sonnenblick (49) make stiffness measurements on the same preparation using quick-release and stretch techniques. They, too, find a linear relation between stiffness and tension when releases are made either at different tensions during a twitch, at the same time but at different muscle lengths, or following deactivation induced by a quick stretch at constant time and muscle length.

McLaughlin & Sonnenblick (48) refined their quick-release apparatus and techniques to obtain high-precision stress-strain curves of the series elastic component at various times during the twitch. They find the stiffness of the series elastic component to be a unique function of force level independent of time during a contraction.

Quick-release stiffness measurements have also been made during contracture responses at various calcium concentrations in membrane-free preparations. Riermann et al (59) find stiffness to be directly proportional to contracture tension (and ATPase activity) in glycerol-treated pig heart papillary muscles and trabeculae when the pCa is varied between 8 and 5. Maughan et al (47) find stiffness to be directly proportional to tension during releases from calcium contractures in disrupted ventricular fragments from guinea pig hearts; the proportionality constant is not different at 4×10^{-6} M Ca^{2+} (65% maximum active force) from what it is at 10^{-4} M Ca^{2+} (100% maximum active force). Alterations in creatine phosphate levels between 15 and 25 mM also are without effect on series elastic properties of this preparation.

Although all of these studies demonstrate a lack of influence of resting tension on the stiffness–active tension relation, more recent work by Templeton et al (65) indicates that when resting tension is increased by stretch the slope of the stiffness–active tension relation decreases while its intercept increases. This dependency results in the surprising finding that stiffness is higher at a given tension if that tension is achieved by diastolic stretch than if it is achieved by contraction from a lower resting tension.

DEPENDENCE OF STIFFNESS ON PERTURBATION FREQUENCY
Templeton et al (66) find a 16% increase in slope and a 28% increase in intercept of the stiffness–tension relation in going from 10 to 30 Hz oscillation frequency. Use of the higher frequency also increases the perturbation-induced depression of peak twitch tension from 9% to 33%; hence the stiffness changes may be complicated by a deactivation effect. In a subsequent study Templeton et al (67) demonstrate that the stiffness–tension relation remains linear for all frequencies below 150 Hz providing the perturbation amplitude is below 2% L_{max}. The slope of the dynamic stiffness continually increases with frequency, reaching a maximum between 80 and 100 Hz. Since frequency analysis demonstrates linear second-order system response the elastic and viscous components of the muscle's dynamic stiffness can be evaluated. Viscous stiffness is about six-fold greater than elastic stiffness and exhibits a strong, inverse dependence on temperature but only a slight dependence on muscle tension. Elastic stiffness exhibits a small temperature dependence and a large tension dependence. Pressure-volume studies on intact hearts (dog) reveal similar dependence of myocardial stiffness on pressure and temperature; however, volume perturbations do not cause deactivation (67).

A more extensive study of the frequency dependence (0.1–35 Hz) of elastic and viscous stiffness in cat papillary muscles is reported by Loeffler & Sagawa (43). While the time and tension dependence of the elastic and viscous component stiffness in their model for active muscle is similar to the above results, they find that the elastic stiffness (but not the viscous stiffness) declines above 95% L_{max}. In addition viscous stiffness reaches a plateau by the first third of the contraction time and then nearly doubles during the early relaxation phase of the twitch.

NONLINEAR TRANSIENT RESPONSE   Steiger (63) examines the length-step induced tension transients of glycerinated rabbit papillary muscle to test the applicability of the Huxley-Simmons (34) crossbridge model. While all phases of tension recovery found in frog muscle can be identified in the papillary muscle response, the dependence of the rate of fast-phase tension recovery on amplitude of length step is opposite to the dependence in frog muscle. The results are interpreted to indicate changes in number of attached crossbridges rather than rotation of crossbridge heads without cycling. In addition a release of about 30 nm per sarcomere is needed to discharge tension to zero—about double that required in frog muscle.

Similar differences between glycerinated rabbit papillary muscle and skeletal muscle are exhibited in the behavior of the short-range elastic component (SREC) as demonstrated by Moss et al (52). The elastic modulus of the SREC in the papillary muscle is only 44% of the skeletal muscle value. Furthermore the length change required to induce slip is 20 nm sarcomere^{-1} in heart vs 9.2 nm sarcomere^{-1} in skeletal muscle. Similar values (17–22 nm sarcomere^{-1}) proposed to correspond to back rotation of crossbridge heads are found in the second phase of three-step length-yielding caused by stepwise increases in load in intact cat papillary muscle (12, 33). The rapid, phase-three lengthening beyond 22 nm sarcomere^{-1} would seem to be the counterpart of slip in the SREC response to ramp stretching reported by Moss et al (52). These results may be interpreted in either of two ways. Crossbridge head rotation in cardiac muscle may be twice that in skeletal muscle while series compliance is no different; or, more likely, head rotation is similar in both muscles, but an extra series compliance is present in the cardiac muscle preparation.

Resting Stiffness and Stress Relaxation

Mirsky & Parmley (50) find an exponential stress–strain relation in nonbeating cat papillary muscles subjected to ramp stretches (0.02 mm sec^{-1}). Estimation of stiffness values in intact human hearts using end diastolic pressure and ventricular volume : mass ratio indicates only about half the value obtained in the isolated cat muscle preparation. Noble (55) subjected cat papillary muscles to ramp stretches of varying speed during diastole. Below 1 muscle-length sec^{-1} (5 mm sec^{-1}) the stress-strain curve is approximately exponential and equal to the static tension-length curve. With velocities of 1–3 muscle-lengths sec^{-1} progressively more force is generated during the stretch due to viscous properties. This increase is greater as initial muscle length is increased. Calculated stretch velocity occurring in situ during early diastole is 2.6–4.2 muscle-lengths sec^{-1}, which, according to these isolated muscle data, would give rise to a left-ventricular pressure increase of 6 mm Hg. Such a velocity-dependent pressure can be erroneously interpreted as a change in diastolic compliance when in reality it is caused by increased filling rate. Using 20 Hz sinusoidal length perturbations, Templeton et al (65) find that the viscous component of dynamic stiffness is forty-fold stiffer than the elastic component and that both components are directly proportional to resting tension.

Loeffler & Sagawa (43) analyze the passive behavior of cat papillary muscle by applying step stretches of 1% L_{max}. Semilog plots of the stress-relaxation responses reveal a double exponential time course leading to a five-component model for resting muscle consisting of two viscoelastic branches in parallel with an elasticity. All five passive parameter values show exponential-like increases with increasing muscle length.

Sources of Compliance

All of the above studies confirm the exponential nature of the active stiffness-tension relation in heart muscle. Since the absolute stiffness values are 3–5 times lower than in skeletal muscle, and in view of the almost universal finding of exponential stress-strain behavior for most passive biological tissue, serious consideration must be given to the possibility that the stiffness values for cardiac muscle represent passive tissue in series with the sarcomere. That both resting and active muscle display exponential stress-strain behavior further supports this possibility. If the rise in stiffness with active tension is a reflection of recruitment of crossbridges in parallel, i.e. if crossbridge compliance is the dominant contributor to muscle compliance, then a common release distance should suffice to discharge active force at any time during a twitch. McLaughlin & Sonnenblick could not confirm this expectation (48), which suggests an extra-sarcomeric origin of the compliance. Meiss & Sonnenblick (49) suggest that a good deal of the extra compliance could reside in load-dependent changes in cellular branching angles. More recent studies by Krueger & Pollack (42) demonstrate that changes in sarcomere length average 7% during an isometric muscle twitch as a result of stretching of damaged tissue near the clamped ends of rat papillary muscles. Maughan et al (47) observe sarcomeres to elongate by only 10% when guinea pig ventricular bundles with clamped ends are stretched by 20%. Winegrad (71) finds that while sarcomere length cannot easily be increased beyond 2.6 μm by stretching frog atrial trabeculae, local spontaneous contraction of sarcomeres lengthen adjacent resting sarcomeres in series with them to as much as 3.2 μm.

These observations suggest poor mechanical coupling between experimental apparatus and sarcomeres in cardiac muscle preparations. The intervening passive tissue is thus a good candidate for the series elastic element and active stiffness in this muscle. It may be possible to test this hypothesis by correlating series elastic stiffness with the number of series sarcomeres in various preparations. The zero-sarcomere intercept would indicate the nonsarcomeric contribution to total compliance.

The recent finding by Maruyama et al (45) of a filamentous network composed of connectin filaments less than 2 nm in diameter within sarcomeres of skeletal and cardiac muscle may provide a structural counterpart for the intracellular parallel elastic component of muscle. The connectin content of bovine heart myofibrils was about 18% of the total myofibrillar protein—three times as much as in skeletal myofibrils (44). This could account for the greater stiffness of resting cardiac muscle myofibrils as compared with skeletal muscle. The presence of dense connectin networks linking Z lines in cardiac muscle would make crossbridge compliance changes even more difficult to detect in the presence of series compliance in damaged ends.

SUMMARY

The goal implicit in the research reviewed above is to describe the contractile behavior of heart muscle in terms of crossbridge and filament behavior. It is necessary to elucidate these details in cardiac muscle because of the distinct biochemical differences between skeletal and cardiac myosin. As is evident in this review, significant advances have been made toward describing unique mechanical properties of cardiac muscle crossbridges. Several major problems now require attention: (a) Activation parameters are labile, making mechanical measurements sensitive to measurement perturbation; (b) significant structural inhomogeneities at the cellular and sarcomere level prevent precise assignment of externally measured force to internal structures (force generators, passive elements) within whole cardiac muscle and individual cells; (c) high resting stiffness and forces of poorly understood origin and properties confound attempts to interpret force measurements and dynamics.

The differences between heart and skeletal muscle myosin may provide the means for identifying structural counterparts of the Huxley-Simmons model (33); they may also be useful in evaluating the electrostatic and quantum-mechanical models.

ACKNOWLEDGMENTS

We thank Katharine A. Fenn and Robert P. Goulette for assistance in the preparation of this manuscript.

Literature Cited

1. Abbott, B. C., Mommaerts, W. F. H. M. 1959. A study of inotropic mechanisms in the papillary muscle preparations. *J. Gen. Physiol.* 42:533–51
2. Anderson, P. A. W., Mauring, A., Johnson, E. A. 1977. The force of contraction of isolated papillary muscle: A study of the interaction of its determining factors. *J. Mol. Cell. Cardiol.* 9: 131–50
3. Bass, B. G. 1975. Enhanced contractility during relaxation of cat papillary muscle. *Am. J. Physiol.* 228: 1708–16
4. Best, P. M., Donaldson, S. K. B., Kerrick, W. G. L. 1977. Tension in mechanically disrupted mammalian cardiac cells: effects of magnesium adenosine triphosphate. *J. Physiol. (London)* 265:1–17
5. Bloom, S. 1970. Spontaneous rhythmic contractions of separated heart muscle cells. *Science* 167:1727–29
6. Bodem, R., Sonnenblick, E. H. 1975. Mechanical activity of mammalian heart muscle: variable onset, species differences, and the effect of caffeine. *Am. J. Physiol.* 228:250–61
7. Bremel, R. D., Weber, A. 1972. Cooperation within actin filaments in vertebrate skeletal muscles. *Nature* 238:97–101
8. Brutsaert, D. L., Claes, V. A. 1974. Onset of mechanical activation of mammalian heart muscle in calcium- and strontium-containing solutions. *Circ. Res.* 35:345–57
9. Brutsaert, D. L., Claes, V. A., Goethals, M. A. 1973. Effect of calcium on force-velocity-length relations of heart muscle of the cat. *Circ. Res.* 32:385–92
10. Brutsaert, D. L., Claes, V. A., Sonnenblick, E. H. 1971. Effects of abrupt load alterations on force-velocity-length and time relations during isotonic contractions of heart muscle: load clamping. *J. Physiol.* 216:319–30
11. Brutsaert, D. L., Claes, V. A., Sonnenblick, E. H. 1971. Velocity of shortening of unloaded heart muscle and the length-tension relation. *Circ. Res.* 29: 63–75
12. Brutsaert, D. L., Housmans, P. R. 1977. Load clamp analysis of maximal force potential of mammalian cardiac muscle. *J. Physiol.* 271:587–603
13. Brutsaert, D. L., Sonnenblick, E. H. 1969. Force-velocity-length-time relations of the contractile elements in heart muscle of the cat. *Circ. Res.* 24:137–49
14. Brutsaert, D. L., Sonnenblick, E. H. 1971. The early onset of maximum velocity of shortening in heart muscle of the cat. *Pfluegers Arch.* 324:91–99
15. Brutsaert, D. L., Vermeulen, F. E., Sonnenblick, E. H. 1970. The early occurrence of maximum velocity of shortening in heart muscle. *Arch. Int. Physiol. Biochem.* 78:563–65
16. Cattell, M., Gold, H. 1938. The influence of digitalis glycosides on the force of contraction of mammalian cardiac muscle. *J. Pharmacol. Exp. Ther.* 62: 116–25
17. DeClerck, N. M., Claes, V. A., Brutsaert, D. L. 1977. Force velocity relations of single cardiac muscle cells. *J. Gen. Physiol.* 69:221–41
18. Donald, T. C., Unnoppetchara, K., Peterson, D., Hefner, L. L. 1972. Effect of initial muscle length on Vmax in isotonic contraction of cardiac muscle. *Am. J. Physiol.* 223:262–67
19. Edman, K. A. P., Nilsson, E. 1972. Relationships between force and velocity of shortening in rabbit papillary muscle. *Acta Physiol. Scand.* 85:488–500
20. Fabiato, A., Fabiato, F. 1973. Activation of skinned cardiac cells. Subcellular effects of cardioactive drugs. *Eur. J. Cardiol.* 1/2:143–55
21. Fabiato, A., Fabiato, F. 1975. Effects of magnesium on contractile activation of skinned cardiac cells. *J. Physiol. (London)* 249:497–517
22. Fabiato, A., Fabiato, F. 1976. Dependence of calcium release, tension generation and restoring forces on sarcomere length in skinned cardiac cells. *Eur. J. Cardiol.* 4:13–27
23. Fabiato, A., Fabiato, F. 1977. Causes for the more negative ionotropic effect of intracellular acidosis in cardiac than in skeletal muscle. *Circulation* 55/56: (Suppl III) 166
24. Gulch, R. W., Jacob, R. 1975. Length-tension diagram and force-velocity relations of mammalian cardiac muscle under steady state conditions. *Pfluegers Arch.* 355:331–46
25. Grimm, A. F., Katele, K. V., Kubota, R., Whitehorn, W. V. 1970. Relation of sarcomere length and muscle length in resting myocardium. *Am. J. Physiol.* 218:1412–16
26. Grimm, A. F., Wohlfart, B. 1974. Sarcomere lengths at the peak of the length-tension curve in living and fixed rat papillary muscle. *Acta Physiol. Scand.* 92:575–77

27. Hamrell, B. B. 1978. Unloaded shortening (Vmax) and maximal force (Po): interaction with time and Ca²⁺. *Fed. Proc.* 37:461

28. Hamrell, B. B., Alpert, N. R. 1977. The mechanical characteristics of hypertrophied rabbit cardiac muscle in the absence of congestive heart failure: the contractile and series elastic elements. *Circ. Res.* 40:20–25

29. Henderson, A. H., Claes, V. A., Brutsaert, D. L. 1973. Influence of caffeine and other inotropic interventions on the onset of unloaded shortening velocity in mammalian heart muscle. *Circ. Res.* 33:291–302

30. Henry, P. D., Ahumada, G. G., Friedman, W. F., Sobel, B. E. 1972. Simultaneously measured isometric tension and ATP hydrolysis in glycerinated fibers from normal and hypertrophied rabbit heart. *Circ. Res.* 31:740–49

31. Hill, A. V. 1956. The design of muscles. *Brit. Med. Bull.* 12:165–66

32. Hill, A. V., Macpherson, L. 1954. The effect of nitrate, iodide and bromide on the duration of the active state in muscle. *Proc. R. Soc. London Ser. B* 143:81–102

33. Housmans, P. R., Brutsaert, D. L. 1976. Three-step yielding of load-clamped mammalian cardiac muscle. *Nature* 262:56–58

34. Huxley, A. F., Simmons, R. M. 1971. Proposed mechanisms of force generation in striated muscle. *Nature* 233:533–38

35. Jewell, B. R. 1977. A reexamination of the influence of muscle length on myocardial performance. *Circ. Res.* 40:221–30

36. Jewell, B. R., Rovell, J. M. 1973. Influence of previous mechanical events on the contractility of isolated cat papillary muscle. *J. Physiol.* 235:715–40

37. Julian, F. J. 1971. The effect of calcium on the force-velocity relation of briefly glycerinated frog muscle fibres. *J. Physiol. (London)* 218:117–45

38. Julian, F. J., Sollins, M. R. 1975. Sarcomere length-tension relations in living rat papillary muscle. *Circ. Res.* 37:299–308

39. Julian, F. J., Sollins, M. R., Moss, R. L. 1976. Absence of a plateau in length-tension relationship of rabbit papillary muscle when internal shortening is prevented. *Nature* 260:340–42

40. Kerrick, W. G. L., Best, P. M. 1974. Calcium ion release in mechanically disrupted heart cells. *Science* 183:435–37

41. Krueger, J. W. 1978. Isometric sarcomere relaxation in intact cardiac muscle. *Fed. Proc.* 37:461

42. Krueger, J. W., Pollack, G. H. 1975. Myocardial sarcomere dynamics during isometric contraction. *J. Physiol.* 251:627–43

43. Loeffler, L., Sagawa, K. 1975. A one-dimensional viscoelastic model of cat heart muscle studied by small length perturbations during isometric contraction. *Circ. Res* 36:498–512

44. Maruyama, K., Kimura, S., Kuroda, M., Handa, S. 1977. Connectin, an elastic protein of muscle. *J. Biochem.* 82:347–50

45. Maruyama, K., Matsubara, S., Natori, R., Nonomura, Y., Kimura, S., Ohashi, K., Murakami, F., Handa, S., Eguchi, G. 1977. Connectin, an elastic protein of muscle. *J. Biochem.* 82:317–37

46. Mattiazzi, A. R., Nilsson, E. 1976. The influence of temperature on the time course of the mechanical activity in rabbit papillary muscle. *Acta Physiol. Scand.* 97:310–18

47. Maughan, D. W., Low, E. S., Alpert, N. R. 1978. Isometric force development, isotonic shortening, and elasticity measurements from Ca²⁺-activated ventricular muscle of the guinea pig. *J. Gen. Physiol.* 71:431–51

48. McLaughlin, R. J., Sonnenblick, E. H. 1974. Time behavior of series elasticity in cardiac muscle. *Cir. Res.* 34:798–811

49. Meiss, R. A., Sonnenblick, E. H. 1974. Dynamic elasticity of cardiac muscle as measured by controlled length changes. *Am. J. Physiol.* 226:1370–81

50. Mirsky, I., Parmley, W. W. 1973. Assessment of passive elastic stiffness for isolated heart muscle and the intact heart. *Circ. Res.* 33:233–43

51. Morad, M., Rolett, E. L. 1972. Relaxing effects of catecholamines on mammalian heart. *J. Physiol.* 224:537–58

52. Moss, R. L., Sollins, M. R., Julian, F. J. 1976. Calcium activation produces a characteristic response to stretch in both skeletal and cardiac muscle. *Nature* 260:619–21

53. Niedergerke, R. 1956. The "staircase" phenomenon and the action of calcium on the heart. *J. Physiol.* 134:569–83

54. Nilsson, E. 1972. Influence of muscle length on the mechanical parameters of myocardial contraction. *Acta Physiol. Scand.* 85:1–23

55. Noble, M. I. M. 1977. The diastolic viscous properties of cat papillary muscle. *Circ. Res.* 40:288–92

56. Parmley, W. W., Chuck, L., Sonnenblick, E. H. 1972. Relation of Vmax to different models of cardiac muscle. *Circ. Res.* 30:34–43
57. Pollack, G. H., Huntsman, L. L. 1974. Sarcomere length–active force relations in living mammalian cardiac muscle. *Am. J. Physiol.* 227:383–89
58. Pollack, G. H., Krueger, J. W. 1976. Sarcomere dynamics in intact cardiac muscle. *Eur. J. Cardiol* 4: (Suppl.) 53–65
59. Reiermann, H. J., Herzig, J. W., Ruegg, J. C. 1977. Ca^{++} activation of ATPase activity, ATP-P_1 exchange, and tension in briefly glycerinated heart muscle. *Basic Res. Cardiol* 72:133–39
60. Reuben, J. P., Brandt, P. W., Berman, M., Grundfest, H. 1971. Regulation of tension in the skinned crayfish muscle fiber. I. Contraction and relaxation in the absence of Ca (pCa > 9.0). *J. Gen. Physiol.* 57:385–407
61. Robinson, T. F., Winegrad, S. 1977. Variations of thin filament length in heart muscle. *Nature* 267:74–75
62. Rutleu, D. L., Powell, W. J. Jr. 1973. Interaction of rate and preload on developed tension in isometric papillary muscle. *Am. J. Physiol.* 225:1015–19
63. Steiger, G. J. 1977. Tension transients in extracted rabbit heart muscle preparations. *J. Mol. Cell Cardiol.* 9:671–85
64. Tamiya, K., Kikkawa, S., Gunji, A., Hori, M., Sakurai, Y. 1977. Maximum rate of tension fall during isometric relaxation at end-systolic fiber length in canine papillary muscle. *Circ. Res.* 40:584–89
65. Templeton, G., Adcock, R., Willerson, J. T., Nardizzi, L., Wildenthal, K., Mitchell, J. 1976. Relationships between resting tension and mechanical properties of papillary muscle. *Am. J. Physiol.* 231:1679–85
66. Templeton, G. H., Donald, T. C. III, Mitchell, J. H., Hefner, L. L. 1973. Dynamic stiffness of papillary muscle during contraction and relaxation. *Am. J. Physiol.* 224:692–98
67. Templeton, G. H., Wildenthal, K., Willerson, J. T., Reardon, W. C. 1974. Influence of temperature on the mechanical properties of cardiac muscle. *Circ. Res.* 34:624–34
68. Thames, M. D., Teichholz, L. E., Podolsky, R. J. 1974. Ionic strength and the contraction kinetics of skinned muscle fibers. *J. Gen. Physiol.* 63:509–30
69. Ullrich, W. C., Whitehorn, W. V. 1956. A muscle column preparation from the rat's left ventricle. *Circ. Res.* 4:499–501
70. Wilkie, D. R. 1956. Measurement of the series elastic component at various times during a single muscle twitch. *J. Physiol.* 134:527–30
71. Winegrad, S. 1974. Resting sarcomere length–tension relation in living frog heart. *J. Gen. Physiol.* 64:343–55
72. Winegrad, S. 1971. Studies in cardiac muscle with a high permeability to calcium produced by treatment with ethylenediaminetetraacetic acid. *J. Gen. Physiol.* 58:71–93
73. Wise, R. M., Rondione, J. F., Briggs, F. N. 1971. Effect of calcium on force-velocity characteristics of glycerinated skeletal muscle. *Am. J. Physiol.* 221:978–79
74. Wohlfart, B., Grimm, A. F., Edman, K. A. P. 1977. Relationship between sarcomere length and active force in rabbit papillary muscle. *Acta Physiol. Scand.* 101:155–64

Ann. Rev. Physiol. 1979. 41:539–52
Copyright © 1979 by Annual Reviews Inc. All rights reserved

MOLECULAR ASPECTS
OF CARDIAC HYPERTROPHY

♦1236

Radovan Zak and Murray Rabinowitz

Cardiology Section of the Department of Medicine and the Department
of Biochemistry, University of Chicago and the Franklin McLean
Memorial Research Institute [operated by the University of Chicago
for the U.S. Research and Development Administration
under Contract E(11–1)–69] Chicago, Illinois 60637

INTRODUCTION

The response of cardiac growth to physiological changes that alter the
hemodynamic load is a biological problem of general interest. In the early
phase of work overload, cardiac growth is an adaptive response that allows
the individual to survive. When the overload is prolonged, however,
changes in the organization of muscle cells occur, with consequent diminished contractile function and eventual heart failure. The nature of the
pathological lesions as well as the transition or distinction between physiological and pathological growth are the points of interest. Another interesting problem concerns the mechanisms by which the synthesis of cellular
components is regulated and adjusted to physiological demands. The extent
of ATP utilization serves in some way as a signal stimulating gene activity.

Many of the reaction steps involved in the translation of genetic information into the amino acid sequence of polypeptide chains have already been
elucidated in studies of rather simple biological systems, such as cell-free
preparations, bacteria, or cells in culture. Much less is known about the
regulatory mechanisms involved in the switching on and off of individual
genes during cell differentiation and growth. Studies of gene activity in
higher organisms, where several types of cells are present within the same
organ, are much more difficult. The heart, for example, contains at least
eight distinct cell types, the nonmuscle cells outnumbering myocytes three
to one. Even muscle-specific proteins, such as myosin, cannot be considered

539

an unequivocal cellular marker, since myosin isozymes are found in a great variety of cells. It is thus obvious that the study of molecular events in developing cardiac hypertrophy must proceed in the direction of analysis of products of specific genes. Any advancement in this area of heart physiology is contingent upon our current knowledge of molecular biology. For this reason, we present in this article an overview of mechanisms regulating gene activity and discuss the most recent information on the molecular aspects of cardiac hypertrophy published subsequent to reviews by Meerson (51) and us (57).

CONTROL OF TRANSCRIPTION

The first level of control that is almost certainly implicated in the activation of synthetic processes in hemodynamically overloaded heart is the transcription of messenger RNA. The information available so far about regulation of genetic activity in eukaryotes is still fragmentary; nevertheless, it is apparent that the regulatory mechanisms in higher organisms are much more complex than those operating in prokaryotes.

Two characteristics of DNA organization in higher organisms reflect the complexity of the mechanisms regulating genetic expression. First, DNA is intimately associated with chromosomal proteins believed to maintain the DNA in a largely repressed condition. The DNA in eukaryotic chromosomes exists in a form of chromatin composed of DNA closely associated with two classes of proteins: the highly basic histones and the mildly acidic nonhistones. The DNA is arranged in small, repeating nucleoprotein units along chromatin fibers.

Second, the amount of DNA in the haploid nuclei of higher organisms, in contrast to prokaryotes, vastly exceeds the number of genes needed. The genomes of higher cells contain segments of repeated nucleotide sequences distributed throughout the length of the DNA fiber. The repeated sequences have been postulated as being important in the regulation of transcription of structural genes (see 21). Different classes of repeated sequences are presumed to interact with cellular regulators, perhaps mediated through receptors and chromosomal proteins, to activate specific groups of structural genes. The mechanism of structural-gene activation is still unknown, but RNA or protein products of repeated sequences have been postulated to result in a cascade of activity, so that a small number of molecules are capable of activating large numbers of structural genes. Of great interest are recent observations that many eukaryotic genes contain sequences that are not produced by the mature messenger RNA (31). The gene is thus a mosaic of expressed sequences (exons) in a matrix of silent regions (introns). The regulatory function of the silent sequences is still a mystery.

The exact means by which cellular metabolites interact with the chromosomes to alter transcription is not known, but important information is being obtained from studies of the mechanism of action of anabolic hormones (45). It has been demonstrated in several models that the action of steroid hormones involves initial binding of the hormone to a receptor molecule in the cytoplasm of target cells. Subsequently, the hormone-receptor complex migrates into the nucleus, where it becomes associated with chromatin. Interaction of the receptor with the nuclear site results in activation of RNA polymerase and in subsequent cellular response.

The actual process that leads to an opening of the repressed gene for transcription is still obscure. It is generally believed, however, that some uncoiling or loosening of DNA fibers within the chromatin is necessary for transcription to occur. How this loosening takes place is not known, although it is recognized that histones act as blocking agents and inhibitors of RNA synthesis from DNA templates (68). The relative constancy among diverse cell types and among different physiological states nevertheless makes it unlikely that histones are specific regulators of gene expression. The acidic nonhistones of chromatin are more likely candidates for the regulatory role. They are highly heterogeneous in molecular weight, show tissue specificity, bind preferentially to homologous DNA, and stimulate the transcription by RNA polymerase of isolated DNA or chromatin. It is of interest that these activities of acidic proteins can be altered by phosphorylation. The extent of nuclear nonhistone protein phosphorylation could be related to the transcriptional activity of various tissues (13), including hearts of hyperthyroid rats (44). The elevated synthesis of RNA in hearts of animals treated with thyroid hormone seems to correlate with the activity of cyclic-AMP–dependent nuclear protein kinase.

Kun et al (43) have suggested another covalent modification of chromatin proteins that might be involved in regulation. They postulate that ADP-ribose, which can be liberated enzymatically from chromatin-bound poly-(ADP-ribose), may form a Schiff base with the ϵ-amino group of lysine residues of proteins, and may consequently alter DNA transcription. It is of particular interest that polyamines, which are present in elevated amounts in growing organs, have been shown to serve as a trap for aldehydes and might thus prevent chromatin modification by the degradation product of poly(ADP-ribose).

Besides changes in template activity, control of transcription could also involve modulation of the activity of RNA polymerase. Several types of RNA polymerase have been separated (see 7). The most abundant are the nucleolar polymerase, which synthesizes ribosome-like RNA (polymerase I), and the polymerase associated with chromatin (polymerase II), which is involved in the synthesis of RNA having a base composition similar to that of DNA, presumably messenger RNA. Activities of these two types are distinguished by preferential inhibition of polymerase II by a by-cyclic octapeptide, α-amanitin. Other enzymatic activities have been reported, such as α-amanitin-insensitive polymerase III, which is present in the nucleoplasm.

Studies of transcriptional control in heart are hampered by tissue heterogeneity, since nearly two thirds of the total nuclei in heart belong to nonmuscle cells (see 81). The time sequence and the intensity of response to a growth stimulus, such as hemodynamic overload, vary according to the cell type.

One of the best-documented and most striking changes in the enlarging myocardium is an increased synthesis of RNA, which can be demonstrated by labeling experiments several hours after imposition of a work-overload (57). The activity of DNA-dependent RNA polymerase in nuclei isolated from unfractionated hypertrophic myocardium rises rapidly after aortic constriction, and a peak value is reached on the second postoperative day (see 57). The main increase occurs in the activity of ribosomal RNA polymerase. This change is preceded by increased template activity of cardiac chromatin (27).

Techniques have been developed recently for the separation of nuclei of muscle and of nonmuscle cells (18, 20). In hypertrophied heart the activity of polymerases II and III increased in nuclei of both cell populations while the activity of polymerase I, which showed the greatest change, occurred only in the muscle-cell nuclei. Assays of polymerase activity in the presence of ammonium sulfate of high molarity provide a measure of total RNA polymerase activity that is independent of chromatin activity. Molar ammonium sulfate removes most of the chromosomal proteins, allowing the endogenous DNA template to be fully utilized. Using this technique, it has been concluded that the observed changes in developing hypertrophy represent an increase either in the activity or in the amount of RNA polymerase. Of interest, however, is the observation that the elevation of polymerase activity lags behind the increase in RNA synthesis. Changes in chromatin activity may account for the early rise in RNA synthesis, while an increase in the activity or amount of polymerase takes place later during the development of hypertrophy (20).

Very little is known about factors that affect the activity of RNA polymerase. It is of interest, however, that polyamines have the ability in vitro to stimulate nuclear RNA polymerase (11) and labeling of proteins with amino acids (30). The polyamine levels are elevated early in the development of cardiac hypertrophy (10, 62), and the activity of ornithin decarboxylase, a key enzyme in the biosynthetic pathway of spermine and spermidine, has been found to be elevated two hours after left ventricular pressure-overload (40, 47).

A rigorous demonstration of preferential synthesis of messenger RNA in cardiac hypertrophy is still elusive. Analysis of newly synthesized, pulse-labeled RNA by sucrose density-gradient centrifugation has revealed equal incorporation of label into ribosomal RNA and tRNA, with no evidence of the presence of messenger RNA with high specific radioactivity (57). These results are supported by the demonstration that the rates of tracer incorporation into RNA containing or lacking poly(A) segments are the same (74). Very early after aortic constriction, however, the activity of polymerase II is increased to a moderately greater extent than polymerase I (36). Also, Meerson et al (80) have recently reported that the proportion of heavy polysomes increases in developing hypertrophy. A conclusive answer concerning changes of messenger RNA concentration in hypertrophy, however, still awaits the development of techniques that allow quantitation of specific mRNAs. Messenger RNA for myosin heavy chain has been isolated from embryonic chick muscle (e.g. 63) but not yet from mammalian heart, in part because of technical difficulties in obtaining intact heavy polysomes from differentiated heart muscle. When perfected, the use of cDNAs to measure the concentration of specific mRNA sequences may become extremely valuable in assaying the contributions of transcriptional and translational controls to the increase in protein synthesis during developing hypertrophy.

Another level at which gene expression may be regulated involves processes that alter the activity of mRNA (post-transcriptional control) (e.g. 8). Three regulatory sites can be envisioned: (a) transport of mRNA from the nucleus to the cytoplasm; (b) post-transcriptional processing of the mRNA molecule, such as methylation of the 5' end of RNA or addition of poly(A) to the 3' end; or (c) modulation of functional levels of mRNA. The importance of post-transcriptional control, at least during the development of skeletal muscle, is indicated by the demonstration that the mRNA sequence for myosin heavy chain is present in the myoblast prior to active myosin synthesis in association with RNP particles (9, 34). At this time, only one study of possible post-transcriptional control in myocardium is available. In perfused hearts of reserpine-treated rabbits, the administration of norepinephrine resulted in enhanced activity of cytoplasmic Mn^{2+}-stimulated polyadenylate activity (12).

CONTROL OF TRANSLATION

The translation of mRNA is a highly complex process, and consequently a large variety of regulatory mechanisms are operative, including: (a) modulation of the interaction of ribosomes with mRNA and aminoacyl-tRNA, which requires several protein factors; (b) changes in the activity of peptidyl transferase and in the extent of tRNA charging with available amino acids, including the activity of aminoacyl-tRNA synthetase and the availability of energy; and (c) modification of the functional state of ribosomal subunits.

Information concerning translational control in cardiac hypertrophy is only fragmentary. In skeletal muscle, aminoacyl-tRNA synthetase activity has been found to fluctuate according to the rates of protein synthesis (55). In developing cardiac hypertrophy, in contrast, the activity of synthetase remains unaltered (28, 29). It is possible, however, that certain amino acids might be limiting since the enzymatic activities of synthetase with respect to different amino acids vary considerably (29).

Initiation and elongation processes have been evaluated mostly by analaysis of distribution of ribosomal classes. The proportion of polysomes, monoribosomes, and ribosomal subunits depends on the state and activity of the protein-synthesizing machinery. For example, a decreased rate of protein synthesis, coupled with a decreased proportion of polysomes and increased fraction of subunits, indicates decreased initiation. By such analyses, the action of anabolic hormones has been shown to enhance the initiation of polypeptide formation in skeletal muscle (70). Similarly, in perfused heart, increased pressure-load is accompanied by accelerated peptide-chain initiation (35).

Initiation factors appear to be involved in the selection of mRNA for translation. Thus a subfraction of initiation factor IF_3 has been obtained that is required for translation of myosin mRNA in cell-free system (33). In addition, a new class of RNA called tcRNA (for translational control) has been isolated from IF_3 (41). The tcRNA appears to be capable of discriminating against the translation of heterologous mRNA (e.g. globin synthesis by the reticulocyte-cell-free system is inhibited by muscle-derived tcRNA).

PROTEIN TURNOVER AND CARDIAC HYPERTROPHY

It has been established during the last several years that all intracellular proteins turn over with half-lives varying from a few minutes to several days or weeks (60, 82). Since turnover involves continuous degradation and resynthesis, the rate at which the level of a given protein changes is determined by the balance of rates of synthesis and degradation. For example, in developing hypertrophy the rate of synthesis is the sum of two processes: (a) protein synthesis balanced by protein degradation in the turnover process, and (b) synthesis of protein in excess of degradation, which leads to cardiac enlargement. Similarly, in regression of hypertrophy, the rate of degradation includes degradation balanced by resynthesis in the turnover process, plus degradation in excess of resynthesis. In both cases, the transition to the new steady state may be accomplished while the rate of protein turnover either remains unchanged or is increased or decreased compared to the steady state in the heart before the imposition of hemodynamic overload.

Studies of protein turnover in heart, as well as in other organs, are frustrated by technical problems, mostly related to the absence of precursors that would allow pulse-labeling of intracellular proteins. Amino acids are recycled, and the extent of recycling depends on the physiological state of the animal. Moreover, equilibria between various compartments of precursor amino acids are very complex, and as a result the specific radioactivity of the immediate protein precursor, the aminoacyl-tRNA, differs from that of free amino acid in the intracellular compartment (46, 48). Available studies of protein synthesis in hypertrophic heart do not allow unequivocal interpretation. However, published data based on analyses of the specific radio-activities of intracellular free amino acids, rather than on measurements of aminoacyl-tRNA, indicate a rather modest increase in the rate of amino acid incorporation into total protein (24) and into myosin (52, 67) of the overloaded heart in vivo. Similarly, acute pressure-overload in the perfused heart leads to elevated labeling of myocardial proteins (37). The increased amino acid incorporation is unrelated to enhanced coronary flow, as was shown using the elegant perfusion systems of Schreiber et al (64).

Measurements of protein degradation are subject to similar technical difficulties. Use of a nonreutilizatable precursor of heme, however, indicates that degradation of cytochrome c decreases considerably during the first 24 hours of pressure-overload (58). In contrast, the rate of myosin degradation, which was calculated by comparing the amount of myosin in the enlarged heart with the increased rate of its synthesis, was found to increase in developing hypertrophy (52).

In regard to the activities of proteases involved in cardiac hypertrophy, only cathepsin D has been studied. The data are contradictory. Some studies indicate no correlation between cathepsin D activity and the change in protein breakdown, either during development or regression of pressure-induced hypertrophy (79), or in hormone-induced hypertrophy (78). In one study, however, an increased latency of cathepsin D was found within the first two days of pressure-overload (37).

CONSEQUENCES OF CARDIAC HYPERTROPHY— CHANGES IN HEART STRUCTURE AND FUNCTION

Cell Proliferation

Activation of biosynthetic processes in myocardium that has been subjected to a sustained hemodynamic overload eventually results in cardiac enlargement. The most recent studies of the cellular features of cardiac growth, reviewed by Rumyantsev (61), are consistent with previous observations. DNA synthesis and the consequent mitotic activity of cardiac myocytes continuously decline after birth and eventually cease altogether, at about 3–4 weeks of age in the rat. However, not every nuclear division results in cell proliferation since cells with more than one nucleus increase in number after birth (32, 39). The decline in mitotic activity is correlated in time with the loss of activities both of DNA polymerase (14, 17, 23) and of thymidine kinase (14). The measurements of enzymatic activities reported so far, however, have only a limited value since no distinction has been made between the nuclei of muscle and of nonmuscle cells. The control of DNA synthesis is quite different in the two cell populations. While the mitotic activity declines with age in both cell types, the rate of decline is much smaller in nonmuscle cells and, in contrast to myocytes, the repression of DNA synthesis is readily reversed by a variety of growth stimuli (see 81). Recently, however a procedure has been developed that allows separation of the nuclei of muscle and nonmuscle cells (18); the problems of regulation of DNA synthesis can thus be reexamined in a more rigorous way.

Very little is know about the factors regulating DNA replication. ADP-ribosylation of chromosomal proteins has been suggested in studies of a variety of differentiating cells as one possible regulatory factor. For example, in mixed nuclei isolated from heart, Claycomb (16) has detected an increase in the activity of poly(ADP-ribose) synthetase, with cell differentiation that seems inversely related to the rate of DNA synthesis. Unfortunately, these results are difficult to interpret quantitatively, since the concentration of NAD^+ used in the assay system was much lower than the K_m determined for this enzyme in rat tissues (25). Appearance of functional adrenergic innervation was also implicated in the control of DNA replication, with noradrenaline and cyclic AMP as the chemical mediators (15).

In animal studies the imposition of work-overload produces a cellular response that depends on age and on the state of DNA synthesis. Overloading in the neonatal period results in an increased labeling with ^{3}H-thymidine of nuclei in both muscle and nonmuscle cells (22, 75). In contrast, similar interventions in the adult result in labeling of the nuclei of connective cells only (6, 22).

Radioautographic procedures for measurements of cell proliferation have been supplemented recently with procedures for estimating changes in the cellular volume during cardiac growth. Radioautographic studies have several limitations: DNA synthesis does not necessarily indicate either cell division (see the discussion above of increased number of nuclei per cell) or nuclear division (e.g. endoreplication of DNA resulting in nuclei having more than two sets of chromosomes might contribute to nuclear labeling). Estimates of the total number of cells prior to and after growth stimulus thus may be a more direct approach. Unfortunately, the available procedures are not entirely satisfactory. However several promising new techniques have recently been applied to this century-old problem. By the use of the point-counting technique, the volume of heart occupied by myocytes can be determined in histological sections (56). Three different methods have been used recently to calculate the total number of muscle cells in the myocardium. In the first method, the two dimensions of myocytes have been measured after their separation by enzyme treatment (42). In the second, the cell diameter has been measured in histological sections and the volume calculated from the assumed length-width ratio (59). In the third method the cell width has been determined stereologically and the cell length defined in units of sarcomeres (69). The main advantage of the third method is its independence of the contractile state of myofibrils.

The application of the first method (42) to cardiac hypertrophy corroborates the radioautographic evidence that in adult rat myocardial growth can be explained by enlargement of existing myocytes.

Recently studies of human autopsy material lends support to previous observations indicating essential differences between primates and other experimental animals. The appearance of polyploid nuclei is prominent in primates; the age of sequence of DNA endoreplication has been delineated in detail, and the times of onset thus indicated are 7 and 12 years of age in normally growing left and right ventricles, respectively (1). Moreover, the cytometric study of Astori et al (3), using sterological techniques, lends support to Linzbach's classical observation (see 81) that there is a critical weight during progressing cardiac enlargment at which cellular hypertrophy is supplemented by addition of new muscle cells. The analysis of the frequency distribution of cell diameters and lengths is consistent with longitudinal splitting of a certain cellular population.

Changes in Cardiac Ultrastructure

Recent data (2, 3, 54) are consistent with previous observations (see 58) that the volume of mitochondria relative to cell volume increases within the first day of pressure-overload and progressively decreases later on. The relationships between plasma membrane and cell volume, as well as between sarcotubular membrane area and myofibrillar volume, remain constant in left ventricular hypertrophy caused by aortic constriction (53) and by administration of thyroxine (53).

Changes in Myosin ATPase

Correlation of depressed contractility following hemodynamic overload with changes in enzymatic properties of cardiac myosin continues to be actively investigated. Despite considerable improvement in the purity of isolated myofibrillar and myosin preparations, recent results, reviewed by Swynghedauw et al (71), are still contradictory. The major disagreement concerns the Ca^{2+}-stimulated and (K^+)-EDTA-stimulated ATPase of purified myosin, which was found to increase in dogs three weeks after pulmonary constriction by one group of investigators (76), but to decrease when another group used the rabbit as the experimental animal (65, 72). Changes in right ventricular (RV) systolic pressure and increases in cardiac weight were found to be comparable by both groups. In chronically overloaded myocardium, most investigators agree that myosin ATPase is reduced (50, 71, 76, 77).

From our current knowledge of myosin structure and function, we can postulate that the alteration in ATPase activity of myosin isolated from hypertrophic heart may be related to changes in either the molecular species or relative amounts of individual myosin light chains, to the synthesis of another type of myosin heavy chain, or to changes in the reactivity of sulfhydryl residues, SH_1 or SH_2.

No change in the relative content of light chains has been found in myosin when its ATPase activity was reduced (38, 72), while their content was altered in myosin with elevated ATPase (49, 76). Thyrotoxicosis, however, was found to result in elevated ATPase activity with no change in light-chain content (4). The role of sulfhydryl residues in the regulation of the ATPase activity of myosin has been studied by Alpert et al (65, 72). Analysis of ATPase activity after chemical modification of myosin gave results consistent with conformational change in the vicinity of the fast-reacting SH_1 group of myosin isolated from hypertrophic heart. Since the most likely explanation for altered conformation of the SH_1 moiety is an amino acid substitution, the results were interpreted as evidence for the appearance of a new cardiac isozyme of myosin.

Studies of myosin isolated from hearts of thyrotoxic animals (4, 5, 26) lend further support to the belief that synthesis of a new species of myosin heavy chains may occur in enlarged heart. These results agree with the conclusion of Alpert (65, 72) that the region near SH_1 residues is important for the observed effects of thyroxine. Moreover, the electrophoreograms of cyanobromide (CNBr) digests indicate a substitution of methionine residues in thyrotoxic animals (26), substantiating the previous claim of altered primary structure of myosin produced by thyroxine treatment (73).

CONCLUSION

Despite continuous interest in cardiac hypertrophy, our knowledge of its molecular aspects is still elementary. Recently, however, several advancements of particular interest have been made: (*a*) Nuclei of muscle and nonmuscle cells have been separated, allowing for the first time the study of nuclear activity in specified cells (18). (*b*) Cardiac growth induced by pressure-overload (72) or by hormone treatment (26) has been shown to lead to myosin of altered ATPase, and strong evidence suggests that new species of myosin molecules thus appear. (*c*) The basis for assessment of protein synthesis and degradation has been established (46, 48). (*d*) Methods are being developed to supplement radioautography in evaluating cell proliferation (42, 59, 69). (*e*) In spontaneously hypertensive rats it has been shown that blood pressure might not be the sole factor responsible for cardiac enlargement, but that hypertrophy can be the result of genetic cardiovascular abnormality (19, 66). (*f*) A hypothesis relating the extent of energy utilization to the nuclear activity via NAD^+ metabolism has been proposed, which allows for experimental verification (43).

ACKNOWLEDGMENTS

This work was supported in part by U.S. Public Health Service Grants HL09172, HL04442, HL16637, and 1–P17–HL17648 (Specialized Center of Research in Ischemic Heart Disease), and by grants from the National Heart and Lung Institute, from the Muscular Dystrophy Association of America, from the Chicago and Illinois Heart Association, and from the Louis Block Fund of The University of Chicago.

Literature Cited

1. Adler, C.-P. 1976. DNA in growing hearts of children. Biochemical and cytophotometric investigations. *Beitr. Pathol.* 158:173–202
2. Anversa, P., Loud, A. V., Vitali-Massa, L. 1976. Morphometry and autoradiography of early hypertrophic changes in the ventricular myocardium of adult rat: an electron microscopic study. *Lab. Invest.* 35:475–83
3. Astorri, E., Bolognesi, R., Colla, B., Chizzola, A., Visioli, O. 1977. Left ventricular hypertrophy: a cytometric study on 42 human hearts. *J. Mol. Cell. Cardiol.* 9:763–75
4. Banerjee, S. K., Kabbas, E. G., Morkin, E. 1977. Enzymatic properties of the heavy meromyosin subfragment of cardiac myosin from normal and thyrotoxic rabbit. *J. Biol. Chem.* 252:6925–29
5. Banerjee, S. K., Morkin, E. 1977. Actin-activated adenosine triphosphatase activity of native and N-ethylmaleimide-modified cardiac myosin from normal and thyrotoxic rabbits. *Circ. Res.* 41:630–34

6. Bishop, S. P., Melsen, L. R. 1976. Myocardial necrosis, fibrosis, and DNA synthesis in experimental cardiac hypertrophy induced by sudden pressure overload. *Clin. Res.* 39:238–45
7. Biswas, B. B., Ganguly, A., Das, A. 1975. Eukaryotic RNA polymerases and the factors that control them. *Prog. Nucl. Acid. Res. Mol. Biol.* 15:145–84
8. Both, G. W., Banerjee, A. K., Shatkin, A. J. 1975. Methylation-dependent translation of viral messenger RNAs *in vitro. Proc. Natl. Acad. Sci. USA* 72:1189–93
9. Buckingham, M. E., Cohen, A., Gros, F. 1976. Cytoplasmic distribution of pulse labelled poly(A)-containing RNA, particularly 26S RNA, during myoblast growth and differentiation. *J. Mol. Biol.* 103:611–26
10. Caldarera, C. M., Orlandini, G., Casti, A., Moruzzi, G. 1974. Polyamines and nucleic acid metabolism in myocardial hypertrophy of the overloaded heart. *J. Mol. Cell. Cardiol.* 6:95–103
11. Caldarera, C. M., Casti, A., Guanieri, C., Moruzzi, G. 1975. Regulation of

550   ZAK & RABINOWITZ

ribonucleic acid synthesis by polyamines. *Biochem. J.* 152:91–98
12. Casti, A., Corti, A., Reali, N., Nezzetti, G., Orlandini, G., Caldarera, C. M. 1977. Modification of major aspects of myocardial ribonucleic acid metabolism as a response to noradrenaline. Behaviour of polyadenylate polymerase and ribonucleic acid polymerase, acetylation of histones and rat of synthesis of polyamines. *Biochem. J.* 168:333–40
13. Chiu, J.-F., Brade, W. P., Thomson, J., Tsai, Y.-H., Hnilica, L. S. 1975. Nonhistone protein phosphorylation in normal and neoplastic rat liver chromatin. *Exp. Cell Res.* 91:200–6
14. Claycomb, W. C. 1975. Biochemical aspects of cardiac muscle differentiation. Deoxyribonucleic acid synthesis and nuclear cytoplasmic deoxyribonucleic acid polymerase activity. *J. Biol. Chem.* 250:3229–35
15. Claycomb, W. C. 1976. Biochemical aspects of cardiac muscle differentiation. Possible control of deoxyribonucleic acid synthesis and cell differentiation by adrenergic innervation and cyclic adenosine 3',5'-monophosphate. *J. Biol. Chem.* 251:6082–89
16. Claycomb, W. C. 1976. Poly (adenosine diphosphate ribose) polymerase activity and nicotonamide adenine dinucleotide in differentiating cardiac muscle. *Biochem. J.* 154:387–93
17. Claycomb, W. C. 1977. DNA synthetic activity of nuclei isolated from differentiating cardiac muscle and association of DNA polymerase with the outer nuclear membrane. *Devel. Biol.* 61:245–51
18. Cutilletta, A. F., Aumont, M.-C., Nag, A. C., Zak, R. 1977. Separation of muscle and non-muscle cells from adult rat myocardium: an application to the study of RNA polymerase. *J. Mol. Cell. Cardiol.* 9:399–407
19. Cutilletta, A. F., Erinoff, L., Heller, A., Low, J., Oparil, S. 1977. Development of left ventricular hypertrophy in young spontaneously hypertensive rats after peripheral sympathectomy. *Circ. Res.* 40:428–34
20. Cutilletta, A. F., Rudnik, M., Zak, R. 1978. Muscle and non-muscle cell RNA polymerase activity during the development of myocardial hypertrophy. *J. Mol. Cell. Cardiol.* 10:677–87
21. Davidson, E. H., Klein, W. H., Britten, R. J. 1977. Sequence organization in animal DNA and a speculation on hnRNA as a coordinate regulatory transcript. *Devel. Biol.* 55:69–84

22. Dowell, R. T., McManus, R. E. 1978. Pressure-induced cardiac enlargement in neonatal and adult rats: left ventricular functional characteristics and evidence of cardiac muscle cell proliferation in the neonate. *Circ. Res.* 42:303–10
23. Doyle, C. M., Zak, R., Fischman, D. A. 1974. The correlation of DNA synthesis and DNA polymerase activity in the developing chick heart. *Devel. Biol.* 37:133–45
24. Everett, A. W., Taylor, R. R., Sparrow, M. P. 1977. Protein synthesis during right-ventricular hypertrophy after pulmonary-artery stenosis in the dog. *Biochem. J.* 166:315–21
25. Ferro, A. M., Kun, E. 1976. Macromolecular derivatives of NAD$^+$ in heart nuclei: poly(adenosine diphosphoribose) and adenosine diphosphoribose proteins. *Biochem. Biophys. Res. Commun.* 71:150–54
26. Flink, I. L., Morkin, E. 1977. Evidence for a new cardiac myosin species in thyrotoxic rabbit. *FEBS Lett.* 81:391–94
27. Florini, J. R., Dankberg, F. L. 1971. Changes in ribonucleic acid and protein synthesis during induced cardiac hypertrophy. *Biochemistry* 10:530–35
28. Gibson, K., Harris, P. 1972. Effect of hypobaric oxygenation, hypertrophy and diet on some myocardial cytoplasmic factors concerned with protein synthesis. *J. Mol. Cell. Cardiol.* 4:651–60
29. Gibson, K., Harris, P. 1973. Aminoacyl-tRNA synthestase activities specific to twenty amino acids in rat, rabbit and human myocardium. *J. Mol. Cell. Cardiol.* 5:419–25
30. Gibson, R., Harris, P. 1974. The *in vitro* and *in vivo* effects of polyamines on cardiac protein biosynthesis. *Cardiovasc. Res.* 8:668–73
31. Gilbert, W. 1978. Why genes in pieces? *Nature* 271:501
32. Grabner, W., Pfitzer, P. 1974. Number of nuclei in isolated myocardial cells in pigs. *Virchow's Arch. B. Cell. Pathol.* 15:279–94
33. Heywood, S. M., Kennedy, D. S., Bester, A. J. 1974. Separation of specific initiation factors involved in the translation of myosin and myoglobin messenger RNAs and the isolation of a new RNA involved in translation. *Proc. Natl. Acad. Sci. USA* 71:2428–31
34. Heywood, S. M., Kennedy, D. S., Bester, A. J. 1975. Stored myosin messenger in embryonic chick muscle. *FEBS Lett.* 53:69–72

35. Hjalmarson, A., Isaksson, O. 1972. *In vitro* work load and rat heart metabolism. III. Effect on ribosomal aggregation. *Acta Physiol. Scand.* 86:342–52

36. Kako, K. J., Varnai, K., Beznak, M. 1972. RNA synthesis and RNA content of nuclei prepared from hearts during hypertrophy. *Cardiovasc. Res.* 6:57–66

37. Kao, R., Rannels, D. E., Whitman, V., Morgan, H. E. 1978. In *Recent Advances in Studies on Cardiac Growth and Metabolism*, ed. T. Kobayashi, I. Ito, G. Rona, 12:105–13 Baltimore: University Park Press

38. Katagiri, R., Morkin, E. 1974. Studies on the substructure of myosin in cardiac hypertrophy; characterization of light chains. *Biochim. Biophys. Acta* 342: 262–74

39. Katzberg, A. A., Farmer, B. B., Harris, R. A. 1977. Predominance of binucleation in isolated rat heart myocytes. *Am. J. Anat.* 149:489–500

40. Krelhaus, W., Gibson, K. I., Harris, P. 1975. The effects of hypertrophy, hypobaric conditions, and diet on myocardial ornithine decarboxylase activity. *J. Mol. Cell. Cardiol.* 7:63–69

41. Kennedy, D. S., Bester, A. J., Heywood, S. M. 1974. The regulation of protein synthesis by translation control RNA. *Biochem. Biophys. Res. Commun.* 61:415–23

42. Korecky, B., Rakusan, K. 1978. Normal and hypertrophic growth of the rat heart: changes in cell dimensions and number. *Am. J. Physiol.* 234:H123–28

43. Kun, E., Chang, A. C. Y., Sharma, M. L., Ferro, A. M., Nitecki, D. 1976. Covalent modification of proteins by metabolites of NAD⁺. *Proc. Natl. Acad. Sci. USA* 73:3131–35

44. Limas, C. J., Chan-Stier, C. 1978. Myocardial chromatin activation in experimental hyperthyroidism in rats: role of nuclear non-histone proteins. *Circ. Res.* 42:311–36

45. Liao, S. 1975. Cellular receptors and mechanism of action of steroid hormones. *Int. Rev. Cytol.* 41:87–172

46. Martin, A. F., Rabinowitz, M., Blough, R., Prior, G., Zak, R. 1977. Measurement of half-life of rat cardiac myosin heavy chain with leucyl-tRNA used as precursor pool. *J. Biol. Chem.* 252: 3422–29

47. Matsushita, S., Sogani, R. K., Raben, M. S. 1972. Ornithin decarboxylase in cardiac hypertrophy in the rat. *Circ. Res.* 31:699–709

48. McKee, E. E., Cheung, J. Y., Rannels, D. E., Morgan, H. E. 1978. Measure-

ment of the rate of protein synthesis and compartmentation of heart phenylalanine. *J. Biol. Chem.* 253:1030–38

49. Medugorac, I., Kammereit, A., Jacob, R. 1975. Influence of long-term swimming training on the structure and enzyme activity of myosin in rat myocardium. *Hoppe-Seyler's Z. Physiol. Chem.* 356:1161–71

50. Medugorac, I., Jacob, R. 1976. Concentration and adenosine triphosphatase activity of left ventricular actomyosin in Goldblatt rats during the compensatory stage of hypertrophy. *Hoppe-Seyler's Z. Physiol. Chem.* 357:1495–1503

51. Meerson, F. Z. 1975. Role of synthesis of nucleic acids and protein in adaptation to the external environment. *Physiol. Rev.* 55:79–123

52. Morkin, E., Kimata, S., Skillman, J. J. 1972. Myosin synthesis and degradation during development of cardiac hypertrophy in the rabbit. *Circ. Res.* 30:690–702

53. Page, E., McCallister, L. P. 1973. Quantitative electron microscopic description of heart muscle cells: application to normal, hypertrophied, and thyroxin-stimulated hearts. *Am. J. Cardiol.* 31:172–81

54. Page, E., Oparil, S. 1978. Effect of peripheral sympathectomy on left ventricular ultrastructure in young spontaneously hypertensive rats. *J. Mol. Cell. Cardiol.* 10:301–5

55. Pain, V. M. 1973. Influence of streptozotocin diabetes on the ability of muscle cell sap to support protein synthesis by ribosomes in cell free systems. *Biochim. Biophys. Acta* 308:180–87

56. Polimeni, P. I. 1974. Extracellular space and ionic distribution in rat ventricle. *Am. J. Physiol.* 227:676–83

57. Rabinowitz, M., Zak, R. 1972. Biochemical and cellular changes in cardiac hypertrophy. *Ann. Rev. Med.* 23:245–61

58. Rabinowitz, M., Zak, R. 1975. Mitochondria and cardiac hypertrophy. *Circ. Res.* 36:367–76

59. Rakusan, K., Raman, S., Layberry, R., Korecky, B. 1978. The influence of aging and growth on the postnatal development of cardiac muscle in rats. *Circ. Res.* 42:213–17

60. Rechcigl, M. 1971. In *Enzyme Synthesis and Degradation in Mammalian Systems*, ed. M. Rechcigl, pp. 236–310. Baltimore: University Park Press

61. Rumyantsev, P. P. 1977. Interrelations of the proliferation and differentiation processes during cardiac myogenesis

and regeneration. *Int. Rev. Cytol.* 51: 187–273

62. Russel, D. N., Shiverick, K. T., Hamrell, B. B., Alpert, N. R. 1971. Polyamine synthesis during initial phases of stress-induced cardiac hypertrophy. *Am. J. Physiol.* 221:1287–91

63. Sarkar, S., Mukherjee, S. P. 1973. Isolation of messenger ribonucleic acid for myosin heavy chain. *Prep. Biochem.* 3:583–604

64. Schreiber, S. S., Rothschild, M. A., Evans, C., Reff, F., Oratz, M. 1975. The effect of pressure or flow stress on right ventricular protein synthesis in the face of constant and restricted coronary perfusion. *J. Clin. Invest.* 55:1–11

65. Shiverick, K. T., Hamrell, B. B., Alpert, N. R. 1976. Structural and functional properties of myosin associated with the compensatory cardiac hypertrophy in the rabbit. *J. Mol. Cell. Cardiol.* 8:837–851

66. Sen, S., Tarazi, R. C., Bumpus, M. F. 1976. Biochemical changes associated with development and reversal of cardiac hypertrophy in spontaneously hypertensive rats. *Cardiovasc. Res.* 10: 254–62

67. Skosey, J. L., Zak, R., Aschenbrenner, V., Rabinowitz, M. 1972. Biochemical correlates of cardiac hypertrophy. V. Labelling of collagen, myosin and nuclear DNA during experimental myocardial hypertrophy in the rat. *Circ. Res.* 31:145–57

68. Stein, G., Spelsberg, T. C., Kleinsmith, L. J. 1974. Nonhistone chromosomal proteins and gene regulation. *Science* 183:817–24

69. Steward, J., Page, E. 1978. Improved stereological techniques for studying myocardial cell growth: application to external sarcolemma, T-system, and intercalated disks of rabbit and rat hearts. *J. Ultrastruct. Res.* In press

70. Stirewalt, W. S., Wool, I. G., Cavicchi, P. 1967. The relation of RNA and protein synthesis to the sedimentation of muscle ribosomes: effect of diabetes and insulin. *Proc. Natl. Acad. Sci. USA* 57:1885–92

71. Swynghedauw, B., Leger, J. J., Schwartz, K. 1976. The myosin isozyme hypothesis in chronic heart overloading. *J. Mol. Cell. Cardiol.* 8:915–24

72. Thomas, L. L., Alpert, N. R. 1977. Functional integrity of the SH₁ site in myosin from hypertrophied myocardium. *Biochim. Biophys. Acta* 481: 680–88

73. Thyrum, P. T., Kritcher, E. M., Luci, R. J. 1970. Effect of L-thyroxine on the primary structure of cardiac myosin. *Biochim. Biophys. Acta* 197:335–36

74. Turto, H. 1977. Experimental cardiac hypertrophy and the synthesis of poly(A)-containing RNA of myocardial proteins in the heart: the effect of digitoxin treatment. *Acta Physiol. Scand.* 101:114–54

75. Wachtlova, M., Mares, V., Ostadal, B. 1977. DNA synthesis in the ventricular myocardium of young rats exposed to intermittent high altitude hypoxia. *Virchow's Arch. B. Cell Pathol.* 24:335–42

76. Wilkman-Coffelt, J., Fenner, C., McPherson, J., Zelis, R., Mason, D. T. 1975. Alterations of subunit composition and ATPase activity of myosin in early hypertrophied right ventricles of dogs with mild experimental pulmonic stenosis. *J. Mol. Cell. Cardiol.* 7:513–22

77. Wikman-Coffelt, J., Walsh, R., Fenner, C., Kamiyama, T., Salel, A., Mason, D. T. 1976. Effects of severe hemodynamic pressure overload on the properties of canine left ventricular myosin: mechanism by which myosin ATPase activity is lowered during chronic increased hemodynamic stress. *J. Mol. Cell. Cardiol.* 8:263–70

78. Wildenthal, K., Mueller, E. A. 1974. Increased myocardial cathepsin D activity during regression of thyrotoxic cardiac hypertrophy. *Nature* 249: 478–79

79. Wildenthal, K., Mueller, E. A. 1977. Lysosomal enzymes in the development and regression of myocardial hypertrophy induced by systemic hypertension. *J. Mol. Cell. Cardiol.* 9:121–30

80. Yavich, M. P., Lerman, M. I., Meerson, F. Z. 1976. Incorporation *in vitro* of labeled amino acids into myocardial ribosomes in early and late stages of compensatory hyperfunctioning of heart. *Biokhimiya* 41:2110–18

81. Zak, R. 1974. Development and proliferative capacity of cardiac muscle cells. *Circ. Res.* 34 & 35:(Suppl. II) 11–17

82. Zak, R., Martin, A. F., Prior, G., Rabinowitz, M. 1977. Comparison of turnover of several myofibrillar proteins and critical evaluation of double isotope method. *J. Biol. Chem.* 252:3430–35

ENDOCRINOLOGY AND METABOLISM

Introduction

In line with the new policy of in-depth coverage of relatively restricted areas of rapid progress, we chose to review two topics for the current volume: hypophysiotropic hormones of the hypothalamus, and the physiological significance of the prostaglandins.

Hypothalamic control over the anterior pituitary is now recognized to be exerted by a family of neurohormones termed "releasing and inhibiting hormones." At least three of these have been isolated; their structures have been determined, and synthetic products have been made available for widespread use. These dramatic achievements were recognized by the award of the Nobel Prize in October 1977 to Drs. Guillemin and Schally. It is well established that these neurohormones are released in the external layer of the median eminence into the capillaries of the hypophyseal portal system of veins, which carry them to the hypophyseal sinusoids where they exert their action on particular pituitary cells. There they rapidly increase or decrease release of the hormone in question. It was originally thought that each of these hormones would affect only a single pituitary cell, but it is now clear that in some instances more than one cell type can be affected. Thyrotropin releasing hormone (TRH) can increase release not only of TSH but also of prolactin. LHRH augments FSH as well as LH release, and somatostatin appears to have widespread inhibitory effects not only on growth hormone release but also on TSH and prolactin release, and on release of other hormones such as insulin, glucagon, and gastrin. The chapters that follow consider most aspects of the physiology of these new hormones. Fernand Labrie et al discuss the mechanism of action of the peptides on the pituitary, including aspects of feedback by target gland hormones. The details of the complex feedback actions of target hormones, particularly gonadal steroids, on hypothalamus and pituitary are considered by George Fink. The localization of the hypophysiotropic peptides has been facilitated by new advances in immunohistochemistry, and it has also become apparent that a number of other biologically active peptides are found within the brain. Elde & Hökfelt assemble information that provides a clear view of the widespread distribution of these peptides in neurons within the brain. Possible roles in other CNS functions as well as in pituitary control are immediately suggested by these distributions. Knowledge of the localization of the hypophysiotropic peptides leads naturally to consideration of putative synaptic transmitters that may control the release of the hypophysiotropic hormones. This subject is discussed by Lad Krulich. Also following naturally from the wide distribution of these peptides in the brain is the consideration that the hypophysiotropic hormones may indeed act on the brain—for example to induce sexual behavior. Recent evidence concerning this new aspect is reviewed by Robert Moss.

The possible role of the prostaglandins in physiologic processes represents another area in which there has been explosive progress in the last few years. William Lands reviews the biosynthesis and metabolism of the prostaglandins in an article that provides the background for a consideration of the mechanism of action of these remarkable compounds. This topic is considered by Harris, Ramwell & Gilmer, who discuss cellular mechanisms of prostaglandin action, limiting the discussion largely to the actions on platelets. This serves as a framework for understanding the possible mechanisms of actions in other tissues and leads naturally to consideration of the role of prostaglandins in organ systems. Unfortunately, the wealth of information and the relative lack of space precluded consideration of a number of organ systems (such as the kidney) in which the prostaglandins play an active role. Only two examples of the role of prostaglandins in organ systems could be considered. The role of these powerful agents in the central nervous system is reviewed by Wolfe & Coceani, and a consideration of the current views of the complex role of the prostaglandins in reproductive processes is ably presented by Harold Behrman.

S. M. McCann
Section Editor

Ann. Rev. Physiol. 1979. 41:555–69

MECHANISM OF ACTION OF HYPOTHALAMIC HORMONES IN THE ADENOHYPOPHYSIS

♦1237

Fernand Labrie, Pierre Borgeat, Jacques Drouin,
Michèle Beaulieu, Lisette Lagacé, Louise Ferland
and Vincent Raymond

Medical Research Council Group in Molecular Endocrinology,
Le Centre Hospitalier de l'Université Laval, Quebec G1V 4G2, Canada

INTRODUCTION

The secretion of anterior pituitary hormones is under specific control by hypothalamic hormones and by the feedback action of gonadal, adrenal, and thyroid hormones. The neurohormones are released from nerve endings in the median eminence (47) and transported to their site of action by a small vascular portal system. A new era in neuroendocrinology started with the isolation, determination of structure, and synthesis of the first hypothalamic hypophysiotropic hormone, thyrotropin-releasing hormone (TRH) (7, 14). This achievement was soon followed by the isolation of LHRH, the neurohormone that stimulates the release of both LH and FSH (13, 45). More recently, somatostatin has been isolated from ovine and porcine hypothalami (12, 51).

Although important information about the role of hypothalamic hormones in the control of anterior pituitary function could be obtained using hypothalamic extracts at different stages of purification, the relative ease of synthesis of these peptides and their analogs has opened new possibilities.

Studies of hypothalamic hormones were much facilitated by another important recent development, the pituitary-cell culture system. Thus, adenohypophyseal cells in primary culture have been extremely useful, not only for assessment of biological activity of analogs of TRH, LHRH, and somatostatin (38, 39), but also for determination of the characteristics of

555

0066-4278/79/0301-0555$01.00

interaction between hypothalamic and peripheral hormones at the anterior pituitary level (20, 21, 23). Furthermore, although peripheral hormones have long been known to be important modulators of anterior pituitary hormone secretion, it has been difficult until now to distinguish between hypothalamic and pituitary sites of action by in vivo approaches.

ROLE OF CYCLIC AMP IN THE CONTROL OF ADENOHYPOPHYSEAL ACTIVITY

The first suggestive evidence for a role of adenosine 3',5'-monophosphate (cAMP) as mediator of the action of the hypothalamic regulatory hormones in the anterior pituitary gland stems from the observations that cAMP derivatives or theophylline, an inhibitor of cyclic nucleotide phosphodiesterase, stimulate the release of all six main anterior pituitary hormones (34, 42, 52). Definite proof of a role of the adenylyl cyclase system could only be obtained from measurements of adenohypophyseal adenylyl cyclase activity or cAMP concentrations under the influence of pure or synthetic neurohormones. Such evidence has now been obtained for TRH (34), LHRH (8, 9, 30), and somatostatin (10).

Addition of synthetic LHRH to rat anterior pituitary tissue in vitro leads to parallel stimulation of cAMP accumulation and LH and FSH release, both as a function of time of incubation and concentration of the decapeptide (8). Moreover, when LHRH analogs having a spectrum of biological activity ranging from 0.001–500–1000% the activity of LHRH itself were used, the same close parallelism between stimulation of cyclic AMP accumulation and both LH and FSH release was found under all experimental conditions (9). That LHRH exerts its action by activation of adenylyl cyclase, and not by inhibition of cyclic nucleotide phosphodiesterase, is indicated by the observation that a similar effect of the neurohormone is observed in the presence or absence of theophylline.

Further evidence for a role of cAMP as mediator of LHRH action was obtained with antagonists of the neurohormone. At appropriate concentrations, these analogs incubated in vitro with rat hemipituitaries lead to parallel inhibition of both LHRH-induced LH and FSH release and cAMP accumulation in anterior pituitary tissue (3).

Although the changes are of somewhat smaller magnitude, addition of TRH to anterior pituitary tissue also leads to increased intracellular levels of cAMP accompanied by increased TSH release (34). More recently it has been shown that synthetic somatostatin leads to a rapid inhibition of cAMP accumulation in anterior pituitary gland in vitro (10), this effect being accompanied by a marked inhibition of both GH and TSH release. The effect of somatostatin on the three mentioned parameters is observed under both basal and prostaglandin E_2- or theophylline-induced conditions, which suggests an inhibitory action of the peptide on adenylyl cyclase activity.

These data clearly show that two stimulatory hypothalamic hormones (TRH and LHRH) lead to parallel stimulation of cyclic AMP accumulation and specific hormone release, while one inhibitory hypothalamic peptide (somatostatin) leads to parallel inhibition of cAMP accumulation and GH and TSH release. Such findings strongly suggest that the adenylyl cyclase system is involved in the mechanism of action of these three peptides in the anterior pituitary gland.

PROPOSED MODE OF ACTION OF HYPOTHALAMIC HORMONES IN THE ANTERIOR PITUITARY GLAND

Based on the characteristics of TRH binding (17, 32), the close association between changes of pituitary cAMP levels and specific hormone release under the influence of LHRH, TRH and somatostatin (8, 9, 10, 34), the properties of adenohypophyseal adenylyl cyclase (41), cAMP-dependent protein kinase (36, 43), and phosphorylation of adenohypophyseal substrates (2, 29, 41), the mode of action schematically illustrated in Figure 1 is proposed for the three hypothalamic hormones studied so far: LHRH, TRH, and somatostatin. While TRH and LHRH lead to increased adenylate cyclase activity and stimulation of cellular activity, opposite effects are associated with somatostatin action.

MODULATION OF TRH ACTION BY PERIPHERAL HORMONES

Soon after elucidation of the structure of TRH, the tritium-labelled hormone became available for studies of its metabolism and interaction with target cells. Using plasma membranes purified from bovine anterior pituitary gland, we have found that interaction of the peptide with its receptor follows standard bimolecular reaction kinetics and has the expected specificity (32). Recent studies indicate that the tissue concentration of some peptide and steroid receptors is not static and can be influenced by a variety of hormonal agents. For example, estrogens and prolactin can increase prolactin-receptor concentrations in liver (48).

Estradiol is well known to increase PRL secretion in humans (28) and rats (17), and a stimulatory effect of this steroid has also been observed on TSH secretion in the rat (37). Since the binding of TRH to TSH- and PRL-secreting cells has been characterized (32), it was of interest to study the possible effect of estrogens and thyroid hormone on the level of pituitary

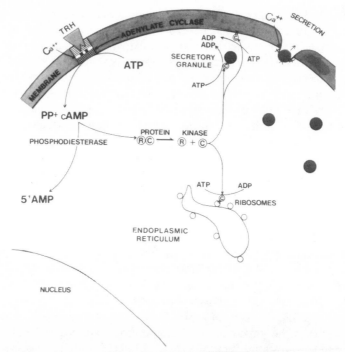

Figure 1   Schematic representation of a proposed mode of action of hypothalamic regulatory hormones in the adenohypophyseal cell. First, binding of the neurohormone to a receptor located in the plasma membrane would stimulate (LHRH or TRH) or inhibit (somatostatin) adenylate cyclase activity. Changes in intracellular cAMP levels would then modulate cAMP-dependent protein kinase activity and lead to changes of the levels of phosphorylation of different intracellular protein substrates. Increased (under the influence of TRH or LHRH) or decreased (under the influence of somatostatin) cAMP levels could then lead to changes in the activity of the various specialized processes of the corresponding adenohypophyseal cells.

TRH receptors and to correlate such modifications of the concentration of TRH receptors with changes of the TSH and PRL responses to the neuro-hormone.

Daily administration of 25 μg of estradiol benzoate to adult female rats for 9 days led to an approximately three-fold increase in the number of pituitary TRH binding sites, from 120 ± 4 to 315 ± 9 fmoles mg^{-1} protein (17). Estrogen treatment was, however, without significant effect on the TRH dissociation constant (3.6 ± 0.4 versus 4.1 ± 0.4 × 10^{-8}M).

Since thyroid hormones are potent inhibitors of the TSH response to TRH (56), we next studied the effect of thyroid hormone on TRH binding in anterior pituitary tissue. It was found that the injection of a single dose of L-thyroxine into hypothyroid animals led to a progressive decrease of the number of TRH binding sites to approximately 50% of control after 24 hr, while a further decrease to 40% of control was measured at 48 hr (17).

We next studied the effect of estrogen and thyroid hormone treatment on plasma TSH and PRL responses to exogenous TRH. Such a parameter should permit a correlation between changes of TRH receptor levels and specific cellular activity. In a large series of experiments performed in intact or castrated male and female rats (17, 18, 19), it was found that estrogens stimulated while thyroid hormone inhibited the TSH and PRL responses to TRH. Such a close correlation observed between changes of the number of TRH binding sites and TSH and PRL responses to the neurohormone indicates that the availability of TRH receptors could be a rate-limiting step in the action of TRH in both thyrotrophs and mammotrophs. The marked influence of estrogens and thyroid hormone is exerted exclusively on the number of TRH receptor sites, while the apparent affinity for the neurohormone remains unchanged.

The present evidence of a modulation of TRH receptors by estrogens and thyroid hormone may provide some explanation for the clinical observations of the inhibition of both TSH and PRL secretion by thyroxine in hypothyroid subjects (54), higher TSH response to TRH in women than in men (11), and reports that oral contraceptives can increase the TSH response to TRH (49).

Although the pituitary has been suggested as the site of the positive action of estrogens (27), negative and inhibitory effects of estrogens on the pituitary-thyroid axis have also been reported. To obtain more precise evaluation of the effect of estradiol at the pituitary level and to eliminate possible changes in the metabolism and distribution of thyroid hormones after estrogen treatment in vivo, we investigated the effect of estradiol on the TSH response to TRH in anterior pituitary cells in culture. A preincubation of rat anterior pituitary cells for 48 hr in the presence of 3 nM estradiol led to increased TSH responsiveness to TRH (J. Drouin and F. Labrie, unpublished data).

We have recently observed that in vivo estrogen treatment leads to an increased sensitivity of the TSH response to TRH with no alteration in the pituitary TSH content. The present findings of parallel changes in pituitary TRH receptor levels and TSH responsiveness to TRH suggest that the number of TRH receptors is important in control of activity of the TSH-secreting cells (Figure 2). A similar antagonism between estrogens and thyroid hormones has also been found for prolactin secretion. The predominant effect of estrogens is on prolactin secretion, while the important effect of thyroid hormone is on TSH secretion. Although the sensitivity appears somewhat different, both prolactin- and TSH-secreting cells possess qualitatively similar mechanisms responsive to estrogens and thyroid hormones.

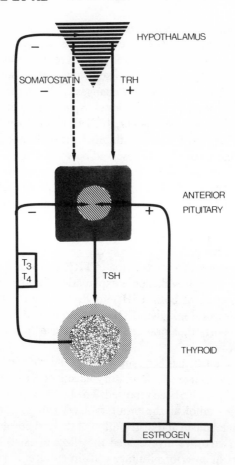

Figure 2 Schematic representation of the antagonistic effects of 17β-estradiol and thyroid hormone at the anterior pituitary level in the control of TSH secretion and at the hypothalamic level (probably on TRH secretion).

MODULATION OF LH AND FSH SECRETION BY GONADAL STEROIDS AND INHIBIN

Since LH-releasing hormone (LHRH) stimulates both LH and FSH release (8), the divergence observed between LH and FSH secretion under various physiological conditions (6) could be best explained by the differential effects of steroids at the pituitary level on the secretion of these two hormones. Moreover, the suggestions derived from implantation studies of a direct pituitary site of action of steroids (31) stimulated us to undertake studies of the direct effect of androgens and estrogens on LH and FSH secretion in pituitary cells in primary culture.

Pretreatment with 17β-estradiol (E_2) for 40 hr decreased the LHRH ED_{50} value for LH release while, on the other hand, preincubation of cells with testosterone (T) had the opposite effect (21). These changes of sensitivity of LH-secreting cells induced by E_2 and T markedly influenced the concentration of LHRH required to reach a given rate of LH secretion. For example, using the ED_{50} values derived from the dose-response curves, it could be calculated that E_2-treated cells require only one third the concentration of LHRH necessary to release 2000 ng LH rat reference preparation–1 (LHRP–1) per ml per 6 hr in control cells. Conversely, a 3-fold higher concentration of LHRH is required in T-treated cells (as compared to controls). The positive feedback action of E_2 may well be responsible for the increased pituitary responsiveness to LHRH observed in the preovulatory period in both humans (58) and laboratory animals (25).

Our data clearly show that androgens have not only specific but also opposite effects at the pituitary level on the control of LH and FSH secretion. In fact, pretreatment of pituitary cells in culture with T markedly inhibits the LH response to LHRH, while its effect on FSH is stimulatory (21). More recently we have studied the effect of progestins on gonadotropin secretion in rat anterior pituitary cells in culture (L. Lagacé, J. Massicotte, and F. Labrie, unpublished data). It could be shown that progesterone, although inactive alone, has a biphasic effect on the sensitizing effect of E_2 on LHRH-induced LH release. At short time intervals (4–8 hr) progesterone increases the LH responsiveness to LHRH, while after 24–48 hr of incubation it inhibits the stimulatory effect of E_2 on LH release. The effect of progesterone on FSH secretion is exclusively stimulatory at all time intervals.

These data indicate that sex steroids have not only specific but also opposite effects on LH secretion (Figure 3). However, the action of the three classes of sex steroids at the adenohypophyseal level on FSH secretion is exclusively stimulatory.

Since, moreover, LHRH is a more potent stimulator of LH than FSH secretion (26), the more rapid rise of FSH than LH secretion observed after ovariectomy (15) is difficult to explain by removal of the feedback effect of sex steroids on LHRH secretion at the hypothalamic level. These data could be best explained by the presence of an ovarian inhibitor acting specifically on FSH secretion. In order to study the effect of this inhibin-like activity at the adenohypophyseal level, we took advantage of the precision of the pituitary cell system to examine the effect of porcine follicular fluid on basal as well as on LHRH-induced LH and FSH secretion. Incubation of rat anterior pituitary cells in culture with porcine follicular fluid (treated with charcoal to remove steroids) led to a marked inhibition of spontaneous FSH release while no effect was observed on basal LH secretion (40). The inhibitory effect of follicular fluid was, however, less specific on LHRH-induced gonadotropin release. Although more potent on FSH than LH release, a significant inhibition of LH release induced by the neurohormone was also observed. Similar findings resulted when anterior pituitary cells were incubated with Sertoli cell culture medium (35), which suggests the similar nature of inhibin activity of ovarian and testicular origin. Coupled with the in vivo data obtained in many laboratories, our studies on the effects of sex steroids and inhibin on LH and FSH secretion can be summarized in Figure 3. While estrogens exert stimulatory effects on both LH and FSH secretion at the pituitary level, androgens inhibit LH but stimulate FSH release. The effect of progesterone is biphasic on LH secretion in cells primed with estrogens (stimulation followed by inhibition) while the effect on FSH is only stimulatory. Recent data obtained with inhibin of ovarian and testicular origin suggest that this(these) substance(s) could well be involved with sex steroids and LHRH in the fine regulation of LH and FSH secretion (Figure 3).

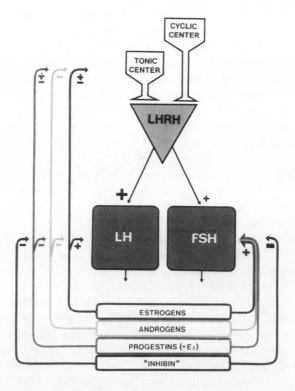

Figure 3 Schematic representation of the pituitary and/or hypothalamic sites of sex steroids and inhibin action on gonadotropin secretion.

ANTAGONISM AT THE PITUITARY LEVEL BETWEEN THE EFFECTS OF DOPAMINE AND ESTROGENS ON PROLACTIN SECRETION

Secretion of prolactin from the anterior pituitary gland is controlled by stimulatory and inhibitory influences of hypothalamic origin. The predominant influence of the hypothalamus on prolactin secretion is, however, inhibitory (46). Rapidly accumulating evidence suggests that dopamine (DA) may be the main or even the only inhibitory substance involved.

It thus appeared important to study in detail the specificity of the control of prolactin secretion and the properties of the adenohypophyseal dopaminergic receptor. Since estrogens are known to be potent stimulators of prolactin secretion, we then studied the interaction of estrogens with dopaminergic action at the pituitary level both in vitro and in vivo.

Much information about the factors controlling prolactin release could be obtained using rat hemipituitaries. However, since adenohypophyseal cells in primary culture proved to be a more precise system in which to study control of the secretion of many pituitary hormones (21, 22), we used this model to investigate in detail the specificity of action of a large series of DA agonists and antagonists on prolactin release. The high degree of precision obtained with the pituitary cell system made possible study of the correlation between the biological activity (effect on prolactin release) of the various substances and their affinity for the adenohypophyseal DA receptor (16, 33).

It could be clearly demonstrated that the order of potency of various inhibitors of prolactin release in anterior pituitary cells in culture (apomorphine > DA > epinephrine ≥ norepinephrine ≫ isoproterenol = phenylephrine) is typical of a dopaminergic process (16, 33). The high degree of stereoselectivity of the prolactin response is well illustrated by the relative potencies of the neuroleptics (+) and (−)butaclamol, α- and β-flupenthixol, and cis- and trans-thiothixene. The stereospecificity of dopamine action is also well demonstrated by the finding that (−)epinephrine and (−)norepinephrine are approximately 8 times more potent inhibitors of prolactin release than the (+)enantiomers. The high degree of precision of the system used has permitted the somewhat unexpected findings that compounds so far classified as DA antagonists, such as haloperidol and pimozide, do in fact have mixed agonist-antagonist properties.

The present data clearly demonstrate that the control of prolactin release, as assessed by the specificity of action of a large variety of compounds of known pharmacological potency, is a typically dopaminergic process.

Our original goal was to study control of prolactin secretion and binding of a specific dopaminergic ligand in the rat anterior pituitary system. In preliminary experiments, we have been able to demonstrate binding of [³H]dihydroergocryptine, which appears to possess features of dopaminergic specificity, to rat anterior pituitary membranes or whole cells in culture. However, due to the very small amount of membrane protein that can be derived from rat anterior pituitary, the relatively low concentration of receptors in these preparations, and the modest specific activity of the labelled ligand, it was felt that the bovine anterior pituitary would be a preferable tissue to study. Binding of [³H]dihydroergocryptine to bovine anterior pituitary membranes displayed a specificity typical of a dopaminergic process (16). Agonists competed for [³H]dihydroergocryptine binding with the following order of potency: apomorphine > dopamine > epinephrine ⩾ norepinephrine ⪢ isoproterenol = clonidine. This relative order of potency closely resembles the potency of these agonists in inhibiting prolactin secretion from rat anterior pituitary. Ergot alkaloids that act as potent dopaminergic agonists on prolactin secretion are also potent competitors of [³H]dihydroergocryptine binding. These ergot compounds did in fact compete for binding with a potency that closely parallels their inhibitory effect on prolactin release in anterior pituitary cells in culture.

The present data indicate that the anterior pituitary gland should represent a useful model for detailed study of the mechanisms of dopaminergic action. In fact, changes of [³H]dihydroergocryptine binding to the dopaminergic receptor can be correlated with an easily accessible and highly precise parameter of biological activity: prolactin release by cells in culture. Such a model of dopamine action has not been previously available and should be useful for a better understanding of the mechanisms controlling dopamine receptor–mediated actions.

It is well known that estrogens are potent stimulators of prolactin secretion in both humans (28) and rats (18). Moreover, the increased rate of prolactin secretion in the afternoon of proestrus in the rat is presumably under estrogenic influence. These in vivo effects of estrogens could, however, be exerted at the hypothalamic and/or pituitary level(s). Since anterior pituitary cells in culture proved to be an excellent system in which to study the specificity of action of sex steroids at the anterior pituitary level (21), we used this system, instead of intact pituitaries, to study the interactions of 17β-estradiol and dopamine on prolactin release. These studies clearly demonstrated that estrogens have potent antidopaminergic activity on prolactin secretion, not only in anterior pituitary cells in culture (50), but also in vivo, the effect being qualitatively similar in both female and male animals. As reflected by an increase of the ED_{50} value of dopamine agonists, the in vitro effect of estrogens was due to a decreased sensitivity to dopaminergic agents. Since the effect of estrogens is predominant at low doses of dopamine, the in vivo antidopaminergic activity of estrogens is also apparently due to a decreased sensitivity of prolactin release to dopamine action at the anterior pituitary level. Such findings indicate that higher concentrations of dopamine in the hypothalamo-hypophyseal portal blood system are likely to be required to inhibit prolactin secretion under conditions of high estrogenic influence. The almost complete reversal of the inhibitory effect of low doses of dopamine by estrogen treatment clearly indicates an important interaction between estrogens and dopamine at the adenohypophyseal level (Figure 4).

As mentioned above, dopamine appears to be the main factor of hypothalamic origin involved in the control of prolactin secretion (33, 44). Moreover, using the dopamine agonist [³H]dihydroergocryptine as a tracer

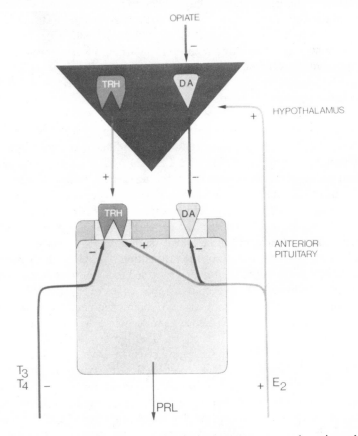

Figure 4 Schematic representation of the interaction between estrogens, dopamine and TRH in the control of prolactin secretion at the anterior pituitary level. The stimulatory effect of estrogens on prolactin secretion appears to be exerted mainly through blockade of the activity of the dopaminergic receptor.

and measuring prolactin release in pituitary cells in culture, we have found that the characteristics of binding to the pituitary receptor and the control of prolactin secretion are typically dopaminergic (50).

The role of dopamine in various brain functions has become increasingly evident during recent years (1, 5). Moreover, malfunction of dopaminergic systems can lead to neurological and psychiatric diseases (53, 55). It is thus hoped that knowledge gained about the pituitary dopaminergic system, where the effects (changes of prolactin secretion) can be measured with a high degree of precision, can help our understanding of less accessible dopaminergic systems in the central nervous system. It is of great interest that treatment with estrogens has recently been found to inhibit the action of dopaminergic agents on circling behavior in rats bearing a unilateral lesion of the nigrostriatal dopaminergic pathways (4) and on striatal acetylcholine accumulation in the rat (24). Moreover, symptoms of tardive dyskinesia following chronic treatment with neuroleptics have been found to be improved by estrogen treatment in the human (57).

CONCLUSION

The observation of a close parallelism between changes of cAMP accumulation and specific hormone release under the influence of two stimulatory hypothalamic hormones (TRH and LHRH) and one inhibitory peptide (somatostatin) strongly suggest that the adenylate cyclase system is involved in the mechanism of action of these three peptides in the anterior pituitary gland. Such a mechanism is supported by data obtained on the characteristics of the TRH receptor and properties of adenohypophyseal cAMP-dependent protein kinase and its substrates.

Following characterization of the interaction of TRH with its receptor, it was found that estrogen treatment in vivo led to an increase of the number of adenohypophyseal TRH receptors, while opposite effects were seen following thyroid hormone administration. Such treatments showed parallel effects on TRH binding and TSH-prolactin responses to TRH, thus suggesting that the number of TRH receptors is an important site for control of activity in TSH- and prolactin-secreting cells. In order to dissociate hypothalamic and pituitary sites of sex steroid action on gonadotropin secretion, experiments were performed in pituitary cells in primary culture. Estrogens stimulated both LH and FSH secretion while androgens had opposite effects on the secretion of the two hormones: marked inhibition of LH and stimulation of FSH release. The effect of progesterone in estradiol-primed cells is biphasic on LH secretion (stimulation at short time intervals followed by inhibition) while the effect on FSH secretion is exclusively stimulatory. Inhibin activity of ovarian and testicular origin is a potent inhibitor of basal FSH release.

Recent data indicate that dopamine may be the main or even the only inhibitory substance of hypothalamic origin controlling prolactin secretion. As assessed by the specificity of a large variety of dopamine agonists and antagonists of known pharmacological potency, the control of prolactin secretion is a typical dopaminergic process that shows a close correlation with the binding of the ergot alkaloid [^{3}H]dihydroergocryptine to the pituitary receptor. Estrogens were found to stimulate prolactin secretion directly at the pituitary level and, more surprisingly, to reverse the inhibitory effect of dopamine agonists on prolactin secretion. This potent antidopaminergic activity of estrogens at the pituitary level may serve as a model of the effect of peripheral hormones on other dopaminergic systems in the central nervous system.

Literature Cited

1. Anden, N. E. 1972. Dopamine turnover in the corpus striatum and the limbic system after treatment with neuroleptic and anti-acetylcholine drugs. *J. Pharmacol.* 24:905–6

2. Barden, N., Labrie, F. 1973. Cyclic adenosine 3',5'-monophosphate-dependent phosphorylation of ribosomal proteins from bovine anterior pituitary gland. *Biochemistry* 12:3096–102

3. Beaulieu, M., Labrie, F., Coy, D. H., Coy, E. J., Schally, A. V. 1975. Parallel inhibition of LHRH-induced cyclic AMP accumulation and LH and FSH release by LHRH antagonists *in vitro*. *J. Cyclic Nucleotide Res.* 1:243–50

4. Bedard, P., Dankova, J., Boucher, R., Langelier, P. 1978. Effect of estrogens on apomorphine-induced circling behavior in the rat. *Can. J. Physiol. Pharmacol.* 56:538–41

5. Beiger, D., Larochelle, L., Hornykiewicz, O. 1972. A model for the quantitative study of central dopaminergic and serotoninergic activity. *Eur. J. Pharmacol.* 18:128–34

6. Bogdanove, E. M. 1967. Analysis of histophysiologic responses of the rat hypophysis to androgen treatment. *Anat. Rec.* 157:117–35

7. Bøler, J., Enzman, F., Folkers, K., Bowers, C. Y., Schally, A. V. 1969. The identity of chemical and hormonal properties of the thyrotropin-releasing hormone and pyroglutamyl-histidyl-proline amide. *Biochem. Biophys. Res. Commun.* 37:705–10

8. Borgeat, P., Chavancy, G., Dupont, A., Labrie, F., Arimura, A., Schally, A. V. 1972. Stimulation of adenosine 3',5'-cyclic monophosphate accumula-

tion in anterior pituitary gland *in vitro* by synthetic luteinizing hormone – releasing hormone/follicle-stimulating hormone–releasing hormone (LH-RH/FSH-RH). *Proc. Natl. Acad. Sci. USA* 69:2677–81

9. Borgeat, P., Labrie, F., Côté, J., Ruel, F., Schally, A. V., Coy, D. H., Coy, E. J., Yanaihara, N. 1974. Parallel stimulation of cyclic AMP accumulation and LH and FSH release by analogs of LHRH *in vitro*. *J. Mol. Cell. Endocrinol.* 1:7–20

10. Borgeat, P., Labrie, F., Drouin, J., Belanger, A., Immer, H., Sestanj, K., Nelson, V., Gotz, M., Schally, A. V., Coy, D. H., Coy, E. J. 1974. Inhibition of adenosine 3',5'-monophosphate accumulation in anterior pituitary gland *in vitro* by growth hormone release-inhibiting hormone. *Biochem. Biophys. Res. Commun.* 56:1052–1059

11. Bowers, C. Y., Friesen, H. G., Hwang, P., Guyda, H. J., Folkers, K. 1971. Prolactin and thyrotropin release in man by synthetic pyroglutamyl-histidyl-prolinamide. *Biochem. Biophys. Res. Commun.* 45:1033–41

12. Brazeau, P., Vale, W., Burgus, R., Ling, N., Butcher, M., Rivier, J., Guillemin, R. 1973. Hypothalamic polypeptide that inhibits the secretion of immunoreactive pituitary growth hormone. *Science* 179:77–79

13. Burgus, R., Butcher, M., Ling, N., Monahan, M., Rivier, J., Fellows, R., Amos, M., Blackwell, R., Vale, W., Guillemin, R. 1971. Structure moléculaire du facteur hypothalamique (LRF) d'origine ovine contrôlant la sécrétion de l'hormone gonadotrope hypo-

physaire de lutéinisation. *C. R. Acad. Sci. Ser. D.* 273:1611–13

14. Burgus, R., Dunn, T. F., Desiderio, D., Guillemin, R. 1969. Structure moléculaire du facteur hypothalamique hypophysiotrope TRH d'origine ovine: mise en évidence par spectrométrie de masse de la séquence PCA-His-Pro-NH$_2$. *C. R. Acad. Sci. Ser. D.* 269:1870–73

15. Campbell, C. S., Schwartz, N. B., Firlit, M. G. 1977. The role of adrenal and ovarian steroids in the control of serum LH and FSH. *Endocrinology* 101:162–72

16. Caron, M. G., Beaulieu, M., Raymond, V., Gagné, B., Drouin, J., Lefkowitz, R. J., Labrie, F. 1978. Dopamine receptors in the anterior pituitary gland: correlation of [^{3}H]dihydroergocryptine binding with the dopaminergic control of prolactin release. *J. Biol. Chem.* 253:2244–53

17. De Léan, A., Ferland, L., Drouin, J., Kelly, P. A., Labrie, F. 1977. Modulation of pituitary TRH receptor levels by estrogens and thyroid hormones. *Endocrinology* 100:1496–1504

18. De Léan, A., Garon, M., Kelly, P. A., Labrie, F. 1977. Changes of pituitary thyrotropin releasing hormone receptor level and prolactin response to TRH during the rat estrous cycle. *Endocrinology* 100:1505–10

19. De Léan, A., Labrie, F. 1977. Sensitizing effect of treatment with estrogens on the TSH response to TRH in male rats. *Am. J. Physiol.* 2(3):E235–E239

20. Drouin, J., De Léan, A., Rainville, D., Lachance, R., Labrie, F. 1976. Characteristics of the interaction between TRH and somatostatin for thyrotropin and prolactin release. *Endocrinology* 98:514–21

21. Drouin, J., Labrie, F. 1976. Selective effect of androgens on LH and FSH release in anterior pituitary cells in culture. *Endocrinology* 98:1528–34

22. Drouin, J., Labrie, F. 1978. Interactions of 17β-estradiol and progesterone in the control of LH and FSH release in anterior pituitary cells in culture. *Endocrinology.* In press

23. Drouin, J., Lagacé, L., Labrie, F. 1976. Estradiol-induced increase of the LH responsiveness to LHRH in anterior pituitary cells in culture. *Endocrinology* 99:1477–81

24. Euvrard, C., Labrie, F., Boissier, J. R. 1978. Antagonism between estrogens and dopamine in the rat striatum. *Proc. 4th Int. Catecholamines Symp.*, ed. E. Usdin. NY: Pergamon. In press

25. Ferland, L., Borgeat, P., Labrie, F., Bernard, J., De Léan, A., Raynaud, J. P. 1975. Changes of pituitary sensitivity to LHRH during the rat estrous cycle. *J. Mol. Cell. Endocrinol.* 2:107–15

26. Ferland, L., Drouin, J., Labrie, F. 1976. Role of sex steroids on LH and FSH secretion in the rat. In *Hypothalamus and Endocrine Functions*, ed. F. Labrie, J. Meites, G. Pelletier, pp. 191–209. New York: Plenum

27. Fisher, J. S., D'Angelo, A. 1971. Stimulatory and inhibitory action of estradiol on TSH secretion. *Endocrinology* 88:687–91

28. Frantz, A. G., Kleinberg, D. L., Noel, G. L. 1972. Studies on prolactin in man. *Rec. Prog. Horm. Res.* 28:527–90

29. Jolicoeur, P., Labrie, F. 1974. Phosphorylation of nuclear proteins from bovine anterior pituitary gland induced by adenosine 3',5'-monophosphate. *Eur. J. Biochem.* 48:1–9

30. Jutisz, M., Kerdelhue, G., Berault, A., Paloma de la Llosa, M. 1972. On the mechanism of action of the hypothalamic gonadotropin releasing factors. In *Gonadotropins*, ed. B. B. Saxena, G. G. Beling, H. M. Gandy, p. 64. New York: Wiley Interscience

31. Kamberi, I. A., McCann, S. M. 1969. Effect of testosterone implants in the anterior pituitary (AP) on FSH secretion. *Fed. Proc.* 28:382

32. Labrie, F., Barden, N., Poirier, G., De Léan, A. 1972. Characteristics of binding of [^{3}H]thyrotropin-releasing hormone to plasma membranes of bovine anterior pituitary gland. *Proc. Natl. Acad. Sci. USA* 69:283–89

33. Labrie, F., Beaulieu, M., Caron, M., Raymond, V. 1978. The adenohypophyseal dopamine receptor: specificity and modulation of its activity by estradiol. In *Progress in Prolactin Physiology and Pathology*, ed. C. Robyn, M. Harter, pp. 121–36. Amsterdam: Elsevier

34. Labrie, F., Borgeat, P., Lemay, A., Lemaire, S., Barden, N., Drouin, J., Lemaire, I., Jolicoeur, P., Belanger, A. 1975. Role of cyclic AMP in the action of hypothalamic regulatory hormones. *Adv. Cyclic Nucleotide Res.* 5:787–801

35. Labrie, F., Lagacé, L., Ferland, L., Kelly, P. A., Drouin, J., Massicotte, J., Bonne, C., Raynaud, J. P., Dorrington, J. H. 1978. Interactions between LHRH, sex steroids and "inhibin" in the control of LH and FSH secretion. *Int. J. Androl.*, Suppl. 2, Geilo, 81–101

36. Labrie, F., Lemaire, S., Poirier, G.,

Pelletier, G., Boucher, R. 1971. Adenohypophyseal secretory granules: I. Their phosphorylation and association with protein kinase. *J. Biol. Chem.* 246:7311–17

37. Labrie, F., Pelletier, G., Labrie, R., Ho-Kim, M. A., Delgado, A., MacIntosh, B., Fortier, C. 1968. Liaison transcortine-corticosterone et contrôle de l'activité hypophyso-surrénalienne chez le rat. *Ann. Endocrinol. Paris* 29:29–44

38. Labrie, F., Pelletier, G., Lemay, A.. Borgeat, P., Barden, N., Dupont, A., Savary, M., Côté, J., Boucher, R. 1973. In *Control of Protein Synthesis in Anterior Pituitary Gland, 6th Symp. Protein Synth. Reprod. Tiss.*, ed. E. Diczfalusy, pp. 301–40. Geneva:

39. Labrie, F., Savary, M., Coy, D. H., Coy, E. J., Schally, A. V. 1976. Inhibition of LH release by analogs of LH-releasing hormone (LHRH) *in vitro. Endocrinology* 98:289–94

40. Lagacé, L., Labrie, F., Lorenzen, J., Schwartz, N. B., Channing, C. 1978. Selective inhibitory effect of porcine follicular fluid on FSH secretion in anterior pituitary cells in culture. *Clin. Endocrinol.* In press

41. Lemay, A., Deschenes, M., Lemaire, S., Poirier, G., Poulin, L., Labrie, F. 1974. Phosphorylation of adenohypophyseal plasma membranes and properties of associated protein kinase. *J. Biol. Chem.* 248:323–28

42. Lemay, A., Labrie, F. 1972. Calcium dependent stimulation of prolactin release in rat anterior pituitary *in vitro* by N⁶-monobutyryl adenosine 3',5'-monophosphate. *FEBS Lett.* 20:7–10

43. Lemaire, S., Pelletier, G., Labrie, F. 1971. Adenosine 3',5'-monophosphate-dependent protein kinase from bovine anterior pituitary gland: II. Subcellular distribution. *J. Biol. Chem.* 246: 7303–10

44. MacLeod, R. M., Lehmeyer, J. E. 1974. Restoration of prolactin synthesis and release by the administration of monoaminergic blocking agents to pituitary tumor-bearing rats. *Cancer Res.* 34:345–50

45. Matsuo, H., Baba, Y., Nair, R. M. G., Arimura, A., Schally, A. V. 1971. Structure of the porcine LH- and FSH-releasing hormone. I. The proposed amino acid sequence. *Biochem. Biophys. Res. Commun.* 43:1334–39

46. Meites, J., Nicoll, C. S., Talwalker, P. K. 1963. The central nervous system

and the secretion and release of prolactin. In *Advances in Neuroendocrinology,* ed. A. V. Nalbandov, 3:238–88. Urbana: Univ. Illinois Press

47. Pelletier, G., Labrie, F., Arimura, A., Puviani, R., Schally, A. V. 1974. Immunohistochemical localization of luteinizing hormone–releasing hormone in the rat median eminence. *Endocrinology* 97:314–17

48. Posner, B. I., Kelly, P. A., Friesen, H. G. 1975. Prolactin receptors in rat liver: possible induction by prolactin. *Science* 188:57–59

49. Ramey, J. N., Burrow, G. N., Polack-Wich, R. J., Donabedian, R. K. 1975. The effect of oral contraceptive steroids in the response of thyroid-stimulating hormone to thyrotropin-releasing hormone. *J. Clin. Endocrinol. Metab.* 40:712–14

50. Raymond, V., Beaulieu, M., Labrie, F., Boissier, J. R. 1978. Potent antidopaminergic activity of estradiol at the pituitary level on prolactin release. *Science* 200:1173–75

51. Schally, A. V., Dupont, A., Arimura, A., Redding, T. W., Linthicum, G. L. 1975. Isolation and structure of somatostatin from porcine hypothalami. *Biochemistry* 15:509–14

52. Schofield, J. G. 1967. Measurement of growth hormone released by ox anterior pituitary slices *in vitro. Biochem. J.* 103:331–41

53. Snyder, S. H., Banerjee, S. P., Yamamura, H. I., Greenberg, D. 1974. Drugs, neorotransmitters and schizophrenia. *Science* 184:1243–53

54. Snyder, P. J., Jacobs, L. S., Utiger, R. D., Daughaday, W. H. 1973. Thyroid hormone inhibition of the prolactin response to thyrotropin releasing hormone. *J. Clin. Invest.* 52:2324–30

55. Stevens, J. R. 1973. An anatomy of schizophrenia? *Arch. Gen. Psychiatry* 29:177–89

56. Vale, W., Blackwell, R., Grant, G., Guillemin, R. 1973. TRF and thyroid hormones on prolactin secretion by rat anterior pituitary cells *in vitro. Endocrinology* 93:26–33

57. Villeneuve, A., Langelier, P., Bedard, P. 1977. Estrogens, dopamine and dyskinesias. *Can. Psych. Assoc. J.* 23:68–70

58. Yen, S. S. C., Vandenberg, G., Rebar, R., Ehara, Y. 1972. Variation of pituitary responsiveness to synthetic LRF during different phases of the menstrual cycle. *J. Clin. Endocrinol.* 35:931–34

Ann. Rev. Physiol. 1979. 41:571–85
Copyright © 1979 by Annual Reviews Inc. All rights reserved

FEEDBACK ACTIONS
OF TARGET HORMONES ON
HYPOTHALAMUS AND PITUITARY
WITH SPECIAL REFERENCE
TO GONADAL STEROIDS[1]

❖1238

George Fink

Department of Human Anatomy, University of Oxford, England

INTRODUCTION

The various components of the forward and feedback loops involved in target hormone regulation of gonadotropin, thyrotropin (TSH), and adrenocorticotropin (ACTH) secretion have been delineated (8). Each of these systems depends upon a neural drive mediated respectively by gonadotropin, thyrotropin, and corticotropin releasing hormones [GnRH, TRH, CRH (36, 94)], which are conveyed to the pituitary by the hypophysial portal system. Target hormones modulate the net output of the hypothalamo-adenohypophysial system (HAS) by altering the magnitude of the neural drive and/or the responsiveness of the anterior pituitary to the releasing hormone. The net effect of the pituitary hormones on the target glands, and of the target hormones on the HAS, depends upon distribution, breakdown and amount (especially in the case of the target hormones) of *free* hormone in plasma.

Removal of the target gland, the most reproducible and reproduced experiment in endocrinology, demonstrates that in the extreme, all three target gland–HAS systems behave as negative feedback regulator systems. This has been reviewed extensively; the present review therefore emphasizes the stimulatory (so-called *positive feedback*) effects of gonadal steroids on the output of gonadotropins. The elegant studies of Everett, Sawyer, Mar-

[1]Dedicated to the memory of Mukund Aiyer.

571

0066-4308/79/0201-0571$01.00

kee and their co-workers (31, 32, 93) established the basis for recent work, which, carried out with the aid of radio-ligand assays and synthetic GnRH, has provided many of the details necessary for the future development of sophisticated biochemical and mathematical models.

GONADAL-HYPOTHALAMIC-PITUITARY SYSTEM

Stimulatory Effects of Steroids on Gonadotropin Release

SPONTANEOUS AND EXPERIMENTALLY INDUCED GONADOTROPIN SURGE The spontaneous preovulatory surge of luteinizing hormone (LH) depends upon the significant increase in the plasma concentration of estradiol-17β (E$_2$) that precedes the surge (11, 26, 37, 38, 66, 74, 95, 104). The stimulatory effect of E$_2$ is enhanced in some but not all species (11) by ovarian progesterone secreted in response to LH (2, 14, 31, 69, 74, 76, 89). The facilitatory effect of progesterone can be blocked by sodium pentobarbitone and only occurs in E$_2$-primed animals (2, 14, 31, 93). In unprimed animals, progesterone inhibits gonadotropin release (14, 31, 69). In the rat, adrenal progesterone secretion increases before the spontaneous LH surge; however, this seems to be crucial for the development of behavioral estrus rather than the LH surge (1, 34, 76).

Several workers have confirmed these points by using a preparation (*model 1*) designed to simulate the changes in plasma steroid concentrations that occur before and during the spontaneous LH surge. Rats are ovariectomized and given an injection of estradiol benzoate (EB) on diestrus followed by an injection of progesterone on the next day (expected proestrus) (2, 41, 62, 76, 101). Though not as robust as *models 2* and *3* (below) (10), *model 1* provides data that may be more physiologically relevant (including greater between-animal and between-experimenter variation). Studies using this model have highlighted the marked sex difference in response to steroids. Manipulation of steroids had no effect on the low plasma LH levels in female rats to which testosterone propionate (TP) had been administered on the fourth postnatal day (androgenized females), and in contrast to the normal female, castration increased while steroids reduced the concentration of plasma LH in males (41).

The second type of preparation (*model 2*) used to study the stimulatory effect of steroids consists of injecting progesterone 72 hr after injecting EB into long-term ovariectomized rats (15). Plasma LH concentrations are reduced by EB; progesterone induces a surge of LH, which reaches a peak 5 hr after injection. The stimulatory effect of progesterone cannot be elicited in EB-primed castrated males, and can be blocked in females by the simultaneous administration of sodium pentobarbitone (9). Because of their high signal-to-noise ratio, this and *model 3* (below) have been used to investigate several questions—e.g. the role of monoaminergic systems in the control of gonadotropin release (21, 57, 63). However, until it has been established that the differences in pituitary responsiveness and GnRH output (below) between these models and the intact rat are only quantitative, extrapolations should be made with caution.

The replacement of EB by TP in *model 1* does not stimulate LH release in either males or females (41); however, TP but not its active metabolite 5α-dihydrotestosterone (5α-DHT), can be used to prime *model 2* (9). The facilitatory effect of progesterone in *model 2* can be mimicked by EB, TP, 20α-hydroxy-progesterone (20α-OH-prog) or 5α-dihydroprogesterone (5α-DHP) (9). Replacement of progesterone by 17α-hydroxy-progesterone (17α-OH-prog) or 5α-DHP, but not 20α-OH-prog, also enhanced LH release in *model 1,* but the potencies of 17α-OH-prog and 5α-DHP were only about 0.5 and 0.05 that of progesterone (41).

Effect of steroids on GnRH output   When long-term ovariectomized rats are given two or more injections of EB, or are exposed to constant, elevated levels of E_2, a diurnal rhythm of LH release occurs with peak levels at 17.00 hr of each day [*model 3* (16, 56, 70)]. The LH surges can be blocked by sodium pentobarbitone and cannot be elicited in the male (56). This, together with other types of preparation (71, 85), has confirmed the existence of a daily neural signal for LH release (33) which, for its expression, depends upon the prolonged maintenance of elevated plasma E_2 concentrations. It has generally been assumed that this neural signal is mediated by the increased release of GnRH into hypophysial portal vessel blood. Direct evidence for this hypothesis has been obtained recently. With the aid of a specific and sensitive radioimmunoassay for GnRH (82) and a steroid anaesthetic (Althesin; alphaxalone and alphadolone acetate) that only partially blocks the LH surge, Sarkar et al (91) showed that in the rat a surge in the concentration of hypophysial portal plasma GnRH occurs about the time of the LH surge. Ovariectomy on the morning of diestrus significantly reduced the concentration of hypophysial portal plasma GnRH on the afternoon of expected proestrus, while the injection of EB immediately after ovariectomy (*model 1*) restored the GnRH concentration to that seen in intact animals (44, 92). Progesterone significantly reduced the stimulatory effect of E_2, but not in long-term adrenalectomized rats (44, 92). Explanation of this phenomenon awaits further study of the possible roles played by the adrenal and the ovary in progesterone conversion.

Because of the large LH surge in *models 2* and *3* we (G. Fink, D. K. Sarkar, unpublished) expected to find clear-cut surges of GnRH in portal plasma of animals anaesthetized with Althesin. However, in *model 2,* the GnRH concentration 3–5 hr after progesterone treatment was not greater than that after treatment with oil. In *model 3* there was a significant increase in the GnRH concentration in the afternoon of Day 4 following the implantation of a Silastic capsule containing E_2, but this increase was slight compared with that of the surge in intact or acutely ovariectomized, EB-treated rats (*model 1*). Perhaps the exceedingly high sensitivity of the pituitary to GnRH in *models 2* and *3* (below) obviates the need for a surge of GnRH sufficiently high to stand out clearly against considerable between-animal variation.

A mid-cycle surge of portal plasma GnRH concentration has also been found in rhesus monkeys anaesthetized with phencyclidine hydrochloride (81).

Effects of steroids on pituitary responsiveness Numerous studies have shown that in the rat, hamster, sheep, and human there is a marked increased in pituitary responsiveness to GnRH before and during the spontaneous LH surge (11, 37, 38, 102, 104). In the rat, the LH response at 17.00–18.00 hr (time of LH surge peak) is about fifty times that at diestrus. The increase in responsiveness depends upon the rise in plasma E_2 concentration and is enhanced considerably by progesterone. The administration of 5α-DHP, but not 17α- or 20α-OH-prog, also enhanced responsiveness in E_2-primed ovariectomized rats (*model 1*), but the potency of 5α-DHP was only about 0.05 that of progesterone (41). Testosterone propionate given instead of EB, either alone or followed by progesterone, had no significant effect on the response to GnRH (41).

Pituitary responsiveness in androgenized females was low and was not affected significantly by manipulating steroid hormones; in males, responsiveness was increased by castration and reduced by the administration of EB, EB plus progesterone, TP, or TP plus progesterone (*model 1*) (41).

In *model 2* the LH response to GnRH increased about 2.5-fold 72 hr after EB injection and 7-fold 4 hr after progesterone injection, at which time it was about 3 times what it had been at 17.00 hr of proestrus (3). The facilitatory effect of progesterone could be blocked by sodium pentobarbitone and was not seen in EB-primed castrated males (3). Pituitary responsiveness in *model 3* was 1.5–2.3 times that at 17.00 hr of proestrus. However, there was no difference between morning and afternoon values, and the response in males was higher than in females (56).

REFLEX GONADOTROPIN SURGE Most studies have been carried out in the rabbit in which LH release, initiated by the neural stimulus produced by mating (estrogen-dependent), stimulates the secretion of 20α-OH-prog, which is thought to ensure, by a positive feedback effect, the development of a full ovulatory surge (58).

Female albino rats exposed to constant light are converted to reflex ovulators. The brisk and relatively large post-coital surge of LH can be simulated by injecting progesterone (12). The profile of the LH surge that follows progesterone administration parallels that of GnRH in hypophysial portal vessel blood (92). However, in view of the low pituitary responsiveness to GnRH in these animals (35, 98) it is surprising how relatively little GnRH is released by progesterone (92).

Inhibitory Effects of Steroids on Gonadotropin Release

Since the classic paper by Moore & Price (77) it has been accepted that a negative feedback system operates between output of gonadal steroids and the "tonic" output of gonadotropins (11, 74, 75). Careful quantitative studies of female rhesus monkeys (65), sheep (53), and rats (51) have demonstrated a potent synergism between progesterone and estradiol shown earlier by McCann (73). These studies (51, 65) and a similar quantitative study carried out on the effect of testosterone on LH secretion in the male (25) show that the control of gonadotropin output by steroids has either a very narrow range or is of an all-or-none type (11).

Gonadectomy in several species including humans is followed by episodic gonadotropin release (11, 27, 49). The administration of steroids suppresses the bursts of hormone release and thereby produces steady but elevated gonadotropin output. However, though attractive, the hypothesis that a major role of steroids is to smooth out the erratic gonadotropin secretion that occurs in the open-loop system cannot be accepted without reservation, because gonadotropin secretion is also episodic in intact males and females of some species, especially humans (4, 11, 90, 105), in which the frequency and amplitude of the fluctuations change during the menstrual cycle (90, 105). There is no clear causal association between the episodic fluctuations in plasma gonadotropins and gonadal steroids (4, 11, 78).

Site and Mode of Steroid Action

Analysis of the site and mode of action of steroids in vivo is complicated by the priming effect of GnRH—i.e. the capacity of GnRH to increase significantly the responsiveness of pituitary gonadotropes in the rat (1, 39, 43), sheep (22), and human (102). Although they do not mediate the priming effect (at least in the rat), steroids, especially E_2, determine the magnitude of the effect (1, 3). The significance of the priming effect in the context of steroid action is that the increased responsiveness of the pituitary produced by E_2 and progesterone may be due, at least in part, to an increase in GnRH output.

Nevertheless, although the priming effect must be born in mind when assessing experiments carried out in vivo, studies carried out in animals subjected to pituitary stalk section or hypothalamic deafferentation (42), and on single-cell suspensions (68), show that E_2 and progesterone do increase the responsiveness of the gonadotropes by a direct action. Furthermore, the tenfold increase in pituitary responsiveness that occurs between 14.00 hr of diestrus and 14.00 hr of proestrus occurs in the absence of any significant change in the concentration of LH in peripheral plasma and GnRH in portal plasma (38, 91).

Interpretation of data obtained from implanting steroids into brain and pituitary has been difficult because of steroid diffusion (6). The most recent and perhaps best-controlled study suggests that the preoptic area is the main site at which E_2 exerts its stimulatory effect (52). This agrees with the finding that E_2 enhanced significantly the GnRH output produced by preoptic but not median eminence stimulation (96). However, studies using hypothalamic deafferentation have shown that an action of E_2 at other brain sites cannot be excluded (20).

The stimulatory effect of E_2 on GnRH output (44, 92) is compatible with the fact that E_2 increases the firing rate of hypothalamic neurons (23, 40, 54) and the responsiveness of the preoptic GnRH system to electrical stimulation (96). Progesterone reduces the firing rate of hypothalamic neurons (23, 40, 54). The intracellular events responsible for the effect of E_2 have not been elucidated, but it is reasonable to assume that protein synthesis is involved. This may result in the provision of more releasable GnRH, changes in the release apparatus of GnRH, and/or changes in the membrane of the neuron leading to increased sensitivity or excitability (74). Analysis is complicated by the fact that the output of GnRH may be modulated by central monoaminergic systems whose activity is also significantly affected by steroids (40, 48, 63, 74).

Estrogen takes a relatively long time to exert its full stimulatory effect, as might have been expected from the duration of the preovulatory E_2 surge. To stimulate the LH surge in the rhesus monkey, plasma E_2 concentrations had to be raised above 100 pg ml^{-1} for at least 36 hr (66). The LH surge began and ended in the presence of high, but physiological, concentrations of E_2, showing that the LH surge resulted from an E_2 stimulus rather than from a disinhibition produced by a fall in E_2 at the end of its surge (66). This has been confirmed in the sheep (53) and the rat (71). The initial effect of elevated plasma E_2 concentrations on pituitary responsiveness is inhibitory; the facilitatory effect is first seen after 6–9 hr (55). The facilitatory effect of E_2 was blocked by sodium pentobarbitone (55), which could be taken as evidence that E_2 increased pituitary responsiveness by increasing the output of GnRH and thereby invoking the priming effect of GnRH. The more likely explanation, for reasons mentioned above, is that exposure of the gonadotropes to at least 'basal' concentrations of GnRH in portal vessel blood is necessary for E_2 to exert its full facilitatory effect.

As for hypothalamic neurons, it is also reasonable to assume that the effect of E_2 on the gonadotropes involves protein synthesis; it is therefore relevant that the nuclear and total concentrations of estradiol-receptor complexes in the pituitary are significantly greater at proestrus than at other times of the cycle (97). The newly synthesized proteins may be gonadotropins, proteins concerned in the reception of GnRH, and/or protein components of the release apparatus for gonadotropins. Recent evidence suggests that E_2 can stimulate the synthesis of GnRH receptors (A. V. Schally, personal communication). Audits of gonadotropin turnover are made difficult by considerable between-animal variation, the relatively small amounts of hormone released relative to the amount stored, and the fact that assays of whole pituitary glands may measure hormone not available for release [in the extreme case still attached to polysomes (100)]. Nevertheless, using a 3 point moving average to smooth out considerable intergroup variations, Naftolin et al (79) were able to disclose the occurrence of an increase in the pituitary content and concentration of LH in the 24 hr before the LH surge. However, in *model 2* there was no correlation between pituitary gonadotropin content and the response to GnRH, which suggests that changes in responsiveness may be due to changes in sensitivity rather than in capacity of the gland (3).

The range of steroids, so far tested is small compared with the number secreted by the ovary (28). Under some conditions C19 as well as C18 steroids can stimulate the HAS, but from the ineffectiveness of 5α-DHT compared with TP (9, 96) it seems that the A ring must be capable of being aromatized by the HAS (80). Progesterone is by far the most potent of the progestins tested for a stimulatory effect, and although the HAS is capable of reducing progesterone to 5α-DHP (18, 107), the physiological significance of this metabolite and that of 17α-OH- or 20α-OH-prog in the rat is not clear (41). Hydroxylated derivatives of 5α-DHP, 5α-pregnan-3α-ol-20-one (which can be produced in the HAS) and its 3β epimer (secreted by the ovary) were more potent than progesterone or 5α-DHP in stimulating LH release in ovariectomized E_2-treated rats (108).

The mechanism of the inhibitory effect of steroids on the HAS is not understood, but it is clear that a significant part of steroid action is exerted directly on the pituitary (6, 59). As for the stimulatory effects of steroids, the role of metabolites may be important; 5α-androstane-3β- and 3α-17β-diol, for example, are more effective than testosterone in inhibiting LH release in castrated males (108).

Steroids and the One-Releasing-Hormone–Two-Gonadotropins Controversy

Several physiological and experimental situations exhibit dissociation between the release of LH and follicle stimulating hormone (FSH) (11, 38, 74, 108). The most clear cut are seen in the guinea pig (5) and rabbit (29), in which the ovulatory LH surge is not accompanied by a FSH surge. In the absence of biochemical evidence for a specific FSH-RH, workers have attempted to explain this dissociation by postulating differences in the responsiveness of the gonadotropes to GnRH, and/or differences betᵥ een the synthesis and release of the two gonadotropins perhaps brought about by steroid hormones. The peaks of the LH and FSH surges in the rat are separated by about 11 hr; however, the peak LH and FSH responses to GnRH coincide (37, 38). Manipulations of steroids in plasma have qualitatively similar effects on the LH and FSH response to GnRH (41), but the effects on spontaneous release differ (2, 41, 74). Thus, differences in responsiveness of the gonadotropes do not seem to play an important role; rather, steroids may have different effects on the synthesis and release apparatus for LH and FSH. Here it is relevant that steroids appear to affect the quality of gonadotropin synthesis (6), and that the part of the FSH surge that occurs after the LH surge in rats can be inhibited by the administration of anti-androgen-serum (50). In the human and the rat, once established, FSH release continues for much longer than LH (13, 106); the administration of sodium pentobarbitone in the rat can interrupt the LH but not the FSH surge (13).

ADRENAL- AND THYROID-HYPOTHALAMIC-PITUITARY SYSTEMS

There is good evidence that the circadian rhythm of ACTH and (the consequent) glucocorticoid secretion, which has a peak at the end and a nadir at the beginning of the sleep phase, is driven by a neural mechanism mediated by CRH (19, 30, 67). However, the degree of amplification of the ACTH signal (a two-fold increase compared with a nine-fold corticosterone increase; 19, 30) is dependent upon the responsiveness of the adrenal, which is also greater at the end than at the beginning of sleep (30). The data obtained so far fit the prediction of Yates & Maran (103) that in the unstressed state the adrenocortical system is operating in an approximately linear domain with all the loop variables exhibiting circadian periodicity. Ultradian rhythms in plasma cortisol concentration, independent of ACTH concentrations, occur in humans (67) and the rhesus monkey (60), in which they are highly synchronized between animals with a predominant periodicity of 85–90 min.

Superimposed upon these basal types of secretion is the rapid and intensity-dependent ACTH/glucocorticoid response to stress. The sophisticated analysis by Yates and his co-workers (reviewed in 103) has shown that glucocorticoids inhibit ACTH output by a fast rate-sensitive (inhibition only during plasma corticoid increase) and a delayed (about 2 hr in the rat) level-sensitive mechanism. The former modifies the stress-induced secretion of ACTH (30) while the latter is probably responsible for setting the output of ACTH when there is a prolonged increase or decrease in plasma glucocorticoid concentrations (103). This simple picture is complicated by changes in the neural drive mechanism. For example, the ACTH response to stress can be enhanced significantly by previous exposure to a stressful stimulus (24), and, in adrenalectomized rats, the ACTH response to stress is significantly greater at the beginning than at the end of the sleep period (30). Numerous investigations have shown that glucocorticoids exert their inhibitory effect at the central nervous as well as the pituitary level (103). Precise localization of action is hampered by the fact that no purified CRH is available, and that the system is exquisitely sensitive to experimental manipulation.

By way of contrast, we are reasonably certain that the negative feedback control of TSH secretion by the thyroid is due to modulation of pituitary responsiveness to TRH by triiodothyronine (T3) and thyroxine (T4) (7, 86). The role of steroid-binding proteins in the control of ACTH has been analyzed extensively (47, 84, 103); binding proteins in plasma are even more important in the regulation of TSH output since only 0.05% T4 and 0.5% T3 are present as free hormone in plasma (8). Recently, emphasis has been placed on the control exerted on the thyroid-TSH system by extrathyroidal deiodination of T4 to the more active T3 and the virtually inactive reverse T3 (64, 83, 88).

SUMMARY AND HYPOTHESIS

A stimulatory effect of target organ hormones on the HAS has only been shown to operate in the case of the gonadotropin surge. In spontaneous ovulators, at low plasma progesterone levels, E_2 first increases pituitary responsiveness and then permits the expression of a daily neural signal that results in the increased release of GnRH into portal vessel blood. Increased GnRH in portal vessel blood releases LH, and at the same time further increases pituitary responsiveness by its priming effect. The increased plasma LH concentration stimulates the secretion of progesterone, which further increases pituitary responsiveness. This cascade of events leads to the LH surge. The priming effect of GnRH obviates the need for a massive release of GnRH and ensures that the peak of the GnRH surge coincides with the peak in pituitary responsiveness. To be affected fully by E_2 and progesterone, the gonadotropes must be exposed to GnRH (basal levels will do); this is why neural blocking agents can inhibit the effect of these steroids. The secretion of LH, but not FSH, is dependent upon continuous exposure of the gonadotropes to GnRH. The factors that terminate the

GnRH surge are not known, though progesterone may play a role. This scheme also operates in the production of the first (pubertal) LH surge in the rat (45). Here, as in the control of seasonal reproductive function (72), changes in the neural drive mechanism (HAS) appear to be crucial (11). In reflex ovulators the initial stimulus for LH release is neural but is probably reinforced by the stimulatory effect of progestins on an HAS that is presumably primed by E_2.

The sex difference in the stimulatory effect of gonadal steroids appears to be due to the lack of a regularly occurring neural signal for LH release in the male. This may be genetically determined, and/or induced during sexual differentiation of the brain by early exposure to androgens. The stimulatory effect of E_2 can, however, be elicited in male primates, this order being less susceptible than rodents to the differentiating effect of androgens on the brain (10).

In the rat the increase in E_2 secretion occurs in the absence of any significant increase in plasma gonadotropins, and it is therefore debatable whether the stimulatory effect of E_2 is, strictly speaking, *positive feedback.* In the sheep, however, the rise in E_2 occurs together with a rise in LH (53). Positive feedback does correctly describe the effect of progesterone since the increase in ovarian progesterone secretion depends upon increasing plasma LH concentrations. The periodic destruction of ovarian follicles and the corpus luteum may be taken as an argument (87), albeit superficial, for using positive feedback to describe the stimulatory effect of both steroids (8).

Under "resting" conditions a negative feedback mechanism maintains the plasma concentrations of the pituitary hormones within a range lower than that found when the target gland is removed or undergoes atrophy (loop opened). However, within this range there is a circadian rhythm in the HAS-adrenal system that is neurally driven and seems to be linear, and in the adrenal-HAS and gonadal-HAS the pituitary and target hormones are released in pulses that are independent of each other. It is not clear whether the fluctuations that occur in the "basal" secretion of steroids, gonadotropins, and ACTH have a functional significance. However, the priming effect of GnRH, the possible episodic release of GnRH (17), and the finding of an optimal frequency of preoptic stimulation for LH release (61) suggest that the action of these components may depend as much on frequency as amplitude. The importance of oscillatory hormone release in the male has been examined mathematically (99). In the gonadal-HAS system, negative feedback is brought about by a nice balance between plasma E_2 and progesterone concentrations, the latter being able to extinguish the expression by E_2 of the daily neural signal for LH release (46). The net effect of target hormone secretion is determined by the amount of free hormone circulating in plasma, especially in the thyroid-HAS system where peripheral conversion of thyroid hormones and the concentration of receptors for T4 and T3 in plasma may play a more important role than neural drive.

ACKNOWLEDGMENT

The author is supported by the Medical Research Council.

Literature Cited

1. Aiyer, M. S., Chiappa, S. A., Fink, G. 1974. A priming effect of luteinizing hormone releasing factor on the anterior pituitary gland in the female rat. *J. Endocrinol.* 62:573–88
2. Aiyer, M. S., Fink, G. 1974. The role of sex steroid hormones in modulating the responsiveness of the anterior pituitary gland to luteinizing hormone releasing factor in the female rat. *J. Endocrinol.* 62:553–72
3. Aiyer, M. S., Sood, M. C., Brown-Grant, K. 1976. Pituitary response to exogenous luteinizing hormone releasing factor in steroid-treated gonadectomized rats. *J. Endocrinol.* 69:255–62
4. Baker, H. W. G., Santen, R. J., Burger, H. G., de Kretser, D. M., Hudson, B., Pepperell, R. J., Bardin, C. W. 1975. Rhythms in the secretion of gonadotropins and gonadal steroids. *J. Steroid Biochem.* 6:793–801
5. Blatchley, F. R., Donovan, B. T., ter Haar, M. B. 1976. Plasma progesterone and gonadotrophin levels during the estrous cycle of the guinea pig. *Biol. Reprod.* 15:29–38
6. Bogdanove, E. M., Nolin, J. M., Campbell, G. T. 1975. Qualitative and quantitative gonad-pituitary feedback. *Recent Prog. Horm. Res.* 31:567–619
7. Brown-Grant, K. 1960. The hypothalamus and the thyroid gland. *Brit. Med. Bull.* 16:165–69
8. Brown-Grant, K. 1969. Regulation and control of the thyroid-pituitary system. *J. Basic Eng.* 91:313–20
9. Brown-Grant, K. 1974. Steroid hormone administration and gonadotrophin secretion in the gonadectomized rat. *J. Endocrinol.* 62:319–32
10. Brown-Grant, K. 1976. In *Subcellular Mechanisms in Reproductive Neuroendocrinology*, ed. F. Naftolin, K. J. Ryan, J. Davies, pp. 485–501. Amsterdam: Elsevier. 529 pp.
11. Brown-Grant, K. 1977. In *International Review of Physiology, Reproductive Physiology II*, ed. R. O. Greep, 13:57–83 Baltimore: University Park Press. 284 pp.
12. Brown-Grant, K., Davidson, J. M., Greig, F. 1973. Induced ovulation in albino rats exposed to constant light. *J. Endocrinol.* 57:7–22
13. Brown-Grant, K., Greig, F. 1975. A comparison of changes in the peripheral plasma concentrations of luteinizing hormone and follicle stimulating hormone in the rat. *J. Endocrinol.* 65:359–97
14. Brown-Grant, K., Naftolin, F. 1972. Facilitation of luteinizing hormone secretion in the female rat by progesterone. *J. Endocrinol.* 53:37–46
15. Caligaris, L., Astrada, J. J., Taleisnik, S. 1968. Stimulating and inhibiting effects of progesterone on the release of luteinizing hormone. *Acta. Endocrinol. Copenhagen* 59:177–85
16. Caligaris, L., Astrada, J. J., Taleisnik, S. 1971. Release of luteinizing hormone induced by estrogen injection into ovariectomized rats. *Endocrinology* 88:810–15
17. Carmel, P. W., Araki, S., Ferin, M. 1976. Pituitary stalk portal blood collection in rhesus monkeys: evidence for pulsatile release of gonadotropin-releasing hormone (GnRH). *Endocrinology* 99:243–48
18. Cheng, Y-J., Karavolas, H. J. 1973. Conversion of progesterone to 5α-pregnane-3, 20-dione and 3α-hydroxy-5α-pregnan-20-one by rat medial basal hypothalami and the effects of estradiol and stage of estrous cycle on the conversion. *Endocrinology* 93:1157–62
19. Chiappa, S. A., Fink, G. 1977. Hypothalamic luteinizing hormone releasing factor and corticotrophin releasing activity in relation to pituitary and plasma hormone levels in male and female rats. *J. Endocrinol.* 72:195–210
20. Chiappa, S. A., Fink, G., Sherwood, N. M. 1977. Immunoreactive luteinizing hormone releasing factor (LRF) in

582   FINK

pituitary stalk plasma from female rats: effects of stimulating diencephalon, hippocampus and amygdala. *J. Physiol. London.* 267:625–40

21. Coen, C. W., MacKinnon, P. C. B. 1976. Serotonin involvement in oestrogen-induced luteinizing hormone release in ovariectomized rats. *J. Endocrinol.* 71:49P-50P

22. Crighton, D. B., Foster, J. P. 1977. Luteinizing hormone release after two injections of synthetic luteinizing hormone releasing hormone in the ewe. *J. Endocrinol.* 72:59–67

23. Cross, B. A. 1973. In *Frontiers in Neuroendocrinology*, ed. W. F. Ganong, L. Martini, pp. 133–71. Oxford: Oxford Univ. Press. 438 pp.

24. Dallman, M. F., Jones, M. T. 1973. Corticosteroid feedback control of ACTH secretion: effect of stress-induced corticosterone secretion on subsequent stress responses in the rat. *Endocrinology* 92:1367-75

25. Damassa, D. A., Kobashigawa, D., Smith, E. R., Davidson, J. M. 1976. Negative feedback control of LH by testosterone: a quantitative study in male rats. *Endocrinology* 99:736–42

26. Davidson, J. M. 1969. In *Frontiers in Neuroendocrinology*, ed. W. F. Ganong, L. Martini, pp. 342–88, Oxford: Oxford Univ. Press. 442 pp.

27. Dierschke, D. J., Bhattacharya, A. N., Atkinson, L. F., Knobil, E. 1970. Circhoral oscillations of plasma LH levels in the ovariectomized rhesus monkey. *Endocrinology* 87:850–53

28. Dorfman, R. I., Ungar, F. 1965. *Metabolism of Steroid Hormones* New York: Academic Press. 716 pp.

29. Dufy-Barbe, L., Franchimont, P., Faure, J. M. A. 1973. Time-courses of LH and FSH release after mating in the female rabbit. *Endocrinology* 92:1318-21

30. Engeland, W. C., Shinsako, J., Winget, C. M., Vernikos-Danellis, J. Dallman, M. F. 1977. Circadian patterns of stress induced ACTH secretion are modified by corticosterone responses. *Endocrinology* 100:138-47

31. Everett, J. W. 1964. Central neural control of reproductive functions of the adenohypophysis. *Physiol. Rev.* 44:373–431

32. Everett, J. W. 1977. The timing of ovulation. *J. Endocrinol.* 75:3P-13P

33. Everett, J. W., Sawyer, C. H. 1950. A 24-hour periodicity in the 'LH release apparatus' of female rats, disclosed by barbiturate sedation. *Endocrinology* 47:198–218

34. Feder, H. H., Brown-Grant, K., Corker, C. S. 1971. Pre-ovulatory progesterone, the adrenal cortex and the 'critical period' for luteinizing hormone release in rats. *J. Endocrinol* 50:29–39

35. Fink, G. 1975. The responsiveness of the anterior pituitary gland to luteinizing hormone releasing factor in rats exposed to constant light. *J. Endocrinol.* 65:439–45

36. Fink, G. 1976. The development of the releasing factor concept. *Clin. Endocrinol.* 5: (Suppl) 245s–60s

37. Fink, G. 1976. In *Ovulation in the Human*, ed. P. G. Crosignani, D. R. Mishell, pp. 95–114. London: Academic. 317 pp.

38. Fink, G. 1977. In *Recent Advances in Obstetrics and Gynaecology*, ed. J. Stallworthy, G. Bourne, pp. 4–54. Edinburgh: Churchill Livingstone. 368 pp. 12th ed.

39. Fink, G., Chiappa, S. A., Aiyer, M. S. 1976. Priming effect of luteinizing hormone releasing factor elicited by preoptic stimulation and by intravenous infusion and multiple injections of the synthetic decapeptide. *J. Endocrinol.* 69:359–72

40. Fink, G., Geffen, L. B. 1978. In *International Review of Physiology: Neurophysiology III*, Vol. 17, ed. R. Porter, pp. 1–48. Baltimore: University Park Press

41. Fink, G., Henderson, S. R. 1977. Steroids and pituitary responsiveness in female, androgenized female and male rats. *J. Endocrinol.* 73:157–64

42. Fink, G., Henderson, S. R. 1977. Site of modulatory action of oestrogen and progesterone on gonadotrophin response to luteinizing hormone releasing factor. *J. Endocrinol.* 73:165–70

43. Fink, G., Pickering, A. J. M. C. 1977. In *Molecular Endocrinology*, ed. I. MacIntyre, M. Szelke, pp. 293–308. Amsterdam: Elsevier. 366 pp.

44. Fink, G., Sarkar, D. K., Chiappa, S. A. 1977. Gonadotrophin releasing hormone surge during pro-oestrus: role of steroid hormones. *J. Endocrinol.* 75:46p-47p

45. Fink, G., Sarkar, D. K. 1978. Mechanism of first surge of luteinizing hormone and vaginal opening in the normal rat, and effect of neonatal androgen. *J. Physiol. London* 282:34–35P

46. Freeman, M. C., Dupke, K. C., Croteau, C. M. 1976. Extinction of the estrogen-induced daily signal for LH release in the rat: a role for the proestrous

surge of progesterone. *Endocrinology* 99:223–29

47. Fortier, C., Labrie, F., Pelletier, G., Raynaud, J. P., Ducommun, P., Delgado, A., Labrie, R., Ho-Kim, M. A. 1970. In *Ciba Foundation Symposium on Control Processes in Multicellular organisms,* ed. G. E. W. Wolstenholme, J. Knight, pp. 178–200. London: Churchill, 424 pp.

48. Fuxe, K., Hökfelt, T., Nilsson, O. 1972. Effect of constant light and androgen-sterilization on the amine turnover of the tubero-infundibular dopamine neurons: blockade of cyclic activity and induction of a persistent high dopamine turnover in the median eminence. *Acta Endocrinol. Copenhagen* 69:625–39

49. Gay, V. L., Midgley, A. R. Jr. 1969. Response of the adult rat to orchidectomy and ovariectomy as determined by radioimmunoassay. *Endocrinology* 84:1359–64

50. Gay, V. L., Tomacari, R. L. 1974. Follicle-stimulating hormone secretion in the female rat: cyclic release is dependent on circulating androgen. *Science* 184:75–77

51. Goodman, R. L. 1978. A quantitative analysis of the physiological role of estradiol and progesterone in the control of tonic and surge secretion of luteinizing hormone in the rat. *Endocrinology* 102:142–50

52. Goodman, R. L. 1978. The site of the positive feedback action of estradiol in the rat. *Endocrinology* 102:151–59

53. Hauger, R. L., Karsch, F. J., Foster, D. L. 1977. A new concept for control of the estrous cycle of the ewe based on temporal relationships between luteinizing hormone, estradiol and progesterone in peripheral serum and evidence that progesterone inhibits tonic LH secretion. *Endocrinology* 101:807–17

54. Hayward, J. N. 1977. Functional and morphological aspects of hypothalamic neurons. *Physiol. Rev.* 57:574–658

55. Henderson, S. R., Baker, C., Fink, G. 1977. Oestradiol-17β and pituitary responsiveness to luteinizing hormone releasing factor in the rat: a study using rectangular pulses of oestradiol-17β monitored by non-chromatographic radioimmunoassay. *J. Endocrinol.* 73:441–53

56. Henderson, S. R., Baker, C., Fink, G. 1977. Effect of oestradiol-17β exposure on the spontaneous secretion of gonadotrophin in chronically gonadectomized rats. *J. Endocrinol.* 73:455–62

57. Héry, M., Laplante, E., Kordon, C. 1976. Participation of serotonin in the phasic release of LH. I. Evidence from pharmacological experiments. *Endocrinology* 99:496–503

58. Hilliard, J., Penardi, R., Sawyer, C. H. 1967. A functional role for 20α-hydroxypregn-4en-3-one in the rabbit. *Endocrinology* 80:901–9

59. Hilliard, J., Schally, A. V., Sawyer, C. H. 1971. Progesterone blockade of the ovulatory response to intrapituitary infusion of LH-RH in rabbits. *Endocrinology* 88:730–36

60. Holaday, J. W., Martinez, H. M., Natelson, B. H. 1977. Synchronized ultradian cortisol rhythms in monkeys: persistence during corticotropin infusion. *Science* 198:56–58

61. Jamieson, M. G., Fink, G. 1976. Parameters of electrical stimulation of the medial preoptic area for release of gonadotrophins in male rats. *J. Endocrinol.* 68:57–70

62. Kalra, P. S., Fawcett, C. P., Krulich, L., McCann, S. M. 1973. The effects of gonadal steroids on plasma gonadotropins and prolactin in the rat. *Endocrinology* 92:1256–68

63. Kalra, P. S., McCann, S. M. 1973. Involvement of catecholamines in feedback mechanisms. *Prog. Brain Res.* 39:158–97

64. Kaplan, M. M., Schimmel, M., Utiger, R. 1977. Changes in serum 3,3'5'-triiodothyronine (reverse T3) concentrations with altered thyroid hormone secretion and metabolism. *J. Clin. Endocrinol. Metab.* 45:447–56

65. Karsch, F. J., Weick, R. F., Hotchkiss, J., Dierschke, D. J., Knobil, E. 1973. An analysis of the negative feedback control of gonadotropin secretion utilizing chronic implantation of ovarian steroids in ovariectomized rhesus monkeys. *Endocrinology* 93:478–86

66. Knobil, E. 1974. On the control of gonadotropin secretion in the rhesus monkey. *Recent Prog. Horm. Res.* 30:1–36

67. Krieger, D. T. 1975. Rhythms of ACTH and corticosteroid secretion in health and disease and their experimental modification. *J. Steroid Biochem.* 6:785–91

68. Labrie, F., Drouin, J., Ferland, L., Deléan, A., Lagacé, L., Borgeat, P. 1977. In *Endocrinology,* ed. V. H. T. James, 1:168–74. Amsterdam: Excerpta Medica. 603 pp.

69. Lawton, I. E. 1972. Facilitatory feedback effects of adrenal and ovarian hor-

mones on LH secretion. *Endocrinology* 90:575–79

70. Legan, S. J., Coon, G. A., Karsch, F. J. 1975. Role of estrogen as initiator of daily LH surges in the ovariectomized rat. *Endocrinology* 96:50–56

71. Legan, S. J., Karsch, F. J. 1975. A daily signal for the LH surge in the rat. *Endocrinology* 96:57–62

72. Legan, S. J., Karsch, F. J., Foster, D. L. 1977. The endocrine control of seasonal reproductive function in the ewe: a marked change in response to the negative feedback of estradiol on luteinizing hormone secretion. *Endocrinology* 101:818–24

73. McCann, S. M. 1962. Effect of progesterone on plasma luteinizing hormone activity. *Am. J. Physiol.* 202:601–4

74. McCann, S. M. 1974. In *Handbook of Physiology*, Sect. 7, Vol. IV, pt. 2, ed. E. Knobil, W. H. Sawyer, pp. 489–517. Washington DC: *Am. Physiol. Soc.* 601 pp.

75. McCann, S. M. Ramirez, V. D. 1964. The neuroendocrine regulation of hypophyseal luteinizing hormone secretion. *Recent Prog. Horm. Res.* 20:131–70

76. Mann, D. R., Barraclough, C. A. 1973. Role of estrogen and progesterone in facilitating LH release in 4-day cyclic rats. *Endocrinology* 93:694–99

77. Moore, C. R., Price, D. 1932. Gonad hormone functions, and the reciprocal influence between gonads and hypophysis with its bearing on the problem of sex hormone antagonism. *Am. J. Anat.* 50:13–67

78. Murray, M. A. F., Corker, C. S. 1973. Levels of testosterone and luteinizing hormone in plasma samples taken at 10-minute intervals in normal men. *J. Endocrinol.* 56:157–58

79. Naftolin, F., Brown-Grant, K., Corker, C. S. 1972. Plasma and pituitary luteinizing hormone and peripheral plasma oestradiol concentrations in the normal oestrous cycle of the rat and after experimental manipulation of the cycle. *J. Endocrinol.* 53:17–30

80. Naftolin, F., Ryan, K. J., Davies, I. J., Reddy, V. V., Flores, F., Petro, Z., Kuhn, M., White, R. J., Takaoka, Y., Wolin, L. 1975. The formation of estrogen in central neuroendocrine tissues. *Recent Prog. Horm. Res.* 31:295–315

81. Neill, J. D., Dailey, R. A., Tsou, R. C., Patton, J., Tindall, G. 1976. In *Ovulation in the Human*, ed. P. G. Crosignani, D. R. Mishell, 115–125. London: Academic Press. 317 pp.

82. Nett, T. M., Akbar, A. M., Niswender, G. D., Hedlund, M. T., White, W. F. 1973. A radioimmunoassay for gonadotropin releasing hormone (GnRH) in serum. *J. Clin. Endocrinol. Metab.* 36:880–885

83. Oppenheimer, J. H., Surks, M. I., Schwartz, H. L. 1969. The metabolic significance of exchangeable cellular thyroxine. *Recent Prog. Horm. Res.* 25:381–414

84. Perrin, F., Normand, M., Fortier, C. 1974. Modèle de la corticostérone plasmatique chez le rat. *J. Physiol., Paris* 68:273–290

85. Ramirez, V. D., Sawyer, C. H. 1974. Differential dynamic responses of plasma LH and FSH to ovariectomy and to a single injection of estrogen in the rat. *Endocrinology* 94:987–993.

86. Reichlin, S., Martin, J. B., Mitnick, M. A., Boshaus, R. L., Grimm, Y., Bollinger, J., Gordon, J., Malacara, J. 1972. The hypothalamus in pituitary-thyroid regulation. *Recent Prog. Horm. Res.* 28:229–277.

87. Riggs, D. S. 1963. *The Mathematical Approach to Physiological Problems.* Boston; MIT Press. 445 pp.

88. Robbins, J., Braverman, L. F. 1976. *Thyroid Research.* Amsterdam: Excerpta Medica. 638 pp.

89. Rothchild, I. 1965. Interrelations between progesterone and the ovary, pituitary, and central nervous system in the control of ovulation and the regulation of progesterone secretion. *Vitam. Horm.* 23:209–327

90. Santen, R. J., Bardin, C. W. 1973. Episodic luteinizing hormone secretion in man: pulse analysis, clinical interpretation, physiologic mechanisms. *J. Clin. Invest.* 52:2617–28

91. Sarkar, D. K., Chiappa, S. A., Fink, G., Sherwood, N. M. 1976. Gonadotropin-releasing hormone surge in pro-oestrous rats. *Nature* 264:461–63

92. Sarkar, D. K., Fink, G. 1979. Effects of gonadal steroids on output of luteinizing hormone releasing factor into hypophysial portal blood in the female rat. *J. Endocrinol.* 80. In press

93. Sawyer, C. H., Hilliard, J. 1971. In *Hormonal Steroids*, ed. L. Martini, V. H. T. James, pp. 716–21. Amsterdam: Excerpta Medica. 1063 pp.

94. Schally, A. V., Arimura, A. Kastin, A. J. 1973. Hypothalamic regulatory hormones. *Science* 179:341–50

95. Schwartz, N. B. 1969. A model for the regulation of ovulation in the rat. *Recent Prog. Horm. Res.* 25:1–43

96. Sherwood, N. M., Chiappa, S. A., Fink, G. 1976. Immunoreactive luteinizing hormone releasing factor in pituitary stalk blood from female rats: sex steroid modulation of response to electrical stimulation of preoptic area or median eminence. *J. Endocrinol.* 70:501–11

97. Sen, K. K., Menon, K. M. J. 1978. Oestradiol receptors in the rat anterior pituitary gland during the oestrous cycle: quantitation of receptor activity in relation to gonadotrophin releasing hormone–mediated luteinizing hormone release. *J. Endocrinol.* 76:211–18

98. Smith, E. R., Davidson, J. M. 1974. Luteinizing hormone releasing factor in rats exposed to constant light: effects of mating. *Neuroendocrinology* 14:129–38

99. Smith, W. R. 1979. A mathematical model of the hypothalamic-pituitary-gonadal axis II. Feedback control of gonadotropin secretion. *Bull. Math. Biol.* In press

100. Stachura, M. E., Frohman, L. A. 1974. "Large" growth hormone: ribonucleic acid–associated precursor of other growth hormone forms in rat pituitary. *Endocrinology* 94:701–12

101. Tapper, C. M., Greig, F., Brown-Grant, K. 1974. Effects of steroid hormones on gonadotrophin secretion in female rats after ovariectomy during the oestrous cycle. *J. Endocrinol.* 62:511–25

102. Wang, C. F., Lasley, B. L., Lein, A., Yen, S. S. C. 1976. The functional changes in the pituitary gonadotrophs during the menstrual cycle. *J. Clin. Endocrinol. Metab.* 42:718–28

103. Yates, F. E., Maran, J. W. 1974. In *Handbook of Physiology,* Sect. 7, Vol. IV, pt. 2, ed. E. Knobil, W. H. Sawyer, pp. 367–404. Washington DC: Am. Physiol. Soc. 601 pp.

104. Yen, S. S. C., Lasley, B. L., Wang, C. F., Leblanc, H., Siler, T. M. 1975. The operating characteristics of the hypothalamic-pituitary system during the menstrual cycle and observations of biological action of somatostatin. *Recent Prog. Horm. Res.* 31:321–57

105. Yen, S. S. C., Tsai, C. C., Naftolin, F., Vandenberg, G., Ajabor, L. 1972. Pulsatile patterns of gonadotropin release in subjects with and without ovarian function. *J. Clin. Endocrinol. Metab.* 34:671–75

106. Yen, S. S. C., Vandenberg, G., Rebar, R., Ehara, Y. 1972. Variation of pituitary responsivensss to synthetic LRF during different phases of the menstrual cycle. *J. Clin. Endocrinol. Metab.* 35:931–34

107. Zanisi, M., Martini, L. 1975. Effects of progesterone metabolites on gonadotrophin secretion. *J. Steroid Biochem.* 6:1021–23

108. Zanisi, M., Motta, M., Martini, L. 1976. In *Basic Applications and Clinical Uses of Hypothalamic Hormones,* ed. A. L. Charro Salgado, R. Fernandez-Durango, J. G. Lopez Del Campo, pp. 178–91. Amsterdam: Excerpta Medica. 350 pp.

Ann. Rev. Physiol. 1979. 41:587–602

LOCALIZATION OF HYPOPHYSIOTROPIC PEPTIDES AND OTHER BIOLOGICALLY ACTIVE PEPTIDES WITHIN THE BRAIN

♦1239

Robert Elde

Department of Anatomy, University of Minnesota Medical School,
Minneapolis, Minnesota 55455

Tomas Hökfelt

Department of Histology, Karolinska Institute, S-104 01, Stockholm 60, Sweden

INTRODUCTION

Within the past decade three hypophysiotropic hormones (thyrotropin releasing hormone, luteinizing hormone releasing hormone, somatostatin) have been isolated from hypothalamic extracts. They have been characterized with respect to their primary structure and neuroendocrinological activity. Using immunohistochemical localization techniques, as well as bioassay and radioimmunoassay analysis of extracts of the hypothalamus, it has been found that these peptide hormones are contained within neurosecretory systems whose axonal terminals are juxtaposed to the capillary loops of the hypothalamo-hypophyseal portal plexus. Such an anatomical arrangement was proposed by Harris (37) as the means by which the hypothalamus exerts control over the release of hormones from the anterior lobe of the pituitary.

Surprisingly, localization studies have also revealed that the hypophysiotropic peptides are not restricted to neuroendocrine systems, but that these peptides are also contained within neurons in many regions of the central and peripheral nervous system. This, along with other evidence, suggests a neurotransmitter role for peptides in these areas. In addition, a growing

587

number of biologically active peptides have been isolated and purified from the brain and characterized for their activity in systems other than the neuroendocrine. For instance, substance P was purified by following its activity to stimulate saliva production (18). The opioid peptides were purified according to their ability to serve as ligands for opiate receptors (50). These "nonneuroendocrine" peptides have been localized in neuronal systems throughout much of the central and peripheral nervous system, and may serve as neurotransmitters in these neurons. However, localization studies have revealed that certain of these peptides may, in some species, serve as hypophysiotropic hormones or regulate the release of other hypophysiotropic hormones. This suggestion is based on the finding of high concentrations of the peptides in nerve terminals juxtaposed to the capillaries of the portal system in the external layer of the median eminence.

For findings relevant to the distribution of the presently characterized neuropeptides see (6, 14, 24, 26, 28, 38–40, 52, 56, 67, 85, 92). We focus here on recent findings obtained from immunohistochemical localization studies of peptides that suggest new concepts in neural control mechanisms.

METHODOLOGICAL ASPECTS

Most of the data reviewed here were derived from immunofluorescence histochemical localizations as originally described by Coons (21). The technique has been modified for localization of neuropeptides and enzymes and has been more thoroughly discussed (44). Briefly, experimental animals were anesthetized and tissues fixed with ice-cold 4% paraformaldehyde by vascular perfusion. The brain and spinal cord were removed and rinsed in phosphate-buffered sucrose (5%) prior to cutting 10-μm sections in a cryostat. The sections were covered with antipeptide antiserum diluted 1 : 10–1 : 100 and incubated at 37°C for 30 min. After rinsing, the sections were covered with fluorescein-labeled antiserum directed against the immunoglobulin of the species providing the antipeptide serum. They were incubated as before and were rinsed; cover slips were applied. The slides were viewed and photographed in a fluorescence microscope equipped for transmitted and reflected illumination.

The specificity of the resultant fluorescent images was established by incubating adjacent sections of brain as above, except that the antipeptide antiserum was pretreated with an excess of the appropriate antigen prior to its exposure to the tissue section. Structures normally fluorescent using untreated antisera, but dark when using antisera pretreated with the appropriate antigen, are considered "specific" localizations. In many cases the antisera used for immunohistochemistry have been characterized for possible cross-reactivity with other peptides by radioimmunoassay techniques.

Although an antiserum with limited cross-reactivity to other presently identified peptides is most desirable, we are unable to rule out cross-reactivity with unidentified tissue antigens using even the most carefully characterized antisera. Further discussion of this matter has recently appeared (70, 81).

The adaptation of the indirect immunofluorescence technique to the use of peroxidase-labeled antibodies (64) or the unlabeled antibody–peroxidase–antiperoxidase complex (79) has enabled localization of neuropeptides with brightfield light microscopy and electron microscopy.

Most of the peptide localizations reviewed here have been obtained in studies of the rat and guinea pig central nervous system. It will be noted at several points that there are species differences in the distribution of peptides.

HYPOPHYSIOTROPIC HORMONES

A great deal of experimental evidence has suggested the existence of specific factors produced by hypothalamic neurons that are released from nerve terminals into capillaries of the hypothalamo-hypophyseal portal system and delivered in a relatively undiluted form to the sinusoids of the adenohypophysis. From these sinusoids they diffuse to receptors associated with the specific cell types of the adenohypophysis. Of the numerous releasing and release-inhibiting factors tentatively identified, only three (by conventional criteria) have been chemically characterized and synthesized.

Thyrotropin Releasing Hormone

Although the tripeptide thyrotropin releasing hormone (TRH) was the first of the hypophysiotropic hormones to be characterized structurally (16, 63), only a few immunohistochemical reports describe its distribution (20, 45, 46). This may be due to the small size of the hormone. For such a small molecule, the fact that the antigenic determinant site must differ from the site available for covalent interaction with the fixative severely limits the varieties of antibodies and fixatives appropriate for localization studies.

Terminals containing TRH immunoreactivity are found in the external layer of the median eminence (20, 45). These terminals are most evident in the median aspect of the median eminence and extend throughout the rostral-caudal extent of the median eminence and for some distance into the pituitary stalk. Other hypothalamic areas containing TRH-immunoreactive nerve terminals include the dorsomedial, paraventricular, ventromedial, and periventricular nuclei. A striking amount of the total TRH immunoreactivity of the central nervous system is found outside of the hypothalamus (13, 51, 66, 91). Areas containing TRH terminals include nucleus accumbens, nucleus interstitialis stria terminalis, and the lateral septal nuclei. Several brainstem nuclei, as well as the ventral and intermediolateral horns of the spinal cord, contain TRH-immunofluorescent fibers and terminals (46). Neuronal cell bodies containing TRH immunoreactivity have been found thus far in the hypothalamic dorsomedial nucleus and perifornical area. Lesion studies suggest that some of these cell bodies send their axons to the external layer of the median eminence (39, 26). It is known that the TRH immunoreactivity in the spinal cord arises from supraspinal cell bodies (40), although the precise details of this and other pathways are not known.

Luteinizing Hormone Releasing Hormone

Luteinizing hormone releasing hormone (LHRH) is a decapeptide (2, 73) that stimulates gonadotropin release. Numerous reports describe the distribution of LHRH in the median eminence of several species (see 6, 7, 14, 34, 52, 56, 75, 92). The median eminence of the rat, for example, contains densely packed LHRH-immunoreactive fibers and terminals in the lateral portion of the external layer. The pituitary stalk is virtually devoid of LHRH immunoreactivity. A second neurohemal juxtaposition of LHRH-immunoreactive terminals and fenestrated capillaries is found in the organum vasculosum lamina terminalis (39). In contrast to most other peptidergic systems, only small numbers of LHRH fibers and terminals appear in other nuclei.

The distribution and connections of LHRH-immunoreactive cell bodies have been a subject of considerable controversy. The disparate findings reported by several laboratories may have arisen because of the use of antisera directed against different portions of the LHRH molecule. It has recently been reported that LHRH antisera (depending upon the antigenic determinant site) will react with cell bodies in either the hypothalamic arcuate nucleus or the preoptic area, or, alternatively, will not react with any neuronal cell bodies (52). All of these antisera could specifically localize LHRH immunoreactivity in axon terminals of the median eminence and organum vasculosum lamina terminalis. From this it is argued that different physicochemical arrangements of the LHRH molecule must exist within the LHRH neurons of these nuclei.

Recent immunohistochemical analysis combined with lesions of the LHRH systems of the guinea pig has revealed that LHRH cell bodies in the medial basal hypothalamus project solely to the median eminence (75). Immunoreactive-LHRH neurons in the medial preoptic area project to organum vasculosum lamina terminalis, to the suprachiasmatic nucleus, and, to a limited extent, to the median eminence. An LHRH projection also arises from this area that traverses the mammillary nuclei and terminates in the ventral tegmental area. A more dorsally situated LHRH projection arises from both the preoptic area and the medial septal nucleus, traverses the stria medullaris to the medial habenular nucleus and the fasiculus retroflexus, and terminates in the interpeduncular nucleus. Somewhat similar LHRH projections have been suggested for the human brain (7).

Somatostatin

The tetradecaptide somatostatin (SOM) was isolated from the ovine hypothalamus (11). The distribution of SOM has been described using bioassay (55, 56, 86), radioimmunoassay (14, 30), and immunohistochemical approaches (26, 38–40, 67). Nerve terminals with SOM immunoreactivity extend the length and width of the external layer of the rat median eminence and extend for some distance into the pituitary stalk. Evaluated by immunohistochemical techniques, SOM-immunoreactive terminals are the most abundant of the presently identified terminal networks in the external layer of the median eminence. The organum vasculosum lamina terminalis also contains SOM-immunoreactive neurohemal contacts. The hypothalamic arcuate, ventromedial, and suprachiasmatic nuclei contain numerous terminals with SOM immunoreactivity. Extrahypothalamic-SOM terminal fields include the amygdaloid complex, nucleus accumbens and the medial portion of the caudate nucleus, the olfactory tubercle, the cerebral cortex and in substantia gelatinosa of the spinal trigeminal nucleus and the dorsal horn of the spinal cord. The substantia gelatinosa terminals represent the central processes of a population of small-diameter primary afferent neurons whose processes and cell bodies contain SOM immunoreactivity (41).

Other neuronal cell bodies containing SOM immunoreactivity include those of the hypothalamic periventricular nucleus (1, 29, 38), the zona incerta, the amygdala, hippocampus, and neocortex (39, 40). Of these, it is established that the hypothalamic periventricular group project to the median eminence (26, 28, 30) and, as such, function as a neuroendocrine system to inhibit the release of growth hormone and thyroid stimulating hormone (4, 83).

OTHER NEUROPEPTIDES

Vasopressin, Oxytocin, and Neurophysins

The posterior pituitary hormones were the first biologically active peptides to be isolated to purity for amino acid sequence analysis and subsequent synthesis (25). The use of immunochemical techniques to study these peptides and the associated proteins (neurophysins) confirmed the prevailing notion that neuronal cell bodies in the supraoptic and paraventricular nuclei synthesize oxytocin and vasopressin and send axons caudally through the internal layer of the median eminence to terminate adjacent to capillaries of the posterior lobe of the pituitary (see 24). Attention has recently focused upon the vasopressin/neurophysin terminals in the external layer of the median eminence (24, 87). They have been shown in the monkey and rat to arise from cell bodies in the paraventricular nucleus (3, 26). Furthermore, these terminals demonstrate increased immunoreactivity following adrenalectomy—an increase that can be suppressed by glucocorticoid replacement (80). In addition, vasopressin/neurophysin terminals of the external layer of the median eminence are specifically depleted after acute reserpine administration (26, 74). The rate of depletion correlates with the depletion of corticotropin releasing factor from the external layer of the hypothalamus as measured by bioassay (8). Taken together, these data suggest a role for the external layer vasopressin/neurophysin system as a possible corticotropin releasing factor.

Further recent interest in the posterior pituitary peptides arises from several reports of extrahypothalamic vasopressin, oxytocin, and neurophysin. A descending neurophysin projection to the spinal cord, possibly arising from the paraventricular nucleus, has been described (26, 82). Others have described projections to the choroid fissure of the lateral ventricles (12), the thalamus, amygdala, and septum (15, 78).

Substance P (SP)

The undecapeptide SP (18) is found unevenly distributed in areas of the central nervous system except in the cerebral cortex and cerebellum. The neurons containing this peptide are so extensive that only a brief discussion of the most interesting findings is possible. Recent mapping studies present a comprehensive view of SP-neuronal systems (22, 59).

The rat hypothalamus contains numerous nerve terminals, axons, and cell bodies with SP immunoreactivity. Prominent terminal fields include those found in the medial preoptic area with somewhat less in the dorsomedial nucleus, the lateral hypothalamus, the arcuate nucleus, a portion of the ventromedial nucleus, and the anterior hypothalamic nucleus. Hypothalamic cell bodies with SP immunoreactivity include those found in the dorsomedial and ventromedial nuclei, the premammillary nuclei, and the lateral preoptic nucleus.

Although the rat median eminence is virtually devoid of SP, the external layer of the primate median eminence contains a rather striking SP-terminal network (47). The position of these terminals in the primate suggests a neuroendocrine role for SP, either as a hypophysiotropic hormone per se, or more likely, as an axo-axonic regulator of the release of other hypophysiotropic hormones (47).

The most prominent extra-hypothalamic areas containing SP immunoreactivity include amygdaloid nuclei; the olfactory tubercle, the thalamus, habenula, substantia nigra, raphe nuclei and substantia gelatinosa of the spinal trigeminal nucleus and spinal cord (22, 58). Most of the substantia gelatinosa terminals represent the central processes of some of the small-diameter primary afferent neurons (41). The occurrence of SP in neurons of the medullary raphe nuclei projecting to the spinal cord is most intriguing since these neurons have recently been shown to contain simultaneously serotonin (19, 48). This finding is significant if it represents a violation of Dale's principle (one-neuron–one-transmitter hypothesis) in the mammalian central nervous system.

Enkephalins and Endorphins

Several endogenous morphinomimetic peptides have been characterized. They include the pentapeptides methionine- and leucine-enkaphalin (50), and α- and β-endorphin (35, 36). These peptides share an amino acid sequence from their amino terminus that is also homologous with the sequence of β-lipotropin beginning at its sixty-first residue.

The enkephalins appear to be the most abundant and widely distributed of the opioid peptides. Several groups have made preliminary reports on the distribution of enkephalin fibers and terminals (27, 77, 89) and cell bodies (42) using immunohistochemical techniques. The anti-enkephalin antisera used in these reports were shown to be specific for the enkephalins in that they did not cross-react with the large endorphins. These studies did not, however, reveal potential differences between the distribution of methionine-enkephalin and leucine-enkephalin.

The globus pallidus contains the densest plexus of enkephalin-immunoreactive fibers and terminals. Other prominent regions of axons and terminals include the nucleus accumbens, nucleus interstitialis stria terminalis, the amygdaloid nuclei, the intralaminar thalamic nuclei, several hypothalamic nuclei, mesencephalic periaqueductal grey, nucleus parabrachialis, the medullary raphe and reticular nuclei, the substantia gelatinosa of the spinal trigeminal nucleus, and the dorsal horn of the spinal cord.

Neuronal cell bodies with enkephalin immunoreactivity have been described in more than 25 areas of the central nervous system (42). In many of these areas the enkephalin cell bodies appear to be in the same vicinity as their terminals, a finding consistent with the hypothesis that enkephalin is important in interneuronal or local circuits. The most prominent groups of cell bodies include those found in the caudate nucleus, nucleus interstitialis stria terminalis, nucleus paraventricularis and the adjacent perifornical area, the premammillary nuclei, mesencephalic periaqueductal central grey, the medullary raphe nuclei, the substantia gelatinosa of the spinal trigeminal nucleus, and the dorsal horn of the spinal cord. The enkephalin cell bodies and terminals in the periaqueductal grey, the medullary raphe nuclei, and the substantia gelatinosa of the spinal trigeminal nucleus and dorsal horn are of interest with regard to mechanisms of analgesia (see 49).

The distribution of nerve terminals with enkephalin immunoreactivity is also remarkable because of its striking parallel with the distribution of opiate receptors (77). This relationship provides strong additional support for the suspected neurotransmitter role of the enkephalins.

The enkephalins may also serve as hypophysiotropic hormones; alternatively, they may regulate the release of other hypophysiotropic hormones by axo-axonic contacts in the external layer of the median eminence. This suggestion is based on the recent demonstration of a substantial number of terminals with enkephalin immunoreactivity in the external layer of the median eminence of rat (39) and cat (61). Several groups have also reported increases in secretion of prolactin and growth hormone in response to enkephalins (23, 58). Finally, the opiate antagonist naloxone prevents the stress-induced rise in prolactin (88), a finding that implicates *endogenous* opioids in regulation of anterior pituitary function.

β-endorphin, β-lipotropin, and ACTH immunoreactivity coexist in most parenchymal cells of the intermediate lobe of the pituitary and in some cells of the anterior pituitary (9, 69). This finding is in accord with the recent demonstration of a common biosynthetic precursor to these molecules (60). These peptides have been localized in the brain (10, 90, 93), where they may also coexist in single cells. Neuronal cell bodies with such immunoreactivity are found almost exclusively in the hypothalamic arcuate and premammillary nuclei. Axons and terminals are found mostly in the diencephalon. Their morphology and limited number distinguish them from enkephalinergic systems, indicating that the endorphin-liptropin-ACTH neurons exist separately from those containing enkephalin. Furthermore, the existence of enkephalins and endorphins in the brain is not dependent upon the pituitary (53, 72).

Several other biologically active peptides have been localized in the central nervous system by immunohistochemical techniques. They each appear to be uniquely distributed, although all of them are found in high concentrations in the hypothalamus. Neurotensin is a tridecapeptide originally isolated from bovine hypothalamus (17). Briefly it has been localized in the substantia gelatinosa of the spinal cord and spinal trigeminal nucleus, and in various hypothalamic and amygdaloid nuclei [(84); F. Bloom, M. Brown, and T. Hökfelt, in preparation].

The octapeptide angiotensin II has been localized in neuronal cell bodies, fibers, and terminals (31). Cell bodies are found in the paraventricular nucleus and perifornical area of the hypothalamus. High concentrations of immunoreactive terminals are found in the hypothalamic dorsomedial nucleus and basal hypothalamus, including the external layer of the median eminence. The spinal cord contains angiotensin II–immunoreactive fibers in the dorsal horn and the sympathetic intermediolateral cell column.

Vasoactive intestinal polypeptide (VIP) is a 28–amino acid peptide originally characterized as a gut hormone (62). It is also widely distributed in the central nervous system, especially in the hypothalamus and cerebral cortex (32, 39, 57).

A cholecystokinin-like peptide that cross-reacts with certain antisera to gastrin has been localized in some hypothalamic areas, including the external layer of the median eminence and in cortical areas, especially in the hippocampus (39).

SUBCELLULAR DISTRIBUTION
OF NEUROPEPTIDES

Several major questions concerning the distribution of neuropeptides remain unanswered by immunohistochemical analysis at the light-microscopic level and by regional radioimmunoassay and bioassay analysis. These questions relate to (a) the subcellular organelles that store and participate in the release of neuropeptides; (b) the possible coexistence of neuropeptides and conventional neurotransmitters within a single nerve terminal; (c) the relationship of peptidergic terminals to other axons and dendrites in the surrounding neuropil; and (d) the relationship of peptidergic terminals to specific peptidergic receptors. Immunohistochemical analysis at the electron-microscopic level may serve to answer these questions.

A number of reports now suggest that neuropeptides are stored in large-diameter (100 – 300 nm) granules (34, 39, 68, 76). Because of the presence of numerous small-diameter (40 – 60 nm) "synaptic vesicles" in peptidergic terminals (Figure 1) it has been tempting to speculate that the smaller vesicles may contain a conventional neurotransmitter. Very recently this possibility has been strengthened on the basis of findings in the mammalian peripheral and central nervous systems. In the peripheral nervous system, SOM has been localized in adrenergic neuronal cell bodies (43). Centrally, SP and serotonin appear to coexist in some neuronal cell bodies of the medullary raphe nuclei (19, 48). These findings are based upon light-microscopic examination of cell bodies but suggest that the terminals also contain both factors. However, critical analysis of the latter will require immunohistochemical analysis at the ultrastructural level.

The relationship of peptidergic terminals to other axons and dendrites also requires immunohistochemical analysis at the ultrastructural level. For example, it is clear that several peptidergic systems are represented in the

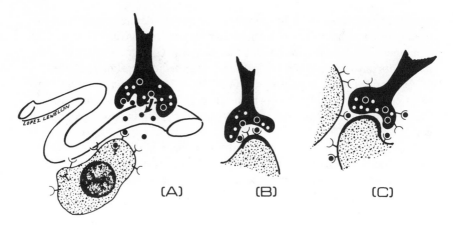

(A)   (B)   (C)

Figure 1   Schematic representation of possible relationships of peptidergic nerve terminals with structures containing peptidergic receptors. Within the terminal, neuropeptides are probably stored in large-diameter (100–300 nm) granules. Small-diameter (40–60 nm) "synaptic vesicles" may contain unidentified substances, or in some cases, a conventional neurotransmitter. (A) A neurohemal juxtaposition in which the peptidergic terminal releases its products into the extracellular spaces adjacent to fenestrated capillaries. The peptide is carried by the vascular system to its target, where it interacts with receptors. (B) A synaptic arrangement whereby the peptide (possibly along with a conventional neurotransmitter) is released into the synaptic cleft, where it interacts with receptors in the specialization of the post-synaptic membrane. (C) A "parasynaptic" arrangement whereby the peptide may be released from the terminal to diffuse and interact with receptors at sites other than the specialization of the post-synaptic membrane. The receptors may be elsewhere on the post-synaptic membrane, on nearby neural membranes not synaptically related to the peptidergic terminal, or on the peptidergic terminal itself. In the latter case, the receptor may act as an autoreceptor (54). If a conventional neurotransmitter coexists in the peptidergic terminal, it may act upon receptors at the synapse proper.

substantia gelatinosa, but the relationship of the peptidergic elements to the complex synaptic glomeruli of this region (33) is not known. Such knowledge is clearly necessary for a better understanding of mechanisms of pain and analgesia.

Finally, ultrastructural immunohistochemistry combined with localization of peptide receptors promises to distinguish among several modes of action presently hypothesized for peptidergic terminals and their putative receptors (Figure 1). It is clear that neuropeptides affect the ionic potential of receptive membranes, but these effects are not identical to those produced by conventional neurotransmitters (see 5, 65, 71). This may be due, in part, to the relationship of peptidergic terminals to peptide receptors. In some cases, peptide receptors may be restricted to the specialization of the post-synaptic membrane (Figure 1B). Alternatively, peptide receptors may be related to specific terminal elements in a "parasynaptic" fashion (Figure

1C). These configurations may be explored by further refinements of immunohistochemical techniques at the ultrastructural level, combined with autoradiographic demonstration of labeled ligands bound to their receptors.

CONCLUSIONS

Immunohistochemical analysis of hypophysiotropic and other neuropeptides reveals unique and striking neural perikarya, axons, and terminals containing specific peptide immunoreactivity. The hypophysiotropic peptides are most highly concentrated in nerve terminals in the external layer of the median eminence. From this site they may be released and carried via the portal circulation to the adenohypophysis. The occurrence of hypophysiotropic peptides in other areas of the nervous system suggests that they may act, at these sites, as neurotransmitters.

Enkephalins, SP, angiotensin II, and cholecystokinin-like immunoreactivity are also found in nerve terminals in the external layer of the median eminence of some species. Although these peptides have not been considered hypophysiotropic hormones, the location of their terminals in the median eminence suggests that they participate indirectly in regulation of anterior pituitary hormone release. This control may be accomplished via axo-axonal influences of terminals containing these peptides upon the terminals containing the genuine hypophysiotropic peptides. An analogous interaction is thought to be exerted by dopamine terminals upon LHRH terminals in the median eminence (39).

All of the neuropeptides discussed above are found within neuronal structures in the hypothalamus. Most of these peptides are also found, at least to a limited extent, in the brainstem, spinal cord, and deep nuclei of the telencephalon. Few peptides have been localized in neurons of the cerebral cortex. These include SOM, VIP, and cholecystokinin-like immunoreactivity. The cerebellum, to date, has not been shown to contain significant immunoreactivity for any of the presently identifiable neuropeptides.

The demonstration of the coexistence of neuropeptides (SOM and SP) in some monoaminergic (adrenergic and serotonergic) neurons raises questions about the one-neuron–one-transmitter hypothesis. It is presently unknown whether or not such coexistence is widespread in the mammalian nervous system. For those neurons that contain two neuroeffector substances, it will be important to determine whether or not both substances play an active role in the function of the neuron. Finally, the details of the morphological interactions of peptidergic elements with other neuronal systems offer the possibility to understand more completely the circuitry of many regions of the central nervous system.

ACKNOWLEDGMENTS

Recent studies from the authors' laboratories have been supported by the Graduate School of the University of Minnesota and the American Diabetes Association, Immuno Nuclear Corporation, and the McKnight Foundation (R.E.); and by the Swedish Medical Research Council, Magnus Bergwalls Stiftelse, Knut och Alice Wallenbergs Stiftelse, and Harald och Greta Jeanssons Stiftelse (T.H.). The secretarial assistance of R. Nelson is gratefully acknowledged.

Literature Cited

1. Alpert, L. C., Brawer, J. R., Patel, Y. C., Reichlin, S. 1976. Somatostatinergic neurons in anterior hypothalamus: Immunohistochemical localization. *Endocrinology* 98:255–58
2. Amoss, M., Burgus, R., Blackwell, R., Vale, W., Fellows, R., Guillemin, R. 1971. Purification, amino acid composition and N-terminus of the hypothalamic luteinizing hormone releasing factor (LRF) of ovine origin. *Biochem. Biophys. Res. Commun.* 44:205–10
3. Antunes, J. L., Carmel, P. W., Zimmerman, E. A. 1977. Projections from the paraventricular nucleus to the zone externa of the median eminence of the rhesus monkey: An immunohistochemical study. *Brain Res.* 137:1–10
4. Arimura, A., Smith, W. F., Schally, A. V. 1976. Blockade of the stress-induced decrease in blood GH by anti-somatostatin serum in rats. *Endocrinology* 98:540–51
5. Barker, J. L. 1977. Physiological roles of peptides in the nervous system. In *Peptides in Neurobiology*, ed. H. Gainer, pp. 295–344. New York: Plenum. 464 pp.
6. Barry, J. 1976. Immunohistochemical localization of hypothalamic hormones (especially LRF) at the light microscopy level. In *Hypothalamus and Endocrine Functions*, ed. F. Labrie, J. Meites, G. Pelletier, pp. 451–74. New York: Plenum
7. Barry, J. 1977. Immunofluorescence study of LRF neurons in man. *Cell Tiss. Res.* 181:1–14
8. Bhattacharya, A. N., Marks, B. H. 1969. Reserpine- and chlorpromazine-induced changes in hypothalamo-hypophyseal-adrenal system in rats in the presence and absence of hypothermia. *J. Pharmacol. Exp. Ther.* 165:108–16
9. Bloom, F., Battenberg, E., Rossier, J., Ling, N., Leppaluoto, J., Vargo, T. M.,

Guillemin, R. 1977. Endorphins are located in the intermediate and anterior lobes of the pituitary gland, not in the neurohypophysis. *Life Sci.* 20:43–48
10. Bloom, F., Battenberg, E., Rossier, J., Ling, N., Guillemin, R. 1978. Neurons containing β-endorphin in rat brain exist separately from those containing enkephalin: Immunocytochemical studies. *Proc. Natl. Acad. Sci. USA* 75:1591–95
11. Brazeau, P., Vale, W., Burgus, R., Ling, N., Butcher, M., Rivier, J., Guillemin, R. 1973. Hypothalamic polypeptide that inhibits the secretion of immunoreactive pituitary growth hormone. *Science* 179:77–79
12. Brownfield, M. S., Kozlowski, G. P. 1977. The hypothalamo-choroidal tract. I. Immunohistochemical demonstration of neurophysin pathways to telencephalic choroidal plexuses and cerebrospinal fluid. *Cell Tissue Res.* 178: 111–27
13. Brownstein, M., Palkovits, M., Saavedra, J. M., Bassiri, R., Utiger, R. D. 1974. Thyrotropin-releasing hormone in specific nuclei of rat brain. *Science* 185:267–69
14. Brownstein, M. J. 1977. Biologically active peptides in the mammalian central nervous system. See Ref. 5, pp. 147–70
15. Buijs, R. M., Swaab, D. F., Dogterom, J., van Leeuwen, F. W. 1978. Intra- and extrahypothalamic vasopressin and oxytocin pathways in the rat. *Cell Tiss. Res.* 186:423–33
16. Burgus, R., Dunn, T. F., Desiderio, D., Ward, D. N., Vale, W., Guillemin, R. 1970. Characterization of ovine hypothalamic hypophysiotropic TSH-releasing factor. *Nature* 226:321–25
17. Carraway, R., Leeman, S. E. 1975. The amino acid sequence of a hypothalamic peptide, neurotensin. *J. Biol. Chem.* 250:1907–11

18. Chang, M. M., Leeman, S. E., Niall, H. D. 1971. Amino acid sequence of substance P. *Nature New Biol.* 232:86–87

19. Chan-Palay, V., Jonsson, G., Palay, S. L. 1978. Serotonin and substance P coexist in neurons of the rat's central nervous system. *Proc. Natl. Acad. Sci. USA* 75:1582–86

20. Choy, V. J., Watkins, W. B., 1977. Immunohistochemical localization of thyrotropin-releasing factor in the rat median eminence. *Cell Tiss. Res.* 177:371–74

21. Coons, A. H. 1958. Fluorescent antibody methods. In *General Cytochemical Methods,* ed. J. F. Danielli, pp. 399–422. New York: Academic

22. Cuello, A. C., Kanazawa, I. 1978. The distribution of substance P immunoreactive fibers in the rat central nervous system. *J. Comp. Neurol.* 178:129–56

23. Cusan, L., Dupont, A., Garon, M., Coy, D. H. 1976. Stimulatory effect of met-enkephalin, (D-Ala²)met-enkephalin and β-endorphine on growth hormone secretion. *Clin. Res.* 24:656A

24. Defendini, R., Zimmerman, E. A. 1978. The magnocellular neurosecretory system of the mammalian hypothalamus. In *The Hypothalamus,* ed. S. Reichlin, R. J. Baldessarini, J. B. Martin, pp. 137–52. New York: Raven. 490 pp.

25. duVigneaud, V. 1954. Hormones of the posterior pituitary gland: Oxytocin and vasopressin. *Harvey Lect., Ser. L,* pp. 1–26

26. Elde, R., Hökfelt, T. 1978. Distribution of hypothalamic hormones and other peptides in the brain. In *Frontiers in Neuroendocrinology,* ed. W. F. Ganong, L. Martini, 5:1–33. New York: Raven Press

27. Elde, R., Hökfelt, T., Johansson, O., Terenius, L. 1976. Immunohistochemical studies using antibodies to leucine-enkephalin: Initial observations on the nervous system of the rat. *Neuroscience* 1:349–51

28. Elde, R. P., Hökfelt, T., Johansson, O., Ljungdahl, A., Nilsson, G., Jeffcoate, S. L. 1978. Immunohistochemical localization of peptides in the nervous system. In *Centrally Acting Peptides,* ed. John Hughes, pp. 17–35. Hampshire, England: Macmillan

29. Elde, R. P., Parsons, J. A. 1975. Immunocytochemical localization of somatostin in cell bodies of the rat hypothalamus. *Am. J. Anat.* 144: 541–48

30. Epelbaum, J., Willoughby, J. O., Brazeau, P., Martin, J. B. 1977. Effects of brain lesions and hypothalamic deafferentation on somatostatin distribution in the rat brain. *Endocrinology* 101: 1495–1502

31. Fuxe, K., Ganten, D., Hökfelt, T., Bolme, P. 1976. Immunohistochemical evidence for the existence of angiotensin II–containing nerve terminals in the brain and spinal cord of the rat. *Neurosci. Lett.* 2:229–34

32. Fuxe, K., Hökfelt, T., Said, S., Mutt, V. 1977. Evidence for the existence of VIP-containing nerve terminals in the rat brain. *Neurosci. Lett.* 5:241–46

33. Gobel, S. 1974. Synaptic organization of the substantia gelatinosa glomeruli in the spinal trigeminal nucleus of the adult cat. *J. Neurocytol.* 3:219–43

34. Goldsmith, P. C., Ganong, W. F. 1975. Ultrastructural localization of luteinizing hormone–releasing hormone in the median eminence of the rat. *Brain Res.* 97:181–91

35. Guillemin, R. 1978. Biochemical and physiological correlates of hypothalamic peptides. The new endocrinology of the neuron. See Ref. 24, pp. 155–94

36. Guillemin, R., Ling, N., Burgus, R. 1976. Endorphines, peptides, d'origine hypothalamique et neurohypophysaire a activite morphinomimetique. Isolement et structure moleculaire de l'α-endorpine. *C. R. Acad. Sci. Ser. D* 282:783–85

37. Harris, G. W. 1955. *Neural Control of the Pituitary Gland.* London: Edward Arnold

38. Hökfelt, T., Efendic, S., Hellerström, C., Johansson, O., Luft, R., Arimura, A. 1975. Cellular localization of somatostatin in endocrine-like cells and neurons of the rat with special references to the A₁ cells of the pancreatic islets and to the hypothalamus. *Acta Endocrinol. Copenhagen Suppl.* 200: 5–41

39. Hökfelt, T., Elde, R., Fuxe, K., Johansson, O., Ljungdahl, A., Goldstein, M., Luft, R., Nilsson, G., Said, S., Fraser, H., Jeffcoate, S. L., White, N., Ganten, D., Rehfeld, J. 1977. Aminergic and peptidergic pathways in the nervous system with special reference to the hypothalamus. See Ref. 24, pp. 69–135

40. Hökfelt, T., Elde, R. P., Johansson, O., Ljungdahl, A., Schultzberg, M., Fuxe, K., Goldstein, M., Nilsson, G., Pernow, B., Terenius, L., Ganten, D., Jeffcoate, S. L., Rehfeld, J., Said, S. 1978. The

distribution of peptide containing neurons in the nervous system. In *Psychopharmacology: A generation of Progress,* ed. M. A. Lipton, A. DiMascio, K. F. Killam, pp. 39–66. New York: Raven

41. Hökfelt, T., Elde, R., Johansson, O., Luft, R., Nilsson, G., Arimura, A. 1976. Immunohistochemical evidence for separate populations of somatostatin-containing and substance P–containing primary afferent neurons. *Neuroscience* 1:131–36

42. Hökfelt, T., Elde, R., Johansson, O., Terenius, L., Stein, L. 1977. The distribution of enkephalin immunoreactive cell bodies in the rat central nervous system. *Neurosci. Lett.* 5:25–31

43. Hökfelt, T., Elfvin, L.-G., Elde, R., Schultzberg, M., Goldstein, M., Luft, R. 1977. Occurrence of somatostatin-like immunoreactivity in some peripheral sympathetic noradrenergic neurons. *Proc. Natl. Acad. Sci. USA* 74:3587–91

44. Hökfelt, T., Fuxe, K., Goldstein, M. 1975. Applications of immunohistochemistry to studies on monoamine cell systems with special references to nervous tissues. *Ann. N.Y. Acad. Sci.* 254:407–32

45. Hökfelt, T., Fuxe, K., Johansson, O., Jeffcoate, S. L., White, N. 1975. Distribution of thyrotropin-releasing hormone (TRH) in the central nervous system as revealed with immunohistochemistry. *Eur. J. Pharmacol.* 34: 389–92

46. Hökfelt, T., Fuxe, K., Johansson, O., Jeffcoate, S., White, N. 1975. Thyrotropin-releasing hormone (TRH)–containing nerve terminals in certain brain stem nuclei and in the spinal cord. *Neurosci. Lett.* 1:133–39

47. Hökfelt, T., Pernow, B., Nilsson, G., Welterberg, L., Goldstein, M., Jeffcoate, S. L. 1978. Dense plexus of substance P immunoreactive nerve terminals in eminentia medialis of the primate hypothalamus. *Proc. Natl. Acad. Sci. USA* 75:1013–15

48. Hökfelt, T., Ljungdahl, A., Steinbusch, H., Verhofstad, A., Nilsson, G., Brodin, E., Pernow, B., Goldstein, M. 1978. Immunohistochemical evidence for substance P–like immunoreactivity in some 5-hydroxytryptamine–containing neurons in the rat central nervous system. *Neuroscience* 3:517–38

49. Hökfelt, T., Ljungdahl, A., Terenius, L., Elde, R., Nilsson, G. 1977. Immunohistochemical analysis of peptide pathways possibly related to pain and

analgesia: Enkephalin and substance P. *Proc. Natl. Acad. Sci. USA* 74:3081–85

50. Hughes, J., Smith, F. W., Kosterlitz, H. W., Fothergill, L. H., Morgan, B. A., Morris, H. R. 1975. Identification of two related pentapeptides from the brain with potent opiate agonist activity. *Nature* 258:577–79

51. Jackson, I. M. D., Reichlin, S. 1974. Thyrotropin-releasing hormone (TRH): Distribution in hypothalamic and extrahypothalamic brain tissue of mammalian and submammalian chordates. *Endocrinology* 95:854–62

52. Knigge, K. M., Joseph, S. A., Hoffman, G. E. 1978. Organization of LRF- and SRIF- neurons in the endocrine hypothalamus. See Ref. 24, pp. 49–68

53. Kobayashi, R. M., Palkovits, M., Miller, R. J., Chang, K.-J., Cuatrecasas, P. 1978. Brain enkephalin distribution is unaltered by hypophysectomy. *Life Sci.* 22:527–30

54. Kosterlitz, H. W., Hughes, J. 1976. Some thoughts on the significance of enkephalin, the endogenous ligand. *Life Sci.* 17:91–96

55. Krulich, L., Dhariwal, A. P. S., McCann, S. M. 1968. Stimulatory and inhibitory effects of purified hypothalamic extracts on growth hormone release from rat pituitary in vitro. *Endocrinology* 83:783–90

56. Krulich, L., Quijada, M., Wheaton, J. E., Illner, P., McCann, S. M. 1977. Localization of hypophysiotropic neurohormones by assay of sections from various brain regions. *Fed. Proc.* 36: 1953–59

57. Larsson, L.-I., Fahrenkrug, J., Schaffalitzky de Muckadell, O., Sundler, F., Hakanson, R., Rehfeld, J. F. 1976. Localization of vasoactive intestinal polypeptide (VIP) to central and peripheral neurons. *Proc. Natl. Acad. Sci. USA* 73:3197–200

58. Lien, E. L., Fenichel, R. L., Garsky, V., Sarantakis, D., Grant, N. H. 1976. Enkephalin-stimulated prolactin release. *Life Sci.* 19:837–40

59. Ljungdahl, A., Hökfelt, T., Nilsson, G. 1978. Distribution of substance P–like immunoreactivity in the central nervous system of the rat. I. Cell bodies and nerve terminals. *Neuroscience* 3: 861–943

60. Mains, R. E., Eipper, B. A., Ling, N. 1977. Common precursor to corticotropins and endorphins. *Proc. Natl. Acad. Sci. USA* 74:3014–18

61. Micevych, P., Elde, R. 1978. Comparative immunohistochemistry of met-

enkaphalin, vasopressin and oxytocin in the median eminence and hypothalamus of the cat. *Neurosci. Abstr.* 4:411

62. Mutt, V., Said, S. I. 1974. Structure of the porcine vasoactive intestinal octacosa-peptide. The amino-acid sequence. Use of kallikrein in its determination. *Eur. J. Biochem.* 42:581–89

63. Nair, R. M. G., Barrett, J. F., Bowers, C. Y., Schally, A. V. 1970. Structure of porcine thyrotropin releasing hormone. *Biochemistry* 9:1103–6

64. Nakane, P. K. 1971. Application of peroxidase-labelled antibodies to the intracellular localization of hormones. In *Karolinska Symposia on Research Methods in Reproductive Endocrinology, Vol. 3: In Vitro Methods in Reproductive Cell Biology*, ed. A. Dickfalusy, pp. 190–204. Copenhagen: Forum

65. Nicoll, R. A. 1975. Promising peptides. In *Neuroscience Symposia, Vol. I: Neurotransmitters, Hormones and Receptors: Novel Approaches*, ed. J. A. Ferrendelli, B. S. McEwen, S. H. Snyder, pp. 99–122. Bethesda, Md.: Soc. Neurosci.

66. Oliver, C., Eskay, R. L., Ben-Jonathan, N., Porter, J. C. 1974. Distribution and concentration of TRH in the rat brain. *Endocrinology* 96:540–46

67. Parsons, J., Erlandsen, S., Hegre, O., McEvoy, R., Elde, R. P. 1976. Central and peripheral localization of somatostatin. Immunoenzyme immunocytochemical studies. *J. Histochem. Cytochem.* 24:872–82

68. Pelletier, G., Labrie, F., Arimura, A., Schally, A. V. 1974. Electron microscopic immunohistochemical localization of growth hormone release inhibiting hormone (somatostatin) in the rat median eminence. *Am. J. Anat.* 140:445–50

69. Pelletier, G., Leclerc, R., Labrie, F., Cote, J., Chretien, M., Lis, M. 1977. Immunohistochemical localization of β-lipotropic hormone in the pituitary gland. *Endocrinology* 100:770–76

70. Petrusz, P., Sar, M., Ordronneau, P., DiMeo, P. 1976. Specificity in immunocytochemical staining. *J. Histochem. Cytochem.* 24:1110–15

71. Renaud, L. P. 1978. Neurophysiological organization of the endocrine hypothalamus. See Ref. 24, pp. 269–302

72. Rossier, J., Vargo, T. M., Minick, S., Ling, N., Bloom, F. E., Guillemin, R. 1977. Regional dissociation of β-endorphin and enkephalin contents in rat brain and pituitary. *Proc. Natl. Acad. Sci. USA* 74:5162–65

73. Schally, A. V., Arimura, A., Baba, Y., Nair, R. M. G., Matsuo, J., Redding, T. W., Debeljuk, L., White, W. F. 1971. Isolation and properties of the FSH- and LH-releasing hormone. *Biochem. Biophys. Res. Commun.* 43:393–99

74. Seybold, V. S., Elde, R., Hökfelt, T. 1978. Effects of reserpine on vasopressin/neurophysin in the external layer of the median eminence in the rat. *Neurosci. Abstr.* 4:355

75. Silverman, A. J., Krey, L. C. 1978. The luteinizing hormone–releasing hormone (LHRH) neuronal networks of the guinea pig. I. Intra- and extra-hypothalamic projections. *Brain Res.* In press

76. Silverman, A. J., Zimmerman, E. A. 1975. Ultrastructural immunocytochemical localization of neurophysin and vasopressin in the median eminence and posterior pituitary of the guinea pig. *Cell Tiss. Res.* 159:291–301

77. Simantov, R., Kuhar, M. J., Uhl, G. R., Snyder, S. H. 1977. Opioid peptide enkephalin: Immunohistochemical mapping in the rat central nervous system. *Proc. Natl. Acad. Sci. USA* 74:2167–71

78. Sofroniew, M. V., Weindl, A. 1978. Extra-hypothalamic neurophysin–containing perikarya, fiber pathways and fiber clusters in the rat brain. *Endocrinology* 102:334–37

79. Sternberger, L. A. 1974. *Immunocytochemistry.* Englewood Cliffs, N.J.: Prentice-Hall

80. Stillman, M. A., Recht, L. D., Rosario, S. L., Seif, S. M., Robinson, A. G., Zimmerman, E. A. 1977. The effects of adrenalectomy and glucocorticoid replacement on vasopressin and vasopressin-neurophysin in the zona externa the median eminence of the rat. *Endocrinology* 101:42–49

81. Swaab, D. F., Pool, C. W., Van Leeuwen, F. W. 1977. Can specificity ever be proved in immunocytochemical staining? *J. Histochem. Cytochem.* 25:388–91

82. Swanson, L. W. 1977. Immunohistochemical evidence for a neurophysin-containing autonomic pathway arising in the paraventricular nucleus of the hypothalamus. *Brain Res.* 128:346–53

83. Terry, L. C., Willoughby, J. O., Brazeau, P., Martin, J. B. 1976. Antiserum to somatostatin prevents stress-induced inhibition of growth hormone in the rat. *Science* 192:565–68

84. Uhl, G. R., Kuhar, M. J., Snyder, S. H. 1977. Neurotensin: Immunohistochemical localization in rat central ner-

vous system. *Proc. Natl. Acad. Sci. USA* 74:4059–63
85. Vale, W., Rivier, C., Brown, M. 1977. Regulatory peptides of the hypothalamus. *Ann. Rev. Physiol.* 39:473–528
86. Vale, W., Brazeau, P., Rivier, C., Brown, M., Boss, B., Rivier, J., Burgus, R., Ling, N., Guillemin, R. 1975. Somatostatin. *Recent Prog. Horm. Res.* 31:365
87. Vandesande, F., Dierickx, K., DeMey, J. 1975. Identification of separate vasopressin-neurophysin II and oxytocin-neurophysin I containing nerve fibers in the external region of the bovine median eminence. *Cell Tiss. Res.* 158:509–16
88. Van Vugt, D. A., Bruni, J. F., Meites, J. 1978. Naloxone inhibition of stress-induced increase in prolactin secretion. *Life Sci.* 22:85–89
89. Watson, S. J., Akil, H., Sullivan, S., Barchas, J. D. 1977. Immunocyto-chemical localization of methionine enkephalin: Preliminary observations. *Life Sci.* 21:733–38
90. Watson, S. J., Barchas, J. D., Li, C. H. 1977. β-lipotropin: Localization of cells and axons in rat brain by immunocytochemistry. *Proc. Natl. Acad. Sci. USA* 74:5155–58
91. Winokur, A., Utiger, R. D. 1974. Thyrotropin-releasing hormone: Regional distribution in rat brain. *Science* 185:265–67
92. Zimmerman, E. A. 1976. Localization of hypothalamic hormones by immunocytochemical techniques. In *Frontiers in Neuroendocrinology*, ed. L. Martini, W. F. Ganong, pp. 25–62. New York: Raven Press
93. Zimmerman, E. A., Liotta, A., Krieger, D. T. 1978. β-lipotropin in brain: Localization in hypothalamic neurons by immunoperoxidase technique. *Cell Tiss. Res.* 186:393–98

Ann. Rev. Physiol. 1979. 41:603–15
Copyright © 1979 by Annual Reviews Inc. All rights reserved

CENTRAL NEUROTRANSMITTERS ❖1240
AND THE SECRETION
OF PROLACTIN, GH, LH AND TSH

Ladislav Krulich

Department of Physiology, University of Texas Health Science Center,
Dallas, Texas 75235

The role of the central neurotransmitters in the regulation of the secretion of hypophysial hormones has enjoyed the unflagging interest of both the experimental and clinical endocrinologists during the past few years. I review here the most recent developments, with several restrictions: The achievements in the mapping of the aminergic and peptidergic systems of the CNS are not included; experimental studies on animals are preferred to clinical observations; and, with few exceptions, only selected papers published during the past two years are cited. Further information can be found in Müller's monograph (1) and in several excellent general reviews (2, 3, 4).

PROLACTIN

The concept is well established and generally accepted that prolactin secretion is under a tonic inhibitory influence generated by the activity of the tuberoinfundibular *dopaminergic system* (reviewed in 5). This system's major physiological function seems to be that of keeping the prolactin secretion low during resting conditions. It probably does not participate, by decreased activity, in the activation of prolactin secretion by suckling or stress. On the contrary, its activity is probably enhanced in these situations (6, 7), which may explain the observations that inhibition of dopamine (DA) synthesis with α-methyl-p-tyrosine augmented the prolactin releasing effect of suckling in lactating rats (8) and that blockade of DA receptors with pimozide augmented the effect of stress in male rats (9). It is possible, however, that

603

0066-4278/79/0301-0603$01.00

the decreased activity of the DA system during proestrus in cyclic female rats facilitates the induction of the prolactin surge (10).

The mechanism of the dopaminergic inhibition of prolactin secretion, i.e. whether there is a prolactin-inhibiting factor (PIF) different from dopamine, remains controversial.

The concept that dopamine released into the portal circulation is itself the inhibitor of the pituitary lactotrophs has gained support from detection of dopamine in portal blood (11) and from the demonstration that its concentration might be sufficient to impose the inhibition (12). Furthermore, the DA receptors of the pituitary lactotrophs are supersensitive to apomorphine in rats following mechanical destruction of the mediobasal hypothalamus (13), which implies that in intact animals the receptors are exposed to activation by DA.

The concept that dopamine is the inhibitor of prolactin secretion was supported indirectly by the so far fruitless attempts to isolate a PIF from hypothalamic extracts, which led first to isolation of catecholamine-rich fractions and later to identification of gamma aminobutyric acid (GABA) as the carrier of the prolactin-inhibiting activity in other fractions (14, 15). GABA certainly inhibits prolactin secretion by a direct effect on the pituitary lactotrophs, but the required doses seem to be too high to make it a likely authentic PIF. However, another line of support for the dopamine theory, based on demonstration that the PIF activity of hypothalamic extracts can be accounted for by their catecholamine content (16), was challenged by Enjalbert et al (17), who claim a catecholamine-free PIF activity in synaptosomal fractions prepared from hypothalamic tissue. Therefore, the possibility that there is a PIF different from DA cannot be discounted.

The possible role of the central *noradrenergic system* in the regulation of prolactin secretion is still largely unknown and the available information is confusing. Intraventricular injections of norepinephrine (NE) elevated serum prolactin in ovariectomized estrogen-progesterone-primed rats (OEP rats) (18) but injections of either α or β blockers did the same (19). Systemic administration of the central α receptor agonist clonidine induced modest-to-marked elevation of prolactin levels (20, 21, 22); however, administration of the α receptor blocker, phenoxybenzamine, had a similar effect, whereas α blockade with phentolamine or β blockade with propranolol had no consistent influence (21, 23, 24).

However, there are indications that the central NE system may play a role in the stress-induced activation of prolactin secretion and in the induction of the prolactin surge during proestrus. Depletion of brain NE following destruction of the central NE terminals with 6-OH-dopamine abolished the prolactin response to stress (25); selective destruction of the ventral adrenergic pathway abolished proestrous surges in cyclic females (26), and systemic administration of either α or β blockers suppressed the afternoon prolactin surges induced by estrogen in ovariectomized rats, respectively (27).

Recent work confirmed earlier studies showing that activation of the central *serotoninergic* (SER) *system* stimulates secretion of prolactin. Blockade of serotonin (5-HT) re-uptake with fluoxetine augmented the prolactin releasing effect of small doses of 5-OH-tryptophan [5-HTP; (28, 29)] and activation of prolactin secretion was described following administration of the serotonin receptor agonist, quipazine (29, 30, 31)

It is probable that the SER system plays a role in activation of prolactin secretion in several physiological situations. Blockade of serotonin receptors with methysergide or inhibition of serotonin synthesis with p-chlorophenylalanine abolished the suckling-induced prolactin release in lactating rats (32, 33) or the prolactin surges in ovariectomized females treated with estrogen (34, 35). The participation of the SER system in the activation of prolactin secretion by suckling was further substantiated by demonstration of increased metabolism of brain serotonin in suckled females (6), and the possibility that release of prolactin-releasing factor (PRF) is involved was suggested by a recent preliminary report (36). Participation of the SER system in the activation of prolactin secretion by stress is more problematical. Blockade of serotonin receptors with methysergide suppressed it (37), and blockade of serotonin re-uptake had an augmenting effect (28); depletion of brain serotonin had no influence (9, 38, 39).

Pharmacologic activation of the *cholinergic system* through either muscarinic or nicotinic receptors inhibits prolactin secretion, possibly by stimulation of the activity of the tuberoinfundibular DA system (40, 41). In addition to this indirect mechanism, a direct inhibitory effect of muscarinic receptor agonists on the pituitary lactotrophs must be considered (42). The physiological role of the cholinergic system in the regulation of prolactin secretion is not known, because receptor blockade had no influence on prolactin secretion, either basal or stimulated (21, 34).

There are indications for a physiological role of the *histaminergic system* in the regulation of prolactin secretion; intraventricular injection of histamine stimulated prolactin secretion in rats (43), whereas blockade of histamine receptors of the H_1 type prevented stimulation of prolactin secretion by stress or suckling (44). However, the situation is complicated by findings that stimulation or blockade of the H_2 histamine receptors seems to have effects on prolactin secretion opposite to those after analogous manipulations of the H_1 receptors (44).

Finally, recent work shows that pharmacological manipulations of the *GABA-ergic system* have influence on prolactin secretion. Intraventricular injections of large doses of GABA stimulated prolactin secretion whereas smaller doses had an inhibitory effect (45, 46). The stimulating effect of the large doses was blocked by the GABA antagonist bicuculline, which by itself did not influence serum prolactin levels, and it was converted into an inhibitory effect by blockade of the DA receptors with pimozide (47). However, according to another report, bicuculline stimulated prolactin secretion, whereas intracisternal injection of GABA had no effect by itself, but blocked the prolactin-releasing effect of several other agents as, for instance, histamine, neurotensin, haloperidol, and clonidine (48).

GROWTH HORMONE

The secretion of GH has several characteristics of its own. One of them is the very marked pulsatile character of its release, especially in the rat, in which species fluctuations of the serum GH levels are typically extreme. In contrast to primates, rats react to stress by an inhibition of GH secretion. Both factors make the study of the role of the central neurotransmitters rather difficult, and stress-free experimental conditions, especially in studies on rats, are a necessary prerequisite for meaningful results (reviewed in 49).

The role of the central *dopaminergic system* has been studied quite extensively, and the evidence is rather conclusive that in primates it is stimulatory to GH secretion. Contrary to earlier work (50, 51), recent studies suggest a stimulating role for the DA system also in rats. Stimulation of GH secretion was seen following systemic administration of small doses of apomorphine (52) or following intraventricular injection of DA (53). Conversely, blockade of DA receptors with butaclamol, which has a minimal effect on adrenergic receptors, decreased the amplitude of the secretory pulses without affecting the pulsatile pattern (54). This implies that the DA system makes a physiological contribution to the regulation of GH secretion, the precise significance of which is not yet clear.

Several recent reports have confirmed the large body of earlier evidence for a stimulatory role of the central *noradrenergic system* in primates operating through α-adrenergic receptors. In human subjects, secretion of GH was activated by clonidine (55) or by desimipramine, which augments the effect of central NE activity by blocking NE re-uptake into the NE terminals (56). The NE precursor, dihydroxyphenylserine (DOPS) proved effective in monkeys (57). Conversely, blockade of α receptors abolished the GH releasing effect of electroshock therapy in psychiatric patients (58).

Recent research work suggests a similar function of the NE system in rats. Intraventricular injections of NE stimulated GH secretion in rats (53), whereas blockade of α receptors with phenoxybenzamine abolished the GH secretory surges, as did inhibition of catecholamine synthesis with α-MT (22, 23). The pulsatile pattern in the α-MT treated animals could be restored with clonidine but not with apomorphine (23). It seems, therefore, that the central NE system represents the major drive for GH secretion both in primates and in rats and that in primates it mediates the GH releasing effect of stressful stimuli.

The central *serotoninergic system* also has a stimulatory role in both primates and rats. Administration of 5-HTP elevated GH serum levels in human subjects (59), monkeys (57), and rats (60). Equally effective in rats was intraventricular injection of serotonin or of the serotonin receptor agonist, quipazine (50, 61). The effects of both drugs were abolished by the serotonin-receptor blocker methysergide (61).

It is probable that the serotoninergic system participates in physiological regulation of GH secretion. In humans, blockade of serotonin receptors suppressed both the sleep-related activation of GH secretion (63) and the activation of GH secretion by insulin hypoglycemia (62). In rats the pulsatile secretion was abolished by inhibition of serotonin synthesis with pCPA and was considerably diminished by methysergide (23).

Little is known about the possible roles of the histamine- and GABA-ergic systems. In human subjects, administration of the H_1 antihistaminic was seen to blunt the GH-secretory response to administration of arginine but not to insulin hypoglycemia (64), while injection of GABA into the cerebral ventricles in rats stimulated GH secretion (65, 66, 67).

In view of the existence of somatostatin, it is remarkable that there are no reported inhibitory effects on the secretion of GH of any of the transmitters themselves or of appropriate receptor agonists. In primates this may mean that release of hypothalamic somatostatin does not participate in the regulation of GH secretion. However, in the rat there is evidence that release of somatostatin is instrumental in the stress-induced inhibition of GH secretion, and the absence of inhibiting effects may mean that the releaser of somatostatin has not yet been found. A recent preliminary report that both catecholamines stimulate release of somatostatin from hypothalamic tissue in vitro (68) is difficult to align with their effects in vivo. Perhaps the catecholamines stimulate in vivo release of somatostatin and GRF simultaneously, with GRF overriding the inhibiting effect of somatostatin.

LUTEINIZING HORMONE

The study of the role of the neurotransmitters in the regulation of the secretion of LH has been rather uneven. Considerable energy has been spent on the elucidation of the role of the catecholamines, which doubtlessly play an important role, whereas the other systems have received much less attention.

The large body of earlier findings (69) that the central *noradrenergic system* is the major activator of LH secretion has been substantiated further by recent work. Intraventricular injections of NE stimulated LH secretion in the OEP rat (18, 70). NE also released LRH from hypothalamic fragments in vitro (68).

A role for the NE system in the induction of the proestrous LH surge received additional support from findings that the NE turnover and NE concentration in the median eminence are increased prior to the LH surge in adult cyclic rats or in prepubertal females treated with pregnant mare's serum gonadotropin (10, 71, 72). Conversely, the LH surges were reduced or abolished following destruction of the ventral noradrenergic pathway (73). Also in accord with earlier experience, interference with the function of the NE system abolished the circhoral LH pulses and decreased serum LH and LRH levels in castrated animals (74, 75, 76).

In contrast to that of the central NE system, the role of the *dopaminergic system* in the regulation of LH secretion is controversial. Intraventricular injections of DA were once more shown to stimulate LH secretion in the OEP female rat (18), and DA also stimulated LRH release from hypothalamic fragments in vitro (68, 77) suggesting an LRH-releasing function of the DA system. There is, however, considerable evidence that the central DA system inhibits LRH-LH secretion. Both infusion of DA and administration of L-dopa or of DA receptor agonists reduced LH levels in normal women (78); the DA receptor agonists had similar effects in intact or ovariectomized rats (52, 79). Implantation of pituitaries under the kidney capsule, which leads to a lasting elevation of serum prolactin levels that in turn stimulate the activity of tuberoinfundibular DA system (80), prevented the postcastration rise of LH levels (81) and temporarily decreased LH levels in castrated rats (80, 82). However, according to Vijayan & McCann (83), infusion of DA or intravenous injection of apomorphine elevated serum LH in ovariectomized rats, but when the drugs were injected intraperitoneally they reduced the LH levels. Blockade of DA receptors either had no effect on LH levels in castrated rats (75, 79) or caused a further elevation (74).

Several DA receptor agonists also inhibited LH surge induced in immature females by pregnant mare's serum gonadotropin, but some DA receptor blockers (chlorpromazine) had the same effect (71). However, according to Clemens (84), administration of a DA receptor agonist in the morning of proestrus advanced the LH surge by several hours. This might indicate that the DA system plays a role in the complex sequence of events that culminates in the LH surge; but it is improbable that in the rat the DA system has an active part in induction of the surge itself, because at that time in the ovarian cycle both the turnover of DA in the median eminence and the concentration of DA in portal blood are at their lowest levels (10, 11, 71).

Activation of the central *serotoninergic system* is generally thought to inhibit secretion of LH. This notion is indirectly supported by recent findings that the inhibition of proestrous LH surge by electrical stimulation of the hippocampus or lateral amygdala is abolished by depletion of brain serotonin with PCPA (85) and that electrical stimulation of arcuate nucleus, which in nontreated ovariectomized rats inhibits the circhoral pulsations of serum LH, had stimulating effect in animals treated with PCPA (86). However, there is evidence that the serotoninergic system may also have some positive input. The afternoon LH surges in ovariectomized-estrogenized rats were abolished by treatment with PCPA and restored by subsequent administration of 5-HTP (35). Destruction of 5-HT terminals with 5,7-dihydroxytryptamine reduced serum LH in male rats, and the return of LH to normal values coincided with the regrowth of the nerve fibers (38).

The information on the role of the remaining neurotransmitters is still very limited and confusing. Intraventricular injections of histamine had some LH releasing effect in females but not in normal males (43, 87). Intraventricular GABA stimulated LH secretion in male rats anesthetized with pentobarbital, but not in unanesthetized males (88); however, it was effective in unanesthetized ovariectomized females or in OEP rats (67).

THYROID-STIMULATING HORMONE

The available information on the role of the central neurotransmitters in the regulation of TSH secretion is still quite fragmentary. However, certain patterns are already emerging.

Artificial activation of central DA receptors inhibits TSH secretion in rats. A marked decrease of serum TSH has been described following both systemic administration of apomorphine or piribedil (52, 89, 90, 91) and intraventricular injection of dopamine (53). Activation of DA receptors inhibited not only resting secretion of TSH but also the cold-stimulated TSH release (89, 90, 91). However, the physiological role of the DA system is not clear because DA receptor blockade does not influence either basal TSH levels or the stimulation by cold (52, 89, 91). There is also considerable evidence that the central NE system stimulates TSH secretion. Intraventricular injection of clonidine or NE increased TSH secretion (53, 92), whereas blockade of synthesis of NE or blockade of α-adrenergic receptors caused a conspicuous decrease of serum TSH (89, 91). It is almost certain that the cold-induced TSH release is mediated by the NE system (89, 91, 93).

In contrast, the role of the central 5-HT system is controversial. In one study, intraventricular injection of 5-HT caused a transient elevation of serum TSH (94); in another, both this same intervention and injection of quipazine were seen to decrease TSH levels in male rats (31). Systemic administration of 5-HTP, which has a dramatic effect on secretion of prolactin, had no consistent effect on TSH. In contrast, systemic administration of tryptophan drastically reduced serum TSH but had only minimal prolactin-releasing effect despite a demonstratable activation of brain-serotonin metabolism (95).

Pharmacological manipulations of the neurotransmitter systems usually have no effect on serum TSH levels in normal human subjects.

NONHORMONAL NEUROPEPTIDES

In addition to the hypothalamic hypophysiotropic hormones LRH, TRH, and somatostatin, the CNS contains a variety of other biologically active neuropeptides: opioid peptides, substance P, neurotensin, angiotensin, the vasoactive intestinal polypeptide (VIP), arginine-vasotocin, gastrin, bombesin, and others. Although their physiological role is still unknown and their mechanisms of action are mostly uncertain, several of them have a marked influence on the secretion of adenopituitary hormones.

The opioid peptides, β-endorphin, met-enkephalin, and several synthetic met-enkephalin analogs stimulated secretion of prolactin and growth hormone in rats (96, 97, 98) and inhibited secretion of LH and TSH (99) in accord with previous experience with morphine. All of these effects were blocked by the specific opiate receptor blocker, naloxone. A possible physiological role of endogenous opioid peptides in the regulation of adenohypophysial secretion is suggested by observations that the antagonists naloxone and naltrexone decreased basal prolactin and GH levels, respectively, and inhibited activation of prolactin secretion by stress or estrogen (98, 100, 101).

Substance P and neurotensin were also seen to stimulate secretion of prolactin and GH (102), but in contrast to the opioid peptides these effects were not blocked by naloxone but by blockade of H_1 histamine receptors (103). According to results from one laboratory (104), arginine-vasotocin elevated serum prolactin in male rats; however, according to another group of workers, the peptide suppressed the proestrous surges of both LH and prolactin in normal cyclic rats (105). It is uncertain how the effects of arginine-vasotocin relate to the function of the pineal gland, which contains the peptide in large concentrations.

ACKNOWLEDGMENT

I would like to thank Mrs. M. A. Mayfield for her help in collecting the literature for the present review, which at the last count amounted to 350 papers. (And I wish I could have cited them all.)

Literature Cited

1. Müller, E. E., Nistico, G., Scapagnini, U. 1978. In *Neurotransmitters and Anterior Pituitary Function.* New York: Academic. 435 pp.
2. Rose, J. C., Ganong, W. F. 1976. Neurotransmitter regulation of pituitary secretion. In *Current Developments in Psychopharmacology,* ed. W. B. Essman, L. Valzelli, pp. 87–123. New York: Halsted
3. McCann, S. M., Ojeda, S. R. 1976. Synaptic transmitters involved in the release of hypothalamic releasing and inhibiting hormones. In *Reviews of Neuroscience,* ed. S. Ehrenpreis, J. Kopin, pp. 91–110. New York: Raven
4. Del Pozo, E., Lancranjan, I. 1978. Clinical use of drugs modifying the release of anterior pituitary hormones. *Front. Neuroendocrinol.* 5:207–47
5. MacLeod, R. M. 1976. Regulation of prolactin secretion. *Front. Neuroendocrinol.* 4:169–94
6. Mena, F., Enjalbert, A., Carbonell, L., Priam, M., Kordon, C. 1976. Effect of suckling on plasma prolactin and hypothalamic monoamine levels in the rat. *Endocrinology* 99:445–51
7. Kvetnansky, R., Palkovits, M., Mitro, A., Torda, T., Mikulaj, L. 1977. Catecholamines in individual hypothalamic nuclei of acutely and repeatedly stressed rats. *Neuroendocrinology* 23:257–67
8. Voogt, J. L., Carr, L. A. 1975. Potentiation of suckling induced release of prolactin by inhibition of brain catecholamine synthesis. *Endocrinology* 97:811
9. Meltzer, H. Y., Fang, V. S., Daniels, S. 1976. Biogenic amines and serum prolactin levels during stress in male rats. *Fed. Proc.* 35:554 (Abstr.)
10. Löfström, A. 1977. Catecholamine turnover alterations in discrete areas of the median eminence of the 4- and 5-day cyclic rats. *Brain Res.* 120:113–31
11. Ben-Jonathan, N., Oliver, C., Weiner, H. J., Mical, R. S., Porter, J. C. 1977. Dopamine in hypophysial portal plasma of the rat during the estrous cycle and during pregnancy. *Endocrinology* 100:452–58
12. Gibbs, D. M., Neill, J. D. 1978. Dopamine levels in hypophysial stalk blood in the rat are sufficient to inhibit prolactin secretion *in vivo. Fed. Proc.* 37:555 (Abstr.)
13. Cheung, C. Y., Weiner, R. I. 1976. Supersensitivity of anterior pituitary dopamine receptors involved in the inhibition of prolactin secretion following destruction of the medial basal hypothalamus. *Endocrinology* 99:914–17
14. Arimura, A., Schally, A. V. 1977. Prolactin release inhibiting and stimulating factors in the hypothalamus. *Adv. Exp. Med. Biol.* 87:237–52
15. Schally, A. V., Redding, T. W., Arimura, A., Dupont, A., Linthicum, G. L. 1977. Isolation of gamma-aminobutyric acid from pig hypothalami and demonstration of its prolactin release inhibiting (PIF) activity *in vivo* and *in vitro. Endocrinology* 100:681
16. Shaar, C. J., Clemens, J. A. 1974. The role of catecholamines in the release of anterior pituitary prolactin *in vitro. Endocrinology* 95:1202–12
17. Enjalbert, A., Priam, M., Kordon, C. 1977. Evidence in favor of the existence of a dopamine free prolactin-inhibiting factor (PIF) in rat hypothalamic extracts. *Eur. J. Pharmacol.* 41:243–44
18. Vijayan, E., McCann, S. M. 1978. Reevaluation of the role of catecholamines in control of gonadotropin and prolactin release. *Neuroendocrinology.* 25:150–65
19. Gala, R. R., Janson, P. A., Kuo, E. Y. 1972. The influence of neural blocking agents injected into the third ventricle of the rat brain and hypothalamic electrical stimulation on serum prolactin. *Proc. Soc. Exp. Biol. Med.* 140:569–72
20. Stevens, R. W., Lawson, D. M. 1977. The influence of estrogen on plasma prolactin levels induced by thyrotrophin-releasing hormone (TRH), clonidine and serotonin in ovariectomized rats. *Life Sci.* 20(2):261–65
21. Lawson, D. M., Gala, R. R. 1975. The influence of adrenergic, dopaminergic, cholinergic and serotoninergic drugs on plasma prolactin levels in ovariecto-

mized, estrogen-treated rats. *Endocrinology* 96:313–18

22. Durand, D., Martin, J. B., Brazeau, P. 1977. Evidence for a role of α-adrenergic mechanisms in the regulation of episodic growth hormone secretion in the rat. *Endocrinology* 100:722–28

23. Martin, J. B., Durand, D., Gurd, W., Faille, G., Audet, J., Brazeau, P. 1978. Neuropharmacological regulation of episodic growth hormone and prolactin secretion in the rat. *Endocrinology* 102:106–13

24. Marchlewska-Koj, A. 1976. Effect of catecholamines and serotonin on the secretion of prolactin from the pituitary of the rat. *Acta Biol. Cracoviensia* XIX:107–44

25. Fenske, M., Wuttke, W. 1976. Effects of intraventricular 6-hydroxydopamine injections on serum prolactin and LH levels: absence of stress-induced pituitary prolactin release. *Brain Res.* 104:68–70

26. Langelier, P., McCann, S. M. 1977. The effects of interruption of the ventral noradrenergic pathway on the proestrous discharge of prolactin in the rat. *Proc. Soc. Exp. Biol. Med.* 154:553–57

27. Subramanian, M. G., Gala, R. R. 1976. The influence of cholinergic, adrenergic and serotoninergic drugs on the afternoon surge of plasma prolactin in ovariectomized, estrogen-treated rats. *Endocrinology* 98:842–48

28. Krulich, L. 1975. The effect of a serotonin uptake inhibitor (Lilly 110140) on the secretion of prolactin in the rat. *Life Sci.* 17:1141–44

29. Clemens, J. A., Sawyer, B. D., Cerimele, B. 1977. Further evidence that serotonin is a neurotransmitter involved in the control of prolactin secretion. *Endocrinology* 100:692–98

30. Meltzer, H. Y., Fang, V. S., Paul, S. M., Kaluskar, R. 1976. Effect of quipazine on rat plasma prolactin levels. *Life Sci.* 19:1073–78

31. Krulich, L., Vijayan, E., Giachetti, A., Mayfield, M. A., McCann, S. M. 1978. On the role of the central serotoninergic system in the regulation of the secretion of TSH and prolactin. Effects of quipazine and 5-hydroxytryptamine (5-HT). *Endocrinology.* In press

32. Gallo, R. V., Rabii, J., Moberg, G. P. 1975. Effect of methysergide, a blocker of serotonin receptors, on plasma prolactin levels in lactating and ovariectomized rats. *Endocrinology* 97:1096–1105

33. Kordon, C., Blake, T. S., Terkel, J., Sawyer, C. H. 1974. Participation of serotonin-containing neurons in the suckling-induced rise in plasma prolactin levels in lactating rats. *Neuroendocrinology* 13:213–23

34. Subramanian, M. G., Gala, R. R. 1976. Further studies on the effect of adrenergic, serotoninergic and cholinergic drugs on the afternoon surge of plasma prolactin in ovariectomized, estrogen-treated rats. *Neuroendocrinology* 22:240–49

35. Héry, M., Laplante, E., Kordon, C. 1976. Participation of serotonin in the phasic release of LH. I. Evidence from pharmacological experiments. *Endocrinology* 99:496–503

36. Brandstaetter, J., Terkel, J. 1978. *In vivo* evidence for a prolactin releasing factor (PRF) in lactating rats. *Fed. Proc.* 37:1789 (Abstr.)

37. Marchlewska-Koj, A., Krulich, L. 1975. The role of central monoamines in the stress-induced prolactin release in the rat. *Fed. Proc.* 34:191 (Abstr.)

38. Wuttke, W., Björklund, A., Baumgarten, H. G., Lachenmeyer, L., Fenske, M., Klemm, H. P. 1977. De- and regeneration of brain serotonin neurons following 4,7-dihydroxytryptamine treatment: effects on serum LH, FSH and prolactin levels in male rats. *Brain Res.* 134:317–31

39. Coppings, R. J., Giachetti, A., Krulich, L. 1978. Inhibition of prolactin secretion by a direct effect of methysergide on pituitary lactotrophs. *Fed. Proc.* 37:2231 (Abstr.)

40. Grandison, L., Meites, J. 1976. Evidence for adrenergic mediation of cholinergic inhibition of prolactin release. *Endocrinology* 99:775–79

41. Eneroth, P., Fuxe, K., Gustaffsson, J. A., Hökfelt, T., Löfström, A., Skett, P., Agnati, L. 1977. The effect of nicotine on central catecholamine neurons and gonadotropin secretion. III. Studies on prepubertal female rats treated with pregnant mare serum gonadotropin. *Med. Biol.* 55:167–76

42. Subramanian, M. G., Gala, R. R. 1977. Specificity of arecoline and apomorphine and site of action of arecoline in inhibiting diurnal prolactin surge. *Proc. Soc. Exp. Biol. Med.* 155:353–56

43. Libertun, C., McCann, S. M. 1976. The possible role of histamine in the control of prolactin and gonadotropin release. *Neuroendocrinology* 20:110–20

44. Arakelian, M. C., Libertun, C. 1977. H_1 and H_2 histamine receptor participa-

tion in the brain control of prolactin secretion in lactating rats. *Endocrinology* 100:890–95

45. Mioduszewski, R., Grandison, L., Meites, J. 1976. Stimulation of prolactin release in rats by GABA. *Proc. Soc. Exp. Biol. Med.* 151:44–46

46. Vijayan, E., McCann, S. M. 1978. The effects of intraventricular injection of γ-aminobutyric acid (GABA) on prolactin and gonadotropin release in conscious female rats. *Brain Res.* 155: 35–43

47. Vijayan, E., McCann, S. M. 1978. The effect of blockade of dopamine (DA) receptors with pimozide on pituitary hormone release in response to intraventricular injection of γ-aminobutyric acid in conscious rats. *Brain Res.* In press

48. Rivier, C., Vale, W. 1977. Effects of γ-aminobutyric acid and histamine on prolactin secretion in the rat. *Endocrinology* 101:506–71

49. Martin, J. B., Brazeau, P., Tannenbaum, G. S., Willoughby, J. O., Epelbaum, J., Terry, L. C., Durand, D. 1978. Neuroendocrine organization of growth hormone regulation. In *The Hypothalamus*, ed. S. Reichlin, R. J. Baldessarini, J. B. Martin, pp. 329–355. New York: Raven

50. Collu, R., Fraschini, F., Martini, L. 1973. Role of indoleamines and catecholamines in the control of gonadotropin and growth hormone secretion. *Progr. Brain Res.* 39:289–300

51. Kato, Y., Dupre, J., Beck, J. C. 1973. Plasma growth hormone in the anesthetized rat: Effect of dibutyryl cyclic AMP, prostaglandin E_1, adrenergic agents, vasopressin, chlorpromazine, amphetamine and L-dopa. *Endocrinology* 93:135–46

52. Mueller, G. P., Simpkins, J., Meites, J., Moore, K. E. 1976. Differential effects of dopamine agonists and haloperidol on release of prolactin, thyroid-stimulating hormone, growth hormone and luteinizing hormone in rats. *Neuroendocrinology* 20:121–35

53. Vijayan, E., Krulich, L., McCann, S. M. 1978. Catecholaminergic regulation of TSH and growth hormone release in ovariectomized and ovariectomized, steroid-primed rats. *Neuroendocrinology* 26:174–85

54. Willoughby, J. O., Brazeau, P., Martin, J. B. 1977. Pulsatile secretion of growth hormone and prolactin: effects of (+)-butaclamol, a dopamine receptor blocking agent. *Endocrinology* 101:1298–1303

55. Lal, S., Tolis, G., Martin, J. B., Brown, G. M., Guyda, H. 1975. Effects of clonidine on growth hormone, prolactin, luteinizing hormone, follicle stimulating hormone and thyroid stimulating hormone in the serum of normal man. *J. Clin. Endocrinol. Metab.* 41: 703–8

56. Laakman, G., Schumacher, G., Benkert, O., Werder, K. R., 1977. Stimulation of growth hormone secretion by disimipramine and chlorimipramine in man. *J. Clin. Endocrinol. Metab.* 44:1010–13

57. Chambers, J. W., Brown, G. M. 1976. Neurotransmitter regulation of growth hormone and ACTH in the rhesus monkey: Effects of biogenic amines. *Endocrinology* 98:420–28

58. Vigaš, M., Wiederman, V., Németh, S., Jurčovičová, J., Žigo, L. 1976. Alpha-adrenergic regulation of growth hormone release after electroconvulsive therapy in man. *Neuroendocrinology* 21:42–48

59. Lancranjan, I., Wirz-Justice, A., Pühringer, W., Del Pozo, E. 1977. Effect of 1- 5-hydroxytryptophan infusion on growth hormone and prolactin secretion in man. *J. Clin. Endocrinol. Metab.* 45:588–93

60. Smythe, G. A., Brandstater, J. F., Lazarus, L. 1975. Serotoninergic control of rat growth hormone secretion. *Neuroendocrinology* 17:245–57

61. Vijayan, E., Krulich, L., McCann, S. M. 1978. Effect of activation of the central serotoninergic system with quipazine or 5-hydroxytryptamine (5-HT) on the secretion of growth hormone in unanesthetized rats. *Proc. Soc. Exp. Biol. Med.* In press

62. Smythe, G. A., Lazarus, L. 1974. Suppression of human growth hormone secretion by melatonin and cyproheptadine. *J. Clin. Invest.* 54:116–21

63. Chihara, K., Kato, Y., Maeda, K., Matsukura, S., Imura, H. 1976. Suppression by cyproheptadine of human growth hormone and cortisol secretion during sleep. *J. Clin. Invest.* 57:1393–1402

64. Pontirolli, A. E., Viberti, G., Vicari, A., Pozza, G. 1976. Effect of the antihistamic agents meclastine and dexchlorpheniramine on the response of human growth hormone to arginine infusion and insulin hypoglycemia. *J. Clin. Endocrinol. Metab.* 43:582–86

65. Bruni, J. F., Mioduszewski, R. J., Grandison, L. J., Simpkins, J. W., Meites, J. 1977. Effect of cholinergic

and GABA-ergic drugs on serum GH in male rats. *Fed. Proc.* 285 (Abstr.)

66. Abe, H., Kato, Y., Chihara, K., Ohgo, S., Iwasaki, Y., Imura, H. 1977. Growth hormone release by gamma-aminobutyric acid (GABA) and gamma-amino-β-hydroxybutyric acid (GABOB) in the rat. *Endocrinol. Jpn.* 24:229–31

67. Vijayan, E., McCann, S. M. 1978. Effect of intraventricular injection of γ-aminobutyric acid (GABA) on plasma growth hormone (GH) and thyrotropin (TSH) in conscious ovariectomized rats. *Endocrinology* 103:1888–93

68. Negro-Vilar, A., Ojeda, S. R. 1978. *In vitro* release of somatostatin and LRH by MBH and ME fragments: effect of catecholamines (CAs). *Fed. Proc.* 37:445 (Abstr.)

69. McCann, S. M., Moss, R. L. 1975. Putative neurotransmitters involved in discharging gonadotropin-releasing neurohormones and the action of LH-releasing hormone on the CNS. *Life Sci.* 16:833–52

70. Krieg, R. J., Sawyer, C. H. 1976. Effects of intraventricular catecholamines on luteinizing hormone release in ovariectomized–steroid-primed rats. *Endocrinology* 99:411–19

71. Agnati, L., Fuxe, K., Löfström, A., Hökfelt, T. 1977. Dopaminergic drugs and ovulation: Studies on PMS-induced ovulation and changes in median eminence DA and NE turnover in immature female rats. *Adv. Biochem. Psychopharmacol.* 16:159–68

72. Negro-Vilar, A., Chiocchio, S. R., Tramezzani, J. H. 1977. Changes in catecholamine content of the median eminence precede the proestrous surges of luteinizing hormone and prolactin. *J. Endocrinol.* 75:339–40

73. Martinovič, J. V., McCann, S. M. 1977. Effect of lesions in the ventral noradrenergic tract produced by microinjections of 6-hydroxydopamine on gonadotropin release in the rat. *Endocrinology* 100:1206–13

74. Gnodde, H. P., Schuiling, G. A. 1976. Involvement of catecholaminergic and cholinergic mechanisms in the pulsatile release of LH in the long-term ovariectomized rat. *Neuroendocrinology* 20:212–23

75. Drouva, S. V., Gallo, R. V. 1976. Catecholamine involvement in episodic luteinizing hormone release in adult ovariectomized rats. *Endocrinology* 99:651–58

76. Kalra, S. P. 1977. Suppression of serum LHRH and LH in rats by an inhibitor of norepinephrine synthesis. *J. Reprod. Fertil.* 49:371–73

77. Rotszstein, W. H., Charli, J. L., Pattou, E., Epelbaum, J., Kordon, C. 1976. *In vitro* release of luteinizing hormone-releasing hormone (LHRH) from rat mediobasal hypothalamus: Effects of calcium, potassium and dopamine. *Endocrinology* 99:1663–66

78. Lachelin, G. C., Leblanc, H., Yen, S. S. 1977. The inhibitory effect of dopamine agonists on LH release in women. *J. Clin. Endocrinol. Metab.* 44:728–32

79. Drouva, S. V., Gallo, R. V. 1977. Further evidence for inhibition of episodic luteinizing hormone release in ovariectomized rats by stimulation of dopamine receptors. *Endocrinology* 100:792–98

80. Gudelsky, G. A., Simpkins, J., Mueller, G. P., Meites, J., Moore, K. E. 1976. Selective actions of prolactin on catecholamine turnover in the hypothalamus and on serum LH and FSH. *Neuroendocrinology* 22:206–15

81. Grandison, L., Hodson, C., Chen, H. T., Advis, J. P., Simpkins, J., Meites, J. 1977. Inhibition by prolactin of postcastration rise in LH. *Neuroendocrinology* 23:312–22

82. Beck, W., Engelbart, S., Gelato, M., Wuttke, W. 1977. Antigonadotrophic effect of prolactin in adult castrated and in immature female rats. *Acta Endocrinol.* 84:62–71

83. Vijayan, E., McCann, S. M. 1978. The effect of systemic administration of dopamine and apomorphine on plasma LH and prolactin concentrations in conscious rats. *Neuroendocrinology.* 25:221–35

84. Clemens, J. A., Tinsley, F. C., Fuller, R. W. 1977. Evidence for a dopaminergic component in the series of neural events that lead to the proestrous surge of LH. *Acta Endocrinol.* 85:18–24

85. Kawakami, M., Kimura, F., Kawagoe, S. 1976. Cholinergic and serotoninergic neural links and the inhibitory effects of hippocampus, lateral amygdala and central gray matter on gonadotropin release. *Endocrinol. Jpn.* 23:11–21

86. Gallo, R. V., Moberg, G. P. 1977. Serotonin mediated inhibition of episodic luteinizing hormone release during electrical stimulation of the arcuate nucleus in ovariectomized rats. *Endocrinology* 100:945–54

87. Donoso, A. O., Bannza, A. M. 1976. Acute effects of histamine on plasma

prolactin and luteinizing hormone levels in male rats. *J. Neural Transm.* 39:95–101

88. Pass, K. A., Ondo, J. G. 1977. The effects of γ-aminobutyric acid on prolactin and gonadotropin secretion in the unanesthetized rat. *Endocrinology* 100:1437–42

89. Tuomisto, J., Ranta, T., Männistö, P., Saarinen, A., Leppäluoto, J., 1975. Neurotransmitter control of thyrotropin secretion in the rat. *Eur. J. Pharmacol.* 30:221–29

90. Ranta, T., Männistö, P., Tuomisto, J. 1977. Evidence for dopaminergic control of thyrotrophin secretion in the rat. *J. Endocrinol.* 72:329–35

91. Krulich, L., Giachetti, A., Marchlewska-Koj, A., Hefco, E., Jameson, H. E. 1977. On the role of the central noradrenergic and dopaminergic systems in the regulation of TSH secretion in the rat. *Endocrinology* 100:496–505

92. Annunziato, L., Di Renzo, G., Lombardi, G., Scopacasa, F., Schettini, G., Preziosi, P., Scapagnini, U. 1977. The role of central noradrenergic neurons in the control of thyrotropin secretion in the rat. *Endocrinology* 100:738–44

93. Onaya, T., Hashizume, K. 1976. Effects of drugs that modify brain biogenic amine concentration on thyroid activation induced by exposure to cold. *Neuroendocrinology* 20:47–58

94. Jordan, D., Ponsin, G., Mornex, R. 1976. Serotoninergic stimulation of thyrotropic function in the rat. *Vth Int. Cong. Endocrinol., Hamburg, 1976.* Abstr. 151

95. Mueller, G. P., Twohy, C. P., Chen, H. T., Advis, J. P., Meites, J. 1976. Effect of L-tryptophan and restraint stress on hypothalamic and brain turnover, and pituitary TSH and prolactin release in rats. *Life Sci.* 18:715–24

96. Lien, E. L., Fenichel, R. L., Garsky, V., Sarantakis, D., Grant, N. H. 1976. Enkephalin-stimulated prolactin release. *Life Sci.* 19:837–40

97. Rivier, C., Vale, W., Ling, N., Brown, M., Guillemin, R. 1977. Stimulation *in vivo* of the secretion of prolactin and growth hormone by β-endorphin. *Endocrinology* 100:238–41

98. Shaar, C. J., Frederickson, R. C. A., Dininger, N. B., Jackson, L. 1977. Enkephalin analogues and naloxone modulate the release of growth hormone and prolactin: evidence for regulation by an endogenous opiod peptide in brain. *Life Sci.* 21:853–60

99. Bruni, J. F., Van Vugt, D., Marshall, S., Meites, J. 1977. Effect of naloxone, morphine and methionin enkephalin on serum prolactin, luteinizing hormone, follicle stimulating hormone, thyroid stimulating hormone and growth hormone. *Life Sci.* 21:461–66

100. Grandison, L., Guidotti, A. 1977. Regulation of prolactin release by endogenous opiates. *Nature* 270:357–59

101. Van Vugt, D. A., Bruni, J. F., Meites, J. 1978. Naloxone inhibition of stress-induced increase in prolactin secretion. *Life Sci.* 22:85–90

102. Kato, Y., Chihara, K., Ohgo, S., Iwasaki, Y., Abe, H., Imura, H. 1976. Growth hormone and prolactin release by substance P in rats. *Life Sci.* 19:441–46

103. Rivier, C., Brown, M., Vale, W. 1977. Effect of neurotensin, substance P and morphine sulfate on the secretion of prolactin and growth hormone in the rat. *Endocrinology* 100:751–54

104. Vaughan, M. K., Blask, D. E., Vaughan, G. M., Reiter, R. J. 1976. Dose-dependent prolactin releasing activity of arginine vasotocin in intact and pinealectomized estrogen-progesterone treated adult male rats. *Endocrinology* 99:1319–22

105. Cheesman, D. W., Osland, R. B., Forsham, P. H. 1977. Suppression of the preovulatory surge of luteinizing hormone and subsequent ovulation in the rat by arginine vasotocin. *Endocrinology* 101:1194–1201

Ann. Rev. Physiol. 1979. 41:617–31
Copyright © 1979 by Annual Reviews Inc. All rights reserved

ACTIONS OF HYPOTHALAMIC-HYPOPHYSIOTROPIC HORMONES ON THE BRAIN

♦1241

Robert L. Moss

Department of Physiology, University of Texas Health Science Center at Dallas, Southwestern Medical School, Dallas, Texas 75235

This review is devoted to consideration of the extra-pituitary actions of the hypothalamic hypophysiotropic hormones—thyrotropin-releasing hormone (TRH), luteinizing hormone–releasing hormone (LHRH), and somatostatin—in the central nervous system (CNS). The review will touch upon three topics: (*a*) the capacity of the hypothalamic peptide hormones to initiate and maintain extra-pituitary behaviors; (*b*) the ability of the hypothalamic peptide hormones to alter neuronal excitability; and finally (*c*) the consideration of the hypothalamic hormones as neurotransmitters in the CNS. References have frequently been chosen for their recentness and bibliography rather than for any priority in the field. Many aspects of the neurobiology of the hypothalamic peptides have been reviewed previously (1, 2, 51–53, 66, 84).

BEHAVIORAL ACTIONS OF THE HYPOTHALAMIC HYPOPHYSIOTROPIC HORMONES IN THE CNS

The localization of peptidergic neurons in the CNS has indicated an emerging pattern with respect to distribution of TRH, LHRH, and somatostatin cell bodies and nerve terminals [see the review by Elde & Hökfelt (22) in this volume]. Peptidergic neurons are localized within the hypophysiotropic area as well as within extra-hypophysiotropic sites. Thus besides mediating anterior pituitary secretions, hypothalamic peptide hormones may also play an integral role in brain function by mediating extra-pituitary events. Several laboratories have recently shown the hypothalamic hypophysiotropic

617

hormones to have unquestionable effects on behavior. [For reviews see (36, 45, 52, 53, 95).] The action of the peptide hormones appears to be sufficient to modulate the functions of the CNS, and subsequently to initiate a specific behavioral pattern, independently of the anterior pituitary gland. These data clearly indicate that peptide hormones have intrinsic CNS actions.

Thyrotropin-Releasing Hormone (TRH)

The tripeptide TRH releases thyroid-stimulating hormone and prolactin from the anterior pituitary gland (8, 23, 106) and is widely distributed throughout the brain and spinal cord (12, 35, 44, 68, 102, 110). That TRH initiated actions on the CNS not mediated by the pituitary was first demonstrated in a number of pharmacological tests to screen psychotropic effects of drugs. TRH, for example, potentiates the behavioral activation induced by pargyline-L-dopa and 5-hydroxy-tryptophan (5-HTP) (10, 74, 75) even in hypophysectomized and thyroidectomized animals. These data demonstrate that TRH can enhance general activity induced by antidepressant drugs. Intraventricular administration of microgram quantities of TRH increases locomotion in the free-roving rat (98), and potentiates L-dopa-induced stereotyped behavior. Administration of TRH increases strychnine-induced seizure duration (11) and 5-HTP-induced tremor in mice (32, 33). TRH has also been shown to antagonize sleep and hypothermia caused by pentobarbital (10, 78) and ethanol (10) independently of the anterior pituitary gland. In addition, TRH suppresses feeding and drinking behavior (107). Thus, TRH increases general activity in animals, and this increase occurs independently of the pituitary gland and under a variety of conditions. TRH opposes the action of centrally acting drugs, including chloral hydrate, reserpine, diazepam, and several barbiturates other than pentobarbital.

Since TRH is endogenous and widely distributed throughout the brain and spinal cord, it is therefore not inconceivable that TRH should exert such a generalized action as increased activity. TRH appears to be a CNS stimulant. Interestingly, TRH appears to have some beneficial effects in man; it produces partial, transient, and variable relief of depression, schizophrenia, hyperkinesis, and alcohol withdrawal (80).

Somatostatin

The tetradecapeptide somatostatin (SS) is also found in extra-hypothalamic brain regions (13, 31). SS inhibits the release of growth hormone (9, 100) and thyroid-stimulating hormone (105). The behavioral action of SS appears to be opposite to that of TRH: SS reduces locomotion (98), prolongs pentobarbital sleeping time (78) and anabarbital sleeping time (15), and decreases the duration of strychnine-induced seizure. When given alone it causes sedation and hypothermia (15). Thus, SS appears to be a CNS depressant. Like TRH, SS has a wide CNS distribution; this may account for the general decrease in activity following its administration. Its behavioral effects have not been studied in humans. [For detailed information and references on the clinical behavioral effects of TRH and SS, see (37, 80).]

Luteinizing Hormone–Releasing Hormone (LHRH)

LHRH, a decapeptide, augments follicle-stimulating-hormone (FSH) as well as luteinizing-hormone (LH) release from the anterior pituitary gland (106). Data on the distribution of LHRH neurons (cell bodies and/or nerve terminals) in the CNS show them to be confined mainly to the hypophysiotropic area, i.e. the medial basal hypothalamus and preoptic area (3, 4, 18, 30, 41, 70, 99, 101, 109). However, some extra-hypothalamic LHRH neurosecretory pathways have been observed recently in a variety of species including rat, guinea pig, and cat. Most notable among the extra-hypothalamic pathways is the hypothalamo-mesencephalic tract (3, 101). Thus, of the three characterized hypothalamic peptides discussed here, LHRH has the most limited CNS distribution.

A more specific behavioral effect has been found with LHRH than with TRH or SS. In fact, investigation of this compound in animals has offered the most direct evidence thus far of a central action for hypothalamic polypeptides. LHRH has been demonstrated to have a specific action on mating behavior (potentiation) in the estrogen-primed ovariectomized (and in the ovariectomized and adrenalectomized or hypophysectomized) rat (56, 63, 64, 72). This increase in lordosis behavior has been found to be specific to LHRH; subcutaneous injections of estrone alone, or of estrone in combination with either TRH, LH, or FSH, were ineffective in initiating mating activities. The LHRH-induced mating behavior thus appears to be independent of anterior pituitary and adrenal hormones. Supportive experiments have demonstrated that the mechanism by which vaginal stimulation activates lordosis responsiveness appears to be due to some process other than release of pituitary hormones (92) and may be mediated by LHRH. LHRH also has been shown to facilitate sexual behavior in dihydrotestosterone- and estradiol benzoate–treated mice (46).

Prostaglandins (PGs), which have been implicated along with LHRH in the neural control of LH secretion from the anterior pituitary gland (47), have also been shown to modify sexual behavior. More specifically, PGE_2, whether administered systemically (19, 93) or intracranially (27), can induce mating behavior in estrogen-primed, ovariectomized (and in ovariectomized, adrenalectomized) rats. PGE_2 has recently been shown to facilitate the lordosis response in ovariectomized rats even without estrogen priming (93, 94). The data suggest that PGE_2 might have the capacity to modulate firing of preoptic-hypothalamic LHRH neurons (76) implicated in the control of mating behavior as well as gonadotropin secretion. The evidence described thus far is based on the effects of LHRH and PGE_2 in estrogen-primed, ovariectomized female rats and mice. However, LHRH and PGE_2 also affect sexual behavior in male rats. LHRH accelerates ejaculation in intact male rats and in castrated rats maintained on testosterone (56); intracerebral infusion of PGE_2 facilitated copulatory behavior in castrated male rats given daily systemic injections of testosterone propionate (50 mg) (14). It is interesting to note that LHRH-induced copulatory behavior is dependent on the presence of testosterone in the male and estrogen in the female. Furthermore, in nonsexual-behavioral tests, LHRH, unlike TRH and SS, has no effect on pentobarbital responses and on eating and drinking behavior in rodents (79, 107).

That the behavioral effects of LHRH are mediated by direct actions on the CNS is further indicated by recent experiments demonstrating that intrahypothalamic [medial preoptic area (MPOA) and arcuate-ventromedial nucleus (ARC-VM)] infusion of LHRH potentiates lordosis behavior (24, 25, 29, 59). TRH infusions resulted in less mating behavior than control infusions. Similar infusions of LHRH and TRH into the lateral hypothalamus and cerebral cortex resulted in no change in the mating behavior pattern. The microinfusion of FSH into the MPOA and ARC-VM did not alter the behavioral response, while LH suppressed the lordotic behavior normally observed in estrogen-LHRH primed, ovariectomized female rats (26). The deposition of LH onto nerve cell membranes results in a marked inhibition of hypophysiotropic neurons, which may explain the LH suppression of mating behavior (38, 96). Certainly supportive of the concept of a hypothalamo-mesencephalic LHRH tract (3, 101) is the finding that LHRH infusions into the midbrain central grey region of estrone-primed, ovariectomized female rats initiated significantly more lordosis behavior than that observed with TRH and saline infusions (91). Furthermore, LHRH has been localized via radioimmunoassay in the midbrain central grey region (personal communication, W. Samson and S. M. McCann, 1978). To date, the most convincing evidence in support of a LHRH neural system that mediates lordosis behavior comes from experiments in which anti-LHRH-antibody was infused into the 3rd ventricle. The antibody decreased the lordosis behavior normally observed in the estrogen-progesterone primed, ovariectomized female rat (42). This study provided the first evidence that antiserum to LHRH can act on the brain and subsequently decrease sexual receptivity, presumably by affecting the animal's endogenous LHRH levels.

The aforementioned findings are indicative of a facilitative action of LHRH and an inhibitory action of TRH on mating behavior. LHRH- and TRH-sensitive sites in the hypothalamus are confined to the MPOA, ARC-

VM, and midbrain central grey; the peptides were not active when infused into either the lateral hypothalamus or the cerebral cortex. It should be mentioned that as studied so far (48, 63, 64, 72) LHRH does not have as great an effect on the lordosis response as progesterone. However, the results with the decapeptide, in conjunction with the decreased receptivity following the infusion of antibody to LHRH into the 3rd ventricle, suggest that in the female rat the peptide hormone may be acting directly on neural tissue in the hypothalamic and/or extra-hypothalamic area to potentiate or depress lordotic behavior independently of the pituitary and adrenal gland.

The observation that synthetic LHRH facilitates mating behavior in the rat has generated considerable interest in the possibility that LHRH therapy may be useful in the teatment of human sexual impotence. Experiments utilizing a variety of routes of administration from nasal spray to subcutaneous injections suggested an LHRH-induced increase in sexual activity (libido and/or behavior) in normal adult, hypogonadal, and impotent males (7, 50, 65, 97). However, the LHRH-induced increase has not been marked or consistent. A number of experiments have demonstrated negative findings. For instance, intravenous injection of LHRH in three normal adult males resulted in no measurable change in sexual activity (21), and subcutaneous administration every 8 hr for one month resulted in no improvement in libido in sexually impotent patients (17). Quite obviously, the clinical usefulness of LHRH in the treatment of sexual dysfunction remains to be ascertained. The evidence of LHRH's ability to enhance human sexual potency is suggestive at best, requiring support by rigorously controlled clinical studies conducted on many patients.

NEUROPHYSIOLOGICAL ACTION OF HYPOTHALAMIC HYPOPHYSIOTROPIC HORMONES IN THE CNS

The behavioral effects of TRH, LHRH, and SS, together with evidence of their CNS distribution and identification in hypothalamic synaptosome fractions (5, 6, 81), suggest a possible role for the hypophysiotropic hormones in the modulation of neuronal excitability. [For current reviews see (1, 2, 52, 66, 84, 85).] Microelectrophoresis has been used to determine the identity of peptide-sensitive neurons in the CNS. By this technique, minute quantities (femtomoles) of peptide hormones (0.001–0.01 M solutions) can be applied directly to the surface of single neurons to circumvent the blood-brain barrier without disturbing the gonadotropin-releasing ability (40).

Microelectrophoresis of the peptide hormones has revealed both excitatory and inhibitory effects of TRH, LHRH, and SS on hypothalamic as well as extra-hypothalamic neurons (20, 38, 39, 51, 52, 60, 61, 73, 77, 87, 89,

90). Examination of these data revealed that the peptide effects in the male rat were predominantly inhibitory (87, 89) while the deposition of peptides in either the female guinea pig or rat (intact-cyclic or ovariectomized) yielded a combination of excitatory and inhibitory actions (38, 39, 51, 52, 54, 60–62, 77). Recently the ovarian hormones have been shown to modulate neuronal membrane responsiveness to LHRH, LHRH agonist analog, and TRH (54). In the estrogen-progesterone primed animal as compared to the untreated, ovariectomized rat, more MPOA neurons were excited by LHRH and its agonist analog, while fewer neurons were responsive to TRH. In addition, the responsiveness of medial basal hypothalamic nerve cells to LHRH has been shown to fluctuate during the estrous cycle, with a larger percentage of responsive neurons occurring on proestrus than on diestrus (38).

Microelectrophoretic experiments have shown TRH-sensitive neurons to be found in the medial basal hypothalamus, preoptic area, septum, ventromedial nucleus of the hypothalamus, cerebral cortex, cerebellar cortex, and cuneate nucleus (52, 57, 87, 89, 90), while somatostatin-sensitive neurons are found in the ventromedial nucleus of the hypothalamus, cerebral cortex, and cerebellar cortex (89, 90). The predominant effect of microelectrophoretically applied TRH on nerve cells in several areas of the brain is inhibition (52, 87); however, in the spinal motoneurons TRH has a stimulatory effect (67). Behavioral data may be related to the neurophysiological data by a behavioral disinhibition since, aside from mating behavior, the general behavioral effects of TRH are of an excitatory nature. Thus, it appears that TRH acts directly on mating-sensitive neurons to inhibit sexual receptivity, while the tripeptide acts indirectly (perhaps through interneurons) to initiate general excitatory behavioral effects. As previously mentioned, such effects were demonstrated in studies showing that the tripeptide antagonized the effects of barbiturates, ethanol, chloral hydrate, and reserpine (10).

On the other hand, LHRH-responsive neurons are more widely distributed in the CNS than the decapeptide itself, as determined by radioimmunoassay and immunohistochemistry. Microelectrophoresis of LHRH has revealed peptide-sensitive neurons throughout the hypothalamus, preoptic area, and septum as well as in the cerebral cortex and in the general area of the midbrain central grey (51, 52, 55, 57, 89, 90). A more detailed analysis of the hypophysiotropic area showed that LHRH excited more ARC neurons than it inhibited, and TRH inhibited more of the same ARC neurons than it excited (38, 52, 77). This predominant excitatory action of LHRH and inhibitory action of TRH on ARC neurons that do not send their axons to the median eminence (ME) coincides with the LHRH facilitation and TRH diminution of the lordotic reflex as observed in mating-behavior experiments (25, 59). The intraventricular infusion of LHRH also increased the amplitude-discriminated multiple unit spike activity of ARC neurons (43).

Actually, the aforementioned neurophysiological data may explain the LHRH-induced sexual behavior observed in both animals and humans (7, 50, 53). For instance, it is thought that the hypothalamic decapeptide is synthesized in specialized nerve cells located within the hypophysiotropic area, namely, in those MPOA and ARC neurons that send their axons to the ME. With the proper hormonal and/or neural stimulus, the specialized nerve cells release LHRH into the hypothalamo-hypophyseal portal system, where it initiates the release of LH from the anterior pituitary gland. However, these ME-terminating ARC neurons may also exert a second influence on the brain itself by a system of collateral connections to other ARC and/or VM neurons. Thus, the collateral fibers would terminate within the ARC-VM complex and synapse on neurons that project to other hypothalamic or extra-hypothalamic areas where LHRH could modulate their neuronal activity, either directly, or indirectly through an amine system, to initiate various behaviors. ARC neurons that terminate in the ME have been shown recently to have collateral fibers (28, 86, 88, 112, 113). In addition, there is also some evidence for recurrent facilitation and recurrent inhibition in these ARC neurons (112) which suggests transmitter or neuromodulator roles for the hypothalamic peptides.

Several important observations concerning the specificity of LHRH in modulating the electrical activity of MPOA nerve cells have been made (58) by comparing its action with that of the LHRH analogs: (a) D–TRP^6, Pro^9-NHEt-LRH, agonist analog [LHRH$^+$], LH releasing potency in vitro 150 times that of LHRH; (b) D-Phe^2, D-TRP^6-LHRH, antagonist analog [LHRH$^-$], releasing potency in vitro 15 times that of LHRH; and (c) des-Pro^9-GLY^{10}-LHRH, inactive analog [LHRH^0], LH releasing potency in vitro ≤ 0.001 that of LHRH. There appears to be no consistent linear relationship between the effectiveness of the agonist analog in vitro and the agonist's potential to increase single nerve cell discharges. However, in most cases, LHRH and LHRH$^+$ microelectrophoresis resulted in responses that were similar in direction (excitatory or inhibitory) and magnitude. It also should be noted that, on occasion, the LHRH$^+$-induced effect was greater and longer lasting than responses observed from LHRH.

The concentration at the neuronal membrane of the material that is being iontophoresed must be established in order to compare different agents for potency. Unfortunately, a shortcoming of the microelectrophoretic technique is its inability to provide accurate concentration measurements of material released at the electrode tip. Aside from this, two situations have been observed that implicate LHRH agonist analog as more effective than

LHRH at the single nerve cell level (58). First, LHRH was sometimes ineffective in modulating nerve cell activity while LHRH$^+$ produced a marked response at the same ejecting current level. Secondly, the analog LHRH$^+$ was capable in some cases of producing a response similar in magnitude to that produced by LHRH but with a lower ejecting current.

The LHRH$^-$ antagonist analog produced a completely different response profile from those of LHRH and LHRH$^+$ (58). In ovariectomized females, LHRH$^-$ produced more inhibition than excitation. On the other hand, LHRH^0 inactive analog was just as effective as LHRH and LHRH$^+$ agonist analog in terms of its ability to modulate neuronal activity (58). At present these findings cannot be explained; however, they may be an expression of the inactive analog's slight potency in releasing some gonadotropin or an indication that the specificity of receptor sites in the brain is quite different from that in the pituitary.

Finally, additional support for LHRH-responsive neurons within the MPOA and ARC-VM region is present in studies demonstrating a short-loop feedback of LH. The microinfusion of LH, for example, into the MPOA and ARC-VM region diminishes the lordotic behavior normally observed in the ovariectomized, estrogen-LHRH treated female rat (26). This finding is in agreement with the previous proposals of LH suppression of mating behavior in male and female rats (16, 71). Moreover, these inhibitory effects of LH upon sexual behavior are also correlated with the inhibitory effects observed upon hypothalamic single cell activity (96), multi-unit activity (103, 111), oxidative metabolism (49), and RNA transcription (34). These effects also parallel the inhibitory effects of LH described for LHRH secretion (82, 104). The parallelisms in LH suppression of neuronal activity, endocrine function, and behavioral responses indicate that LH may feed back upon hypothalamic neurons involved in the coordination of reproductive processes. Further, the LH blockade of LHRH effects suggest that LH may act upon LHRH-responsive neurons within the hypophysiotropic area.

CONSIDERATION OF THE HYPOTHALAMIC HYPOPHYSIOTROPIC HORMONES AS NEUROTRANSMITTERS IN CNS

Until recently, many endocrinologists considered the hypothalamic hypophysiotropic hormones to be solely involved in pituitary function, while many neuropharmacologists considered all the major neurotransmitters to be accounted for. However, it is now quite clear that a new class of substances, the hypothalamic hypophysiotropic peptides, do mediate extra-pituitary behaviors and participate in neuronal excitability and thus must be included in any list of putative CNS neurotransmitters.

In establishing the role of peptides in CNS function as synaptic transmitters, it is necessary to satisfy certain criteria similar to those utilized to identify such other agents such as acetylcholine and norepinephrine as neurotransmitters (108). Satisfying such criteria in the CNS is extremely difficult, but the hypothalamic hypophysiotropic hormones have in part done so. For example, LHRH and TRH have been identified in synaptosomal preparations (5, 6, 81), and the release of peptides from nerve terminals has been shown to be Ca^{2+}-dependent (69). In addition, both LHRH and TRH have been (a) localized in cell bodies and nerve terminals (18, 70), (b) shown to be involved in the initiation of specific CNS-dependent behaviors (63, 64), and (c) shown to be involved in neuronal excitability of hypothalamic as well as extra-hypothalamic neurons (38, 39, 52, 57, 58, 89). Interestingly, the peptides in the CNS are characterized by their extreme potency (active in picomole concentrations for pituitary effects, nanogram concentrations for mating behavior, and femtomole concentration for neurophysiological effects), their capacity for having bifunctional properties (i.e. acting as possible transmitters and simultaneously as hormones), and finally, their time course for inducing neural cellular and behavioral actions. The time course for the neural response was virtually instantaneous and coterminous with the period of peptide hormone microelectrophoresis. On the other hand, the behavioral response was initiated approximately 2–5 hr following subcutaneous administration and 30 min following intrahypothalamic microinfusion. [For a review of the peptides as probable transmitter candidates in CNS, see (83).]

In conclusion, the hypothalamic hypophysiotropic hormones have been shown to have extra-pituitary behavioral actions as well as neurophysiological postsynaptic membrane effects in addition to their specific endocrine effects. Whether these peptides are neurotransmitters (i.e. whether they are released from terminal endings, diffuse across a narrow cleft, and subsequently act on the receptors of the postsynaptic membrane) or neuromodulators [i.e. circulating substances that interact with receptors on neurons within the CNS (66)] is open to some question and controversy. Peptide hormones are certainly localized within axonal terminals and are apparently released into the synaptic space. These peptide hormones do initiate changes in neuronal excitability in some nerve cells but not in others, are found in only selective CNS sites (although in some cases they are widely but not ubiquitously distributed), and, in the case of LHRH, mediate a specific CNS-dependent behavior. This would suggest a neurotransmitter role for the hypothalamic peptides. The question of whether the hypothalamic peptides are transmittters or modulators is of considerable interest but not of paramount importance. What is of major importance, is the fact that the hypothalamic hypophysiotropic hormones can mediate three distinct events—i.e. pituitary, behavioral, and neural outflow—and can be considered as multisignal integrator(s) in the physiology of animal and man.

ACKNOWLEDGMENTS

The authors express their appreciation to Donna King for typing the manuscript and Carol A. Dudley and Peter Riskind for their critical analysis of the manuscript. Synthetic luteinizing hormone–releasing hormone (LRH) and its agonist analog D-ala^6, des-gly^{10} LRH ethylamide were generously provided by Drs. M. Götz and R. Deghenghi of Ayerst Research Laboratories, Montreal, Canada. Thyrotropin releasing hormone was supplied by Drs. J. Dorn and J. Weinstein and Mr. C. Flanagan of Abbott Laboratories, North Chicago, Illinois, and Dr. J. Rivier of the Salk Institute at San Diego supplied the LRH analog peptides (*a*) D-TRP^6, Pro^9 – NHEt-LRH, agonist analog (LHRH$^+$), (*b*) D-Phe^2, D-TRP^6 -LHRH, antagonist analog (LHRH$^-$), (*c*) des-Pro^9-GLY^{10}-LHRH inactive analog (LHRH^0), and ([τ-ME-His^2] TRH).

Research from the author's laboratory referred to in this review was supported by the National Institutes of Health Research Grant NIH-USPHS-10434 END and the National Science Foundation Grant NSF-GB-43494. The author is the recipient of a USPHS-NIH Career Development Award K04-00146.

Literature Cited

1. Barker, J. L. 1976. Peptides: Roles in neuronal excitability. *Physiol. Rev.* 56(2):435–452
2. Barker, J. L. 1977. Physiological roles of peptides in the nervous system. In *Peptides in Neurobiology,* ed. Harold Gainer, pp. 295–343. New York and London: Plenum
3. Barry, L., Dubois, M. P. 1976. Immunoreactive LRH neurosecretory pathways in mammals. *Acta Anat.* 94:497–503
4. Barry, J., Dubois, M. P., Carette, B. 1974. Immunofluorescent study of the preoptic-infundibular LRH neurosecretion pathway in normal, castrated or testosterone-treated male guinea-pig. *Endocrinology* 95:1416–23
5. Barnea, A., Ben-Jonathan, N., Porter, J. C. 1975. Characterization of hypothalamic particles containing luteiniz-

ing hormone and thyrotropin releasing hormone. *J. Neurochem.* 27:477–84
6. Barnea, A., Ben-Jonathan, N., Colston, C., Johnston, J. M., Porter, J. C. 1975. Differential sub-cellular compartmentalization of thyrotropin-releasing hormones (TRH) and gonadotropin-releasing hormones (LRH) in hypothalamic tissue. *Proc. Natl. Acad. Sci. USA* 72:3153
7. Benkert, O., Jordan, R., Dahlen, H. G., Schneider, H. P. G., Gammel, G. 1975. Sexual impotence: a double blind study of LHRH nasal spray. *Neuropsychobiology* 1:203–10
8. Bowers, C. Y., Friesen, H. G., Hwang, P., Guyda, H. J., Folkers, K. 1971. Prolactin and thyrotropin release in man by synthetic pyroglutamyl-histadyl-prolineamide. *Biochem. Biophys. Res. Commun.* 45:1033–41

9. Brazeau, P., Vale, W., Burgus, R., Ling, N., Butcher, M., Rivier, J., Guillemin, R. 1973. Hypothalamic polypeptide that inhibits the secretion of immunoreactive pituitary growth hormone. *Science* 179:77–79

10. Breese, G. R., Cooper, B. R., Prange, A. J. Jr., Cott, J. M., Lipton, M. A. 1974. Interactions of thyrotropin-releasing hormone with centrally acting drugs. In *The Thyroid Axis, Drugs, and Behavior,* ed. A. J. Prange, Jr., pp. 115–27. New York: Raven

11. Brown, M., Vale, W. 1975. Growth hormone release in the rat: effects of somatostatin and thyrotropin-releasing factor. *Endocrinology* 97:1151–56

12. Brownstein, M. J. 1977. Biologically active peptides in the mammalian central nervous system. See Ref. 2, pp. 145–70

13. Brownstein, M., Arimura, A., Sato, H., Schally, A. V., Kizer, J. S. 1975. The regional distribution of somatostatin in the rat brain. *Endocrinology* 96: 1456–61

14. Clemens, L. G., Gladue, B. A. 1977. The effect of prostaglandin E_2 on masculine sexual behavior in the rat. *J. Endocrinol.* 75:383–89

15. Cohn, M. L. 1975. Cyclic AMP, thyrotropin releasing factor and somatostatin: key factors in the regulation of the duration of narcosis. In *Molecular Mechanisms of Anesthesia,* ed. B. R. Fink, pp 485–500. New York: Raven

16. Crowley, W. R., Rodriguez-Sierra, J. F., Komisaruk, B. R. 1976. Hypophysectomy facilitates sexual behavior in female rats. *Neuroendocrinology* 20:328–38

17. Davies, T. F., Mountjoy, C. Q., Gomez-Pan, A., Watson, M. J., Hanker, J. P., Besser, G. M., Hall, R. 1977. Reduced gonadotrophin: response to releasing hormone after chronic administration to impotent men. *Clin. Endocrinol. Oxford* 6(3):213–18

18. Dubois, M. P. 1976. Immunocytological evidence of LH-RF in hypothalamus and median eminence: a review. *Ann. Biol. Anim. Biochim. Biophys.* 16(2):177–94

19. Dudley, C. A., Moss, R. L. 1976. Prostaglandin E_2: facilitatory action on the lordotic response. *J. Endocrinol.* 71: 457–58

20. Dyer, R. G., Dyball, R. E. J. 1974. Evidence for a direct effect of LRF and TRF on single unit activity in the rostral hypothalamus. *Nature* 252:486–88

21. Ehrensing, R. H., Kastin, A. J. 1976. Clinical investigations for emotional effects of neuropeptide hormones. *Pharmacol. Biochem. Behav.* 5(1):89–93

22. Elde, R., Hokfelt, T. 1979. Localization of hypophysiotropic peptides and other biologically active peptides within the brain. *Ann. Rev. Physiol.* 41:587–602

23. Fleischer, N., Burgus, R., Vale, W., Dunn, T., Guillemin, R. 1970. Preliminary observations on the effect of synthetic thyrotropin releasing factor on plasma thyrotropin levels in man. *J. Clin. Endocrinol. Metab.* 31:109–12

24. Foreman, M. M., Moss, R. L. 1975. Enhancement of lordotic behavior by intrahypothalamic infusion of luteinizing hormone–releasing hormone. *Soc. Neurosci., 5th Annu. Meet., New York City,* Abstr. #15.4, p. 675

25. Foreman, M. M., Moss, R. L. 1977. Effects of subcutaneous injection and intrahypothalamic infusion of releasing hormones upon lordotic response to repetitive coital stimulation. *Horm. Behav.* 8:219–34

26. Foreman, M. M., Moss, R. L. 1978. Roles of gonadotropins and releasing hormones in the hypothalamic control of lordotic behavior in the ovariectomized–estrogen primed female rat. Submitted to *J. Comp. Physiol. Psychol.*

27. Hall, N. R., Luttge, W. G., Berry, R. B. 1975. Intracerebral prostaglandin E_2: effect upon sexual behavior, open activity and body temperature in ovariectomized female rats. *Prostaglandins* 10: 877–88

28. Harris, M., Sanghera, M. 1974. Projection of medial basal hypothalamic neurones to the preoptic anterior hypothalamic areas and the paraventricular nucleus in the rat. *Brain Res.* 81:401–11

29. Herrenkohl, R. L., Verhalst, I. M. 1975. Interacerebral infusions of luteinizing hormone–releasing factor induce lordosis in rats. See Ref. 28, p. 676

30. Hoffman, G. E., Melnyk, V., Hayes, T., Bennett-Clarke, C., Fowler, E. 1978. Immunocytology of LHRH neurons. See Ref. 49, pp. 67–82

31. Hokfelt, T., Johansson, O., Fuxe, K., Lofstrom, A., Goldstein, M., Park, D., Ebstein, R., Fraser, H., Jeffcoate, S., Efendic, S., Luft, R., Arimura, A. 1975. Mapping and relationship of hypothalamic neurotransmitters and hypothalamic hormones. *Proc. Sixth Int. Congr. Pharmacol.,* Vol. 3

32. Huidoboro-Toro, J. P., Scotti de Carolis, A., Longo, V. G. 1974. Action of two hypothalamic factors (TRH, MIF) and of angiotensin II on the behavioral effects of L-DOPA and 5-hydroxytrop-

tophan in mice. *Pharmacol. Biochem. Behav.* 2:105–9

33. Huidoboro-Toro, J. P., Scotti de Carolis, A., Longo, V. G. 1975. Intensification of central catecholaminergic and serotonergic processes by the hypothalamic factors MIF and TRF and by angiotensin II. *Pharmacol. Biochem. Behav.* 3:235–42

34. Ifft, J. D. 1965. Further evidence on an internal feedback from the adenohypophysis to the hypothalamus. *Neuroendocrinology* 1:350–57

35. Jackson, I. M. D., Reichlin, S. 1974. Thyrotropin releasing hormone distribution in hypothalamus and extrahypothalamic brain tissues of mammalian and submammalian chordates. *Endocrinology* 95:854–62

36. Kastin, A. J., Plotnikoff, N. P., Schally, A. V., Sandman, C. A. 1976. Endocrine and CNS effects of hypothalamic peptides and MSH. In *Reviews in Neuroscience*, pp 111–48. New York: Raven. Vol. 2

37. Kastin, A. J., Sandman, C. A., Schally, A. V., Ehrensing, R. H. 1978. Clinical effects of hypothalamic-pituitary peptides upon the central nervous system. In *Clinical Neuropharmacology*, ed. H. L. Klawans, Vol. 3. New York: Raven Press. In press

38. Kawakami, K., Sakuma, Y. 1974. Responses of hypothalamic neurons to the microiontophoresis of LH-RH, LH and FSH under various levels of circulatory ovarian hormones. *Neuroendocrinology* 15:290–307

39. Kawakami, K., Sakuma, Y. 1976. Electrophysiological evidences for possible participation of periventricular neurons in anterior pituitary regulation. *Brain Res.* 101:79–94

40. Kelly, M. J., Moss, R. L. 1976. Quantitative evaluation and determination of the biological potency of iontophoretically applied luteinizing hormone-releasing hormone (LRH). *Neuropharmacology* 15:325

41. King, J. C., Elkind, K. E., Gerall, A. A., Millar, R. P. 1978. Investigation of the LH-RH system in the normal and neonatally steroid-treated male and female rat. Brain-Endocrine Interaction III. *Neural Hormones and Reproduction, 3rd Int. Symp., Wurzburg.* Basel: Karger pp. 97–107

42. Kozlowski, G. P., Hostetter, G. 1978. Cellular and subcellular localization and behavioral effects of gonadotropin-releasing hormone (Gn-RH) in the rat. See Ref. 41, pp. 138–53

43. Krieg, R. J. Jr., Tandon, O. P., Whitmoyer, D. I., Sawyer, C. H. 1976. Differential effects of intraventricular luteinizing hormone–releasing hormone (LH–RH) and norepinephrine on electrical activity of the arcuate nucleus in the proestrus rat. *Neuroendocrinology* 22:152–63

44. Krulich, L., Quijada, M., Wheaton, J., Illner, P., McCann, S. M. 1977. Localization of hypophysiotropic neurohormones by assay of sections from various brain areas. *Fed. Proc.* 36:1953–59

45. Lipton, M. A., Breese, G. R., Prange, A. J., Wilson, I. C., Cooper, B. R. 1976. Behavioral effects of hypothalamic polypeptide hormones in animals and man. *Hormones, Behavior, Psychopathology*, ed. Edward J. Sachar, pp. 15–29. New York: Raven

46. Luttge, W. G., Sheets, C. S. 1977. Further studies on the restoration of estrogen-induced sexual receptivity in ovariectomized mice treated with dihydrotestosterone: effects of progesterone, dihydroprogesterone and LH-RH. *Pharmacol. Biochem. Behav.* 7:563–66

47. McCann, S. M., Ojeda, S. R. 1976. Synaptic transmitters involved in the release of hypothalamic releasing and inhibiting hormones. *Rev. Neurosci.* Vol. 2, pp. 91–110

48. Modianos, D., Pfaff, D. 1976. Steroid and peptide hormones, and the neural mechanisms for reproductive behavior. *Endocrinol. Proc. V Int. Congr. Endocrinol., Hamburg*, ed. V. H. T. James, pp 67–71. Amsterdam: Excerpta Medica

49. Moguilevsky, J. A. 1971. Effects of gonadotropins on the oxidative metabolism of hypothalamus. In *Influence of Hormones on the Nervous System, Proceedings of the International Society of Psychoneuroendocrinology*, ed. D. H. Ford, pp. 366–77. New York: Karger

50. Mortimer, C. H., McNeilly, A. S., Fisher, R. A., Murray, M. A. F., Besser, G. M. 1974. Gonadotrophin-releasing hormone therapy in hypogonadal males with hypothalamic or pituitary dysfunction. *Br. Med. J.* 14:617–21

51. Moss, R. L. 1976. Unit responses in preoptic and arcuate neurons related to anterior pituitary function. *Front. Neuroendocrinol.* 4:95–128

52. Moss, R. L. 1977. Role of hypophysiotropic neurohormones in mediating neural and behavioral events. *Fed. Proc.* 36:1978–83

53. Moss, R. L. 1978. Effects of hypothalamic peptides on sex behavior in an-

imal and man. *Psychopharmacology: A Generation of Progress,* ed. M. A. Lipton, A. DiMascio, K. F. Killam, pp. 431–440. New York: Raven

54. Moss, R. L., Dudley, C. A. 1978. Changes in responsiveness of medial preoptic neurons to the microelectrophoresis of releasing hormones as a function of ovarian hormones. *Brain Res.* 149:511–15

55. Moss, R. L., Dudley, C. A., Chud, L. 1978. Unpublished observations

56. Moss, R. L., Dudley, C. A., Foreman, M. M., McCann, S. M. 1975. Synthetic LRF: a potentiator of sexual behaviour in the rat. In *Hypothalamic Hormones,* ed. M. Motta, P. G. Crosignani, L. Martini, pp. 269–78. London: Academic

57. Moss, R. L., Dudley, C. A., Kelly, M. 1978. Hypothalamic polypeptide releasing hormones: modifiers of neuronal activity. *Neuropharmacology* 17:87–93

58. Moss, R. L., Dudley, C. A., Vale, W. 1978. Hypothalamic peptides: putative modulators of neural activity. See Ref. 41, pp. 313–26

59. Moss, R. L., Foreman, M. M., 1976. Potentiation of lordosis behavior by intrahypothalamic infusion of synthetic luteinizing hormone–releasing hormone (LRH). *Neuroendocrinology* 20:176–81

60. Moss, R. L., Kelly, M., Dudley, C. A. 1975. Responsiveness of medial-preoptic neurons to releasing hormones and neurohumoral agents. *Fed. Proc.* 34:219

61. Moss, R. L., Kelly, M., Dudley, C. A. 1976. Effect of peptide hormones on extracellular electrical activities of preoptic-hypothalamic neurons. *Neurosci. Abstr.* 2(2):652

62. Moss, R. L., Kelly, M., Foreman, M. M., Dudley, C. A. 1975. Luteinizing hormone–releasing hormone (LRH) regulation of neural events controlling mating behavior. *Physiologist* 18:326

63. Moss, R. L., McCann, S. M. 1973. Induction of mating behavior in rats by luteinizing hormone–releasing factor. *Science* 181:177–79

64. Moss, R. L., McCann, S. M. 1975. Action of luteinizing hormone–releasing factor (LRF) in the initiation of lordosis behavior in the estrone-primed ovariectomized female rat. *Neuroendocrinology* 17:309–18

65. Moss, R. L., Riskind, P., McCann, S. M., Danhof, I., Rochefort, G. 1978. In preparation

66. Nicoll, R. A. 1976. Promising peptides. *Soc. Neurosci. Symp.* 1:99–122

67. Nicoll, R. A. 1977. Excitatory action of TRH on spinal motoneurones. *Nature* 265:242–43

68. Oliver, C., Eskay, R. L., Ben-Jonathan, N., Porter, J. C. 1974. Distribution and concentration of TRH in the rat brain. *Endocrinology* 548:46

69. Peck, E. J., Tytell, M., Clark, J. H. 1975. Hypothalamic synaptosomes and in vitro LRF secretion. *Endocrine Soc. Abstr.* #89, p. 95

70. Pelletier, G., Labrie, F., Puviani, R., Arimura, A., Schally, A. V. 1974. Electron microscopic localization of luteinizing hormone releasing hormone in the rat median eminence. *Endocrinology* 95:314–15

71. Pfaff, D. W. 1970. Mating behavior of hypophysectomized rats. *J. Comp. Physiol. Psychol.* 72:45–50

72. Pfaff, D. W. 1973. Luteinizing hormone–releasing factor (LRF) potentiates lordosis behavior in hypophysectomized ovariectomized female rats. *Science* 182:1148–49

73. Pittman, Q. J., Blume, H. W., Renaud, L. P. 1978. Depressant effect of thyrotropin releasing hormone (TRH) and TRH analogs on central neuronal excitability. *Proc. Can. Fed. Biol. Soc.* #21. (Abstr.)

74. Plotnikoff, N. P., Prange, A. J. Jr., Breese, G. R., Anderson, M. S., Wilson, I. C. 1971. Thyrotropin releasing hormone: enhancement of DOPA activity by a hypothalamic hormone. *Science* 178:417–18

75. Plotnikoff, N. P., Prange, A. J. Jr., Breese, G. R., Anderson, M. S., Wilson, I. C. 1974. See Ref. 10, pp. 103–13

76. Poulain, P., Carette, B. 1974. Iontophoresis of prostaglandins on hypothalamic neurons. *Brain Res.* 79: 311–14

77. Poulain, P., Carette, B. 1978. Septal afferents to the arcuate-median eminence region in the guinea pig: microiontophoretically applied LRF effects. *Brain Res.* 137:154–57

78. Prange, A. J. Jr., Breese, G. R., Cott, J. M., Martin, B. R., Cooper, B. R., Wilson, I. C., Plotnikoff, N. P. 1974. Thyrotropin releasing hormone: antagonism of pentobarbital in rodents. *Life Sci.* 14:447–55

79. Prange, A. J. Jr., Breese, G. R., Jahnke, G. D., Martin, B. R., Cooper, B. R., Cott, J. M., Wilson, I. C., Alltop, L. B., Lipton, M. A., Bissette, G., Neneroff, C. B., Lossen, P. T. 1975. Modification of pentobarbital effects by natural and synthetic polypeptides: dissociation of

brain and pituitary effects. *Life Sci.* 16:1907–14

80. Prange, A. J. Jr., Nemeroff, C. B., Lipton, M. A. 1978. Behavioral effects of peptides: basic and clinical studies. *Psychopharmacology: A Generation of Progress,* ed. M. A. Lipton, A. DiMascio, K. F. Killam, pp. 441–58. New York: Raven

81. Ramirez, V. D., Kordon, C. 1975. Studies on luteinizing hormone–releasing hormone (LH-RH). See Ref. 56, pp. 57–74

82. Ramirez, V. D., Sawyer, C. H. 1965. Fluctuations of hypothalamic luteinizing hormone–releasing factor during the estrous cycle. *Endocrinology* 76:282–89

83. Reichelt, K. L., Edminson, P. D. 1977. Peptides containing probable transmitter candidates in the central nervous system. In *Peptides in Neurobiology,* ed. H. Gainer, pp. 171–82. New York: Plenum

84. Renaud, L. P. 1978. Peptides as neurotransmitters or neuromodulators. See Ref. 80, pp. 423–30

85. Renaud, L. P., Blume, H. W., Pittman, Q. J. 1978. Neurophysiology and neuropharmacology of the hypothalamic tuberoinfundibular system. *Front. Neuroendocrinol.* 5:135–62

86. Renaud, L. P., Martin, J. B. 1974. Antidromic and orthodromic activation of basomedial and periventricular hypothalamic neurons. *Proc. Soc. Neurosci. 4th Annu. Meet., October 20–24, St. Louis, Mo.*

87. Renaud, L. P., Martin, J. B. 1975. Thyrotropin releasing hormone (TRH): depressant action on central neuronal activity. *Brain Res.* 86:150–54

88. Renaud, L. P., Martin, J. B. 1975. Electrophysiological studies of connections of hypothalamic ventromedial nucleus neurons in the rat: evidence for a role in neuroendocrine regulation. *Brain Res.* 93:145–51

89. Renaud, L. P., Martin, J. B., Brazeau, P. 1975. Depressant action of TRH, LHRH and somatostatin on activity of central neurons. *Nature* 255:233–35

90. Renaud, L. P., Martin, J. B., Brazeau, P. 1976. Hypothalamic releasing factors: physiological evidence for a regulatory action on central neurons and pathways for their distribution in brain. *Pharmacol. Biochem. Behav.* 5(1):171–78

91. Riskind, P., Moss, R. L. 1977. Midbrain central grey: an extrahypothalamic site for LRH potentiation of lordosis behavior in female rat. *Soc. Neurosci. Abstr.* Vol. III, p. 356

92. Rodriguez-Sierra, J. F., Crowley, W. R., Komisaruk, B. R. 1977. Induction of lordosis responsiveness by vaginal stimulation in rats is independent of anterior or posterior pituitary hormones. *Horm. Behav.* 8(3):348–55

93. Rodriguez-Sierra, J. F., Komisaruk, B. R. 1977. Effects of prostaglandin E_2 and indomethacin on sexual behavior in the female rat. *Horm. Behav.* 9:281–89

94. Rodriguez-Sierra, J. F., Komisaruk, B. R. 1979. Lordosis induction in the rat by prostaglandin E_2 systematically or intracranially in the absence of ovarian hormones. *Prostaglandins.* In press

95. Sandman, C. A., Miller, L. H., Kastin, A. J. 1977. Introduction: perspectives on the behavioral effects of the neuropeptides. In *Neuropeptide Influences on the Brain and Behavior.* New York: Raven Press. p. 1

96. Sanghera, M., Harris, M. C., Morgan, R. A. 1978. Effects of microiontophoretic and intravenous application of gonadotropic hormones on the discharge of medial basal hypothalamic neurones in the rat. *Brain Res.* 140:63–74

97. Schwarzstein, L., Aparicio, N. J., Turner, D., Calamera, J. C., Mancini, J. F., Schally, A. V. 1975. Use of synthetic luteinizing hormone–releasing hormone in treatment of oligospermia men: a preliminary report. *Fertil. Steril.* 25:331–36

98. Segal, D. S., Mandell, A. J. 1974. Differential behavioral effects of hypothalamic polypeptides. See Ref. 10, pp. 129–33

99. Setalo, G., Vigh, S., Schally, A. V., Arimura, A., Flerko, B. 1976. Immunohistological study of the origin of LH-RH containing nerve fibers of the rat hypothalamus. *Brain Res.* 103:597–602

100. Siler, T. M., VanderBerg, G., Yen, S. S. C. 1973. Inhibition of growth hormone release in humans by somatostatin. *J. Clin. Endocrinol. Metab.* 37:632–34

101. Silverman, A. J., Zimmerman, E. A. 1978. Pathways containing luteinizing hormone–releasing hormone (LHRH) in the mammalian brain. See Ref. 41, pp. 83–96

102. Stumpf, W. E., Sar, M. 1973. ^{3}H-TRH and ^{3}H-proline radioactivity localization in pituitary and hypothalamus. *Fed. Proc.* 32:211

103. Terasawa, E. I., Whitmoyer, D. I., Sawyer, C. H. 1969. Effects of luteinizing

hormone on multiple-unit activity in the rat hypothalamus. *Am. J. Physiol.* 217:1119–26

104. Turgeon, J. L., Barraclough, C. A. 1976. The existence of a possible short-loop negative feedback action of LH in proestrous rat. *Endocrinology* 98: 639–44

105. Vale, W., Blackwell, R., Grant, G., Guillemin, R. 1973. TRF and thyroid hormones on prolactin secretion by rat anterior pituitary cells *in vitro. Endocrinology* 93:26–33

106. Vale, W., Rivier, C., Brown, M. 1977. Regulatory peptides of the hypothalamus. *Ann. Rev. Physiol.* 39:473–527

107. Vijayan, E., McCann, S. M. 1977. Suppression of feeding and drinking activity in rats following intraventricular injection of thyrotropin releasing hormone (TRH). *Endocrinology* 100(6):1727–30

108. Werman, R. 1966. Criteria for identification of a central nervous system trans-mitter. *Comp. Biochem. Physiol.* 18: 745–66

109. Wheaton, J. E., Krulich, L., McCann, S. M. 1975. Localization of luteinizing hormone–releasing hormone in the preoptic area and hypothalamus of the rat using radioimmunoassay. *Endocrinology* 97:30–38

110. Winokur, A., Utiker, R. D. 1974. Thyrotropin releasing hormone: Regional distribution in rat brain. *Science* 185:265–67

111. Wuttke, W. 1974. Preoptic unit activity and gonadtropin release. *Exp. Brain Res.* 19:205–16

112. Yagi, K., Sawaki, Y. 1975. Recurrent inhibition and facilitation: demonstration in the tuberoinfundibular system and effects of strychnine and picrotoxin. *Brain Res.* 84:155–59

113. Yagi, K., Sawaki, Y. 1978. Electrophysiological characteristics of identified tubero-infundibular neurons. *Neuroendocrinology* 26:50–64

Ann. Rev. Physiol. 1979. 41:633–52

THE BIOSYNTHESIS AND METABOLISM OF PROSTAGLANDINS

♦1242

William E. M. Lands

Department of Biological Chemistry, University of Michigan,
Ann Arbor, Michigan 48109

To evaluate the different and sometimes paradoxical physiologic roles for prostaglandins (PGs), we may best regard them as evanescent agents whose transient existence modulates and modifies many physiologic events. The speed with which the various compounds in this family of autacoids appear and disappear has made it difficult to determine accurately their abundance and to relate it to the physiologic effects observed. Many existing reports deal with only a few of the prostaglandins involved. Closely related compounds can have opposite physiologic effects—e.g. PGE vs PGF, or thromboxane A_2 (TXA$_2$) vs PGI$_2$. Highly selective differences in tissue responses to different prostaglandins [e.g. with stomach and artery strips (94)] may reflect differences in types of receptors or in ways that receptors interact with cellular adenyl cyclase and β-adrenergic receptors (17) to cause tissue response. The response of each tissue is in turn influenced by the abundance of its specific receptors (17) and of the appropriate prostaglandin available to the receptor. This review examines factors regulating the flow of materials from cellular lipid to the fatty acid precursor to the different active agents to their various inactive metabolites, which eventually appear in the urine. Quantitative assays of the various prostaglandins and their metabolites are not presented since they were extensively reviewed in Volume 5 of *Advances in Prostaglandin and Thromboxane Research*. An excellent review of prostaglandin interactions with cyclic nucleotides (125) covers aspects omitted here.

BIOSYNTHESIS

Overall, the biosynthetic reactions involved are simple; few cofactors are required. Molecular oxygen is inserted into a polyunsaturated fatty acid,

633

and the acyl chain is rearranged to form the various autacoids. Figure 1 illustrates these rearrangements and shows the essential role of the cyclooxygenase in producing the different derivatives. In examining the physiologic control of prostaglandin biosynthesis particular attention should be given to the abundance of two types of material: the non-esterified acid(s) that are substrates, and the hydroperoxide(s) that serve as cyclooxygenase activators. Neither is normally present in appreciable amounts in cells at steady state, and the cyclooxygenase that is present in many tissues cannot function at a significant rate unless the concentration of these ligands is raised to the magnitude of their respective K_m values. An oversimplified relationship (see 130) for these factors serves to remind us of the conditions ($S \ll K_s$ and/or $P \ll K_p$) that allow large amounts of cyclooxygenase to be present without any appreciable synthetic activity. Synthetic rate may be expressed as:

$$\text{synthetic rate} = v = \frac{k_3 \text{ (enzyme)}}{1 + K_s/[S] + K_p/[P] + K_s K_p/[S]\,[P]}.$$

An increased synthetic rate caused by increased accessibility of [S] and [P] may occur by the processes described below. These processes can account for the fact that much less prostaglandin is formed in vivo (100, 152) than would be predicted from tissue levels of cyclooxygenase activity.

Substrate Availability

Arachidonate (20:4), the precursor of the predominant (dienoic) type of prostaglandins shown in Figure 1, is formed from the essential fatty acid, linoleate (18:2), by elongation and desaturation (reviewed in 133). A less abundant intermediate fatty acid, eicosatrienoate (20:3), is the precursor of the monoenoic prostaglandins (PGE_1, PGH_1, etc). Few tissues contain the large amounts of 20:3 found in vesicular glands (80), and the monoenoic type is not generally abundant, although PGE_1 is often studied experimentally. An exception to this concept is 6-keto-$PGF_{1\alpha}$, which is formed from PGI_2. [Ironically, effects noted with PGE_1 may be due to its action at PGI_2 receptors (91).] The substrate acids are seldom free, but are esterified with other acids to cellular lipids; the highest concentration of arachidonate is generally in phospholipids, although the greatest total amount may be in triglycerides.

STIMULATED RELEASE   Early studies of release following autonomic nerve stimulation (e.g. 40) and mechanical agitation (e.g. 119) showed that new synthesis was involved (22, 100) requiring release of esterified precursors (80). The early studies led to several models of activated acyl hydrolysis now used in the laboratories of Needleman (64), Flower & Vane (10) and

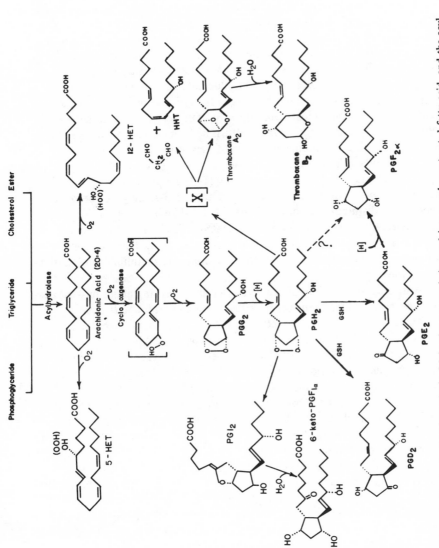

Figure 1 Prostaglandin biosynthesis. Molecular oxygen is inserted into a polyunsaturated fatty acid, and the acyl chain is rearranged to form the various autacoids.

Levine (63). Stimulated release has been shown for bradykinin and angiotensin II in kidney, spleen, heart, and cells in culture, and angiotensin III appears even more potent in stimulating prostaglandin release (15).

Arachidonate is released in a Ca^{2+}-dependent process from adrenocortical phospholipids by the peptide corticotrophin (81), and from thyroid phosphatidyl inositol by thyrotropin (58). These receptor-mediated activations are more selective than stimulation with an ionophore (70), the basic protein mellitin (142), or a small peptide isolated recently from guinea pig lungs during anaphylaxis (98). The blockade of stimulated release by a serine protease inhibitor suggests that proteolytic action may be needed for activation of phospholipase activity (36). The serine protease activity involved in such cell responses may in turn be formed from a zymogen or by a cycloheximide-inhibitable synthesis of new protein (120).

A particularly interesting stimulator of prostaglandin release is SRS-A (90), which may occur preformed in lung (143) and is released upon antigen challenge (44). The bioassays used to detect SRS-A may not be selective enough to distinguish among different SRS-A-like materials (139), and the characteristics described for isolated SRS-A (107) may not apply to all forms of the activity. These multiple forms may be the basis for conflicting reports on whether release of SRS-A is enhanced or inhibited by anticyclooxygenase agents.

Anti-inflammatory steroids appear to reduce prostaglandin biosynthesis by lowering the availability of the substrate acid (47, 53) to the cyclooxygenase. The phospholipase A_2 activity in lungs that is suppressed by steroids is in cellular membranes other than lysosomal (13). Alternatively, the steroids may reduce transport of the non-esterified arachidonic acid to the cyclooxygenase (144) or block efflux of the prostaglandins from their site of synthesis (see the section below on Transport).

Once liberated, the substrate acids may still encounter several impediments to interacting with the cyclooxygenase. They are: binding to other proteins in the cytosol or extracellular fluids; competition at the substrate site with other fatty acids; activation by acid:CoA ligase (and subsequent esterification to lipid); oxygenation by lipoxidase(s). Thus, even when the total cellular content of non-esterified acid is elevated, little may be avilable for sustained synthesis of prostaglandins.

Recent experiments examined the possibility of a regionally selective release that would provide the acid closer to the major cyclooxygenase locations (64). Further evidence on the cellular and subcellular localization of cyclooxygenase (e.g. 131) will help to evaluate this concept.

COMPETITION BY OTHER ACIDS   All fatty acids are potential competitors for the substrate binding site. Such competition means that higher levels of the substrate acid must occur to achieve the same cyclooxygenase activity. Competition was especially evident with long-chain polyunsaturated acids (77). If the stimulated acylhydrolase activity released all fatty acids equally from the site of attack (e.g. the 2-position of phosphatidylcholine) then the relative effectiveness of arachidonate in producing prostaglandins would tend to parallel its mole percent content. The striking results of Bills et al (6), however, indicated that arachidonate may be hydrolyzed by a hitherto unrecognized selective phospholipase activity. Subsequent studies support the possible existence of a phospholipase highly selective for a particular fatty acid (64). Since highly selective hydrolases are still relatively unknown, we cannot yet estimate the extent to which this type of efficient release mechanism is acting.

PROTEIN BINDING   The hydrophobic nature of free fatty acids causes them to occur bound to hydrophobic sites on cellular proteins and membranes rather than as free, solvated molecules. Thus their availability to the cyclooxygenase is much less than indicated by their overall content in nmoles g^{-1} wet tissue. The nearly 100 mg of protein per ml of cell contents tends to keep the cyclooxygenase in an almost arachidonate-free condition. Also, extracellular serum albumin has several particularly avid binding sites for lipophilic anions (reviewed in 132). Thus, when cyclooxygenase activity resides in a cell other than the one stimulated to release arachidonate, these binding effects may greatly depress the percent conversion.

REACYLATION   Activation of non-esterified arachidonate to acyl-CoA by acid:CoA ligase followed by acyltransferase-catalyzed transfer to phospholipid can occur rapidly in most tissues [see the review of acyl-transferase in (75)]. In this way the cellular lipids may recover their ability to release the prostaglandin precursor upon subsequent stimulation. Since continued incorporation requires a supply of ATP, ischemic and hypoxic conditions could be expected to reduce the tissue's reesterification activity without markedly affecting the hydrolytic activity. In this situation, an increased steady-state concentration of non-esterified arachidonate seems likely, and is often observed (64) associated with increased prostaglandin formation (14).

LIPOXYGENASE ACTIVITY   Lipoxygenase activity has been recognized in many tissues (50), including platelets (62, 99), neutrophils (16), and skin (56). Like the cyclooxygenase, the lipoxygenase may be present but inoperant until the non-esterified fatty acid level is elevated. If tissue lipoxygenases have K_m values comparable to that for the soybean enzyme [$\sim 1 \ \mu M$ (129)] they could effectively lower the pool of prostaglandin precursors available to the cyclooxygenase. This competitive role, however, may be much less significant than the consequences of producing the stimulatory unsaturated hydroperoxides (see below) that are in turn rapidly reduced to form the chemotactic hydroxy acids (42, 144). In this way, lipoxygenase action may increase prostaglandin levels in a tissue by stimulating the rate of prostaglandin biosynthesis and by increasing the entry of more prostaglandin-forming cells into the region. Lack of such stimulation may cause the inadequate platelet aggregation associated with myeloproliferative disorders (68).

Cyclooxygenase Action

Cyclooxygenase activity has been purified from vesicular glands of rams (59, 146) and bulls (92) and found to contain subunits of about 70,000 daltons. Antibodies developed with the ram enzyme also bind with the cyclooxygenase activity in many tissues from other species (131). This result, and the similar responses of prostaglandin formation in many tissues to aspirin-like drugs (see the section on Interactions of Drugs at Substrate and Activator Sites, below) suggest that cyclooxygenase protein is similar in most systems examined. Thus much of the biosynthetic information obtained with one system may be applied to others.

OXYGEN REQUIREMENT   The requirement of the reaction for molecular oxygen (126) creates a paradox: Many investigators have observed that reduced oxygen levels can lead to an increased production of prostaglandins. Total anoxia, however, as achieved in vitro (e.g. 145), does prevent biosynthesis and the paradox may be resolved in knowing the level of oxygen needed to give appreciable oxygenation activity: around 5 μM (79). At tissue O_2 levels greater than 20 μM, synthesis seems limited by substrate acid availability. Apparently the arachidonate accumulating in hypoxic (ischemic) conditions can elevate the rate of prostaglandin synthesis as long as O_2 concentrations are still sufficient (5–10 μM) to maintain near-optimal cyclooxygenase rates. Only when the available O_2 drops below 5 μM would hypoxic conditions begin appreciably to lower the rate of prostaglandin synthesis.

HEME REQUIREMENT   The first definitive report of a heme requirement (154) came from study of bovine cyclooxygenase. Subsequent purification of the sheep enzyme (59) allowed unequivocal proof that it, too, had a complete dependence upon heme (60), which it bound very tightly. This requirement means that cyclooxygenase activity in a tissue depends upon adequate heme availability, and that competition for the heme by various proteins may be a means of regulating prostaglandin biosynthesis. Only one heme is required per two subunits (60), which indicates that the holoenzyme contains two different types of peptide chain. Interactions of these chains with each other and with the essential heme provide added points for regulation of prostaglandin biosynthesis.

POSITIVE AND NEGATIVE FEEDBACK   Positive feedback is demonstrable in the accelerating rates observed as PGG_2 is formed (24), and very small amounts of hydroperoxide (0.1 μM) can trigger this synthesis. A continued presence of hydroperoxide seems necessary for continued reaction, and the cellular peroxide tone can regulate prostaglandin synthesis (25). For these reasons activity of cellular lipoxygenases and glutathione peroxidase can be significant in physiologic regulation. An interesting example of stimulated synthesis of prostaglandin that seems related to the regulatory actions of peroxides occurs in mollusks (95).

Kinetic studies of cyclooxygenase have consistently been complicated by a progressive inactivation as the reaction proceeds (130). The negative feedback inherent in the self-catalyzed inactivation means that a molecule of enzyme can produce only a limited amount of product. This provides the cell with yet another way to avoid overproduction of these potent autacoids.

PEROXIDASE ACTION OF CYCLOOXYGENASE   Although PGG_2 is the first product formed from arachidonate and O_2, the more abundant product isolated has been the 15-hydroxy derivative, PGH_2. Even highly purified preparations convert PGG_2 to PGH_2 so that peroxidase activity seems inherent in the holoenzyme (92). The peroxidase activity causes cooxidation of other organic materials (89), thus providing the basis for a colorimetric (140) and a histochemical (66) assay. The peroxidase activity was proposed to cause the irreversible self-inactivation of the cyclooxygenase due to "oxygen-centered radicals" formed in the reduction of PGG_2 to PGH_2 (33), but it has not been established whether that reduction is causally or only correlatively related to inactivation. One consequence of the peroxidase action plus that of other tissue peroxidases (e.g. 18) is that relatively little PGG_2 will be available to maintain the cyclooxygenase in a fully activated state (25). In the suboptimal conditions normally found in the cytosol, any increased removal of PGG_2 (or other peroxides) would tend to reduce the ability to synthesize prostaglandins. PGG_2 and its free radical derivatives (and not the derived prostaglandins) have been proposed as major agents in inflammatory processes (73). Careful analysis of tissue prostaglandin levels will be needed to determine if anti-inflammatory agents that reduce hydroperoxide levels also cause a lowered production of prostaglandins in vivo.

INTERACTIONS OF DRUGS AT SUBSTRATE AND ACTIVATOR SITES
Many nonsteroidal anti-inflammatory agents inhibit cyclooxygenase activity (reviewed in 46, 127). The unusual kinetic features of the cyclooxygenase have complicated the standard assessments of inhibitor action and may be the basis for some conflicting reports (reviewed in 78). With four types of ligand necessary for the reaction (heme, oxygen, hydroperoxide activator, and substrate acid) a variety of competitive and noncompetitive inhibitory events are possible. For example, some interesting thiol analogs of prostaglandin bind reversibly and noncompetitively with substrate (105). A dominant principle controlling the competitive events is that the competing native ligand is present in suboptimal amounts. For example, agents competing with substrate fatty acid are more effective when little substrate is present (reviewed in 78; see also 26). Acetamidophenol was reported to compete reversibly at both the substrate and peroxide activator sites (74), and its inhibition was particularly marked when both ligands were present at low levels. Differences in substrate or activator contents in various model systems may partially account for paradoxical results that led to the suggestions that some agents are inhibiting inflammation by mechanisms other than inhibition of PG synthesis (41, 73). Some measurements of the in vivo suppression of prostaglandin synthesis by several reversible and irreversible agents have been evaluated constructively by Fitzpatrick & Wynalda (39). Irreversible inactivation of the cyclooxygenase (128) provides more dramatic inhibitory effects (39) that are less dependent upon other ligand concentrations. Aspirin binds at the substrate site and, in addition, causes a progressive irreversible inactivation (124) that is associated with, and may actually precede (123), acetylation of the subunits. Irreversible inactivation that is clearly independent of acetylation also occurs with other anti-inflammatory agents that have their carboxylic group intact (122). Conversion of the acids to methyl esters did not greatly alter their competitive binding to the substrate site ($k_I = 1$–5 μM), but it completely eliminated the irreversible inactivation (122). Recovery from irreversible inactivation requires biosynthesis of new enzyme, and slower rates of renewal in platelets compared to vascular endothelium (88) may explain the effectiveness of aspirin in reducing thrombosis.

Thromboxane Synthase

Once the novel metabolic product TXB_2 was recognized in human platelets, its short-lived precursor TXA_2 was proposed and demonstrated (55). The rapid, spontaneous hydrolytic conversion of TXA_2 to TXB_2 makes the latter compound the form that is isolated. The above findings, paralleled by similar results with guinea pig lung (53), greatly altered the previous concept that these tissues primarily produce PGE_2 and $PGF_{2\alpha}$. The specificity of the thromboxane synthase is uncertain, with one report of TXB_1 being formed by platelets (35) and subsequent studies unable to demonstrate TXA_1 formation (29, 97). Apparently PGH_3 can be converted to TXA_3 (97), and so the synthase is not absolutely specific for only 20:4 products. Also, the microsomal synthase converts PGH_1 to hydroxyheptadecadienoate (35, 148) and forms nearly equal amounts of thromboxane and hydroxyheptadecatrienoate from PGH_2 (148, 155). This dismutation reaction seems an alternate activity of the same catalytic site since it copurifies with the synthase and is inhibited (29) to the same degree by various inhibitors. The synthase is now recognized in many tissues (e.g. see 136), and the high levels in brain (151) may provide important modulators of neurotransmission.

Selective inhibitors of thromboxane synthase are of considerable interest in attempts to reduce formation of this proaggregatory, vasoconstricting material while permitting normal rates of formation of the other prostaglandins. Inhibition occurs with N0164 (30, 32, 96), L-8027 (30, 48), dipyridamole (3), imidazole (30, 96), as well as the azo (30, 38, 96) and epoxymethano (135) analogs of PGH_2.

Prostacyclin Synthase

The growing awareness of the existence of another cyclic metabolite of arachidonate in the rat stomach (110, 118) became intense when it was found to be related to the potent antiaggregatory, hypotensive agent (PGI_2) formed by vascular endothelium (93). The prostacyclin synthase converts PGH_2 into the relatively unstable PGI_2, which then spontaneously hydrolyzes to 6-keto-$PGF_{1\alpha}$ (67), the form most readily observed. The synthase is present in many different tissues (116), and we now recognize that different cells within an organ may selectively form either PGI_2 (lung vascular endothelium) or TXA_2 (lung parenchyma). The synthase appears to form active products from either PGH_2 or PGH_3, and the exceptionally high levels of the 20:5 (n-3) precursor of PGH_3 in Eskimos (31) may help to interpret the low incidence of myocardial infarction in these people. Improved analytic methods have let us recognize the prostacyclin metabolites as major products in ductus arteriosis (117), heart (28), uterus (37), corpus luteum (136); they also share a major role with thromboxanes in lung (27, 138) and granuloma (21). Attention has now moved away from PGE and PGF and toward these two very potent metabolites.

Isomerase

11-KETO-ISOMERASE PGD_2 is formed from PGH_2 in the presence of glutathione by the supernatant of some rat tissues (102), by a sheep lung transferase (23), and by serum albumin (23, 51). It was a major prostaglandin identified in brain (1) and platelets (2, 103). Although PGD_2 has been regarded as biologically inactive, it inhibits platelet aggregation, causes long-lasting erythema, and has selective receptors on platelets (91).

9-KETO-ISOMERASE   This reaction is catalyzed by a microsomal isomerase (76, 101) that requires glutathione. The isomerase was solubilized and separated from the cyclooxygenase by column chromatography (104). Different 9-keto-isomerase activities are described for rat liver and sheep lung (23). Some evidence suggests that PGG_2 conversion to 15-hydroperoxy PGE_2 may be a preferred pathway. However, Ogino (104) observed PGG_2 to react at approximately half the rate of PGH_2, and the cellular peroxidases might be expected to keep the PGG_2 levels in a cell rather low relative to PGH_2 (102). Inhibition of the isomerase occurs with a bicyclo analog of the endoperoxide (150) and with the substrate analog eicosatrienoate [20:3 (n − 9) (147)]. In contrast, benzydamine and flazalone appeared to stimulate the 9-keto-isomerase (26) under some conditions.

Reductase

Two routes may operate in forming $PGF_{2\alpha}$ from PGH_2: direct reduction of the endoperoxide, and isomerization followed by reduction of the keto derivative. The most consistent type of evidence for endoperoxide reduction is the retention of the 9-H of arachidonate in the $PGF_{2\alpha}$ that is isolated. This would have been removed if isomerase action were in the pathway. Although thiols (82) and catechols (152) facilitate PGF formation, direct evidence for enzymatic endoperoxide reductase activity has not been convincing (19). The increased ratio of PGF/PGE in uterus following estrogen treatment (72) might be due to elevated endoperoxide reductase, but there was an accompanying increase in 9-keto reductase that may have produced the effect. In vitro results with cow and guinea pig microsomes (149) provide the best evidence to date for enzymic endoperoxide reductase.

9-KETO REDUCTASE   This activity converting PGE to PGF is found in blood, heart, liver (61), kidney, brain (71), and skin (156). The reductase does not act on the 11-keto isomer, PGD (84), and, in what may be an important regulatory response, it appears to be stimulated by bradykinin to a greater degree in veins than arteries (84, 153). Reports of the regional distribution and nucleotide specificity of the enzyme in kidney, and of its inhibition by diuretics, need more data before its role in physiological regulation is established. More data on the K_m and specific activity are also needed to estimate its action on $10^{-7}M$ prostaglandins rather than the $10^{-5}M$ often used in in vitro assays.

TRANSPORT AND METABOLISM

The rapid appearance and disappearance of physiologically active prostaglandins seem to be catalyzed by intracellular enzymes, and the high affinity receptors (K_d - $10^{-9}M$) mediating the physiologic responses appear to be on the cellular plasma membranes [e.g. thymocytes (45) and corpus luteum (87)]. We do not yet know the extent to which prostaglandins function at cells other than the ones catalyzing their biosynthesis, and the topological relationships of the different cells must be learned. However, it is clear that intercellular and intertissue actions are often sharply constrained by a mediated transport into various cells containing enzymes that rapidly convert the active agents to inactive derivatives.

Transport

Although many discussants regard prostaglandins as freely diffusable agents, reports of apparent concentrative uptake led to evidence that uptake of $PGF_{2\alpha}$ could be a saturable process inhibited by $PGF_{2\beta}$ (9). PGE_1 and $PGF_{2\alpha}$ had delayed pulmonary transition times due to removal from the circulation (7), whereas PGA_1 and PGB_1 were not removed. Interference with the mediated transport increases the circulating concentration that is not metabolized on passage through a tissue (34). Several agents, including some nonsteroidal anti-inflammatory agents (8) at high concentrations are capable of interfering with this transport and metabolism.

A different phenomenon—decreased efflux of prostaglandins from adipose tissue in the presence of glucocorticoid, while uptake seemed unaffected—led to the suggestion of a carrier-mediated release (20). This hypothesis provides a challenging alternative to the interpretation that steroids reduce substrate availability to the cyclooxygenase (see the section on Stimulated Release, above).

Metabolism

A rapid loss of biological activity is associated with both the enzymatic oxidation of the 15-hydoxyl group of the active prostaglandins (4) and the spontaneous hydrolytic reactions of PGI_2 and TXA_2 described above. In some cells, the enzyme-catalyzed oxidation is rapid enough to precede the spontaneous hydrolysis. This oxidation, which forms a conjugated ketone, is usually followed by reduction of the 13,14-*trans*-double bond to give the dihydro keto derivative, a major metabolite in the peripheral circulation (reviewed in 126). Subsequent oxidations of the carbon chain provide the shorter mono- and dicarboxylic acids, which are predominant metabolites observed in urine.

15-HYDROXYDEHYDROGENASE Two types of activity are recognized on the basis of cofactor selectivity (83): a NAD^+-linked enzyme in lung, heart, kidney, spleen, and placenta; and a $NADP^+$-linked enzyme in brain, kidney, and erythrocytes. An excellent review of the enzymatic and physiologic aspects of the two enzymes appeared in 1976 (57). Improved methods for estimating 15-hydroxydehydrogenase activity are based on the stereospecific removal of a ^3H from the 15-R position (12, 137). This avoids errors due to further metabolism of the 15-keto derivative and NADH by the 13-reductase (see the section on Metabolism, below). The 15-dehydrogenase acts on many different prostaglandins, although an unusually selective form of the enzyme from rabbit kidney papillae was reported to act only on PGA (106). The K_m values of 1–20 μM suggest that the dehydrogenase is not operating at optimum efficiency with the low levels of prostaglandin usually available. Increasing levels of dehydrogenase in lung and kidney of early postnatal rats (109) and altered levels in developing sheep lung (112) support a concept of a "critical prostaglandin period" (115). Prostaglandin dehydrogenase activity in tissues appears to be very short-lived, and its rapid turnover is modulated by steroid estrogen and hormones (11).

Inhibition of the dehydrogenase may be an important mechanism in the action of diuretics. Alternatively, elevated blood pressure in the spontaneously hypertensive (SHR) Wistar-Okamoto-Aoki rat may be preceded by decreased 15-hydroxy dehydrogenase activity (86, 111); and the disorder may be amplified by increased prostaglandin "synthetase" activity (86). An interesting discussion of genetic hypertension (GH) in New Zealand rats (5) proposes that a local elevation of PGE_2 might improperly modulate the adrenergic system.

13-REDUCTASE This activity using NADH (and perhaps NADPH) appears in the supernatant fraction of many tissue homogenates associated with the 15-hydroxy dehydrogenase (4). The 13-reductase does not act on the 15-hydroxy derivative, but the conjugated 15-keto derivative is rapidly reduced to the 15-keto-13,14-dihydro derivative (52). The latter type of compound is the form that seems most available to the 9-keto reductase (108) and is the form in which prostaglandins tend to occur in peripheral blood. The relative ratio of 15-keto-13-dihydro to 15-keto probably reflects different ratios of 13-reductase to 15-dehydrogenase (4). The two enzyme activities vary during development, with proportionately high reductase activity in rat lung at birth (114).

β-OXIDATION Although many investigators have observed the results of chain shortening, particularly with urinary metabolites, little direct experimental work has appeared since the early report of Hamberg (49). The chain-shortened dinor (C_{18}) and tetranor (C_{16}) derivatives are generally formed after 15-dehydrogenation and 13,14-reduction. Exceptions are found in the appearance in urine of dinor-$PGF_{1\alpha}$ with rats (43), dinor thromboxane B_2 with primates (121), and dinor 6-keto-$PGF_{1\alpha}$ with rats (113). These may reflect in part some pharmacokinetic aspects of the administered compounds and may not be the major metabolites of the endogenously produced prostaglandins. Better knowledge of the major catabolic form of each prostaglandin could allow us to monitor its daily production.

ω-OXIDATION   This process was also examined directly by the Karolinska group (65), and little subsequent work has appeared. The reaction in liver provides both the ω-(20-) and (ω-1)-(19-)hydroxy derivatives (65% and 35%, respectively); in urine (241) the oxidized form, ω-COOH, is most prevalent. Again, kinetics of prostaglandin transport and distribution probably play a dominant role in influencing these ratios (134). The ω-1 hydroxy derivatives of PGE_1 and PGE_2 are major components in primate semen (54, 69), where they have unknown roles.

SUMMARY

With improved techniques for isolation and identification of materials, thromboxane (TXA_2) and prostacyclin (PGI_2) derivatives are now recognized as more abundant in some tissues and more potent than PGE_2 and $PGF_{2\alpha}$. The rapid appearance and disappearance of these autacoids can be regulated at many points along the enzymatic path. Two important features affecting the rate of overall prostaglandin formation are the availability of non-esterified substrate and the availability of hydroperoxide activator for the cyclooxygenase. The fate of the endoperoxide formed by this reaction then depends upon the different relative amounts of the synthases and dehydrogenases in each type of synthesizing cell. Important future developments will indicate ways in which the amounts of these enzyme activities are altered and the ways in which the prostaglandin receptors interact with cellular adenyl cyclase and adrenergic receptors.

ACKNOWLEDGMENT

This review was partially supported by a National Science Foundation Grant (BMS-75-13157). The author acknowledges the stimulating encouragement of A. M. Lands, who had to cease pursuing his curiosity just as we began to recognize important relationships between prostaglandins and the α- and β-adrenergic systems.

Literature Cited

1. Abdel-Halim, M. S., Hamberg, M., Sjöquist, B., Änggard, E. 1977. Identification of prostaglandin D_2 as a major prostaglandin in homogenates of rat brain. *Prostaglandins* 14:633–43
2. Ali, M., Cerskus, A. L., Zamecnik, J., McDonald, J. W. D. 1977. Synthesis of prostaglandin D_2 and thromboxane B_2 by human platelets. *Thromb. Res.* 11:485–96
3. Ally, A. I., Manku, M. S., Horrobin, D. F., Morgan, R. O., Karmazin, M., Karmali, R. A. 1977. Dipyridamole: A possible potent inhibitor of thromboxane A_2 synthetase in vascular smooth muscle. *Prostaglandins* 14:607–9
4. Änggard, E., Larsson, C., Samuelsson, B. 1970. The distribution of 15-hydroxyprostaglandin dehydrogenase and prostaglandin-Δ^{13}-reductase in tissues of the swine. *Acta Physiol. Scand.* 81:396–404
5. Armstrong, J. M., Blackwell, G. J., Flower, R. J., McGiff, J. C., Mullane, K. M., Vane, J. R. 1976. Genetic hypertension in rats is accompanied by a defect in renal prostaglandin catabolism. *Nature* 260:582–86
6. Bills, T. K., Smith, J. B., Silver, M. J. 1977. Selective release of arachidonic acid from the phospholipids of human platelets in response to thrombin. *J. Clin. Invest.* 60:1–6
7. Bito, L. Z., Baroody, R. A., Reitz, M. E. 1977. Dependence of pulmonary prostaglandin metabolism on carrier-mediated transport processes. *Am. J. Physiol.* 232:E382–87
8. Bito, L. Z., Salvador, E. V. 1976. Effects of anti-inflammatory agents and some other drugs on prostaglandin biotransport. *J. Pharmacol. Exp. Ther.* 198:481–88
9. Bito, L. Z., Spellane, P. J. 1974. Saturable, "carrier-mediated" absorption of prostaglandin $F_{2\alpha}$ from the in vivo rabbit vagina and its inhibition by prostaglandin $F_{2\beta}$. *Prostaglandins* 8:345–52
10. Blackwell, G. J., Duncombe, W. G., Flower, R. J., Parsons, M. F., Vane, J. R. 1977. The distribution and metabolism of arachidonic acid in rabbit platelets during aggregation and its modification by drugs. *Br. J. Pharmacol.* 59:353–66
11. Blackwell, G. J., Flower, R. J. 1975. Effects of steroid hormones on tissue levels of prostaglandin 15-hydroxydehydrogenase in the rat. *Proc. B.P.S., December 17th–19th,* pp. 343P–44P

12. Blackwell, G. J., Flower, R. J. 1976. A rapid method for the estimation of prostaglandin 15-hydroxydehydrogenase activity and its application to pharmacology. *Br. J. Pharmacol.* 57:589–97
13. Blackwell, G. J., Flower, R. J., Nijkamp, F. P., Vane, J. R. 1978. Phospholipase A_2 activity of guinea-pig isolated perfused lungs: stimulation, and inhibition by anti-inflammatory steroids. *Br. J. Pharmacol.* 62:79–89
14. Block, A. J., Feinberg, H., Herbaczynska-Cedro, K., Vane, J. R. 1975. Anoxia-induced release of prostaglandins in rabbit isolated hearts. *Cir. Res.* 36:34–42
15. Blumberg, A., Denny, S., Nishikawa, K., Pure, E., Marshall, G. R., Needleman, P. 1976. Angiotensin III—induced prostaglandin (PG) release. *Prostaglandins* 11:195–97
16. Borgeat, P., Hamberg, M., Samuelsson, B. 1976. Transformation of arachidonic acid and homo-γ-linolenic acid by rabbit polymorphonuclear leukocytes. *J. Biol. Chem.* 251:7816–20
17. Brunton, L. L., Maguire, M. E., Anderson, H. J., Gilman, A. G. 1977. Expression of genes for metabolism of cyclic adenosine 3':5'-monophosphate in somatic cells. *J. Biol. Chem.* 252:1293–1302
18. Burk, R. F., Nishiki, K., Lawrence, R. A., Chance, B. 1977. Peroxide removal by selenium-dependent and selenium-independent glutathione peroxidases in hemoglobin-free perfused rat liver. *J. Biol. Chem.* 253:43–46
19. Chan, J. A., Nagasawa, M., Takeguchi, C., Sih, C. J. 1975. On agents favoring prostaglandin F formation during biosynthesis *Biochemistry* 14:2987–91
20. Chang, J., Lewis, G. P., Piper, P. J. 1977. Inhibition by glucocorticoids of prostaglandin release from adipose tissue in vitro. *Br. J. Pharmacol.* 59:425–32
21. Chang, W.-C., Murota, S.-I., Tsurufuji, S. 1978. Inhibition of thromboxane B_2 and 6-ketoprostaglandin $F_{1\alpha}$ formation by anti-inflammatory drugs in carrageenin-induced granuloma. *Biochem. Pharmacol.* 27:109–11
22. Christ, E. J., VanDorp, D. A. 1972. Comparative aspects of prostaglandin biosynthesis in animal tissues. *Biochim. Biophys. Acta* 270:537–45
23. Christ-Hazelhof, E., Nugteren, D. H., VanDorp, D. A. 1976. Conversions of prostaglandin endoperoxides by glutathione-s-transferases and serum albu-

mins. *Biochim. Biophys. Acta* 450:
450–61

24. Cook, H. W., Lands, W. E. M. 1975.
Evidence for an activating factor
formed during prostaglandin biosynthesis. *Biochem. Biophys. Res. Commun.*
65:464–71

25. Cook, H. W., Lands, W. E. M. 1976.
Mechanism for suppression of cellular
biosynthesis of prostaglandins. *Nature*
260:630–32

26. Cushman, D. W., Cheung, H. S. 1976.
Effect of substrate concentration on inhibition of prostaglandin synthetase of
bull seminal vesicles by anti-inflammatory drugs and fenamic acid analogs.
Biochim. Biophys. Acta 424:449–59

27. Dawson, W., Boot, J. R., Cockerill, A.
F., Mallen, D. N. B., Osborne, D. J.
1976. Release of novel prostaglandins
and thromboxanes after immunological
challenge of guinea pig lung. *Nature*
262:699–702

28. deDeckere, E. A. M., Nugteren, D. H.,
TenHoor, F. 1977. Prostacyclin is the
major prostaglandin released from the
isolated perfused rabbit and rat heart.
Nature 268:160–63

29. Diczfalusy, U., Falardeau, P., Hammarström, S. 1977. Conversion of
prostaglandin endoperoxides to C_{17}
hydroxy acids catalyzed by human
platelet thromboxane synthase. *FEBS
Lett.* 84:271–74

30. Diczfalusy, U., Hammarström, S. 1977.
Inhibitors of thromboxane synthase in
human platelets. *FEBS Lett.* 82:107–10

31. Dyerberg, J., Bang, H. O., Stofferson,
E., Moncada, S., Vane, J. R. 1978.
Eicosapentaenoic acid and prevention
of thrombosis and atherosclerosis. *Lancet* 00:117–19

32. Eakins, K. E., Kulkarni, P. S. 1977. Selective inhibitory actions of sodium *p*-benzyl-4-[1-OXO-2-(4-Chlorobenzyl)-3-Phenyl Propyl] phenyl phosphate (N-0164) and indomethacin on the biosynthesis of prostaglandins and thromboxanes from arachidonic acid. *Br. J. Pharmacol.* 60:135–40

33. Egan, R. W., Paxton, J., Kuehl, F. A.
Jr. 1976. Mechanism for irreversible
self-deactivation of prostaglandin synthetase. *J. Biol. Chem.* 251:7329–35

34. Eling, T. E., Anderson, M. W. 1976.
Transport and metabolism of prostaglandins by lung. *Prostaglandins* 11:
471–73

35. Falardeau, P., Hamberg, M., Samuelsson, B. 1976. Metabolism of 8,11,14-eicosatrienoic acid in human platelets.
Biochim. Biophys. Acta 441:193–200

36. Feinstein, M. B., Becker, E. L., Fraser,
C. 1977. Thrombin, collagen and
A23187 stimulated endogenous platelet
arachidonate metabolism: differential
inhibition by PGE_1, local anesthetics
and a serine-protease inhibitor. *Prostaglandins* 14:1075–93

37. Fenwick, L., Jones, R. L., Naylor, B.
1977. Production of prostaglandins by
the pseudopregnant rat uterus in vitro,
and the effect of tamoxifen with the
identification of 6-keto-prostaglandin
$F_{1\alpha}$ as a major product. *Br. J. Pharmacol.* 59:191–99

38. Fitzpatrick, F. A., Gorman, R. R. 1978.
A comparison of imidazole and 9,11-azoprosta-5,13-dienoic acid. Two selective thromboxane synthetase inhibitors.
Biochim. Biophys. Acta 539:162–72

39. Fitzpatrick, F. A., Wynalda, M. A.
1976. In vivo suppression of prostaglandin biosynthesis by non-steroidal antiinflammatory agents. *Prostaglandins*
12:1037–44

40. Gilmore, N., Vane, J. R., Wyllie, J. H.
1968. Prostaglandins released by the
spleen. *Nature* 218:1135–40

41. Glenn, E. M., Bowman, B. J., Rohloff,
N. A. 1977. Anti-inflammatory and PG
inhibitory effects of phenacetin and
acetaminophen. *Agents and Actions*
7:513–16

42. Goetzl, E. J., Woods, J. M., Gorman,
R. R. 1977. Stimulation of human
eosinophil and neutrophil polymorphonuclear leukocyte chemotaxis and
random migration by 12-L-hydroxy-5,8,10,14-eicosatetraenoic acid. *J. Clin.
Invest.* 59:179–83

43. Granström, E., Inger, U., Samuelsson,
B. 1965. The structure of a urinary
metabolite of prostaglandin $F_{1\alpha}$ in the
rat. *J. Biol. Chem.* 240:457–50

44. Grant, J. A., Lichtenstein, L. M. 1974.
Release of slow reacting substance of
anaphylaxis from human leukocytes. *J.
Immunol.* 112:897–904

45. Grunnet, I., Bojesen, E. 1976. Prostaglandin E_1 high affinity binding sites of
rat thymocytes. Specificity and blockade by non-steroidal antiinflammatory
drugs and localization in a plasma
membrane-enriched fraction. *Biochim.
Biophys. Acta* 419:365–78

46. Gryglewski, R. J. 1974. Structure-activity relationships of some prostaglandin synthetase inhibitors. In *Prostaglandin Synthetase Inhibitors,* ed. H. J.
Robinson, J. R. Vane, p. 33. New York:
Raven

47. Gryglewski, R. J., Panczenko, B., Korbut, R., Grodzinska, L., Ocetkiewics,

A. 1975. Corticosteroids inhibit prostaglandin release from perfused mesenteric blood vessels of rabbit and from perfused lungs of sensitized guinea pig. *Prostaglandins* 10:343–55

48. Gryglewski, R. J., Zmuda, A., Dembinska-Kieć, A., Krecioch, E. 1977. A potent inhibitor of thromboxane A_2 biosynthesis in aggregating human blood platelets. *Pharmacol. Res. Commun.* 9:109–16

49. Hamberg, M. 1968. Metabolism of prostaglandins in rat liver mitochondria. *Eur. J. Biochem.* 6:135–46

50. Hamberg, M. 1976. On the formation of thromboxane B_2 and 12-L-hydroxy-5,8,10,14-eicosatetraenoic acid (12ho-20:4) in tissues from the guinea pig. *Biochim. Biophys. Acta* 431:651–54

51. Hamberg, M., Fredholm, B. B. 1976. Isomerization of prostaglandin H_2 into prostaglandin D_2 in the presence of serum albumin. *Biochim. Biophys. Acta* 431:189–93

52. Hamberg, M., Samuelsson, B. 1971. Metabolism of prostaglandin E_2 in guinea pig liver. II. Pathways in the formation of the major metabolites. *J. Biol. Chem.* 246:1073–77

53. Hamberg, M., Samuelsson, B. 1974. Prostaglandin endoperoxides. VII. Novel transformations of arachidonic acid in guinea pig lung. *Biochem. Biophys. Res. Commun.* 61:942

54. Hamberg, M., Samuelsson, B. 1966. Prostaglandins in human seminal plasma. Prostaglandins and related factors 46. *J. Biol. Chem.* 241:257–63

55. Hamberg, M., Svensson, J., Samuelsson, B. 1975. Thromboxanes: a new group of biologically active compounds derived from prostaglandin endoperoxides. *Proc. Natl. Acad. Sci. USA* 72:2994–98

56. Hammarström, S., Hamberg, M., Samuelsson, B., Duell, E. A., Stawiski, M., Voorhees, J. J. 1975. Increased concentrations of nonesterified arachidonic acid, 12-L-hydroxy-5,8,10,14-eicosatetraenoic acid, prostaglandin E_2, and prostaglandin F_{2a} in epidermis of psoriasis. *Proc. Natl. Acad. Sci. USA* 72:5130–34

57. Hansen, H. S. 1976. 15-Hydroxyprostaglandin dehydrogenase. *Prostaglandins* 12:647–79

58. Haye, B., Jacquemin, C. 1977. Incorporation of [^{14}C]arachidonate in pig thyroid lipids and prostaglandins. *Biochim. Biophys. Acta* 487:231–42

59. Hemler, M., Lands, W. E. M. 1976. Purification of the cyclooxygenase that forms prostaglandins. Demonstration of two forms of iron in the holoenzyme. *J. Biol. Chem.* 251:5575–79

60. Hemler, M. E., Lands, W. E. M. 1977. Biosynthesis of prostaglandins. *Lipids* 12:591–95

61. Hensby, C. N. 1975. Distribution studies on the reduction of prostaglandin E_2 to prostaglandin F_{2a} by tissue homogenates. *Biochim. Biophys. Acta* 409:225–34

62. Ho, P. P. K., Walters, C. P., Sullivan, H. R. 1977. A particulate arachidonate lipoxygenase in human blood platelets. *Biochem. Biophys. Res. Commun.* 76:398–405

63. Hong, S.-C., Levine, L. 1976. Inhibition of arachidonic acid release from cells as the biochemical action of anti-inflammotory corticosteroids. *Proc. Natl. Acad. Sci. USA* 73:1730–34

64. Hsueh, W., Isakson, P. C., Needleman, P. 1977. Hormone selective lipase activation in the isolated rabbit heart. *Prostaglandins* 13:1073–89

65. Israelsson, U., Hamberg, M., Samuelsson, B. 1969. Biosynthesis of 19-hydroxy-prostaglandin A_1. *Eur. J. Biochem.* 11:390–94

66. Janszen, F. H. A., Nugteren, D. H. 1974. Histochemical localisation of prostaglandin synthetase. *Histochemie* 27:159–64

67. Johnson, R. A., Morton, D. R., Kinner, J. H., Gorman, R. R., McGuire, J. C., Sun, F. F. 1976. The chemical structure of prostaglandin X (prostacyclin). *Prostaglandins* 12:915–28

68. Keenan, J. P., Wharton, J., Shepherd, A. J. N., Bellingham. A. J. 1977. Defective platelet lipid peroxidation in myeloproliferative disorders: a possible defect of prostaglandin synthesis. *Br. J. Haematol.* 35:275

69. Kelly, R. W., Taylor, P. L., Hearn, J. P., Short, R. V., Martin, D. E., Marston, J. H. 1976. 19-Hydroxyprostaglandin E_1 as a major component of the semen of primates. *Nature* 260:544–45

70. Knapp, H. R., Oelz, O., Roberts, L. J., Sweetman, B. J., Oates, J. A., Reed, P. W. 1977. Ionophores stimulate prostaglandin and thromboxane biosynthesis. *Proc. Natl. Acad. Sci. USA* 74:4251–55

71. Kröner, E. E., Peskar, B. A. 1976. On the metabolism of prostaglandins by rat brain homogenate. *Experientia* 32:1114–15

72. Kuehl, F. A. Jr., Cirillo, V. J., Zanetti, M. E., Beveridge, G. C., Ham, E. A. 1976. The regulatory role of steroid hor-

mones on the PGF/PGE ratio in target tissues. *Agents and Actions* 6:165–70

73. Kuehl, F. A. Jr., Humes, J. L., Egan, R. W., Ham, E. A., Beveridge, G. C., VanArman, C. G. 1977. Role of prostaglandin endoperoxide PGG₂ in inflammatory processes. *Nature* 265:170–73

74. Lands, W. E. M., Cook, H. W., Rome, L. H. 1976. Prostaglandin biosynthesis: consequences of oxygenase mechanism upon in vitro assays of drug effectiveness. In *Advances in Prostaglandin and Thromboxane Research*, ed. B. Samuelsson, R. Paoletti, 1:7–17. New York: Raven

75. Lands, W. E. M., Crawford, C. G. 1976. Enzymes of membrane phospholipid metabolism in animals. In *The Enzymes of Biological Membranes—Biosynthesis of Cell Components*, ed. A. Martonosi, 2:3–85. New York: Plenum

76. Lands, W., Lee, R., Smith, W. 1971. Factors regulating the biosynthesis of various prostaglandins. *Ann. NY Acad. Sci.* 180:107–22

77. Lands, W. E. M., LeTellier, P. R., Rome, L. H., Vanderhoek, J. Y. 1973. Inhibition of prostaglandin biosynthesis. *Adv. Biosci.* 9:15–28

78. Lands, W. E. M., Rome, L. H. 1975. Inhibition of prostaglandin biosynthesis. In *Prostaglandins: Chemical and Biochemical Aspects*, ed. S. M. M. Karim, 3:87–126. England: MTP Press Ltd.

79. Lands, W. E. M., Sauter, J., Stone, G. W. 1978. Oxygen requirement for prostaglandin synthesis. *Prostagl. Med.* 1: In press

80. Lands, W. E. M., Samuelsson, B. 1968. Phospholipid precursors of prostaglandins. *Biochim. Biophys. Acta* 164: 426–29

81. Laychock, S. G., Franson, R. C., Weglicki, W. B., Rubin, R. P. 1977. Identification and partial characterization of phospholipases in isolated adrenocortical cells. The effects of synacthen [corticotropin-(1–24)-tetracosapeptide] and calcium ions. *Biochem. J.* 164:753–56

82. Lee, R. E., Lands, W. E. M. 1972. Cofactors in the biosynthesis of prostaglandins F₁α and F₂α. *Biochim. Biophys. Acta* 260:203–11

83. Lee, S.-C., Levine, L. 1975. Prostaglandin metabolism. II. Identification of two 15-hydroxyprostaglandin dehydrogenase types. *J. Biol. Chem.* 250:548–52

84. Lee, S.-C., Levine, L. 1975. Purification and regulatory properties of chicken heart prostaglandin E 9-ketoreductase. *J. Biol. Chem.* 250:4549–55

85. Limas, C. J. 1977. Selective stimulation of venous prostaglandin E 9-ketoreductase by bradykinin. *Biochim. Biophys. Acta* 498:306–15

86. Limas, C. J., Limas, C. 1977. Prostaglandin metabolism in the kidneys of spontaneously hypertensive rats. *Am. J. Physiol.* 233:H87–H92

87. Lin, M. T., Rao, Ch. V. 1977. [³H] Prostaglandins binding to dispersed bovine luteal cells: evidence for discrete prostaglandin receptors. *Biochem. Biophys. Res. Commun.* 78:510–16

88. Livio, M., Villa, S., deGaetano, G. 1978. Aspirin, thromboxane and prostacyclin in rats: a dilemma resolved? *Lancet*: 1307

89. Marnett, L. J., Wlodawer, P., Samuelsson, B. 1975. Co-oxgenation of organic substrates by the prostaglandin synthetase of sheep vesicular gland. *J. Biol. Chem.* 250:8510–17

90. Mathé, A. A., Strandberg, K., Yen, S.-S. 1977. Prostaglandin release by slow reacting substance from guinea pig and human lung tissue. *Prostaglandins* 14:1105–15

91. Miller, O. V., Gorman, R. R. 1978. Evidence for distinct PGI₂ and PGD₂ receptors in human platelets. *J. Pharmacol. Exp. Ther.* In press

92. Miyamoto, T., Ogino, N., Yamamoto, S., Hayaishi, O. 1976. Purification of prostaglandin endoperoxide synthetase from bovine vesicular gland microsomes. *J. Biol. Chem.* 251:2629–36

93. Moncada, S., Gryglewski, R., Bunting, S., Vane, J. R. 1976. An enzyme isolated from arteries transforms prostaglandin endoperoxides to an unstable substance that inhibits platelet aggregation. *Nature* 263:663–65

94. Moncada, S., Mugridge, K. G., Whittle, B. J. R. 1977. The differential response of a novel bioassay tissue, the rabbit transverse stomach-strip, to prostacyclin (PGI₂) and other prostaglandins. *Br. J. Pharmacol.* 61:451P-52P

95. Morse, D. E., Duncan, H., Hooker, N., Morse, A. 1977. Hydrogen peroxide induces spawning in mollusks, with activation of prostaglandin endoperoxide synthetase. *Science* 196:298–300

96. Needleman, P., Bryan, B., Wyche, A., Bronson, S. D., Eakins, K., Ferrendelli, J. A., Minkes, M. 1977. Thromboxane synthetase inhibitors as pharmacological tools: differential biochemical and biological effects on platelet. *Prostaglandins* 14:897–907

97. Needleman, P., Minkes, M., Raz, A. 1976. Thromboxanes: selective biosyn-

thesis and distinct biological properties. *Science* 193:163–65

98. Nijkamp, F. P., Flower, R. J., Moncada, S., Vane, J. R. 1976. Partial purification of rabbit aorta contracting substance–releasing factor and inhibition of its activity by anti-inflammatory steroids. *Nature* 263:479–82

99. Nugteren, D. H. 1975. Arachidonate lipoxygenase in blood platelets. *Biochim. Biophys. Acta* 380:299–307

100. Nugteren, D. H. 1975. The determination of prostaglandin metabolites in human urine. *J. Biol. Chem.* 250:2808–12

101. Nugteren, D. H., Beerthuis, R. K., Van-Dorp, D. A. 1966. The enzymic conversion of *all-cis* 8,11,14-eicosatrienoic acid into prostaglandin E_1. *Recueil* 85:405–19

102. Nugteren, D. H., Hazelhof, E. 1973. Isolation and properties of intermediates in prostaglandin biosynthesis. *Biochim. Biophys Acta* 326:448–61

103. Oelz, O., Oelz, R., Knapp, H. R., Sweetman, B. J., Oates, J. A. 1977. Biosynthesis of prostaglandin D_2. 1. Formation of prostaglandin D_2 by human platelets. *Prostaglandins* 13:225–34

104. Ogino, N., Miyamoto, T., Yamamoto, S., Hayaishi, O. 1977. Prostaglandin endoperoxide E isomerase from bovine vesicular gland microsomes, a glutathione-requiring enzyme. *J. Biol. Chem.* 252:890–95

105. Ohki, S., Ogino, N., Yamamoto, S., Hayaishi, O., Yamamoto, H., Miyake, H., Hayashi, M. 1977. Inhibition of prostaglandin endoperoxide synthetase by thiol analogues of prostaglandin. *Proc. Natl. Acad. Sci. USA* 74:144–48

106. Oien, H. G., Ham, E. A., Zanetti, M. E., Ulm, E. H., Kuehl, F. A. Jr. 1976. A 15-hydroxyprostaglandin dehydrogenase specific for prostaglandin A in rabbit kidney. *Proc. Natl. Acad. Sci. USA* 73:1107–11

107. Orange, R. P., Murphy, R. C., Karnovsky, M. L., Austen, K. F. 1973. The physicochemical characteristics and purification of slow-reacting substance of anaphylaxis. *J. Immunol.* 110:760–70

108. Pace-Asciak, C. 1975. Prostaglandin 9-hydroxydehydrogenase activity in the adult rat kidney. Identification, assay, pathway, and some enzyme properties. *J. Biol. Chem.* 250:2789–94

109. Pace-Asciak, C. 1975. Activity profiles of prostaglandin 15- and 9-hydroxydehydrogenase and 13-reductase in the developing rat kidney. *J. Biol. Chem.* 250:2795–2800

110. Pace-Asciak, C. 1976. Isolation, structure, and biosynthesis of 6-ketoprostaglandin $F_{1\alpha}$ in the rat stomach. *J. Am. Chem. Soc.* 98:2348–49

111. Pace-Asciak, C. 1976. Decreased renal prostaglandin catabolism precedes onset of hypertension in the developing spontaneously hypertensive rat. *Nature* 263:510–12

112. Pace-Asciak, C. 1977. Prostaglandin biosynthesis and catabolism in the developing fetal sheep lung. *Prostaglandins* 13:649–60

113. Pace-Asciak, C. R., Carrara, M. C., Domazet, Z. 1977. Identification of the major urinary metabolites of 6-keto-prostaglandin $F_{1\alpha}$ (6K-PGF1$_\alpha$) in the rat. *Biochem. Biophys. Res. Commun.* 78:115–21

114. Pace-Asciak, C., Miller, D. 1973. Prostaglandins during development. I. Age-dependent activity profiles of prostaglandin 15-hydroxy-dehydrogenase and 13,14-reductase in lung tissue from late prenatal, early postnatal and adult rats. *Prostaglandins* 4:351–62

115. Pace-Asciak, C. R., Rangaraj, G. 1976. Prostaglandin biosynthesis and catabolism in the developing fetal sheep brain. *J. Biol. Chem.* 251:3381–85

116. Pace-Asciak, C. R., Rangaraj, G. 1977. Distribution of prostaglandin biosynthetic pathways in several rat tissues. Formation of 6-keto-prostaglandin $F_{1\alpha}$. *Biochim. Biophys. Acta* 486:579–82

117. Pace-Asciak, C. R., Rangaraj, G. 1977. The 6-ketoprostaglandin $F_{1\alpha}$ pathway in the lamb ductus arteriosus. *Biochim. Biophys. Acta* 486:583–85

118. Pace-Asciak, C., Wolfe, L. S. 1971. A novel prostaglandin derivative formed from arachidonic acid by rat stomach homogenates. *Biochemistry* 10:3657–69

119. Palmer, M. A., Piper, P. J., Vane, J. R. 1973. Release of rabbit aorta contracting substance (RCS) and prostaglandins induced by chemical or mechanical stimulation of guinea-pig lungs. *Br. J. Pharmacol.* 49:226–42

120. Pong, S.-S., Hong, S.-C. L., Levine, L. 1977. Prostaglandin production by methylcholanthrene-transformed mouse BALB/3T3. Requirement for protein synthesis. *J. Biol. Chem.* 252:1408–13

121. Roberts, L. J. II., Sweetman, B. J., Payne, N. A., Oates, J. A. 1977. Metabolism of thromboxane B_2 in man. Identification of the major urinary metabolite. *J. Biol. Chem.* 252:7415–17

122. Rome, L. H., Lands, W. E. M. 1975. Structural requirements for time-dependent inhibition of prostaglandin

biosynthesis by anti-inflammatory drugs. *Proc. Natl. Acad. Sci. USA* 72:4863–65

123. Rome, L. H., Lands, W. E. M., Roth, G. J., Majerus, P. W. 1976. Aspirin as a quantitative acetylating reagent for the fatty acid oxygenase that forms prostaglandins. *Prostaglandins* 11: 23–30

124. Roth, G. J., Majerus, P. W. 1975. The mechanism of the effect of aspirin on human platelets. I. Acetylation of a particulate fraction protein. *J. Clin. Invest.* 56:624–32

125. Samuelsson, B., Goldyne, M., Granström, E., Hamberg, M., Hammarström, S., Malmsten, C. 1978. *Ann. Rev. Biochem.* 47:997–1029

126. Samuelsson, B., Granström, E., Green, K., Hamberg, M., Hammarström, S. 1975. Prostaglandins. *Ann. Rev. Biochem.* 44:669–95

127. Shen, T. Y., Ham, E. A., Cirillo, V. J., Zanetti, M. 1974. Structure-activity relationship of certain prostaglandin synthetase inhibitors. See Ref. 46, p. 19

128. Smith, W. L., Lands, W. E. M. 1971. Stimulation and blockade of prostaglandin biosynthesis. *J. Biol. Chem.* 246: 6700–4

129. Smith, W. L., Lands, W. E. M. 1972. Oxygenation of unsaturated fatty acids by soybean lipoxygenase. *J. Biol. Chem.* 247:1038–47

130. Smith, W. L., Lands, W. E. M. 1972. Oxygenation of polyunsaturated fatty acids during prostaglandin biosynthesis by sheep vesicular gland. *Biochemistry* 11:3276–85

131. Smith, W. L., Wilkin, G. P. 1977. Immunochemistry of prostaglandin endoperoxide-forming cyclooxygenases: the detection of the cyclooxygenases in rat, rabbit, and guinea pig kidneys by immunofluorescence. *Prostaglandins* 13:873–92

132. Spector, A. A. 1975. Fatty acid binding to plasma albumin. *J. Lipid Res.* 16:165–76

133. Sprecher, H. 1977. Biosynthesis of polyunsaturated fatty acids and its regulation. In *Polyunsaturated Fatty Acids,* ed. W.-H. Kunau, R. T. Holman, P.1. Chicago, Ill: Am. Oil Chem. Soc.

134. Sun, F. F. 1974. Metabolism of prostaglandin $F_{2\alpha}$ in the rat. *Biochim. Biophys. Acta* 348:249–62

135. Sun, F. F. 1977. Biosynthesis of thromboxanes in human platelets. I. Characterization and assay of thromboxane synthetase. *Biochem. Biophys. Res. Commun.* 74:1432–40

136. Sun, F. F., Chapman, J. P., McGuire, J. C. 1977. Metabolism of prostaglandin endoperoxide in animal tissues. *Prostaglandins* 14:1055–74

137. Tai, H.-H. 1976. Enzymatic synthesis of $(15S)$-$[15$-$^3H]$prostaglandins and their use in the development of a simple and sensitive assay for 15-hydroxyprostaglandin dehydrogenase. *Biochemistry* 15:4586–92

138. Tai, H.-H., Yuan, B., Wu, A. T. 1978. Transformation of arachidonate into 6-oxoprostaglandin $F_{1\alpha}$ thromboxane B_2 and prostaglandin E_2 by sheep lung microsomal fraction. *Biochem. J.* 170:441–44

139. Takahashi, H., Webster, M. E., Newball, H. H. 1976. Separation of slow reacting substance of anaphylaxis (SRS-A) from human lung into four biologically active fractions. *J. Immunol.* 117:1039–44

140. Takeguchi, C., Sih, C. J. 1972. A rapid spectrophotometric assay for prostaglandin synthetase: application to the study of nonsteroidal antiinflammatory agents. *Prostaglandins* 2:169–85

141. Tam, S., Hong, S.-C. L., Levine, L. 1977. Relationships, among the steroids, of anti-inflammatory properties and inhibition of prostaglandin production and arachidonic acid release by transformed mouse fibroblasts. *J. Pharmacol. Exp. Ther.* 203:162–68

142. Tashjian, A. H. Jr., Ivey, J. L., Delclos, B., Levine, L. 1978. Stimulation of prostaglandin production in bone by phorbol diesters and melittin. *Prostaglandins.* In press

143. Turnbull, L. S., Jones, D. G., Kay, A. B. 1976. Slow reacting substance as a preformed mediator from human lung. *Immunology* 31:813

144. Turner, S. R., Tainer, J. A., Lynn, W. S. 1975. Biogenesis of chemotactic molecules by the arachidonate lipoxygenase system of platelets. *Nature* 257:680–81

145. Vanderhoek, J. Y., Lands, W. E. M. 1973. Acetylenic inhibitors of sheep vesicular gland oxygenase. *Biochim. Biophys. Acta* 296:374–81

146. Van der Ouderaa, F. J., Buytenhek, M., Nugteren, D. H., Van Dorp, D. A. 1977. Purification and characterisation of prostaglandin endoperoxide synthetase from sheep vesicular glands. *Biochim. Biophys. Acta* 487:315–31

147. van Evert, W. C., Nugteren, D. H., Van Dorp, D. A. 1978. Inhibition of prostaglandin biosynthesis by *c*-5, *c*-8, *c*-11-

eicosatrienoic acid. *Prostaglandins* 15:267–72

148. Wlodawer, P., Hammarström, S. 1978. Thromboxane synthase from bovine lung—solubilization and partial purification. *Biochem. Biophys. Res. Commun.* 80:525–32

149. Wlodawer, P., Kindahl, H., Hamberg, M. 1976. Biosynthesis of prostaglandin $F_{2\alpha}$ from arachidonic acid and prostaglandin endoperoxides in the uterus. *Biochim. Biophys. Acta* 431:603–14

150. Wlodawer, P., Samuelsson, B., Albonico, S. M., Corey, E. J. 1971. Selective inhibition of prostaglandin synthetase by a bicyclo[2.2.1] heptene derivative. *J. Am. Chem. Soc.* 93:2815–16

151. Wolfe, L. S., Rostworowski, K., Marion J. 1976. Endogenous formation of the prostaglandin endoperoxide metabolite, thromboxane B_2, by brain tissue. *Biochem. Biophys. Res. Commun.* 70:907–13

152. Wolfe, L. S., Rostworowski, K., Pappius, H. M. 1976. The endogenous biosynthesis of prostaglandins by brain tissue in vitro. *Can. J. Biochem.* 54:629–40

153. Wong, P. Y.-K., Terragno, D. A., Terragno, N. A., McGiff, J. C. 1977. Dual effects of bradykinin on prostaglandin metabolism: relationship to the dissimilar vascular actions of kinins. *Prostaglandins* 13:1113–25

154. Yoshimoto, A., Ito, H., Tomita, K. 1970. Cofactor requirements of the enzyme synthesizing prostaglandin in bovine seminal vesicles. *J. Biochem.* 68:487–99

155. Yoshimoto, T., Yamamoto, S., Okuma, M., Hayaishi, O. 1977. Solubilization and resolution of thromboxane synthesizing system from microsomes of bovine blood platelets. *J. Biol. Chem.* 252:5871–74

156. Ziboh, V. A., Lord, J. T., Penneys, N. S. 1977. Alterations of prostaglandin E_2-9-ketoreductase activity in proliferating skin. *J. Lipid Res.* 18:37–43

Ann. Rev. Physiol. 1979. 41:653–68
Copyright © 1979 by Annual Reviews Inc. All rights reserved

CELLULAR MECHANISMS
OF PROSTAGLANDIN ACTION

◆1243

R. H. Harris and P. W. Ramwell

Department of Physiology and Biophysics, Georgetown University
Medical Center, Washington DC 20007

P. J. Gilmer

Institute of Molecular Biophysics, The Florida State University,
Talahassee, Florida 32306

INTRODUCTION

In the platelet it is possible to determine systematically (*a*) the profile of biological activity of the arachidonate metabolites, (*b*) the effects of interconversion, (*c*) the intracellular mediators of arachidonate action, and (*d*) the arachidonate metabolites involved in the response to other stimuli. On the other hand, the erythrocyte displays a quite different activity profile toward arachidonate metabolites, and its study is uncomplicated by endogenous prostaglandin production. Since both human platelets and erythrocytes can be harvested in a relatively pure form, they are ideally suited for introductory investigations into the cellular mechanisms of prostaglandin action.

PLATELETS

The endoperoxides (PGG_2 and PGH_2), thromboxane (TXA_2), and prostacyclin (PGI_2) are the arachidonate metabolites most active in directly affecting platelet function. Therefore, this section focuses primarily on the activity of these compounds and only touches on that of the prostaglandins.

653

0066-4278/79/0301-0653$01.00

Cascade Effects

ENDOPEROXIDES AND THROMBOXANES   Initial experiments support the contention that TXA_2 rather than the endoperoxides is the primary mediator of arachidonate-induced platelet aggregation (33, 93). When washed platelets were incubated with arachidonate a substance was produced that aggregated washed platelets previously treated with indomethacin. The endoperoxides were ruled out because only low levels were found at the height of the response. Incubation of the filtrate at 37°C indicated that the unstable substance had a 30–40 sec half-life, which was similar to that of both "rabbit aorta contracting substance" (RCS) and the trapped TXA_2. Incubation of PGG_2 with washed platelets produced an aggregating substance displaying the same properties.

Although these studies suggested that TXA_2 is the primary pro-aggregator of the arachidonate cascade, other information makes this conclusion less certain. The half-lives of the endoperoxides and TXA_2 in aqueous media are approximately five minutes and thirty seconds, respectively (33), but TXA_2-like activity may persist in plasma for over 10 minutes, while measurable endoperoxide levels have become negligible (90). Albumin appears to be the plasma factor responsible for providing stability for the preformed TXA_2 (22). The production of TXA_2 may also differ depending on the presence of plasma. In platelet-rich plasma (PRP), aggregation induced by PGG_2 proceeds with little TXA_2 production, whereas in washed platelets TXA_2 is rapidly formed and destroyed (48). If platelet aggregation is inhibited with EDTA, TXA_2 production can continue for at least three minutes, perhaps due to the slow release and metabolism of arachidonate and endoperoxide bound to plasma proteins (90). Other studies have indicated that in plasma, PGH_2 may undergo accelerated degradation to PGD_2, thus shortening its plasma lifetime (91). Thus, changes in the production and decomposition of PGG_2, PGH_2, and TXA_2 (depending on the conditions) makes comparison of their relative activities difficult.

The release of other and more well-known mediators into the incubates of washed platelets by arachidonate also complicates the assessment of activity due to the endoperoxides or TXA_2. Arachidonate (89), PGG_2 (48), and PGH_2 (99) induce release of serotonin in platelet-rich plasma (PRP), and the removal of plasma constituents or extracellular calcium does not prevent release (24). Thus, serotonin and ADP could be likely contaminants in any incubate; and, in fact, stable aggregatory mediators were present in the transfer experiments mentioned above (93). Although neither ADP nor serotonin alone causes aggregation in washed platelets (34), a pronounced synergism has been demonstrated with arachidonate in human platelets (86) and with PGH_2 in dog platelets (14). This synergism may partially explain some of the enhanced activity attributed to TXA_2. Similarly, the concentration of endoperoxides needed may be much lower, owing to a synergistic response. However, arachidonate also induces aggregation in degranulated platelets (40), and the endoperoxides can induce reversible aggregation without secretion (77). Thus, the arachidonate intermediates affect more than one platelet function.

The use of relatively nonspecific thromboxane synthetase inhibitors has yielded equivocal results about the role of thromboxanes. Imidazole inhibits thromboxane synthetase from platelet microsomes (56), and blocks the production of TXA_2 by the lung and spleen (62). Several other inhibitors of the thromboxane synthetase have also been discovered (5). However, they produce diverse effects when tested in a platelet-aggregating system stimulated by arachidonic acid or PGG_2. Imidazole may not inhibit aggregation even when all TXA_2 production is blocked. In contrast, 9,11-azoprosta-5,13-dienoic acid (U51605) inhibits both aggregation and TXA_2 synthesis, while N-0164 inhibits aggregation at concentrations that do not inhibit synthesis (59, 60). This emphasizes the necessity of evaluating the other actions of TXA_2 inhibitors before they can be confidently used as pharmacological tools. The thromboxane synthetase has been solubilized from bovine platelet microsomes and resolved from the cyclo-oxygenase (101). The enzyme converts PGH_2 into TXA_2 and TXB_2, and the reaction mixture stimulates platelet aggregation to a greater level than PGH_2 alone (101). However, considerable TXA_2 is produced in this system before enhanced stimulation is observed.

Several stable endoperoxide analogs have been studied. The $9\alpha,11\alpha$, and $11\alpha,9\alpha$ epoxymethano and the 9,11 azo PGH_2 analogs induce both platelet aggregation and the release reaction, which can be blocked by indomethacin (16, 45). Two analogs of PGE_2 possess similar properties, but secondary aggregation and release require higher concentrations and only these are blocked by indomethacin (15). The 9,11-dithio PGH_2 analog induces irreversible aggregation after a dose-dependent lag time, and thus differs from the above compounds; in this case indomethacin does not prevent the aggregation, which is temporally associated with serotonin release (64). The 9,11-azoprosta-5,13-dienoic acid inhibits the platelet thromboxane synthetase, but has little intrinsic endoperoxide-like activity (26). This compound delays aggregation induced by arachidonic acid, inhibits the secondary aggregation induced by both ADP and epinephrine, but does not alter aggregation induced by the 9,11 epoxymethano PGH_2 analog. Although these results suggest that thromboxane synthesis is required for the aggregation process, an antagonism of endoperoxide action cannot be ruled out. Incubation of platelets with 4,7,10,13-nonadecatetraenoic acid produces an intermediate (endoperoxide or thromboxane?) that aggregates platelets but does not contract the rabbit aorta; incubation with 5,8,11,14,17-eicosapentaenoic acid produces an RCS-like intermediate, but aggregation does not ensue (69). Although the endoperoxide analogs have shed light on the mode of endoperoxide action because of their chemical and biological stability and potency, their effects on cascade enzymes and mediator release prevent unequivocal interpretation of their activity.

Thus none of the approaches used so far has conclusively defined the primary mediator of arachidonate-induced aggregation. The ability to induce or modulate aggregation, or to induce mediator release, may be the exclusive property of one or a shared property of both the endoperoxides and thromboxanes.

PROSTACYCLIN   Of the inhibitory metabolites, prostacyclin (PGI_2) is the most potent in preventing aggregation induced by a variety of stimuli (30, 58). It is up to thirty times more active than either PGE_1 or PGD_2, which are approximately equipotent (95). PGI_2 also promotes disaggregation initiated by PGG_2 and PGH_2 (27), but significant PGI_2 synthesis has not been observed in the platelet (94). However, vascular tissues and their microsomes produce predominantly PGI_2 from arachidonate and the endoperoxides (30, 58). The microsomal prostacyclin synthetase is more sensitive to inhibition by hydroperoxy fatty acids than are the other enzymes of the prostanoate pathway, which suggests that such products may have an indirect influence on the profile of the metabolite (57). At pH <7, PGI_2 rapidly transforms into 6-keto-$PGF_{1\alpha}$, a relatively inactive compound by comparison. However, the primary metabolite is probably 6,15-diketo-$PGF_{1\alpha}$, and recent studies by Axen indicate 6-keto-$PGF_{1\alpha}$ can also be converted to 6-keto-PGE_1, which is as active as PGE_1.

The instability of PGI_2 limits its usefulness as an antithrombotic agent. However, stable analogs of PGI_2 (17, 46) have been synthesized and one, 6,9-thiaprostacyclin (61), has activity comparable to the natural compound.

Intracellular Mediators

CYCLIC AMP   Increased cAMP is associated with inhibition of (a) platelet shape change, (b) internal contraction, (c) secretion of mediators, (d) phospholipase activation, and (e) aggregation; decreased levels are associated with the activation of these processes. Thus the properties of the individual metabolites of arachidonate may be associated with cAMP formation and breakdown.

PGE_1 elevates platelet intracellular cAMP levels by stimulating adenylate cyclase (78). Most of the parent prostaglandins also increase cAMP levels but are much less potent (50); this is consistent with their virtual inactivity in the platelet. PGD_1 and PGD_2 in human platelets are exceptions (43). During platelet aggregation PGD_2 may arise from the enzymatic or nonenzymatic breakdown of PGH_2 (63) but not enough is produced to provide a feedback regulator.

Prostacyclin also elevates cAMP levels, and the potency relative to PGE_1 and PGD_2 correlates well with the anti-aggregatory potency (95). However, in response to PGE_1 the cAMP maximum occurs earlier than with PGD_2 or PGI_2, though the greatest increase is attained with PGI_2 (27). Also, the cAMP increase in response to PGE_1 declines rapidly, whereas with PGD_2 and PGI_2 the level remains elevated longer. Unlike the case in the intact cell, both PGE_1 and PGI_2 stimulate the particulate adenylate cyclase over the same concentration range (27). PGI_2 binds to plasma membranes at a high affinity site that is competitively antagonized by PGE_1, and a low affinity site that is antagonized by PGD_2 (85). The presence of two receptors in human platelets may partially explain why PGI_2 stimulation is greater than that of either PGE_1 or PGD_2 alone. In addition, rapid reversal of platelet aggregation by PGE_1 argues for a plasma membrane receptor for these prostaglandins (96).

ADP, epinephrine, thrombin, and collagen reduce cAMP levels and initiate the sequence of events leading to platelet aggregation (12, 49, 80). Although basal cAMP levels are not altered by PGG_2 and PGH_2, the increase in response to PGE_1 (53) or PGI_2 (27) can be attenuated. ADP and epinephrine produce a similar effect (54). TXA_2 appears to be the responsible metabolite, since the PGH_2 effect is abolished with a thromboxane synthetase inhibitor (28).

The endoperoxide PGH_1 partially antagonizes the effect of PGH_2; but, as indicated by its ability to contract gerbil colon, this may be the result of decomposition to PGE_1 and PGD_1, which are both stimulants of adenylate cyclase (29).

PGE_2 has a biphasic effect on platelet aggregation (84). Low concentrations, which potentiate secondary aggregation to other stimuli, are associated with decreased cAMP levels; higher inhibitory concentrations elevate cAMP. This biphasic characteristic of PGE_2 has been invoked to explain both the decline of cAMP upon platelet washing (79) and the anomalous increase in cAMP upon stimulation with thrombin (18). The PGE_2 potentiation is calcium-dependent (99), which suggests that calcium influx is increased resulting in inhibition of adenylate cyclase and lowered cAMP levels (73). The net balance between this and the stimulation of adenylate cyclase activity may determine the final disposition of the platelet.

Other substances may affect platelet reactivity toward the prostaglandins. For example, cholesterol-enriched platelets are more aggregable to thrombotic stimuli, and PGE_1 is a less effective inhibitor (87). Inhibitors of adenylate cyclase activity enhance platelet aggregation induced by PGG_2 (77).

At high concentrations the other cascade products, such as HETE, HHT, and TXB_2, are without effect on basal or PGE_1-stimulated cAMP levels (53). Interestingly, the stable endoperoxide analog, $11\alpha,9\alpha$-epoxymethano PGH_2 does not lower stimulated cAMP levels (54) even though aggregation is induced. Thus the correlation between inhibition of platelet stimulation and increased cAMP levels seems more firmly entrenched than that of the decreased levels with stimulation.

CYCLIC GMP   Increased cGMP levels occur following stimulation with collagen (13, 14, 35, 36, 44, 45, 98), thrombin (98), epinephrine (13, 98), ADP (7, 14, 44), serotonin (1), and phorbol myristate (98). The increase observed with collagen is not blocked by aspirin at concentrations that inhibit aggregation (35, 36); cytochalasin B, an inhibitor of microfilament formation, potentiates the aggregation and release reaction to subthreshold concentrations of collagen but does not alter cGMP (35). Whether arachidonate elevates or depresses cGMP is debated; cGMP levels were reportedly lowered within one minute of arachidonate stimulation (7), but others (25) observed an increase that followed aggregation and was not blocked by aspirin. Perhaps this increase in cGMP is the result of lipoperoxide formation by the lipoxygenase pathway or by nonenzymatic oxidation of arachidonate, since neither reaction is blocked by aspirin. Such hydroperoxides of arachidonate and other unsaturated fatty acids stimulate the soluble guanylate cyclase of the platelet, in contrast to PGE_1, PGE_2, and $PGF_{2\alpha}$ (6). In addition, no increase in platelet cGMP levels occurs with PGH_2, TXA_2, TXB_2, HHT, and HETE (53). Thus, changes in cGMP may be associated with platelet aggregation but are probably not part of the mechanism.

CALCIUM   Calcium may be the ultimate regulator of the platelet shape change, internal contraction, release reaction, and aggregation induced by most stimuli (20, 51). Increased calcium necessary for these processes may arise from extracellular uptake or intracellular translocation. A model has been suggested proposing that TXA_2 acts as a calcium ionophore, translocating calcium from sequestered sites in the dense tubular system into the cytoplasm (24). Undirectional movement of calcium is maintained because the TXA_2 after its synthesis binds and transports calcium from the dense tubular system and spontaneously breaks down in the cytoplasm. The preferential transport of calcium into a diethyl ether phase by TXA_2 provides some support for this model. In contrast, PGE_2 requires extracellular calcium for its potentiating effect and may even induce aggregation if sufficient calcium is present (44).

If increased cytoplasmic calcium is associated with platelet activation, then its removal would be expected to inhibit aggregation. Two recent models have involved cAMP in this action, thus indirectly implicating the inhibitory prostaglandins (PGE, PGD, PGI) (8, 24). The accumulation of calcium into a subcellular fraction is stimulated by cAMP and a platelet protein kinase, which suggests that phosphorylation of a protein is necessary. Although there is a parallel with the cAMP stimulated uptake of calcium into sarcoplasmic reticulum in smooth muscle, the relationship between calcium and cAMP in the platelet is still not clear.

The Arachidonic Acid Cascade as Mediator

Initally, PGE_2, $PGF_{2\alpha}$ (79), and later the endoperoxides (100) were isolated from platelets aggregated with thrombin. Other aggregating agents, including ADP, collagen, and epinephrine, also induce platelet prostaglandin synthesis (88). Aspirin and nonsteroidal anti-inflammatory drugs partially inhibit the aggregating response to thrombin and collagen; they completely abolish secondary aggregation induced by ADP, while inhibiting formation of products of arachidonate (65). These findings indicate that arachidonate acts in concert with other mechanisms to effect the response. Additionally, thrombin stimulates the consumption of oxygen by platelets; this can be mimicked by exogenous arachidonate and prevented by prior incubation with aspirin (66). Acetylation of the cycloxygenase by aspirin can be inhibited by thrombin as well as by the substrate arachidonate (55).

The site of thrombin activation of arachidonate appears to be at the level of the acyl hydrolase. Mepacrine, an inhibitor of the acyl hydrolase, prevents release; whereas aspirin, a cyclo-oxygenase inhibitor, and eicosatetraynoic acid, a cyclo-oxygenase and lipoxygenase inhibitor, do not (11). Most platelet phospholipid fractions contain a substantial amount of arachidonate, and incubation of platelets with radiolabeled fatty acids results in rapid incorporation of arachidonate relative to linoleate or oleate (10). The rate of incorporation into the specific phospholipid fractions does not resemble their arachidonate composition, which suggests that separate pools or more selective uptake and release mechanisms exist (9). The arachidonate of the membrane phosphatidyl choline and phosphatidyl inositol, which are more rapidly labeled, is also preferentially liberated upon stimulation by thrombin. In addition to metabolism via the cascade, an enrichment of arachidonate is found in the phosphatidyl ethanolamine plasmalogen fraction following thrombin stimulation (71). This increase is not the result of de novo phospholipid synthesis or of increased exposure of plasmalogen at the plasma surface. Turnover through this phosphatide may be the primary source of arachidonate for the cyclo-oxygenase and lipoxygenase (72).

Agents that elevate intracellular cAMP levels block not only platelet internal contraction, release reaction, and the aggregation stimulated by thrombin, but also the release of arachidonate (23, 55) from platelet phospholipid. Platelet aggregation induced by arachidonate is inhibited by PGE_1, PGI_2, the combination of PGE_1 and theophylline, or dibutyryl cAMP; however, the metabolism of arachidonate is not inhibited and the product profile is not changed (23, 55). This contrasts with earlier work which proposed that dibutyryl cAMP appears to inhibit cyclo-oxygenase activity in addition to its effects on other processes (47).

Thrombin activates at least three pathways that lead to platelet aggregation (65). Aggregation proceeds even when the production of endoperoxides is blocked and the released mediators are neutralized with a regenerating system. Thrombin, collagen, ADP, arachidonic acid, and A23187, a calcium ionophore, produce the same sequence of ultrastructural changes in the platelet, which suggests that all pathways converge or interact at a common point (97). Because of the similarities to the effects of A23187, internal calcium shifts have been proposed as the third mechanism of thrombin stimulation of platelet aggregation, mediator release, and arachidonate hydrolysis. Indeed, thrombin enhances $^{45}Ca^{2+}$ uptake by platelets, and this can be blocked by PGE_1; but several antagonists that inhibit thrombin activation do not affect A23187 activation (21). Increased acyl hydrolase activity may be due to increased cytoplasmic calcium rather than to the release of hydrolytic enzymes (70). Despite the differences, calcium may serve as the key intermediate in the third thrombin pathway and also in release of endogenous arachidonic acid.

ERYTHROCYTES

Cascade Effects

The human red cell is sensitive to the lowest concentrations of prostaglandins yet reported for any cell. PGE_2 has a biphasic effect on the deformability of erythrocytes; the maximal response is with $10^{-10}M$ PGE_2 at 70% hematocrit, which is equivalent to ten PGE_2 molecules per cell; epinephrine and isoproterenol have similar effects at $10^{-9}M$ and $10^{-7}M$, respectively (2). Responses to the prostaglandins are not observed when precautions are not taken to minimize endogenous prostaglandin levels in the blood (37). In addition to changing deformability, PGE_2 affects the response of the red cell to osmotic shock. PGE_2 ($2 \times 10^{-11}M$) increases hypotonic hemolysis by about 3%, and the process is complete in 20–30 sec. The oscillatory nature (with a period of approximately 15 sec) of the susceptibility of red cells to hypotonic hemolysis is not altered by PGE_2 but is dampened by 10^{-9} M epinephrine (3). Regular oscillations in the size of the Ca ion pool are observed. Introduction of PGE_2 (10^{-11}M) to red cells decreases the size of the Ca ion pool and of cytoplasmic ATP levels while membrane-associated ATP levels rise. However, PGE_1 increases the size of the Ca ion pool (68).

This potent effect of PGE_2 on the red blood cell has been confirmed and extended using electron paramagnetic resonance (EPR) measurements (42). PGE_2 (10^{-11}M) has a maximal effect in increasing the relaxation time for shear-oriented erythrocytes to become randomly oriented. This orientation relaxation time is measured by stopping the flow of the oriented ery- throcytes and observing the change with time in the EPR spectrum of fatty acid spin-labeled erythrocytes. Opposite in effect to PGE_2, PGE_1 at the same low concentration increases the orientation relaxation time. Both these effects are biphasic, and both require the presence of external Ca ion in the medium. A cooperative phenomenon must be operating for so few PGE molecules per cell to affect the flow properties and deformability of a population of cells. Indeed, the EPR spectra, and therefore the mobility of the spin-label fatty acid probe, are affected by these low concentrations of the prostaglandins (10^{-11} M): PGE_2 decreases and PGE_1 increases the overall fluidity of the membrane. This is apparently a surface-related phe- nomenon, since the spin probe is most sensitive to hormone-induced changes when the nitroxide label is close to the carboxyl end of the fatty acid chain (42).

Similar concentrations of PGE_1 and PGE_2 alter the circular dichroism spectra of erythrocyte ghost membranes; PGE_1 causes a 13% decrease in membrane protein helicity (52). This phenomenon is temperature-depend- ent with a persistent alteration occurring at 37°C, a transient change at 25°, and no change at lower temperatures. The antagonist, 7-oxa-13-prostynoic acid, blocks the PGE_1 effect on membrane ellipticity.

Mediators

CYCLIC NUCLEOTIDES   Rat red blood cells respond to low levels of prostaglandins with an increase in cAMP concentration (68, 83). In fact, exogenous cAMP added to either rat (68) or human (41) erythrocytes alters the osmotic fragility and EPR parameters the way PGE_2 does. In the human erythrocyte there is no increase in cAMP or cGMP on prostaglan- din treatment (68) except perhaps at very high (10^{-6}M) PGE_1 concentra- tions (74).

Prostaglandin-induced changes in membrane fluidity can be mimicked by sealing human erythrocyte ghosts with cyclic nucleotides (41). These changes parallel the cyclic nucleotide–stimulated phosphorylation of membrane proteins by a membrane-associated protein kinase (32) that may be part of the mechanism.

Many other studies have examined endogenous and cAMP-stimulated phosphorylation of human erythrocyte membranes by protein kinase (75, 76, 82). The proteins phosphorylated and the amount of stimulation by cAMP vary considerably with changes in ionic conditions. The presence of Ca ion affects the selection of the protein kinase substrate and the amount of phosphate incorporated (19). In an intact erythrocyte system, one of the proteins phosphorylated is glycophorin (82). In the avian erythrocyte, which has a hormone-activated adenylate cyclase, cAMP-dependent phosphorylation of spectrin is observed (76). In the human erythrocyte, changes in phosphorylation upon hormone treatment may still occur, but in this case the protein kinase activity could be regulated by changes in the calcium ion concentration rather than by changes in cyclic nucleotide levels.

ION TRANSPORT   Internal Na and K ion concentrations rise or fall in proportion to their internal concentration following treatment of the red cell with PGE_1 or PGE_2, as if the red cell were shrinking or swelling by 3%, respectively, due to the change in the cell volume by transport of water. This may be a secondary consequence of the initial prostaglandin-induced changes in the membrane. The EPR parameters that are sensitive to hormone-induced changes are not sensitive to osmotically induced volume changes in the red cell.

At high concentrations of PGE_1 or PGE_2 ($10^{-7}M$), activation of the Na,K-ATPase occurs, but these effects probably do not relate to the deformability observed at much lower concentrations (39), due to the biphasic nature of the response.

No alteration in calcium efflux or calcium-dependent Mg-ATPase activity is observed in resealed ghosts with $10^{-10}M$ PGE_1 or PGE_2 (81). However, PGE_2 can decrease and PGE_1 can increase the soluble Ca ion pool by up to 20% (68). Thus, a plausible mechanism for prostaglandin action in the human erythrocyte is a primary hormone-induced change in the ratio of bound to free Ca ion, which then affects the protein kinase activity by its calcium ion sensitivity. The resulting change in membrane-associated protein phosphorylation at nucleation sites would affect the association of the cytoskeletal spectrin network with the membrane, thereby altering the overall membrane lipid fluidity and cell deformability.

Significance

High concentrations of PGE_2 ($10^{-7}M$) may induce sickling of susceptible (SS) erythrocytes at reduced oxygen tension (38) in addition to effects on cation flux (67). However, PGE_2 ($10^{-7}M$) has no adverse effect on plasma-suspended SS erythrocytes, and $10^{-5}M$ PGE_2 can transform cell shape in saline but not in autologous plasma (92). Thus, PGE_2 probably does not affect sickling in vivo because of plasma binding.

Therefore, the functional significance of the response of erythrocytes to prostaglandins and vasoactive hormones may be to control blood flow through capillaries (4). Because the red blood cell needs to bend and alter its shape in order to traverse capillaries, any physiological substances that alter the flexibility or deformability of the membrane could potentially regulate blood flow.

CONCLUSION

The human platelet and erythrocyte differ quite dramatically in relation to the arachidonic acid cascade. The platelet synthesizes its own characteristic products, while the erythrocyte lacks cyclo-oxygenase activity but possesses other metabolic enzymes. In these and other cell types the metabolites are potentially determined by the cascade enzymes, the availability of cofactors, the presence of specific activators and inhibitors, and the selective binding or transport of intermediates.

Endogenously synthesized metabolites may have intracellular actions or may be released and exert their effects extracellularly. Study of the cellular mechanisms mediating these effects, like study of the fast-acting hormones, has focused primarily on the cyclic nucleotides and calcium. Considering the diverse activities of several metabolites in the platelet however, these mechanisms seem to need reevaluation or refining.

The released cascade metabolites may also act as intercellular signals over a short range. The range depends on their chemical stability in the absence of protective carriers and their selective uptake and metabolism by surrounding cells. Additionally, the effects will reflect the selective interaction of responsive cells with the spectrum of metabolites released. Answering these questions of complex intercellular interactions requires the identification and classification of characteristic responses and the metabolic profile of individual cell types in each tissue. Consequently, this type of analysis may best be done with isolated cells, such as the platelet and erythrocyte.

Literature Cited

1. Agarwal, K. C., Steiner, M. 1976. Effect of serotonin on cyclic nucleotides of human platelets. *Biochem. Biophys. Res. Commun.* 69:962–69
2. Allen, J. E., Rasmussen, H. 1971. Human red blood cells: prostaglandin E_2, epinephrine, and isoproterenol alter deformability. *Science* 174:512–14
3. Allen, J. E., Rasmussen, H. 1972. Some effects of vasoactive hormones on the mammalian red blood cell. In *Prostaglandins in Cellular Biology,* ed. P. W. Ramwell, B. B. Pharriss, pp. 27–60. New York: Plenum
4. Allen, J. E., Valeri, C. R. 1974. Prostaglandins in hematology. *Arch. Intern. Med.* 133:86–96
5. Alusy, U. D., Hammarstrom, S. 1977. Inhibitors of thromboxane synthetase in human platelets. *FEBS Lett.* 82(1):107–10
6. Asano, T., Hidaka, H. 1977. Purification of guanylate cyclase from human platelets and effect of arachidonic acid peroxide. *Biochem. Biophys. Res. Commun.* 78(3):910–18
7. Barber, A. J. 1976. Cyclic nucleotides and platelet aggregation. Effect of aggregating agents on the activity of cyclic nucleotide–metabolizing enzymes. *Biochem. Biophys. Acta* 444:579–95
8. Berridge, M. J. 1975. The interaction of cyclic nucleotides and calcium in the control of cellular activity. In *Advances in Cyclic Nucleotide Research,* ed. P. Greengard, G. A. Robison, 6:1–98. New York: Raven Press
9. Bills, T. K., Smith, J. B., Silver, M. J. 1976. Metabolism of ^{14}C-arachidonic acid by human platelets. *Biochem. Biophys. Acta* 424(2):303–14
10. Bills, T. K., Smith, J. B., Silver, M. J. 1977. Selective release of arachidonic acid from the phospholipids of human platelets in response to thrombin. *J. Clin. Invest.* 60(1):1–6
11. Blackwell, G. J., Duncombe, W. G., Flower, R. J., Parsons, M. F., Vane, J. R. 1977. The distribution and metabolism of arachidonic acid in rabbit platelets during aggregation and its modification by drugs. *Br. J. Pharmacol.* 59(2):353–66
12. Chiang, T. M., Beachey, E. H., Kang, A. H. 1975. Interaction of a chick skin collagen fragment (alpha 1-CB5) with human platelets. Biochemical studies during the aggregation and release reaction. *J. Biol. Chem.* 250:6916–22
13. Chiang, T. M., Dixit, S. N., Kang, A. H. 1976. Effect of cyclic 3',5'-guanosine monophosphate on human platelet function. *J. Lab. Clin. Med.* 88:215–21
14. Chignard, M., Vergaftig, B. B. 1976. Dog platelets fail to aggregate when they form aggregating substances upon stimulation with arachidonic acid. *Eur. J. Pharmacol.* 38:7–18
15. Corey, E. J., Gordon, J. L., MacIntyre, D. E., Salzman, E. W. 1977. Effects of synthetic prostaglandin analogues on platelet aggregation and secretion. *Br. J. Pharmacol.* 59(3):446P–47P (Abstr.)
16. Corey, E. J., Nicolaou, K. C., Machida, Y., Malmsten, C. L., Samuelsson, B. 1975. Synthesis and biological properties of a 9,11-azo-prostanoid: Highly active biochemical mimic of prostaglandin endoperoxides. *Proc. Natl. Acad. Sci. USA* 72:3355–58
17. Crane, B. H., Maish, T. L., Maddox, Y. T., Corey, E. J., Szekely, I., Ramwell, P. W. 1978. The effect of prostaglandin I_2 and analogues on platelet aggregation and smooth muscle contraction. *J. Pharmacol. Exp. Ther.* 206(1):132–38
18. Droller, J. J. 1976. Thrombin induced platelet prostaglandin and cyclic AMP production and a possible intrinsic modulation of platelet function. *Scand. J. Haematol.* 17(3):167–78
19. Fairbanks, G., Avruch, J. 1974. Phosphorylation of endogenous substrates by erythrocyte membrane protein kinases. II. Cyclic adenosine monophosphate-stimulated reactions. *Biochemistry* 13:5514–21
20. Feinman, R. D., Detwiler, T. C. 1974. Platelet secretion induced by divalent cation ionophores. *Nature* 249:172–73
21. Feinstein, M. B., Becher, E. L., Fraser, C. 1977. Thrombin, collagen, and A23187 stimulated endogenous platelet arachidonate metabolism: Differential inhibition by PGE_1. *Prostaglandins* 14:1075–93
22. Folco, G., Granstrom, E., Kindahl, H. 1977. Albumin stabilizes thromboxane A_2. *FEBS Lett.* 82(2):321–24
23. Gerrard, J. M., Peller, J. D., Krick, T. P., White, J. G. 1977. Cyclic AMP and platelet prostaglandin synthesis. *Prostaglandins* 14(1):39–50
24. Gerrard, J. M., Townsend, D., Stoddard, S., Witkop, C. J., White, J. G. 1977. The influence of prostaglandin G_2 on platelet ultrastructure and platelet secretion. *Am. J. Pathol.* 86(1):99–115
25. Glass, D. B., Gerrard, J. M., White, J. G., Goldberg, N. D. 1975. Cyclic AMP formation in human platelets aggre-

gated by arachidonic acid. *Blood* 46:1033 (Abstr.)

26. Gorman, R. R., Bundy, G. L., Peterson, D. C., Sun, F. F., Miller, O. V., Fitzpatrick, F. A. 1977. Inhibition of human platelet thromboxane synthetase by 9,11-azoprosta-5,13-dienoic acid. *Proc. Natl. Acad. Sci. USA* 74(9):4007–11

27. Gorman, R. R., Bunting, S., Miller, O. V. 1977. Modulation of human platelet adenylate cyclase by prostacyclin (PGX). *Prostaglandins* 13(3):377–88

28. Gorman, R. R., Fitzpatrick, F. A., Miller, O. V. 1977. A selective synthetase inhibitor blocks the cAMP lowering activity of PGH₂. *Biochem. Biophys. Res. Commun.* 79(1):305–13

29. Gorman, R. R., Sun, F. F., Miller, O. V. Johnson, R. A. 1977. Prostaglandins H₁ and H₂. Convenient biochemical synthesis and isolation. Further biological and spectroscopic characterization. *Prostaglandins* 13:1043–53

30. Gryglewski, R. J., Bunting, S., Moncada, S., Flower, R. J., Vane, J. R. 1976. Arterial walls are protected against deposition of platelet thrombi by a substance (prostaglandin X) which they make from prostaglandin endoperoxides. *Prostaglandins* 12:685–713

31. Gryglewski, R. J., Zmuda, A., Dembinska-Kiec, A., Krecioch, E. 1977. A potent inhibitor of thromboxane A₂ biosynthesis in aggregating human blood platelets. *Pharmacol. Res. Commun.* 9(2):109–16

32. Guthrow, C. E. Jr., Allen, J. E., Rasmussen, H. 1972. Phosphorylation of an endogenous membrane protein by an endogenous, membrane-associated cyclic adenosine 3',5'-monophosphate-dependent protein kinase in human erythrocyte ghosts. *J. Biol. Chem.* 247: 8145–53

33. Hamberg, M., Svensson, J., Samuelsson, B. 1975. Thromboxanes: A new group of biologically active compounds derived from prostaglandin endoperoxides. *Proc. Natl. Acad. Sci. USA* 72:2994–98

34. Haslam, R. J. 1967. Mechanisms of blood platelet aggregation. In *Physiology of Hemostasis and Thrombosis*, ed. S. A. Johnson, W. H. Seegers, pp. 88–112. Springfield, Ill: Thomas

35. Haslam, R. J., Davidson, M. M. L., McClenaghan, M. D. 1975. Cytochalasin B, the blood platelet release reaction and cyclic GMP. *Nature* 253: 455–57

36. Haslam, R. J., McClenaghan, M. D. 1974. Effects of collagen and of aspirin on the concentration of guanosine

3',5'-cyclic monophosphate in human blood platelets: Measurement by a prelabelling technique. *Biochem. J.* 138: 317–20

37. Jay, A. W. L., Rowlands, S., Skibo, L. 1973. Red blood cell deformability and the prostaglandins. *Prostaglandins* 3:871–77

38. Johnson, M., Rabinowitz, I., Willis, A. L., Wolf, P. L. 1973. Detection of prostaglandin induction of erythrocyte sickling. *Clin. Chem.* 19:23–26

39. Johnson, M., Ramwell, P. W. 1973. Prostaglandin modification of membrane bound enzyme activity: A possible mechanism of action? *Prostaglandins* 3:703–19

40. Kinlough-Rathbone, R. L., Reimers, H. J., Mustard, J. F., Packham, M. A. 1976. Sodium arachidonate can induce platelet shape change and aggregation which are independent of the release reaction. *Science* 192:1011–12

41. Kury, P. G., McConnell, H. M. 1975. Regulation of membrane flexibility in human erythrocytes. *Biochemistry* 14: 2798–803

42. Kury, P. G., Ramwell, P. W., McConnell, H. M. 1974. The effect of prostaglandins E₁ and E₂ on the human erythrocyte as monitored by spin labels. *Biochem. Biophys. Res. Commun.* 56:478–83

43. MacFarlane, D. E., Smith, J. B., Mills, D. C. B., Silver, M. J. 1974. Inhibition of platelet aggregation by D-type prostaglandins. *Blood* 44:947 (Abstr.)

44. MacIntyre, D. E., Gordon, J. L. 1975. Calcium-dependent stimulation of platelet aggregation by PGE₂. *Nature* 258:337–38

45. Malmsten, C. 1976. Some biological effects of prostaglandin endoperoxide analogs. *Life Sci.* 18:169–76

46. Malmsten, C., Claesson, H. E., Hammarstrom, S., Fried, J., Barton, J. 1977. Biological activities of 13,14-dehydroprostacyclin methyl ester. *Prostaglandins* 13:1009 (Abstr.)

47. Malmsten, C., Granstrom, E., Samuelsson, B. 1976. Cyclic AMP inhibits synthesis of prostaglandin endoperoxide (PGG₂) in human platelets. *Biochem. Biophys. Res. Commun.* 68(2):569–76

48. Malmsten, C., Hamberg, M., Svensson, J., Samuelsson, B. 1975. Physiological role of an endoperoxide in human platelets: hemostatic defect due to platelet cyclo-oxygenase deficiency. *Proc. Natl. Acad. Sci. USA* 72:1446–50

49. Marquis, N. R., Becher, J. A., Vigdahl, R. L. 1970. Platelet aggregation. 3. An epinephrine induced decrease in cAMP

synthesis. *Biochem. Biophys. Res. Commun.* 39:783–89

50. Marquis, N. R., Vigdahl, R. L., Tavormina, P. A. 1969. Platelet aggregation. I. Regulation by cAMP and PGE$_1$. *Biochem. Biophys. Res. Commun.* 36:965–72

51. Massini, P., Luscher, E. F. 1974. Some effects of ionophores for divalent cations on blood platelets. Comparison with the effects of thrombin. *Biochem. Biophys. Acta* 372:109–21

52. Meyers, M. B., Swislocki, N. I. 1974. Conformational changes in erythrocyte membranes by prostaglandins as measured by circular dichroism. *Arch. Biochem. Biophys.* 164:544–50

53. Miller, O. V., Johnson, R. A., Gorman, R. R. 1977. Inhibition of PGE$_1$-stimulated cAMP accumulation in human platelets by thromboxane A$_2$. *Prostaglandins* 13(4):599–609

54. Mills, D. C. B., MacFarlane, D. E. 1977. Prostaglandins and platelet adenylate cyclase. In *Prostaglandins and Hematology*, ed. M. J. Silver, J. B. Smith, J. J. Kocsis, pp. 219–33. New York: Spectrum

55. Minkes, M., Stanford, N., Chi, M. M., Roth, G. J., Raz, A., Needleman, P., Majerus, P. W. 1977. Cyclic adenosine 3',5'-monophosphate inhibits the availability of arachidonate to prostaglandin synthetase in human platelet suspensions. *J. Clin. Invest.* 59(3):449–54

56. Moncada, S., Bunting, S., Vane, J. R., Mullane, K., Thorogood, P., Raz, A., Needleman, P. 1977. Imidazole: A selective antagonist of thromboxane synthetase. *Prostaglandins* 13:611–18

57. Moncada, S., Gryglewski, R. J., Bunting, S., Vane, J. R. 1976. A lipid peroxide inhibits the enzyme in blood vessel microsomes that generates from prostaglandin endoperoxides the substance (prostaglandin X) which prevents platelet aggregation. *Prostaglandins* 12:715–37

58. Moncada, S., Gryglewski, R. J., Bunting, S., Vane, J. R. 1976. An enzyme isolated from arteries transforms prostaglandin endoperoxides to an unstable substance that inhibits platelet aggregation. *Nature* 263:663–65

59. Needleman, P., Bryan, B., Wyche, A., Bronson, S. D., Eakins, K. Ferrendelli, J. A., Minkes, M. 1977. Thromboxane synthetase inhibitors as pharmacological tools: Differential biochemical and biological effects on platelet suspensions. *Prostaglandins* 14(5):897–907

60. Needleman, P., Raz, A., Ferrendelli, J. A., Minkes, M. 1977. Application of imidazole as a selective inhibitor of thromboxane synthetase in human platelets. *Proc. Natl. Acad. Sci. USA* 74:1716–20

61. Nicolaou, K. C., Barnette, W. E., Gasic, G. P., Magolda, R. L. 1977. 6,9-thiaprostacyclin. A stable and biologically potent analog of prostacyclin (PGI$_2$). *J. Am. Chem. Soc.* 99:7736–38

62. Nijkamp, F. P., Moncada, S., White, H. L., Vane, J. R. 1977. Diversion of prostaglandin endoperoxide metabolism by selective inhibition of thromboxane A$_2$ biosynthesis in lung, spleen or platelets. *Eur. J. Pharmacol.* 44(2):179–86

63. Oelz, O., Oelz, R., Knapp, H. R., Sweetman, B. J., Oates, J. A. 1977. Biosynthesis of prostaglandin D$_2$. 1. Formation of prostaglandin D$_2$ by human platelets. *Prostaglandins* 13(2):225–34

64. Okuma, M., Yoshimoto, T., Yamamoto, S. 1977. Human platelet aggregation induced by prostaglandin endodisulfide. *Prostaglandins* 14:891–907

65. Packham, M. A., Kinlough-Rathbone, R. L., Reimers, H. J., Scott, S., Mustard, J. F. 1977. Mechanisms of platelet aggregation independent of adenosine diphosphate. See Ref. 54, pp. 247–76

66. Pickett, W. C., Cohen, P. 1976. Mechanism of the thrombin-mediated burst in oxygen consumption by human platelets. *J. Biol. Chem.* 251(8):2536–38

67. Rabinowitz, I. N., Wolf, P. L., Berman, S., Shikuma, N., Edwards, P. 1975. Prostaglandin E$_2$ effects on cation flux in sickle erythrocyte ghosts. *Prostaglandins* 9:545–55

68. Rasmussen, H., Lake, W., Allen, J. E. 1975. The effect of catecholamines and prostaglandins upon human and rat erythrocytes. *Biochim. Biophys. Acta* 411:63–73

69. Raz, A., Minkes, M., Needleman, P. 1977. Endoperoxides and thromboxanes: Structural determinants for platelet aggregation and vasoconstriction. *Biochim. Biophys. Acta* 488:305–11

70. Rittenhouse-Simmons, S., Deykin, D. 1977. The mobilization of arachidonic acid in platelets exposed to thrombin or ionophore A23187. Effects of adenosine triphosphate deprivation. *J. Clin. Invest.* 60(2):495–98

71. Rittenhouse-Simmons, S., Russell, F. A., Deykin, D. 1976. Transfer of arachidonic acid to human platelet plasmalogen in response to thrombin. *Biochem. Biophys. Res. Commun.* 70(1):295–301

72. Rittenhouse-Simmons, S., Russell, F. A., Deykin, D. 1977. Mobilization of arachidonic acid in human platelets. Kinetics and Ca^{2+} dependency. *Biochim. Biophys. Acta* 488(3):370–80

73. Rodan, G. A., Feinstein, M. B. 1976. Interrelationships between Ca^{2+} and adenylate cyclase and guanylate cyclase in the control of platelet secretion and aggregation. *Proc. Natl. Acad. Sci. USA* 73(6):1829–33

74. Rodan, S. B., Rodan, G. A., Sha'afi, R. I. 1976. Demonstration of adenylate cyclase activity in human red blood cell ghosts. *Biochim. Biophys. Acta* 428: 509–15

75. Rubin, C. S. 1975. Adenosine 3',5'-monophosphate–regulated phosphorylation of erythrocyte membrane proteins. *J. Biol. Chem.* 250:9044–52

76. Rudolph, S. A., Greengard, P. 1974. Regulation of protein phosphorylation and membrane permeability by β-adrenergic agents and cyclic adenosine 3',5'-monophosphate in the avian erythrocyte. *J. Biol. Chem.* 249:5684–87

77. Salzman, E. W. 1977. Interrelation of prostaglandin endoperoxide (prostaglandin G_2) and cyclic 3',5'-adenosine monophosphate in human blood platelets. *Biochim. Biophys. Acta* 499(1): 48–60

78. Salzman, E. W., Levine, L. 1971. Cyclic 3',5'-adenosine monophosphate in human blood platelets. II. Effect of N^6-2'-O'dibutyryl cyclic 3',5'-adenosine monophosphate on platelet function. *J. Clin. Invest.* 50:131–41

79. Salzman, E. W., Lindon, J. N., Rodvien, R. 1976. Cyclic AMP in human blood platelets: relation to platelet prostaglandin synthesis induced by centrifugation or surface contact. *J. Cyclic Nucleotide Res.* 2(1):25–37

80. Salzman, E. W., Neri, L. L. 1969. Cyclic 3',5'-adenosine monophosphate in human blood platelets. *Nature* 224:609–10

81. Schrier, S. L., Bensch, K. G., Johnson, M., Junga, I. 1975. Energized endocytes in human erythrocyte ghosts. *J. Clin. Invest.* 56:8–22

82. Shapiro, D. L., Marchesi, V. T. 1977. Phosphorylation in membranes of intact human erythrocytes. *J. Biol. Chem.* 252:508–17

83. Sheppard, H., Burghardt, C. R. 1970. The stimulation of adenylate cyclase of rat erythrocyte ghosts. *Molec. Pharmacol.* 6:425–29

84. Shio, H., Ramwell, P. W. 1972. Effect of prostaglandin E_2 and aspirin on the sec-

ondary aggregation of human platelets. *Nature New Biol.* 263:45–46

85. Siegl, A. M., Smith, J. B., Silver, M. J., Nicolaou, K. C., Gasic, G., Burnette, W. E. 1978. Binding of prostacyclin by platelets. *Fed. Proc.* 37:260 (Abstr.)

86. Silver, M. J., Smith, J. B., Ingerman, C. M., Kocsis, J. J. 1973. Arachidonic acid–induced human platelet aggregation and prostaglandin formation. *Prostaglandins* 4:863–75

87. Sinha, A. K., Shattil, S. J., Colman, R. W. 1977. Cyclic AMP metabolism in cholesterol-rich platelets. *J. Biol. Chem.* 252(10):3310–14

88. Smith, J. B., Ingerman, C., Kocsis, J. J., Silver, M. J. 1973. Formation of prostaglandins during the aggregation of human blood platelets. *J. Clin. Invest.* 52:965–69

89. Smith, J. B., Ingerman, C. M., Kocsis, J. J., Silver, M. J. 1974. Formation of an intermediate in prostaglandin biosynthesis and its association with the platelet release reaction. *J. Clin. Invest.* 53:1468–72

90. Smith, J. B., Ingerman, C., Silver, M. J. 1976. Persistence of thromboxane A_2-like material and platelet release-inducing activity in plasma. *J. Clin. Invest.* 58(5):1119–22

91. Smith, J. B., Ingerman, C. M., Silver, M. J. 1976. Formation of prostaglandin D_2 during endoperoxide-induced platelet aggregation. *Thromb. Res.* 9:413–18

92. Sobota, J. T., Gruber, C. A., Gilbertson, T. J., Wilson, J. 1977. Prostaglandin E_2-hemoglobin AA and SS erythrocyte interaction. *Am. J. Hematol.* 2:133–43

93. Svensson, J., Hamberg, M., Samuelsson, B. 1975. Prostaglandin endoperoxides. IX. Characterization of rabbit aorta contracting substance (RCS) from guinea pig lung and human platelets. *Acta Physiol. Scand.* 94: 222–28

94. Tansik, R. L., Namm, D. H., White, H. L. 1978. Synthesis of prostaglandin 6-keto-$F_{1\alpha}$ by cultured aortic smooth muscle cells and stimulation of its formation in a coupled system with platelet lysates. *Prostaglandins* 15:399–409

95. Tateson, J. E., Moncada, S., Vane, J. R. 1977. Effects of prostacyclin (PGX) on cyclic AMP concentrations in human platelets. *Prostaglandins* 13(3):389–97

96. Wang, T. Y., Hussey, C. V., Garancis, J. C. 1977. Effects of dibutyryl cyclic adenosine monophosphate and prostaglandin E_1 on platelet aggregation and shape change. *Am. J. Clin. Pathol.* 67:362–67

97. White, J. G., Gerrard, J. M. 1977. Prostaglandins and platelet ultrastructure. See Ref. 54, pp. 293–319

98. White, J. G., Goldberg, N. D., Estensen, R. D., Haddox, M. K., Rao, G. H. R. 1973. Rapid increase in platelet cyclic 3',5'-guanosine monophosphate (cGMP) levels in association with irreversible aggregation, degranulation and secretion. *J. Clin. Invest.* 52:89 (Abstr.)

99. Willis, A. L. 1974. An enzymatic mechanism for the anti-thrombotic and anti-haemostatic action of aspirin. *Science* 183:325–27

100. Willis, A. L., Vane, F. M., Kuhn, D. C., Scott, C. A., Petrin, M. 1974. An endoperoxide aggregator (LASS) formed in platelets in response to thrombotic stimuli: Purification, identification and unique biological significance. *Prostaglandins* 8:453–507

101. Yoshimoto, T., Yamamoto, S., Okuma, M., Hayaishi, O. 1977. Solubilization and resolution of thromboxane synthesizing system from microsomes of bovine blood platelets. *J. Biol. Chem.* 252(16):5871–74

Ann. Rev. Physiol. 1979. 41:669–84
Copyright © 1979 by Annual Reviews Inc. All rights reserved

THE ROLE OF PROSTAGLANDINS IN THE CENTRAL NERVOUS SYSTEM

♦1244

Leonhard S. Wolfe

Department of Neurology and Neurosurgery, McGill University, Montreal, Quebec H3A 2B4, Canada

Flavio Coceani

Research Institute, The Hospital for Sick Children, Toronto, Ontario M5G 1X8, Canada

INTRODUCTION

The prostaglandin system is implicated in physiological and pathological responses of most tissues of the body. The background and breadth of this subject are documented in many reviews and recent symposia (15, 25, 27, 28, 51, 108, 112, 114, 135). This review on the CNS covers advances in the past three years and concerns specifically the possible involvement of the prostaglandin system in the regulation of physiological and pathophysiological processes.

A wide range of stimuli (hormones, enzymes, trauma, inflammation, pyrogens, immune and allergic reactions, etc) activate a plasma membrane enzyme sequence in mammalian cells that leads to the rapid de novo synthesis of several prostaglandin types and in certain tissues thromboxanes as well. The biologically active compounds do not accumulate intracellularly and, therefore, under physiological conditions they occur only in trace amounts in tissues and most body fluids. Following formation, action and release, the compounds are rapidly converted by several enzymatic sequences to less active or inactive metabolites, which appear in blood and urine. Arachidonic acid, the predominant precursor unsaturated fatty acid in mammalian cells, becomes oxygenated to the prostaglandin endoperox-

669

0066-4278/79/0301-0669$01.00

ides and their products. Arachidonic acid must be released from a complex lipid precursor by deacylases before it can be transformed. The biosynthesis of prostaglandins and thromboxanes by central nervous tissue and factors that affect it have been reviewed recently (42, 135, 136). A new finding is that PGD_2 is formed in excess of $PGF_{2\alpha}$ by cerebral tissues of the rat (1).

CEREBROSPINAL FLUID

The existence of prostaglandin-like material in cerebrospinal fluid (CSF) of experimental animals has been recognized for some time (25, 135). Recent studies show CSF levels of $PGF_{2\alpha}$ in human subjects without neurological disease usually to be below 100 pg ml^{-1} (range 30–140 pg ml^{-1}) in cell-free fluid (55, 73, 137). Either PGE_2 is not detectable or it is present at the same low levels as $PGF_{2\alpha}$. Thromboxane B_2 is also a normal constituent (range 80–300 pg ml^{-1}), at least in the cat (F. Coceani, unpublished results). In contrast to most other tissues (89, 135), the brain has very low capacity either to take up or metabolize $PGF_{2\alpha}$ and PGE_2 to the 15-keto and 15-keto-13,14-dihydro metabolites. Consequently, prostaglandins normally produced endogenously are primarily cleared into the general circulation through choroidal and extra-choroidal transport mechanisms (16, 55).

Marked increases in CSF $PGF_{2\alpha}$ levels are found in patients with epilepsy, meningoencephalitis, hydrocephalus, and after surgical trauma; but levels are variable even in the same patient. Likewise, patients with vascular lesions, subarachnoid hemorrhage, and stroke also show significant albeit variable (200–3000 pg ml^{-1}) increases in $PGF_{2\alpha}$ and PGE_2 levels (22, 55, 74, 137). Prostaglandins in the CSF may affect brain function directly or through local changes in the circulation.

CEREBRAL CIRCULATION

It is now well accepted that prostaglandins and thromboxanes contribute to vascular homeostasis through a direct action on smooth muscle in the vessel wall and, possibly, a modulation of muscle responses to neural and hormonal stimuli (27, 78, 125). The evidence supporting this concept is as follows: (a) Vessels are endowed with an enzyme system for the synthesis of primary prostaglandins and PGI_2, the latter being the predominant prostaglandin. With one exception (umbilical artery), all vessels lack the thromboxane A_2 synthetic enzyme. (b) Prostaglandins and thromboxane A_2 exert potent and varied actions on vessels. While the action of the primary prostaglandins changes depending on the species and the vascular bed, PGI_2 and thromboxane A_2 are relaxant and constrictor agents, respectively, at all sites. Prostaglandin endoperoxides are also vasoactive, and their action may be direct or mediated by the intramural formation of primary prostaglandins and PGI_2. (c) Indomethacin and other nonsteroidal anti-inflammatory drugs constrict or dilate vessels in vitro and in vivo.

Although these findings implicate intramural prostaglandins in the control of vascular tone, extramural prostaglandins may also be important, particularly under pathological conditions. Thromboxane A_2, which is released in great amounts from aggregating platelets, may gain access to muscle cells in the vessel wall and cause constriction. Furthermore, prostaglandins and thromboxane A_2 formed within the parenchyma of organs may act upon small resistance vessels.

The above scheme may also apply to the cerebral circulation. All primary prostaglandins and PGI_2 are formed in cerebral vessels (56, 133). Moreover, indomethacin reduces cerebral blood flow (99, 101), which implies that vessels are normally maintained in a relaxed state by a prostaglandin. The identity of the active compound is not known. However, evidence obtained in other vascular beds and the demonstration that PGE_2 and $PGF_{2\alpha}$ are both constrictors on cerebral vessels (100, 139) suggest that this compound is PGI_2. Thromboxane A_2, though not formed in cerebral vessels (56), is a potent constrictor (39). In fact, thromboxane A_2 is the most potent vasoconstrictor among agents acting on the cerebral circulation.

According to current ideas, prostaglandins and allied compounds, besides being involved in the normal control of cerebral blood flow, are also responsible for the hemodynamic changes occurring under certain pathological conditions—in particular, cerebral vasospasm (132). For example, thromboxane A_2, formed in damaged brain tissue or in aggregating platelets, is considered a prime determinant of the vasospasm-complicating thromboembolism and subarachnoid hemorrhage (39, 131). Thromboxane A_2 action may be complemented by that of the prostaglandins and other vasoactive agents (5-hydroxytryptamine) (2). Indeed, thrombin stimulates $PGF_{2\alpha}$ and PGE_2 synthesis when injected intrathecally (54). Brain ischemia following head injury is possibly another prostaglandin-mediated process. Prostaglandins, specifically PGE_2, have also been implicated in the pathogenesis of migraine (58, 131). PGE_2, a constrictor of intracranial vessels, dilates extracranial vessels (100); therefore, it may be involved both in the prodromal phase and in the headache phase of the migraine attack.

HYPOTHALAMIC FUNCTION

Prostaglandins have been implicated in several hypothalamic mechanisms. Only temperature regulation, water balance, and food intake are considered here. Involvement of prostaglandins in hypothalamo-adenohypophyseal function has been discussed in recent reviews (53, 68, 70, 110).

Temperature Regulation

The subject of hypothalamic transmitters involved in thermal homeostasis has been well covered recently (29, 42, 62, 77, 99, 107, 128, 140) and does not require further elaboration here. It is sufficient to say that three compounds, 5-hydroxytryptamine (5-HT), norepinephrine (NE), and acetylcholine (ACh) are generally assigned a key role in temperature regulation. According to most authors, body temperature is controlled through the opposing actions of 5-HT and NE on neurons in the anterior hypothalamic/preoptic region (AH/POA). These amines have species-specific signs of action while maintaining reciprocal effects. ACh is considered a transmitter in the temperature-raising pathway in all species. The extracellular concentration of ions within the posterior hypothalamus, and specifically the balance between sodium and calcium, may be an additional controlling factor. This ionic mechanism is thought to work in concert with the neurohumoral mechanism to determine the "set-point" around which body temperature is regulated.

The prostaglandins are a relatively recent addition to the field of thermoregulation. Interest in these compounds dates back to the early 1970s when it was found that PGE_1 was a potent pyretic agent (84) and that antipyretics blocked prostaglandin synthesis in various organs including brain (48, 112). These two findings implicated a prostaglandin in the genesis of fever. Research in this area developed actively and led to the demonstration that: (a) PGE_2, a normal constituent of hypothalamic tissue (70), is as potent as PGE_1 in producing fever (45–47, 57, 65, 76, 86, 93, 94, 102, 106, 121); moreover, both compounds are like pyrogens in that their action is not influenced by ambient temperature (57, 65, 121, 126); (b) PGE_2 acts upon neurons in the AH/POA that are also the main target for pyrogens (121, 126); (c) thermo-sensitive neurons in AH/POA respond in the same manner to PGE_2 and pyrogens (117); (d) PGE_2 fever, unlike pyrogen fever, does not abate following administration of antipyretics (24, 79, 84, 85); and (e) pyrogen fever is associated with elevated levels in the CSF of a prostaglandin with the biological and immunological properties of PGE_2 (34, 37, 43, 44, 83, 95). Collectively, these findings indicate that PGE_2 is well suited for being the "central messenger" of fever and specifically of pyrogen fever (cf 62, 80, 128). According to current knowledge, pyrogens from outside the body (*exogenous pyrogen*), and foremost among them bacterial endotoxin, as well as pathological conditions causing tissue inflammation and damage (e.g. infarction, malignancy) elicit the formation of a pyrogenic substance (*endogenous pyrogen*) in neutrophils and in cells of the reticuloendothelial system. The endogenous pyrogen, which is therefore a key intermediate in the sequence of events leading to fever, is then carried to the rostral region of the hypothalamus by the circulation. Because the blood-brain barrier is seemingly impermeable to endogenous pyrogen (cf 80), and because prostaglandins are rapidly removed from the circulation (cf 124), one must assume that the vessel wall is the main site where pyrogen action is translated into increased prostaglandin synthesis. Consistent with this hypothesis is the notion that vessels, including cerebral vessels, are endowed with an active prostaglandin-generating system and that hypothalamic blood flow is increased during pyrogen fever (109). The latter finding implies activation of prostaglandin synthesis in the vessel wall. Alternatively, PGE_2 could be released from phagocytosing leucocytes sequestered in the capillary bed of AH/POA (128). Any pyrogen crossing the blood-brain barrier may stimulate prostaglandin synthesis in neural tissue (140). PGE_2, whether formed in the tissue of the AH/POA or from the vessels, acts at appropriate sites in the thermoregulatory pathways to elevate the "set-point" for temperature regulation, thus causing fever. Once its action is completed, PGE_2 is either inactivated enzymatically in situ or enters the extracellular fluid and CSF whence it is transported into the circulation. Interference with the latter mechanism results in enhancement of pyrogen effects (30).

Although the experimental evidence implicating PGE_2 in the pathogenesis of fever seems quite convincing, there have been reports contradicting the above scheme. In the monotreme, *Tachyglossus aculeatus* (Echidna), PGE_1 and PGE_2 are hypothermic agents, whereas endotoxin causes fever (12). Dissociation between pyrogen and PGE effects also occurs in the newborn lamb which, after appropriate sensitization, may develop fever in response to pyrogens but not in response to prostaglandins (103, 105). A similar phenomenon has been described in the adult animal following destruction of AH/POA (126). Potentially germane to these findings is the demonstration that prostaglandin antagonists block PGE_2 but not pyrogen fever (31).

Because pyrogen fever is susceptible to antipyretic treatment in the above experiments, a possible explanation for the inconsistencies could be that an arachidonic acid metabolite other than PGE_2 contributes to, or is the main determinant of pyrogen effects. Consistent with this is the finding that fever following administration of arachidonic acid, while abolished by antipyretics, is only partially blocked by prostaglandin antagonists (71). Theoretically, several compounds could have this role; however, available data limit the choice to two compounds, PGI_2 and thromboxane A_2, because prostaglandin endoperoxides and PGD_2 are inactive (41, 59), and $PGF_{2\alpha}$ is a pyretic agent but only in high doses (41, 47, 86). While no information is available on the central action of PGI_2, recent work showing that levels of thromboxane B_2 in the cerebrospinal fluid rise during pyrogen fever (F. Coceani, unpublished results) suggests that thromboxane A_2 might be the hypothetical mediator. If so, it would not be a coincidence that intracranial bleeding, a condition in which AH/POA may be exposed to massive amounts of thromboxane A_2 formed in aggregating platelets, is commonly associated with fever (113).

Some findings suggest that fever may develop independently of the prostaglandin system. In the rabbit, salicylate at certain doses has little or no effect on the febrile response to pyrogen while it completely reverses the elevation in prostaglandin levels in the CSF (34). The question remains whether the dose of salicylate used was sufficient to block the synthesis of PGE_2 or any other pyrogenic derivative of arachidonic acid in the AH/-POA. However, more cogent evidence against the involvement of the prostaglandin system in fever is afforded by recent work in the chick (4, 5) in which it was shown that PGEs are hyper- or hypothermic agents depending on the ambient temperature and that pyrogen fever is only marginally affected by indomethacin at a dose exceeding the therapeutic range (cf 48). Etiocholanolone fever in man, which is mediated by endogenous pyrogen (19), is also resistant to antipyretic treatment.

Summing up, a large body of evidence supports the existence of a "PGE_2 link" in the central action of endogenous pyrogen; but this prostaglandin may work in concert with another product, or more than one product, of arachidonic acid metabolism. Some forms of pyrogen fever, however, do not involve the prostaglandin system, and their central mechanism remains obscure.

Prostaglandins probably do not contribute to normal temperature regulation. Antipyretics, whether given systemically (24, 66, 79) or injected into the anterior hypothalamus (6, 35), produce little or no hypothermia in the afebrile animal, nor do they reverse the hyperthermia following cold stress (32, 104). Furthermore, prostaglandin levels in the CSF remain unchanged during thermoregulatory adjustments to cold or hot environments (21, 33). When present, hypothermic effects of antipyretics (cf 115) are ascribed to activation of the heat loss mechanism rather than to blockade of prostaglandin synthesis (79). Indeed, iontophoretically applied salicylate may stimulate warm-sensitive neurons in the AH/POA of the afebrile animal (13).

The intimate mechanism of prostaglandin action in producing fever remains a subject of speculation. It has been debated for some time (cf 28, 62) whether the prostaglandin and monoaminergic mechanisms are functionally interdependent, and this issue is far from being settled. In essence, two schemes have been proposed for linking the prostaglandins, specifically PGE_1 and PGE_2, to the monoamines. According to one (7), monoamine actions leading to elevation in body temperature are mediated in part by a prostaglandin. In support of this concept is the finding that 5-HT stimulates the release of PGEs from brain (64) and that epinephrine as well as 5-HT-induced hyperthermia are suppressed by antipyretics (7, 69, 82, 85). However, the validity of results with the antipyretics has been questioned (36, 82), moreover, this hypothesis is not easily reconciled with the notion that monoamine effects (17, 62), unlike prostaglandin effects (57, 65, 121, 126), are affected by ambient temperature. Alternatively, it has been suggested on the basis of work with specific monoamine depletors and antagonists that monoamines are intermediates in the action of prostaglandins on temperature-raising mechanisms. Again, no firm conclusion can be drawn from these studies (cf 28) because positive results in one species [rabbit (20, 66, 72)] contrast with inconsistent results in another [cat (82, 126)]. Furthermore, an explanation for the constancy of prostaglandin effects at different ambient temperatures must be provided before accepting this hypothesis. Equally controversial is the question of the role of cyclic nucleotides in PGE fever. While findings in the rabbit suggest that cyclic AMP is a central mediator of PGE fever (138), findings in the cat argue against this idea (81).

Control of Body Water

The homeostatic regulation of body water content is dependent on the concerted action of two brain mechanisms, namely, the function of a "thirst sensor" possibly located in the subfornical organ (40) and other circumventricular organs (97), and the secretion of antidiuretic hormone (ADH). Both mechanisms are under the direct control of angiotensin II (40, 118) and may also be influenced by the prostaglandins. Angiotensin, whether formed in situ or blood-borne, stimulates thirst and the formation of ADH. The latter action is exerted on the synthesis [supraoptic and paraventricular neurons (87)] and release [neurohypophysis (50, 63)] of the hormone. When injected into the common carotid artery or the cerebral ventricles, PGE_1 and PGE_2 mimic angiotensin in stimulating ADH release (75, 129). Moreover, these prostaglandins share with angiotensin a dual site of action (50, 75, 129). Prostaglandin action on thirst mechanisms is a subject of controversy. While it has been reported that PGE_1 and PGE_2 (but not $PGF_{2\alpha}$) antagonize the dipsogenic effect of angiotensin in the rat (40, 91), the same compounds have opposite effects in the goat (3, 75). This discrepancy is unlikely due to the dose of prostaglandin used (40, 75), because the sign of responses in the rat remained the same over a wide range of doses. Differences may reflect a genuine species variation, the significance of which is not known.

Because low doses of PGE_1 and PGE_2 given by the ventricular route affect water balance without altering thermoregulatory neurons, responses are possibly indicative of a physiological process. This applies specifically to PGE_2, which is present in brain. Future experiments employing blockers of prostaglandin synthesis may confirm this point. Regardless of whether responses are physiological or pharmacological, the mechanism of prostaglandin action remains to be elucidated. Prostaglandins and angiotensin, which are both vasoactive agents, may act, or interact, on blood vessels supplying target neurons in the subfornical organ and the hypothalamus. Alternatively, their action may be exerted directly on neurons. Indeed, subfornical and supraoptic neurons respond to iontophoretically applied angiotensin (92, 96). It is still a question whether the same holds true with the prostaglandins.

Regulation of Food Intake

It is generally assumed that food intake is primarily controlled through the opposing action of two neuronal systems located in the hypothalamus: a lateral system signalling the urge for food ("feeding center"), and a ventromedial system suppressing food intake ("satiety center") (60). Several neurohumoral agents, including the prostaglandins, have been implicated in the function of these neurons (cf 8). When given systemically, various prostaglandin types, including PGE_1, PGE_2, and $PGF_{2\alpha}$, inhibit food intake without overtly affecting behavior, body temperature, and water intake (116). PGE_1 is also effective when injected into the hypothalamus; however, its site of action varies with the species. While in the rat responsive sites are located in the anterior commissure region and the lateral hypothalamus (11), in the ewe they are located in the anterior and medial hypothalamus (10). Furthermore, in the ewe PGE_1 may also stimulate feeding (10). Prostaglandin effects occur in both food-deprived and satiated animals (38), which implies a central action for these compounds.

Although these findings implicate the prostaglandins in the hypothalamic control of energy balance, some facts are inconsistent with this possibility. PGE_2, even though it suppresses feeding by the systemic route, has no effect on sites in the hypothalamus that are sensitive to PGE_1 (10). Moreover, effective doses of PGE_1 by the intrahypothalamic route are in the microgram range (10, 11, 127, 134), indicating a pharmacological rather than a physiological action. Another difficulty in accepting this idea arises from the fact that distribution of prostaglandin-sensitive sites in the hypothalamus is species-specific in spite of a seemingly constant organization of the neuronal systems controlling feeding behavior (9).

INTERACTION WITH CYCLIC NUCLEOTIDES AND NEUROTRANSMITTERS

A large body of evidence suggests that cyclic nucleotides, and particularly adenosine 3',5'-monophosphate (cyclic AMP), play a role in peripheral and central synapses (52, 67, 90). In the CNS, cyclic AMP has been implicated in the mediation of postsynaptic effects of several neurotransmitters (52, 67, 90); however, evidence of such a role is strongest in the case of dopaminergic synapses on caudate neurons (120) and β-adrenergic synapses between fibers originating in the locus coeruleus (LC) and cells in the cerebellum (Purkinje cells) and the hippocampus (pyramidal cells) (18). Some data also suggest that guanosine 3',5'-monophosphate (cyclic GMP) is involved in the muscarinic actions of ACh (52, 88, 90, 118). In fact, it has been proposed that cyclic AMP and cyclic GMP have a reciprocal function in the regulation of neuronal activity (123).

Prostaglandins may also interact with the cyclic nucleotides. Findings in cerebellar Purkinje cells afford a model of some of their possible functions in synaptic events. In brief, it is proposed (cf 28; 18, 90) that NE released from LC fibers impinging upon Purkinje cells triggers the postsynaptic formation of cyclic AMP, which in turn causes an appropriate change in membrane potential (i.e. hyperpolarization) through the phosphorylation of specific membrane proteins. The same model assumes that PGE_2, formed in response to NE or cyclic AMP action, modulates the synaptic process by inhibiting the synthesis of cyclic AMP. A similar sequence of events is thought to occur in other noradrenergic synapses (90), whereas prostaglandins are assigned a stimulatory action on the cyclic AMP–generating system in dopaminergic synapses (120).

Although supported by findings in peripheral synapses (52), the above scheme has been challenged on various grounds. The idea that cyclic AMP is an essential intermediate in the postsynaptic action of NE has been questioned, and the points of contention are discussed in several reviews (28, 90, 98). Furthermore, different investigators (cf 23, 28, 122) have been unable to confirm at several sites in the CNS (cerebral cortex, hypothalamus and brain stem in mammals, and spinal cord in the frog) that E-type prostaglandins modify neuronal responses to the monoamines. Negative results with spinal neurons (23) are particularly significant because the amphibian CNS, unlike the mammalian CNS, is endowed with an active enzyme system for prostaglandin inactivation (26; F. Coceani, unpublished results) and would, therefore, seem to be a well-suited site for prostaglandin involvement in synaptic events. It is conceivable, however, that prostaglandins may influence postsynaptic actions of the monoamines only in certain neuronal systems. Future work must take into consideration effects of the endoperoxides and thromboxanes, which may turn out to be more important endogenous modulators of adenylate cyclase than the primary prostaglandins.

A separate line of investigation suggests that PGE_2 may modulate noradrenergic and dopaminergic transmission through inhibition of transmitter release. However, this concept is based on work in peripheral synapses (61), whereas findings in the CNS are negative (130) or inconsistent (14, 111, 119).

CONCLUSIONS

Facts

Central nervous tissue has a complete system for the biosynthesis of prostaglandins and thromboxanes. The prostaglandin system is either directly or indirectly connected with neuronal activity, and its possible function is best documented in the case of hypothalamic homeostatic mechanisms. Cerebral blood vessels synthesize prostaglandins, which likely contribute to normal hemodynamics. There is compelling evidence that prostaglandins are formed at multiple sites in the CNS, both neural and non-neural, and interact in a varied manner in physiological and pathological situations.

Outstanding Issues

The activity and control of synthetic enzymes in neural and non-neural constituents of CNS; the identity of compounds active at various sites; the role of $PGF_{2\alpha}$ and PGD_2, which are relatively inactive in spite of being formed in excess of PGE_2; the likelihood of prostaglandin-degrading enzymes being confined to certain neuronal types and the importance of such enzymes in the termination of prostaglandin effects; and the specific involvement of prostaglandins in synaptic events are the outstanding issues.

Prospectives

Most of the outstanding issues will be hard to resolve because of limitations in assay methodology, the multitude of compounds to be assayed, the potential for new compounds or pathways in the metabolism of arachidonic acid, and difficulties in following the time-sequence of biosynthetic events in vivo. In spite of these problems, refinements in assay methods and the development of new and more selective blockers of arachidonic acid metabolism should afford a better knowledge of the functional organization of the prostaglandin system in the CNS. Advances in this field should also have an impact in the clinic—particularly in the management of neurological diseases in which the neural deficit follows a vascular insult.

ACKNOWLEDGMENTS

Work of the authors of this review was supported by the Medical Research Council of Canada.

Literature Cited

1. Abdel-Halim, M. S., Hamberg, M., Sjöquist, B., Änggard, E. 1977. Identification of prostaglandin D_2 as a major prostaglandin in homogenates of rat brain. *Prostaglandins* 14:633–43
2. Allen, G. S., Gross, C. J., French, L. A., Chou, S. N. 1976. Cerebral arterial spasm: *In vitro* contractile activity of vasoactive agents including human CSF on human basilar and anterior cerebral arteries. *J. Neurosurg.* 44:594–600
3. Andersson, B., Leksell, L. G. 1975. Effects on fluid balance of intraventricular infusions of prostaglandin E_1. *Acta Physiol. Scand.* 93:286–88
4. Artunkal, A. A., Marley, E., Stephenson, J. D. 1977. Some effects of prostaglandins E_1 and E_2 and of endotoxin injected into the hypothalamus of young chicks: dissociation between endotoxin fever and the effects of prostaglandins. *Br. J. Pharmacol.* 61:39–46
5. Artunkal, A. A., Marley, E., Stephenson, J. D. 1977. Some effects of intravenous prostaglandin E_1 and endotoxin in young chickens. *Br. J. Pharmacol.* 61:29–37
6. Avery, D. D., Penn, P. E. 1974. Blockage of pyrogen induced fever by intrahypothalamic injections of salicylate in the rat. *Neuropharmacology* 13:1179–85
7. Avery, D. D., Penn, P. E. 1976. Interaction of salicylate and body temperature changes caused by injections of neurohumours into the anterior hypothalamus: possible mechanisms of salicylate antipyresis. *Neuropharmacology* 15:433–38
8. Baile, C. A. 1974. Putative neurotransmitters in the hypothalamus and feeding. *Fed. Proc.* 33:1166–75
9. Baile, C. A., Forbes, J. M. 1974. Control of feed intake and regulation of energy balance in ruminants. *Physiol. Rev.* 54:160–214
10. Baile, C. A., Martin, F. H., Forbes, J. M., Webb, R. L., Kingsbury, W. 1974. Intrahypothalamic injections of prostaglandins and prostaglandin antagonists and feeding in sheep. *J. Dairy Sci.* 57:81–88
11. Baile, C. A., Simpson, C. W., Bean, S. M., McLaughlin, C. L., Jacobs, H. L. 1973. Prostaglandins and food intake of rats: a component of energy balance regulation? *Physiol. Behav.* 10:1077–85
12. Baird, J. A., Hales, J. R. S., Lang, W. J. 1974. Thermoregulatory responses to the injection of monoamines, acetylcholine and prostaglandins into a lateral

ventricle of the echidna. *J. Physiol. London* 236:539–48
13. Beckman, A. L., Rozkowska-Ruttimann, E. 1974. Hypothalamic and septal neuronal responses to iontophoretic application of salicylate in rats. *Neuropharmacology* 13:393–98
14. Bergström, S., Farnebo, L.-O., Fuxe, K. 1973. Effect of prostaglandin E_2 on central and peripheral catecholamine neurons. *Eur. J. Pharmacol.* 21:362–368
15. Berti, F., Samuelsson, B., Velo, G. P., eds. 1976. *Prostaglandins and Thromboxanes*, NATO Advanced Study Institute Series A., Vol. 13. New York: Plenum. 449 pp.
16. Bito, L. Z., Davson, H., Hollingsworth, J. R. 1976. Facilitated transport of prostaglandins across the blood–cerebrospinal fluid and blood-brain barriers. *J. Physiol. London* 256:273–85
17. Bligh, J., Cottle, W. H., Maskrey, M. 1971. Influence of ambient temperature on the thermoregulatory responses to 5-hydroxytryptamine, noradrenaline and acetylcholine injected into the lateral cerebral ventricles of sheep, goats and rabbits. *J. Physiol. London* 212:377–92
18. Bloom, F. E., Siggins, G. R., Hoffer, B. J., Segal, M., Oliver, A. P. 1975. Cyclic nucleotides in the central synaptic actions of catecholamines. In *Advances in Cyclic Nucleotide Research,* ed. G. I. Drummond, P. Greengard, G. A. Robinson, 5:603–18. New York: Raven. 872 pp.
19. Bodel, P., Dillard, M. 1968. Studies on steroid fever. I. Production of leukocyte pyrogen in vitro by ethiocholanolone. *J. Clin. Invest.* 47:107–17
20. Borsook, D., Laburn, H. P., Rosendorff, C., Willies, G. H., Woolf, C. J. 1977. A dissociation between temperature regulation and fever in the rabbit. *J. Physiol. London* 266:423–33
21. Cammock, S., Dascombe, M. J., Milton, A. S. 1976. Prostaglandins in thermoregulation. See Ref. 114, 1:375–80
22. Carasso, R. L., Vardi, J., Rabay, J. M., Zor, U., Streifler, M. 1977. Measurement of prostaglandin E_2 in cerebrospinal fluid in patients suffering from stroke. *J. Neurol. Psychiatr.* 40:967–69
23. Caulford, P. G., Coceani, F. 1977. Microiontophoresis of 5-hydroxytryptamine, epinephrine and prostaglandin E_1 on spinal neurons in the frog. *Can. J. Physiol. Pharmacol.* 55:293–300
24. Clark, W. G., Cumby, H. R. 1975. The

antipyretic effect of indomethacin. *J. Physiol. London* 248:625–38

25. Coceani, F. 1974. Prostaglandins and the central nervous system. *Arch. Intern. Med.* 133:119–29

26. Coceani, F. 1978. Studies of the prostaglandins in the frog spinal cord. In *Iontophoresis and Transmitter Mechanisms in the Mammalian Central Nervous System*, ed. R. W. Ryall, J. S. Kelly, pp. 456–58. New York: Elsevier. 494 pp.

27. Coceani, F., Olley, P. M., eds. 1978. Prostaglandins and perinatal medicine. In *Advances in Prostaglandin and Thromboxane Research*, Vol. 4. New York: Raven. 412 pp.

28. Coceani, F., Pace-Asciak, C. R. 1976. Prostaglandins and the central nervous system. In *Prostaglandins: Physiological, Pharmacological and Pathological Aspects*, ed. S. M. M. Karim, pp. 1–36. Lancaster, Pa.: MTP Press. 367 pp.

29. Cooper, K. E., Lomax, P., Schönbaum, E., eds. 1977. *Drugs, Biogenic Amines and Body Temperature*. Basel: Karger. 283 pp.

30. Cooper, K. E., Veale, W. L. 1972. The effect of injecting an inert oil into the cerebral ventricular system upon fever produced by intravenous leucocyte pyrogen. *Can. J. Physiol. Pharmacol.* 50:1066–71

31. Cranston, W. I., Duff, G. W., Hellon, R. F., Mitchell, D., Townsend, Y. 1976. Evidence that brain prostaglandin synthesis is not essential in fever. *J. Physiol. London* 259:239–49

32. Cranston, W. I., Hellon, R. F., Luff, R. H., Rawlins, M. D., Rosendorff, C. 1970. Observations on the mechanism of salicylate-induced antipyresis. *J. Physiol. London* 210:593–600

33. Cranston, W. I., Hellon, R. F., Mitchell, D. 1975. Is brain prostaglandin synthesis involved in responses to cold? *J. Physiol. London* 249:425–34

34. Cranston, W. I., Hellon, R. F., Mitchell, D. 1975. A dissociation between fever and prostaglandin concentration in cerebrospinal fluid. *J. Physiol. London* 253:583–92

35. Cranston, W. I., Rawlins, M. D. 1972. Effects of intracerebral microinjection of sodium salicylate on temperature regulation in the rabbit. *J. Physiol. London* 222:257–66

36. Dey, P. K., Feldberg, W., Gupta, K. P., Milton, A. S., Wendlandt, S. 1974. Further studies on the role of prostaglandins in fever. *J. Physiol. London* 241:629–46

37. Dey, P. K., Feldberg, W., Wendlandt, S. 1974. Lipid A and prostaglandin. *J. Physiol. London* 239:102–3P

38. Doggett, N. S., Jawaharlal, K. 1977. Some observations on the anorectic activity of prostaglandin $F_{2\alpha}$. *Br. J. Pharmacol.* 60:409–15

39. Ellis, E. F., Nies, A. S., Oates, J. A. 1977. Cerebral arterial smooth muscle contraction by thromboxane A_2. *Stroke* 8:480–83

40. Epstein, A. N. 1978. The neuroendocrinology of thirst and salt appetite. In *Frontiers in Neuroendocrinology*, ed. W. F. Ganong, L. Martini, 5:101–34. New York: Raven. 399 pp.

41. Ewen, L., Milton, A. S., Smith S. 1976. Effects of prostaglandin $F_{2\alpha}$ and prostaglandin D_2 on the body temperature of conscious cats. *J. Physiol. London* 258:121–22P

42. Feldberg, W. 1975. Body temperature and fever: changes in our views during the last decade. *Proc. R. Soc. London Ser. B* 191:199–229

43. Feldberg, W., Gupta, K. P. 1973. Pyrogen fever and prostaglandin-like activity in cerebrospinal fluid. *J. Physiol. London* 228:41–53

44. Feldberg, W., Gupta, K. P., Milton, A. S., Wendlandt, S. 1973. Effect of pyrogen and antipyretics on prostaglandin activity in cisternal c.s.f. of unanaesthetized cats. *J. Physiol. London* 234:279–303

45. Feldberg, W., Saxena, P. N. 1971. Fever produced by prostaglandin E_1. *J. Physiol. London* 217:547–56

46. Feldberg, W., Saxena, P. N. 1971. Further studies on prostaglandin E_1 fever in cats. *J. Physiol. London* 219:739–45

47. Feldberg, W., Saxena, P. N. 1975. Prostaglandins, endotoxin and lipid A on body temperature in rats. *J. Physiol. London* 249:601–15

48. Flower, R. J. 1974. Drugs which inhibit prostaglandin synthesis. *Pharmacol. Rev.* 26:33–67

49. Fumagalli, R., Folco, G. C., Longiave, D. 1976. Influence of prostaglandins on central functions. See Ref. 15, pp. 383–421

50. Gagnon, D. J., Cousineau, D., Boucher, P. J. 1973. Release of vasopressin by angiotensin II and prostaglandin E_2 from the rat neurohypophysis in vitro. *Life Sci.* 12:487–97

51. Galli, C., Galli, G., Porcellati, G., eds. 1978. Phospholipases and prostaglandins. In *Advances in Prostaglandin and Thromboxane Research*, Vol. 3. New York: Raven. 206 pp.

52. Greengard, P. 1976. Possible role for cyclic nucleotides and phosphorylated membrane proteins in post-synaptic actions of neurotransmitters. *Nature* 260:101–8

53. Hafs, H. D., Haynes, N. B. 1977. Prostaglandins and pituitary hormone secretion. In *Prostaglandins and Therapeutics*, ed. D. K. Silver, 3(3):3–4. Kalamazoo, Mich.: The Upjohn Company. 4 pp.

54. Hagen, A. A., Gerber, J. N., Sweeley, C. C., White, R. P., Robertson, J. T. 1977. Pleocytosis and elevation of prostaglandin $F_{2\alpha}$ and E_2 in cerebrospinal fluid following intracisternal injection of thrombin. *Stroke* 8:236–38

55. Hagen, A. A., Gerber, J. N., Sweeley, C. C., White, R. P., Robertson, J. T. 1977. Levels and disappearance of prostaglandin $F_{2\alpha}$ in cerebral spinal fluid: a clinical and experimental study. *Stroke* 8:672–75

56. Hagen, A. A., White, R. P., Terragno, N. A., Robertson, J. T. 1978. Synthesis of prostaglandins (PGs) by bovine cerebral arteries. *Fed. Proc.* 37:384

57. Hales, J. R. S., Bennett, J. W., Baird, J. A., Fawcett, A. S. 1973. Thermoregulatory effects of prostaglandins E_1, E_2, $F_{1\alpha}$ and $F_{2\alpha}$ in the sheep. *Pfleugers Arch.* 339:125–33

58. Harper, A. M., McCulloch, J., MacKenzie, E. T., Pickard, J. D. 1977. Migraine and the blood-brain barrier. *Lancet* 1:1034–36

59. Hawkins, M., Lipton, J. M. 1977. Analogs of endoperoxide precursors of prostaglandins: failure to affect body temperature when injected into primary and secondary central temperature controls. *Prostaglandins* 13:209–18

60. Hayward, J. N. 1977. Functional and morphological aspects of hypothalamic neurons. *Physiol. Rev.* 57:574–658

61. Hedqvist, P. 1973. Autonomic neurotransmission. See Ref. 108, 1:101–31

62. Hellon, R. F. 1974. Monoamines, pyrogens and cations: their actions on central control of body temperature. *Pharmacol. Rev.* 26:289–321

63. Hisada, S., Fujimoto, S., Kamiya, T., Endo, Y., Tsushima, H. 1977. Antidiuresis of centrally administered amines and peptides and release of antidiuretic hormone from isolated rat neurohypophysis. *Jpn. J. Pharmacol.* 27:153–61

64. Holmes, S. W. 1970. The spontaneous release of prostaglandins into the cerebral ventricles of the dog and the effect of external factors on this release. *Br. J. Pharmacol.* 38:653–58

65. Hori, T., Harada, Y. 1974. The effects of ambient and hypothalamic temperatures on the hyperthermic responses to prostaglandins E_1 and E_2. *Pfleugers Arch.* 350:123–34

66. Kandasamy, B., Girault, J.-M., Jacob, J. 1975. Central effects of a purified bacterial pyrogen, prostaglandin E_1 and biogenic amines on the temperature in the awake rabbit. See Ref. 77, pp. 124–32

67. Kebabian, J. W. 1977. Biochemical regulation and physiological significance of cyclic nucleotides in the nervous system. In *Advances in Cyclic Nucleotide Research*, ed. P. Greengard, G. A. Robinson, 8:421–508. New York: Raven. 582 pp.

68. Kenimer, J. G., Goldberg, V., Blecker, M. 1977. The endocrine system: interactions of prostaglandins with adenyl cyclase-cyclic AMP systems. See Ref. 108, 3:77–108

69. Komiskey, H. L., Rudy, T. A. 1975. The involvement of methysergide-sensitive receptors and prostaglandins in the hyperthermia evoked by 5-HT in the cat. *Res. Commun. Chem. Path. Pharmacol.* 11:195–208

70. Labrie, F., Pelletier, G., Borgeat, P., Drouin, J., Ferland, L., Belanger, A. 1976. Mode of action of hypothalamic regulatory hormones in the adenohypophysis. In *Frontiers in Neuroendocrinology*, ed. L. Martini, W. F. Ganong, 4:63–93. New York: Raven. 294 pp.

71. Laburn, H., Mitchell, D., Rosendorff, C. 1977. Effects of prostaglandin antagonism on sodium arachidonate fever in rabbits. *J. Physiol. London* 267:559–70

72. Laburn, H., Woolf, C. J., Willies, G. H., Rosendorff, C. 1975. Pyrogen and prostaglandin fever in the rabbit. II. Effects of noradrenaline depletion and adrenergic receptor blockade. *Neuropharmacology* 14:405–11

73. Landau, I. S., Young, C. W. 1977. Measurement of prostaglandin $F_{2\alpha}$ levels in cerebrospinal fluid of febrile and afebrile patients with advanced cancer. *Prostaglandins* 14:343–53

74. Latorre, E., Patrono, C., Fortuna, A., Grossi-Belloni, D. 1974. Role of prostaglandin $F_{2\alpha}$ in human cerebral vasospasm. *J. Neurosurg.* 41:293–99

75. Leksell, L. G. 1976. Influence of prostaglandin E_1 on cerebral mechanisms involved in the control of fluid balance. *Acta Physiol. Scand.* 98:85–93

76. Lipton, J. M., Fossler, D. E. 1974 . Fever produced in the squirrel monkey by

intravenous and intracerebral endotoxin. *Am. J. Physiol.* 226:1022–27
77. Lomax, P., Schönbaum, E., Jacob, J., eds. 1975. *Temperature Regulation and Drug Action.* Basel: Karger. 405 pp.
78. Malik, K. U. 1978. Prostaglandins—modulation of adrenergic nervous system. *Fed. Proc.* 37:203–7.
79. Milton, A. S. 1973. Prostaglandin E_1 and endotoxin fever, and the effects of aspirin, indomethacin, and 4-acetamidophenol. *Adv. Biosci.* 9:495–500
80. Milton, A. S. 1976. Modern views on the pathogenesis of fever and the mode of action of antipyretic drugs. *J. Pharm. Pharmacol.* 28:393–99
81. Milton, A. S., Dascombe, M. J. 1977. Cyclic nucleotides in thermoregulation and fever. In *Drugs, Biogenic Amines, and Body Temperature,* ed. K. E. Cooper, P. Lomax, E. Schönbaum, pp. 129–35. Basel: Karger. 283 pp.
82. Milton, A. S., Harvey, C. A. 1975. Prostaglandins and monoamines in fever. See Ref. 77, pp. 133–42
83. Milton, A. S., Smith, S., Tomkins, K. B. 1977. Levels of prostaglandin F and E in cerebrospinal fluid of cats during pyrogeninduced fever. *Br. J. Pharmacol.* 59:447–48P
84. Milton, A. S., Wendlandt, S. 1970. A possible role for prostaglandin E_1 as a modulator for temperature regulation in the central nervous system of the cat. *J. Physiol. London* 207:76–77P
85. Milton, A. S., Wendlandt, S. 1971. The effects of 4-acetamidophenol (paracetamol) on the temperature response of the conscious rat to the intracerebral injection of prostaglandin E_1, adrenaline and pyrogen. *J. Physiol. London* 217:33–34P
86. Milton, A. S., Wendlandt, S. 1971. Effects on body temperature of prostaglandins of the A, E, and F series on injection into the third ventricle of unanaesthetized cats and rabbits. *J. Physiol. London* 218:325–36
87. Mouw, D., Bonjour, J. P., Malvin, R. L., Vander, A. 1971. Central action of angiotensin in stimulating ADH release. *Am. J. Physiol.* 220:239–42
88. Nahorski, S. R., Pratt, C. N. F. W., Rogers, K. J. 1976. Increased cerebral cyclic GMP concentration induced by muscarinic cholinergic agonists and prostaglandin $F_{2\alpha}$. *Br. J. Pharmacol.* 57:445–46P
89. Nakano, J., Prancan, A. V., Moore, S. E. 1972. Metabolism of prostaglandin E_1 in cerebral cortex and cerebellum of the dog and rat. *Brain Res.* 39:545–48

90. Nathanson, J. A. 1977. Cyclic nucleotides and the nervous system function. *Physiol. Rev.* 57:157–256
91. Nicolaides, S., Fitzsimmons, J. T. 1975. La dépendance de la prise d'eau induite par l'angiotensine II envers la fonction vasomotrice cérébrale locale chez le Rat. *C. R. Acad. Sci. Paris Ser. D* 281:1417–20
92. Nicoll, R. A., Barker, J. L. 1971. Excitation of supraoptic neurosecretory cells by angiotensin II. *Nature* 233:172–74
93. Nisticó, G., Marley, E. 1973. Central effects of prostaglandin E_1 in adult fowls. *Neuropharmacology* 12:1009–16
94. Nisticó, G., Marley, E. 1976. Central effects of prostaglandins E_2, A_1 and $F_{2\alpha}$ in adult fowls. *Neuropharmacology* 15:737–41
95. Philipp-Dormston, W. K., Siegert, R. 1974. Prostaglandins of the E and F series in rabbit cerebrospinal fluid during fever induced by Newcastle Disease Virus, *E. coli*—endotoxin, or endogenous pyrogen. *Med. Microbiol. Immunol.* 159:279–84
96. Phillips, M. I., Felix, D. 1976. Specific angiotensin II receptive neurons in the cat subfornical organ. *Brain Res.* 109:531–40
97. Phillips, M. I., Hoffman, W. E. 1977. Sensitive sites in the brain for the blood pressure and drinking responses to antiotensin II. In *Central Actions of Angiotensin and Related Hormones,* ed. J. P. Buckley, C. Ferrario, pp. 325–56. New York: Pergamon. 580 pp.
98. Phillis, J. W. 1977. The role of cyclic nucleotides in the CNS. *Can. J. Neurol. Sci.* 4:151–95
99. Pickard, J. D., MacDonell, L. A., MacKenzie, E. T., Harper, A. M. 1977. Response of the cerebral circulation in baboons to changing perfusion pressure after indomethacin. *Circ. Res.* 40:198–203
100. Pickard, J. D., MacDonell, L. A., MacKenzie, E. T., Harper, A. M. 1977. Prostaglandin-induced effects in the primate cerebral circulation. *Eur. J. Pharmacol.* 43:343–51
101. Pickard, J. D., MacKenzie, E. T. 1973. Inhibition of prostaglandin synthesis and the response of baboon cerebral circulation to carbon dioxide. *Nature* 245:187–88
102. Pittman, Q. J., Veale, W. L., Cockeram, A. W., Cooper, K. E. 1976. Changes in body temperature produced by prostaglandins and pyrogens in the chicken. *Am. J. Physiol.* 230:1284–87

103. Pittman, Q. J., Veale, W. L., Cooper, K. E. 1975. Temperature responses of lambs after centrally injected prostaglandins and pyrogens. *Am. J. Physiol.* 228:1034–38

104. Pittman, Q. J., Veale, W. L., Cooper, K. E. 1976. Observations on the effect of salicylate in fever and the regulation of body temperature against cold. *Can. J. Physiol. Pharmacol.* 54:101–6

105. Pittman, Q. J., Veale, W. L., Cooper, K. E. 1977. Effect of prostaglandin, pyrogen and noradrenaline injected into the hypothalamus, on thermoregulation in newborn lambs. *Brain Res.* 128:473–83

106. Potts, W. J., East, P. F. 1972. Effects of prostaglandin E_2 on the body temperature of conscious rats and cats. *Arch. Int. Pharmacodyn. Ther.* 197:31–36

107. Preston, E., Schönbaum, E. 1976. Monoaminergic mechanisms in thermoregulation. In *Brain Dysfunction in Infantile Febrile Convulsions,* ed. M. A. B. Brazier, F. Coceani, pp. 75–87. New York: Raven. 370 pp.

108. Ramwell, P. W., ed. 1973, 1974, 1977. *The Prostaglandins,* Vols. 1, 2, 3. New York: Plenum. 400 pp.; 350 pp.; 359 pp.

109. Rawlins, M. D., Luff, R. H., Cranston, W. I. 1973. Regional brain salicylate concentrations in afebrile and febrile rabbits. *Biochem. Pharmacol.* 22: 2639–42

110. Roberts, J. S., Carlson, J. C., McCracken, J. A. 1976. Prostaglandin $F_{2\alpha}$ production by the brain and its role in LH secretion. See Ref. 114, 2:609–19

111. Roberts, P. J., Hillier, K. 1976. Facilitation of noradrenaline release from rat brain synaptosomes by prostaglandin *Brain Res.* 112:425–28

112. Robinson, H. J., Vane, J. R., eds. 1974. *Prostaglandin Synthetase Inhibitors.* New York: Raven. 395 pp.

113. Rudy, T. A., Westergaard, J. L., Yaksh, T. L. 1978. Hyperthermia produced by simulated intraventricular hemorrhage in the cat. *Exp. Neurol.* 58:296–310

114. Samuelsson, B., Paoletti, R., eds. 1976. *Advances in Prostaglandin and Thromboxane Research,* Vols. 1, 2. New York: Raven. 1028 pp.

115. Satinoff, E. 1972. Salicylate: action on normal body temperature in rats. *Science* 176:532–33

116. Scaramuzzi, O. E., Baile, C. A., Mayer, J. 1971. Prostaglandins and food intake of rats. *Experientia* 27:256–57

117. Schoener, E. P., Wang, S. C. 1976. Effects of locally administered prostaglandin E_1 on anterior hypothalamic neurons. *Brain Res.* 117:157–62

118. Severs, W. B., Daniels-Severs, A. E. 1973. Effects of angiotensin on the central nervous system. *Pharmacol. Rev.* 25:415–49

119. Shenoy, A., Ziance, R. 1978. Modulation of ^{3}H-norepinephrine release in rat cerebral cortex by prostaglandin E_2 and autonomic drugs. *Fed. Proc.* 37:688

120. Siggins, G. R., Hoffer, B. J., Bloom, F. E., Understedt, U. 1976. Cytochemical and electrophysiological studies of dopamine in the caudate nucleus. *Res. Publ. Assoc. Res. Nerv. Ment. Dis.* 55: 227–48

121. Stitt, J. T. 1973. Prostaglandin E_1 fever induced in rabbits. *J. Physiol. London* 232:163–79

122. Stitt, J. T., Hardy, J. D. 1975. Microelectrophoresis of PGE_1 onto single units in the rabbit hypothalamus. *Am. J. Physiol.* 229:240–45

123. Stone, T. W., Taylor, D. A., Bloom, F. E. 1975. Cyclic AMP and cyclic GMP may mediate opposite neuronal responses in the rat cerebral cortex. *Science* 187:845–47

124. Vane, J. R. 1969. The release and fate of vasoactive hormones in the circulation. *Br. J. Pharmacol.* 35:209–42

125. Vane, J. R., McGiff, J. C. 1975. Possible contribution of endogenous prostaglandins to the control of blood pressure. *Circ. Res.* 36, 37: (Suppl.) I68–75

126. Veale, W. L., Cooper, K. E. 1975. Comparison of sites of action of prostaglandin E and leucocyte pyrogen in brain. See Ref. 77, 218–26

127. Veale, W. L., Cooper, K. E., Malkinson, T. 1976. Temperature and feeding responses in the unanaesthetized cat following injections of prostaglandin E into the hypothalamus. *Canada Physiol.* 7:64

128. Veale, W. L., Cooper, K. E., Pittman, Q. J. 1977. Role of prostaglandins in fever and temperature regulation. See Ref. 108, 3:145–62

129. Vilhardt, H., Hedqvist, P. 1970. A possible role of prostaglandin E_2 in the regulation of vasopressin secretion in rats. *Life Sci.* 9:825–30

130. VonVoigtlander, P. F. 1976. In vivo dopamine release and prostaglandin E_2 *Res. Comm. Chem. Pathol. Pharmacol.* 14:431–36

131. Welch, K. M. A., Spira, P. J., Knowles, L., Lance, J. W. 1974. Effects of prostaglandins in the internal and external carotid blood flow in the monkey. *Neurology* 24:705–10

132. White, R. P., Hagen, A. A., Morgan, H., Dawson, W. N., Robertson, J. T.

1975. Experimental study on the genesis of cerebral vasospasm. *Stroke* 6:52–57

133. White, R., Terragno, D. A., Terragno, N. A., Hagen, A. A., Robertson, J. T. 1977. Prostaglandins in porcine cerebral blood vessels. *Stroke* 8:135

134. Wishaw, I. Q., Veale, W. L. 1974. Comparison of the effect of prostaglandin E_1 and norepinephrine injected into the brain on ingestive behaviour in the rat. *Pharmacol. Biochem. Behav.* 2:421–25

135. Wolfe, L. S. 1975. Possible roles of prostaglandins in the nervous system. In *Advances in Neurochemistry*, ed. M. Aprison, B. W. Agranoff, 1:1–49. New York: Plenum. 309 pp.

136. Wolfe, L. S. 1978. Some facts and thoughts on the biosynthesis of prostaglandins and thromboxanes in brain. See Ref. 27, pp. 215–20

137. Wolfe, L. S., Mamer, O. A. 1974. Measurement of prostaglandin $F_{2\alpha}$ levels in human cerebrospinal fluid in normal and pathological conditions. *Prostaglandins* 9:183–92

138. Woolf, C. J., Willies, G. H., Rosendorff, C. 1977. Pyrogen, prostaglandin and cyclic AMP fevers in the rabbit. In *Drugs, Biogenic Amines and Body Temperature,* ed. K. E. Cooper, P. Lomax, E. Schönbaum, pp. 136–39. Basel: Karger. 283 pp.

139. Yamamoto, Y. L., Feindel, W., Wolfe, L. S., Katoh, H., Hodge, C. P. 1972. Experimental vasoconstriction of cerebral arteries by prostaglandins. *J. Neurosurg.* 37:385–97

140. Ziel, R., Krupp, P. 1976. Influence of endogenous pyrogen on the cerebral prostaglandin-synthetase system. *Experientia* 32:1451–53

Ann. Rev. Physiol. 1979. 41:685–700

PROSTAGLANDINS IN HYPOTHALAMO-PITUITARY AND OVARIAN FUNCTION

❖1245

Harold R. Behrman

Reproductive Biology Section, Departments of Obstetrics and Gynecology and Pharmacology, Yale University School of Medicine, New Haven, CT 06510

INTRODUCTION

In this review attention is focused on the role of prostaglandins (PGs) in the hypothalamus and pituitary in control of gonadotropin secretion, and in the control of ovulation, luteinization, and corpus luteum regression. The role of prostaglandins in uterine function, fetal-placental function and parturition is not reviewed here.

ROLE OF PGs IN GONADOTROPIN SECRETION

On the basis of present evidence it is clear that PGs affect gonadotropin secretion; PGs may play a role in regulation of gonadotropin secretion. Our present information is based largely on the effects of PGs on LH secretion, to a lesser extent on FSH secretion, and to a minor extent on prolactin secretion.

PGs and the Anterior Pituitary

The "mixed-cell" feature of the anterior pituitary and the independent humoral regulation of the different cell types make interpretation of the specificity of PG action on gonadotropin secretion difficult since isolated gonadotrophs have not yet been studied directly.

It is accepted that PGs, particularly PGE_1, act directly on the anterior pituitary to stimulate an increase in cyclic AMP levels and hormone secretion. For example, PGs stimulate release of GH from pituitary tissue in vitro (24, 44, 53, 59, 79, 83). Hedge (39, 40) has reported that PGs act

685

0066-4278/79/0301-0685$01.00

directly on the pituitary to inhibit ACTH secretion in the presence and absence of corticotropin releasing factor. However, direct effects of PGs on the secretion of LH, FSH, and prolactin have not been clearly shown, and most evidence indicates that PGs do not stimulate gonadotropin secretion by a direct action on the pituitary. There is a well documented relationship between cAMP and gonadotropin secretion (50, 53, 75, 89), as well as a relationship between PGs and stimulation of cAMP levels in the pituitary (16, 60, 76, 89). Although Zor et al (90) demonstrated that both a crude hypothalamic extract and PGE_1 stimulated adenylate cyclase activity and cAMP accumulation, only the hypothalamic extract increased LH secretion from intact pituitary tissue. More recently, Drouin et al (29) showed that neither PGE_1 nor PGE_2 had an effect on basal or LHRH-stimulated LH release in cultured pituitary cells. In further studies, Drouin & Labrie (30) found that PGE_1 had little effect on release of LH, FSH, TSH, or prolactin in cultured pituitary cells, although PGE_1 did produce a dose-dependent release of GH. Furthermore, PGE_2 was shown to have no effect on LH release from hemipituitaries (21). This evidence conflicts with earlier reports that a stimulation of LH secretion occurred with addition of PGE_1 (60, 76). The basis of these conflicting reports is not clear, but most workers agree that the pituitary is not a predominant site of PG action in stimulating LH release.

Although PGs stimulate cAMP formation in pituitary tissue and gonadotropin release appears to depend on cAMP, the absence of effect of PGs on gonadotropin release from the pituitary implies that PGs probably do not increase cAMP levels in gonadotrophs. On the other hand, the observation that PGs directly stimulate GH release from pituitary tissue indicates that the increase in pituitary cAMP levels produced by PGs may be limited to specific cell types. These observations may be taken as indirect evidence for specificity of PG action on target cells in the pituitary and that stimulation of cAMP may not be a generalized response to PG in all pituitary cells. Future studies that identify specific receptors for PGs in pituitary cells may yield interesting information in this area.

Prostaglandins and the Hypothalamus

Systemic administration of PGs has been shown to increase circulating levels of GH (45, 48, 53, 67), ACTH (26, 41, 71), prolactin (37, 65, 77), FSH (77), and LH (18, 38, 53, 76, 78, 86). In general, PGs of the E series are more potent than PGs of the F series; with regard to LH secretion, PGE_2 is more potent than PGE_1 (53). In vivo evidence that PGs may be involved in gonadotropin secretion was derived from indirect experiments in which rats treated with indomethacin during the follicular phase failed to ovulate (68).

On the basis of present evidence the systemic action of PGs in stimulating gonadotropin release appears to be due to an hypothalamic site of action. This conclusion is based on several observations. First, PGs have little direct effect on pituitary release of gonadotropins (reviewed above). Second, direct administration of PGs into the brain ventricle mimics the intravenous effect of PGs on gonadotropin secretion (38, 53, 81). Third, pretreatment of male and female rats (21) and proestrous rats (29) with antisera against LHRH blocks the PGE_2-stimulated increase in systemic blood levels of LH. Taken together these observations indicate that PGs stimulate release of LHRH, thereby producing a stimulation of gonadotropin secretion. These observations also provide provocative evidence that PGs may be physiological mediators (regulators) of LHRH secretion. It has not been established whether PGs act directly on LHRH-containing neurons to stimulate LHRH release or whether they act on other neurons that synapse with LHRH-neurons to modify LHRH release.

The site of PG action in stimulating increased levels of circulating prolactin also appears to be at the hypothalamic level based on the positive effects of intraventricular injection of PG and the lack of a direct effect of intrapituitary injections of PG (37, 65). It has been suggested that PGE_2 may act in the hypothalamus by inhibiting release of a prolactin-secretion-inhibiting factor, which would result in an increase in prolactin secretion (66).

General Considerations of PG Action on Gonadotropin Secretion

Although there is clear evidence that PGs may act at hypothalamic sites to stimulate release of gonadotropins and prolactin, it is not clear whether PGs play a physiological role in this process. One problem is the inability to control adequately the localization and concentration of PG applied to hypothalamic areas to prevent expression of pharmacological and/or indirect actions of PGs. Until hypothalamic neurons can be successfully isolated and tested in vitro, or tested in highly controlled environments in vivo, direct administration of PGs will yield little information on their physiological actions. An alternative approach that is technically feasible but about which no information is available is the use of "tagging procedures" to identify sites of prostaglandin localization in the hypothalamus. Studies that utilize inhibitors of PG synthesis, such as aspirin and indomethacin, have provided provocative information on the role of PGs in gonadotropin secretion. However, such drugs are not entirely specific in their actions and the results must be interpreted with caution.

The generalized action of PGs in stimulating release of a wide spectrum of pituitary hormones implies that if PGs are physiological regulators of hypothalamic control of pituitary hormone secretion, they probably act as intermediaries in reactions common to release of many hypothalamic products. Since independent control of secretion of most pituitary hormones does occur, it follows that positive or negative effectors that regulate hypothalamic function may be dependent on a common action of PGs, but specificity would be directed by receptors of such effectors within the hypothalamus. If this is the case, it is expected that changes in PG levels may be highly restricted and localized within areas of the hypothalamus, either through control of synthesis-degradation or by the presence of specific PG receptors.

ROLE OF PGs IN OVULATION

The involvement of PGs in ovulation was first suspected when inhibitors of PG synthesis, indomethacin and aspirin, were found to block ovulation in the rat (3, 68). This action of indomethacin on ovulation was confirmed in the rabbit (36, 63). The indomethacin-induced block of ovulation was reversed by injection of animals with PGs (68, 87). To avoid possible central actions of indomethacin on gonadotropin secretion Armstrong et al (4) injected indomethacin directly into rabbit follicles and showed that ovulation was blocked. Intrafollicular injections of an antiserum to PGF blocked ovulation in the rabbit (4), and elevated levels of PGs in preovulatory follicles were demonstrated in the rabbit (57), in the rat (87), and later in the pig (1).

Gonadotropin Effects on Follicular PG Production

Present evidence indicates that elevation of PGs in preovulatory follicles is induced by gonadotropin. For example, LeMaire et al (57) isolated rabbit follicles one, five, and nine hours after treatment with human chorionic gonadotropin to induce ovulation. Levels of PGE and PGF were markedly increased nine hours after gonadotropin treatment, but at five hours only a modest change was seen. This response was seen only in follicles that were destined to ovulate (88). A similar observation was made later in the pig (1).

In vitro, LH stimulates PG production in preovulatory rabbit follicles, but FSH and prolactin were shown to have no effect (61). In the rat however, Bauminger & Lindner (7) reported that either LH or FSH stimulated PG production in isolated follicles with a latency period of about two to four hours. Elevation of follicular PG content was shown in bovine follicles exposed to LH in vitro (80) and in follicles of women pretreated with human menopausal gonadotropin followed by human chorionic gonadotropin (73). Thus there appears to be a species difference in the nature of the gonadotropins that stimulate follicular PG production.

Effect of Cyclic Nucleotides on Follicular PG Production

Cyclic nucleotides may be involved in mediating the action of gonadotropins on follicular PG production. Marsh et al (61) reported that cAMP mimicked the effect of LH on PG production in the rabbit follicle in vitro. Zor et al (91) reported that both cAMP and cGMP stimulated PGE production in isolated rat follicles. On the other hand, Clark et al (23) reported that cAMP, but not cGMP, stimulated PG production in isolated rat follicles. The difference between these reports may be due to the use of analogs of cAMP and cGMP by Zor et al (91). It is interesting that cholera toxin, a nonhumoral agent that elevates cAMP levels in a variety of cells, was also shown to elevate PGE levels in rat follicles (23, 91).

Macromolecular Synthesis and PG Production

The time lag following exposure of the follicle to gonadotropin or cyclic nucleotide indicates that macromolecular synthesis may be involved in follicular PG production. Bauminger & Lindner (7) found that the increase in prostaglandin synthetase activity in rat follicles exposed in vivo to the ovulatory surge of gonadotropin was blocked by neutralization of circulating LH with a specific antiserum. It was suggested that the delay in follicular PG production in response to LH may require de novo synthesis of PG synthetase rather than direct stimulation of enzyme activity. This conclusion was based on studies using inhibitors of protein synthesis (22, 91) and nucleic acid synthesis (91) to block the LH- and cyclic nucleotide-stimulated increase in PG production. However, no direct evidence for PG synthetase induction by gonadotropin is available. The possibility that gonadotropins modify other rate-limiting factors necessary for PG production, such as arachidonic acid availability, has not been examined.

Plasminogen Activator Production by the Follicle

Recently, it was suggested by Beers et al (15) that plasminogen activator may play a role in the process of follicular rupture that leads to ovulation. The protease, plasmin, a product of the reaction catalyzed by plasminogen activator, was able to weaken follicle wall strips in vitro (14). In addition, it was shown that rat granulosa cells released plasminogen-dependent fibrinolytic activity, and such activity was greatest in granulosa cells obtained from preovulatory follicles. This activity was inducible by exposure of the cells in vitro to LH or dibutyryl cAMP (15). It was shown that plasminogen activator production increased as ovulation was approached and occurred only in follicles destined to ovulate (82). In this same study, PGE_1 and PGE_2 stimulated granulosa cells to produce the enzyme activator, but $PGF_{1\alpha}$ and $PGF_{2\alpha}$ were inactive. FSH was found to be more active than LH, TSH showed substantial activity, while GH and prolactin were inactive (82).

Although FSH may have a role in ovulation, it is generally assumed that LH is the major signal in initiating the ovulatory process. On the other hand, in the studies on plasminogen activator, FSH was more active than LH, and $PGF_{2\alpha}$ was found to be inactive (82). It has been shown that intrafollicular injections of $PGF_{2\alpha}$ induce ovulation (5) and intrafollicular injection of antiserum against $PGF_{2\alpha}$ blocks ovulation (4). The hypothesis that ovulation is due to LH (FSH) stimulation of cAMP production followed by increased follicular PG levels and resultant granulosa cell secretion of plasminogen activator is interesting, but the discrepancies between hormone and PG specificity are disturbing. Nonetheless the time course for appearance of plasminogen activator activity following exposure of rat granulosa cells to LH approximates the time course for PG release in rat follicles exposed to LH (7).

Summary

In Figure 1 a model of a possible mechanism of gonadotropin-follicular-PG interaction in ovulation is shown. The cell type in the follicle responsible for PG production is not known, although LH and to some extent FSH (6) appear to activate processes leading to this response. Results that show FSH to be more active than LH in stimulating plasminogen activator secretion by granulosa cells (82) are not consistent with the hormone specificity for PG production. However, since it has been shown that granulosa cells respond to FSH with cAMP production and elevated aromatase activity (2), it is not surprising that isolated granulosa cells respond better to FSH than to LH with plasminogen activator secretion. Presumably this may be due to the presence of distinct receptors for FSH but few for LH. Theca cells, on the other hand, appear to respond specifically to LH with increased androgen synthesis (2), and follicle wall tissue was shown to produce plasminogen activator (14). Thus, it is possible that PG production and plasminogen activator secretion may occur in the theca compartment (follicle wall) under the control of LH and in the granulosa compartment under the control of FSH.

The site and mechanism of action of follicular PG in the ovulatory process are not known. PGs may mediate hormone dependent–adenylate cyclase stimulation of plasminogen-activator release, or they may mediate another process, such as contraction of follicle wall smooth muscle (27). Prostaglandin production appears to be independent of follicular steroidogenesis (6) but is elevated by cAMP (23, 61, 91). Conversely PGs, particularly the E series, elevate cAMP levels (20), but this response is rapid whereas elevation of PGs by cAMP shows a lag of several hours (91). Since inhibitors of prostaglandin synthesis do not block LH-induced steroido-

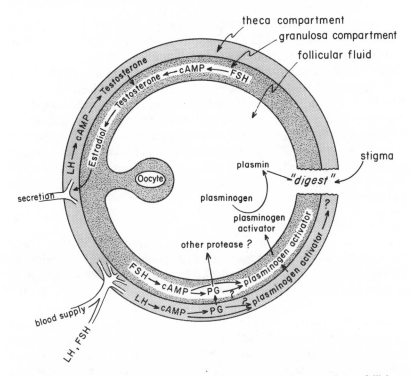

Figure 1   Prostaglandin-gonadotropin interactions in the rat pre-ovulatory follicle.

genesis and oocyte maturation, and because of the time delay in PG production after addition of hormone, it is probable that PGs do not mediate the hormone-induced elevation of cAMP levels. Thus, the increase in plasminogen activator secretion produced by PGE_1 and PGE_2 (82) may reflect stimulation of adenylate cyclase but it does not necessarily show a direct role of PGs in plasminogen activator secretion. In this regard it was reported that indomethacin did not affect gonadotropin-dependent plasminogen activator secretion (82). It is possible that both PG production and plasminogen activator secretion are parallel but not interdependent events involved in ovulation.

ROLE OF PGs IN LUTEAL FUNCTION

Luteinization

A physiological role of PGs in the luteinization process has been suggested but not confirmed. Channing showed that granulosa cells cultured in the presence of PGE_1 and PGE_2 luteinized, and increased progesterone secretion occurred (19, 20). While the evidence is somewhat equivocal, cAMP appears to be involved in the luteinization process (20, 32). In general, luteinization induced by LH appears to be mediated by cAMP, and PGE_1 or PGE_2 may mimic this action of LH.

However, evidence that PG is an obligatory intermediate of LH-induced luteinization is less clear. Doses of indomethacin that block ovulation in vivo (3, 36, 63) do not prevent luteinization in the rat or the rabbit. Yet, it was reported that indomethacin reduced the incidence of luteinization of follicles exposed to LH in vitro and then permitted to luteinize in vivo (32). In this same study PGE_2 prevented the indomethacin effect, but the possibility of nonspecific effects of the drug cannot be excluded. An obligatory role of PGs in the luteinization process has not been established, and further work in this area is necessary.

Corpus Luteum Regression

It is now clear that PGs, particularly $PGF_{2\alpha}$, secreted by the uterus, cause luteal regression in many species—with one possible notable exception: the human. Evidence for a physiological role of $PGF_{2\alpha}$ in corpus luteum regression is based upon several observations. First, direct administration of $PGF_{2\alpha}$ causes luteal regression. Second, active immunization of the animal against $PGF_{2\alpha}$ prolongs the life span of the corpus luteum. Third, inhibition of PG synthesis with indomethacin prolongs the life span of the corpus luteum. Fourth, an increase in the blood level of $PGF_{2\alpha}$ occurs at or near the time of luteal regression. Evidence in support of a physiological role of $PGF_{2\alpha}$ in corpus luteum regression has recently been reviewed (33, 47).

Although $PGF_{2\alpha}$ has been shown to induce transient decreases in blood levels of progesterone that are most marked with increased age of the corpus luteum (33, 55), the physiological signal involved in human luteolysis remains to be established. In other species such as the sheep, cow, and rat, newly formed corpora lutea appear to be refractory to the luteolytic activity of $PGF_{2\alpha}$. The basis for such refractoriness is not known but studies on this problem may elucidate the cause for the resistance of the human corpus luteum to $PGF_{2\alpha}$.

Several mechanisms have been postulated for the luteolytic action of $PGF_{2\alpha}$. These include restriction of blood supply to the ovary (31) or corpus luteum (85), stimulation of a lytic level of LH secretion from the pituitary (52), or antagonism of gonadotropin support of the corpus luteum (12). It is now clear that the site of action of $PGF_{2\alpha}$ in luteolysis is directly on the corpus luteum. This conclusion is based upon observations that show that $PGF_{2\alpha}$ is luteolytic in hypophysectomized rats in which the corpora lutea were maintained with exogenous gonadotropin (10). Thus stimulation or inhibition of pituitary hormone secretion appears not to play a major role in $PGF_{2\alpha}$-induced luteolysis.

Ovarian and Luteal Blood Flow Effects of $PGF_{2\alpha}$

Present evidence indicates that luteal tissue blood flow comprises the major part of the ovarian blood flow and that at regression luteal blood flow is significantly reduced. This observation has been made in the sheep (62), the rabbit (17), and the rat (69). Several studies have reported on the interrelationship between blood flow and progesterone secretion following $PGF_{2\alpha}$ treatment (17, 51, 62, 72). It is clear that at pharmacological doses $PGF_{2\alpha}$ reduces ovarian blood flow, but no data have been reported in which a dose-response of $PGF_{2\alpha}$ on blood flow and progesterone secretion was examined. However, at lower doses it has been reported that reduced progesterone secretion precedes the decrease in blood flow (17, 49, 51, 58).

In the rat, 200 μg $PGF_{2\alpha}$ (i.v.) reduced utero-ovarian blood flow (72), but 20 μg $PGF_{2\alpha}$ (i.v.) had no effect on ovarian blood flow within 30 min, although progesterone secretion was reduced (12). Rats given $PGF_{2\alpha}$ at a dose of 1 mg kg^{-1} (s.c.) showed no change of ovarian blood flow 6 hr and 12 hr later, but progesterone secretion was reduced (13). Pang & Behrman (69) reported recently that in physiological luteal regression of the rat, blood flow was unchanged until after a significant decrease in progesterone levels occurred. These same workers reported that $PGF_{2\alpha}$ at a dose of 3 mg kg^{-1} (s.c.) reduced luteal blood flow at 30 min after treatment, but blood flow returned to control levels within 1 hr and remained unchanged at 4 hr, 8 hr, and 24 hr, but was reduced 36 hr after treatment (70). In this study, plasma progesterone levels were reduced at all times examined after $PGF_{2\alpha}$ treatment. These observations support the conclusion that $PGF_{2\alpha}$ at physiological concentrations may not induce functional luteal regression by reducing luteal blood flow.

$PGF_{2\alpha}$ Antagonism of Gonadotropins in the Corpus Luteum

The first evidence that $PGF_{2\alpha}$ may be an antagonist of gonadotropin action in the corpus luteum arose from studies in which acute inhibition of progesterone secretion by $PGF_{2\alpha}$ was reversed by a simultaneous injection of LH (12). In this same study but in hypophysectomized rats, $PGF_{2\alpha}$ blocked the acute stimulation of progesterone secretion produced by LH. In hypophysectomized rats, luteal function maintained with exogenous prolactin was also lost following $PGF_{2\alpha}$ treatment (10). Since gonadotropin support is necessary for luteal function, it was suggested (10, 12) that luteolysis may arise from a loss of hormone action by an antagonistic action of $PGF_{2\alpha}$ against both LH and prolactin. Herlitz et al (42) have shown that rat luteal tissue, at or near regression, becomes refractory to LH with respect to cAMP production. Refractoriness could occur by a loss of receptors on the luteal cell; it has been shown that LH receptors are lost in rat corpora lutea at regression (56). Hichens et al (46) showed that $PGF_{2\alpha}$ reduced luteal LH receptors in the rat within 24 hr and suggested that this may be the basis for refractoriness to LH in regressing luteal tissue. This effect is also accompanied by a marked decrease in serum progesterone and reduced functional activity of the LH receptor (34). The depletion of LH receptors by $PGF_{2\alpha}$ is probably not due to a direct action on the LH receptor since $PGF_{2\alpha}$ has no effect on binding of LH to isolated luteal membranes (46). $PGF_{2\alpha}$-induced loss of LH receptors in rat corpora lutea appears to be due to inhibition of prolactin action. This conclusion is based on demonstrations that ergocryptine (35) and hypophysectomy (9) mimicked the effect of $PGF_{2\alpha}$. Furthermore, prolactin treatment prevents the loss of LH receptors produced by $PGF_{2\alpha}$, ergocryptine, or hypophysectomy (9, 35).

Grinwich et al (35) found that progesterone levels in serum are reduced within 2 hr of $PGF_{2\alpha}$ treatment in the rat, whereas the first measurable decrease in LH receptor binding capacity did not occur for at least 8 hr. However, functional luteolysis, marked by elevated serum 20-α-dihydro-progesterone, was seen within 8 hr of PG treatment (35). Thus, loss of LH receptors per se is probably not the cause of the early decrease in progesterone production produced by $PGF_{2\alpha}$. On the other hand, loss of receptors for LH would insure that corpora lutea whose function was lost would not reinitiate progesterone secretion.

A possible basis for the rapid effect of $PGF_{2\alpha}$ on progesterone secretion is reduced binding of LH to preexisting receptors. In this regard, $PGF_{2\alpha}$ produces a prompt and marked fall in uptake of radiolabelled hormone by the corpus luteum in vivo (8). This effect occurs as early as 30 min after $PGF_{2\alpha}$ coincident with a significant decrease in plasma progesterone. In later studies it was shown that prolactin prevented the rapid effect of $PGF_{2\alpha}$ on luteal uptake of radiolabelled chorionic gonadotropin (9). Moreover, $PGF_{2\alpha}$ also reduced luteal uptake of radiolabelled prolactin, but no effect of $PGF_{2\alpha}$ was seen on either LH or prolactin receptor binding capacity in luteal membranes from rats treated with $PGF_{2\alpha}$ 2 hr before sacrifice (9). These observations indicate that block of hormone uptake by $PGF_{2\alpha}$ in vivo is not hormone-specific.

One explanation for the rapid action of $PGF_{2\alpha}$ on block of hormone uptake in vivo may be reduction of blood flow to the corpus luteum. But, at the same concentration, $PGF_{2\alpha}$ had no effect on blood flow 1 hr after treatment (70) and in other studies no effect was seen at 2, 4, or 24 hr after treatment (C. Y. Pang, H. R. Behrman, unpublished observations). $PGF_{2\alpha}$ has no direct effect on binding of radiolabelled chorionic gonadotropin to isolated luteal membranes (46). From these data it is concluded that $PGF_{2\alpha}$ in some unknown manner reduces accessibility of the intact luteal cell to circulating hormone. Clearly, further research in this area is necessary.

An additional basis for the rapid effect of $PGF_{2\alpha}$ on progesterone production may be inhibition of events in LH-dependent steroidogenesis that follow binding of LH to its receptor. Direct antagonism of gonadotropin action by $PGF_{2\alpha}$ in vitro has been demonstrated. For example, progesterone secretion by hamster corpora lutea induced either by co-incubation with hamster pituitary tissue or LH was blocked by $PGF_{2\alpha}$ (11). In monkey granulosa cells Channing (20) showed that $PGF_{2\alpha}$ and PGE_2 inhibited LH-stimulated progesterone secretion. Henderson & McNatty (43) showed antagonism by $PGF_{2\alpha}$ of gonadotropin- (LH- and FSH-) stimulated progesterone production in porcine granulosa cells cultured over a period of eight days. The same workers reported that $PGF_{2\alpha}$ inhibited progesterone secretion by cultured granulosa cells from the cow and human when progesterone production was low but not when high. In the latter studies the effects of $PGF_{2\alpha}$ on LH-stimulated progesterone secretion were not reported, and also $PGF_{2\alpha}$ was present in the incubation media for long periods of time. $PGF_{2\alpha}$ had a similar effect on long-term culture of explants of rat (25) and rabbit (64) corpora lutea in organ culture. Both $PGF_{2\alpha}$ and PGE_2 produce a rapid block of LH-dependent progesterone secretion by rat luteal cells in culture within 2 hr (84). In this same study no effect on specific binding to the LH receptor by $PGF_{2\alpha}$ was seen, but the effect of $PGF_{2\alpha}$ was reversed by addition of exogenous dibutyryl cAMP. In addition, direct inhibition of LH-dependent cAMP accumulation by $PGF_{2\alpha}$ was shown, but no effect of $PGF_{2\alpha}$ on phosphodiesterase activity was evident. These results confirm the preliminary observation of Lahav et al (54) in which $PGF_{2\alpha}$ inhibited cAMP accumulation induced by LH in slices of rat luteal tissue.

In preparations of isolated rat luteal plasma membranes $PGF_{2\alpha}$ had no effect on LH-stimulated adenylate cyclase activity (28). However, in dispersed luteal cells $PGF_{2\alpha}$ blocked cholera toxin stimulation of progesterone secretion; this action of $PGF_{2\alpha}$ was prevented by dibutyryl cAMP (L. J. Dorflinger, H. R. Behrman, unpublished observations). The mechanisms of these actions of $PGF_{2\alpha}$ have not been elucidated but the ionophore A23187 was found to mimic the action of $PGF_{2\alpha}$ in dispersed luteal cells, and addition of calcium to isolated plasma membranes produced a dose-dependent inhibition of LH-stimulated adenylate cyclase activity (L. J. Dorflinger, H. R. Behrman, unpublished observations). Thus, the rapid anti-LH action of $PGF_{2\alpha}$ is expressed only in the intact cell, which implies an indirect action possibly through some mediator that blocks LH receptor complex activation of adenylate cyclase. Preliminary evidence indicates that an initial action of $PGF_{2\alpha}$ in the luteal cell may be an increase in calcium influx (or intracellular release of bound calcium) that then inhibits activation of adenylate cyclase. More direct studies are necessary to determine if calcium mediates the anti-gonadotropic action of $PGF_{2\alpha}$. This action of $PGF_{2\alpha}$ appears to be specific since $PGF_{2\alpha}$ was not active in blocking the action of LH in interstitial cells of rat testes (J. P. Thomas, H. R. Behrman, unpublished observations).

It is possible that specific PG receptors are necessary for expression of the adenylate cyclase inhibition by $PGF_{2\alpha}$. Such receptors have been identified in luteal tissue of the pig, cow, and human, and this subject was recently reviewed by Powell et al (74). Specific binding of $PGF_{2\alpha}$ has been demonstrated in rat luteal membrane preparations (K. Wright, H. R. Behrman, unpublished observations), and such receptors have been localized on the luteal cell plasma membrane with ultrastructural studies using a ferritin conjugate of $PGF_{2\alpha}$ (J. L. Luborsky-Moore, K. Wright, H. R. Behrman, unpublished observations).

Proposed Mechanism of $PGF_{2\alpha}$-Induced Luteolysis in the Rat

The sequence of events in luteal regression produced by $PGF_{2\alpha}$ include several time-dependent phenomena. First there is a rapid (within minutes) inhibition of LH-activated adenylate cyclase. This process appears to be reversible since luteal cells incubated with LH (or cholera toxin) and $PGF_{2\alpha}$ respond to LH (or cholera toxin) after washing (L. J. Dorflinger, H. R. Behrman, unpublished observations). The longer-term effect of $PGF_{2\alpha}$ on the luteal cell of the rat appears to be inhibition of prolactin action that results in a loss of LH receptors. This process takes more than eight hours in the rat (35). After substantial loss of LH receptors this process appears to be irreversible because of the time necessary to generate new receptors and the need for constant gonadotropin action for continued luteal function. The mechanism of the anti-prolactin action of $PGF_{2\alpha}$ is unknown and, although specific receptors for prolactin are present on rat luteal cells (9), the mechanism of prolactin action is unknown. Inhibition of gonadotropin uptake by luteal tissue produced by $PGF_{2\alpha}$ in vivo is a rapid and additional facet of $PGF_{2\alpha}$ action in the rat. The mechanism of this action of $PGF_{2\alpha}$ is presently unexplained. Thus the luteolytic impact of $PGF_{2\alpha}$ (Figure 2) includes rapid inhibition of LH action and eventual loss of LH receptors.

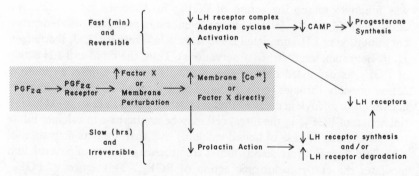

Figure 2 Summary of the rapid and slow antigonadotropic actions of $PGF_{2\alpha}$ in the rat luteal cell. Factor X unknown.

The combination of these events results in isolation of the luteal cell from the tropic and trophic influences of gonadotropins necessary for continued function of the luteal cell culminating in luteolysis.

ACKNOWLEDGMENTS

The author wishes to acknowledge Drs. J. L. Luborsky-Moore, K. Wright, C. Pang, and L. Dorflinger for their assistance in the preparation and editing of the manuscript. Supported by NIH HD 10718 and The Ford Foundation 770-0534.

Literature Cited

1. Ainsworth, L., Baker, R. D., and Armstrong, D. T. 1975. Pre-ovulatory changes in follicular fluid prostaglandin F levels in swine. *Prostaglandins* 9:915–25
2. Armstrong, D. T., Dorrington, J. H. 1977. Estrogen biosynthesis in the ovaries and testes. *Advances in Sex Hormone Research,* ed. J. A. Thomas, R. L. Singhal, 3:217–58. Baltimore: University Park Press
3. Armstrong, D. T., Grinwich, D. L. 1972. Blockade of spontaneous and LH-induced ovulation in rats by indomethacin, an inhibitor of prostaglandin biosynthesis. *Prostaglandins* 1:21–8
4. Armstrong, D. T., Grinwich, D. L., Moon, Y. S., Zamecnik, J. 1974. Inhibition of ovulation in rabbits by intrafollicular injection of indomethacin and prostaglandin F antiserum. *Life Sci.* 14:129–40
5. Armstrong, D. T., Moon, Y. S., Zamecnik, J. 1974. Evidence for a role of ovarian prostaglandin in ovulation. In *Gonadotropins and Gonadal Function,* ed. N. R. Moudgal, pp. 345–63. New York: Academic
6. Bauminger, S., Lieberman, M. E., Lindner, H. R. 1975. Steroid-independent effect of gonadotropins on prostaglandin synthesis in rat graafian follicles *in vitro. Prostaglandins* 9:753–63
7. Bauminger, S., Lindner, H. R. 1975. Periovulatory changes in ovarian prostaglandin formation and their hormonal control in the rat. *Prostaglandins* 9: 737–51
8. Behrman, H. R. Hichens, M. 1976. Rapid block of gonadotropin uptake by corpora lutea *in vivo* induced by prostaglandin $F_{2\alpha}$. *Prostaglandins* 12:83–95
9. Behrman, H. R., Grinwich, D. L., Hichens, M., Macdonald, G. J. 1978. Effect of hypophysectomy, prolactin

and prostaglandin $F_{2\alpha}$ on gonadotropin binding *in vivo* and *in vitro* in the corpus luteum. *Endocrinology* 103:349–57
10. Behrman, H. R., Macdonald, G. J., Greep, R. O. 1971. Regulation of ovarian cholesterol esters:evidence for the enzymatic sites of prostaglandin-induced loss of corpus luteum function. *Lipids* 6:791–96
11. Behrman, H. R., Ng, T. S., Orczyk, G. P. 1974. Interactions between prostaglandins and gonadotropins on corpus luteum function. See Ref. 5, pp. 332–43
12. Behrman, H. R., Yoshinaga, K., Greep, R. O. 1971. Extra luteal effects of prostaglandins. *Ann. N.Y. Acad. Sci.* 180: 426–35
13. Behrman, H. R., Yoshinaga, K., Greep, R. O. 1971. Effects of prostaglandin on ovarian steroid secretion and biosynthesis during pregnancy. *Am. J. Physiol.* 221:189–93
14. Beers, W. H. 1975. Follicular plasminogen and plasminogen activator and the effect of plasmin on ovarian follicle wall. *Cell* 6:379–86
15. Beers, W. H., Strickland, S., Reich, E. 1975. Ovarian plasminogen activator: relationships to ovulation and hormonal regulation. *Cell* 6:387–94
16. Borgeat, P., Labrie, F., Garneau, P. 1975. Characteristics of action of prostaglandins on cyclic AMP accumulation in rat anterior pituitary gland. *Can. J. Biochem.* 53:455–60
17. Bruce, N. W., Hillier, K. 1974. The effect of prostaglandin $F_{2\alpha}$ on ovarian blood flow and corpora lutea regression in the rabbit. *Nature* 249:176–77
18. Carlson, J. C., Barcikowski, B., McCracken, J. A. 1973. Prostaglandin $F_{2\alpha}$, and the release of LH in the sheep. *J. Reprod. Fertil.* 34:357–61
19. Channing, C. P. 1972. Effects of prostaglandin inhibitors 7-oxa-13-prostynoic

acid and eicosa-5,8,11,14-tetraynoic acid upon luteinization of rhesus monkey granulosa cells in culture. *Prostaglandins* 2:351–67

20. Channing, C. P. 1972. Stimulatory effects of prostaglandins upon luteinization of rhesus monkey granulosa cell cultures. *Prostaglandins* 2:331–50

21. Chobsieng, P., Naor, Z., Koch, Y., Zor, U., Lindner, H. R. 1975. Stimulatory effect of prostaglandin E_2 on LH release in the rat:evidence for hypothalamic site of action. *Neuroendocrinology* 17:12–17

22. Clark, M. R., Marsh, J. M., LeMaire, W. J. 1976. The role of protein synthesis in the stimulation by LH on prostaglandin accumulation in rat preovulatory follicles *in vitro. Prostaglandins* 12:209–16

23. Clark, M. R., Marsh, J. M., LeMaire, W. J., 1978. Stimulation of prostaglandin accumulation in preovulatory rat follicles by adenosine3',5'-monophosphate. *Endocrinology* 102:39–44

24. Cooper, R. A., McPherson, M., Schofield, J. G. 1972. The effect of prostaglandins on ox pituitary content of adenosine3',5'-cyclic monophosphate and the release of growth hormone. *Biochem. J.* 127:143–54

25. Demers, L., Behrman, H. R., Greep, R. O. 1972. Effects of prostaglandins and gonadotrophins on luteal prostaglandin and steroid biosynthesis. *Adv. Biosci.* 9:701–7

26. deWied, D., Witter, A., Versteeg, D. H. G., Mulder, A. H., 1969. Release of ACTH by substances of central nervous system origin. *Endocrinology* 85:561–69

27. Diaz-Infante, A., Wright, K. H., Wallach, E. E., 1974. Effects of indomethacin and prostaglandin $F_{2\alpha}$ on ovulation and ovarian contractility in the rabbit. *Prostaglandins* 5:567–81

28. Dorflinger, L. J., Behrman, H. R. 1978. Evidence for the role Ca^{++} in the acute effect of $PGF_{2\alpha}$ on LH-stimulated adenylate cyclase activity. *Biol. Reprod.* 18: (Suppl. 1) 62A

29. Drouin, J., Ferland, L., Bernard, J., Labrie, F. 1976. Site of the *in vivo* stimulatory effect of prostaglandins on LH release. *Prostaglandins* 11:367–75

30. Drouin, J., Labrie, F. 1976. Specificity of the stimulatory effect of prostaglandins on hormone release in rat anterior pituitary cells in culture. *Prostaglandins* 11:355–64

31. Duncan, G. W., Pharriss, B. B. 1970. Effect of nonsteroidal compounds on fertility. *Fed. Proc.* 29:1232–39

32. Ellsworth, L. R., Armstrong, D. T. 1974. Effect of indomethacin and 7-oxa-13-prostynoic acid in luteinization of transplanted rat ovarian follicles induced by luteinizing hormone and prostaglandin E_2. *Prostaglandins* 7:165–74

33. Goldberg, V. J., Ramwell, P. W. 1975. Role of prostaglandins in reproduction. *Physiol. Rev.* 55:325–51

34. Grinwich, D. L., Ham, E. A., Hichens, M., Behrman, H. R. 1976. Binding of human chorionic gonadotropin and response of cyclic nucleotides to luteinizing hormone in luteal tissue from rats treated with prostaglandin $F_{2\alpha}$. *Endocrinology* 98:146–50

35. Grinwich, D. L., Hichens, M., Behrman, H. R. 1976. Control of the LH receptor by prolactin and prostaglandin $F_{2\alpha}$ in rat corpora lutea. *Biol. Reprod.* 14:212–18

36. Grinwich, D. L., Kennedy, T. G., Armstrong, D. T. 1972. Dissociation of ovulatory and steroidogenic actions of luteinizing hormone in rabbits with indomethacin, an inhibitor of prostaglandin synthesis. *Prostaglandins* 1:89–96

37. Harms, P. G., Ojeda, S. R., McCann, S. M. 1973. Prostaglandin involvement in hypothalamic control of gonadotropin and prolactin release. *Science* 181:760–61

38. Harms, P. G., Ojeda, S. R. McCann, S. M. 1974. Prostaglandin induced release of pituitary gonadotropins: central nervous system and pituitary sites of action. *Endocrinology* 94:1459–64

39. Hedge, G. A. 1976. Hypothalamic and pituitary effects of prostaglandins on ACTH secretion. *Prostaglandins* 11:293–301

40. Hedge, G. A. 1977. Stimulation of ACTH secretion by indomethacin and reversal by exogenous prostaglandins. *Prostaglandins* 14:145–50

41. Hedge, G. A., Hanson, S. D. 1972. The effects of prostaglandins on ACTH secretion. *Endocrinology* 91:925–33

42. Herlitz, H., Hamberger, L., Rosberg, S., Ahren, K. 1974. Cyclic AMP in isolated corpora lutea of the rat: influence of gonadotropins and prostaglandins. *Acta Endocrinol.* 77:739–52

43. Henderson, K. M., McNatty, K. D. 1977. A possible interrelationship between gonadotropin stimulation and prostaglandin $F_{2\alpha}$ inhibition of steroidogenesis by granulosa luteal cells *in vitro. J. Endocrinol.* 73:71–78

44. Hertelendy, F. 1971. Studies on growth hormone secretion. II. Stimulation by

prostaglandins *in vitro. Acta Endocrinol.* 68:355–62

45. Hertelendy, F., Todd, H., Ehrhart, K., Blute, R. 1972. Studies on growth hormone secretion: IV. *In vivo* effects of prostaglandin E_1. *Prostaglandins* 2:79–91

46. Hichens, M., Grinwich, D. L., Behrman, H. R. 1974. $PGF_{2\alpha}$-induced loss of corpus luteum gonadotropin receptors. *Prostaglandins* 7:449–58

47. Horton, E. W., Poyser, N. L. 1976. Uterine luteolytic hormone: a physiological role for prostaglandin $F_{2\alpha}$. *Physiol. Rev.* 56:595–651

48. Ito, H., Momose, G., Katayama, T., Takagishi, H., Ito, L., Nakajima, H., Takei, Y. 1971. Effect of prostaglandins on the secretion of human growth hormone. *J. Clin. Endocrinol.* 32:857–59

49. Janson, P. O., Albrecht, I., Ahren, K. 1975. Effects of prostaglandin $F_{2\alpha}$ on ovarian blood flow and vascular resistance in the pseudopregnant rabbit. *Acta. Endocrinol.* 79:337–50

50. Jutisz, M., Paloma de la Llosa, M. 1970. Requirement of Ca^{++} and Mg^{++} ions for the *in vitro* release of follicle stimulating hormone from rat pituitary glands and its subsequent biosynthesis. *Endocrinology* 86:761–68

51. Kirton, K. T., Kimball, F. A., Portena, S. E. 1976. Reproductive physiology: prostaglandin associated events. In *Advances in Prostaglandin and Thromboxane Research,* ed. B. Samuelsson, R. Paoletti, 2:621–25. NY: Raven Press

52. Labhsetwar, A. 1973. Do prostaglandins stimulate LH release and thereby cause luteolysis? *Prostaglandins* 3:729–32

53. Labrie, F., Pelletier, G., Borgeat, P., Drouin, J., Ferland, L., Belanger, A. 1976. Mode of action of hypothalamic regulatory hormones in the adenohypophysis. In *Frontiers in Neuroendocrinology,* ed. L. Martini, W. F. Ganong, 4:63–93. NY: Raven Press

54. Lahav, M., Freud, A., Lindner, H. R. 1976. Abrogation by prostaglandin $F_{2\alpha}$ of LH stimulated cyclic AMP accumulation in isolated rat corpora lutea of pregnancy. *Biochem. Biophys. Res. Commun.* 68:1294–99

55. Lehmann, F., Peters, F., Brechwoldt, M., Bettendorf, G. 1972. Plasma progesterone levels during the infusion of prostaglandin $F_{2\alpha}$. *Prostaglandins* 1:269–77

56. Lee, C. Y., Tateishi, K., Ryan, R. J., Jiang, N. S. 1975. Binding of human chorionic gonadotropin by rat ovarian slices: dependence on the functional state of the ovary. *Proc. Soc. Exp. Biol. Med.* 148:505–7

57. LeMaire, W. J., Yang, N. S. T., Behrman, H. R., Marsh, J. M. 1973. Preovulatory changes in the concentration of prostaglandins in rabbit graafian follicles. *Prostaglandins* 3:367–76

58. McCracken, J. A., Barcikowski, B., Carlson, J. C., Green, K., Samuelsson, B. 1973. The physiological role of prostaglandin $F_{2\alpha}$ in corpus luteum regression. *Adv. Biosci.* 9:599–624

59. Macleod, R. M., Lehmeyer, J. E. 1970. Release of pituitary growth hormone by prostaglandins and dibutyryl adenosine cyclic 3',5'-monophosphate in the absence of protein synthesis. *Proc. Natl. Acad. Sci. USA* 67:1172–79

60. Makino, T. 1973. Study of the intracellular mechanism of LH release in the anterior pituitary. *Am. J. Obstet. Gynecol.* 115:606–14

61. Marsh, J. M., Yang, N. S. T., LeMaire, W. J. 1974. Prostaglandin synthesis in rabbit Graafian follicles *in vitro.* Effect of luteinizing hormone and cyclic AMP. *Prostaglandins* 7:269–83

62. Niswender, G. D., Akbar, A. M., Diekman, M. A., Nett, T. M. 1973. Relative blood flow to the ovaries of cycling and pregnant ewes. *Biol. Reprod.* 9:87

63. O'Grady, J. P., Caldwell, B. V., Auletta, E. J., Speroff, L. 1972. The effects of an inhibitor of prostaglandin synthesis (indomethacin) on ovulation, pregnancy, and pseudopregnancy in the rabbit. *Prostaglandins* 1:97–106

64. O'Grady, J. P., Kohorn, E. I., Glass, R. H., Caldwell, B. V., Brock, W. A., Speroff, L. 1972. Inhibition of progesterone synthesis *in vitro* by prostaglandin $F_{2\alpha}$. *J. Reprod. Fertil.* 30:153–56

65. Ojeda, S. R., Harms, P. G., McCann, S. M. 1974. Central effect of prostaglandin E_1 on prolactin release. *Endocrinology* 95:613–18

66. Ojeda, S. R., Harms, P. G., McCann, S. M. 1974. Possible role of cyclic AMP and prostaglandin E_1 in the dopaminergic control of prolactin release. *Endocrinology* 95:1694–1703

67. Ojeda, S. R., Jameson, H. E., McCann, S. M. 1977. Prostaglandin E_2 induced growth hormone release: effect of intrahypothalamic and intrapituitary implants. *Prostaglandins* 13:943–55

68. Orczyk, G. P., Behrman, H. R. 1972. Ovulation blockade by aspirin or indomethacin: *in vivo* evidence for a role of prostaglandin in gonadotropin secretion. *Prostaglandins* 1:3–21

69. Pang, C. Y., Behrman, H. R. 1978. Relationship of corpus luteum function with ovarian and luteal blood flow. *Can. Fed. Biol. Soc.* 21:76

70. Pang, C. Y., Behrman, H. R. 1978. Acute effect of prostaglandin $F_{2\alpha}$ on luteal and ovarian function and blood flow. *Biol. Reprod.* 18: (Suppl. 1) 66A

71. Peng, T.-C., Six, K. M., Munson, P. L. 1970. Effects of prostaglandin E_1 on the hypothalamo-hypophysial-adrenocortical axis in rats. *Endocrinology* 86:202–6

72. Pharriss, B. B., Cornette, J. C., Gutknecht, G. D. 1970. Vascular control of luteal steroidogenesis. *J. Reprod. Fertil. Suppl.* 10:97–103

73. Plunkett, E. R., Moon, Y. S., Zamecnik, J., Armstrong, D. T. 1975. Preliminary evidence of a role for prostaglandin F in human follicular function. *Am. J. Obstet. Gynecol.* 123:391–97

74. Powell, W. S., Hammarstrom, S., Kylden, U., Samuelsson, B. 1976. *NATO Adv. Studies Inst. Ser. A: Life Sci.* 2:455–72

75. Ratner, A. 1970. Stimulation of LH release *in vitro* by dibutyryl cyclic-AMP and theophylline. *Life Sci.* 9:1221–26

76. Ratner, A., Wilson, M. C., Srivastava, L., Peake, G. T. 1974. Stimulatory effects of prostaglandin E_1 on rat anterior pituitary cyclic AMP and luteinizing hormone release. *Prostaglandins* 5:165–74

77. Sato, T., Jyujyo, T., Iesaka, T., Ishikawa, J., Igarashi, M. 1974. Follicle stimulating hormone and prolactin release induced by prostaglandins in rat. *Prostaglandins* 5:483–90

78. Sato, T., Taya, K., Jyujyo, T., Hirono, M., Igarashi, M. 1974. The stimulatory effect of prostaglandins on luteinizing hormone release. *Am. J. Obstet. Gynecol.* 118:875–76

79. Schofield, J. G. 1970. Prostaglandin E_1 and the release of growth hormone in vitro. *Nature* 228:179–80

80. Shemesh, M., Hansel, W. 1975. Stimulation of prostaglandin synthesis in bovine ovarian tissues by arachidonic acid and luteinizing hormone. *Biol. Reprod.* 13:448–52

81. Spies, H. G., Norman, R. L. 1973. Luteinizing hormone release and ovulation induced by the intraventricular infusion of prostaglandin E_1 into pentobarbital blocked rats. *Prostaglandins* 4:131–42

82. Strickland, S., Beers, W. H. 1976. Studies on the role of plasminogen activator in ovulation. *J. Biol. Chem.* 251:5694–702

83. Sundberg, D. K., Fawcett, C. P., Illner, P., McCann, S. M. 1975. The effect of various prostaglandins and a prostaglandin synthetase inhibitor on rat anterior pituitary cyclic AMP levels and hormone release in vitro. *Proc. Soc. Exp. Biol. Med.* 148:54–59

84. Thomas, J. P., Dorflinger, L. J., Behrman, H. R. 1978. Mechanism of the rapid antigonadotropic action of prostaglandins in cultured luteal cells. *Proc. Natl. Acad. Sci. USA* 75:1344–48

85. Thorburn, G. D., Hales, J. R. S. 1972. Selective reduction in blood flow to the ovine corpus luteum after infusion of prostaglandin $F_{2\alpha}$ into a uterine vein. *Proc. Aust. Physiol. Pharmacol. Soc.* 3:145

86. Tsafriri, A., Koch, Y., Lindner, H. R. 1973. Ovulation rate and serum LH levels in rats treated with indomethacin or prostaglandin E_2. *Prostaglandins* 3:461–67

87. Tsafriri, A., Lindner, H. R., Zor, U., Lamprecht, S. A. 1972. Physiological role of prostaglandins in the induction of ovulation. *Prostaglandins* 2:1–10

88. Yang, N. S. T., Marsh, J. M., LeMaire, W. J. 1974. Postovulatory changes in the concentrations of prostaglandins in rabbit graafian follicles. *Prostaglandins* 6:37–44

89. Zor, U., Kaneko, T., Schenider, H. P. G., McCann, S. M., Lowe, I. P., Bloom, G., Borland, B., Field, J. B. 1969. Stimulation of anterior pituitary adenyl cyclase activity and adenosine3',5'-cyclic phosphate by hypothalamic extract and prostaglandin E_1. *Proc. Natl. Acad. Sci. USA* 63:918–25

90. Zor, U., Lamprecht, S. A., Kaneko, T., Schneider, H. P. G., McCann, S. M., Field, J. B., Tsafriri, A., Lindner, H. R. 1972. Functional relations between cyclic AMP, prostaglandins, and luteinizing hormone in rat pituitary and ovary. *Adv. Cyclic Nucleotide Res.* 1:503–19

91. Zor, U., Strulovici, B., Nimrod, A., Lindner, H. R. 1977. Stimulation by cyclic nucleotides of prostaglandin E production in isolated graafian follicles. *Prostaglandins* 14:947–59

CELL AND MEMBRANE PHYSIOLOGY

Introduction

Three of the four articles in this section deal with contractility and its relation to structure in a variety of cells. They are complemented by one reviewing a novel way of studying cell metabolism—a prerequisite of motion—by a nondestructive process.

Goldman et al deal with the wide variety of filaments found in mammalian cells. In addition to filaments made up of proteins analogous to those found in the muscle cell, other filaments or fibers exist that differ in morphology from actin- and myosin-containing filaments. A number of proteins have been recognized as their constituents. The functional role of these filaments in maintaining cell structure and in cellular contractility—a fast growing field—is the main theme of the review.

Tregear & Marston cover the more conventional contractile apparatus, i.e. that found in skeletal muscle. They review current views on the mechanism by which the portion of the myosin molecule that carries the active site for the ATP hydrolysis interacts with actin. In the view of the large majority of workers in this field, myosin molecules interacting with actin form the so-called crossbridges, whose cyclic formation and breaking, coupled to ATP hydrolysis, is the basis of force generation. Tregear & Marston present an up-to-date review on the topic, together with some suggestions of their own.

While knowledge of the striated muscle system has reached a high level of development, information concerning smooth muscle has been lagging in many areas. Recent work has cleared up several uncertainties (particularly in regard to structure), has led to progress in energetics, and has brought to light some novel aspects of control. The chapter by Murphy is, therefore, a timely review of a rapidly developing field.

The relation between cell metabolism and cell function, whether that function be muscle contraction, secretion, or the generation of an electrical signal, has been recognized as a fundamental problem of biology. Classical methods of metabolic study have usually required the destruction of cells or tissue for quantitative determination of specific metabolites. Thus continuous metabolic and concomitant functional measurements have, with some exceptions, been impractical. The NMR methods reviewed by Radda & Seeley contribute an important new tool for studying specific metabolites in a nondestructive fashion. They promise important developments in bioenergetics.

John Gergely
Section Editor

Ann. Rev. Physiol. 1979. 41:703–22
Copyright © 1979 by Annual Reviews Inc. All rights reserved

CYTOPLASMIC FIBERS IN MAMMALIAN CELLS: Cytoskeletal and Contractile Elements

♦1246

Robert D. Goldman, Amy Milsted, Jeffery A. Schloss, *
Judith Starger, and Marie-Jeanne Yerna

Department of Biological Sciences, Mellon Institute of Science,
Carnegie-Mellon University, Pittsburgh, Pennsylvania 15213

Cells derived from many types of nonmuscle tissues contain three classes of cytoplasmic fibers: microfilaments, 10 nm filaments, and microtubules. Since many excellent reviews have appeared recently on the subject of microtubules (see 63, 74, 130, 142, 174, 181, 198) we have chosen to emphasize the microfilament and 10 nm filament systems. Microtubules are discussed only with regard to their possible interactions with these systems.

In order to narrow the scope of this review even further, we emphasize studies of normal mammalian cell systems and stress those investigations that relate structure to biochemical and molecular function.

MICROFILAMENTS AND THEIR ASSOCIATED PROTEINS: Actin, Myosin, Tropomyosin, α-Actinin, Actin Binding Protein, Filamin, etc.

Actin

Actin has been isolated from a variety of cells ranging from the simplest pleuropneumonia-like organisms (138) to the highly organized multi-nucleated cells of skeletal muscle (92). Proteins similar to myosin have also been isolated from a diversity of cell types. In nonmuscle cells actin is seen ultrastructurally as a class of cytoplasmic fibers known as microfilaments. Nonmuscle cell myosin is rarely seen in situ by electron microscopy, but

*Present address: Department of Biology, Yale University, New Haven, Connecticut 06520

703

0066-4278/79/0301-0703$01.00

it can be isolated as a complex with actin (actomyosin). These observations have led to the general acceptance of the idea that actomyosin complexes occur in vivo and probably function in cell motility.

For general background information on the biochemistry and localization of actin, myosin, and other related proteins in nonmuscle cells see (32, 151). Articles have appeared covering possible actomyosin functions in neurons (19), chromosome movement (56, 57), cytokinesis (166), and regulation of motility (86). For purposes of comparison with skeletal and smooth muscle, excellent reviews are available (see 80, 92, 123, 124, 185, 190).

Actin appears in several different forms as determined by both urea and two-dimensional gel electrophoretic analyses. Three major types of actin, designated α, β, and γ, have been defined in several cell systems (see 32). More recently the β and γ forms have been found in platelets (113). Differences in amino acid sequence of nonmuscle relative to muscle actin may account for the different isoelectric forms in brain, platelets, and other tissues (49, 120, 187). No functional differences have been demonstrated for the different forms of actin, but this will obviously be an area of intense study and excitement over the next few years.

Actin has been localized in plasma membrane fractions by electron microscopy and by sodium dodecyl sulfate polyacrylamide gel electrophoresis (Na-dod-SO_4-PAGE). A band of protein of ~42,000 daltons has been identified as actin in, or demonstrated capable of interacting with, membranes obtained from fibroblasts (79, 195), secretory vesicles (29, 144), platelets (184), erythrocytes (140; see also 178), synapses (10, 12), lymphocytes (6), and macrophages (43). The relationship of actin with membranes requires the consideration of several other proteins that are thought to play a role in membrane-actin interactions.

Spectrin, Actin-Binding Protein (or Filamin), and α-Actinin

Spectrin is a major protein of the erythrocyte membrane (32, 107, 178). Its molecular weight is 480,000 daltons and it consists of two different polypeptide chains of 220,000 and 240,000 daltons (104). A copolymer of actin and spectrin appears to function in maintaining red blood cell shape (122) and the distribution of intramembranous proteins (208). Spectrin-actin interactions may be regulated by phosphorylation of the 220,000-dalton subunit (149). This reaction requires ATP and precedes cell shape changes (11, 168).

A group of high molecular weight proteins distinct from spectrin includes filamin from chicken gizzard (171, 188, 189), actin-binding protein from macrophages (81), leukocytes (16), and platelets (121), and a similar protein from cultured fibroblasts (79, 192). These proteins have a subunit molecular weight greater than that of myosin heavy chain (sometimes they co-migrate with the smaller spectrin subunit), and they appear in association with actin and membranes (15, 43, 85, 188). These proteins appear to cross-link actin during a temperature-dependent gelation [see Stossel & Hartwig, Pollard et al, and Weihing in (74); see also (189)] that can be inhibited by cytochalasin B (82, 192). Contraction of this gel can occur in the presence (16, 82, 193) or in the absence (189) of myosin. Determination of the specific functions and control of these high molecular weight actin-associated proteins awaits future investigations.

α-Actinin is a major protein comprising skeletal muscle Z-lines (the sites of actin filament anchorage). Evidence for a similar protein in nonmuscle cells is based on immunocytochemical observations with antibodies directed against muscle α-actinin. It appears to be localized at points of actin attachment to membranes [Schollmeyer et al in (74)] and in association with actin-rich structures known as stress fibers in cultured cells (114). Others have suggested its presence in purified secretory vesicles (100) and in kidney microvillus membranes (14). Muscle α-actinin interacts with erythrocyte actin in a specific molar ratio and alters the interaction of actin with myosin (153). α-Actinin has been implicated in linking microfilaments within microvilli to each other and to plasma membranes (133).

Proteins similar to those regulating actin-myosin interactions in muscle have been isolated from nonmuscle cells (see 32, 86). One such protein is tropomyosin. The major difference observed is the lower molecular weight of the nonmuscle species. It has been shown to consist of two different peptide chains (consisting of a 30,000-dalton doublet in Na-dod-SO$_4$ gels) in bovine brain (22) and in baby hamster kidney (BHK-21) cells (163). Tropomyosin-like components have been localized in actin-containing stress fibers in cultured cells by immunofluorescence using muscle tropomyosin antibody (114). A search for proteins similar to skeletal muscle troponin has also been initiated. This protein complex is of particular interest because it provides a calcium sensitive on-off switch for regulating muscle contraction. Calcium sensitive actomyosin preparations, which contain the expected Na-dod-SO$_4$-gel profiles, have been isolated from mammalian nonmuscle cells. They are discussed by Hitchcock (86), who also considers the possible confusion of troponin with a calcium sensitive modulator protein (136) (see the section below on myosin regulation).

Several other polypeptides bind to actin. Profilin (16,000 daltons) coisolates with actin from calf spleen and thymus in a 1:1 complex and prevents globular (G) actin from polymerizing into fibrous (F) actin (31). Actin is capable of inhibiting deoxyribonuclease I (DNAse I) in these tissues. DNAase I binds with high affinity to F-actin, causes its depolymerization, and prevents polymerization of G-actin (87). Polymerization of actin is also affected by phalloidin, a mushroom toxin, which causes a proliferation of microfilaments in hepatocytes (reviewed in 196). Fructose diphosphate aldolase binds to muscle actin thin filaments apparently via troponin (134), and actin may be a subunit of phosphorylase kinase, an enzyme of carbohydrate metabolism (54). The significance of actin's binding to enzymes involved in various metabolic pathways (such as those involving DNAse I and phosphorylase kinase) awaits future investigations.

Actin Localization

Actin has been identified in nonmuscle cells by several methods. Microfilaments can be observed directly in the cytoplasm of many cells by electron microscopy. They resemble muscle thin filaments morphologically (4–7 nm) and can be shown to bind skeletal muscle heavy meromyosin (HMM) to form arrowhead complexes or decorated microfilaments in glycerinated cells (97). These complexes are similar to those described for muscle actin–HMM complexes (92). HMM binding has been applied to many cell and tissue types [for detailed reviews see (56, 151)]. The major drawback of this technique is that glycerination (used to permeabilize cells for HMM entry) causes deterioration of cytoplasmic structure, which may result in artifact formation. However, several laboratories have demonstrated that varying the conditions for glycerination results in the relatively normal preservation of microfilaments in situ, which subsequently can be shown to bind HMM as well as another myosin fragment, HMM S-1 [(56, 68, 164); Goldman et al in (74)].

Use of HMM as a light microscope probe was introduced by Aronson (3). He conjugated fluorescein to HMM (F-HMM) and demonstrated specific binding in myofibrils. More recently others have applied the technique to nonmuscle cells using various methods of conjugation (161) and subsequent purification (112, 164) to improve the specificity of binding of labelled myosin fragments to microfilaments in situ. Immunofluorescence employing various types of antibody directed against actin has also been used for localizations in nonmuscle tissues and cells (62, 102, 115). In cultured mouse 3T3 cells anti-actin stains stress fibers, which are coincident with the microfilament bundles resolved by electron microscopic methods (24, 73).

Two major forms of microfilament organization have been described primarily in cultured cells: (a) Well-organized bundles and sheets consisting of parallel arrays of microfilaments are found in extended cell processes; (b) networks or meshworks usually containing less well-organized arrays of microfilaments are observed in actively moving areas of the periphery, such as ruffles and blebs, nonattached cortical areas of substrate-attached cells, and throughout the cortex of suspended cells (24, 25, 68, 112, 116, 117, 126, 127, 156, 160, 175, 194, 201). The two organizational forms are apparently interconvertible, as demonstrated by a change from meshworks to bundles [Goldman et al in (74); see also (69, 72)]. The latter are seen to form rapidly upon contact with another cell or a growth substrate (17, 69, 72, 83, 84, 119).

Microfilaments have been seen in cells found in tissues and body fluids far too numerous to list [see (56) for summary]. Microfilaments have been implicated in various functions ranging from retinal pigment migration (26) to tissue morphogenesis (175). Blood platelets are one of the more extensively studied systems in which microfilaments may function directly in platelet activation (7, 137). The microvilli of the brush-border cells comprising the intestinal epithelium contain a bundle of microfilaments running from their insertion point at the tip into a terminal web at their base (132, 133, 135, 159). In this latter instance, HMM binding indicates that the arrowhead configurations have similar polarity and tend to point away from the microvillus tip. The terminal web itself also contains microfilaments and possibly a myosin-like protein. The interaction of these two microfilament systems may function in the movement of microvilli, which in turn could increase their efficiency and aid in food uptake by endocytosis.

Nonmuscle Myosin

A class of proteins with properties similar to muscle myosin has been found in many types of cells and tissues. These myosins interact with actin filaments to form a complex that is dissociated in the presence of Mg^{2+}-ATP and whose ATPase activity is stimulated by actin under physiological conditions. Other properties shared by muscle and nonmuscle myosins are: a similar native molecular weight, the ability to form synthetic thick filaments similar to those seen in situ in muscle cells, and an ATPase activity stimulated by Ca^{2+} and by K^+-EDTA.

Myosin has been isolated from platelets (150, 151, 170), leukocytes (169, 182), macrophages (81), brain (19, 28), liver (18), adrenal medulla (34, 101), thyroid gland (108), and cultured mammalian cells (4, 131, 145, 151, 206). On the basis of Na-dod-SO_4-gel densitometry and ATPase measurements, myosin has been estimated to represent 0.3–5.0% of the total cell protein in these nonmuscle systems (4, 18, 19, 28, 81, 145, 150, 206).

The physical properties of nonmuscle and smooth muscle myosins are similar. Their partition coefficient during column chromatography indicates similar native molecular weights (18, 28, 81, 150, 169). Analysis by Na-dod-SO_4-PAGE of nonmuscle myosins show three major bands: one heavy chain and two light chains (4, 18, 19, 28, 34, 81, 101, 150, 169, 170, 182, 206). The mass of the heavy chain is ~200,000 daltons based upon its coelectrophoresis with muscle myosin heavy chains (4, 18, 81, 150, 169, 206). However, a slight difference between smooth muscle and nonmuscle heavy chain mobility has been reported (28). Peptides produced by cleavage of muscle and nonmuscle myosin heavy chains at cysteine residues show that they are not identical (28). Different Na-dod-SO$_4$-PAGE patterns are obtained even among different nonmuscle myosins (28). The two light chains are similar to those of smooth muscle myosin. The molecular weights are 20,000 and 16,000 daltons (4, 18, 19, 28, 34, 81, 101, 150, 169, 170, 206). Comparison of the tryptic peptide maps of smooth muscle and nonmuscle light chains indicate that these subunits may be identical (19, 27). The molar ratios for the heavy chain and the two light chains appear to be 1:1:1 (4, 34, 81, 150, 206).

Nonmuscle myosins are similar to smooth muscle myosin in that they possess ATPase activities that in high salt are stimulated by K$^+$-EDTA and usually to a lesser extent by Ca^{2+}. The values reported for specific activities vary considerably; in general they resemble those found for smooth muscle (80) and are significantly lower that those reported in skeletal muscle (4, 18, 19, 28, 81, 101, 145, 150, 169, 206).

At low ionic strength, mammalian nonmuscle myosin molecules aggregate into synthetic bipolar thick filaments similar in shape to, but shorter than, muscle filaments formed under analogous conditions (28, 81, 108, 150, 151, 169, 206). Nonmuscle thick filaments are typically ~0.3 μm long. However, longer filaments have been reported for glial cell myosin (4). Millimolar concentrations of divalent cations affect the length (150) and state of aggregation (81) of some types of myosin filaments. If the sliding filament model used to explain skeletal muscle contraction does indeed apply to nonmuscle actomyosin systems, a minimal requirement appears to be the simultaneous presence of thin actin-containing filaments and the thicker myosin-containing filaments. However, thick filaments have not been seen in the vast majority of nonmuscle mammalian cells examined by electron microscopy. There are only a few exceptions, including the myosin-like tactoids seen in some platelets of retracted clots (see 133, 139) and in some BHK-21 cells observed by electron microscopy both in the presence (67) and absence of cytochalasin B (155). This problem has been discussed extensively (139); it appears that even if myosin filaments are present they would be very few and therefore very difficult to visualize directly.

Regulation of Actin-Myosin Interaction

In skeletal muscle, Ca^{2+} regulation is mediated through the interactions of the thin (actin) filament proteins (185, 190). In smooth muscle at least part of the regulatory system appears to involve phosphorylation of the 20,000-dalton myosin light chain by a specific kinase (76). This kinase requires Ca^{2+} and is composed of two proteins with molecular weights of 105,000 and 17,000 daltons (36). The 17,000-dalton protein appears to be identical to the Ca^{2+} binding modulator protein that has been isolated from several tissues, including brain. This protein acts as a cofactor for brain phosphodiesterase and adenylate cyclase (37). As mentioned above, it may be the same as the troponin C-like proteins reported in nonmuscle cells (136). There is some evidence that Ca^{2+} may be involved in regulating mammalian nonmuscle cell movements (99, 132); however, none of the relevant myosins or actomyosins isolated thus far has shown significant Ca^{2+} regulation. Actin activation of mammalian cell myosin ATPase at low ionic strength and in the presence of Mg^{2+} is usually very low and is not affected by Ca^{2+} (4, 18, 19, 28, 34, 81, 206). Adelstein & Conti (1) have shown that phosphorylation of the 20,000-dalton light chain of platelet myosin stimulates the low ionic strength actin activated ATPase, but there is no calcium requirement for either phosphorylation or actin activation. However, Dabrowska et al (38) have prepared a partially purified platelet kinase that promotes both phosphorylation and actin activation of myosin in the presence of Ca^{2+}. A factor that causes the actin stimulation of rabbit macrophage myosin has been described; however, Ca^{2+} is not required (183).

In cultured mouse cells an endogenous kinase appears to be present that catalyzes the phosphorylation of the 20,000-dalton light chain; however, the effect of phosphorylation on actin activation of myosin ATPase has not been described (167). Another approach to elucidating regulatory factors consists of a hybrid system containing baby hamster kidney (BHK-21) cell myosin and smooth muscle kinase (206). Under these conditions the simultaneous Ca^{2+}-sensitive phosphorylation of myosin 20,000-dalton light chains and actin activated ATPase has been reported (206). More recently it has been shown that there is an endogenous BHK-21 kinase system containing a 17,000-dalton modulator and 105,000-dalton kinase that has properties very similar to those of the smooth muscle kinase system (207). These data indicate that phosphorylation of the 20,000-dalton light chain could be involved in regulating the interactions of nonmuscle actin and myosin. Since regulation of actomyosin-linked motile phenomena in nonmuscle systems is undoubtedly very complicated, it is probable that future research will reveal several regulatory mechanisms that could be used simultaneously or sequentially during different types of cell movements.

Localization of Myosin

The localization of myosin in nonmuscle cells is essential for elucidating its possible functions in cell motility. Since myosin molecules cannot be seen directly by electron microscopy, several laboratories have attempted to localize myosin in nonmuscle systems using immunological techniques (e.g. 34, 59, 131, 146, 157, 169, 197, 206). Antibodies against smooth muscle and nonmuscle myosins do not cross-react as determined by immunodiffusion analyses (150, 197, 206). However both types of antisera generate similar or identical localization patterns in nonmuscle cells. This finding suggests that there may be similar antigenic determinants in different myosins from different cell types. In well-spread cultured cells, the fluorescence is usually found in cytoplasmic stress fibers (59, 146, 191, 206). Some laboratories have also reported the presence of myosin associated with the plasma membrane (78, 141, 146, 152, 157, 197). However, some antimyosin antibody preparations appear to react with the outer surface of the plasma membrane (78, 152, 197) while others appear bound to the cytoplasmic side of the plasma membrane (146, 157). The differences observed have been explained by suggesting either that myosin is present in different positions in different cell types or that the antibodies used by different laboratories react with different portions of the myosin molecule, some of which may penetrate from the cytoplasm to the outer surface of the plasma membrane. Since there is very little data available on the latter possibilities, the existence of myosin molecules in whole or in part on the external surface of the plasma membrane awaits further and much more extensive analysis. This is especially true if the possible artifacts inherent in the cell-fixation and permeabilization techniques used for immunocytochemical studies are taken into consideration.

Function of Actin and Myosin in Cell Motility

Although the information available on the biochemistry and localization of contractile proteins has increased significantly over the past few years, very little is known about their specific functions in nonmuscle cells. Actin, myosin, α-actinin, tropomyosin, and filamin (actin-binding protein) antibodies, as well as fluorescein-labelled HMM or HMMS-1, all demonstrate uniform or periodic staining of the stress fibers of cultured cells as determined by fluorescence microscope techniques. These stress fibers are coincident with the sub-membranous bundles of microfilaments seen by electron microscopy in the region of cell-substrate adhesion (24, 70). Such observations imply that stress fibers may contain "primitive sarcomeres" that may be involved in motile functions such as locomotion [see Goldman et al in (74); see also (73)]. In this case, they may provide the force necessary to move cells across solid substrates. Myosin antibody and HMM also bind to microfilament-enriched regions of mammalian-cell cleavage furrows and contractile rings indicating an actomyosin function in cytokinesis (59, 166). More specific information regarding the functions of actomyosin awaits the development and refinement of lysed or model cell systems that are Ca^{2+}-sensitive and respond specifically to the addition of Mg^{2+}-ATP. Some evidence is available that glycerinated models of locomoting cultured cells [Goldman et al in (74)] and cells in cytokinesis (89) can be reactivated with Mg^{2+}-ATP. However, Ca^{2+}-sensitive contractile models of mammalian cell systems have only been demonstrated in a few cases, most notably in isolated intestinal brush borders (e.g. see 132).

Actin and myosin may be present along with microtubules, in the mitotic apparatus between chromosomes and poles. Therefore actomyosin may function in motive force production for chromosome movement (reviewed in 57). A possible close relationship between spindle microtubules and HMM or HMM S-1 decorated microfilaments has been reported from electron-microscopic observations of dividing Pt K1 cells (164; see also 57). However, other investigators claim that there are no microfilaments within the mitotic apparatus [for a detailed discussion of these discrepancies see (57)]. Other evidence in favor of possible actomyosin and microtubule relationships within the mitotic apparatus of mammalian cells comes from the observations that, following immunofluorescence procedures, tubulin (61), actin (30), and myosin (59) antibodies all stain chromosome-to-pole regions of various types of cultured cells. In addition, F-HMM and F-S-1 also stain the same regions as determined by fluorescence microscopy (3, 30, 57, 161, 164). Based on these observations from several different laboratories, it appears that spindle microtubules may act as a skeletal system directing force production by actomyosin-like contractile elements. Working in concert, these systems could participate in chromosome-to-pole migration. It is also relevant to note that purified muscle F-actin and brain microtubules interact as determined by both viscometric analysis and the fact that microtubules bind to actin coupled to agarose beads (77). In addition, actin appears to co-purify with polymerizable tubulin obtained from isolated sea urchin mitotic apparatuses even following several cycles of disassembly and reassembly (105). Therefore biochemical evidence is becoming available that supports the idea that microtubules and microfilaments interact in in vitro systems.

10 nm FILAMENTS

The term 10 nm filaments refers to a class of cytoplasmic fibers intermediate in size between microtubules and microfilaments. They have been described in many types of cells, and in each system they have been given a different name. This has led to some confusion in the literature. Most information has been obtained from the nervous system, smooth muscle, epithelial tissues, and more recently from cultured cells.

Nerve Tissue

Two classes of 10 nm filaments have been described in the vertebrate nervous system. Neurofilaments are abundant running parallel to the long axis of nerve cell axons, few of which continue into dendritic processes. Glial filaments are seen in the perikaryon and processes of neuroglial astrocytes (147). They are 7.0–11.0 nm in diameter (40, 65, 147, 162) and appear tubular in cross section with a 2.5–3.5 nm light core and walls ~ 3.0 nm thick (202). Glial filaments generally appear thinner than neurofilaments (202). Lateral projections or side arms have been reported along neurofilaments (64, 147); these appear to connect to other neurofilaments, microfilaments, or microtubules (128, 147). Glial filaments rarely show such projections (202).

Neurofilaments were first obtained from the squid axon (91). These neurofilaments can be dissociated in dilute urea or guanidine-hydrochloride. Reconstitution of neurofilaments has been achieved upon removal of denaturing agents by dialysis. Enriched preparations of bovine brain neurofilaments are insoluble at low ionic strength but can be dissociated in 8 M urea or 4–6 M guanidine-HCl (47) to give rise to a major 54,000-dalton protein subunit (205) that reassembles into ∼ 10 nm filaments upon removal of guanidine-HCl (47). Antibodies against calf brain neurofilament protein do not cross-react with squid, frog, chicken, *Myxicola,* or cod nerve extracts (45). Cross-reaction is seen with human, dog, cat, owl, monkey, and rabbit nerve extracts (45). Up to three major protein subunits in the range 50,-000–212,000 daltons have been found in other mammalian neurofilament preparations (88, 95, 162). Neurofilament protein is the major protein phosphorylated in squid, *Myxicola,* and mammalian axoplasm (146a). A partial explanation for these discrepancies may lie in the anomalous behavior of neurofilament protein in Na-dod-SO$_4$ gels. Molecular weights of 50,000, 68,000, and 90,000 daltons have been obtained for a single major subunit on three different electrophoretic systems (51). The protein contains little or no carbohydrate (51) to account for the different electrophoretic mobilities. However, there is a possibility that lipid is responsible since it has been reported to be present in some neurofilament preparations (165). Other possible explanations for discrepancies in the molecular weights of major subunits may lie in sample proteolysis (39), polypeptide aggregation (8, 91), and diverse methods of preparation. In addition, a Ca^{2+}-activated protease that breaks down major subunits can be found in *Myxicola* neurofilament preparations (2, 65).

Structural information obtained from *Myxicola* neurofilament preparations indicates a coiled-coil configuration typical of the k-m-e-f class of α-helical proteins (64, 110); this agrees with early studies on glial filament bundles (5). The basic building unit appears to be an asymmetric fibrous molecule that is incorporated into four protofilaments (8, 110).

Glial fibrillary acid protein (GFA) is the presumptive subunit of glial 10 nm filaments (39, 50). This protein co-migrates with the major neurofilament protein as determined by Na-dod-SO$_4$-PAGE, has similar amino acid composition, and exhibits similar tryptic, chymotryptic, and cyanogen bromide peptide maps when compared directly with the neurofilament subunit (40, 41, 45, 205). Calf brain neurofilament antibodies cross-react with GFA (45, 205) while antisera directed against GFA do not cross-react with neurofilament protein (42).

Muscle

The presence of 10 nm filaments (morphologically similar to neurofilaments) in muscle was first recognized in embryonic skeletal muscle cells (96), although no morphological correlates have been reported in adult skeletal muscle (55). In developing and adult cardiac muscle they are found in association with intercalcated discs and appear to form transverse connections between adjacent Z bands and the outer nuclear membrane (53, 55, 154). In smooth muscle cells they occur singly or in small groups and are separated from actin and myosin filaments. They are sometimes concentrated in a juxtanuclear position and appear to constitute an integrated filamentous network with dense bodies (33, 186).

Smooth muscle 10 nm filaments are resistant to low and high salt extraction and are solubilized in 8 M urea (33, 98) or 1 M acetic acid (173) to yield a major subunit [also called skeletin (173)] in the 50,000–55,000 dalton range. These subunits have different tryptic and chymotryptic peptide maps when compared to neurofilament subunits (46). A presumptive 50,000-dalton subunit (desmin) of 10 nm filaments has been obtained from chicken skeletal and cardiac muscle and appears to exist as two isoelectric variants (98). [For more recent work, see 115a.] Filaments will reform upon removal by dialysis of 8 M urea (33) or 1 M acetic acid (173). Structural information obtained by optical diffraction analysis of negatively stained preparations indicates that the basic building unit appears to be 60 nm long and 3.5 nm in diameter (173).

Epidermis

The term tonofilament is confusing, as it has been widely applied to various sizes (3–12 nm) of cytoplasmic fibers in cells comprising the epidermal layers (94). It is possible that some of the fibers with smaller dimensions represent actin-like microfilaments, but this awaits further investigation. We shall use the term tonofilament for those fibers in the larger ($\sim$ 10 nm) size range.

Cells of the basal layer (stratum basale) eventually form the outer, dead layer of epidermis (stratum corneum) by a process called keratinization (20, 60). Tonofilaments (also termed keratin filaments) increase in number during this process and become compacted to form bundles (termed tonofibrils) that appear to loop within and around desmosomes to form an intracellular network (106, 125).

Tonofilaments resist solubilization at neutral pH but are soluble at $\sim$ pH 2.5 (125) or in 8 M urea (35, 180) and give rise to as many as seven different low sulfur–containing α-helical polypeptides (180). These vary in molecular weight from 47,000 (180) to 68,000 daltons (35). Until recently there has been no direct evidence that these proteins are derived from tonofilaments since filamentous structures have not been isolated intact. However it is now known that filaments with the same structure as tonofilaments seen in situ (keratin filaments) can be assembled in dilute salt solutions with combinations of two or three of the seven polypeptides (179, 180).

Cultured Cells

An abundance of 10 nm filaments in various types of cultured cells is well documented (13, 21, 69, 70, 90, 97). Arrays of 8–10 nm filaments radiate from "synthesis and organizing centers" and terminate in desmosomes in Pt K1 cells (21). 10 nm filaments encircle the nucleus in guinea pig vascular endothelial cells (13) and form circles and coils in mouse neuroblastoma cells (103, 176). In BHK-21 cells, 10 nm filaments are dispersed singly or in small groups throughout the cytoplasm and are frequently found in association with microtubules (72). During the early stages of BHK-21 cell spreading, 10 nm filaments are found aggregated in a juxtanuclear position and are redistributed as the cells flatten and take on fibroblastic shapes (71). Similar juxtanuclear aggregates can be induced to form in the presence of agents (e.g. colchicine) that cause microtubule breakdown (13, 66, 90, 158).

Juxtanuclear accumulations of 10 nm filaments have been isolated and purified from BHK-21 cells and the major proteins are resolved as a 54,000 and 55,000-dalton doublet by Na-dod-SO$_4$-PAGE (176, 177). BHK-21 filaments are partially solubilized in low ionic strength solutions [similar to the properties of *Myxicola* neurofilaments (2)] and will reassemble upon addition of salt at physiological concentrations (176). X-ray data recently obtained from BHK-21 10 nm filaments indicate a structure very similar to keratin filaments and *Myxicola* neurofilaments (180a). Other approaches have involved analysis of cellular remains after detergent extraction (23, 93, 143), and identification of the target antigen of rabbit autoimmune sera as 10 nm filament protein in cultured cells (75). Despite the use of widely different approaches for determining 10 nm filament-related proteins in cultured cell systems, the reported subunit molecular weights are remarkably similar and reside in the narrow range between 52,000 (23) and 58,000 daltons (93, 143). This indicates that homogeneous populations of cultured cells may be ideal for biochemical characterization of 10 nm filaments.

Filamentous Proliferation

Accumulations of 10 nm filaments occur in a wide variety of abnormal cells as a reflection of a diseased or injured state. Neurofilaments appear to proliferate in response to numerous neurotoxins and neurological diseases (see 109, 200, 203). Abnormal accumulations are also seen in a hereditary disease of mucous membranes (58) and as Mallory bodies in the livers of alcoholics (172). The functional significance of 10 nm filament accumulation and proliferation remains to be determined.

10 nm Filaments and Microtubules

The apparent increases in the numbers of 10 nm filaments following microtubule breakdown has led some investigators to suggest the interconversion of microtubules and 10 nm filaments (129, 148, 199, 200). Others have considered a direct interconversion unlikely (48, 63, 66, 204). There is some biochemical and immunological evidence for tubulin–10 nm filament protein homology (95, 118); however, in these instances cross-contamination of protein preparations may have occurred (9). Other recent data indicate that the two proteins differ by various criteria including their immunological properties [(103, 111, 176, 205); see Shelanski et al in (74)], peptide maps [(176, 205); see Shelanski et al in (74)], and amino acid composition (47, 176).

Functions of 10 nm Filaments

The most widely discussed role for 10 nm filaments in mammalian cells is that of a cytoskeletal system involved in maintaining shape and intracellular support (21, 33, 53, 88, 106). They also appear to function along with microtubules in axonal transport (44, 88), distribution of pigment granules within melanocytes (129), organelle movements in cultured BHK-21 cells (66, 72), and cell locomotion (52, 66, 69).

Literature Cited

1. Adelstein, R. S., Conti, M. A. 1975. Phosphorylation of platelet myosin increases actin-activated myosin ATPase. *Nature* 256:597–98
2. Anderton, B. H., Bell, C. W., Newby, B. J., Gilbert, D. S. 1976. Neurofilaments. *Biochem. Soc. Trans.* 4:544–48
3. Aronson, J. F. 1965. The use of fluorescein-labeled heavy meromyosin for the cytological demonstration of actin. *J. Cell Biol.* 26:293–98
4. Ash, J. F. 1975. Purification and characterization of myosin from the clonal rat glial cell strain C-6. *J. Biol. Chem.* 250:3560–66
5. Bairati, A. 1958. Fibrillar structure of astrocytes. In *Biology of Neuroglia,* ed. W. F. Windle, pp. 66–72. Springfield, Ill: C. C. Thomas
6. Barber, B. H., Crumpton, M. J. 1976. Actin associated with purified lymphocyte plasma membrane. *FEBS Lett.* 66:215–20
7. Behnke, O., Kristensen, B. I., Nielsen, L. E. 1971. Electron microscopical observations on actinoid and myosinoid filaments in blood platelets. *J. Ultrastruct. Res.* 37:351–69

8. Bell, C. W. 1977. Hydrodynamic properties of neurofilaments. *J. Physiol. London* 266:83–84
9. Berkowitz, S., Katagim, J., Binder, H., Williams, R. 1977. Separation and characterization of microtubule proteins from calf brain. *Biochemistry* 16:5610–17
10. Berl, S., Puszkin, S., Nicklas, W. 1973. Actomyosin-like protein in brain. Actomyosin-like protein may function in the release of transmitter material at synaptic endings. *Science* 179:441–46
11. Birchmeier, W., Singer, S. J. 1977. On the mechanism of ATP-induced shape changes in human erythrocyte membranes. II. The role of ATP. *J. Cell Biol.* 73:647–59
12. Blitz, A. L., Fine, R. E. 1974. Muscle-like contractile proteins and tubulin in synaptosomes. *PNAS* 71:4472–76
13. Blose, S. H., Chacko, S. 1976. Rings of intermediate (100 Å) filament bundles in the perinuclear region of vascular endothelial cells. *J. Cell Biol.* 70:459–66
14. Booth, A. G., Kenny, A. J. 1976. Proteins of the kidney microvillus membrane. Identification of subunits after sodium dodecyl sulfate polyacrylamide

gel electrophoresis. *Biochem. J.* 159:
395–407

15. Boxer, L. A., Richardson, S., Floyd, A.
1976. Identification of actin-binding
protein in membrane of polymorphonuclear leukocytes. *Nature* 263:249–51

16. Boxer, L. A., Stossel, T. P. 1976. Interactions of actin, myosin, and an actin-binding protein of chronic myeloge-
nous leukemia leukocytes. *J. Clin. Invest.* 57:964–76

17. Bragina, E. E., Vasiliev, Ju. M., Gel-
fand, I. M. 1976. Formation of bundles
of microfilaments during spreading of
fibroblasts on the substrate. *Exp. Cell
Res.* 97:241–48

18. Brandon, D. L. 1976. The identification
of myosin in rabbit hepatocytes. *Eur. J.
Biochem.* 65:139–46

19. Bray, D. 1977. Actin and myosin in
neurons: a first review. *Biochimie* 59:
1–6

20. Breathnach, A. S. 1975. Aspects of epidermal ultrastructure. *J. Invest. Dermatol.* 65:2–15

21. Brecher, S. 1975. The occurrence and
possible role of 80–100 Å filaments in Pt
K1 cells. *Exp. Cell Res.* 96:303–10

22. Bretscher, A., Weber, K. 1978.
Tropomyosin from bovine brain contains two polypeptide chains of slightly
different molecular weights. *FEBS Lett.*
85:145–48

23. Brown, S., Levinson, W., Spudich, J.
1976. Cytoskeletal elements of chick
embryo fibroblasts revealed by detergent extraction. *J. Supramol. Struct.*
5:119–30

24. Buckley, I. K., Porter, K. R. 1967.
Cytoplasmic fibrils in living cultured
cells. A light and electron microscope
study. *Protoplasma* 64:349–80

25. Buckley, I. K., Raju, T. R. 1976. Form
and distribution of actin and myosin in
non-muscle cells: A study using cultured chick embryo fibroblasts. *J. Microsc.* 107:129–49

26. Burnside, M. B. 1976. Possible roles of
microtubules and actin filaments in retinal pigmented epithelium. *Exp. Eye
Res.* 23:257–75

27. Burridge, K. 1974. A comparison of
fibroblast and smooth muscle myosins.
FEBS Lett. 45:14–17

28. Burridge, K., Bray, D. 1975. Purification and structural analysis of myosins
from brain and other non-muscle tissues. *J. Mol. Biol.* 99:1–14

29. Burridge, K., Phillips, J. 1975. Association of actin and myosin with secretory
granule membranes. *Nature* 254:
526–29

30. Cande, W. Z., Lazarides, E., McIntosh,
J. R. 1977. A comparison of the distribution of actin and tubulin in the mammalian mitotic spindle as seen by indirect immunofluorescence. *J. Cell Biol.*
72:552–67

31. Carlsson, L., Nyström, L.-E., Sundk-
vist, I., Markey, F., Lindberg, U. 1977.
Actin polymerizability is influenced by
profilin, a low molecular weight protein
in non-muscle cells. *J. Mol. Biol.*
115:465–83

32. Clarke, M., Spudich, J. A. 1977. Nonmuscle contractile proteins: The role of
actin and myosin in cell motility and
shape determination. *Ann. Rev. Biochem.* 46:797–822

33. Cooke, P. 1976. A filamentous cytoskeleton in vertebrate smooth muscle
fibers. *J. Cell Biol.* 68:539–56

34. Creutz, C. E. 1977. Isolation, characterization and localization of bovine adrenal medullary myosin. *Cell Tiss. Res.*
178:17–38

35. Culbertson, V., Freedberg, I. 1977.
Mammalian epidermal keratin isolation
and characterization of the α-helical
proteins from newborn rat. *Biochim.
Biophys. Acta* 490:178–91

36. Dabrowska, R., Aromatorio, D.,
Sherry, J., Hartshorne, D. J. 1977.
Composition of the myosin light chain
kinase from chicken gizzard. *Biochem.
Biophys. Res. Commun.* 78:1263–72

37. Dabrowska, R., Sherry, J., Aromatorio,
D., Hartshorne, D. 1978. Modulator
protein as a component of the myosin
light chain kinase from chicken gizzard.
Biochemistry 17:253–58

38. Dabrowska, R., Sherry, J., Hartshorne,
D. 1978. Phosphorylation of myosin: A
possible regulatory mechanism in
smooth muscle. In *Motility in Cell Formation.* New York: Academic. In press

39. Dahl, D. 1976. Glial fibrillary acidic
protein from bovine and rat brain degradation in tissues and homogenates.
Biochim. Biophys. Acta 420:142–54

40. Dahl, D. 1976. Isolation and initial
characterization of glial fibrillary acidic
protein from chicken, turtle, frog, and
fish central nervous systems. *Biochim.
Biophys. Acta* 446:41–50

41. Dahl, D., Bignami, A. 1976. Isolation
from peripheral nerve of a protein similar to the glial fibrillary acidic protein.
FEBS Lett. 66:281–84

42. Dahl, D., Bignami, A. 1976. Immuno-
genic properties of the glial fibrillary
acidic protein. *Brain Res.* 116:150–57

43. Davies, W. A., Stossel, T. P. 1977. Pe-

ripheral hyaline blebs (podosomes) of macrophages. *J. Cell Biol.* 75:941–55

44. Davison, P. 1975. Neuronal fibrillar proteins and axoplasmic transport. *Brain Res.* 100:73–80
45. Davison, P. F., Hong, B. S. 1977. Structural homologies in mammalian neurofilament proteins. *Brain Res.* 134:287–95
46. Davison, P. F., Hong, B. S., Cooke, P. 1977. Classes of distinguishable 10 nm cytoplasmic filaments. *Exp. Cell Res.* 109:471–74
47. Davison, P. F., Winslow, B. 1974. The protein subunit of calf brain neurofilament. *J. Neurobiol.* 5:119–33
48. DeBrabander, J., Aerts, F., Van de Veire, R., Borgers, M. 1975. Evidence against interconversion of microtubules and filaments. *Nature* 253:119–20
49. Elzinga, M., Maron, B., Adelstein, R. 1976. Human heart and platelet actins are products of different genes. *Science* 191:94–95
50. Eng, L. F., Vandenhaeghen, J. J., Bignami, A., Gerstl, B. 1971. An acidic protein isolated from fibrous astrocytes. *Brain Res.* 28:351–54
51. Feit, H., Neudeck, U., Shay, J. 1977. Anomalous electrophoretic properties of brain filament protein subunits. *Brain Res.* 133:341–49
52. Felix, H., Sträuli, P. 1976. Different distribution pattern of 100 Å filaments in resting and locomotive leukaemia cells. *Nature* 261:604–6
53. Ferrans, V., Roberts, W. 1973. Intermyofibrillar and nuclear-myofibrillar connections in human and canine myocardium; an ultrastructural study. *J. Mol. Cell Cardiol.* 5:247–57
54. Fischer, E. H., Becker, J.-U., Blum, H. E., Lehky, P. Malencik, D. A., Pocinwong, S. 1975. Concerted regulation of carbohydrate metabolism and muscle contraction. *Hoppes-Seyler's. Z. Physiol. Chem.* 356:381
55. Fischman, D. 1970. The synthesis and assembly of myofibrils in embryonic muscle. *Curr. Top. Dev. Biol.* 5:235–80
56. Forer, A. 1978. Electron microscopy of actin. In *Principles and Techniques of Electron Microscopy,* ed. M. A. Hayat. New York: Van Nostrand. In press
57. Forer, A. 1978. Chromosome movements during cell division: possible involvement of actin filaments. In *Mitosis in Fungi,* ed. I. B. Heath. New York: Academic
58. Frithiof, L., Banoczy, J. 1976. White sponge nevus (leukoedema exfoliativum

mucosae oris): ultrastructural observations. *Oral Surg.* 41:607–22
59. Fujiwara, K., Pollard, T. D. 1976. Fluorescent antibody localization of myosin in the cytoplasm, cleavage furrow, and mitotic spindle of human cells. *J. Cell Biol.* 71:848–75
60. Fukuyama, K., Inoue, N., Suzuki, H., Epstein, W. 1976. Keratinization. *Int. J. Dermatol.* 15:473–89
61. Fuller, G. M., Brinkley, B. R., Boughton, J. M. 1975. Immunofluorescence of mitotic spindles by using monospecific antibody against bovine brain tubulin. *Science* 187:948–50
62. Gabbiani, G., Ryan, G., Lamelin, J., Vassalli, P., Majno, G., Cruchaud, A., Lüscher, E. 1973. Human smooth muscle antibody. Its identification as antiactin antibody and a study of its binding to non-muscle cells. *Am. J. Pathol.* 72:473–89
63. Gaskin, F., Shelanski, M. L. 1976. Microtubules and intermediate filaments. *Essays Biochem.* 12:115–46
64. Gilbert, D. S. 1975. Axoplasm architecture and physical properties as seen in the *Myxicola* giant axon. *J. Physiol. London* 253:257–301
65. Gilbert, D., Newby, B., Anderton, B. 1975. Neurofilament disguise, destruction and discipline. *Nature* 256:586–89
66. Goldman, R. D. 1971. The role of three cytoplasmic fibers in BHK-21 cell motility. I. Microtubules and the effects of colchicine. *J. Cell Biol.* 51:752–62
67. Goldman, R. D. 1972. The effects of cytochalasin B on the microfilaments of baby hamster kidney (BHK-21) cells. *J. Cell Biol.* 52:246–54
68. Goldman, R. D. 1975. The use of heavy meromyosin binding as an ultrastructural cytochemical method for localizing and determining the possible functions of actin-like microfilaments in non-muscle cells. *J. Histochem. Cytochem.* 23:529–42
69. Goldman, R. D., Berg, G., Bushnell, A., Chang, C.-M., Dickerman, L., Hopkins, N., Miller, M. L., Pollack, R., Wang, E. 1973. Fibrillar systems in cell motility. *Ciba Found. Symp.* 14 (NS):83–102
70. Goldman, R. D., Follett, E. A. C. 1969. The structure of the major cell processes of isolated BHK-21 fibroblasts. *Exp. Cell Res.* 57:263–76
71. Goldman, R. D., Follett, E. A. C. 1970. Birefringent filamentous organelle in BHK-21 cells and its possible role in cell spreading and motility. *Science* 169:286–88

72. Goldman, R. D., Knipe, D. M. 1972. Functions of cytoplasmic fibers in non-muscle cell motility. *Cold Spring Harbor Symp. Quant. Biol.* 37:523–34
73. Goldman, R. D., Lazarides, E., Pollack, R., Weber, K. 1975. The distribution of actin in non-muscle cells. *Exp. Cell Res.* 90:333–44
74. Goldman, R. D., Pollard, T., Rosenbaum, J., eds. 1976. *Cell Motility.* Cold Spring Harbor, New York: Cold Spring Harbor Laboratory
75. Gordon, W., Bushnell, A., Burridge, K. 1978. Characterization of the intermediate (10 nm) filaments of cultured cells using an auto-immune rabbit antiserum. *Cell* 13:249–61
76. Gorecka, A., Aksoy, M. O., Hartshorne, D. J. 1976. The effect of phosphorylation of gizzard myosin on actin activation. *Biochem. Biophys. Res. Commun.* 71:325–31
77. Griffith, L., Pollard, T. 1978. Quantitative analysis of the interaction of microtubules with actin and with each other. *Biophys. J.* 21:23a
78. Gröschel-Stewart, U., Jones, B. M., Kemp, R. B. 1970. Detection of actomyosin-type protein at the surface of dissociated embryonic chick cells. *Nature* 227:280
79. Gruenstein, E., Rich, A., Weihing, R. R. 1975. Actin associated with membranes from 3T3 mouse fibroblast and HeLa cells. *J. Cell Biol.* 64:223–34
80. Hartshorne, D., Gorecka, A. The biochemistry of the contractile smooth muscle. In *Handbook of Physiology on Circulation.* In press
81. Hartwig, J. H., Stossel, T. P. 1975. Isolation and properties of actin, myosin, and a new actin-binding protein in rabbit alveolar macrophages. *J. Biol. Chem.* 250:5696–705
82. Hartwig, J. H., Stossel, T. P. 1976. Interactions of actin, myosin and an actin-binding protein of rabbit pulmonary macrophage. III. Effects of cytochalasin B. *J. Cell Biol.* 71:295–303
83. Heath, J. P., Dunn, G. A. 1978. Cell to substratum contacts of chicken fibroblasts and their relation to the microfilament system. A correlated interference-reflexion and high-voltage electron microscope study. *J. Cell Sci.* 29:197–212
84. Heaysman, J. E. M., Pegrum, S. M. 1973. Early contacts between fibroblasts. *Exp. Cell Res.* 78:71–78
85. Heggeness, M. H., Wang, K., Singer, S. J. 1977. Intracellular distributions of mechano-chemical proteins in cultured fibroblasts. *Proc. Natl. Acad. Sci. USA* 74:3883–3887
86. Hitchcock, S. E. 1977. Regulation of motility in non muscle cells. *J. Cell Biol.* 74:1–15
87. Hitchcock, S. E., Carlsson, L., Lindberg, U. 1976. Depolymerization of F-actin by deoxyribonuclease I. *Cell* 7:531–42
88. Hoffman, P., Lasek, R. 1975. The slow component of axonal transport: Identification of major structural polypeptides of the axon and their generality among mammalian neurons. *J. Cell Biol.* 66:351–66
89. Hoffmann-Berling, H. 1957. Die glycerin-in-wasserextrahierte Telophasezelle als Modell der Zytokinese. *Biochem. Biophys. Acta* 15:332–39
90. Holtzer, H., Croop, J., Dienstman, S., Ishikawa, H., Somlyo, A. P. 1975. Effects of cytochalasin B and colcemid on myogenic cultures. *Proc. Natl. Acad. Sci. USA* 72:513–17
91. Huneeus, F., Davison, P. 1970. Fibrillar proteins from squid axons. I. Neurofilament protein. *J. Mol. Biol.* 52:415–28
92. Huxley, H. E. 1972. Molecular basis of contraction in cross-striated muscle. In *The Structure and Function of Muscle,* ed. Bourne, G. H., pp. 302–87. New York: Academic. 2nd ed.
93. Hynes, R., Destree, A. 1978. 10 nm filaments in normal and transformed cells. *Cell* 13:151–63
94. Inoué, S., Dionne, G. 1977. Tonofilaments in normal human bronchial epithelium and in squamous cell carcinoma. *Am. J. Pathol.* 88:345–54
95. Iqbal, K., Grundke-Iqbal, I., Wisniewski, H., Terry, R. 1977. On neurofilament and neurotubule proteins from human autopsy tissue. *J. Neurochem.* 29:417–24
96. Ishikawa, H., Bischoff, R., Holtzer, H. 1968. Mitosis and intermediate-sized filaments in developing skeletal muscle. *J. Cell Biol.* 38:538–55
97. Ishikawa, H., Bischoff, R., Holtzer, H. 1969. Formation of arrowhead complexes with heavy meromyosin in a variety of cell types. *J. Cell Biol.* 43:312–28
98. Izant, J. G., Lazarides, E. 1977. Invariance and heterogeneity in the major structural and regulatory proteins of chick muscle cells revealed by two-dimensional gel electrophoresis. *Proc. Natl. Acad. Sci. USA* 74:1450–54
99. Izzard, C. S., Izzard, S. L. 1975. Calcium regulation of the contractile state of isolated mammalian fibroblast cytoplasm. *J. Cell Sci.* 18:241–56

100. Jockush, B. M., Burger, M. M., Da-Prada, M., Richards, J. G., Chaponnier, C., Gabbiani, G. 1977. α-Actinin attached to membranes of secretory vesicles. *Nature* 270:628-29

101. Johnson, D. H., McCubbin, W. D., Kay, C. M. 1977. Isolation and characterization of a myosin-like protein from bovine adrenal medulla. *FEBS Lett.* 77:69-74

102. Johnson, G., Holborow, E., Glynn, L. 1965. Antibody to smooth muscle in patients with liver disease. *Lancet* 2:878-79

103. Jorgensen, A., Subrahamanyan, L., Turnbull, C., Kalnins, V. I. 1976. Localization of the neurofilament protein in neuroblastoma cells by immunofluorescent staining. *Proc. Natl. Acad. Sci. USA* 73:3192-3196.

104. Kam, Z., Josephs, R., Eisenberg, H., Gratzer, W. B. 1977. Structural study of spectrin from human erythrocyte membranes. *Biochemistry* 16:5568-72

105. Keller, T., Rebhun, L. Personal communication.

106. Kelly, D. 1966. Fine structure of desmosomes, hemidesmosomes, and an adepidermal globular layer in developing newt epidermis. *J. Cell Biol.* 28:51-72

107. Kirkpatrick, F. H. 1976. Spectrin: current understanding of its physical, biochemical, and functional properties. *Life Sci.* 19:1-18

108. Kobayashi, R., Goldman, R. D., Hartshorne, D. J., Field, J. B. 1977. Purification and characterization of myosin from bovine thyroid. *J. Biol. Chem.* 252:8285-91

109. Koch, T., Schultz, P., Williams, R., Lampert, P. 1977. Giant axonal neuropathy. A childhood disorder of microfilaments. *Ann. Neurol.* 1:438-51

110. Krishnan, N., Lasek, R. 1975. The fine structure of neurofilaments in the giant axon of *Myxicola infundibulus*. *J. Cell Biol.* 67:226a

111. Kurki, P., Linder, E., Virtanen, I., Stenman, S. 1977. Human smooth muscle autoantibodies reacting with intermediate (100 Å) filaments. *Nature* 268:240-41

112. Kuzmarski, E. R., Rosenbaum, J. L. 1978. Studies on the organization and localization of actin and myosin in neurons. *J. Cell Biol.* In press

113. Landon, F., Huc, C., Thomé, F., Oriol, C., Olomucki, A. 1977. Human platelet actin. Evidence of β and λ forms and similarity of properties with sarcomeric actin. *Eur. J. Biochem.* 81:571-77

114. Lazarides, E. 1975. Immunofluorescence studies on the structure of actin filaments in tissue culture cells. *J. Histochem. Cytochem.* 23:507-28

115. Lazarides, E., Weber, K. 1974. Actin antibody: The specific visualization of actin filaments in non-muscle cells. *Proc. Natl. Acad. Sci. USA* 71:2268-72

115a. Lazarides, E., Balzer, D. 1978. Specificity of desmin to avian and mammalian muscle cells. *Cell* 14:429-38

116. LeBeux, Y. J., Willemot, J. 1975. An ultrastructural study of the microfilaments in rat brain by means of heavy meromyosin labeling. I. The perikaryon, the dendrites, and the axon. *Cell Tiss. Res.* 160:1-36

117. LeBeux, Y. J., Willemot, J. 1975. An ultrastructural study of the microfilaments in rat brain by means of E-PTA staining and heavy meromyosin labeling. II. The synapses. *Cell Tiss. Res.* 160:37-68

118. Liem, R. K., Yen, S. H., Loria, C. J., Shelanski, M. L. 1977. Immunological and biochemical comparison of tubulin and intermediate brain filament protein. *Brain Res.* 132:167-71

119. Lonchampt, M. O., Laurent, M., Courtois, Y., Trenchev, P., Hughes, R. C. 1976. Microtubules and microfilaments of bovine lens epithelial cells: electron microscopy and immunofluorescence staining with specific antibodies. *Exp. Eye Res.* 23:505-18

120. Lu, R. C., Elzinga, M. 1977. Partial amino acid sequence of brain actin and its homology with muscle actin. *Biochemistry* 16:5801-6

121. Lucas, R. C., Gallagher, M., Stracher, A. 1976. Actin and actin-binding protein in platelets. In *Contractile Systems in Non-Muscle Tissues*, ed. S. V. Perry, A. Margreth, R. S. Adelstein, pp. 133-39. Amsterdam: Elsevier/North Holland

122. Lux, S. E., John, K. M., Karnovsky, M. J. 1976. Irreversible deformation of the spectrin-actin lattice in irreversibly sickled cells. *J. Clin. Invest.* 58:955-63

123. Mannherz, H. G., Goody, R. S. 1976. Proteins of contractile systems. *Ann. Rev. Biochem.* 45:427-65

124. Maruyama, K. 1976. Actinins, regulatory proteins of muscle. *Adv. Biochem.* 9:157-85

125. Matoltsy, A. 1975. Desmosomes, filaments, and keratohyaline granules: Their role in the stabilization and keratinization of the epidermis. *J. Invest. Dermatol.* 65:127-42

126. McNutt, N. S., Culp, L. A., Black, P. H. 1971. Contact-inhibited revertant cell lines isolated from SV40-transformed cells. *J. Cell Biol.* 50:691–708

127. McNutt, N. S., Culp, L. A., Black, P. H. 1973. Contact-inhibited revertant cell lines isolated from SV40-transformed cells. IV. Microfilament distribution and cell shape in untransformed, transformed, and revertant Balb/c 3T3cells. *J. Cell Biol.* 56:412–28

128. Metuzals, J., Mushynski, W. 1974. Electron microscope and experimental investigations of the neurofilamentous network in Dieter's neurons. Relationship with the cell surface and nuclear pores. *J. Cell Biol.* 61:701–22

129. Moellman, G., McGuire, J. 1975. Correlation of cytoplasmic microtubules and 10 nm filaments with the movement of pigment granules in cutaneous melanocytes of *Rana pipiens. Ann. N.Y. Acad. Sci.* 253:711–22

130. Mohri, H. 1976. The function of tubulin in motile systems. *Biochim. Biophys. Acta* 456:85–127

131. Moore, A., Joffe, E. A., Becker, C. G., Nachman, R. L. 1977. Myosin in cultured human endothelial cells. *Br. J. Haematol.* 35:71–79

132. Mooseker, M. S. 1976. Brush border motility. Microvillar contraction in triton-treated borders isolated from intestinal epithelium. *J. Cell Biol.* 71:417–33

133. Mooseker, M. S., Tilney, L. G. 1975. Organization of an actin filament–membrane complex. Filament polarity and membrane attachment in the microvilli of intestinal epithelial cells. *J. Cell Biol.* 67:725–43

134. Morton, D. J., Clarke, F. M., Masters, C. J. 1977. An electron microscope study of the interaction between fructose diphosphate aldolase and actin-containing filaments. *J. Cell Biol.* 74:1016–23

135. Mukherjee, T. M., Staehelin, L. A. 1971. The fine-structural organization of the brush border of intestinal epithelial cells. *J. Cell Sci.* 8:573–99

136. Muszbek, L., Kuznicki, J., Szabo, T., Drabikowski, W. 1977. Troponin C-like protein of blood platelets. *FEBS Lett.* 80:308–12

137. Nachmias, V., Sullender, J., Asch, A. 1977. Shape and cytoplasmic filaments in control and lidocaine-treated human platelets. *Blood* 50:39–53

138. Neimark, H. C. 1977. Extraction of an actin-like protein from the prokaryote *Mycoplasma pneumoniae. Proc. Natl. Acad. Sci. USA* 74:4041–45

139. Niederman, R., Pollard, T. D. 1975. Human platelet myosin. II. *In vitro* assembly and structure of myosin filaments. *J. Cell Biol.* 67:72–92

140. Ohnishi, T. 1977. Isolation and characterization of an actin-like protein from membranes of human red cells. *Br. J. Haematol.* 35:453–58

141. Olden, K., Willingham, M., Pastan, I. 1976. Cell surface myosin in cultured fibroblasts. *Cell* 8:383–90

142. Olmsted, J. B., Borisy, G. G. 1973. Microtubules. *Ann. Rev. Biochem.* 42:507–40

143. Osborn, M., Weber, K. 1977. The detergent-resistant cytoskeleton of tissue culture cells includes the nucleus and the microfilament bundles. *Exp. Cell Res.* 106:339–349

144. Ostlund, R. E., Leung, J. T., Kipnis, D. M. 1977. Muscle actin filaments bind pituitary secretory granules *in vitro. J. Cell Biol.* 73:78–87

145. Ostlund, R. E., Pastan, I. 1976. The purification and quantitation of myosin from cultured cells. *Biochim. Biophys. Acta* 453:37–47

146. Painter, R. G., Sheetz, M., Singer, S. J. 1975. Detection and ultrastructural localization of human smooth muscle myosin-like molecules in human non-muscle cells by specific antibodies. *Proc. Natl. Acad. Sci. USA* 72:1359–63

146a. Pant, H., Schecket, G., Gainer, H., Lasek, R. 1978. Neurofilament protein is phosphorylated in the giant axon. *J. Cell Biol.* 78:R23–27

147. Peters, A., Palay, S., Webster, H. 1970. *The Fine Structure of the Nervous System: The Cells and Their Processes.* New York/Evanston/London: Harper and Row. p. 198

148. Peters, A., Vaughn, J. 1967. Microtubules and filaments in the axons and astrocytes of early post-natal rat optic nerves. *J. Cell Biol.* 32:113–19

149. Pinder, J. C., Bray, D., Gratzer, W. B. 1977. Control of interaction of spectrin and actin by phosphorylation. *Nature* 270:752–54

150. Pollard, T. D., Thomas, S. M., Niederman, R. 1974. Human platelet myosin. I. Purification by a rapid method applicable to other non-muscle cells. *Anal. Biochem.* 60:258–66

151. Pollard, T. D., Weihing, R. R. 1974. Actin and myosin in cell movement. *Crit. Rev. Biochem.* 2:1–65

152. Puszkin, E. G., Maldonado, R., Spaet, T. H., Zucker, M. B. 1977. Platelet myosin localization of the rod myosin fragment and effect of its antibodies on

platelet function. *J. Biol. Chem.* 252:
4371–78

153. Puszkin, S., Puszkin, E., Maimon, J.,
Rouault, C., Schook, W., Ores, C.,
Kochwa, S., Rosenfield, R. 1977. α-
Actinin and tropomyosin interactions
with a hybrid complex of erythrocyte-
actin and muscle-myosin. *J. Biol. Chem.*
252:5529–37

154. Rash, J., Biesele, J., Gey, G. 1970.
Three classes of filaments in cardiac
differentiation. *J. Ultrastruct. Res.* 33:
408–35

155. Rash, J. E., McDonald, T. F., Sachs, H.
G., Ebert, J. D. 1972. Muscle-like ar-
rays in a fibroblast line. *Nature New
Biol.* 237:160

156. Reaven, E. P., Axline, S. G. 1973. Sub-
plasmalemmal microfilaments and microtubules in resting and phagocytizing
cultivated macrophages. *J. Cell Biol.*
59:12–27

157. Rihihisa, Y., Mizuno, D. 1977. Demonstration of myosin on the cytoplasmic
side of plasma membranes of guinea pig
polymorphonuclear leucocytes with immunoferritin. *Exp. Cell Res.* 110:87–92

158. Robbins, E., Gonatas, N. 1967. Histochemical and ultrastructural studies on
HeLa cell cultures exposed to spindle
inhibitors with special reference to the
interphase cell. *J. Histochem. Cytochem.* 12:704–11

159. Rodeward, R., Newman, S. B., Karnovsky, M. J. 1976. Contraction of isolated brush borders from intestinal epithelium. *J. Cell Biol.* 70:541–54

160. Ross, J., Olmsted, J. B., Rosenbaum, J.
L. 1975. The ultrastructure of mouse
neuroblastoma cells in tissue culture.
Tissue & Cell 7:107–36

161. Sanger, J. W. 1975. Intracellular localization of actin with fluorescently labelled heavy meromyosin. *Cell Tiss.
Res.* 161:431–44

162. Schlaepfer, W. 1977. Immunological
and ultrastructural studies of neurofilaments isolated from rat peripheral
nerve. *J. Cell Biol.* 74:226–40

163. Schloss, J., Goldman, R. Unpublished
observations.

164. Schloss, J. A., Milsted, A., Goldman,
R. D. 1977. Myosin subfragment binding for the localization of actin-like microfilaments in cultured cells. *J. Cell
Biol.* 74:794–815

165. Schook, W., Norton, W. 1976. Neurofilaments account for the lipid in myelin-
free axons. *Brain Res.* 118:517–22

166. Schroeder, T. E. 1975. Dynamics of the
contractile ring. In *Molecules and Cell

Movement,* ed. S. Inoué, R. E. Stephens,
pp. 305–32. New York: Raven Press

167. Scordilis, S. P., Anderson, J. L., Pollack, R., Adelstein, R. S. 1977. Characterization of the myosin-phosphorylat-
ing system in normal murine astrocytes
and derivative SV40 wild-type and A-
mutant transformants. *J. Cell Biol.*
74:940–49

168. Sheetz, M. P., Singer, S. J. 1977. On the
mechanism of ATP-induced shape
change in human erythrocyte membranes. I. The role of spectrin. *J. Cell
Biol.* 73:638–46

169. Shibata, N., Tatsumi, N., Tanaka, K.,
Okamura, Y., Senda, N. 1975. Leuco-
cyte myosin and its location in the cell.
Biochim. Biophys. Acta 400:222–43

170. Shimizu, T., Mobuchi, I. 1977. Bovine
platelet myosin. *J. Biochem. (Tokyo)*
81:1879–88

171. Shizuta, Y., Shizuta, H., Gallo, M., Davies, P., Pastan, I., Lewis, M. S. 1976.
Purification and properties of filamin,
an actin binding protein from chicken
gizzard. *J. Biol. Chem.* 251:6562–67

172. Sim, J., Franks, K., French, S., Caldwell, M. 1977. Mallory bodies compared with microfilament hyperplasia.
Arch. Pathol. Lab. Med. 101:401–4

173. Small, J. V., Sobieszek, A. 1977. Studies
on the function and composition of the
10 nm (100 Å) filaments of vertebrate
smooth muscle. *J. Cell Sci.* 23:243–68

174. Soifer, D., ed. 1975. The biology of
cytoplasmic microtubules. *Ann. N.Y.
Acad. Sci.* 253:1–848

175. Spooner, B. S. 1975. Microfilaments,
microtubules, and extracellular materials in morphogenesis. *BioScience* 25:
440–51

176. Starger, J., Brown, W., Goldman, A.,
Goldman, R. 1978. Biochemical and
immunological analysis of 10 nm filaments from baby hamster kidney
(BHK-21) cells. *J. Cell Biol.* 78:93–109

177. Starger, J., Goldman, R. 1977. Isolation
and preliminary characterization of 10
nm filaments from baby hamster kidney
(BHK-21) cells. *Proc. Natl. Acad. Sci.
USA* 74:2422–26

178. Steck, T. L. 1974. The organization of
proteins in the human red blood cell
membrane. A review. *J. Cell Biol.*
62:1–19

179. Steinert, P. M. 1978. Structure of the
three-chain unit of the bovine epidermal
keratin filament. *J. Molec. Biol.* In press

180. Steinert, P., Idler, W., Zimmerman, S.
1976. Self assembly of bovine epidermal
keratin filaments *in vitro. J. Mol. Biol.*
108:547–67

180a. Steinert, P., Zimmerman, W., Starger, J., Goldman, R. 1978. Manuscript submitted

181. Stephens, R. E. 1975. Structural chemistry of the axoneme: Evidence for chemically and functionally unique tubulin dimers in outer fibers. See Ref. 166 pp. 181–206

182. Stossel, T. P., Pollard, T. D. 1973. Myosin in polymorphonuclear leucocytes. *J. Biol. Chem.* 248:8288–94

183. Stossel, T. P., Hartwig, J. H. 1975. Interactions between actin, myosin and an actin-binding protein from rabbit alveolar macrophages. *J. Biol. Chem.* 250:5706–12

184. Taylor, D. G., Mapp, R. J., Crawford, N. 1975. The identification of actin associated with pig platelet membranes and granules. *Biochem. Soc. Trans.* 3:161–64

185. Taylor, E. W. 1972. Chemistry of muscle contraction. *Ann. Rev. Biochem.* 41:577–616

186. Uehara, Y., Campbell, G., Burnstock, G. 1971. Cytoplasmic filaments in developing and adult vertebrate smooth muscle. *J. Cell Biol.* 50:484–97

187. Vandekerckhove, J., Weber, K. 1978. Mammalian cytoplasmic actins are the products of at least two genes and differ in primary structure in at least 25 identified positions from skeletal muscle actin. *Proc. Natl. Acad. Sci. USA* 75:1106–10

188. Wang, K., Ash, J. F., Singer, S. J. 1975. Filamin, a new high-molecular-weight protein found in smooth muscle and non-muscle cells. *Proc. Natl. Acad. Sci. USA* 72:4483–86

189. Wang, K., Singer, S. J. 1977. Interaction of filamin with F-actin in solution. *Proc. Natl. Acad. Sci. USA* 74:2021–25

190. Weber, A., Murray, J. M. 1973. Molecular control mechanisms in muscle contraction. *Physiol. Rev.* 53:612–73

191. Weber, K., Gröschel-Stewart, U. 1974. Antibody to myosin: the specific visualization of myosin-containing filaments in non-muscle cells. *Proc. Natl. Acad. Sci. USA* 71:4561–64

192. Weihing, R. 1976. Cytochalasin B inhibits actin-related-gelation of HeLa cell extracts. *J. Cell Biol.* 71:303–7

193. Weihing, R. R. 1977. Effects of myosin and heavy meromyosin on actin-related gelation of HeLa cell extracts. *J. Cell Biol.* 75:95–103

194. Wessells, N. K., Spooner, B. S., Luduena, M. A. 1973. Surface movements, microfilaments and cell locomotion. *Ciba Found. Symp.* 14 (NS) 53–77

195. Wickus, G., Gruenstein, E., Robbins, P. W., Rich, A. 1975. Decrease in membrane—associated actin of fibroblasts after transformation by vivo sarcoma virus. *Proc. Natl. Acad. Sci. USA* 72:746–49

196. Weiland, T. 1977. Modification of actins by phallotoxins. *Naturwissenschaften* 64:303–9

197. Willingham, M. C., Ostlund, R. E., Pastan, I. 1974. Myosin is a component of the cell surface of cultured cells. *Proc. Natl. Acad. Sci. USA* 71:4144–48

198. Wilson, L., Bryan, J. 1974. Biochemical and pharmacological properties of microtubules. *Adv. Cell Mol. Biol.* 3:21–72

199. Wisniewski, H., Shelanski, M., Terry, R. D. 1968. Effects of mitotic spindle inhibitors on neurotubules and neurofilaments in anterior horn cells. *J. Cell Biol.* 38:224–29

200. Wisniewski, H., Soifer, D. 1978. Neurofibrillary pathology: Current status and research prospectives. *Mech. Aging Dev.* In press

201. Wolosewick, J. J., Porter, K. R. 1976. Stereo high-voltage electron microscopy of whole cells of the human diploid line, WI-38. *Am. J. Anat.* 147:303–24

202. Wuerker, R. 1970. Neurofilaments and glial filaments. *Tissue & Cell* 2:1–9

203. Wuerker, R., Kirkpatrick, J. 1972. Neuronal microtubules, neurofilaments and microfilaments. *Int. Rev. Cytol.* 33:45–75

204. Wuerker, R., Palay, S. 1969. Neurofilaments and microtubules in anterior horn cells of the rat. *Tissue & Cell* 1:387–402

205. Yen, S.-H., Dahl, D., Schachner, M., Shelanski, M. 1976. Biochemistry of the filaments of brain. *Proc. Natl. Acad. Sci. USA* 73:529–33

206. Yerna, M.-J., Aksoy, M., Hartshorne, D. J., Goldman, R. D. 1978. BHK-21 myosin: Isolation, biochemical characterization and intracellular localization. *J. Cell Sci.* 31:411–29

207. Yerna, M.-J. Dabrowska, R., Hartshorne, D. J., Goldman, R. D. 1979. Calcium sensitive regulation of actin-myosin interactions in baby hamster kidney (BHK-21) cells. *Proc. Natl. Acad. Sci. USA* 76(1). In press

208. Yu, J., Branton, D. 1976. Reconstitution of intramembrane particles in recombinants of erythrocyte protein Band 3 and lipid: Effects of spectrin-actin association. *Proc. Natl. Acad. Sci. USA* 73:3891–3895

Ann. Rev. Physiol. 1979. 41:723–36
Copyright © 1979 by Annual Reviews Inc. All rights reserved

THE CROSSBRIDGE THEORY ♦1247

R. T. Tregear and S. B. Marston[1]

Agricultural Research Council Unit of Muscle Mechanism and Insect
Physiology, Department of Zoology, University of Oxford, Oxford, England

INTRODUCTION

This review treats the central issues in present-day research on the problem
of contraction itself. In the first section we give a brief account of the several
schools of experimental study that have dominated the field over the last
half century and show how they have given rise to the crossbridge theory.
In the second we describe more fully the logic of the present form of the
theory and the way in which different experimental modes interact to
produce this logic. The final section contains a brief commentary on the
probable developments in the near future. Because our article is fitted to
very strict limits on length, we have omitted much detail from the evidence.
Many detailed reviews of particular aspects of the contractile process have
appeared in the last few years and may be used to add flesh to our bare bones
(17, 35, 40, 52, 72, 74, 77, 79, 82).

PAST

"Muscle, which is the instrument of voluntary movement . . . becomes
thicker, shortens and gathers itself together and so draws to itself and moves
the part to which it is attached" [Vesalius, 1543 (63)]. How it does so has
become a lot clearer in the last forty years, and is now *almost* a proper
subject of molecular biology; the terms we use are approaching a description
of events during contraction at atomic resolution and millisecond time
scale, but they are not there yet.

The steady-state mechanics of active muscle were described in the first
half of the century in terms of the twin relations between force and either

[1]Present address—ICI Pharmaceuticals, Mereside, Alderley Park, Macclesfield, Cheshire,
England

0066-4278/79/0301-0723$01.00

constant velocity or constant length. These empirical relationships have been remeasured many times since then; the effects of tendon and muscle sheath have been ever more exactly subtracted until the present measurements of these same parameters represent almost entirely what the original workers hoped for: the properties of the contractile elements themselves (26, 43). Despite the excellence of these observations, further measurements of the same class may always be made simply because of the enormous variety of muscles available (15). Meanwhile the leaders in the field have moved on to study the rapidly changing events that follow a sudden deformation during such a steady state (14, 37). Not all of these data can yet be translated into molecular terms, but those that can are essential; they are our only measurements of the system's output.

When muscle contracts at the correct speed it is highly efficient (82). This was shown very early on, but dissection of the metabolic pathway to the actual contractile event took a long time because it required the elucidation of anaerobic and aerobic glycolysis (45). Once this was done the biochemical simplicity of the contraction itself was revealed: ATP is hydrolyzed at a specific site on a specific protein, directly coupled to the mechanical output and totally dissociable from the vast array of support reactions that regenerate the ATP. The final hydrolysis operates at a high efficiency if and only if the contraction velocity is optimal for the particular muscle (10). ATP hydrolysis, or its concomitant heat production, has been studied under the same steady states of constant velocity or constant length as the mechanical output (82). These input-output relationships of the contractile machine form the basis of all thermodynamic treatments of the system. In addition, some of the observations can be interpreted directly in molecular terms.

The muscle proteins that bring about this remarkable coupling of input to output were first prepared in the 1930s (22) but were only properly separated at the end of World War II. The basic protein contraction mechanism was at once recognized. The ATP-hydrolytic site of one protein, myosin, is activated by contact with the second, actin, and in some way coupled to the output of mechanical energy (73). The formal problem of the mechanists was thus transformed into a protein-conformation problem.

Such submicroscopic events require a structural order to have a macroscopic effect. Nineteenth-century optical microscopists had elucidated many of the structural details of the most obviously ordered, the striated muscles (34). Although the details were clear enough they could only be interpreted in protein terms after the proteins themselves had been separated. Thus it was not until the early 1950s, at the inception of electron microscopy, that the optical microscopic images were properly understood. This resulted in simultaneous identical conclusions from the two techniques: There are two overlapping sets of filaments, one of myosin and the other of actin (36, 42). Immediately electron microscopy showed that the filaments remained of constant length while the muscle shortened (38), and the sliding-filament theory was born. Despite repeated fierce attacks it has remained received truth ever since. Virtually ever teacher and his students over the last twenty years, and all but a few heretical workers, have accepted the evidence that muscle shortens because of a force generated between two filaments, which themselves remain macroscopically unaltered. Since the myosin and actin filaments are both bipolar, the sliding action causes the "gathering together" of the ends of the sets of parallel actin filaments interacting with each half of a set of myosin filaments. Many actin and myosin filament-arrays (sarcomeres) are built up in series so that the molecular movements summate to give a macroscopic contraction.

The reason for acceptance of the sliding-filament model is not merely the original structural evidence but also the reinforcement provided by the study both of the molecular order within the filaments and of the shape of the myosin molecule itself. The filament of actin turned out to be a double string of globular beads (28), while the filament of myosin was a set of tails packed together, each tail supporting above the filament's surface a pair of enzymatic globular heads (39). The modus operandi of the sliding of the filaments was therefore obvious: The exposed heads, or "crossbridges," attached to the actin and pulled it alongside the myosin filament. Hence the sliding-filament theory was transposed into the crossbridge theory. The mode of myosin's interaction with actin could be seen when the two proteins were tightly attached in the absence of ATP: The attached myosin head resembled a bent hook. It was as if the molecule had attached and then turned, extending the head's attachment to the filament and tending to pull the actin filament in (68). This rotation of the head became incorporated in the crossbridge theory (40) even though there was at the time no direct evidence for it.

All this concerned the output. The input, the binding and hydrolysis of ATP, produces no bulk change in molecular shape of the myosin in solution (60), although it does produce internal changes in the environment of particular amino acids (69, 78). The steady-state relationship of ATP hydrolysis rate to molecular concentrations of myosin, actin, and nucleotide in solution showed that myosin behaves as a simple enzyme with Mg-ATP as its substrate and actin as an activator (19). A far more detailed picture of the mechanism was obtained by application of transient kinetic methods. It was immediately shown that ATP is bound very rapidly and hydrolyzed almost equally rapidly by myosin (48). Its products then remain attached at the enzymatic site for a long time unless the myosin contacts actin (49). In other words, the myosin of relaxed muscle had already bound and hydrolyzed ATP before activation; it was primed and ready to perform the output action when the actin became available (56).

Thus by the 1970s a contractile-mechanism model had been considerably tested. In this model a primed myosin molecule attached to actin and rotated about its actin attachment, storing mechanical energy locally. While this state lasted such energy could be used to move the filaments. It was terminated by the loss of the ATP hydrolysis products and detachment of the myosin from the actin. As the muscle shortened the myosin attached to actin further down the thin filament and so continued to pull on it.

This model, which must be very familiar to most if not all of our readers, has grown gradually, sometimes preceding and sometimes following the evidence of its correctness. The first and most famous "working cross-bridge" model was put forward by A. F. Huxley in 1957 (34). Mainstream enzymologists and structuralists all produced their own glosses on the conception without altering the basic concepts (16, 29, 37, 40, 49).

Meanwhile others have attacked it and still do. The first challengers claimed both that muscle produced tension without filament overlap and also that thick filaments shortened (11). They were proven wrong on both counts (26, 66); indeed later evidence indicated a slight filament elongation on activation (30). Pollack has recently reopened this controversy (64). Alternative theories of contraction abound, mostly based on the electro-static charge of the filaments (21, 64, 71). They have not been disproven, but the direct coupling between myosin's enzymatic site and the mechanical output proven by recent evidence (46, 54, 57) renders them exceedingly unlikely. McClare mounted the most direct attack on the crossbridge theory (50). He claimed that the system could not work on thermodynamic princi-ples and formulated a "molecular machine" alternative in which the myosin molecules existed in a long-lived excited state after hydrolyzing ATP (51). The existence of such a state has not been disproved, but it is unnecessary to assume it; it is perfectly possible to create working thermo-dynamic crossbridge models (33, 37).

The crossbridge theory has been debated now for twenty years. It has withstood the attacks of its critics and the probings of its friends. In the next section we consider its present condition.

PRESENT

The conceptual framework of the thermodynamic crossbridge model is a set of biochemical states connected by rate-constants. Such states are most easily recognized by biochemical kinetic studies on protein solutions. The reaction between ATP and myosin is now known in some detail (Figure 1). Binding takes place in two steps (44). First a contact intermediate is formed, at a high rate but only a moderate affinity ($10^4 M^{-1}$). Then an internal change takes place in the protein, which is seen as an increase in the fluorescence from tryptophan. This reaction is also very fast and effectively irreversible ($K = 10^6$) so that the overall binding constant of ATP and myosin is very large [$10^{10} M^{-1}$ (24)]. The events that succeed these rapid processes have given rise to much argument, but it is now believed that ATP is immediately hydrolyzed at the enzymatic site (13, 44). Hydrolysis at the site is a moderately rapid equilibrium reaction, accompanied by a further internal protein change seen both as proton release and tryptophan fluorescence increase. Equilibrium is not far from a 1:1 ATP:ADP ratio (6), which may be contrasted with the 1:10^8 ratio required in solutions containing a physiological phosphate concentration (4); protein and ligand are clearly tightly bound to one another and so are able to feed energy across their combined structure. As one might expect, the lifetime of such a complex is long. In the absence of actin it lasts between 10 and 100 sec, and is the rate-limiting step of the overall reaction (48). The subsequent release of both products is relatively fast, phosphate being released faster than ADP (7).

Actin greatly increases the steady-state rate of ATP hydrolysis by interacting with the tight M.ADP.P complex, or some substate thereof (Fig. 1). Usually M.ADP.P is formed faster than the subsequent reactions of the attached complex, but under conditions of low temperature and ionic strength it is formed slowly enough to limit the overall rate of ATP hydrolysis (12, 18). It is likely that the actin-to-M.ADP.P attachment reaction is itself a two-step process (55, 81). An initial collision complex is formed with an affinity of about $10^4 M^{-1}$, followed by an internal change in the proteins. The acto-myosin-product complex so formed is analogous to the myosin-product complex of myosin alone, but it lasts for a much shorter time [(49); Figure 1]. The rate-constant of its decay is normally the rate-limiting step

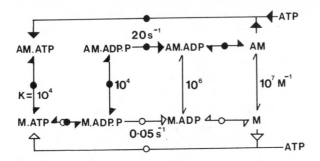

Figure 1 Hydrolysis of ATP by myosin ($\circ$) or actomyosin ($\bullet$). The actomyosin dissociation constants (K) are shown, as are the rate-constants of the slowest step in each of the two cycles (at physiological temperature, pH, and ionic strength). Data from (49, 57, 70, 80)

when excess actin is provided (81) and is characteristic of the source of myosin used; muscles that shorten rapidly have a high actomyosin ATPase and vice versa (8, 55). After the rate-limiting step, loss of products is relatively rapid. As the products are lost the actomyosin affinity rises [(57, 58); Figure 1]. The final complex, actomyosin, has such a high interprotein affinity that it is only physiologically dissociable by ATP. ATP binding to actomyosin can again be subdivided into at least two steps, the formation of a contact complex and then an internal change in the protein (55). The second state appears to be in direct equilibrium with the tight myosin-ATP complex [(44); Figure 1]. The rate-constants of all these process are large, and at physiological ATP concentration the process AM → M.ATP occurs rapidly, the enormous affinity of myosin for ATP overcoming its only slightly lower affinity for actin (81).

These kinetic studies show in outline the sequence of biochemical states on which a model must be built. The preferred biochemical cycle is clearly indicated (Figure 1). It is much faster than the cycle for myosin alone, although hydrolysis itself takes place off the actin. Energy transduction occurs after actin attachment. The interprotein affinity increases as the cycle proceeds [(27, 57); Figure 1], and thus the basic free energy of the attached states decreases. This is required for efficient energy transduction since the basic free energy of the last mechanically significant attached state must lie close to that of the detached state once ATP has been re-bound [(33); Figure 2].

If the progression of myosin and actin through a biochemical cycle with its associated change of interprotein configuration is to be transmitted into a undirectional movement, it is necessary that both myosin and actin monomers are formed into linear aggregates capable of interacting with each other in a stereospecific manner. Two elements of regularity are common to all muscles and are likely to be important for the conversion of molecular conformation change to bulk movement. They are the 14 nm axial repeat of the myosin filament and the 38 nm helical repeat of the actin filament.

The array structure places the actin and myosin molecules in ordered proximity. Their distance apart increases as the muscle shortens [because the cells remain at constant volume (21)], but the surfaces of the two filaments are never more than 20 nm, and usually only 10–15 nm, apart. This is less than the length of the myosin heads (20) and according to fluorescence depolarization and ESR spin-label studies the heads are free to rotate singly about their junctions with the tail (60, 75), although their motion is slowed by the filament matrix (59). It follows that the two proteins should make frequent contact due to thermal motion of the heads. Furthermore the upper part of the tail is not rigidly locked into the thick filament and so can provide the additional flexibility necessary for the myosin head to contact the actin monomer at the right orientation of the intermolecular fit (20, 47). There is more than sufficient actin in the contractile matrix of any muscle to accept all the myosin present (76) and the concentration of each protein is several hundred micromolar (38, 56), which would be sufficient in solution to ensure near-saturation of myosin heads with actin. Whether it is so in the matrix depends on the degree of steric hindrance present. One obvious problem is the steric relation of the two heads of one myosin molecule to different actin monomers; if these are adjacent on a filament a considerable relative displacement of the outer ends of the two heads is demanded (65). This does appear to weaken the binding of the second head, for the affinity of double-headed myosin (HMM) for actin is only ten to a hundred times greater than that of the single head on its own (32, 53).

In relaxed muscle, there is no tendency for the myosin to contact the actin; the X-ray diffraction pattern is that of the two separate filaments, the 15 nm–based regularity of the myosin, and the 38 nm–based regularity of the actin (41, 83). When the muscle is isometrically activated the myosin heads stand away from their regular positions around the thick filament and come closer to the actin monomers (31, 84) but do not form a regular enough array on the actin to be seen in diffraction experiments (5, 41). In the absence of ATP they do. The myosin heads then attach to actin at approximately 55° in groups at each turn of the 38 nm actin helix (68). These crossbridges may be seen directly in electron micrographs (62, 67) and may also be inferred from X-ray diffraction of the intact matrix (61). Each head is bent back at an acute angle relative to its tail. This rigor-crossbridge structure (r-bridge) has been widely used as a model for the structural state from which mechanical energy can be drawn (29, 40, 49). Actually during contraction the state AM, which corresponds to the rigor structure, is very short-lived and could not be involved in mechano-chemical conversion; but it is postulated that there exists a long-lived biochemical state (e.g. AM.ADP.P_{II}) that has the same structure as the rigor crossbridge (41). When the unhydrolyzable ATP analog, β,γ-imido-ATP, is bound to myosin then the 55°-angled rigor crossbridges are replaced by ones closer to right angles to the two filaments (p-bridges) grouped at each 14 nm origin from the thick filament rather than at each 38 nm turn of the actin helix (9, 25, 54). The myosin heads that form p-bridges therefore seem to be sterically related to both filaments, as if their origins fitted to the thick filament tail assembly and their insertions to the binding sites on actin.

These two kinds of bridge constitute all our current structural information about the actomyosin interaction. Are they relevant to active muscle? There are three reasons for believing that they may be. First, β,γ-imido-ATP is the closest structural analog of ATP (85) so that its fit to the enzymatic site is likely to generate the same sort of structural change in the protein; it certainly binds to myosin without detaching it from actin (27). Second, change of p-bridge to r-bridge causes the expected mechanical changes in the muscle: The tension rises and the equilibrium length of the muscle shortens (46, 54, 57). Third, the converse is also true: Muscle extension increases myosin's affinity for those nucleotides that cause a change from r-bridge to p-bridge (46, 57). Thus the transition from p to r is a possible analog of one of the transitions in the actomyosin ATP hydrolysis cycle.

The mechanical output of active muscle shows these transitions in action and allows estimation of the timing and spacing of the events. In order to do so it is necessary to look carefully at theoretically simple situations and in particular at small deformations about the isometric case. During isometric activation both the elasticity of the muscle and the active tension generated in it are proportional to the length of the overlapping actomyosin arrays (23, 26), which shows that within each overlap region there is a constant proportion of the available myosin attached and a constant distribution of these actomyosin links between the various biochemical states. It is therefore reasonable to use para-isometric data as indexes of individual crossbridge behavior; there is no evidence of gross feedback between groups of bridges via the filament tension.

The most obvious observation to make on an isometric muscle is what happens when it is abruptly shortened. In practice it has required great technical development to enforce sufficiently rapid motion and to measure the resultant force, so that it is only now that proper answers to this simple question are available. The tension falls instantaneously as the muscle shortens and reaches zero when it has shortened approximately 5 nm per filament array (23); thus this appears to be the average extension of the actomyosin linkage from mechanical equilibrium or distance of the biochemical states from their point of lowest free energy (alternative statements of the same thing; cf Figure 2).

If the muscle is now held at this new length the tension regenerates in two phases. The first is quick, as if there were a rapid transition either between attached states (35, 37) or in the attachment-detachment equilibrium of a given state (2, 3, 14). This rapid tension recovery can be abolished by increased shortening, to some 10 nm per array. Thus the difference in muscle extension for lowest free energy of the biochemical states before and after transition would also appear to be in the vicinity of 5 nm. The speed of tension regeneration gives some idea of the rate-constants of interstate transitions. These are of the order of $100–1000 \text{ sec}^{-1}$, at least an order faster than the limiting rate-constant of the biochemical cycle. The final phase of tension regeneration is much slower, and probably represents reequilibration via detachment, ATP hydrolysis, and reattachment. These mechanical data fit the general concept of energy transduction from biochemical states. The rate-constants between such states should theoretically be related to extension (33), and indeed the overall speed of the first phase of tension regain is dependent on the amount of shortening that precedes it (37). The first phase can itself be divided into at least two components (1, 3, 23); the proper treatment of the data is under active debate.

Three strands of evidence have gone into the present model; biochemical, structural, and mechanical. The crossbridge cycle can be viewed in all three ways. We end this section with a triple description of the hypothetical events during one cycle as a muscle contracts at constant velocity. Let us start in biochemical terms. Initially suppose the myosin detached, as the tight ligand complex M.ADP.P (Figure 2a). It now attaches via a transient contact intermediate to form $AM.ADP.P_I$. This state is retained for an appreciable time and then changes to $AM.ADP.P_{II}$. Again the state remains for some while and is finally lost via the last slow step. The relative lifetimes of these two states depend on the rate-constants k_1 and k_2, which are themselves functions of the muscle's extension (Figure 2a). If k_1 were much greater than k_2 then the model would reduce to a single mechanically effective state. Further states before dissociation are assumed to have only a transitory existence, and so this completes the mechanically effective part of the cycle. The myosin is returned for recycling via loss of products and gain of ATP.

Structural terms may be added to the biochemical states by assuming that in $AM.ADP.P_I$ there is a high probability that the bridge will be in the p-form, while in $AM.ADP.P_{II}$ it will usually take the r-form (Figure 2b). Mechanical energy is stored in the crossbridge as some form of internal strain (Fig. 2b). Shortening may now be introduced and appears in structural terms as a steady reduction of strain until the p-bridge changes into an r-bridge. This transition is very rapid, and so it occurs at a particular muscle length ($x = b$ in Fig. 2b). It causes an abrupt increase in the internal strain, which then continues to relax at a steady rate until the myosin finally detaches from the actin.

Looking at the same operation in mechanical terms, the p-bridge forms at a certain tension that then steadily falls with time until the p–r transition. At this point it abruptly rises and then again steadily falls as the muscle shortens (Figure 2c).

Finally, this whole description can be put in terms of free energy. The p-bridge forms with a loss of free energy but not at its own minimum free energy, because it comes via a contact intermediate of brief lifetime [OP, Figure 2d; (33)]. Its own lifetime is dependent upon the mechanical events that follow. In the case considered, the muscle is shortening at constant

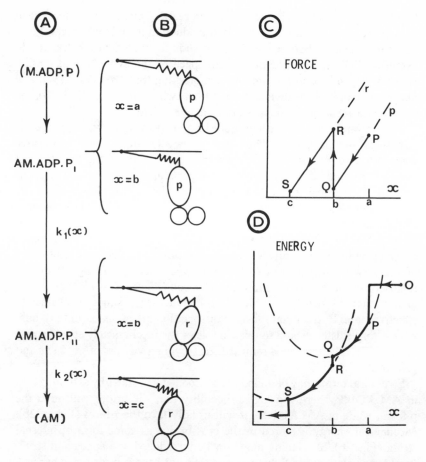

Figure 2 The performance of mechanical work in the constant-velocity shortening of muscle in terms of biochemical states (A), crossbridge movements (B), tension (C), and basic free energy (D). For explanation of symbols see text.

velocity, and the p-bridge releases energy as it does so (PQ). The ratio of forward to backward rate-constant for the p–r transition increases as the muscle shortens (33). We assume here that this is due to increase in the forward rate-constant so that the most probable transition to the r-state is close to the free energy minimum for the p-bridge (QR). The free energy of the r-bridge is released as the muscle shortens (RS) until detachment occurs (ST). The difference in free energy level between the detached bridge (less ATP's chemical potential) and the base of the r-bridge curve must not be great or the efficiency will be low; in other words the interprotein affinity of the r-bridge must be enhanced over that of the p-bridge.

FUTURE

The model described above is a working hypothesis, a way of suggesting experiments and of keeping arguments to the point. How much of it is likely to survive?

The major concept has been well tested and is probably correct. In our opinion it is now almost certain that mechanical energy is delivered from actomyosin states whose existence is directly enforced by the hydrolysis of ATP; the crossbridge model is here to stay.

The details of the present model are not. It is a scheme sketched from enzymatic, structural, and mechanical data. The two-state model has experimental support; in the equilibrium case, when the enzymatic site is empty or occupied by unhydrolyzable nucleotides, all three sorts of data have been firmly connected together. However, this is a very particular case. If there were more observations it is likely that the model would be different. We have interpreted the data in terms of two states, p and r, simply because these are the known states, but this may be a reflection of the inability of structural and spectroscopic probes to distinguish several intermediates. The best we can hope for is that the present model is a crude approximation to the truth.

Each of the three experimental approaches is limited in its potential for immediate advance. Mechanical experiments have reached near-perfection, but they have only one parameter to measure: tension. The interpretation of tension change in biochemical terms is dependent on biochemical experiments; mechanics is exact but derivative. By contrast, enzymological investigation is extremely crude. At the moment light scattering is the only established probe of actin-myosin interaction and it is incapable of distinguishing between different types of attachment. Only when probes that differentiate between the various attached states have been devised and applied will it be possible to properly interpret the mechanical experiments. Structural studies are in even more trouble. Diffraction can in principle, and probably very soon in practice, detect the regular features of structure on a millisecond time scale; but it only detects regularities, and interpretation of the patterns is again highly model-dependent. One way out is to look at individual crossbridges by microscopy, but the necessary preparative processes reduce both the resolution and credibility of the pictures obtained and remove the possibility of dynamic measurements.

Once new methods are applied a more detailed crossbridge mechanism is likely to be revealed. A definitive theory will then replace the working hypothesis. It will even then be only a beginning, the start of a search for the intramolecular mechanism at atomic resolution. That remains for the future.

Literature Cited

1. Abbott, R. H. 1972. Comments on the mechanism of force generation in striated muscles. *Nature New Biol.* 289:183–86
2. Abbott, R. H. 1977. The relationship between biochemical kinetics and mechanical properties. In *Insect Flight Muscle*, ed. R. T. Tregear, pp. 269–76. Amsterdam: North-Holland
3. Abbott, R. H., Steiger, G. J. 1977. Temperature and amplitude dependence of tension transients in glycerinated skeletal and insect fibrillar muscle. *J. Physiol.* 266:13–42
4. Alberty, R. A. 1968. Effect of pH and metal ion concentration on the equilibrium hydrolysis of adenosine triphosphate. *J. Biol. Chem.* 243:1337–43
5. Armitage, P. M., Tregear, R. T., Miller, A. 1975. Effect of activation by calcium on the X-ray diffraction pattern from insect flight muscle. *J. Mol. Biol.* 92:39–53
6. Bagshaw, C. R., Trentham, D. R. 1973. The reversibility of ATP cleavage by myosin. *Biochem. J.* 133:323–28
7. Bagshaw, C. R., Trentham, D. R. 1974. The characterisation of myosin-product complexes and of product release steps. *Biochem. J.* 141:331–49
8. Bárány, M. 1967. ATPase activity of myosin correlated with speed of muscle shortening. *J. Gen. Physiol.* 50:197–218
9. Beinbrech, G. 1977. See ref. 2, pp. 147–55
10. Cain, D. F., Infante, A. A., Davies, R. E. 1962. Chemistry of muscle contraction. *Nature* 196:214–17
11. Carlsen, F., Knappeis, G. G., Buchthal, F. 1961. Ultrastructure of the resting and contracted striated muscle fibre. *J. Biophys. Biochem. Cytol.* 11:95–117
12. Chock, S. P., Chock, P. B., Eisenberg, E. 1977. Pre-steady-state kinetic evidence for a cyclic interaction of myosin subfragment one with actin during the hydrolysis of ATP. *Biochemistry* 15:3244–53
13. Chock, S. P., Eisenberg, E. 1977. Binding ATP to myosin subfragment-1. *Fed. Proc.* 31:830
14. Civan, M. M., Podolsky, R. J. 1966. Contraction kinetics of striated muscle fibres following quick changes in load. *J. Physiol.* 184:511–34
15. Close, R. 1965. The relation between intrinsic speed of shortening and duration of the active state of muscle. *J. Physiol.* 180:542–59
16. Davies, R. E. 1963. A molecular theory of muscle contraction. *Nature* 199:1068–74
17. Eisenberg, E., Hill, T. L. 1978. A crossbridge model of muscle contraction. *Prog. Biophys. Mol. Biol.* 33:55–82
18. Eisenberg, E., Kielley, W. W. 1972. Refractory state of heavy meromyosin and subfragment-1. *Cold Spring Harbor Symp. Quant. Biol.* 37:145–52
19. Eisenberg, E., Moos, C. 1971. Actin activation of heavy meromyosin adenosine triphosphatase. *J. Biol. Chem.* 245:2451–56
20. Elliott, A., Offer, G. 1978. The shape and flexibility of the myosin molecule. *J. Mol. Biol.* 123:505–19
21. Elliott, G. F., Rome, E. M., Spencer, M. 1970. A type of contraction hypothesis applicable to all muscles. *Nature* 226:400–417
22. Engelhardt, V. A., Lyubimova, M. N. 1939. Myosin and adenosine triphosphatase. *Nature* 144:668–69
23. Ford, L. E., Huxley, A. F., Simmons, R. M. 1977. Tension responses to sudden length change in stimulated frog muscle fibres near slack length. *J. Physiol.* 269:441–515
24. Goody, R. S., Hofmann, W., Mannherz, H. G. 1977. The binding constant of ATP to myosin S1 fragment. *Eur. J. Biochem.* 78:317–24
25. Goody, R. S., Holmes, K. C., Mannherz, H. G., Barrington-Leigh, J., Rosenbaum, G. 1975. X-ray studies of insect flight muscle with ADP analogues. *Biophys. J.* 15:687–705
26. Gordon, A. M., Huxley, A. F., Julian, F. J. 1966. Variation in isometric tension with sarcomere length in vertebrate muscle fibres. *J. Physiol.* 184:170–92
27. Greene, L. E., Eisenberg, E. 1978. The formation of a ternary complex: actin-adenyl imidodiphosphate and the subfragments of myosin. *Proc. Natl. Acad. Sci. USA* 75:54–58
28. Hanson, J., Lowy, J. 1963. The structure of F-Actin and of Actin filaments isolated from muscle. *J. Mol. Biol.* 6:46–60
29. Harrington, W. F. 1971. A mechanochemical mechanism for muscle contraction. *Proc. Natl. Acad. Sci. USA* 68:685–89
30. Haselgrove, J. C. 1975. X-ray evidence for conformational changes in the myosin filaments of vertebrate striated muscle. *J. Mol. Biol.* 92:113–43
31. Haselgrove, J. C., Huxley, H. E. 1973. X-ray evidence for radial crossbridge movement. *J. Mol. Biol.* 77:549–68

32. Highsmith, S. 1978. Heavy meromyosin binds actin with negative co-operativity. *Biochemistry* 17:22–26

33. Hill, T. L. 1975. Theoretical formalism for the sliding filament model of contraction of striated muscle. *Prog. Biophys. Mol. Biol.* 28:269–340

34. Huxley, A. F. 1957. Muscle structure and theories of contraction. *Prog. Biophys. Chem.* 7:255–318

35. Huxley, A. F. 1974. Muscular contraction. *J. Physiol.* 243:1–43

36. Huxley, A. F., Niedergerke, R. C. 1954. Structural changes in muscle during contraction. *Nature* 173:971–72

37. Huxley, A. F., Simmons, R. M. 1971. Proposed mechanism of force generation in striated muscle. *Nature* 233:533–38

38. Huxley, H. E. 1957. The double array of filaments in cross-striated muscle. *J. Biophys. Biochem. Cytol.* 3:631–47

39. Huxley, H. E. 1963. Electron microscope studies of the structure of natural and synthetic protein filaments from striated muscles. *J. Mol. Biol.* 7:281–308

40. Huxley, H. E. 1971. The structural basis of muscular contraction. *Proc. R. Soc. London Ser. B.* 160:442–48

41. Huxley, H. E., Brown, W. 1967. X-ray diffraction of vertebrate striated muscle during contraction and in rigor. *J. Mol. Biol.* 30:383–434

42. Huxley, H. E., Hanson, J. 1954. Changes in the cross-striations of muscle during contraction and stretch and their structural interpretation. *Nature* 173:973–76

43. Jewell, B. R., Wilkie, D. R. 1958. The mechanical properties of relaxing muscle. *J. Physiol.* 143:515–40

44. Johnson, K. A., Taylor, E. W. 1978. A re-evaluation of the mechanism of subfragment-1 and actosubfragment-1 ATPase. *Biochemistry* 17:3432–42

45. Kalcar, H. M. 1969. *Biological Phosphorylations.* Englewood Cliffs, New Jersey: Prentice-Hall

46. Kuhn, H. J. 1977. See Ref. 2, pp. 307–16

47. Lowey, S., Slayter, H. S., Weeds, A. G., Baker, H. 1969. Substructure of the myosin molecule-1. Subfragments of myosin by enzymic degradation. *J. Mol. Biol.* 42:1–29

48. Lymn, R. W., Taylor, E. W. 1970. Transient state phosphate production in the hydrolysis of nucleoside triphosphates by myosin. *Biochemistry* 9:2975–91

49. Lymn, R. W., Taylor, E. W. 1971. Mechanism of adenosine triphosphate hydrolysis by actomyosin. *Biochemistry* 10:4617–24

50. McClare, C. W. F. 1971. Biochemical machines, Maxwell's demon and living organisms. *J. Theor. Biol.* 30:1–34

51. McClare, C. W. F. 1972. A 'molecular energy' muscle model. *J. Theor. Biol.* 35:569–95

52. Mannherz, H. G., Goody, R. S. 1976. Proteins of contractile systems. *Ann. Rev. Biochem.* 427–65

53. Margossian, S., Lowey, S. 1976. Interaction of myosin subfragments with actin. *Fed. Proc.* 35:1580

54. Marston, S. B., Rodger, C. D., Tregear, R. T. 1976. Changes in muscle crossbridges when β,γ-imido ATP binds to myosin. *J. Mol. Biol.* 104:263–76

55. Marston, S. B., Taylor, E. W. 1978. Actomyosin ATPase cycle of the four types of vertebrate muscles. *J. Mol. Biol.* In press

56. Marston, S. B., Tregear, R. T. 1972. Evidence for a complex between myosin and ADP in relaxed muscle fibres. *Nature New Biol.* 235:23–24

57. Marston, S. B., Tregear, R. T. Rodger, C. D., Clarke, M. 1979. Coupling between the enzymatic site of myosin and the mechanical output of muscle. *J. Mol. Biol.* In press

58. Marston, S. B., Weber, A. 1975. The dissociation constant of the Actin-heavy meromyosin subfragment-1 complex. *Biochemistry* 14:3868–73

59. Mendelson, R. A., Cheung, P. 1976. Muscle crossbridges: absence of direct effect of calcium on movement away from thick filaments. *Science* 194:190–93

60. Mendelson, R. A., Morales, M. F., Botts, J. 1973. Segmental flexibility of the S-1 moiety of myosin. *Biochemistry* 12:2250–55

61. Miller, A., Tregear, R. T. 1972. Structure of insect flight muscle in the presence and absence of ATP. *J. Mol. Biol.* 70:85–104

62. Moore, P. B., Huxley, H. E., DeRosier, D. J. 1970. Three dimensional reconstruction of thin filaments. *J. Mol. Biol.* 50:279–95

63. Needham, D. M. 1971. *Machina Carnis.* Cambridge: Cambridge Univ. Press. 13 pp.

64. Noble, M. I. M., Pollack, G. H. 1977. Molecular mechanisms of contraction. *Circ. Res.* 40:333–42

65. Offer, G., Elliott, A. 1978. Can a

myosin molecule bind to two actin filaments? *Nature* 271:325–29

66. Page, S. G., Huxley, H. E. 1963. Filament lengths in striated muscle. *J. Cell. Biol.* 19:369–90

67. Reedy, M. K., Garrett, W. E. 1977. See Ref. 2, pp. 115–43

68. Reedy, M. K., Holmes, K. C., Tregear, R. T. 1965. Induced changes in orientation of the crossbridges of glycerinated insect flight muscle. *Nature* 207: 1276–80

69. Seidel, J. C., Gergely, J. 1972. Conformational changes in myosin. *Cold Spring Harbor Symp. Quant. Biol.* 37:187–93

70. Sleep, J. A., Hutton, R. L. 1978. Actin mediated release of ATP from a myosin ATP complex. Personal communication

71. Spencer, M., Worthington, C. R. 1960. A hypothesis of contraction in striated muscle. *Nature* 187:388–91

72. Squire, J. M. 1975. Muscle filament structure and muscle contraction. *Ann. Rev. Biophys. Bioeng.* 4:137–63

73. Szent-Györgyi, A. 1951. *Chemistry of Muscular Contraction.* New York: Academic

74. Taylor, E. W. 1978. Mechanism of actomysin ATPase and the problem of muscle contraction. *Crit. Rev. Biochem.* In press

75. Thomas, D. D., Seidel, J. C., Hyde, J. S., Gergely, J. 1975. Motion of subfragment-1 in myosin and its supramolecular complexes. *Proc. Natl. Acad. Sci. USA* 72:1729–33

76. Tregear, R. T., Squire, J. M. 1973. Myosin content and filament structure in smooth and striated muscle. *J. Mol. Biol.* 77:279–90

77. Weber, A., Murray, J. M. 1973. Molecular control mechanisms in muscle contraction. *Physiol. Rev.* 53:612–73

78. Werber, M. W., Szent-Györgyi, A. G., Fassman, G. D. 1972. Fluorescence studies of heavy meromyosin–substrate interaction. *Biochemistry* 11:2872–83

79. White, D. C. S., Thorson, J. 1973. The kinetics of muscle contraction. *Prog. Biophys.* 27:175–258

80. White, H. D. 1977. Magnesium ADP binding to actomyosin-S-1 and acto-heavy-meromyosin. *Biophys. J.* 17:40a

81. White, H. D., Taylor, E. W. 1976. Energetics and mechanism of actomyosin adenosine triphosphatase. *Biochemistry* 15:5818–26

82. Woledge, R. C. 1971. Heat production and chemical change in muscle. *Prog. Biophys. Mol. Biol.* 22:37–74

83. Wray, J. S., Vibert, P. J., Cohen, C. 1975. Diversity of crossbridge configurations in invertebrate muscles. *Nature* 257:561–64

84. Yagi, N., Ito, M. H., Nakajima, H., Izumi, T., Matsubara, I. 1977. Return of myosin heads to thick filaments after muscle contraction. *Science* 197:685–87

85. Yount, R. G., Ojala, D., Babcock, D. 1971. Interaction of PNP and PCP analogues of adenosine triphosphate with heavy meromyosin, myosin and actomyosin. *Biochemistry* 10:2490–95

Ann. Rev. Physiol. 1979. 41:737–48

FILAMENT ORGANIZATION AND CONTRACTILE FUNCTION IN VERTEBRATE SMOOTH MUSCLE

♦1248

R. A. Murphy

Department of Physiology, University of Virginia School of Medicine,
Charlottesville, Virginia 22901

INTRODUCTION

In a sliding-filament model of muscle contraction, actin and myosin are organized in distinct structures, and cyclic interactions between them generate force and shortening by a translational movement between the two types of filaments. Force developed by a contractile unit (the sarcomere in striated muscle) is the sum of the forces generated by all the interacting sites coupled in parallel. Such a mechanism was confirmed for striated muscles by a synthesis of structural and mechanical data [(24); see also Tregear & Marston in the present volume]. This chapter reviews structural models that have been proposed for the contractile system of vertebrate smooth muscle. Evidence for structures in vertebrate smooth muscle that meet requirements of a sliding-filament model is discussed briefly. Several types of models are described that show promise of accommodating the known facts; and key data that must be obtained before various hypotheses can be discriminated are noted.

RATIONALE FOR SLIDING-FILAMENT MODELS

Structural and Biochemical Evidence

The contractile system of smooth muscle consists of actin and myosin and is qualitatively, if not quantitatively, similar to that in striated muscle (reviewed in 35, 57). Electron microscopic and X-ray diffraction data show that actin and tropomyosin form typical thin filaments and constitute the dominant structural protein in smooth-muscle cells (55). Thin filaments in

737

smooth muscle are attached to dense surface patches on the inside of the plasma membrane and also appear to be associated with osmiophilic amorphous structures, termed dense bodies, in the cytoplasm (1, 40, 42, 45, 54). However, the connection to cytoplasmic dense bodies has been questioned (8, 50–52). Thin filament polarity is unknown in relation to dense bodies, but thin filaments attached to surface dense patches when decorated with heavy meromyosin exhibit "arrowheads" pointing away from the membrane (56). This polarity would be appropriate for force development on the basis of an analogy with the polarity of thin filaments in relation to the Z-band in striated muscle. The length of thin filaments in smooth muscle is unknown. While there is an extensive thin-filament lattice in smooth muscle, no lateral registration is apparent. Double overlap may occur at physiological tissue lengths with interdigitation of thin filaments having opposite polarities.

The in vivo organization of myosin constitutes the major uncertainty concerning the contractile apparatus. Scattered thick filaments can be demonstrated by electron microscopy with suitable procedures (48, 54, 55). The low density of thick filaments is consistent with the low myosin content estimated with biochemical methods (7, 37, 38, 51). However, confirmation of such structures by diffraction methods in living tissues is needed. In low-angle X-ray diffraction experiments a weak 14.4 nm meridional diffraction pattern was observed which may arise from filaments resembling those in striated muscles (28, 29). However, the appearance of the reflection varied with the experimental conditions and was not observed at physiological temperatures (12, 47). Low-angle equatorial X-ray and neutron-diffraction patterns (G. F. Elliott, R. A. Murphy, P. A. Timmons & A. E. Woolgar, unpublished observations) yielded only hints of a thick-filament lattice with an interfilament spacing comparable to that observed in electron micrographs (41). The equivocal diffraction data may reflect the low myosin content and an irregular lattice structure. Biochemical data indicate that the myosin should be aggregated at the concentrations present in smooth-muscle cells (59).

There is reason to question electron-microscopic observations on thick filaments because reports differ on the basic structure, length, and ordering. Tapered ends and an apparent helical organization of crossbridges (1, 54, 55), together with a 14.4 nm meridional reflection (29, 47), are consistent with a conventional bipolar thick filament. However, central bare zones have not been demonstrated in thick filaments, and there is no assurance that such structures are bipolar (50). Smooth-muscle myosin can aggregate in vitro to form rectangular "face-polarized" filaments whose projections on each side have the same polarity along the entire length (10, 53). Small (50) measured the length of "native" thick filaments released from extracted taenia coli homogenates and reported values ranging up to 8 μm. He suggested that shorter filaments reflect breakage (50), but the method is subject to various artifacts and the few long filaments might well represent aggregates of the very numerous filaments less than 3 μm long. Thick-filament lengths of 2.2 ± 0.14 SD μm were measured by Ashton et al (1) by stereoscopic examination of thick sections with high-voltage electron microscopy. This value, obtained in rabbit portal anterior mesenteric vein and main pulmonary artery (55), is subject to little error if fixation is adequate, but data on other tissues are needed. Ashton et al (1) also observed that small groups of 3–5 thick filaments were in transverse register with interfilament lattice spacings of 60–80 nm. This significant result implies that mini-sarcomeres exist within the cell. The appearance of fibrils with striations in smooth-muscle cells stained with fluorescent antibodies to myosin is also consistent with some degree of order in the myosin disposition (4, 5, 26).

Direct evidence for a sliding-filament model is dependent on demonstrating increases in thick- and thin-filament overlap with shortening. Such relationships cannot be resolved in longitudinal sections of smooth muscles. However, electron micrographs of transverse sections in stretched tissues can show large areas of thin filaments (reminiscent of "I-band regions") that are much reduced after shortening (17). This is consistent with the predictions of a sliding-filament model. A rigorous quantitative study of filament organization in cross sections of muscles fixed at known points on the length-force curve is needed.

Sliding-filament contractile mechanisms depend on additional structures for force transmission and for maintaining filament-lattice geometry. The staining of dense bodies and membrane thin filament attachment plaques by antibodies to α-actinin (a constituent of the Z-lines of skeletal muscle) suggests that these structures have a similar role (45). The dense bodies are associated with the descriptively named intermediate ($\sim$10 nm) filaments observed in most cell types, which appear to link dense bodies into a cytoskeletal network (8, 9, 27, 45, 51, 55). Such suggestions remain speculative, but these studies do provide some indication of organized structural elements that play a role in ordering the filament lattice.

Mechanical Evidence

TISSUE MECHANICS   Hollow organs with muscular walls typically exhibit extreme volume changes at fairly low pressures. This has contributed to the impression that by comparison with skeletal muscle smooth muscle combines a very high shortening capacity with low force development and shortening velocity. However, recent mechanical studies on isolated tissues where the cells are oriented in parallel to the axis of force measurement have altered this assessment (reviewed in 34). The classical mechanical relationships described by Hill and others for striated muscle adequately characterize smooth muscle tissues (36). (*a*) Force is a function of length, with an optimum force, F_o, developed at a unique tissue length, L_o. (*b*) Shortening velocity under constant load can be fitted by a hyperbolic relationship described by the Hill equation. (*c*) Fully activated tissues subjected to an imposed stretch can transiently maintain forces of about 1.5 F_o. This qualitative similarity between the mechanical behavior of smooth and striated muscles provides the strongest argument for a common contractile process.

There are, however, quantitative mechanical differences. When expressed relative to the fraction of the cross-sectional area occupied by muscle cells, values of F_o for many smooth muscles equal those of striated muscle, and F_o in arterial tissues is even greater (34). This performance is striking, as the myosin content, and therefore the potential number of sites interacting with actin, is only 20–25% of that in striated muscles (7, 37, 38). Comparisons of working range and shortening capacity are difficult because most smooth muscles cannot be stretched much beyond L_o owing to the presence of connective tissue in the preparation (36). Loaded smooth muscles shorten more than striated muscles relative to L_o, but this difference is not so great as it is often assumed, and there is no direct evidence that the contractile system of smooth muscle, per se, has a greater shortening capacity (34, 36). Smooth muscles do have low maximum shortening velocities and are capable of maintaining a constant force with an economy perhaps two orders of magnitude greater than striated muscle (32, 39). These features probably reflect the kinetics of the actin-myosin interaction (30, 32, 34), although the organization of the proteins in a filament lattice may be a contributing factor.

CELL MECHANICS   The preceding discussion is based on the assumption that mechanical estimates of cellular function can be based on tissue measurements. There is anatomical evidence for lateral attachments between adjacent smooth-muscle cells and between cells and connective-tissue laminae (22,23). Such connections could effectively couple cells in parallel so that high force generation would reflect a mechanical advantage and not a characteristic of individual smooth-muscle cells (20, 23, 34). However, two different experimental approaches indicated that cellular properties are directly estimated in mechanical studies of several tissues. The first approach applied to mammalian muscles showed that (*a*) maximum active force depends only on tissue cross-sectional area and not on the length of a tissue segment or the total number of cells (37), and (*b*) cell length was directly proportional to tissue length (11, 33, 58). These results show that the high force in these tissues is a cellular property and not an inflated value arising from an underestimate of the true cross-sectional area of the cells additively generating force in parallel. The second approach currently applicable only to the stomach of the toad, *Bufo marinus,* involves direct mechanical measurements on individual cells released by enzymatic digestion (2, 14). At least for pig carotid artery (11, 37), rat mesenteric artery (33), *Bufo* stomach (2, 14), and rabbit urinary bladder (58), force, length, and velocity data normalized to cross section of smooth-muscle cells or to optimum tissue length, L_o, provide valid estimates of cellular properties.

CRITERIA FOR STRUCTURAL MODELS

Vertebrate smooth muscles exhibit remarkable functional diversity. Most of this variation probably reflects differences in membrane system properties associated with coupling of stimuli to activation of the contractile system. However, striking differences have been observed in contractile protein contents (7, 37, 51). In porcine tissues, two distinct groups were found in which arterial thin-filament protein contents (actin and tropomyosin) were significantly higher than those in veins and a variety of tissues from other organs (7, 37). This represents substantial variation in the contractile apparatus not observed among vertebrate striated muscles. Differences in thin-filament protein content and actin:myosin ratios may be associated with variations in the structural organization of the contractile proteins and contractile output, since arterial smooth muscle appears to develop higher forces than most other types (37). However, a model for the structural arrangement of the contractile proteins must account for (*a*) a high force-generating capacity for the amount of myosin (which was constant in all the smooth muscles we have studied) and possibly (*b*) variability in terms of thin-filament proteins. This means that the fraction of the total number of sites that act in parallel is several times higher than in striated muscle and/or that each site is capable of generating more force than in striated muscle. Although some models have specifically been proposed to account for a high shortening capacity of smooth muscle (43, 52), most recent studies reviewed above indicate that this is not a parameter that requires a special mechanism.

The familiar sliding-filament model involves bipolar myosin filaments interdigitating with actin filaments with a single zone of overlap in the sarcomere of striated muscle. This image is unnecessarily restrictive. It should be remembered that smooth muscles are physiologically active at lengths less than L_o (25). In the discussion below, the emphasis is on arrangements that accommodate the necessary number of interacting sites in parallel to account for force generation in an arterial smooth muscle and that are consistent with the myosin and actin contents. It seems premature to place restrictions on the nature of the myosin aggregates or their geometrical relationship to the thin filaments given the lack of detailed information on the state and structure of myosin filaments in vivo (48, 54).

Filament Lattice Structure and Contractile Protein Contents

Models of the structure of the filament lattice of smooth muscle must be consistent with anatomical and biochemical observations. The information to be considered has been obtained from large arteries where the most detail is known. Filament counts from electron micrographs of transverse sections indicate that there are 15–18 thin filaments for each thick filament [pulmonary artery (55)]. Cellular contractile protein contents in a series of 10 porcine arteries expressed as mg protein per g cellular wet weight are: myosin, 18.4; actin 49.5; and tropomyosin 13.2 [see (7) for published values of part of this series].

The critical question is whether these high ratios of thin:thick filaments in cross section directly reflect the numbers of thin and thick filaments, or whether they arise from a lattice containing thin filaments that are very long compared to thick filaments. Extreme values can be set and their implications for contractile function estimated in two cases. In the first, one assumes that smooth muscles show the same ratio of thin-filament length to thick-filament length as that observed in striated muscle (about 0.67). The same ratio is found for many striated muscles, although absolute filament lengths vary greatly in invertebrates (19). This allows a prediction of about 15 thin filaments, 1.5 μm long, for each 2.2 μm long thick filament in arterial smooth muscle. This calculation uses Ashton and co-workers' (1) estimate of thick filament length and gives a value consistent with actual counts. Only the relative lengths of thick and thin filaments are assumed, and the result is not dependent on any specific value for thick-filament lengths. For the second case, one assumes that the ratio of the number of thin and thick filaments is the same as in vertebrate striated muscles, i.e. 2:1, and that the thick filaments are 2.2 μm long (1). If so, the excess thin-filament protein content in smooth muscle must be accommodated as longer thin filaments relative to the length of the thick filaments. The calculated thin-filament length in this case is 11 μm. This estimate is also compatible with filament counts from electron micrographs because long thin filaments would be sampled more frequently in thin sections. The following section deals with the implications of these differing arrangements for smooth-muscle force-generation.

Filament Lattice Structure and Force Generation

The maximum force generated at optimum lengths for pig carotid arterial cells is 3.7×10^5 N m^{-2} (38). This value is typical of a number of arterial preparations (37) and is approached by directly measured forces in single cells released by enzymatic digestion from *Bufo marinus* stomach (14). Mammalian striated muscle containing four to five times as much myosin develops 1.8–3.5×10^5 N m^{-2} (corrected for 15% extracellular space) (6). One must assume, therefore, that there is a five- to ten-fold increase in (*a*) the efficiency of chemomechanical transduction, (*b*) the fraction of the interaction cycle times associated with force production (30), or in (*c*) the fraction of the sites arranged to couple force in parallel. A combination of these factors could be involved, but the last appears to be a likely contribution. Certainly, high force-generation in invertebrate smooth and striated muscles is associated with more sites in parallel (owing to longer filaments) in cases where the mechanics have been studied and the structure is known (19, 43, 44). Three structural possibilities to couple more sites in parallel are considered below.

If increased thick-filament length were to account fully for smooth-muscle force-generation, the thick filaments would be roughly five times the length of striated-muscle thick filaments, or about 7.5 μm. The elegant study of Ashton et al (1) suggests that high force-generation in vascular smooth muscle can be only partially (about 30%) explained on the basis of longer filaments (2.2. μm) of conventional structure.

An increase in thin-filament length would also couple more active sites in parallel (32). This is more difficult to visualize, but can be imagined in the context of the segment of a skeletal muscle fiber 5 sarcomeres long. If the thick filaments were removed from the two sarcomeres at each end of the segment, the myosin content would be reduced by 80% with no change in the number of active sites coupled in parallel. However, the length of the thin filaments would have to be increased to bridge the gap from the ends of the segment to the central thick filaments. Shortening capacity will decrease unless overlapping arrays of thin filaments can interdigitate. Were such interdigitation to occur without major interference with normal force-generating site function, it would give very broad peaks in the length-force diagram. This phenomenon is seen to some degree in smooth-muscle tissues (34). Limited data indicate that near-maximum forces can be obtained over even wider length changes in isolated single *Bufo* stomach cells (13).

A third arrangement to increase the number of interacting sites in parallel for a given amount of contractile material is an oblique orientation of the myofilaments relative to the cell membrane and the longitudinal axis of the cell (42). With such an arrangement the functional cross section of the cell is greater than the anatomical cross section used to normalize active force. The evidence for such an arrangement consists of (*a*) clearly documented insertion of thin filaments into cell-membrane dense areas (15, 16, 22, 23, 27, 40, 42); (*b*) electron micrographs indicating that the filaments form an angle with the cell axis (16–18, 42); (*c*) birefringent fibrils whose angle to the cell axis increases with shortening (17, 18, 49); and (d) invaginations of the cell surface in shortening cells that appear to result from an inward force exerted on the cell membrane at the membrane dense areas (15, 16). Such observations have led to several models for an oblique (16, 42, 52) or helical (17, 18, 49) organization of the fibrillar contractile apparatus.

The studies cited above are derived from work on tissues shortening under no load. Most were on isolated cells, usually from *Bufo marinus* stomach. The observations appear to be valid, but the inference that such models adequately represent the contractile apparatus may be questioned. Although high force-generation is readily explained, such models also predict a diminished shortening capacity (34) unless coupled with additional processes such as shearing of thick filaments past each other on shortening (52). Diffraction data (see 34) and electron micrographs of mammalian smooth muscle contracting under some load (22, 46, 48) show that the filaments remain parallel to the cell axis within the limits of resolution. Gabella (21) describes a variety of longitudinal, oblique, and transverse striations in shortened taenia coli that are related to complex surface folding of the cells on contraction. Many of the observations cited in the preceding paragraph may reflect either passive distortions of the fibrillar lattice associated with contraction of adjacent cells, or localized myofibrillar shortening reflecting the slow spread of activation along isolated amphibian smooth-muscle cells. This interpretation is consistent with Bagby & Abercrombie's most recent work (3), in which curved myofibrils were found in shortening *Bufo* cells.

The considerations raised in the preceding paragraph cast doubt on the hypothesis that high force-generation in mammalian smooth-muscle cells is due to oblique filaments. Several studies described above indicate that high force-generation in many smooth muscle tissues is a cellular property and does not arise from a complex anatomical coupling of cells to produce a mechanical advantage. Both of these propositions are in apparent conflict with the clear evidence for (a) filament attachment to the membrane along the length of the cell, and (b) coupling of some such sites to similar structures in adjacent smooth-muscle cells or to connective-tissue laminae (21). This apparent discrepancy would be resolved if contractile units as defined above are linked in series by the desmosome-like structures between adjacent cells. The force developed by such structures could be virtually parallel to the longitudinal axis of the cells and to the direction of force transmission throughout the tissue. This speculative interpretation suggests that the contractile system may be functionally coupled across cell membranes, just as individual smooth-muscle cells are not electrically independent units in many tissues. The merit of this proposal [which has some parallel in cardiac muscle (31)] at present rests on the apparent mechanical stability of the intermediate junctions or desmosome-like attachments (23) and on its ability to reconcile a variety of experimental observations.

SUMMARY AND CONCLUSIONS

The mechanism of contraction in vertebrate smooth muscles remains an area of uncertainty and disagreement. However, the structural, biochemical, and biophysical data are consistent with a sliding-filament mechanism. Some plausible structural modifications of the filament lattice known from striated muscle can explain the quantitative differences between smooth and striated muscles without invoking novel contractile mechanisms. Some models have been examined in terms of the ability of smooth muscle to develop high forces with a low myosin content. This emphasis on filament lattice structure is consistent with comparative data from invertebrate smooth and striated muscles, where sizable differences in absolute force-generating capabilities can be correlated with the number of crossbridges acting in parallel. However, special properties of the interacting sites might also contribute to the force-generating capacity in smooth muscle.

Increasing filament lengths may account for the mechanical properties of smooth muscle. Long thick filaments with high thin-filament:thick-filament ratios are common in invertebrates. Such a mechanism may account for part of the force-generating capacity of arterial smooth muscle. An increase in the ratio of thin- to thick-filament length may also account for the measured mechanical properties of vertebrate smooth muscles. A review of the evidence for an oblique or helical arrangement of myofilaments suggests that this organization may not contribute to force generation in the dramatic way suggested by analysis of simple models.

For an understanding of the mechanism of force generation we now require data (from several types of smooth muscle) on (a) myosin aggregate structure in vivo, together with thin- and thick-filament lengths; (b) the polarity of adjacent thin filaments on both sides of their anchor structures; (c) orientation of filaments with reference to the longitudinal axis of the cell and the resultant force vector; and (d) the number and relationships of thick and thin filaments interacting with each other in transverse register and forming a repeating contractile unit.

ACKNOWLEDGMENTS

While I bear responsibility for inferences and suggestions made on the basis of the somewhat limited and rather controversial literature on this subject, two groups of colleagues have made valuable contributions. One group is composed of my collaborators over the years: Drs. J. T. Herlihy, C. L.

Seidel, J. Megerman, D. M. Cohen, and particularly Dr. S. P. Driska, who analyzed the models involving increases in the ratio of thin : thick filament lengths. I am also indebted to numerous workers in the field whose thoughts, criticisms, and preprints were generously offered. In particular, I would like to thank Drs. Roland Bagby, C. F. Shoenberg, A. V. Somlyo, and Lars Thuneberg. Work from my laboratory was supported by NIH Grants HL 14547 and HL 16881.

Literature Cited

1. Ashton, F. T., Somlyo, A. V., Somlyo, A. P. 1975. The contractile apparatus of vascular smooth muscle: intermediate high voltage stereo electron microscopy. *J. Mol. Biol.* 98:17–29
2. Bagby, R. M. 1974. Time course of isotonic contraction in single cells and muscle strips from *Bufo marinus* stomach. *Am. J. Physiol.* 227:789–93
3. Bagby, R. M., Abercrombie, R. K. 1978. Observations on the 3-dimensional organization of myofibrils in vertebrate smooth muscle. In *Motility in Cell Function*, ed. F. A. Pepe. In press
4. Bagby, R. M., Pepe, F. A. 1977. Striations in antimyosin-stained isolated adult smooth muscle cells. *Fed. Proc.* 36(3):602 (Abstr.)
5. Chamley, J. H., Campbell, G. R., McConnell, J. D., Groeschel-Stewart, U. 1977. Comparison of vascular smooth muscle cells from adult human, monkey and rabbit in primary culture and in subculture. *Cell Tiss. Res.* 177:503–22
6. Close, R. I. 1972. Dynamic properties of mammalian skeletal muscles. *Physiol. Rev.* 52:129–97
7. Cohen, D. M., Murphy, R. A. 1978. Differences in cellular contractile protein contents among porcine smooth muscles: evidence for variation in the contractile system. *J. Gen. Physiol.* 72(3):369–80
8. Cooke, P. 1976. A filamentous cytoskeleton in vertebrate smooth muscle fibers. *J. Cell Biol.* 68:539–56
9. Cooke, P. H., Fay, F. S. 1972. Correlation between fiber length, ultrastructure, and the length-tension relationship of mammalian smooth muscle. *J. Cell Biol.* 52:105–16
10. Craig, R., Megerman, J. 1977. Assembly of smooth muscle myosin into sidepolar filaments. *J. Cell Biol.* 75:990–96
11. Driska, S. P., Damon, D. N., Murphy, R. A. 1978. Estimates of cellular mechanics in an arterial smooth muscle. *Biophys. J.* 24:525–40

12. Elliott, G. F. 1967. Variations of the contractile apparatus in smooth and striated muscles. *J. Gen. Physiol.* 50:171–84
13. Fay, F. S. 1976. Mechanical properties of single isolated smooth muscle cells. In *Smooth Muscle Pharmacology and Physiology*, ed. M. Worcel, G. Vassort, pp. 327–42. Paris: INSERM
14. Fay, F. S. 1977. Mechanics of single isolated smooth muscle cells. In *Excitation-Contraction Coupling in Smooth Muscle*, ed. R. Casteels, T. Godfraind, J. C. Ruegg, pp. 433–39. Amsterdam: Elsevier/North-Holland
15. Fay, F. S., Cooke, P. H., Canaday, P. G. 1976. Contractile properties of isolated smooth muscle cells. In *Physiology of Smooth Muscle*, ed. E. Bulbring, M. F. Shuba, pp. 249–64. New York: Raven
16. Fay, F. S., Delise, C. M. 1973. Contraction of isolated smooth-muscle cells —structural changes. *Proc. Natl. Acad. Sci. USA* 70:641–45
17. Fisher, B. A. 1974. *A model for vertebrate smooth muscle contraction derived from studies of circular stomach muscle from the tropical toad,* Bufo marinus. PhD thesis. Univ. Tennessee, Knoxville, Tenn. 167 pp.
18. Fisher, B. A., Bagby, R. M. 1977. Reorientation of myofilaments during contraction of a vertebrate smooth muscle. *Am. J. Physiol.* 232:C5–C14
19. Franzini-Armstrong, C. 1970. Natural variability in the length of thin and thick filaments in single fibres from a crab, *Portunus depurator*. *J. Cell Sci.* 6:559–92
20. Gabella, G. 1976. The force generated by a visceral smooth muscle. *J. Physiol.* 263:199–213
21. Gabella, G. 1976. Structural changes in smooth muscle cells during isotonic contraction. *Cell Tiss. Res.* 170:187–201
22. Gabella, G. 1977. A morphological study of the mechanical coupling be-

tween smooth muscle cells. See Ref. 14, pp. 3–12

23. Gabella, G. 1977. Arrangement of smooth muscle cells and intramuscular septa in the Taenia coli. *Cell Tiss. Res.* 184:195–212

24. Gordon, A. M., Huxley, A. F., Julian, F. J. 1966. The variation in isometric tension with sarcomere length in vertebrate muscle fibres. *J. Physiol.* 184:170–92

25. Gore, R. W. 1972. Wall stress: a determinant of regional differences in response of frog microvessels to norepinephrine. *Am. J. Physiol.* 222:82–91

26. Groeschel-Stewart, U., Chamley, J. H., Campbell, G. R., Burnstock, G. 1975. Changes in myosin distribution in dedifferentiating and redifferentiating smooth muscle cells in tissue culture. *Cell Tiss. Res.* 165:13–22

27. Lazarides, E., Hubbard, B. D. 1976. Immunological characterization of the subunit of the 100 Å filaments from muscle cells. *Proc. Natl. Acad. Sci. USA* 73:4344–48

28. Lowy, J., Poulsen, F. R., Vibert, P. J. 1970. Myosin filaments in vertebrate smooth muscle. *Nature* 225:1053–54

29. Lowy, J., Vibert, P. J., Haselgrove, J. C., Poulsen, F. R. 1973. The structure of the myosin elements in vertebrate smooth muscles. *Phil. Trans. R. Soc. Ser. B* 265:191–96

30. Marston, S. B., Taylor, E. W. 1978. Mechanism of myosin and actomyosin ATPase in chicken gizzard smooth muscle. *FEBS Lett.* 86:167–70

31. McNutt, N. S. 1975. Ultrastructure of the myocardial sarcolemma. *Circ. Res.* 37:1–13

32. Mrwa, U., Paul, R. J., Kreye, V. A. W., Ruegg, J. C. 1976. The contractile mechanism of vascular smooth muscle. See Ref. 13, pp. 319–26

33. Mulvany, M. J. 1977. Mechanical properties of smooth muscle cells. See Ref. 14, pp. 441–48

34. Murphy, R. A. 1976. Contractile system function in mammalian smooth muscle. *Blood Vessels* 13:1–23

35. Murphy, R. A. 1976. Structural proteins in the myofilaments and regulation of contraction in vertebrate smooth muscle. *Fed. Proc.* 35:1302–6

36. Murphy, R. A. 1979. The mechanics of vascular smooth muscle. In *Handbook of Physiology,* ed. D. F. Bohr, A. P. Somlyo, H. V. Sparks. In press

37. Murphy, R. A., Driska, S. P., Cohen, D. M. 1977. Variations in actin to myosin ratios and cellular force genera-

tion in vertebrate smooth muscles. See Ref. 14, pp. 417–24

38. Murphy, R. A., Herlihy, J. T., Megerman, J. 1974. Force generating capacity and contractile protein content of arterial smooth muscle. *J. Gen. Physiol.* 64:691–705

39. Paul, R. J., Peterson, J. W. 1977. The mechanochemistry of smooth muscle. In *The Biochemistry of Smooth Muscle,* ed. N. L. Stephens, pp. 15–39. Baltimore: University Park Press

40. Pease, D. C., Molinari, S. 1960. Electron microscopy of muscular arteries; pial vessels of the cat and monkey. *J. Ultrastruc. Res.* 3:447–68

41. Rice, R. V., McManus, G. M., Devine, C. E., Somlyo, A. P. 1971. Regular organization of thick filaments in mammalian smooth muscle. *Nature New Biol.* 231:242–43

42. Rosenbluth, J. 1965. Smooth muscle: an ultrastructural basis for the dynamics of its contraction. *Science* 148:1337–39

43. Ruegg, J. C. 1968. Contractile mechanisms of smooth muscle. *Aspects of Cell Motility,* 22:45–66. London: Cambridge Univ. Press

44. Ruegg, J. C. 1971. Smooth muscle tone. *Physiol. Rev.* 51:201–48

45. Schollmeyer, J. E., Furcht, L. T., Goll, D. E., Robson, R. M., Stromer, M. H. 1976. Localization of contractile proteins in smooth muscle cells and in normal and transformed fibroblasts. In *Cell Motility,* Book A, ed. R. Goldman, T. Pollard, J. Rosenbaum, pp. 361–88. Cold Spring Harbor, N.Y.: Cold Spring Harbor Laboratory

46. Shoenberg, C. F. 1969. A study of myosin filaments in extracts and homogenates of vertebrate smooth muscle. *Angiologica* 6:233–46

47. Shoenberg, C. F., Haselgrove, J. C. 1974. Filaments and ribbons in vertebrate smooth muscle. *Nature* 249:152–54

48. Shoenberg, C. F., Needham, D. M. 1976. A study of the mechanism of contraction in vertebrate smooth muscle. *Biol. Rev.* 51:53–104

49. Small, J. V. 1974. Contractile units in vertebrate smooth muscle cells. *Nature* 249:324–27

50. Small, J. V. 1977. Studies on isolated smooth muscle cells: the contractile apparatus. *J. Cell Sci.* 24:327–49

51. Small, J. V., Sobieszek, A. 1977. Studies on the function and composition of the 10-nm (100-Å) filaments of vertebrate smooth muscle. *J. Cell Sci.* 23:243–68

52. Small, J. V., Squire, J. M. 1972. Structural basis of contraction in vertebrate smooth muscle. *J. Mol. Biol.* 67:117–49
53. Sobieszek, A. 1972. Cross-bridges on self-assembled smooth muscle myosin filaments. *J. Mol. Biol.* 70:741–44
54. Somlyo, A. P., Somlyo, A. V., Ashton, F. T., Vallieres, J. 1976. Vertebrate smooth muscle: ultrastructure and function. See Ref. 45, pp. 165–83
55. Somlyo, A. V. 1979. Ultrastructure of vascular smooth muscle. See Ref. 36. In press
56. Somlyo, A. V., Ashton, F. T., Lemanski, L. F., Vallieres, J., Somlyo, A. P.

1977. Filament organization and dense bodies in vertebrate smooth muscle. See Ref. 39, pp. 455–71
57. Stephens, N. L., ed. 1977. *The Biochemistry of Smooth Muscle.* Baltimore: University Park Press. 733 pp.
58. Uvelius, B. 1976. Isometric and isotonic length-tension relations and variations in cell length in longitudinal smooth muscle from rabbit urinary bladder. *Acta Physiol. Scand.* 97:1–12
59. Weber, H. H., Ruegg, J. C. 1966. The contractile fine structure of vertebrate smooth muscle. *Med. Col. Va. Quarterly* 2:72–77

Ann. Rev. Physiol. 1979. 41:749–69
Copyright © 1979 by Annual Reviews Inc. All rights reserved

RECENT STUDIES
ON CELLULAR METABOLISM
BY NUCLEAR MAGNETIC
RESONANCE

❖1249

George K. Radda and P. John Seeley

Department of Biochemistry, University of Oxford,
South Parks Road, Oxford, UK.

INTRODUCTION

The primary concern of the physiologist is to understand function in vivo. We would like to stress the complementary aspects of measurements of this function—perhaps mechanical or electrical—and the activity of cellular metabolism at a molecular level. In particular, we shall describe the use of nuclear magnetic resonance (NMR) for the examination of energy transducing and motile systems and relate it to other ways of observing molecular events within an intact organ or organism. We have applied the following criteria in the selection of material: The measurements should be interpretable in terms of the properties of specific molecules within intact cells; the method should be noninvasive; and there should be minimal perturbation of the system from its physiological state.

SPECTROSCOPY OF MOLECULES IN CELLS

Radiation interacts with matter in either an elastic or inelastic fashion. Inelastic interactions are specific for molecular type, whereas elastic (or quasielastic) collisions give information on molecular shape or motion that cannot necessarily be assigned to individual components in an unordered system such as the cytoplasm. Important physiological information is nevertheless obtained from measurements of inelastic scattering.

749

0066-4278/79/0301-0749$01.00

Studies of protoplasmic streaming in *Nitella flexilis* (94) generated a uniform velocity profile for intracellular particles from Doppler shifts in laser light scattered from the interior of the internodal cell. Streaming was quantified, but no information on the nature of the particles involved in the motion was obtained. It was possible, however, to examine the spatial distribution of cytoplasmic motion. Using a similar technique, the frequency and synchrony of ciliary activity in rabbit fimbria and in oviduct cells were quantified (77). Scattering studies on skeletal muscle (9) postulated random axial motions of individual sarcomeres during tetanus, a phenomenon that would result in tension fluctuations and a decrease in X-ray diffraction intensities.

The most powerful scattering techniques, X-ray and neutron diffraction, are now at a stage where structural changes can be followed in functioning systems—e.g. muscular contraction [(58) and see Tregear, this volume].

The remaining methods to be described are spectroscopic: They depend on the ability of a molecule to absorb electromagnetic radiation. Fluorescence spectroscopy gives a readout of the activity of the surface of a tissue (maximal penetration depth $200 \mu m$). Contrast is controlled by selection of the excitation and emission wavelengths. Cohen (28) has pioneered the examination of extrinsic fluorescent dyes in nerve to quantify electrical changes during the action potential. Chance and his colleagues have been concerned with intrinsic tissue fluorescence from reduced pyridine nucleotide and from mitochondrial flavoproteins. Pyridine nucleotide fluorescence increases and that of flavoprotein decreases as cells become anoxic, and therefore cellular redox states can be assessed in organs such as lung (49), kidney (51), liver (25), heart (7, 90), and brain (26). Studies on kidney (51) quantify the rates and extents of redox transitions induced by anoxia, hypothermia, and metabolic inhibitions. Rates of mitochrondrial NADH oxidation were estimated from reversal of carbon monoxide anoxia by laser flash photolysis. Reduced functional ability of perfused kidneys appeared to correlate with tissue deprivation of oxygen and was interpreted in terms of a heterogeneous pattern of renal metabolism (51). Two dimensional redox heterogeneity has been visualized by fluorescence photography of partially occluded perfused hearts (7). The method has been extended into the third dimension by freezing and sectioning the tissue at liquid nitrogen temperature (25). Results support the "border-zone hypothesis" for cardiac ischemia but indicate that this zone has a maximum width of only 0.3 mm. The heterogeneity of tissue oxygenation is now being examined by microfluorimetry using "flying spot" laser excitation (25). The usefulness of time resolution in fluorescence is illustrated in simultaneous measurements of slow electrical waves and NADH emission of muscle from cat small intestine (32). An increase in NADH on cooling the preparation or with nitrogen anoxia was noted. By signal-averaging over 30–70 contraction cycles an oscillatory response in NADH/NAD was detected; NADH was at a maximum on depolarization and at a minimum for the most polarized state. ATP utilization was greatest during the repolarization phase, though the calculated upper limit for cyclic changes in ATP content was only 10%. Oscillations in ATP level could not be detected by biochemical analysis of muscle extracts.

The redox activity of blood-perfused brain and heart was monitored by absorption in the near infrared (69). Shift of hemoglobin from the oxy- to the deoxy- form was used as an indicator of the redox state of cytochrome a,a_3, in anoxia-normoxia transitions of dog heart and cat brain in situ.

In resonance Raman spectroscopy, the molecules are excited via an ultraviolet or visible absorption band of the parent molecule and it is thus possible to select for the signals of a particular molecule against the general vibrational background. Energy transduction in the purple membrane (80) and vertebrate retinal rod (78, 79) have been studied with this technique. The chromophore, retinal linked to a lysine of opsin by a Schiff base, cycles between two forms and concomitantly transports protons across the bacterial membrane. The signals in the Raman spectrum indicate an association between proton transport and the state of the rhodopsin molecule. The state of the retinal pigment in a live albino rabbit has also been observed (78). Changes in the Raman spectrum were correlated with those in the electroretinogram signal, and protonation-deprotonation of the Schiff base of retinal during visual transduction was postulated (78).

The spectroscopic methods we have outlined have many advantages over the conventional invasive analytical techniques. They give a *continuous* readout of cellular activity, they have *spatial resolution,* and they give information about *specific molecular* events in vivo. NMR combines all these advantages, but its use is frequently limited by low sensitivity.

NUCLEAR MAGNETIC RESONANCE

This section is intended to serve as a guide to terms and concepts. For reviews and references see (35, 43, 47, 48, 71, 76, 111). Many nuclei have a magnetic dipole and these may be oriented by a magnetic field in a way analogous to the alignment of a compass needle by the earth's magnetic field. The orientation behavior is determined by the spin quantum number of the nucleus, I, which is an integer or half-integer. We shall deal with the simplest and most practical case: $I = \frac{1}{2}$. The interaction of such a nucleus with a magnetic field results in alignment of the nuclear magnetic vector along two conical surfaces at $\pm \cos^{-1}(3^{-\frac{1}{2}})$ to the field (B_o), i.e. there are two nuclear states. (Both sets of nuclei are in fact precessing about direction

B_o.) The two states are of unequal energy and a nucleus may be made to flip from the lower to the higher energy state by absorption of an electromagnetic quantum with frequency $\nu = \gamma B_o / 2\pi$ (γ is the "magnetogyric ratio," which depends only on the type of nucleus, and B_o is the flux density of the field.)

An NMR machine is made up of four parts: a sample, a magnet to polarize the magnetic nuclei in the sample, a radiofrequency transmitter that supplies the radiation for excitation, and a radiofrequency detector that registers the "resonance" as a change in sample magnetization. If the sample were water and a superconducting magnet were to generate a field, B_o, of 4.2 T, proton signals would be observed at 180 MHz. A plot of signal intensity against radiofrequency would be an (ideal) Lorentz curve, the area under which is proportional to the total number of spins in the sample.

Frequency Effects

The electrons surrounding a nucleus alter the effective magnetic field it experiences. Thus the signal frequency is dependent on the nature of chemical bonding. The phosphorus NMR spectrum of a solution of ATP has, for example, three signals corresponding to the α-, β-, and γ-phosphates. Frequencies are expressed numerically in parts per million (ppm) relative to a standard signal, the "chemical shift." For biological samples shift ranges are about 15 ppm for ^1H, 40 ppm for ^{31}P, and 200 ppm for ^{13}C. Magnetic nuclei can relay information about their nuclear states from one to another via bonding electrons and this "spin-spin coupling" modifies the spectrum further.

Relaxation Effects

There are two principal "relaxation times" for every NMR signal. T_1, the "longitudinal relaxation time," is the reciprocal first-order rate constant for transfer of nuclei from one magnetic state to the other. Since these magnetic states are in the long term thermally equilibrated with their environment, it also describes the rate of conversion of magnetic to heat energy. T_2, the "transverse relaxation time," is related to the linewidth of a signal at half maximum height, $1/\pi T_2$ (neglecting field inhomogeneity).

Relaxation processes depend on the action of fluctuating magnetic fields at the nucleus and their mechanisms provide much information on the physical chemistry of molecules. Operationally, T_1 and T_2 values depend on the rate at which a molecule tumbles in solution. T_2 decreases—and linewidth increases—monotonically as the rate of the rotational motion of a molecule is lowered. (The dependence of T_1 on motion is more complex.) Macromolecules give broader signals than metabolites, and metabolites bound to macromolecules generate broader signals than those free in solution.

Nuclei with spin greater than ½ have ellipsoidal rather than spherical electrical symmetry. Their NMR signals may relax by coupling between the nuclear *quadrupole* and time-varying electrical field gradients at the nucleus. This frequently results in rather broad signals for the nucleus concerned.

Chemical Exchange

The NMR signals of molecules that exist in more than one environment or state deserve special mention. If the "forms" interchange very slowly, the NMR spectrum is simply the sum of the signals of the components. Conversely, if interchange is very rapid, both frequency and relaxation parameters are the *weighted averages* of those of the components. The determinants of spectral form are the ratios of rates of interconversion to T_1 and T_2 relaxation times and to frequency parameters (22, 84, 107). NMR may therefore be used to measure or place limits on these exchange rates. For example, ^{13}C spectra of a mixture of CO_2 and HCO_3^- in aqueous solution have two peaks separated by 37 ppm. As the pH of the solution is varied in the range of pKa_1 of carbonic acid, the relative intensities of the signals change but their frequencies remain constant. HCO_3^- and CO_2 signals are in "slow exchange." Conversely, ^{31}P NMR spectra of inorganic phosphate near neutrality have only one signal, even though both $H_2PO_4^-$ and HPO_4^{2-} ions are present in significant proportions. The signals are in "fast exchange" and the resonance shifts monotonically by 2.4 ppm as the second pK of orthophosphate is titrated.

Technical Points

If frequency shifts of signals of the order of 1 ppm are to be observed, the homogeneity of the polarizing field B_o over the sample volume must be of at least the same precision. Since signal linewidth determines the effective sensitivity of the spectrometer, it is common to arrange for field homogeneity of 1 part in 10^8.

The voltage changes induced in the primary detector of the spectrometer are $\sim 1\,\mu V$—hence the low sensitivity of NMR. The feasibility of biological studies using NMR arises from an innovation in the signal-averaging process: the Fourier transform technique. The cycle begins with an intense pulse of radiofrequency that lasts for about 1–100 μsec. Pulsing greatly increases the spread of radiation frequency and in this way allows all nuclei of a particular type to be excited simultaneously. The receiver is switched on immediately after the pulse and picks up voltages induced by magnetization changes of resonant nuclei. Data collection follows the decay of transverse magnetization for a period of several T_2 ($\sim$sec). There is then an optional waiting period before the cycle is begun again with a burst of radiation. Successive signals are added coherently in a computer memory and accumulation of data is terminated when adequate signal-to-noise [$\propto$(number cycles)$^{1/2}$] has been achieved. The conventional absorption-vs-frequency spectrum is obtained from the magnetization signal by the mathematical operation of Fourier transformation. The system thus integrates the nuclear output over the total period of spectrum acquisition; it is only for the most intense signals that spectra may be collected after a single pulse of radiation. Signal-to-noise is inversely related to the linewidth of the signal. T_1 values determine the rate at which population differences may be replenished after absorption. Hence, they determine the time between pulses in a Fourier transform experiment: Too high an input-radiofrequency power reduces population differences and the signal intensity ("saturation").

The magnetic properties of biologically important nuclei are presented in Table 1. Because of variations in nuclear properties, spectrometer sensitivity, sample size, T_1 and T_2, it is difficult to predict approximate periods for data collection. However, spectra of moderate signal-to-noise may be collected from 1 μmole of identical nuclei in $10-10^3$ min. There have thus been a large number of biological applications of ^{1}H, ^{31}P, and ^{13}C NMR. ^{15}N studies are now more frequent.

Table 1   Magnetic isotopes of the elements most common in biological systems

Mass number	Nucleus	Spin quantum number	Isotopic abundance (%)	Relative[a] sensitivity
1	H	1/2	99.98	1
2	H	1	0.016	104
13	C	1/2	1.1	63
14	N	1	99.64	990
15	N	1/2	0.37	962
17	O	5/2	0.037	34
23	Na	3/2	100	11
25	Mg	5/2	10	373
31	P	1/2	100	15
33	S	3/2	0.74	442
35	Cl	3/2	75	213
37	Cl	3/2	25	369
39	K	3/2	93	1,970
41	K	3/2	6.9	11,800
43	Ca	7/2	0.13	16

[a]Sensitivity (^{1}H)/sensitivity (equal number nuclei)

What additional problems are there if the sample is a tissue rather than a solution? Extra field inhomogeneity due to macroscopic variations in the electron density of the tissue is small: < 0.4 ppm. Organs cannot normally be perfused if the sample tube is spinning, which may be a problem if the stationary field inhomogeneity of the magnet is large. The presence of tubes required for perfusion circuits may also impair field homogeneity. Losses due to absorption of radiofrequency radiation by conductors in the sample tube (e.g. stimulators) may be minimized by decoupling circuits (see 38).

INTERACTIONS

Cations

A description of metabolism in vivo requires knowledge of hydrogen ion concentration within the cell. In particular there is much interest in the effects of acidosis on coordinated functions like heart contractility (120), the recovery of function from such acidosis (8), control of excitation by pH effects (125), and in the mechanisms of pH homeostasis (2).

Intracellular pH (pH_i) can be determined by dye absorption (85), microelectrodes (1), distribution of a weak acid or base across the plasmalemma (5), or by NMR (21, 101). For a review of methods see (30). Distribution techniques have poor time resolution because of the necessity of equilibration of the marker across cell membranes. They are also subject to uncertainties associated with the state of the marker inside the cell and its partition among subcellular compartments. Measurements of pH are made from the frequency of ^{31}P NMR signals of phosphate ions of pK values close to the pH. (The ionizations are in fast exchange as discussed above.) pH_i has been obtained in this way for erythrocytes (89), yeast (113), *E.coli* (96, 101), skeletal muscle (20, 65), and heart (53, 68). Potential systematic error arises from phosphate interactions in the cell that do not occur in the "standard" solution used for frequency calibration. This problem is analogous to the interference effects that trouble both the distribution (30) and the ion-specific electrode techniques (126). The absolute value of pH_i is more precise if there is more than one phosphate marker—e.g. the inorganic phosphate and diphosphoglycerate signals of the erythrocyte (89). The method has significant advantages: (*a*) It is noninvasive. (*b*) It is relatively rapid. (Our ^{31}P NMR spectrometer can measure inorganic phosphate signal frequency within 10 sec for an adult rat heart.) (*c*) It is possible to measure not only mean pH, but also distribution of pH_i (21, 52, 63, 116) (see below). Besides ^{31}P NMR of phosphates, ^{13}C spectra of carbonate and bicarbonate and ^{1}H and ^{13}C spectra of amino acids are feasible monitors for pH. For erythrocytes, a pH_i value of 7.4 was measured from the ^{1}H NMR signals of hemoglobin histidines (14).

Mg^{2+} is not only an essential cofactor for kinase reactions, it also modulates the functions of other intracellular cations, particularly calcium. Thus the influence of Mg^{2+} on calcium movement in skeletal muscle (121, 122) and the Mg-inhibition of Na^+-K^+ ATPase (41) have been examined. Present methods for investigating intracellular Mg^{2+} are limited. The most indirect is calculation of the levels of various Mg^{2+}-complexes from in vitro association constants (124). Alternatively, the concentration of free Mg^{2+} may be estimated from Mg^{2+} effects on Na^+-K^+ ATPase activity (41), diffusional and electrophoretic mobility (6), or dual-wavelength absorption spectroscopy using a metallochromic indicator (12). The latter determination on single barnacle muscle fibres used a null-point method to avoid interference effects, but required internal dialysis of the fibre. The concentration of free Mg^{2+} was found to be 6 mM (12).

NMR observations of tissue Mg^{2+} have been indirect. ^{31}P signal frequencies of ATP are shifted appreciably on formation of the MgATP complex (31) and existence of the cellular triphosphate in its Mg^{2+}-bound form has been observed for several systems such as muscle (20, 65) and ascites tumor cells (95). Free Mg^{2+} was estimated as 4.4 mM in frog gastrocnemius by measuring T_2 relaxation times for phosphocreatine signals (29). T_2 for Mg^{2+}-phosphocreatine is less than T_2 for phosphocreatine due to an exchange effect, even though T_1 and frequency are unaffected. There have been few observations of the isotope of magnesium, ^{25}Mg, possessing a nuclear magnetic moment (Table 1) (17). Collection of spectra from ^{25}Mg-enriched tissue should be feasible at mM levels for free and complexed Mg^{2+} despite the quadrupolar character of the nucleus. Bryant's data (17) are moderately encouraging: Though the linewidth of MgATP is 1000 Hz, that of Mg^{2+} in solution is only 4 Hz. The chemical shift between Mg^{2+} and MgATP is large enough for two signals to be resolved at high magnetic fields.

The physiological significance of Ca^{2+} and the desirability of tracking intracellular fluxes of this ion are self-evident. Calcium-sensitive electrodes of low selectivity are available (126), but there have been few applications to cellular systems (106). Investigations of concentrations of ionized calcium in squid axons have used light emission from aequorin (42) and light absorption by the metallochromic dye Arsenazo III (13, 42) in conjunction with the internal dialysis technique. There have been no indirect observations of Ca^{2+} by NMR and only one examination of the rather expensive ^{43}Ca nucleus (16). The signal linewidth for Ca^{2+} solutions at pH 6.4 was 0.4 Hz, and that for CaATP (pH 6.4) was estimated to be 83 Hz. (The nucleus is quadrupolar.)

$^{23}Na^+$ and $^{39}K^+$ resonances have been observed in several types of cells and tissue (27, 88), and the difficulties of interpretation have been reviewed (45), as has the use of NMR in the study of cellular water (33).

Anions

Knowledge of intracellular activities of carbon dioxide and bicarbonate is necessary for an understanding of pH homeostasis and transport of CO_2 in tissue. Renewed theoretical interest in mechanisms of CO_2 transport within the cell (56) and across the cell membrane (57) correspond in time to developments in use of bicarbonate-specific microelectrodes (70). Sophisticated isotopic exchange techniques have also been used for continuous monitoring of carbonic anhydrase activity within the erythrocyte (67, 119).

The system is uniquely amenable to ^{13}C NMR studies using enriched carbonates (Table 1). The "slow exchange" between CO_2 and HCO_3^- is accelerated to "intermediate exchange" by carbonic anhydrase. The increases in signal linewidths concomitant with catalysis of the $CO_2 \leftrightarrows HCO_3^-$ reaction have been analyzed to supply rate constants of elementary steps (72). [There are also changes in T_1 values on catalysis (92).] These observations were preceded historically by studies of $^{13}CO_2$ interaction with human red blood cells (87). A signal adjacent to that of bicarbonate was tentatively assigned to the carbamino derivative of the terminal valines of the α- and β-chains of hemoglobin. This observation was confirmed and extended (92), and ^{13}C NMR signals were assigned to carbamino adducts of particular amino acids (91, 93).

The interaction between diphosphoglycerate and components of the red cell will be discussed below.

METABOLISM, CONTRACTILITY, AND ENERGY TRANSDUCTION

^{31}P NMR of Organs

It was first demonstrated in 1974 that ^{31}P NMR spectra could be recorded from muscle. The major resonances were identified as those of ATP, phosphocreatine, and inorganic and sugar phosphates(65). From such spectra the intracellular pH, the interaction of ATP with metal ions, and slow metabolic changes during anoxia could be measured. Burt et al have confirmed and extended these findings in a comparison of different muscle types (20), as have Seeley and colleagues (116). Significant differences were observed in the time-course of changes under anaerobic conditions. Thus the ATP content of Northern frog muscle was maintained for 7 hr while other types of amphibian, avian, and mammalian muscles began to show appreciable breakdown in ATP after 2 hr. Hitherto unsuspected metabolites were detected by their signals in the phosphodiester frequency range of spectra from rabbit muscle, frog gastrocnemius, and dystrophic chicken pectoralis (24, 116). On the basis of chromatographic separation and chemical analysis these compounds were identified as glycerophosphorylcholine (19, 115) and as L-serine ethanolamine phosphodiester in dystrophic chicken muscle (24). The presence of several such compounds in toad muscle was also reported (20, 38).

NMR may help in elucidating the functional role of these phosphodiesters; at present it can give us a quick estimate of these compounds in different tissues, confirming older observations (112). For example, it was shown that the concentration of glycerophosphorylcholine in Duchenne dystrophic quadriceps was significantly lower than that in normal human quadriceps, whereas elevated levels were detected for muscles with Werdnig-Hoffmann syndrome (18).

In view of the extensive work on metabolite levels in muscle, a first requirement has been the comparison of analytical information obtained by NMR and chemical methods. The concentrations of compounds determined by both techniques are in broad agreement for mammalian skeletal muscle (20, 65) and frog sartorii (38). This problem merits detailed study since the conventional freeze-extraction method measures total metabolite concentrations whereas the NMR signals of the intact system arise from relatively mobile (i.e. unbound) molecules.

It is well known that for contracting frog sartorii the energy produced as heat and work cannot be accounted for by the chemical reactions (55). Several aspects of this problem have been studied recently using chemical methods of analysis. Two kinds of energy imbalance were observed for rapidly shortening *Rana pipiens* skeletal muscle (110). (*a*) Approximately 70% of the total energy liberated in a contraction-relaxation cycle can be attributed to phosphocreatine splitting. This result is similar to those obtained in isotonic afterloaded twitches (127) and in isometric twitches and tetani (64, 127). (*b*) There is a temporal energy imbalance; during rapid shortening, energy is produced without equivalent phosphocreatine or ATP splitting; during relaxation, high-energy phosphate is split with little heat production. It was also shown that the energy imbalance was much smaller for the second tetanus than in the first of a closely spaced pair of isometric tetani (36). Kushmerick & Paul concluded from measurements of oxygen consumption during recovery that the contractile history of a muscle plays a significant role in determining the chemical energy cost of an isometric contraction (73).

With these problems in mind, Dawson, Gadian & Wilkie developed the physiological techniques required to maintain muscles for long periods within the NMR spectrometer, to stimulate them, to record tension development, and at the same time to observe ^{31}P NMR signals (38). By synchronizing NMR data collection with the electrical stimulation of the muscle, several important observations were made. Following 25-sec tetani (repeated every 56 min) approximately 20% of the phosphocreatine was broken down in frog sartorii. Both the phosphocreatine and inorganic phosphate recovered with a half-time of about 10 min. Two unexpected observations were (a) the fall in inorganic phosphate concentration below that in the resting muscle, and (b) the maintenance of sugar phosphate at a high and constant level throughout the recovery period, which was not observed when shorter stimulations were used. When frog sartorii were tetanized for 1 sec every 2 min, the changes in phosphocreatine and inorganic phosphate were too small to observe; but large changes in these compounds were seen when toad gastrocnemii were similarly stimulated. The possibility was raised that during the steady state of repeated contraction the energy deficit might disappear (38).

Studies on anaerobic frog muscles undergoing repeated isometric contractions at 4°C have used ^{31}P NMR to link biochemical and energetic changes to force development in fatiguing muscle [(39) and J. Dawson, personal communication]. A novel feature of this study was the use of a measured decline in pH to derive the concentration of lactate from the known buffering capacity of the tissue. It was concluded that the decline in isometric force development is more likely to be linked to changes in metabolites than to any independent changes in conduction of excitation. The decline in force development as the muscle fatigues was proportional to the decrease in rate of phosphorus utilization, which suggests that the hydrolysis of ATP in each crossbridge cycle produces a fixed mechanical impulse and that the economy of ATP hydrolysis remains unchanged.

Studies on thin skeletal muscles such as frog sartorii place considerable limitation on the NMR measurements because only small volumes of tissue can be kept in good physiological condition. In contrast, perfused hearts of almost any size can be kept functioning for many hours; in this case the size of the NMR tube limits the experiments.

Myocardial metabolism has been extensively reviewed by Neely & Morgan (97). In addition to studies on the relation between energy metabolism and cardiac output (66), substantial effort has been directed towards understanding myocardial infarction (103); and it is towards this problem that the NMR experiments reported have been addressed. Of current interest are questions about (a) the nature of the border zone between normal and damaged tissue following the onset of regional ischemia by coronary artery ligation (59); (b) methods for estimating the size of the infarct (10, 25); (c) means of providing protection to the ischemic myocardium (11, 81, 82, 104).

The first ^{31}P NMR experiments were carried out on a small rat heart that was rapidly cooled after removal from the animal (52). The spectrum showed peaks that could be assigned to ATP, phosphocreatine, inorganic phosphate, and sugar phosphate; the integrals, after about half an hour of accumulation, showed that the three ATP signals were in the ratio $\beta:\alpha: \gamma = 0.5:1.5:0.9$, implying that the γ-peak contained a contribution from ADP and that the α-peak, in addition to those from ADP, also contained contributions from other pyrophosphate-diesters.

After the temperature was raised to 30°C a steady increase in the inorganic phosphate level and a run-down of the energy store were observed, together with a progressive shift of the inorganic phosphate signal to lower frequencies. It was suggested that the increased acidity of the ischemic tissue should lead to the possibility of distinguishing normal from damaged tissue in experiments on regionally ischemic hearts and possibly to measurements of infarct volumes based on the proportions of the low and high pH inorganic phosphate signals (52).

Two orthophosphate signals were indeed found in regionally ischemic rabbit hearts following ligation of the left anterior descending coronary artery (63). It was argued, however, that the area under the acidic phosphate peak could not be directly related to the volume of the ischemic tissue because of presumed phosphate washout by coronary arterial collateral flow. We believe that this view is too pessimistic and that there are ways to overcome this problem.

Spectra of perfused rat hearts were reported by two groups (53, 68). Jacobus et al demonstrated the feasibility of the experiment. They claimed that the intracellular pH dropped from 7.4 to 5.7 during total ischemia. After reperfusion only partial recovery of the original metabolite levels was obtained, and the pH_i was reported to remain at 6.1 (68). In our experiments the pH change was much smaller and we did not observe loss of cellular phosphate during perfusion (53). In ischemia-reperfusion sequences the original phosphocreatine and ATP levels were almost entirely restored but the sugar phosphate level remained high, an observation reminiscent of that seen in skeletal muscle after extensive contraction. The early observations of Jacobus et al must be attributed to inadequate perfusion technique; indeed they have reported different data subsequently (123), in agreement with our observations both on rat (53) and mouse hearts (54). For mouse hearts, we measured the extent and time-course of acidification during ischemia. It was noted that the phosphocreatine/ATP ratio was higher at the initial stages of perfusion; coronary flow was also at its high, pre-steady-state level. A rapid and unexpectedly large resynthesis of phosphocreatine was observed following reperfusion after total ischemia. The cellular pH rapidly returned to its value prior to ischemia, whereas the recovery of the nucleotide pool was relatively slow and was accompanied by a fall in the phosphocreatine level. The possibility that this phosphocreatine "overshoot" is related to the existence of two types of creatine kinase (mitochondrial and cytoplasmic) raises some interesting questions.

An investigation of the "calcium paradox" in rat heart by ^{31}P NMR and ultrastructural methods showed that Ca^{2+}-deprivation injury was largely confined to cell junctions, while pH and high-energy phosphates were maintained. Metabolic integrity was only impaired after Ca^{2+} reflow (62).

So far, ^{31}P NMR experiments on isolated rat kidneys have been concerned with establishing conditions under which one could follow the depletion of metabolites during warm and cold ischemia and their recovery following blood perfusion using a circuit with an anesthetized "assist" animal (117). In addition to resonances from ATP, phosphocreatine, and inorganic phosphate, AMP and a large phosphodiester signal are observed in renal tissue. The gradual depletion of the energy pool during cold ischemia is associated with a much smaller change in intracellular pH in this tissue than in muscle, presumably because of the relatively low glycogen content and the slow rates of glycolysis in kidney. When an isolated ischemic kidney is linked up to the blood circulation of an anesthetized animal, ATP is resynthesized to its original level. Kidneys perfused in this way produce urine, and it is therefore possible, using this model, to quantify metabolic effects of the procedures involved in renal transplantation.

Cellular and Subcellular Systems

The first reports of Moon & Richards (89) and Henderson et al (60) on the use of ^{31}P NMR to study erythrocytes were rapidly followed by a series of papers by Shulman and his collaborators. Moon & Richards determined the pH_i while Henderson et al demonstrated that the major metabolites observable by NMR included ATP, inorganic phosphate, 2,3-diphosphoglycerate and hexose- or triosephosphate. Apart from noting that changes in these metabolites could be observed when cells were aged or treated with inosine and pyruvate, the authors concluded that there were two microenvironments for ATP in the red cell. Thus specific intracellular interactions can be studied in the same way as in solution (34). ^{31}P NMR spectra were reported for yeast cells (113), Ehrlich ascites tumor cells (95), E.coli (96, 101), and in lymphoid, Friend erythroleukemic, and HeLa cells (46, 118). For each of these systems several phosphate-containing molecules were detected and identified. Semiquantitative measurements using NMR have confirmed previous conclusions about the metabolic sequences.

Using a sophisticated system to maintain O_2 tension in cellular suspensions, two important types of experiment were carried out. For E.coli it was possible to resolve extracellular and intracellular inorganic phosphate signals and to show that a ΔpH (pH_i-pH_o) of almost one unit was generated either by reversal of the ATPase reaction (anaerobic conditions, ATP synthesized through glycolysis) or by respiration (aerobic conditions with and without ATPase inhibitor) (96, 101). The outward movement of protons during respiration is consistent with the chemiosmotic hypothesis. No appreciable pH gradient was observed across the cell membrane of mammalian cells (118), but pH gradients across isolated liver mitochondria could be followed by NMR (100).

One of the most interesting applications of ^{31}P NMR to the study of cellular suspensions has been the measurement of steady-state ATPase rates by the method of "saturation transfer" (15). Spin magnetization of one chemical species is perturbed from its thermal equilibrium value, and the rate of appearance of the nonequilibrium spin magnetization at the second species is monitored to determine the reaction rate. This technique can measure unidirectional rates under steady-state or equilibrium conditions with time resolution of 1 sec or less. For *E. coli* the unimolecular exchange rates between inorganic phosphate and ATP catalyzed by the dicyclohexyl-carbodiimide-sensitive ATPase were found to be 0.6 sec^{-1} for P_i to ATP and about 20 sec^{-1} for ATP to P_i. This technique has general applicability.

A system for which ^{31}P NMR led to conceptual advance is the catecholamine storage vesicle (chromaffin granule) of the adrenal medulla. In addition to catecholamines, these vesicles contain a high concentration of ATP (128) and the ^{31}P NMR spectrum of this internal ATP can be observed both in intact adrenal glands and isolated chromaffin granules (23, 109). For both situations the phosphorus signal frequency of the γ-phosphate of ATP indicates an intragranular pH of 5.6 in the resting granule. (This value can be derived only if elaborate calibrations are done.) This pH drops by 0.4–0.5 units when ATP is added to isolated granules and hydrolyzed by the membrane ATPase. Because of the differences in composition and pH of the internal and external solutions, the signals of internal and external nucleotides and inorganic phosphate can be resolved. It is thus possible to show that the membrane-bound ATPase is an inwardly directed, electrogenic proton pump (23). By using values of buffering capacity determined from reconstituted intragranular solutions, pH changes were converted into the number of protons translocated per ATP hydrolyzed. This ratio was found to be about 1.0 immediately after external ATP addition and fell towards zero as the pH gradient increased to a new steady state. Theoretical considerations show that the actual H^+/ATP ratio of the proton pump is 2.0; the low experimental value observed resulted from passive proton leakage (98, 99).

Until now the phosphorus nucleus has been the favored choice for NMR studies of cellular systems because it is sensitive, generates relatively simple spectra, and a number of phosphate-containing metabolites are present in high concentrations in cells. The promise of ^{13}C NMR relies largely on the use of selectively enriched compounds because the natural abundance of the magnetic carbon isotope is only 1.1% (Table 1). This method has been employed to great effect in studies of biosynthesis, which represent a rather long-term view of metabolism. Not only does the ^{13}C technique reveal the paths of carbon in genesis of a particular molecule, but the information is obtained without the need for painstaking assessment of isotopic composition of individual carbons by unambiguous degradation procedures (cf ^{14}C) (86).

Using randomly enriched ^{13}C acetate and $(1-^{13}C)$ glucose as substrates, ^{13}C spectra were obtained from yeast cells (44). More recently, plant metabolism has been followed in soybeans labelled by $^{13}CO_2$ (114). We expect that ^{13}C NMR will become much more widely used in cellular studies.

Despite its sensitivity, owing to the ubiquity of the hydrogen nucleus in biological systems and the relatively small chemical shifts, proton NMR generally yields broad undecipherable signals from cellular systems. Recent application of the "spin-echo" method has increased the possibilities for ^1H experiments by allowing selection of the observed resonances, essentially on the basis of molecular mobility. Signals from purine nucleotides, glutathione, lactate, and pyruvate in human erythrocytes have been assigned, plus those from specific residues of hemoglobin (14). The method was used to follow the time-courses of lactate synthesis and glutathione reduction on addition of glucose to red cells.

STRUCTURE

NMR is one of the most powerful methods for studying the structure and conformation of molecules in solution. This type of information is also available for the molecules in a living system if the NMR signals are well resolved. More sophisticated forms of the NMR measurement can be used to determine the spatial distribution of material.

Molecular Components

The structure and motion of molecular components of cells and their membranes have been studied by the use of isotopic enrichment in the case of ^{13}C (83), ^{15}N (74), and ^2H (102), and by the use of selective enhancement of the NMR signals in the case of ^1H NMR (37). ^{31}P NMR has also been used to study membranes of bacteria (40).

Compartmentation

Postulates of intracellular compartmentation of metabolites have often provided the escape route for rationalization of unexplained observations of metabolism [for an excellent review, see (105)]. ^{31}P NMR has already shown promise as a new approach. Fossel & Solomon observed that in human red cells the 2,3-diphosphoglycerate resonances shifted when 10^{-6} M ouabain was added after incubation with glucose (50). They suggested that this was a result of alteration in the interaction of the diphosphate with phosphoglycerate mutase which was mediated through phosphoglycerate kinase. A network of enzymes, interacting with the cell membrane and hence the Na^+-K^+ ATPase, was postulated. Kinetic studies have also provided evidence that membrane-bound phosphoglycerate kinase and Na^+-K^+ ATPase are linked via a compartmented form of ATP (108).

The observed linewidth of the inorganic phosphate signal from skeletal muscle is consistently greater than that for phosphocreatine (21, 38, 116), yet in aqueous solution the two molecules have the same linewidth. Multicomponent orthophosphate signals are also seen during metabolic rundown of anoxic muscles (116). The intrinsic linewidths for phosphate and phosphocreatine in muscle determined from the T_2 measurements are, however, identical (116). It was therefore suggested that the inorganic phosphate experiences several pH environments in the cell. Perturbation of pH_i in muscle by acetate resulted in the detection of two inorganic phosphate and sugar phosphate pools (21). The observations were tentatively interpreted in terms of compartmentation of these molecules between the sarcoplasm and sarcoplasmic reticulum.

Spatial Distribution

In a conventional NMR experiment the sample is placed in the most uniform magnetic field available. Even if the sample is macroscopically nonuniform the observed spectrum will merely be a superposition of the NMR signals of the components. In recent years, several methods for resolving local properties within NMR samples have been developed (3, 75). These methods all depend on the encoding of spacial information into the NMR signals by the use of nonuniform fields and are referred to as "zeugmatographic imaging." To date this imaging in biological systems has, for reasons of sensitivity, been restricted to measurements of the properties of tissue water. Images of a human hand (4, 61), plants, malignant tumors in mice, and other systems have been obtained (75). It is possible to combine imaging with other types of NMR measurement discussed in this article; we can confidently expect "metabolic imaging" of isolated organs in the not-too-distant future.

ACKNOWLEDGMENTS

P. J. S. is a British Heart Foundation Fellow. The authors' own work described in this article was supported by the British Heart Foundation, NIH (Grant HL 18708–0251), and by the Science Research Council.

Literature Cited

1. Aickin, C. C., Thomas, R. C. 1977. Micro-electrode measurement of the intracellular pH and buffering power of mouse soleus muscle fibres. *J. Physiol. London* 267:791–810
2. Aickin, C. C., Thomas, R. C. 1977. An investigation of the ionic mechanism of intracellular pH regulation in mouse soleus muscle fibres. *J. Physiol. London* 273:295–316
3. Andrew, E. R. 1976. *Magnetic Resonance in Condensed Matter—Recent Developments.* Paper presented at IVth Ampere International Summer School, Pula, Yugoslavia.
4. Andrew, E. R., Bottomley, P. A., Hinshaw, W. S., Holland, G. N., Moore, W. S., Simaroj, C. 1977. NMR images by the multiple sensitive point method: application to larger biological systems. *Phys. Med. Biol.* 22:971–74
5. Arieff, A. I., Kerian, A., Massry, S. G., DeLima, J. 1976. Intracellular pH of brain: alterations in acute respiratory acidosis and alkalosis. *Am. J. Physiol.* 230:804–12
6. Baker, P. F., Crawford, A. C. 1972. Mobility and transport of magnesium in squid giant axons. *J. Physiol. London,* 227:855–74
7. Barlow, C. H., Chance, B. 1976. Ischemic areas in perfused rat hearts: measurement by NADH fluorescence photography. *Science* 193:909–10
8. Bing, O. H. L., Brooks, W. W., Messer, J. V. 1973. Heart muscle viability following hypoxia: protective effect of acidosis. *Science* 180:1297–98
9. Bonner, R. F., Carlson, F. D. 1975. Structural dynamics of frog muscle during isometric contraction. *J. Gen. Physiol.* 65:555–81
10. Brachfeld, N. 1976. Characterization of the ischemic process by regional metabolism. *Am. J. Cardiol.* 37:467–73
11. Brachfeld, N. 1976. Metabolic evaluation of agents designed to protect the ischemic myocardium and to reduce infarct size. *Am. J. Cardiol.* 37:528–32
12. Brinley, F. J., Scarpa, A., Tiffert, T. 1977. The concentration of ionized magnesium in barnacle muscle fibres. *J. Physiol. London,* 266:545–65
13. Brinley, F. J., Tiffert, T., Scarpa, A., Mullins, L. J. 1977. Intracellular calcium buffering capacity in isolated squid axons. *J. Gen. Physiol.* 70:355–84
14. Brown, F. F., Campbell, I. D., Kuchel, P. W., Rabenstein, D. C. 1977. Human erythrocyte metabolism studies by ¹H spin echo HMR. *FEBS Lett.* 82:12–16

15. Brown, T. R., Ugurbil, K., Shulman, R. G. 1977. ³¹P nuclear magnetic resonance measurements of ATPase kinetics in aerobic *Escherichia coli* cells. *Proc. Natl. Acad. Sci. USA,* 74:5551–53
16. Bryant, R. G. 1969. Nuclear magnetic resonance study of calcium-43. *J. Am. Chem. Soc.* 91:1870–71
17. Bryant, R. G. 1972. Magnesium-25 nuclear magnetic resonance in aqueous phosphate solutions. *J. Magn. Reson.* 6:159–66
18. Burt, C. T., Danon, M. J., Millar, E. A., Homa, F. L., Vuolo, M. D., Bárány, M., Glonek, T. 1978. Variation of phosphate metabolites in normal and Duchenne human muscle. *Biophys. J.* 21:184a
19. Burt, C. T., Glonek, T., Bárány, M. 1976. Phosphorus-31 nuclear magnetic resonance detection of unexpected phosphodiesters in muscle. *Biochemistry* 15:4850–53
20. Burt, C. T., Glonek, T., Bárány, M. 1976. Analysis of phosphate metabolites, the intracellular pH, and the state of adenosine triphosphate in intact muscle by phosphorus nuclear magnetic resonance. *J. Biol. Chem.* 251:2584–91
21. Busby, S. J. W., Gadian, D. G., Radda, G. K., Richards, R. E., Seeley, P. J. 1978. Phosphorus nuclear-magnetic-resonance studies of compartmentation in muscle. *Biochem. J.* 170:103–14
22. Carrington, A., McLachlan, A. D. 1967. *Introduction to Magnetic Resonance.* New York: Harper and Row
23. Casey, R. P., Njus, D., Radda, G. K., Sehr, P. A. 1977. Active proton uptake by chromaffin granules: observation by amine distribution and phosphorus-31 nuclear magnetic resonance techniques. *Biochemistry* 16:972–77
24. Chalovich, J. M., Burt, C. T., Cohen, S. M., Glonek, T., Bárány, M. 1977. Identification of an unknown ³¹P nuclear magnetic resonance from dystrophic chicken as L-serine ethanolamine phosphodiester. *Arch. Biochem. Biophys.* 182:683–89
25. Chance, B., Barlow, C, Haselgrove, J., Nakase, Y., Matschinsky, F., Mayevsky, A. 1978. Microheterogeneities of redox states of perfused and intact organs. In *The Role of Compartmentation in Metabolic Regulation: Microenvironment,* ed. P. A. Srere, R. W. Estabrook. New York: Academic In press
26. Chance, B., Mayevsky, A. 1974. Repetitive patterns of metabolic changes dur-

ing cortical spreading depression of the awake rat. *Brain Res.* 65:529–33

27. Civan, M. M., McDonald, G. G., Pring, M., Shporer, M. 1976. Pulsed nuclear magnetic resonance study of ^{39}K in frog striated muscle. *Biophys. J.* 16:1385–98

28. Cohen, L. B. 1973. Changes in neuron structure during action potential propagation and synaptic transmission. *Physiol. Rev.* 53:373–418

29. Cohen, S. M., Burt, C. T. 1977. ^{31}P nuclear magnetic relaxation studies of phosphocreatine in intact muscle: determination of intracellular free magnesium. *Proc. Natl. Acad. Sci. USA* 74:4271–75

30. Cohen, R. D., Iles, R. A. 1975. Intracellular pH: measurement, control and metabolic interrelationships. *Crit. Rev. Clin. Lab. Sci.* 6:101–43

31. Cohn, M., Hughes, T. R. 1962. Nuclear magnetic resonance spectra of adenosine di- and triphosphate. *J. Biol. Chem.* 237:176–81

32. Connor, J. A., Kreulen, D. L., Prosser, C. L. 1976. Relation between oxidative metabolism and slow rhythmic potentials in mammalian intestinal muscle. *Proc. Natl. Acad. Sci. USA* 73:4239–43

33. Cooke, R., Kuntz, I. D. 1974. The properties of water in biological systems. *Ann. Rev. Biophys. Bioeng.* 3:95–126

34. Costello, A. J. R., Marshall, W. E., Omachi, A., Henderson, T. O. 1976. Interactions between hemoglobin and organic phosphates investigated with ^{31}P nuclear magnetic resonance spectroscopy and ultrafiltration. *Biochim. Biophys. Acta* 427:481–91

35. Coxon, B. 1972. Proton magnetic resonance spectroscopy: part I. *Adv. Carbohydrate Chem. Biochem.* 27:7–83

36. Curtin, N. A., Woledge, R. C. 1977. A comparison of the energy balance in two successive isometric tetani of frog muscle. *J. Physiol. London* 270:455–71

37. Daniels, A., Williams, R. J. P., Wright, P. E. 1976. Nuclear magnetic resonance studies of the adrenal gland and some other organs. *Nature* 261:321–22

38. Dawson, M. J., Gadian, D. G., Wilkie, D. R. 1977. Contraction and recovery of living muscle studied by ^{31}P nuclear magnetic resonance. *J. Physiol. London* 267:703–35

39. Dawson, M. J., Gadian, D. G., Wilkie, D. R. 1977. Studies of living, contracting muscle by ^{31}P nuclear magnetic resonance. In *NMR in Biology,* ed. R. A. Dwek, I. D. Campbell, R. E. Richards, R. J. P. Williams, pp. 289–322.

New York/London/San Francisco: Academic

40. De Kruijff, B., Cullis, P. R., Radda, G. K., Richards, R. E. 1976. Phosphorus nuclear magnetic resonance of *Acholeplasma laidlawii* cell membranes and derived liposomes. *Biochim. Biophys. Acta* 419:411–24

41. De Weer, P. 1976. Axoplasmic free magnesium levels and magnesium extrusion from squid giant axons. *J. Gen. Physiol.* 68:159–78

42. DiPolo, R., Requena, J., Brinley, F. J., Mullins, L. J., Scarpa, A., Tiffert, T. 1976. Ionized calcium concentration in squid axons. *J. Gen. Physiol.* 67:433–67

43. Dwek, R. A. 1973. *Nuclear Magnetic Resonance in Biochemistry: Applications to Enzyme Systems.* Oxford: Clarendon Press

44. Eakin, R. T., Morgan, L. O., Gregg, C. T., Matwiyoff, N. A. 1972. Carbon-13 nuclear magnetic resonance spectroscopy of living cells and their metabolism of a specifically labelled ^{13}C substrate. *FEBS Lett.* 28:259–64

45. Edzes, H. T., Berendsen, H. J. C. 1975. The physical state of diffusible ions in cells. *Ann. Rev. Biophys. Bioeng.* 4:265–85

46. Evans, F. E., Kaplan, N. O. 1977. ^{31}P nuclear magnetic resonance studies of HeLa cells. *Proc. Natl. Acad. Sci. USA* 74:4909–13

47. Farrar, T. C., Becker, E. D. 1971. *Pulse and Fourier Transform NMR. Introduction to Theory and Methods,* New York/London: Academic

48. Feeney, J. 1977. Carbon-13 nuclear magnetic resonance spectroscopy. *Essays Chem.* 7:67–97

49. Fisher, A. B., Furia, L., Chance, B. 1976. Evaluation of redox state of isolated perfused rat lung. *Am. J. Physiol.* 230:1198–1204

50. Fossel, E. T., Solomon, A. K. 1977. Membrane mediated link between ion transport and metabolism in human red cells. *Biochim. Biophys. Acta* 464:82–92

51. Franke, H., Barlow, C. H., Chance, B. 1976. Oxygen delivery in perfused rat kidney: NADH fluorescence and renal functional state. *Am. J. Physiol.* 231:1082–88

52. Gadian, D. G., Hoult, D. I., Radda, G. K., Seeley, P. J., Chance, B., Barlow, C. 1976. Phosphorus nuclear magnetic resonance studies on normoxic and ischemic cardiac tissue. *Proc. Natl. Acad. Sci. USA* 73:4446–48

53. Garlick, P. B., Radda, G. K., Seeley, P. J., Chance, B. 1977. Phosphorus NMR

studies on perfused heart. *Biochem. Biophys. Res. Commun.* 74:1256–62

54. Garlick, P. B., Seeley, P. J., Battersby, M. K., Radda, G. K. 1978. Phosphorus nuclear magnetic resonance studies on perfused heart. *Regulatory Mechanisms of Carbohydrate Metabolism* ed. V. Esmann, pp 297–302 Oxford/New York: Pergamon Press

55. Gilbert, C., Kretzschmar, K. M., Wilkie, D. R., Woledge, R. C. 1971. Chemical change and energy output during muscular contraction. *J. Physiol. London* 218:163–93

56. Gros, G., Moll, W., Hoppe, H., Gros, H. 1976. Proton transport by phosphate diffusion—a mechanism of facilitated CO_2 transfer. *J. Gen. Physiol.* 67:773–90

57. Gutknecht, J., Bisson, M. A., Tosteson, F. C. 1977. Diffusion of carbon dioxide through lipid bilayer membranes. *J. Gen. Physiol.* 69:779–94

58. Haselgrove, J. C., Stewart, M., Huxley, H. E. 1976. Cross-bridge movement during muscle contraction. *Nature* 261:606–8

59. Hearse, D. J., Opie, L. H., Katzeff, I. E., Lubbe, L. W., van der Werff, T. J., Peisach, M., Boulle, G. 1977. Characterisation of the "border-zone" in acute regional ischemia in the dog. *Am. J. Cardiol.* 40:716–26

60. Henderson, T. O., Costello, A. J. R., Omachi, A. 1974. Phosphate metabolism in intact human erythrocytes: determination by phosphorus-31 nuclear magnetic resonance spectroscopy. *Proc. Natl. Acad. Sci USA* 71:2487–90

61. Hinshaw, W. S., Bottomley, P. A., Holland, G. N. 1977. Radiographic thin-section image of the human wrist by nuclear magnetic resonance. *Nature* 270:722–23

62. Hollis, D. P., Nunnally, R. L., Bulkley, B. H. 1978. ^{31}P NMR and ultrastructural study of 'calcium paradox' in rat heart. *Biophys. J.* 21:218a

63. Hollis, D. P., Nunnally, R. L., Jacobus, W. E., Taylor, G. J. IV. 1977. Detection of regional ischemia in perfused beating hearts by phosphorus nuclear magnetic resonance. *Biochem. Biophys. Res. Commun.* 75:1086–91

64. Homsher, E., Mommaerts, W. F. H. M., Ricchiuti, N. V., Wallner, A. 1972. Activation heat, activation metabolism and tension-related heat in frog semitendinosus muscles. *J. Physiol. London* 220:601–25

65. Hoult, D. I., Busby, S. J. W., Gadian, D. G., Radda, G. K., Richards, R. E.,

Seeley, P. J. 1974. Observation of tissue metabolites using ^{31}P nuclear magnetic resonance. *Nature* 252:285–87

66. Illingworth, J. A., Ford, W. C. L., Kobayashi, K., Williamson, J. R. 1975. Regulation of myocardial energy metabolism. *Recent Adv. Stud. Card. Struct. Metab.* 8:271–90

67. Itada, N., Forster, R. E. 1977. Carbonic anhydrase activity in intact red blood cells measured with ^{18}O exchange. *J. Biol. Chem.* 252:3881–90

68. Jacobus, W. E., Taylor, G. J. IV, Hollis, D. P., Nunnally, R. L. 1977. Phosphorus nuclear magnetic resonance of perfused working rat hearts. *Nature* 265:756–58

69. Jöbsis, F. F. 1977. Noninvasive, infrared monitoring of cerebral and myocardial oxygen sufficiency and circulatory parameters. *Science* 198:1264–66

70. Khuri, R. N., Agulian, S. K., Bogharian, K. K. 1976. Intracellular bicarbonate of skeletal muscle under different metabolic states. *Am. J. Physiol.* 230:228–32

71. Knowles, P. F. 1972. The application of magnetic resonance methods to the study of enzyme structure and action. *Essays Biochem.* 8:79–106

72. Koenig, S. H., Brown, R. D., Needham, T. E., Matwiyoff, N. A. 1973. Kinetic parameters of human carbonic anhydrase B as determined from NMR linewidths of ^{13}C in CO_2 and HCO_3^-. *Biochem. Biophys. Res. Commun.* 53:624–30

73. Kushmerick, M. J., Paul, R. J. 1977. Chemical energetics in repeated contractions of frog sartorious muscles at 0°C. *J. Physiol. London* 267:249–60

74. Lapidot, A., Irving, C. S. 1977. Dynamic structure of whole cells probed by nuclear Overhauser enhanced nitrogen-15 nuclear magnetic resonance spectroscopy. *Proc. Natl. Acad. Sci. USA* 74:1988–92

75. Lauterbur, P. C. 1977. Spatially-resolved studies of whole tissues, organs and organisms by NMR zeugmatography. See Ref. 39, pp. 323–35

76. Lee, A. G., Birdsall, N. J. M., Metcalfe, J. C. 1974. Nuclear magnetic relaxation and the biological membrane. *Methods Membr. Biol.* 2:1–156

77. Lee, W. I., Verdugo, P. 1976. Laser light-scattering spectroscopy. A new application in the study of ciliary activity. *Biophys. J.* 16:1115–19

78. Lewis, A. 1976. Tunable laser resonance Raman spectroscopic investigations of the transduction process in

vertebrate rod cells. *Fed. Proc.*
35:51–53
79. Lewis, A., Fager, R. S., Abrahamson,
E. W. 1973. Tunable laser resonance
Raman spectroscopy of the visual process. I: the spectrum of rhodopsin. *J.
Raman Spectrosc.* 1:465–70
80. Lewis, A., Spoonhower, J., Bogomolni,
R. A., Lozier, R. H., Stoeckenius, W.
1974. Tunable laser Raman spectroscopy of bacteriorhodopsin. *Proc. Natl.
Acad. Sci. USA* 71:4462–66
81. Liedtke, A. J., Hughes, H. C., Neely, J.
R. 1976. Effects of excess glucose and
insulin on glycolytic metabolism during
experimental myocardial ischemia. *Am.
J. Cardiol.* 38:17–27
82. Liedtke, A. J., Nellis, S. H., Neely, J.
R., Hughes, H. C. 1976. Effects of treatment with pyruvate and tromethamine
in experimental myocardial ischemia.
Circ. Res. 39:378–87
83. London, R. E., Hildebrand, C. E., Ol-
son, E. S., Matwiyoff, N. A. 1976. Car-
bon-13 nuclear magnetic resonance
spectroscopy of suspensions of Chinese
hamster ovary cells specifically enriched
with [methyl-^{13}C] choline. *Biochemistry*
15:5480–86
84. Luz, Z., Meiboom, S. 1964. Proton relaxation in dilute solutions of cobalt (II)
and nickel (II) ions in methanol and the
rate of methanol exchange of the solva-
tion sphere. *J. Chem. Phys.* 40:2686–92
85. MacDonald, R. W., Jöbsis, F. F. 1976.
Spectrophotometric studies on the pH
of frog skeletal muscle: pH change during and after contractile activity. *J. Gen.
Physiol.* 68:179–95
86. McInnes, A. G., Wright, J. L. C. 1975.
Use of carbon-13 magnetic resonance
spectroscopy for biosynthetic investigations. *Acc. Chem. Res.* 8:313–20
87. Matwiyoff, N. A., Needham, T. E.
1972. Carbon-13 NMR spectroscopy of
red blood cell suspensions. *Biochem.
Biophys. Res. Commun.* 49:1158–64
88. Monoi, H., Katsukura, Y. 1976. Nuclear magnetic resonance of ^{23}Na in suspensions of pig erythrocyte ghosts: a
comment on the interpretation of tissue
^{23}Na signals. *Biophys. J.* 16:979–81
89. Moon, R. B., Richards, J. H. 1973. Determination of intracellular pH by ^{31}P
magnetic resonance. *J. Biol. Chem.*
248:7276–78
90. Moravec, J., Corsin, A., Owen, P.,
Opie, L. H. 1974. Effect of increased
aortic perfusion pressure on fluorescent
emission of the isolated rat heart. *J.
Mol. Cell. Cardiol.* 6:187–200

91. Morrow, J. S., Keim, P., Gurd, F. R. N.
1974. CO_2 adducts of certain amino
acids, peptides, and sperm whale myoglobin studied by carbon 13 and proton
nuclear magnetic resonance. *J. Biol.
Chem.* 249:7484–94
92. Morrow, J. S., Keim, P., Visscher, R.
B., Marshall, R. C., Gurd, F. R. N.
1973. Interaction of $^{13}CO_2$ and bicarbonate with human hemoglobin preparations. *Proc. Natl. Acad. Sci. USA*
70:1414–18
93. Morrow, J. S., Matthew, J. B., Wit-
tebort, R. J., Gurd, F. R. N. 1976. Carbon 13 resonances of $^{13}CO_2$ carbamino
adducts of α- and β-chains in human
adult hemoglobin. *J. Biol. Chem.*
251:477–84
94. Mustacich, R. V., Ware, B. R. 1976. A
study of protoplasmic streaming in
Nitella by laser Doppler spectroscopy.
Biophys. J. 16:373–88
95. Navon, G., Ogawa, S., Shulman, R. G.,
Yamane, T. 1977. ^{31}P nuclear magnetic
resonance studies of Ehrlich ascites tumor cells. *Proc. Natl. Acad. Sci. USA*
74:87–91
96. Navon, G., Ogawa, S., Shulman, R. G.,
Yamane, T. 1977. High resolution ^{31}P
nuclear magnetic resonance studies of
metabolism in aerobic *Escherichia coli*
cells. *Proc. Natl. Acad. Sci. USA*
74:888–91
97. Neely, J. R., Morgan, H. E. 1974. Relation between carbohydrate and lipid
metabolism and the energy balance of
heart muscle. *Ann. Rev. Physiol.*
36:413–59
98. Njus, D., Radda, G. K. 1978. Bioenergetic processes in chromaffin granules.
A new perspective on some old problems. *Biochim. Biophys. Acta* 463:
219–44
99. Njus, D., Radda, G. K., Ritchie, G. A.,
Seeley, P. J., Sehr, P. A. 1978. Active
proton translocation in chromaffin
granules observed by ^{31}P NMR. *Biophys. J.* 21:58a
100. Ogawa, S., Brown, T. R., Rottenberg,
H., Shulman, R. G. 1978. ^{31}P NMR
study of mitochondria. *Biophys. J.*
21:60a
101. Ogawa, S., Shulman, R. G., Glynn, P.,
Yamane, T., Navon, G. 1978. On the
measurement of pH in *Escherichia coli*
by ^{31}P nuclear magnetic resonance.
Biochim. Biophys. Acta 502:45–50
102. Oldfield, E., Meadows, M., Glaser, M.
1976. Deuterium magnetic resonance
spectroscopy of isotopically labeled
mammalian cells. *J. Biol. Chem.* 251:
6147–49

103. Opie, L. H. 1976. Effects of regional ischemia on metabolism of glucose and fatty acids. *Circ. Res. Suppl.* 38:I-52–74

104. Opie, L. H., Owen, P. 1976. Effect of glucose-insulin-potassium infusions on arteriovenous differences of glucose and of free fatty acids and on tissue metabolic changes in dogs with developing myocardial infarction. *Am. J. Cardiol.* 38:310–21

105. Ottaway, J. H., Mowbray, J. 1977. The role of compartmentation in the control of glycolysis. *Curr. Top. Cell. Reg.* 12:107–208

106. Owen, J. D., Brown, H. M., Pemberton, J. P. 1976. Ca²⁺ in the *Aplysia* giant cell and the *Balanus eburneus* muscle fibre. *Biophys. J.* 16:34a

107. Piette, L. H., Anderson, W. A. 1959. Potential energy barrier determinations for some alkyl nitrites by nuclear magnetic resonance. *J. Chem. Phys.* 30:899–908

108. Proverbio, F., Hoffman, J. F. 1977. Membrane compartmentalized ATP and its preferential use by the Na, K-ATPase of human red cell ghosts. *J. Gen. Physiol.* 69:605–32

109. Radda, G. K. 1975. The dynamic properties of biological membranes. *Philos. Trans. R. Soc. London Ser. B.* 272:159–71

110. Rall, J. A., Homsher, E., Wallner, A., Mommaerts, W. F. H. M. 1976. A temporal dissociation of energy liberation and high energy phosphate splitting during shortening in frog skeletal muscles. *J. Gen. Physiol.* 68:13–27

111. Rattle, H. W. E. 1974. Nuclear magnetic resonance in the study of biopolymers. *Prog. Biophys. Mol. Biol.* 28:3–40

112. Roberts, E., Lowe, I. P. 1954. Occurrence of the O-phosphodiester of L-serine and ethanolamine in turtle tissue. *J. Biol. Chem.* 211:1–12

113. Salhany, J. M., Yamane, T., Shulman, R. G., Ogawa, S. 1975. High resolution ³¹P nuclear magnetic resonance studies of intact yeast cells. *Proc. Natl. Acad. Sci. USA* 72:4966–70

114. Schaefer, J., Stejskal, E. O., Beard, C. F. 1975. Carbon-13 nuclear magnetic resonance analysis of metabolism in soybeans labeled by ¹³CO₂. *Plant Physiol.* 55:1048–53

115. Seeley, P. J. 1975. *Some studies of glycolytic enzymes.* D. Phil. thesis, University of Oxford, England. pp. 224–26

116. Seeley, P. J., Busby, S. J. W., Gadian, D. G., Radda, G. K., Richards, R. E. 1976. A new approach to metabolite compartmentation in muscle. *Biochem. Soc. Trans.* 4:62–64

117. Sehr, P. A., Radda, G. K., Bore, P. J., Sells, R. A. 1977. A model kidney transplant studied by phosphorus nuclear magnetic resonance. *Biochem. Biophys Res. Commun.* 77:195–202

118. Shulman, R. G., Ugurbil, K., Brown, T. R., Rottenberg, H., Ogawa, S., Yamane, T., Navon, G., den Hollander, J. A., Cohen, S. M. 1978. ³¹P NMR studies of metabolism and bioenergetics in suspensions of living cells. *Biophys. J.* 21:154a

119. Silverman, D. N., Tu, C., Wynns, G. C. 1976. Depletion of ¹⁸O from C¹⁸O₂ in erythrocyte suspensions. *J. Biol. Chem.* 251:4428–35

120. Steenbergen, C., Deleeuw, G., Rich, T., Williamson, J. R. 1977. Effects of acidosis and ischemia on contractility and intracellular pH of rat heart. *Circ. Res.* 41:849–58

121. Stephenson, E. W., Podolsky, R. J. 1977. Regulation by magnesium of intracellular calcium movement in skinned muscle fibers. *J. Gen. Physiol.* 69:1–16

122. Stephenson, E. W., Podolsky, R. J. 1977. Influence of magnesium on chloride-induced calcium release in skinned muscle fibers. *J. Gen. Physiol.* 69:17–35

123. Taylor, G. J., Jacobus, W. E., Hollis, D. P., Nunnally, R. L., Weisfeldt, M. L. 1977. Intracellular pH during myocardial ischemia and anoxia measured by ³¹P nuclear magnetic resonance (NMR). *Clin. Res.* 25:257 (Abstr.)

124. Veloso, D., Guynn, R. W., Oskarsson, M., Veech, R. L. 1973. The concentrations of free and bound magnesium in rat tissues. *J. Biol. Chem.* 248:4811–19

125. Vogel, S., Sperelakis, N. 1977. Blockade of myocardial slow inward current at low pH. *Am. J. Physiol.* 233:C99-103

126. Walker, J. L., Brown, H. M. 1977. Intracellular ionic activity measurements in nerve and muscle. *Physiol. Rev.* 57:729–78

127. Wilkie, D. R. 1968. Heat, work, and phosphorylcreatine breakdown in muscle. *J. Physiol. London* 195:157–83

128. Winkler, H. 1976. The composition of adrenal chromaffin granules: an assessment of controversial results. *Neuroscience* 1:65–80

AUTHOR INDEX

SUBJECT INDEX

A

Acetazolamide
proximal tubular effects of, 202–6
Acetylcholine
effect on pacemaker potential, 434
released by K⁺, 166
Acid-base disturbances
kidney potassium transport and, 246–48
Adenohypophysis
cyclic AMP and, 556, 557
hypothalamic hormones acting on
see Hypothalamic hormones action on adenohypophysis and Hypothalamic-hypophysiotropic hormones and brain;
Target hormones feedback on hypothalamus and pituitary
see also Brain, localization of hypophysiotropic hormones
Amiloride
distal tubular acidification and, 207, 208
Amino acids
stimulation of gastrin release by, 36
Aminopyrine, ¹⁴C–
cell accumulation of, 44
Ammonium
kidney excretion of potassium excretion and, 247
Amphibian skin peptides
pancreatic fragment secretion and, 56
Amphioxins
intestinal hormones of, 91
Angiotensin
interactions with prostaglandins, 675, 676
Anticholinergic agents
inhibition of gastric acid secretion by, 41
Arachidonate metabolites
platelet function and, 653–66
Astereognosis
posterior parietal cortex and, 141
Atropine
secretagogue interactions and, 45, 46

Avian orientation and navigation, 353–64
gravity cues, 360
infrasonic cues, 361, 362
integration of cues, 363
magnetic cues, 358–60
animals using, 358, 359
natural geomagnetic anomalies and, 359
meteorological cues, 363
barometric pressure and, 363
wind directions and turbulence, 363
olfactory cues, 360, 361
visual cues, 353–58
clock-shifted bearings of pigeons, 354, 355
compass information and, 353
hormonal influences, 356
polarization of sunlight and, 355
"spring" vs "autumn" orientation, 356, 357
star compass, 355–58
sun compass, 354, 355
ultraviolet light and, 355
Axons
giant squid axons
Kenneth Cole work on, 10–14

B

Benzolamide
proximal kidney tubule and, 201
Bile secretion
see Hepatic biliary secretion regulation
Biophysics
establishment of Biophysical Society, 21, 22
Blood-brain barrier
potassium and, 160, 161
Body fluid volume
prostaglandins and control of, 675, 676
Brain localization of
hypophysiotropic peptides, 587–97
hypophysiotropic hormones, 589–91
luteinizing hormone releasing hormone, 590, 591
"nonneuroendocrine" peptides, 588
outside brain, 587

somatostatin, 591
thyrotropin releasing hormone, 589, 590
methodological aspects, 585, 589
immunofluorescence histochemistry, 588
peroxide-labeled antibody use, 589
other neuropeptides, 591–95
enkephalins and endorphins, 593–95
substance P, 592, 593
vasopressin, oxytocin, and neurophysins, 591, 592
subcellular distribution of neuropeptides, 595–97
"parasynaptic" role of peptide receptors, 596
schema of peptidergic nerve terminals, 596

C

Caerulein
pancreatic secretion and, 56, 60
Calcium
cardiac excitation-contraction coupling, 473–81
intracellular measurements of, 756
pancreatic cell excitation and, 62
ultrafilterable fraction of, 266
uncoupling in heart muscle by, 453
follicular prostaglandin production, 689
cAMP
gastric acid secretagogues and, 47, 48
interaction with prostaglandins, 676, 677
neurological effects of, 677
pancreatic secretion and, 58, 59
Carbonic anhydrase
kidney content of
brush border and, 201
proton secretion by kidney and, 197
Cardiac
see Heart
Catecholamines
cardiac arryhthmias and, 464, 466, 467
effect on pacemaker currents, 435

CUMULATIVE INDEXES

CONTRIBUTING AUTHORS, VOLUMES 36–40

CHAPTER TITLES, VOLUMES 37–41

824   CHAPTER TITLES

Please list on the order blank on the reverse side the volumes you wish to order and whether you wish a standing order (the latest volume sent to you automatically upon publication each year). Volumes not yet published will be shipped in month and year indicated. Prices subject to change without notice. Out of print volumes subject to special order.

NEW.... to be published in 1980

ANNUAL REVIEW OF PUBLIC HEALTH

$17.00 per copy ($17.50 outside USA)

Volume 1 available May 1980

SPECIAL PUBLICATIONS

ANNUAL REVIEW REPRINTS: CELL MEMBRANES, 1975-1977 (published 1978)

A collection of articles reprinted from recent Annual Review series.

Soft cover $12.00 per copy ($12.50 outside USA)

THE EXCITEMENT AND FASCINATION OF SCIENCE (published 1965)

A collection of autobiographical and philosophical articles by leading scientists.

Clothbound $6.50 per copy ($7.00 outside USA)

THE EXCITEMENT AND FASCINATION OF SCIENCE, VOLUME 2:
Reflections by Eminent Scientists (published 1978)

Hard cover $12.00 per copy ($12.50 outside USA)

Soft cover $10.00 per copy ($10.50 outside USA)

HISTORY OF ENTOMOLOGY (published 1973)

A special supplement to the ANNUAL REVIEW OF ENTOMOLOGY series.

Clothbound $10.00 per copy ($10.50 outside USA)

ANNUAL REVIEW SERIES

Annual Review of ANTHROPOLOGY	$17.00 per copy ($17.50 outside USA)
Volumes 1-7 (1972-1978) currently available	Volume 8 available October 1979
Annual Review of ASTRONOMY AND ASTROPHYSICS	$17.00 per copy ($17.50 outside USA)
Volumes 1-16 (1963-1978) currently available	Volume 17 available September 1979
Annual Review of BIOCHEMISTRY	$18.00 per copy ($18.50 outside USA)
Volumes 28-47 (1959-1978) currently available	Volume 48 available July 1979
Annual Review of BIOPHYSICS AND BIOENGINEERING	$17.00 per copy ($17.50 outside USA)
Volumes 1-7 (1972-1978) currently available	Volume 8 available June 1979
Annual Review of EARTH AND PLANETARY SCIENCES	$17.00 per copy ($17.50 outside USA)
Volumes 1-6 (1973-1978) currently available	Volume 7 available May 1979
Annual Review of ECOLOGY AND SYSTEMATICS	$17.00 per copy ($17.50 outside USA)
Volumes 1-9 (1970-1978) currently available	Volume 10 available November 1979
Annual Review of ENERGY	$17.00 per copy ($17.50 outside USA)
Volumes 1-3 (1976-1978) currently available	Volume 4 available October 1979
Annual Review of ENTOMOLOGY	$17.00 per copy ($17.50 outside USA)
Volumes 7-23 (1962-1978) currently available	Volume 24 available January 1979
Annual Review of FLUID MECHANICS	$17.00 per copy ($17.50 outside USA)
Volumes 1-10 (1969-1978) currently available	Volume 11 available January 1979

(continued on reverse side)

Annual Review of GENETICS	$17.00 per copy ($17.50 outside USA)
Volumes 1-12 (1967-1978) currently available	Volume 13 available December 1979
Annual Review of MATERIALS SCIENCE	$17.00 per copy ($17.50 outside USA)
Volumes 1-8 (1971-1978) currently available	Volume 9 available August 1979
Annual Review of MEDICINE: Selected Topics in the Clinical Sciences	$17.00 per copy ($17.50 outside USA)
Volumes 1-3, 5-15, 17-29 (1950-1952, 1954-1964, 1966-1978) currently available	Volume 30 available April 1979
Annual Review of MICROBIOLOGY	$17.00 per copy ($17.50 outside USA)
Volumes 14-32 (1960-1978) currently available	Volume 33 available October 1979
Annual Review of NEUROSCIENCE	$17.00 per copy ($17.50 outside USA)
Volume 1 currently available	Volume 2 available March 1979
Annual Review of NUCLEAR AND PARTICLE SCIENCE	$19.50 per copy ($20.00 outside USA)
Volumes 9-28 (1959-1978) currently available	Volume 29 available December 1979
Annual Review of PHARMACOLOGY AND TOXICOLOGY	$17.00 per copy ($17.50 outside USA)
Volumes 1-3, 5-18 (1961-1963, 1965-1978) currently available	Volume 19 available April 1979
Annual Review of PHYSICAL CHEMISTRY	$17.00 per copy ($17.50 outside USA)
Volumes 9-29 (1958-1978) currently available	Volume 30 available November 1979
Annual Review of PHYSIOLOGY	$17.00 per copy ($17.50 outside USA)
Volumes 19-40 (1957-1978) currently available	Volume 41 available March 1979
Annual Review of PHYTOPATHOLOGY	$17.00 per copy ($17.50 outside USA)
Volumes 1-16 (1963-1978) currently available	Volume 17 available September 1979
Annual Review of PLANT PHYSIOLOGY	$17.00 per copy ($17.50 outside USA)
Volumes 10-29 (1959-1978) currently available	Volume 30 available June 1979
Annual Review of PSYCHOLOGY	$17.00 per copy ($17.50 outside USA)
Volumes 4, 5, 8, 10-29 (1953, 1954, 1957, 1959-1978) currently available	Volume 30 available February 1979
Annual Review of SOCIOLOGY	$17.00 per copy ($17.50 outside USA)
Volumes 1-4 (1975-1978) currently available	Volume 5 available August 1979

To ANNUAL REVIEWS INC., 4139 El Camino Way, Palo Alto, CA 94306 USA (415-493-4400)
Please enter my order for the following publications:
(Standing orders: indicate which volume you wish order to begin with)

_____, Vol(s). _____   Standing order _____
_____, Vol(s). _____   Standing order _____
_____, Vol(s). _____   Standing order _____
_____, Vol(s). _____   Standing order _____

Amount of remittance enclosed $_____   California residents please add sales tax.
Please bill me for the amount $_____   Prices subject to change without notice.

SHIP TO   BILL TO (include institutional purchase order)

Name _____   Name _____

Address _____   Address _____

_____Postal code _____   _____Postal code _____

Signed _____ Date _____   Signed _____ Date _____

___ Send free copy of annual Prospectus for current year

___ Send free back contents brochure for Annual Review(s) of _____